Lial • Hornsby • McGinnis

# Beginning Algebra

## Custom Edition for Fullerton College

Taken from:
*Beginning Algebra*, Eleventh Edition
by Margaret L. Lial, John Hornsby, and Terry McGinnis

Cover Art: Courtesy of Photodisc/Getty Images

Taken from:

*Beginning Algebra,* Eleventh Edition
by Margaret L. Lial, John Hornsby, and Terry McGinnis
Copyright © 2012, 2008, 2004, 2000 by Pearson Education, Inc.
Published by Addison-Wesley
Boston, MA 02116

This special edition published in cooperation with Pearson Learning Solutions.

Pearson Learning Solutions, 501 Boylston Street, Suite 900, Boston, MA 02116
A Pearson Education Company
www.pearsoned.com

Printed in the United States of America

3 4 5 6 7 8 9 10  V092  16 15 14 13


000200010270767337

RR

  ISBN 10: 1-256-27671-5
ISBN 13: 978-1-256-27671-5

# Welcome Students!

*MyMathLab* is an interactive website where you can:
- Self-test & work through practice exercises with step-by-step help to improve your math skills.
- Study more efficiently with a personalized study plan and exercises that match your book.
- Get help when YOU need it. MyMathLab includes multimedia learning aids, videos, animations, and live tutorial help.

# Before You Begin:

To register for MyMathLab you will need:

☑ **A MyMathLab student access code** (packaged with your new text, standalone at your bookstore, or available for purchase with a major credit card at www.coursecompass.com)

☑ **Your instructors' Course ID:**_____

☑ **Your school's zip code:** _____

☑ **A valid email address**

# Student Registration:

- Enter **http://www.coursecompass.com** in your Web Browser.
- Under **Students**, click Register.
- Read the "Before you start" information and click **Next.**
- Enter your **Course ID** exactly as provided by your instructor and click "**Find Course.**" *Your course information should appear. If not, contact your instructor to verify the correct Course ID.*
- Select **Access Code**, type your **Access Code** in the fields provided (one word per field), and click **Next**. *If you do not have an access code, click Buy Now and follow those prompts to purchase and register.*
- Read the License Agreement and Privacy Policy and click "**I Accept.**"
- On the Access Information Screen, you'll be asked whether you already have a Pearson Education Account. Click:

 - "**YES**" if you have registered for other Pearson online products and already have a login name and password. Fields will appear for you to enter your existing login information.
 - "**NO**" if this is the first time you have registered for a Pearson online product. Boxes will appear for you to create your login name and password.
 - "**NOT SURE**" if you want to check for a pre-existing account and receive an email with your login name and password.

Simply follow the registration screens and enter your information as prompted. You will enter your name, email address, school information, and provide a security question/answer to ensure the privacy of your account.

Once your registration is complete, you will see a **Confirmation** screen (this information will also be emailed to you). Simply print your confirmation (remember to **write down your login name and password**) and you are now ready to Log in and access your resources!

# Logging In:

- Go to www.coursecompass.com and click on **Log In**.
- Enter your **login name** and **password** and click **Log in**.
- On the left, click on the name of your course.

The first time you enter your course from your own computer and anytime you use a new computer, click the **Installation Wizard** or **Browser Check** on the Announcements page. After completing the installation process and closing the wizard you will be on your course home page and ready to explore your MyMathLab resources!

# Need help?

Contact Product Support at **http://www.mymathlab.com/student-support** for live CHAT, email, or phone support.

*To Margaret, Cody, and Finley*
"P.P.J."


*To Papa*
T.

# Contents

## Linear Equations and Inequalities in Two Variables; Functions   175

## Systems of Linear Equations and Inequalities   247

## Exponents and Polynomials   295

## Quadratic Equations 553

It is with pleasure that we offer the eleventh edition of *Beginning Algebra*. With each new edition, the text has been shaped and adapted to meet the changing needs of both students and educators, and this edition faithfully continues that process. As always, we have taken special care to respond to the specific suggestions of users and reviewers through enhanced discussions, new and updated examples and exercises, helpful features, updated figures and graphs, and an extensive package of supplements and study aids. We believe the result is an easy-to-use, comprehensive text that is the best edition yet.

Students who have never studied algebra—as well as those who require further review of basic algebraic concepts before taking additional courses in mathematics, business, science, nursing, or other fields—will benefit from the text's student-oriented approach. Of particular interest to students and instructors will be the NEW Study Skills activities and Now Try Exercises.

This text is part of a series that also includes the following books:

▶ *Intermediate Algebra,* Eleventh Edition, by Lial, Hornsby, and McGinnis

▶ *Beginning and Intermediate Algebra,* Fifth Edition, by Lial, Hornsby, and McGinnis

▶ *Algebra for College Students,* Seventh Edition, by Lial, Hornsby, and McGinnis

## NEW IN THIS EDITION

In this edition of the text, we are pleased to offer the following new student-oriented features:

**Study Skills** Poor study skills are a major reason why students do not succeed in mathematics. In these short activities, we provide helpful information, tips, and strategies on a variety of essential study skills, including *Reading Your Math Textbook, Tackling Your Homework, Taking Math Tests,* and *Managing Your Time.* While most of the activities are concentrated in the early chapters of the text, each has been designed independently to allow flexible use with individuals or small groups of students, or as a source of material for in-class discussions. (See pages 48 and 163.)

**Now Try Exercises** To actively engage students in the learning process, we now include a parallel margin exercise juxtaposed with each numbered example. These all-new exercises enable students to immediately apply and reinforce the concepts and skills presented in the corresponding examples. Answers are conveniently located on the same page so students can quickly check their results. (See pages 3 and 87.)

**Revised Exposition** As each section of the text was being revised, we paid special attention to the exposition, which has been tightened and polished. (See Section 1.4 Real Numbers and the Number Line, for example.) We believe this has improved discussions and presentations of topics.

**Specific Content Changes**  These include the following:

▶ We gave the exercise sets special attention. There are approximately 1,100 new and updated exercises, including problems that check conceptual understanding, focus on skill development, and provide review. We also worked to improve the even-odd pairing of exercises.

▶ Real-world data in over 185 applications in the examples and exercises has been updated.

▶ There is an increased emphasis on the difference between expressions and equations, including a new Caution at the beginning of Section 2.1. Throughout the text, we have reformatted many example solutions to use a "drop down" layout in order to further emphasize for students the difference between simplifying expressions and solving equations.

▶ We increased the emphasis on checking solutions and answers, as indicated by the new *CHECK* tag and ✓ in the exposition and examples.

▶ The presentation on solving linear equations in Sections 2.1–2.3 now includes five new examples and corresponding exercises.

▶ Section 2.6 includes entirely new discussion and examples on percent, percent equations, and percent applications, plus corresponding exercises.

▶ Section 3.4 on writing and graphing equations of lines provides increased development and coverage of the slope-intercept form, including two new examples.

▶ Presentations of the following topics have also been enhanced and expanded:

Dividing real numbers involving zero (Section 1.6)
Solving applications involving consecutive integers and finding angle measures
   (Section 2.4)
Solving formulas for specified variables (Sections 2.5 and 7.7)
Using interval notation (Section 2.8)
Graphing linear equations in two variables (Section 3.2)
Solving systems of equations with decimal coefficients (Section 4.2)
Dividing polynomials (Section 5.7)
Factoring trinomials (Section 6.2)
Solving quadratic equations by factoring (Section 6.6)

## HALLMARK FEATURES

We have included the following helpful features, each of which is designed to increase ease-of-use by students and/or instructors.

**Annotated Instructor's Edition**  For convenient reference, we include answers to the exercises "on page" in the *Annotated Instructor's Edition,* using an enhanced, easy-to-read format. In addition, we have added approximately 35 new Teaching Tips and over 50 new and updated Classroom Examples.

**Relevant Chapter Openers**  In the new and updated chapter openers, we feature real-world applications of mathematics that are relevant to students and tied to specific material within the chapters. Examples of topics include the Olympics, student credit card debt, and popular movies. Each opener also includes a section outline. (See pages 85, 175, and 247.)

**Helpful Learning Objectives** We begin each section with clearly stated, numbered objectives, and the included material is directly keyed to these objectives so that students and instructors know exactly what is covered in each section. (See pages 2 and 130.)

**Popular Cautions and Notes** One of the most popular features of previous editions, we include information marked ⚠ CAUTION and NOTE to warn students about common errors and emphasize important ideas throughout the exposition. The updated text design makes them easy to spot. (See pages 2 and 56.)

**Comprehensive Examples** The new edition of this text features a multitude of step-by-step, worked-out examples that include pedagogical color, helpful side comments, and special pointers. We give increased attention to checking example solutions—more checks, designated using a special *CHECK* tag, are included than in past editions. (See pages 87 and 396.)

**More Pointers** Well received by both students and instructors in the previous edition, we incorporate more pointers in examples and discussions throughout this edition of the text. They provide students with important on-the-spot reminders and warnings about common pitfalls. (See pages 204 and 345.)

**Updated Figures, Photos, and Hand-Drawn Graphs** Today's students are more visually oriented than ever. As a result, we have made a concerted effort to include appealing mathematical figures, diagrams, tables, and graphs, including a "hand-drawn" style of graphs, whenever possible. (See pages 182 and 188.) Many of the graphs also use a style similar to that seen by students in today's print and electronic media. We have incorporated new photos to accompany applications in examples and exercises. (See pages 109 and 593.)

**Relevant Real-Life Applications** We include many new or updated applications from fields such as business, pop culture, sports, technology, and the life sciences that show the relevance of algebra to daily life. (See pages 277 and 409.)

**Emphasis on Problem-Solving** We introduce our six-step problem-solving method in Chapter 2 and integrate it throughout the text. The six steps, *Read, Assign a Variable, Write an Equation, Solve, State the Answer,* and *Check,* are emphasized in boldface type and repeated in examples and exercises to reinforce the problem-solving process for students. (See pages 108 and 272.) We also provide students with PROBLEM-SOLVING HINT boxes that feature helpful problem-solving tips and strategies. (See pages 139 and 401.)

**Connections** We include these to give students another avenue for making connections to the real world, graphing technology, or other mathematical concepts, as well as to provide historical background and thought-provoking questions for writing, class discussion, or group work. (See pages 195 and 315.)

**Ample and Varied Exercise Sets** One of the most commonly mentioned strengths of this text is its exercise sets. We include a wealth of exercises to provide students with opportunities to practice, apply, connect, review, and extend the algebraic concepts and skills they are learning. We also incorporate numerous illustrations, tables, graphs, and photos to help students visualize the problems they are solving. Problem types include writing ✍, graphing calculator 📊, multiple-choice, true/false, matching, and fill-in-the-blank problems, as well as the following:

▶ *Concept Check* exercises facilitate students' mathematical thinking and conceptual understanding. (See pages 96 and 196.)

▶ *WHAT WENT WRONG?* exercises ask students to identify typical errors in solutions and work the problems correctly. (See pages 208 and 398.)

▶ *Brain Busters* exercises challenge students to go beyond the section examples. (See pages 119 and 455.)

▶ **RELATING CONCEPTS** exercises help students tie together topics and develop problem-solving skills as they compare and contrast ideas, identify and describe patterns, and extend concepts to new situations. These exercises make great collaborative activities for pairs or small groups of students. (See pages 209 and 539.)

▶ **TECHNOLOGY INSIGHTS** exercises provide an opportunity for students to interpret typical results seen on graphing calculator screens. Actual screens from the TI-83/84 Plus graphing calculator are featured. (See pages 256 and 263.)

▶ **PREVIEW EXERCISES** allow students to *review* previously-studied concepts and *preview* skills needed for the upcoming section. These make good oral warm-up exercises to open class discussions. (See pages 257 and 367.)

**Special Summary Exercises** We include a set of these popular in-chapter exercises in every chapter. They provide students with the all-important ***mixed* review problems** they need to master topics and often include summaries of solution methods and/or additional examples. (See pages 311 and 465.)

**Extensive Review Opportunities** We conclude each chapter with the following review components:

▶ A **Chapter Summary** that features a helpful list of **Key Terms,** organized by section, **New Symbols, Test Your Word Power** vocabulary quiz (with answers immediately following), and a **Quick Review** of each section's contents, complete with additional examples (See pages 238–241.)

▶ A comprehensive set of **Chapter Review Exercises,** keyed to individual sections for easy student reference, as well as a set of **Mixed Review Exercises** that helps students further synthesize concepts (See pages 241–244.)

▶ A **Chapter Test** that students can take under test conditions to see how well they have mastered the chapter material (See pages 244–245.)

▶ A set of **Cumulative Review Exercises** (beginning in Chapter 2) that covers material going back to Chapter 1 (See page 246.)

**Glossary** For easy reference at the back of the book, we include a comprehensive glossary featuring key terms and definitions from throughout the text. (See pages G-1 to G-5.)

## SUPPLEMENTS

For a comprehensive list of the supplements and study aids that accompany *Beginning Algebra,* Eleventh Edition, see pages xvi–xviii.

## ACKNOWLEDGMENTS

The comments, criticisms, and suggestions of users, nonusers, instructors, and students have positively shaped this textbook over the years, and we are most grateful for the many responses we have received. Thanks to the following people for their review work, feedback, assistance at various meetings, and additional media contributions:

Barbara Aaker, *Community College of Denver*
Kim Bennekin, *Georgia Perimeter College*
Dixie Blackinton, *Weber State University*
Callie Daniels, *St. Charles Community College*
Cheryl Davids, *Central Carolina Technical College*
Robert Diaz, *Fullerton College*
Chris Diorietes, *Fayetteville Technical Community College*
Sylvia Dreyfus, *Meridian Community College*
Sabine Eggleston, *Edison State College*
LaTonya Ellis, *Bishop State Community College*
Beverly Hall, *Fayetteville Technical Community College*
Sandee House, *Georgia Perimeter College*
Joe Howe, *St. Charles Community College*
Lynette King, *Gadsden State Community College*
Linda Kodama, *Windward Community College*
Carlea McAvoy, *South Puget Sound Community College*
James Metz, *Kapi'olani Community College*
Jean Millen, *Georgia Perimeter College*
Molly Misko, *Gadsden State Community College*
Jane Roads, *Moberly Area Community College*
Melanie Smith, *Bishop State Community College*
Erik Stubsten, *Chattanooga State Technical Community College*
Tong Wagner, *Greenville Technical College*
Sessia Wyche, *University of Texas at Brownsville*

Special thanks are due all those instructors at Broward Community College for their insightful comments.

Over the years, we have come to rely on an extensive team of experienced professionals. Our sincere thanks go to these dedicated individuals at Addison-Wesley, who worked long and hard to make this revision a success: Chris Hoag, Maureen O'Connor, Michelle Renda, Adam Goldstein, Kari Heen, Courtney Slade, Kathy Manley, Lin Mahoney, and Mary St. Thomas.

We are especially grateful to Callie Daniels for her excellent work on the new Now Try Exercises. Abby Tanenbaum did a terrific job helping us revise real-data applications. Kathy Diamond provided expert guidance through all phases of production and rescued us from one snafu or another on multiple occasions. Marilyn Dwyer and Nesbitt Graphics, Inc. provided some of the highest quality production work we have experienced on the challenging format of these books.

Special thanks are due Jeff Cole, who continues to supply accurate, helpful solutions manuals; David Atwood, who wrote the comprehensive *Instructor's Resource Manual with Tests;* Beverly Fusfield, who provided the new MyWorkBook; Beth Anderson, who provided wonderful photo research; and Lucie Haskins, for yet another accurate, useful index. De Cook, Shannon d'Hemecourt, Paul Lorczak, and Sarah Sponholz did a thorough, timely job accuracy checking manuscript and page proofs. It has indeed been a pleasure to work with such an outstanding group of professionals.

As an author team, we are committed to providing the best possible text and supplements package to help instructors teach and students succeed. As we continue to work toward this goal, we would welcome any comments or suggestions you might have via e-mail to math@pearson.com.

**Margaret L. Lial**
**John Hornsby**
**Terry McGinnis**

## STUDENT SUPPLEMENTS

### Student's Solutions Manual

▶ By Jeffery A. Cole, *Anoka-Ramsey Community College*

▶ Provides detailed solutions to the odd-numbered, section-level exercises and to all Now Try Exercises, Relating Concepts, Summary, Chapter Review, Chapter Test, and Cumulative Review Exercises

ISBNs: 0-321-70245-X, 978-0-321-70245-6

### NEW Lial Video Library

The **Lial Video Library,** available in MyMathLab and on the Video Resources on DVD, provides students with a wealth of video resources to help them navigate the road to success! All video resources in the library include optional subtitles in English. The **Lial Video Library** includes the following resources:

▶ **Section Lecture Videos** offer a new navigation menu that allows students to easily focus on the key examples and exercises that they need to review in each section. Optional Spanish subtitles are available.

▶ **Solutions Clips** show an instructor working through the complete solutions to selected exercises from the text. Exercises with a solution clip are marked in the text and e-book with a DVD icon 🌐.

▶ **Quick Review Lectures** provide a short summary lecture of each key concept from the Quick Reviews at the end of every chapter in the text.

▶ **The Chapter Test Prep Videos** provide step-by-step solutions to all exercises from the Chapter Tests. These videos provide guidance and support when students need it the most: the night before an exam. The Chapter Test Prep Videos are also available on YouTube (searchable using author name and book title).

### NEW MyWorkBook

▶ Provides Guided Examples and corresponding Now Try Exercises for each text objective

▶ Refers students to correlated Examples, Lecture Videos, and Exercise Solution Clips

▶ Includes extra practice exercises for every section of the text with ample space for students to show their work

▶ Lists the learning objectives and key vocabulary terms for every text section, along with vocabulary practice problems

ISBNs: 0-321-70251-4, 978-0-321-70251-7

## INSTRUCTOR SUPPLEMENTS

### Annotated Instructor's Edition

▶ Provides "on-page" answers to all text exercises in an easy-to-read margin format, along with Teaching Tips and extensive Classroom Examples

▶ Includes icons to identify writing ✐ and calculator ▦ exercises. These are in Student Edition also.

ISBNs: 0-321-67585-1, 978-0-321-67585-9

### Instructor's Solutions Manual

▶ By Jeffery A. Cole, *Anoka-Ramsey Community College*

▶ Provides complete answers to all text exercises, including all Classroom Examples and Now Try Exercises

ISBNs: 0-321-70243-3, 978-0-321-70243-2

### Instructor's Resource Manual with Tests

▶ By David Atwood, *Rochester Community and Technical College*

▶ Contains two diagnostic pretests, four free-response and two multiple-choice test forms per chapter, and two final exams

▶ Includes a mini-lecture for each section of the text with objectives, key examples, and teaching tips

▶ Provides a correlation guide from the tenth to the eleventh edition

ISBNs: 0-321-69116-4, 978-0-321-69116-3

### PowerPoint® Lecture Slides

▶ Present key concepts and definitions from the text

▶ Available for download at www.pearsonhighered.com

ISBNs: 0-321-70248-4, 978-0-321-70248-7

### TestGen® (www.pearsonhighered.com/testgen)

▶ Enables instructors to build, edit, print, and administer tests using a computerized bank of questions developed to cover all text objectives

▶ Allows instructors to create multiple but equivalent versions of the same question or test with the click of a button

▶ Allows instructors to modify test bank questions or add new questions

▶ Available for download from Pearson Education's online catalog

ISBNs: 0-321-70244-1, 978-0-321-70244-9

## STUDENT SUPPLEMENTS

### InterAct Math Tutorial Website
### www.interactmath.com

▷ Provides practice and tutorial help online

▷ Provides algorithmically generated practice exercises that correlate directly to the exercises in the textbook

▷ Allows students to retry an exercise with new values each time for unlimited practice and mastery

▷ Includes an interactive guided solution for each exercise that gives helpful feedback when an incorrect answer is entered

▷ Enables students to view the steps of a worked-out sample problem similar to the one being worked on

## INSTRUCTOR SUPPLEMENTS

### Pearson Math Adjunct Support Center

(http://www.pearsontutorservices.com/math-adjunct.html)

▷ Staffed by qualified instructors with more than 50 years of combined experience at both the community college and university levels

Assistance is provided for faculty in the following areas:

▷ Suggested syllabus consultation

▷ Tips on using materials packed with your book

▷ Book-specific content assistance

▷ Teaching suggestions, including advice on classroom strategies

### Available for Students and Instructors

**MyMathLab® Online Course (Access code required.)**

MyMathLab® is a text-specific, easily customizable online course that integrates interactive multimedia instruction with textbook content. MyMathLab gives instructors the tools they need to deliver all or a portion of their course online, whether their students are in a lab setting or working from home.

▷ **Interactive homework exercises,** correlated to the textbook at the objective level, are algorithmically generated for unlimited practice and mastery. Most exercises are free-response and provide guided solutions, sample problems, and tutorial learning aids for extra help.

▷ **Personalized homework** assignments can be designed to meet the needs of the class. MyMathLab tailors the assignment for each student based on their test or quiz scores so that each student's homework assignment contains only the problems they still need to master.

▷ **Personalized Study Plan,** generated when students complete a test or quiz or homework, indicates which topics have been mastered and links to tutorial exercises for topics students have not mastered. Instructors can customize the Study Plan so that the topics available match their course content.

▷ **Multimedia learning aids,** such as video lectures and podcasts, animations, and a complete multimedia textbook, help students independently improve their understanding and performance. Instructors can assign these multimedia learning aids as homework to help their students grasp the concepts.

▷ **Homework and Test Manager** lets instructors assign homework, quizzes, and tests that are automatically graded. They can select just the right mix of questions from the MyMathLab exercise bank, instructor-created custom exercises, and/or TestGen® test items.

▷ **Gradebook,** designed specifically for mathematics and statistics, automatically tracks students' results, lets instructors stay on top of student performance, and gives them control over how to calculate final grades. They can also add offline (paper-and-pencil) grades to the gradebook.

▶ **MathXL Exercise Builder** allows instructors to create static and algorithmic exercises for their online assignments. They can use the library of sample exercises as an easy starting point, or they can edit any course-related exercise.

▶ **Pearson Tutor Center** (www.pearsontutorservices.com) access is automatically included with MyMathLab. The Tutor Center is staffed by qualified math instructors who provide textbook-specific tutoring for students via toll-free phone, fax, email, and interactive Web sessions.

Students do their assignments in the Flash®-based MathXL Player, which is compatible with almost any browser (Firefox®, Safari™, or Internet Explorer®) on almost any platform (Macintosh® or Windows®). MyMathLab is powered by CourseCompass™, Pearson Education's online teaching and learning environment, and by MathXL®, our online homework, tutorial, and assessment system. MyMathLab is available to qualified adopters. For more information, visit our website at www.mymathlab.com or contact your Pearson representative.

### MathXL® Online Course (access code required)

MathXL® is an online homework, tutorial, and assessment system that accompanies Pearson's textbooks in mathematics or statistics.

▶ **Interactive homework exercises,** correlated to your textbook at the objective level, are algorithmically generated for unlimited practice and mastery. Most exercises are free-response and provide guided solutions, sample problems, and learning aids for extra help.

▶ **Personalized homework** assignments are designed by the instructor to meet the needs of the class, and then personalized for each student based on their test or quiz results. As a result, each student receives a homework assignment that contains only the problems they still need to master.

▶ **Personalized Study Plan,** generated when students complete a test or quiz or homework, indicates which topics have been mastered and links to tutorial exercises for topics students have not mastered. Instructors can customize the available topics in the study plan to match their course concepts.

▶ **Multimedia learning aids,** such as video lectures and animations, help students independently improve their understanding and performance. These are assignable as homework, to further encourage their use.

▶ **Gradebook,** designed specifically for mathematics and statistics, automatically tracks students' results, lets instructors stay on top of student performance, and gives them control over how to calculate final grades.

▶ **MathXL Exercise Builder** allows instructors to create static and algorithmic exercises for their online assignments. They can use the library of sample exercises as an easy starting point or the Exercise Builder to edit any of the course-related exercises.

▶ **Homework and Test Manager** lets instructors create online homework, quizzes, and tests that are automatically graded. They can select just the right mix of questions from the MathXL exercise bank, instructor-created custom exercises, and/or TestGen test items.

The new, Flash®-based MathXL Player is compatible with almost any browser (Firefox®, Safari™, or Internet Explorer®) on almost any platform (Macintosh® or Windows®). MathXL is available to qualified adopters. For more information, visit our website at www.mathxl.com, or contact your Pearson representative.

# BEGINNING ALGEBRA

STUDY **SKILLS**

## Using Your Math Textbook

*Your textbook is a valuable resource.* You will learn more if you fully make use of the features it offers.

### General Features

▶ **Table of Contents** Find this at the front of the text. Mark the chapters and sections you will cover, as noted on your course syllabus.

▶ **Answer Section** Tab this section at the back of the book so you can refer to it frequently when doing homework. Answers to odd-numbered section exercises are provided. Answers to ALL summary, chapter review, test, and cumulative review exercises are given.

▶ **Glossary** Find this feature after the answer section at the back of the text. It provides an alphabetical list of the key terms found in the text, with definitions and section references.

▶ **List of Formulas** Inside the back cover of the text is a helpful list of geometric formulas, along with review information on triangles and angles. Use these for reference throughout the course.

### Specific Features

▶ **Objectives** The objectives are listed at the beginning of each section and again within the section as the corresponding material is presented. Once you finish a section, ask yourself if you have accomplished them.

▶ **Now Try Exercises** These margin exercises allow you to immediately practice the material covered in the examples and prepare you for the exercises. Check your results using the answers at the bottom of the page.

▶ **Pointers** These small shaded balloons provide on-the-spot warnings and reminders, point out key steps, and give other helpful tips.

▶ **Cautions** These provide warnings about common errors that students often make or trouble spots to avoid.

▶ **Notes** These provide additional explanations or emphasize important ideas.

▶ **Problem-Solving Hints** These green boxes give helpful tips or strategies to use when you work applications.

*Find an example of each of these features in your textbook.*

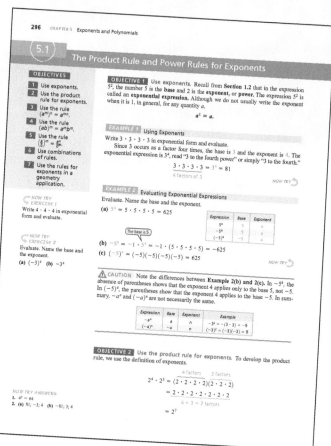

# The Real Number System

The personal savings rate of Americans has fluctuated over time. It stood at a hefty 10.8% of after-tax income in 1984, but dropped to −0.5% by 2005 when Americans actually spent more than they earned. This was the first negative savings rate since the Great Depression of the 1930s. In recent years, Americans have spent less and saved more, and personal savings rates have returned to positive territory, reaching 6.9% in May 2009. (*Source:* U.S. Bureau of Economic Analysis.)

In this chapter, we examine *signed numbers* and apply them to situations such as the personal savings rate of Americans in **Exercise 115** of **Section 1.5.**

## 1.1 Fractions

In everyday life, the numbers seen most often are the **natural numbers,**

$$1, 2, 3, 4, \ldots,$$

the **whole numbers,**

$$0, 1, 2, 3, 4, \ldots,$$

and **fractions,** such as

$$\frac{1}{2}, \quad \frac{2}{3}, \quad \text{and} \quad \frac{15}{7}.$$

The parts of a fraction are named as shown.

$$\text{Fraction bar} \rightarrow \frac{4}{7} \begin{array}{l} \leftarrow \text{Numerator} \\ \leftarrow \text{Denominator} \end{array}$$

***The fraction bar represents division*** $\left(\frac{a}{b} = a \div b\right)$.

A fraction is classified as being either a **proper fraction** or an **improper fraction.**

| Proper fractions | $\dfrac{1}{5}, \dfrac{2}{7}, \dfrac{9}{10}, \dfrac{23}{25}$ | Numerator is **less than** denominator. Value is less than 1. |
|---|---|---|
| Improper fractions | $\dfrac{3}{2}, \dfrac{5}{5}, \dfrac{11}{7}, \dfrac{28}{4}$ | Numerator is **greater than or equal** to denominator. Value is greater than or equal to 1. |

A **mixed number** is a single number that represents the sum of a natural number and a proper fraction.

$$\text{Mixed number} \rightarrow 5\frac{3}{4} = 5 + \frac{3}{4}$$

**OBJECTIVE 1** **Learn the definition of *factor*.** In the statement $3 \times 6 = 18$, the numbers 3 and 6 are called **factors** of 18. Other factors of 18 include 1, 2, 9, and 18. The result of the multiplication, 18, is called the **product.** We can represent the product of two numbers, such as 3 and 6, in several ways.

$$3 \times 6, \quad 3 \cdot 6, \quad (3)(6), \quad (3)6, \quad 3(6) \qquad \text{Products}$$

We *factor* a number by writing it as the product of two or more numbers. Factoring is the reverse of multiplying two numbers to get the product.

| Multiplication | Factoring |
|---|---|
| $3 \cdot 6 = 18$ | $18 = 3 \cdot 6$ |
| ↑   ↑   ↑ | ↑   ↑   ↑ |
| Factors  Product | Product  Factors |

**NOTE** In algebra, a raised dot $\cdot$ is often used instead of the $\times$ symbol to indicate multiplication because $\times$ may be confused with the letter $x$.

A natural number greater than 1 is **prime** if it has only itself and 1 as factors. "Factors" are understood here to mean natural number factors.

$$2, 3, 5, 7, 11, 13, 17, 19, 23, 29, 31, 37 \qquad \text{First dozen prime numbers}$$

A natural number greater than 1 that is not prime is called a **composite number.**

    4, 6, 8, 9, 10, 12, 14, 15, 16, 18, 20, 21    First dozen composite numbers

***By agreement, the number 1 is neither prime nor composite.***

Sometimes we must find all **prime factors** of a number—those factors which are prime numbers.

NOW TRY
EXERCISE 1
Write 60 as the product of prime factors.

**EXAMPLE 1** Factoring Numbers

Write each number as the product of prime factors.

**(a)** 35

Write 35 as the product of the prime factors 5 and 7, or as

$$35 = 5 \cdot 7.$$

**(b)** 24

We show a factor tree on the right. The prime factors are circled.

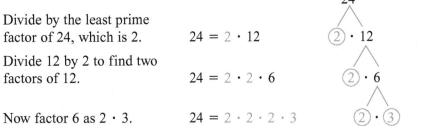

| | |
|---|---|
| Divide by the least prime factor of 24, which is 2. | $24 = 2 \cdot 12$ |
| Divide 12 by 2 to find two factors of 12. | $24 = 2 \cdot 2 \cdot 6$ |
| Now factor 6 as $2 \cdot 3$. | $24 = 2 \cdot 2 \cdot 2 \cdot 3$ |

All factors are prime.                        NOW TRY

**NOTE** When factoring, we need not start with the least prime factor. No matter which prime factor we start with, we will *always* obtain the same prime factorization. Verify this in **Example 1(b)** by starting with 3 instead of 2.

**OBJECTIVE 2** **Write fractions in lowest terms.** Recall the following **basic principle of fractions,** which is used to write a fraction in *lowest terms.*

**Basic Principle of Fractions**

If the numerator and denominator of a fraction are multiplied or divided by the same nonzero number, the value of the fraction is not changed.

A fraction is in **lowest terms** when the numerator and denominator have no factors in common (other than 1).

**Writing a Fraction in Lowest Terms**

*Step 1*  Write the numerator and the denominator as the product of prime factors.

*Step 2*  Divide the numerator and the denominator by the **greatest common factor,** the product of all factors common to both.

NOW TRY ANSWER
1. $2 \cdot 2 \cdot 3 \cdot 5$

⌐ NOW TRY
 ↳ EXERCISE 2
Write $\frac{30}{42}$ in lowest terms.

**EXAMPLE 2**   Writing Fractions in Lowest Terms

Write each fraction in lowest terms.

**(a)** $\dfrac{10}{15} = \dfrac{2 \cdot 5}{3 \cdot 5} = \dfrac{2 \cdot 1}{3 \cdot 1} = \dfrac{2}{3}$

The factored form shows that 5 is the greatest common factor of 10 and 15. Dividing both numerator and denominator by 5 gives $\frac{10}{15}$ in lowest terms as $\frac{2}{3}$.

**(b)** $\dfrac{15}{45}$

By inspection, the greatest common factor of 15 and 45 is 15.

$$\dfrac{15}{45} = \dfrac{15}{3 \cdot 15} = \dfrac{1}{3 \cdot 1} = \dfrac{1}{3} \longleftarrow \boxed{\text{Remember to write 1 in the numerator.}}$$

If the greatest common factor is not obvious, factor the numerator and denominator into prime factors.

$$\dfrac{15}{45} = \dfrac{3 \cdot 5}{3 \cdot 3 \cdot 5} = \dfrac{1 \cdot 1}{3 \cdot 1 \cdot 1} = \dfrac{1}{3} \qquad \text{The same answer results.}$$

*NOW TRY* ↻

⚠ **CAUTION**   When writing fractions like $\frac{15}{45}$ from **Example 2(b)** in lowest terms, be sure to include the factor 1 in the numerator.

**OBJECTIVE 3**   **Multiply and divide fractions.**

### Multiplying Fractions

If $\dfrac{a}{b}$ and $\dfrac{c}{d}$ are fractions, then $\qquad \dfrac{a}{b} \cdot \dfrac{c}{d} = \dfrac{a \cdot c}{b \cdot d}.$

That is, to multiply two fractions, multiply their numerators and then multiply their denominators.

**EXAMPLE 3**   Multiplying Fractions

Find each product, and write it in lowest terms.

**(a)** $\dfrac{3}{8} \cdot \dfrac{4}{9} = \dfrac{3 \cdot 4}{8 \cdot 9}$    Multiply numerators.
          Multiply denominators.

$\qquad\qquad = \dfrac{3 \cdot 4}{2 \cdot 4 \cdot 3 \cdot 3}$    Factor the denominator.

$\boxed{\text{Remember to write 1 in the numerator.}} \qquad = \dfrac{1}{2 \cdot 3}$    Divide numerator and denominator by 3 · 4, or 12.

$\qquad\qquad = \dfrac{1}{6}$    Lowest terms

*NOW TRY ANSWER*
**2.** $\frac{5}{7}$

NOW TRY
EXERCISE 3
Find each product, and write it in lowest terms.

(a) $\dfrac{4}{7} \cdot \dfrac{5}{8}$   (b) $3\dfrac{2}{5} \cdot 6\dfrac{2}{3}$

**(b)**

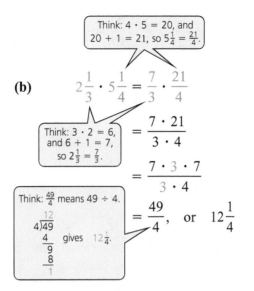

Think: $4 \cdot 5 = 20$, and $20 + 1 = 21$, so $5\frac{1}{4} = \frac{21}{4}$.

$$2\dfrac{1}{3} \cdot 5\dfrac{1}{4} = \dfrac{7}{3} \cdot \dfrac{21}{4}$$    Write each mixed number as an improper fraction.

Think: $3 \cdot 2 = 6$, and $6 + 1 = 7$, so $2\frac{1}{3} = \frac{7}{3}$.

$$= \dfrac{7 \cdot 21}{3 \cdot 4}$$    Multiply numerators. Multiply denominators.

$$= \dfrac{7 \cdot 3 \cdot 7}{3 \cdot 4}$$    Factor the numerator.

Think: $\frac{49}{4}$ means $49 \div 4$.

$$\begin{array}{r} 12 \\ 4\overline{)49} \\ 4 \\ \hline 9 \\ 8 \\ \hline 1 \end{array}$$    gives  $12\frac{1}{4}$.

$$= \dfrac{49}{4}, \quad \text{or} \quad 12\dfrac{1}{4}$$    Write in lowest terms and as a mixed number.

NOW TRY

**NOTE** Some students prefer to factor and divide out any common factors *before* multiplying.

$$\dfrac{3}{8} \cdot \dfrac{4}{9} = \dfrac{3}{2 \cdot 4} \cdot \dfrac{4}{3 \cdot 3}$$    Example 3(a)

$$= \dfrac{1}{2 \cdot 3}$$    Divide out common factors. Multiply.

$$= \dfrac{1}{6}$$    The same answer results.

| Number | Reciprocal |
|--------|-----------|
| $\frac{3}{4}$ | $\frac{4}{3}$ |
| $\frac{11}{7}$ | $\frac{7}{11}$ |
| $\frac{1}{5}$ | 5, or $\frac{5}{1}$ |
| 9, or $\frac{9}{1}$ | $\frac{1}{9}$ |

*A number and its reciprocal have a product of 1.* For example,

$$\tfrac{3}{4} \cdot \tfrac{4}{3} = \tfrac{12}{12} = 1.$$

Two fractions are **reciprocals** of each other if their product is 1. See the table in the margin. Because division is the opposite (or inverse) of multiplication, we use reciprocals to divide fractions.

**Dividing Fractions**

If $\dfrac{a}{b}$ and $\dfrac{c}{d}$ are fractions, then     $\dfrac{a}{b} \div \dfrac{c}{d} = \dfrac{a}{b} \cdot \dfrac{d}{c}.$

That is, to divide by a fraction, multiply by its reciprocal.

As an example of why this method works, we know that $20 \div 10 = 2$ and also that $20 \cdot \frac{1}{10} = 2$. The answer to a division problem is called a **quotient.** For example, the quotient of 20 and 10 is 2.

**EXAMPLE 4**   Dividing Fractions

Find each quotient, and write it in lowest terms.

**(a)** $\dfrac{3}{4} \div \dfrac{8}{5} = \dfrac{3}{4} \cdot \dfrac{5}{8} = \dfrac{3 \cdot 5}{4 \cdot 8} = \dfrac{15}{32}$    Make sure the answer is in lowest terms.

Multiply by the reciprocal of the second fraction.

NOW TRY ANSWERS
**3. (a)** $\frac{5}{14}$ **(b)** $\frac{68}{3}$, or $22\frac{2}{3}$

**(b)** $\dfrac{3}{4} \div \dfrac{5}{8} = \dfrac{3}{4} \cdot \dfrac{8}{5} = \dfrac{3 \cdot 8}{4 \cdot 5} = \dfrac{3 \cdot 4 \cdot 2}{4 \cdot 5} = \dfrac{6}{5}, \quad \text{or} \quad 1\dfrac{1}{5}$

NOW TRY
EXERCISE 4

Find each quotient, and write it in lowest terms.

**(a)** $\dfrac{2}{7} \div \dfrac{8}{9}$  **(b)** $3\dfrac{3}{4} \div 4\dfrac{2}{7}$

**(c)** $\dfrac{5}{8} \div 10 = \dfrac{5}{8} \div \dfrac{10}{1} = \dfrac{5}{8} \cdot \dfrac{1}{10} = \dfrac{5 \cdot 1}{8 \cdot 10} = \dfrac{5 \cdot 1}{8 \cdot 5 \cdot 2} = \dfrac{1}{16}$

Remember to write 1 in the numerator.

Write 10 as $\dfrac{10}{1}$.

**(d)** $1\dfrac{2}{3} \div 4\dfrac{1}{2} = \dfrac{5}{3} \div \dfrac{9}{2}$  Write each mixed number as an improper fraction.

$= \dfrac{5}{3} \cdot \dfrac{2}{9}$  Multiply by the reciprocal of the second fraction.

$= \dfrac{10}{27}$  Multiply numerators. Multiply denominators.

NOW TRY

**OBJECTIVE 4** **Add and subtract fractions.** The result of adding two numbers is called the **sum** of the numbers. For example, $2 + 3 = 5$, so 5 is the sum of 2 and 3.

### Adding Fractions

If $\dfrac{a}{b}$ and $\dfrac{c}{b}$ are fractions, then $\quad \dfrac{a}{b} + \dfrac{c}{b} = \dfrac{a + c}{b}$.

That is, to find the sum of two fractions having the *same* denominator, add the numerators and **keep the same denominator.**

NOW TRY
EXERCISE 5

Find the sum, and write it in lowest terms.

$$\dfrac{1}{8} + \dfrac{3}{8}$$

**EXAMPLE 5** Adding Fractions with the Same Denominator

Find each sum, and write it in lowest terms.

**(a)** $\dfrac{3}{7} + \dfrac{2}{7} = \dfrac{3 + 2}{7} = \dfrac{5}{7}$  Add numerators. Keep the same denominator.

**(b)** $\dfrac{2}{10} + \dfrac{3}{10} = \dfrac{2 + 3}{10} = \dfrac{5}{10} = \dfrac{1}{2}$  Write in lowest terms.

NOW TRY

If the fractions to be added do *not* have the same denominators, we must first rewrite them with a common denominator. For example, to rewrite $\dfrac{3}{4}$ as an equivalent fraction with denominator 32, think,

$$\dfrac{3}{4} = \dfrac{?}{32}.$$

We must find the number that can be multiplied by 4 to give 32. Since $4 \cdot 8 = 32$, we multiply numerator and denominator by 8.

$$\dfrac{3}{4} = \dfrac{3 \cdot 8}{4 \cdot 8} = \dfrac{24}{32}$$

$\dfrac{3}{4}$ and $\dfrac{24}{32}$ are equivalent fractions.

### Finding the Least Common Denominator

To add or subtract fractions with different denominators, find the **least common denominator (LCD)** as follows.

*Step 1* Factor each denominator.

*Step 2* For the LCD, use every factor that appears in any factored form. If a factor is repeated, use the largest number of repeats in the LCD.

NOW TRY ANSWERS
4. (a) $\dfrac{9}{28}$  (b) $\dfrac{7}{8}$
5. $\dfrac{1}{2}$

NOW TRY
EXERCISE 6

Find each sum, and write it in lowest terms.

**(a)** $\dfrac{5}{12} + \dfrac{3}{8}$   **(b)** $3\dfrac{1}{4} + 5\dfrac{5}{8}$

---

**EXAMPLE 6**  Adding Fractions with Different Denominators

Find each sum, and write it in lowest terms.

**(a)** $\dfrac{4}{15} + \dfrac{5}{9}$

To find the least common denominator, first factor both denominators.

$$15 = 5 \cdot 3 \qquad \text{and} \qquad 9 = 3 \cdot 3$$

Since 5 and 3 appear as factors, and 3 is a factor of 9 twice, the LCD is

$$\overset{15 \quad 9}{5 \cdot 3 \cdot 3}, \qquad \text{or} \qquad 45.$$

Write each fraction with 45 as denominator.

$$\dfrac{4}{15} = \dfrac{4 \cdot 3}{15 \cdot 3} = \dfrac{12}{45} \qquad \text{and} \qquad \dfrac{5}{9} = \dfrac{5 \cdot 5}{9 \cdot 5} = \dfrac{25}{45}$$

> At this stage, the fractions are *not* in lowest terms.

$$\dfrac{4}{15} + \dfrac{5}{9} = \dfrac{12}{45} + \dfrac{25}{45} = \dfrac{37}{45} \qquad \text{Add the two equivalent fractions.}$$

**(b)** $3\dfrac{1}{2} + 2\dfrac{3}{4}$

**Method 1** $\quad 3\dfrac{1}{2} + 2\dfrac{3}{4} = \dfrac{7}{2} + \dfrac{11}{4} \qquad$ Write each mixed number as an improper fraction.

> Think: $\frac{7 \cdot 2}{2 \cdot 2} = \frac{14}{4}$

$$= \dfrac{14}{4} + \dfrac{11}{4} \qquad \text{Find a common denominator. The LCD is 4.}$$

$$= \dfrac{25}{4}, \quad \text{or} \quad 6\dfrac{1}{4} \qquad \text{Add. Write as a mixed number.}$$

**Method 2**

$$\begin{aligned}
3\dfrac{1}{2} &= 3\dfrac{2}{4} \\
+\ 2\dfrac{3}{4} &= 2\dfrac{3}{4}
\end{aligned}$$

Write $3\dfrac{1}{2}$ as $3\dfrac{2}{4}$. Then add vertically. Add the whole numbers and the fractions separately.

$$5\dfrac{5}{4} = 5 + 1\dfrac{1}{4} = 6\dfrac{1}{4}, \quad \text{or} \quad \dfrac{25}{4}$$

NOW TRY

The **difference** between two numbers is found by subtracting the numbers. For example, $9 - 5 = 4$, so the difference between 9 and 5 is 4.

---

**Subtracting Fractions**

If $\dfrac{a}{b}$ and $\dfrac{c}{b}$ are fractions, then $\qquad \dfrac{a}{b} - \dfrac{c}{b} = \dfrac{a - c}{b}.$

That is, to find the difference between two fractions having the *same* denominator, subtract the numerators and ***keep the same denominator.***

---

**NOW TRY ANSWERS**
**6.** **(a)** $\dfrac{19}{24}$   **(b)** $\dfrac{71}{8}$, or $8\dfrac{7}{8}$

**NOW TRY**
**EXERCISE 7**

Find each difference, and write it in lowest terms.

**(a)** $\dfrac{5}{11} - \dfrac{2}{9}$  **(b)** $4\dfrac{1}{3} - 2\dfrac{5}{6}$

**EXAMPLE 7**  Subtracting Fractions

Find each difference, and write it in lowest terms.

**(a)** $\dfrac{15}{8} - \dfrac{3}{8} = \dfrac{15 - 3}{8}$   Subtract numerators. Keep the same denominator.

$= \dfrac{12}{8}$

$= \dfrac{3}{2}, \quad \text{or} \quad 1\dfrac{1}{2}$   Write in lowest terms and as a mixed number.

**(b)** $\dfrac{7}{18} - \dfrac{4}{15} = \dfrac{7 \cdot 5}{2 \cdot 3 \cdot 3 \cdot 5} - \dfrac{4 \cdot 2 \cdot 3}{2 \cdot 3 \cdot 3 \cdot 5}$   $18 = 2 \cdot 3 \cdot 3$ and $15 = 3 \cdot 5$, so the LCD is $2 \cdot 3 \cdot 3 \cdot 5 = 90$.

$= \dfrac{35}{90} - \dfrac{24}{90}$   Write the equivalent fractions.

$= \dfrac{11}{90}$   Subtract. The answer is in lowest terms.

**(c)** $\dfrac{15}{32} - \dfrac{11}{45}$

Since $32 = 2 \cdot 2 \cdot 2 \cdot 2 \cdot 2$ and $45 = 3 \cdot 3 \cdot 5$, there are no common factors. The LCD is $32 \cdot 45 = 1440$.

$\dfrac{15}{32} - \dfrac{11}{45} = \dfrac{15 \cdot 45}{32 \cdot 45} - \dfrac{11 \cdot 32}{45 \cdot 32}$   Find a common denominator.

$= \dfrac{675}{1440} - \dfrac{352}{1440}$   Write the equivalent fractions.

$= \dfrac{323}{1440}$   Subtract numerators. Keep the common denominator.

**(d)** $4\dfrac{1}{2} - 1\dfrac{3}{4}$

***Method 1***   $4\dfrac{1}{2} - 1\dfrac{3}{4} = \dfrac{9}{2} - \dfrac{7}{4}$   Write each mixed number as an improper fraction.

$= \dfrac{18}{4} - \dfrac{7}{4}$   Find a common denominator. The LCD is 4.

Think: $\frac{9 \cdot 2}{2 \cdot 2} = \frac{18}{4}$

$= \dfrac{11}{4}, \quad \text{or} \quad 2\dfrac{3}{4}$   Subtract. Write as a mixed number.

***Method 2***   $4\dfrac{1}{2} = 4\dfrac{2}{4} = 3\dfrac{6}{4}$   $4\frac{2}{4} = 3 + 1 + \frac{2}{4} = 3 + \frac{4}{4} + \frac{2}{4} = 3\frac{6}{4}$

$-1\dfrac{3}{4} = 1\dfrac{3}{4} = 1\dfrac{3}{4}$

$\rule{3cm}{0.4pt}$

$2\dfrac{3}{4}, \quad \text{or} \quad \dfrac{11}{4}$

NOW TRY

**NOW TRY ANSWERS**
**7.** **(a)** $\frac{23}{99}$  **(b)** $\frac{3}{2}$, or $1\frac{1}{2}$

NOW TRY
EXERCISE 8

A board is $10\frac{1}{2}$ ft long. If it must be divided into four pieces of equal length for shelves, how long must each piece be?

**OBJECTIVE 5** Solve applied problems that involve fractions.

**EXAMPLE 8** Adding Fractions to Solve an Applied Problem

The diagram in **FIGURE 1** appears in the book *Woodworker's 39 Sure-Fire Projects.* Find the height of the bookcase/desk to the top of the writing surface.

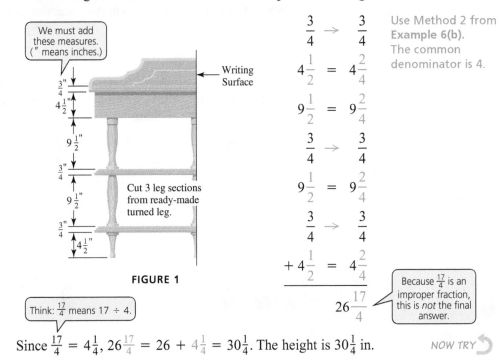

We must add these measures. (″ means inches.)

Writing Surface

Cut 3 leg sections from ready-made turned leg.

**FIGURE 1**

Use Method 2 from Example 6(b). The common denominator is 4.

$$\frac{3}{4} \rightarrow \frac{3}{4}$$
$$4\frac{1}{2} = 4\frac{2}{4}$$
$$9\frac{1}{2} = 9\frac{2}{4}$$
$$\frac{3}{4} \rightarrow \frac{3}{4}$$
$$9\frac{1}{2} = 9\frac{2}{4}$$
$$\frac{3}{4} \rightarrow \frac{3}{4}$$
$$+ 4\frac{1}{2} = 4\frac{2}{4}$$
$$26\frac{17}{4}$$

Because $\frac{17}{4}$ is an improper fraction, this is *not* the final answer.

Think: $\frac{17}{4}$ means $17 \div 4$.

Since $\frac{17}{4} = 4\frac{1}{4}$, $26\frac{17}{4} = 26 + 4\frac{1}{4} = 30\frac{1}{4}$. The height is $30\frac{1}{4}$ in.

NOW TRY

**OBJECTIVE 6** Interpret data in a circle graph. In a **circle graph,** or **pie chart,** a circle is used to indicate the total of all the data categories represented. The circle is divided into *sectors*, or wedges, whose sizes show the relative magnitudes of the categories. The sum of all the fractional parts must be 1 (for 1 whole circle).

**EXAMPLE 9** Using a Circle Graph to Interpret Information

Recently there were about 970 million Internet users worldwide. The circle graph in **FIGURE 2** shows the fractions of these users living in various regions of the world.

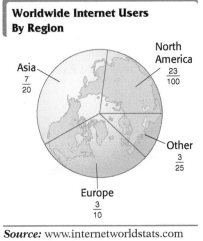

**Worldwide Internet Users By Region**

Asia $\frac{7}{20}$

North America $\frac{23}{100}$

Other $\frac{3}{25}$

Europe $\frac{3}{10}$

*Source:* www.internetworldstats.com

**FIGURE 2**

NOW TRY ANSWER
8. $2\frac{5}{8}$ ft

**NOW TRY**
**EXERCISE 9**
Refer to the circle graph in
**FIGURE 2** on the preceding page.

**(a)** Which region had the least number of Internet users?

**(b)** Estimate the number of Internet users in Asia.

**(c)** How many actual Internet users were there in Asia?

**NOW TRY ANSWERS**
9. **(a)** other
   **(b)** 333 million $\left(\frac{7}{20} \text{ is about } \frac{1}{3}.\right)$
   **(c)** $339\frac{1}{2}$ million, or 339,500,000

**(a)** Which region had the largest share of Internet users? What was that share?

The sector for Asia is the largest, so Asia had the largest share of Internet users, $\frac{7}{20}$.

**(b)** Estimate the number of Internet users in North America.

A share of $\frac{23}{100}$ can be rounded to $\frac{25}{100}$, or $\frac{1}{4}$, and the total number of Internet users, 970 million, can be rounded to 1000 million (1 billion). We multiply $\frac{1}{4}$ by 1000. The number of Internet users in North America would be about

$$\frac{1}{4}(1000) = 250 \text{ million.}$$

**(c)** How many actual Internet users were there in North America?

We multiply the actual fraction from the graph for North America, $\frac{23}{100}$, by the number of users, 970 million.

$$\frac{23}{100}(970) = \frac{23}{100} \cdot \frac{970}{1} = \frac{22,310}{100} = 223\frac{1}{10}$$

> This is reasonable, given our estimate in part (b).

Thus, $223\frac{1}{10}$ million, or 223,100,000 (since $\frac{1}{10}$ million $= \frac{1}{10} \cdot 1,000,000 = 100,000$), people in North America used the Internet.

**NOW TRY**

---

## 1.1 EXERCISES

 *MyMathLab*     Math XL PRACTICE     WATCH     DOWNLOAD     READ     REVIEW

🌐 *Complete solution available on the Video Resources on DVD*

*Concept Check*   Decide whether each statement is true *or* false. *If it is false, say why.*

**1.** In the fraction $\frac{5}{8}$, 5 is the numerator and 8 is the denominator.

**2.** The mixed number equivalent of $\frac{31}{5}$ is $6\frac{1}{5}$.

**3.** The fraction $\frac{7}{7}$ is proper.

**4.** The number 1 is prime.

**5.** The fraction $\frac{13}{39}$ is in lowest terms.

**6.** The reciprocal of $\frac{6}{2}$ is $\frac{3}{1}$.

**7.** The product of 10 and 2 is 12.

**8.** The difference between 10 and 2 is 5.

*Identify each number as* prime, composite, *or* neither. *If the number is composite, write it as the product of prime factors.* ***See Example 1.***

**9.** 19      **10.** 31      **11.** 30      **12.** 50

🌐 **13.** 64      **14.** 81      **15.** 1      **16.** 0

**17.** 57    **18.** 51    **19.** 79    **20.** 83    **21.** 124

**22.** 138    **23.** 500    **24.** 700    **25.** 3458    **26.** 1025

*Write each fraction in lowest terms.* ***See Example 2.***

**27.** $\frac{8}{16}$    **28.** $\frac{4}{12}$    🌐 **29.** $\frac{15}{18}$    **30.** $\frac{16}{20}$    **31.** $\frac{64}{100}$

**32.** $\frac{55}{200}$    **33.** $\frac{18}{90}$    **34.** $\frac{16}{64}$    **35.** $\frac{144}{120}$    **36.** $\frac{132}{77}$

**37.** *Concept Check*   Which choice shows the correct way to write $\frac{16}{24}$ in lowest terms?

**A.** $\frac{16}{24} = \frac{8+8}{8+16} = \frac{8}{16} = \frac{1}{2}$      **B.** $\frac{16}{24} = \frac{4 \cdot 4}{4 \cdot 6} = \frac{4}{6}$

**C.** $\frac{16}{24} = \frac{8 \cdot 2}{8 \cdot 3} = \frac{2}{3}$      **D.** $\frac{16}{24} = \frac{14+2}{21+3} = \frac{2}{3}$

**38.** *Concept Check* Which fraction is *not* equal to $\frac{5}{9}$?

    **A.** $\frac{15}{27}$    **B.** $\frac{30}{54}$    **C.** $\frac{40}{74}$    **D.** $\frac{55}{99}$

*Find each product or quotient, and write it in lowest terms.* ***See Examples 3 and 4.***

**39.** $\frac{4}{5} \cdot \frac{6}{7}$      **40.** $\frac{5}{9} \cdot \frac{2}{7}$      **41.** $\frac{2}{3} \cdot \frac{15}{16}$      **42.** $\frac{3}{5} \cdot \frac{20}{21}$

**43.** $\frac{1}{10} \cdot \frac{12}{5}$      **44.** $\frac{1}{8} \cdot \frac{10}{7}$      **45.** $\frac{15}{4} \cdot \frac{8}{25}$      **46.** $\frac{21}{8} \cdot \frac{4}{7}$

**47.** $21 \cdot \frac{3}{7}$      **48.** $36 \cdot \frac{4}{9}$      **49.** $3\frac{1}{4} \cdot 1\frac{2}{3}$      **50.** $2\frac{2}{3} \cdot 1\frac{3}{5}$

**51.** $2\frac{3}{8} \cdot 3\frac{1}{5}$      **52.** $3\frac{3}{5} \cdot 7\frac{1}{6}$      **53.** $\frac{5}{4} \div \frac{3}{8}$      **54.** $\frac{7}{5} \div \frac{3}{10}$

**55.** $\frac{32}{5} \div \frac{8}{15}$      **56.** $\frac{24}{7} \div \frac{6}{21}$      **57.** $\frac{3}{4} \div 12$      **58.** $\frac{2}{5} \div 30$

**59.** $6 \div \frac{3}{5}$      **60.** $8 \div \frac{4}{9}$      **61.** $6\frac{3}{4} \div \frac{3}{8}$      **62.** $5\frac{3}{5} \div \frac{7}{10}$

**63.** $2\frac{1}{2} \div 1\frac{5}{7}$      **64.** $2\frac{2}{9} \div 1\frac{2}{5}$      **65.** $2\frac{5}{8} \div 1\frac{15}{32}$      **66.** $2\frac{3}{10} \div 1\frac{4}{5}$

**67.** *Concept Check* For the fractions $\frac{p}{q}$ and $\frac{r}{s}$, which one of the following can serve as a common denominator?

    **A.** $q \cdot s$    **B.** $q + s$    **C.** $p \cdot r$    **D.** $p + r$

**68.** *Concept Check* Write a fraction with denominator 24 that is equivalent to $\frac{5}{8}$.

*Find each sum or difference, and write it in lowest terms.* ***See Examples 5–7.***

**69.** $\frac{7}{15} + \frac{4}{15}$      **70.** $\frac{2}{9} + \frac{5}{9}$      **71.** $\frac{7}{12} + \frac{1}{12}$      **72.** $\frac{3}{16} + \frac{5}{16}$

**73.** $\frac{5}{9} + \frac{1}{3}$      **74.** $\frac{4}{15} + \frac{1}{5}$      **75.** $\frac{3}{8} + \frac{5}{6}$      **76.** $\frac{5}{6} + \frac{2}{9}$

**77.** $3\frac{1}{8} + 2\frac{1}{4}$      **78.** $4\frac{2}{3} + 2\frac{1}{6}$      **79.** $3\frac{1}{4} + 1\frac{4}{5}$      **80.** $5\frac{3}{4} + 1\frac{1}{3}$

**81.** $\frac{7}{9} - \frac{2}{9}$      **82.** $\frac{8}{11} - \frac{3}{11}$      **83.** $\frac{13}{15} - \frac{3}{15}$      **84.** $\frac{11}{12} - \frac{3}{12}$

**85.** $\frac{7}{12} - \frac{1}{3}$      **86.** $\frac{5}{6} - \frac{1}{2}$      **87.** $\frac{7}{12} - \frac{1}{9}$      **88.** $\frac{11}{16} - \frac{1}{12}$

**89.** $4\frac{3}{4} - 1\frac{2}{5}$      **90.** $3\frac{4}{5} - 1\frac{4}{9}$      **91.** $6\frac{1}{4} - 5\frac{1}{3}$      **92.** $5\frac{1}{3} - 4\frac{1}{2}$

*Use the table to answer Exercises 93 and 94.*

**93.** How many cups of water would be needed for eight microwave servings?

**94.** How many teaspoons of salt would be needed for five stove-top servings? (*Hint:* 5 is halfway between 4 and 6.)

| | Microwave | Stove Top | | |
|---|---|---|---|---|
| Servings | 1 | 1 | 4 | 6 |
| Water | $\frac{3}{4}$ cup | 1 cup | 3 cups | 4 cups |
| Grits | 3 Tbsp | 3 Tbsp | $\frac{3}{4}$ cup | 1 cup |
| Salt (optional) | Dash | Dash | $\frac{1}{4}$ tsp | $\frac{1}{2}$ tsp |

*Source:* Package of Quaker Quick Grits.

*The Pride Golf Tee Company, the only U.S. manufacturer of wooden golf tees, has created the Professional Tee System, shown in the figure. Use the information given to work Exercises 95 and 96. (Source: The Gazette.)*

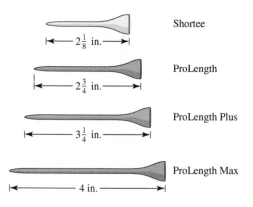

**95.** Find the difference in length between the ProLength Plus and the once-standard Shortee.

**96.** The ProLength Max tee is the longest tee allowed by the U.S. Golf Association's *Rules of Golf.* How much longer is the ProLength Max than the Shortee?

*Solve each problem. **See Example 8.***

**97.** A hardware store sells a 40-piece socket wrench set. The measure of the largest socket is $\frac{3}{4}$ in. The measure of the smallest is $\frac{3}{16}$ in. What is the difference between these measures?

**98.** Two sockets in a socket wrench set have measures of $\frac{9}{16}$ in. and $\frac{3}{8}$ in. What is the difference between these two measures?

**99.** A piece of property has an irregular shape, with five sides, as shown in the figure. Find the total distance around the piece of property. (This distance is called the **perimeter** of the figure.)

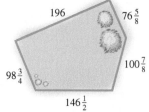

Measurements in feet

**100.** Find the perimeter of the triangle in the figure.

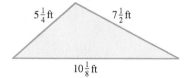

**101.** A board is $15\frac{5}{8}$ in. long. If it must be divided into three pieces of equal length, how long must each piece be?

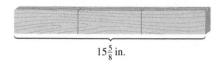

$15\frac{5}{8}$ in.

**102.** Paul Beaulieu's favorite recipe for barbecue sauce calls for $2\frac{1}{3}$ cups of tomato sauce. The recipe makes enough barbecue sauce to serve seven people. How much tomato sauce is needed for one serving?

**103.** A cake recipe calls for $1\frac{3}{4}$ cups of sugar. A caterer has $15\frac{1}{2}$ cups of sugar on hand. How many cakes can he make?

**104.** Kyla Williams needs $2\frac{1}{4}$ yd of fabric to cover a chair. How many chairs can she cover with $23\frac{2}{3}$ yd of fabric?

**105.** It takes $2\frac{3}{8}$ yd of fabric to make a costume for a school play. How much fabric would be needed for seven costumes?

**106.** A cookie recipe calls for $2\frac{2}{3}$ cups of sugar. How much sugar would be needed to make four batches of cookies?

**107.** First published in 1953, the digest-sized *TV Guide* has changed to a full-sized magazine. The full-sized magazine is 3 in. wider than the old guide. What is the difference in their heights? (*Source: TV Guide.*)

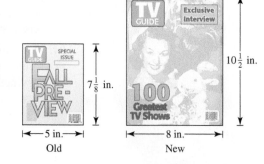

**108.** Under existing standards, most of the holes in Swiss cheese must have diameters between $\frac{11}{16}$ and $\frac{13}{16}$ in. To accommodate new high-speed slicing machines, the U.S. Department of Agriculture wants to reduce the minimum size to $\frac{3}{8}$ in. How much smaller is $\frac{3}{8}$ in. than $\frac{11}{16}$ in.? (*Source:* U.S. Department of Agriculture.)

*Approximately 38 million people living in the United States in 2006 were born in other countries. The circle graph gives the fractional number from each region of birth for these people. Use the graph to answer each question.* **See Example 9.**

**109.** What fractional part of the foreign-born population was from other regions?

**110.** What fractional part of the foreign-born population was from Latin America or Asia?

**111.** How many people (in millions) were born in Europe?

**U.S. Foreign-Born Population By Region of Birth**

*Source:* U.S. Census Bureau.

**112.** At the conclusion of the Pearson Education softball league season, batting statistics for five players were as follows:

| Player | At-Bats | Hits | Home Runs |
|---|---|---|---|
| Courtney Slade | 36 | 12 | 3 |
| Kari Heen | 40 | 9 | 2 |
| Adam Goldstein | 11 | 5 | 1 |
| Nathaniel Koven | 16 | 8 | 0 |
| Jonathan Wooding | 20 | 10 | 2 |

Use the table to answer each question. Estimate as necessary.

**(a)** Which player got a hit in exactly $\frac{1}{3}$ of his or her at-bats?

**(b)** Which player got a hit in just less than $\frac{1}{2}$ of his or her at-bats?

**(c)** Which player got a home run in just less than $\frac{1}{10}$ of his or her at-bats?

**(d)** Which player got a hit in just less than $\frac{1}{4}$ of his or her at-bats?

**(e)** Which two players got hits in exactly the same fractional parts of their at-bats? What was the fractional part, expressed in lowest terms?

**113.** For each description, write a fraction in lowest terms that represents the region described.

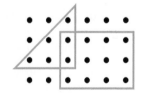

**(a)** The dots in the rectangle as a part of the dots in the entire figure

**(b)** The dots in the triangle as a part of the dots in the entire figure

**(c)** The dots in the overlapping region of the triangle and the rectangle as a part of the dots in the triangle alone

**(d)** The dots in the overlapping region of the triangle and the rectangle as a part of the dots in the rectangle alone

**114.** *Concept Check* Estimate the best approximation for the sum.

$$\frac{14}{26} + \frac{98}{99} + \frac{100}{51} + \frac{90}{31} + \frac{13}{27}$$

**A.** 6    **B.** 7    **C.** 5    **D.** 8

# Reading Your Math Textbook

*Take time to read each section and its examples before doing your homework.* You will learn more and be better prepared to work the exercises your instructor assigns.

## Approaches to Reading Your Math Textbook

**Student A** learns best by listening to her teacher explain things. She "gets it" when she sees the instructor work problems. She previews the section before the lecture, so she knows generally what to expect. **Student A carefully reads the section in her text *AFTER* she hears the classroom lecture on the topic.**

**Student B** learns best by reading on his own. He reads the section and works through the examples before coming to class. That way, he knows what the teacher is going to talk about and what questions he wants to ask. **Student B carefully reads the section in his text *BEFORE* he hears the classroom lecture on the topic.**

*Which reading approach works best for you—that of Student A or Student B?*

## Tips for Reading Your Math Textbook

▶ **Turn off your cell phone.** You will be able to concentrate more fully on what you are reading.

▶ **Read slowly.** Read only one section—or even part of a section—at a sitting, with paper and pencil in hand.

▶ **Pay special attention to important information given in colored boxes or set in boldface type.**

▶ **Study the examples carefully.** Pay particular attention to the blue side comments and pointers.

▶ **Do the Now Try exercises in the margin on separate paper as you go.** These mirror the examples and prepare you for the exercise set. The answers are given at the bottom of the page.

▶ **Make study cards as you read.** (See **page 48.**) Make cards for new vocabulary, rules, procedures, formulas, and sample problems.

▶ **Mark anything you don't understand.** *ASK QUESTIONS* in class—everyone will benefit. Follow up with your instructor, as needed.

*Select several reading tips to try this week.*

## 1.2  Exponents, Order of Operations, and Inequality

**OBJECTIVE 1  Use exponents.** Consider the prime factored form of 81.

$$81 = 3 \cdot 3 \cdot 3 \cdot 3 \qquad \text{The factor 3 appears four times.}$$

In algebra, repeated factors are written with an *exponent*, so the product $3 \cdot 3 \cdot 3 \cdot 3$ is written as $3^4$ and read as "3 to the fourth power."

$$\underbrace{3 \cdot 3 \cdot 3 \cdot 3}_{4 \text{ factors of 3}} = 3^4 \quad \begin{matrix}\text{Exponent}\\\text{Base}\end{matrix}$$

The number 4 is the **exponent,** or **power,** and 3 is the **base** in the **exponential expression** $3^4$. A natural number exponent, then, tells how many times the base is used as a factor. *A number raised to the first power is simply that number.* For example,

$$5^1 = 5 \quad \text{and} \quad \left(\frac{1}{2}\right)^1 = \frac{1}{2}.$$

**EXAMPLE 1  Evaluating Exponential Expressions**

Find the value of each exponential expression.

**(a)** $5^2 = \underbrace{5 \cdot 5}_{} = 25$

  5 is used as a factor 2 times.

Read $5^2$ as "5 to the second power" or, more commonly, "5 squared."

**(b)** $6^3 = \underbrace{6 \cdot 6 \cdot 6}_{} = 216$

  6 is used as a factor 3 times.

Read $6^3$ as "6 to the third power" or, more commonly, "6 cubed."

**(c)** $2^5 = 2 \cdot 2 \cdot 2 \cdot 2 \cdot 2 = 32$   2 is used as a factor 5 times.

Read $2^5$ as "2 to the fifth power."

**(d)** $\left(\frac{2}{3}\right)^3 = \frac{2}{3} \cdot \frac{2}{3} \cdot \frac{2}{3} = \frac{8}{27}$   $\frac{2}{3}$ is used as a factor 3 times.

**(e)** $(0.3)^2 = 0.3(0.3) = 0.09$   0.3 is used as a factor 2 times.   NOW TRY

⚠ **CAUTION** *Squaring, or raising a number to the second power, is NOT the same as doubling the number.* For example,

$$3^2 \quad \textbf{means} \quad 3 \cdot 3, \quad not \quad 2 \cdot 3.$$

Thus $3^2 = 9$, *not* 6. Similarly, cubing, or raising a number to the third power, does *not* mean tripling the number.

**OBJECTIVE 2  Use the rules for order of operations.** When a problem involves more than one operation, we often use **grouping symbols,** such as parentheses ( ), to indicate the order in which the operations should be performed.

Consider the expression $5 + 2 \cdot 3$. To show that the multiplication should be performed before the addition, we use parentheses to group $2 \cdot 3$.

$$5 + (2 \cdot 3) \quad \text{equals} \quad 5 + 6, \quad \text{or} \quad 11.$$

NOW TRY
EXERCISE 1

Find the value of each exponential expression.

**(a)** $6^2$  **(b)** $\left(\frac{4}{5}\right)^3$

NOW TRY ANSWERS
**1. (a)** 36  **(b)** $\frac{64}{125}$

If addition is to be performed first, the parentheses should group $5 + 2$.

$$(5 + 2) \cdot 3 \quad \text{equals} \quad 7 \cdot 3, \quad \text{or} \quad 21.$$

Other grouping symbols are brackets $[\quad]$, braces $\{\quad\}$, and fraction bars. (For example, in $\frac{8 - 2}{3}$, the expression $8 - 2$ is "grouped" in the numerator.)

To work problems with more than one operation, we use the following **order of operations.** This order is used by most calculators and computers.

---

**Order of Operations**

*If grouping symbols are present,* simplify within them, innermost first (and above and below fraction bars separately), in the following order.

*Step 1* Apply all **exponents.**

*Step 2* Do any **multiplications** or **divisions** in the order in which they occur, working from left to right.

*Step 3* Do any **additions** or **subtractions** in the order in which they occur, working from left to right.

*If no grouping symbols are present,* start with Step 1.

---

NOTE In expressions such as $3(7)$ or $(-5)(-4)$, multiplication is understood.

---

**EXAMPLE 2** Using the Rules for Order of Operations

Find the value of each expression.

**(a)** $4 + 5 \cdot 6$ ⟵ Be careful! Multiply first.

$= 4 + 30$ Multiply.

$= 34$ Add.

**(b)** $9(6 + 11)$

$= 9(17)$ Work inside parentheses.

$= 153$ Multiply.

**(c)** $6 \cdot 8 + 5 \cdot 2$

$= 48 + 10$ Multiply, working from left to right.

$= 58$ Add.

**(d)** $2(5 + 6) + 7 \cdot 3$

$= 2(11) + 7 \cdot 3$ Work inside parentheses.

$= 22 + 21$ Multiply.

$= 43$ Add.

$2^3 = 2 \cdot 2 \cdot 2$, not $2 \cdot 3$.

**(e)** $9 - 2^3 + 5$

$= 9 - 2 \cdot 2 \cdot 2 + 5$ Apply the exponent.

$= 9 - 8 + 5$ Multiply.

$= 1 + 5$ Subtract.

$= 6$ Add.

NOW TRY
EXERCISE 2
Find the value of each
expression.

**(a)** $15 - 2 \cdot 6$

**(b)** $6(2 + 4) - 7 \cdot 5$

**(c)** $8 \cdot 10 \div 4 - 2^3 + 3 \cdot 4^2$

**(f)** $72 \div 2 \cdot 3 + 4 \cdot 2^3 - 3^3$  ⟵ Think: $3^3 = 3 \cdot 3 \cdot 3$

$= 72 \div 2 \cdot 3 + 4 \cdot 8 - 27$    Apply the exponents.

$= 36 \cdot 3 + 4 \cdot 8 - 27$    Divide.

$= 108 + 32 - 27$    Multiply.

$= 140 - 27$    Add.

$= 113$    Subtract.

*Multiplications and divisions are done from left to right as they appear. Then additions and subtractions are done from left to right as they appear.*    NOW TRY

**OBJECTIVE 3**  **Use more than one grouping symbol.**  In an expression such as $2(8 + 3(6 + 5))$, we often use brackets, [  ], in place of one pair of parentheses.

NOW TRY
EXERCISE 3
Simplify each expression.

**(a)** $7[(3^2 - 1) + 4]$

**(b)** $\dfrac{9(14 - 4) - 2}{4 + 3 \cdot 6}$

**EXAMPLE 3**  Using Brackets and Fraction Bars as Grouping Symbols

Simplify each expression.

**(a)** $2[8 + 3(6 + 5)]$

$= 2[8 + 3(11)]$    Add inside parentheses.

$= 2[8 + 33]$    Multiply inside brackets.

$= 2[41]$    Add inside brackets.

$= 82$    Multiply.

**(b)** $\dfrac{4(5 + 3) + 3}{2(3) - 1}$    Simplify the numerator and denominator separately.

$= \dfrac{4(8) + 3}{2(3) - 1}$    Work inside parentheses.

$= \dfrac{32 + 3}{6 - 1}$    Multiply.

$= \dfrac{35}{5},$  or  $7$    Add and subtract. Then divide.    NOW TRY

---

**NOTE**  The expression $\frac{4(5 + 3) + 3}{2(3) - 1}$ in **Example 3(b)** can be written as the quotient

$$[4(5 + 3) + 3] \div [2(3) - 1],$$

which shows that the fraction bar "groups" the numerator and denominator separately.

---

**OBJECTIVE 4**  **Know the meanings of $\neq$, $<$, $>$, $\leq$, and $\geq$.**  So far, we have used the equality symbol $=$. The symbols $\neq$, $<$, $>$, $\leq$, and $\geq$ are used to express an **inequality,** a statement that two expressions may not be equal. The equality symbol with a slash through it, $\neq$, means "is not equal to."

$$7 \neq 8 \quad \text{7 is not equal to 8.}$$

If two numbers are not equal, then one of the numbers must be less than the other. The symbol $<$ represents "is less than."

$$7 < 8 \quad \text{7 is less than 8.}$$

NOW TRY ANSWERS
2. **(a)** 3  **(b)** 1  **(c)** 60
3. **(a)** 84  **(b)** 4

The symbol $>$ means "is greater than."

$$8 > 2 \qquad \text{8 is greater than 2.}$$

*To keep the meanings of the symbols $<$ and $>$ clear, remember that the symbol always points to the lesser number.*

$$\text{Lesser number} \rightarrow 8 < 15$$

$$15 > 8 \leftarrow \text{Lesser number}$$

The symbol $\leq$ means "is less than or equal to."

$$5 \leq 9 \qquad \text{5 is less than or equal to 9.}$$

*If either the $<$ part or the $=$ part is true, then the inequality $\leq$ is true.* The statement $5 \leq 9$ is true, since $5 < 9$ is true.

The symbol $\geq$ means "is greater than or equal to."

$$9 \geq 5 \qquad \text{9 is greater than or equal to 5.}$$

---

NOW TRY
EXERCISE 4

Determine whether each statement is *true* or *false*.

**(a)** $12 \neq 10 - 2$

**(b)** $5 > 4 \cdot 2$

**(c)** $7 \leq 7$

**(d)** $\dfrac{5}{9} > \dfrac{7}{11}$

---

**EXAMPLE 4** Using Inequality Symbols

Determine whether each statement is *true* or *false*.

**(a)** $6 \neq 5 + 1$     This statement is false because $6 = 5 + 1$.

**(b)** $5 + 3 < 19$     The statement $5 + 3 < 19$ is true, since $8 < 19$.

**(c)** $15 \leq 20 \cdot 2$     The statement $15 \leq 20 \cdot 2$ is true, since $15 < 40$.

**(d)** $25 \geq 30$     Both $25 > 30$ and $25 = 30$ are false, so $25 \geq 30$ is false.

**(e)** $12 \geq 12$     Since $12 = 12$, this statement is true.

**(f)** $9 < 9$     Since $9 = 9$, this statement is false.

**(g)** $\dfrac{6}{15} \geq \dfrac{2}{3}$

$\dfrac{6}{15} \geq \dfrac{10}{15}$     Get a common denominator.

Both statements $\frac{6}{15} > \frac{10}{15}$ and $\frac{6}{15} = \frac{10}{15}$ are false. Therefore, $\frac{6}{15} \geq \frac{2}{3}$ is false.

NOW TRY

---

**OBJECTIVE 5** Translate word statements to symbols.

---

NOW TRY
EXERCISE 5

Write each word statement in symbols.

**(a)** Ten is not equal to eight minus two.

**(b)** Fifty is greater than fifteen.

**(c)** Eleven is less than or equal to twenty.

---

**EXAMPLE 5** Translating from Words to Symbols

Write each word statement in symbols.

**(a)** Twelve equals ten plus two.

$$12 = 10 + 2$$

**(b)** Nine is less than ten.

$$9 < 10$$

**(c)** Fifteen is not equal to eighteen.

$$15 \neq 18$$

**(d)** Seven is greater than four.

$$7 > 4$$

**(e)** Thirteen is less than or equal to forty.

$$13 \leq 40$$

**(f)** Eleven is greater than or equal to eleven.

$$11 \geq 11$$

NOW TRY

---

NOW TRY ANSWERS

**4. (a)** true **(b)** false
**(c)** true **(d)** false
**5. (a)** $10 \neq 8 - 2$ **(b)** $50 > 15$
**(c)** $11 \leq 20$

**OBJECTIVE 6** **Write statements that change the direction of inequality symbols.** Any statement with $<$ can be converted to one with $>$, and any statement with $>$ can be converted to one with $<$. *We do this by reversing the order of the numbers and the direction of the symbol.* For example,

$$6 < 10 \qquad \text{becomes} \qquad 10 > 6.$$

Interchange numbers.

Reverse symbol.

*NOW TRY*
*EXERCISE 6*

Write the statement as another true statement with the inequality symbol reversed.

$$8 < 9$$

**EXAMPLE 6** Converting between Inequality Symbols

Parts (a)–(c) each show a statement written in two equally correct ways. In each inequality, the inequality symbol points toward the lesser number.

**(a)** $5 > 2$, $2 < 5$  **(b)** $3 \leq 8$, $8 \geq 3$  **(c)** $12 \geq 5$, $5 \leq 12$

*NOW TRY*

Here is a summary of the symbols discussed in this section.

| Symbol | Meaning | Example |
|:---:|:---|:---|
| $=$ | Is equal to | $0.5 = \frac{1}{2}$ means 0.5 is equal to $\frac{1}{2}$. |
| $\neq$ | Is not equal to | $3 \neq 7$ means 3 is not equal to 7. |
| $<$ | Is less than | $6 < 10$ means 6 is less than 10. |
| $>$ | Is greater than | $15 > 14$ means 15 is greater than 14. |
| $\leq$ | Is less than or equal to | $4 \leq 8$ means 4 is less than or equal to 8. |
| $\geq$ | Is greater than or equal to | $1 \geq 0$ means 1 is greater than or equal to 0. |

⚠ **CAUTION** Equality and inequality symbols are used to write mathematical *sentences,* while operation symbols ($+$, $-$, $\cdot$, and $\div$) are used to write mathematical *expressions* that represent a number. Compare the following.

*Sentence:* $\quad 4 < 10 \leftarrow$ Gives the relationship between 4 and 10

*Expression:* $\quad 4 + 10 \leftarrow$ Tells how to operate on 4 and 10 to get 14

NOW TRY ANSWER
6. $9 > 8$

## 1.2 EXERCISES

*MyMathLab*   PRACTICE   WATCH   DOWNLOAD   READ  REVIEW

🌐 *Complete solution available on the Video Resources on DVD*

*Concept Check*  *Decide whether each statement is* true *or* false. *If it is false, explain why.*

**1.** The expression $6^2$ means that 2 is used as a factor 6 times.

**2.** $3^2 = 6$

**3.** $1^3 = 3$

**4.** $3^1 = 1$

**5.** When evaluated, $4 + 3(8 - 2)$ is equal to 42.

**6.** When evaluated, $12 \div 2 \cdot 3$ is equal to 2.

*Find the value of each exponential expression.* ***See Example 1.***

**7.** $3^2$        **8.** $8^2$        🌐 **9.** $7^2$        **10.** $4^2$        **11.** $12^2$

**12.** $14^2$        **13.** $4^3$        **14.** $5^3$        **15.** $10^3$        **16.** $11^3$

**17.** $3^4$        **18.** $6^4$        **19.** $4^5$        **20.** $3^5$        **21.** $\left(\dfrac{1}{6}\right)^2$

**22.** $\left(\dfrac{1}{3}\right)^2$        **23.** $\left(\dfrac{2}{3}\right)^4$        **24.** $\left(\dfrac{3}{4}\right)^3$        **25.** $(0.4)^3$        **26.** $(0.5)^4$

*Find the value of each expression.* ***See Examples 2 and 3.***

**27.** $64 \div 4 \cdot 2$        **28.** $250 \div 5 \cdot 2$        🌐 **29.** $13 + 9 \cdot 5$

**30.** $11 + 7 \cdot 6$        **31.** $25.2 - 12.6 \div 4.2$        **32.** $12.4 - 9.3 \div 3.1$

**33.** $\dfrac{1}{4} \cdot \dfrac{2}{3} + \dfrac{2}{5} \cdot \dfrac{11}{3}$        **34.** $\dfrac{9}{4} \cdot \dfrac{2}{3} + \dfrac{4}{5} \cdot \dfrac{5}{3}$        **35.** $9 \cdot 4 - 8 \cdot 3$

**36.** $11 \cdot 4 + 10 \cdot 3$        **37.** $20 - 4 \cdot 3 + 5$        **38.** $18 - 7 \cdot 2 + 6$

**39.** $10 + 40 \div 5 \cdot 2$        **40.** $12 + 64 \div 8 - 4$        **41.** $18 - 2(3 + 4)$

**42.** $30 - 3(4 + 2)$        **43.** $3(4 + 2) + 8 \cdot 3$        **44.** $9(1 + 7) + 2 \cdot 5$

**45.** $18 - 4^2 + 3$        **46.** $22 - 2^3 + 9$        **47.** $2 + 3[5 + 4(2)]$

**48.** $5 + 4[1 + 7(3)]$        **49.** $5[3 + 4(2^2)]$        **50.** $6[2 + 8(3^3)]$

🌐 **51.** $3^2[(11 + 3) - 4]$        **52.** $4^2[(13 + 4) - 8]$        **53.** $\dfrac{6(3^2 - 1) + 8}{8 - 2^2}$

**54.** $\dfrac{2(8^2 - 4) + 8}{29 - 3^3}$        **55.** $\dfrac{4(6 + 2) + 8(8 - 3)}{6(4 - 2) - 2^2}$        **56.** $\dfrac{6(5 + 1) - 9(1 + 1)}{5(8 - 6) - 2^3}$

*First simplify both sides of each inequality. Then tell whether the given statement is* true *or* false. ***See Examples 2–4.***

🌐 **57.** $9 \cdot 3 - 11 \le 16$        **58.** $6 \cdot 5 - 12 \le 18$

**59.** $5 \cdot 11 + 2 \cdot 3 \le 60$        **60.** $9 \cdot 3 + 4 \cdot 5 \ge 48$

**61.** $0 \ge 12 \cdot 3 - 6 \cdot 6$        **62.** $10 \le 13 \cdot 2 - 15 \cdot 1$

**63.** $45 \ge 2[2 + 3(2 + 5)]$        **64.** $55 \ge 3[4 + 3(4 + 1)]$

**65.** $[3 \cdot 4 + 5(2)] \cdot 3 > 72$        **66.** $2 \cdot [7 \cdot 5 - 3(2)] \le 58$

**67.** $\dfrac{3 + 5(4 - 1)}{2 \cdot 4 + 1} \ge 3$        **68.** $\dfrac{7(3 + 1) - 2}{3 + 5 \cdot 2} \le 2$

**69.** $3 \ge \dfrac{2(5 + 1) - 3(1 + 1)}{5(8 - 6) - 4 \cdot 2}$        **70.** $7 \le \dfrac{3(8 - 3) + 2(4 - 1)}{9(6 - 2) - 11(5 - 2)}$

*Concept Check*    *Insert one pair of parentheses so that the left side of each equation is equal to the right side.*

**71.** $3 \cdot 6 + 4 \cdot 2 = 60$        **72.** $2 \cdot 8 - 1 \cdot 3 = 42$        **73.** $10 - 7 - 3 = 6$

**74.** $15 - 10 - 2 = 7$        **75.** $8 + 2^2 = 100$        **76.** $4 + 2^2 = 36$

*Write each statement in words and decide whether it is* true *or* false. ***See Examples 4 and 5.***

**77.** $5 < 17$        **78.** $8 < 12$        **79.** $5 \ne 8$        **80.** $6 \ne 9$

**81.** $7 \ge 14$        **82.** $6 \ge 12$        **83.** $15 \le 15$        **84.** $21 \le 21$

*Write each word statement in symbols.* **See Example 5.**

**85.** Fifteen is equal to five plus ten.

**86.** Twelve is equal to twenty minus eight.

**87.** Nine is greater than five minus four.

**88.** Ten is greater than six plus one.

**89.** Sixteen is not equal to nineteen.

**90.** Three is not equal to four.

**91.** One-half is less than or equal to two-fourths.

**92.** One-third is less than or equal to three-ninths.

*Write each statement with the inequality symbol reversed while keeping the same meaning.* **See Example 6.**

**93.** $5 < 20$

**94.** $30 > 9$

**95.** $2.5 \geq 1.3$

**96.** $4.1 \leq 5.3$

*One way to measure a person's cardiofitness is to calculate how many METs, or metabolic units, he or she can reach at peak exertion. One MET is the amount of energy used when sitting quietly. To calculate ideal METs, we can use the following expressions.*

$$14.7 - \text{age} \cdot 0.13 \quad \text{For women}$$

$$14.7 - \text{age} \cdot 0.11 \quad \text{For men}$$

(*Source: New England Journal of Medicine.*)

**97.** A 40-yr-old woman wishes to calculate her ideal MET.

**(a)** Write the expression, using her age.

**(b)** Calculate her ideal MET. (*Hint:* Use the rules for order of operations.)

**(c)** Researchers recommend that a person reach approximately 85% of his or her MET when exercising. Calculate 85% of the ideal MET from part (b). Then refer to the following table. What activity can the woman do that is approximately this value?

| Activity | METs | Activity | METs |
|---|---|---|---|
| Golf (with cart) | 2.5 | Skiing (water or downhill) | 6.8 |
| Walking (3 mph) | 3.3 | Swimming | 7.0 |
| Mowing lawn (power mower) | 4.5 | Walking (5 mph) | 8.0 |
| Ballroom or square dancing | 5.5 | Jogging | 10.2 |
| Cycling | 5.7 | Skipping rope | 12.0 |

*Source:* Harvard School of Public Health.

**98.** Repeat parts (a)–(c) of **Exercise 97** for a 55-yr-old man.

**99.** Repeat parts (a)–(c) of **Exercise 97** using your age.

**100.** The table shows the number of pupils per teacher in U.S. public schools in selected states.

**(a)** Which states had a figure greater than 13.9?

**(b)** Which states had a figure that was at most 14.7?

**(c)** Which states had a figure not less than 13.9?

| State | Pupils per Teacher |
|---|---|
| Alaska | 16.7 |
| Texas | 14.7 |
| California | 20.5 |
| Wyoming | 12.5 |
| Maine | 12.3 |
| Idaho | 17.8 |
| Missouri | 13.9 |

*Source:* National Center for Education Statistics.

## Taking Lecture Notes

Study the set of sample math notes given here.

▶ **Include the date and title** of the day's lecture topic.

▶ **Include definitions,** written here in parentheses—don't trust your memory.

▶ **Skip lines and write neatly** to make reading easier.

▶ **Emphasize direction words** (like *simplify*) with their explanations.

▶ **Mark important concepts with stars, underlining, etc.**

▶ **Use two columns,** which allows an example and its explanation to be close together.

▶ **Use brackets and arrows** to clearly show steps, related material, etc.

*With a partner or in a small group, compare lecture notes.*

1. What are you doing to show main points in your notes (such as boxing, using stars, etc.)?

2. In what ways do you set off explanations from worked problems and subpoints (such as indenting, using arrows, circling, etc.)?

3. What new ideas did you learn by examining your classmates' notes?

4. What new techniques will you try in your notes?

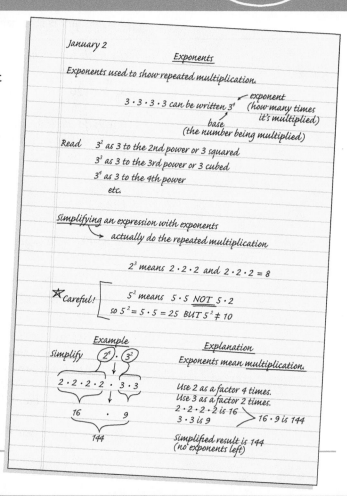

---

## 1.3 Variables, Expressions, and Equations

### OBJECTIVES

**1** Evaluate algebraic expressions, given values for the variables.

**2** Translate word phrases to algebraic expressions.

**3** Identify solutions of equations.

**4** Identify solutions of equations from a set of numbers.

**5** Distinguish between *expressions* and *equations*.

A **variable** is a symbol, usually a letter such as

$$x, \quad y, \quad \text{or} \quad z, \qquad \text{Variables}$$

used to represent any unknown number. An **algebraic expression** is a sequence of numbers, variables, operation symbols, and/or grouping symbols formed according to the rules of algebra.

$$x + 5, \quad 2m - 9, \quad 8p^2 + 6(p - 2) \qquad \text{Algebraic expressions}$$

$2m$ means $2 \cdot m$, the product of 2 and $m$.

$6(p - 2)$ means the product of 6 and $p - 2$.

**OBJECTIVE 1** **Evaluate algebraic expressions, given values for the variables.** An algebraic expression has different numerical values for different values of the variables.

*NOW TRY*
*EXERCISE 1*
Find the value of each algebraic expression for $k = 6$.
**(a)** $9k$   **(b)** $4k^2$

**EXAMPLE 1**   Evaluating Expressions

Find the value of each algebraic expression for $x = 5$.

**(a)** $8x$

$= 8 \cdot x$

$= 8 \cdot 5$     Let $x = 5$.

$= 40$     Multiply.

**(b)** $3x^2$

$= 3 \cdot x^2$     $\boxed{5^2 = 5 \cdot 5}$

$= 3 \cdot 5^2$     Let $x = 5$.

$= 3 \cdot 25$     Square 5.

$= 75$     Multiply.     *NOW TRY*

---

⚠ **CAUTION**   In **Example 1(b)**, $3x^2$ means $3 \cdot x^2$, *not* $3x \cdot 3x$. *Unless parentheses are used, the exponent refers only to the variable or number just before it.* Use parentheses to write $3x \cdot 3x$ with exponents as $(3x)^2$.

---

*NOW TRY*
*EXERCISE 2*
Find the value of each expression for $x = 4$ and $y = 7$.
**(a)** $3x + 4y$   **(b)** $\dfrac{6x - 2y}{2y - 9}$
**(c)** $4x^2 - y^2$

**EXAMPLE 2**   Evaluating Expressions

Find the value of each expression for $x = 5$ and $y = 3$.

**(a)**          $2x + 7y$     $\boxed{\text{We could use parentheses and write } 2(5) + 7(3).}$

$\boxed{\text{Follow the rules for order of operations.}}$

$= 2 \cdot 5 + 7 \cdot 3$     Let $x = 5$ and $y = 3$.

$= 10 + 21$     Multiply.

$= 31$     Add.

**(b)** $\dfrac{9x - 8y}{2x - y}$

$= \dfrac{9 \cdot 5 - 8 \cdot 3}{2 \cdot 5 - 3}$     Let $x = 5$ and $y = 3$.

$= \dfrac{45 - 24}{10 - 3}$     Multiply.

$= \dfrac{21}{7}$, or  $3$     Subtract, and then divide.

**(c)**    $x^2 - 2y^2$     $\boxed{3^2 = 3 \cdot 3}$

$= 5^2 - 2 \cdot 3^2$     Let $x = 5$ and $y = 3$.

$\boxed{5^2 = 5 \cdot 5}$

$= 25 - 2 \cdot 9$     Apply the exponents.

$= 25 - 18$     Multiply.

$= 7$     Subtract.     *NOW TRY*

**OBJECTIVE 2**   Translate word phrases to algebraic expressions.

**EXAMPLE 3**   Using Variables to Write Word Phrases as Algebraic Expressions

Write each word phrase as an algebraic expression, using $x$ as the variable.

**(a)** The sum of a number and 9

$x + 9$,   or   $9 + x$     "Sum" is the answer to an addition problem.

**(b)** 7 minus a number

$7 - x$     "Minus" indicates subtraction.

*NOW TRY ANSWERS*
**1. (a)** 54   **(b)** 144
**2. (a)** 40   **(b)** 2   **(c)** 15

$x - 7$ *is incorrect. We cannot subtract in either order and get the same result.*

NOW TRY
EXERCISE 3

Write each word phrase as an algebraic expression, using $x$ as the variable.

**(a)** The sum of a number and 10

**(b)** A number divided by 7

**(c)** The product of 3 and the difference between 9 and a number

**(c)** A number subtracted from 12

$$12 - x \quad \boxed{\text{Be careful with order.}}$$

Compare this result with "12 subtracted from a number," which is $x - 12$.

**(d)** The product of 11 and a number

$$11 \cdot x, \quad \text{or} \quad 11x$$

**(e)** 5 divided by a number

$$5 \div x, \quad \text{or} \quad \frac{5}{x} \quad \boxed{\tfrac{x}{5} \text{ is } \textit{not} \text{ correct here.}}$$

**(f)** The product of 2 and the difference between a number and 8

We are multiplying 2 times "something." This "something" is the difference between a number and 8, written $x - 8$. We use parentheses around this difference.

$$2 \cdot (x - 8), \quad \text{or} \quad 2(x - 8) \quad \boxed{8 - x, \text{ which means the difference between 8 and a number, is not correct.}}$$

NOW TRY

---

**OBJECTIVE 3**   **Identify solutions of equations.** An **equation** is a statement that two algebraic expressions are equal. *An equation always includes the equality symbol,* **=.**

$$\left.\begin{array}{lll} x + 4 = 11, & 2y = 16, & 4p + 1 = 25 - p, \\[2mm] \dfrac{3}{4}x + \dfrac{1}{2} = 0, & z^2 = 4, & 4(m - 0.5) = 2m \end{array}\right\} \text{Equations}$$

To **solve** an equation means to find the values of the variable that make the equation true. Such values of the variable are called the **solutions** of the equation.

---

NOW TRY
EXERCISE 4

Decide whether the given number is a solution of the equation.

$$8k + 5 = 61; \quad 7$$

**EXAMPLE 4**   Deciding Whether a Number Is a Solution of an Equation

Decide whether the given number is a solution of the equation.

**(a)** $5p + 1 = 36; \quad 7$

$$5p + 1 = 36$$
$$5 \cdot 7 + 1 \overset{?}{=} 36 \qquad \text{Let } p = 7.$$
$$35 + 1 \overset{?}{=} 36 \qquad \text{Multiply.}$$
$$\boxed{\text{Be careful! Multiply first.}} \qquad 36 = 36 \;\checkmark\; \text{True—the left side of the equation equals the right side.}$$

The number 7 is a solution of the equation.

**(b)** $9m - 6 = 32; \quad 4$

$$9m - 6 = 32$$
$$9 \cdot 4 - 6 \overset{?}{=} 32 \qquad \text{Let } m = 4.$$
$$36 - 6 \overset{?}{=} 32 \qquad \text{Multiply.}$$
$$30 = 32 \qquad \text{False—the left side does } \textit{not} \text{ equal the right side.}$$

The number 4 is not a solution of the equation.

NOW TRY

NOW TRY ANSWERS
**3.** **(a)** $x + 10$, or $10 + x$   **(b)** $\frac{x}{7}$
**(c)** $3(9 - x)$
**4.** yes

**OBJECTIVE 4** Identify solutions of equations from a set of numbers. A **set** is a collection of objects. In mathematics, these objects are most often numbers. The objects that belong to the set, called **elements** of the set, are written between **braces.**

$$\{1, 2, 3, 4, 5\} \leftarrow \text{The set containing the numbers 1, 2, 3, 4, and 5}$$

⤹ NOW TRY
▸ EXERCISE 5
Write the word statement as an equation. Then find all solutions of the equation from the set $\{0, 2, 4, 6, 8, 10\}$.

The sum of a number and nine is equal to the difference between 25 and the number.

**EXAMPLE 5** Finding a Solution from a Given Set

Write each word statement as an equation. Use $x$ as the variable. Then find all solutions of the equation from the set

$$\{0, 2, 4, 6, 8, 10\}.$$

**(a)** The sum of a number and four is six.

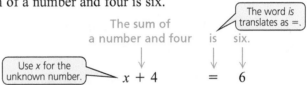

One by one, mentally substitute each number from the given set $\{0, 2, 4, 6, 8, 10\}$ in $x + 4 = 6$. Since $2 + 4 = 6$ is true, $2$ is the only solution.

**(b)** Nine more than five times a number is 49.

Substitute each of the given numbers. The solution is $8$, since $5 \cdot 8 + 9 = 49$ is true.

**(c)** The sum of a number and 12 is equal to four times the number.

Substituting each of the given numbers in the equation leads to a true statement only for $x = 4$, since $4 + 12 = 4(4)$ is true. NOW TRY ⤹

**OBJECTIVE 5** Distinguish between *expressions* and *equations*. Students often have trouble distinguishing between equations and expressions. *An equation is a sentence—it has something on the left side, an = symbol, and something on the right side. An expression is a phrase that represents a number.*

⤹ NOW TRY
▸ EXERCISE 6
Decide whether each of the following is an *expression* or an *equation*.

**(a)** $2x + 5 = 6$

**(b)** $2x + 5 - 6$

| $4x + 5 = 9$ | $4x + 5$ |
|---|---|
| Left side ↑ Right side | ↑ |
| Equation | Expression |
| (to solve) | (to simplify or evaluate) |

**EXAMPLE 6** Distinguishing between Equations and Expressions

Decide whether each of the following is an *equation* or an *expression*.

**(a)** $2x - 5y$   There is no equals symbol. This is an expression.

**(b)** $2x = 5y$   There is an equals symbol with something on either side of it. This is an equation. NOW TRY ⤹

NOW TRY ANSWERS
**5.** $x + 9 = 25 - x$; 8
**6.** **(a)** equation **(b)** expression

## 1.3 EXERCISES

*MyMathLab*  Math XL PRACTICE  WATCH  DOWNLOAD  READ REVIEW

🌐 *Complete solution available on the Video Resources on DVD*

*Concept Check* *Choose the letter(s) of the correct response.*

**1.** The expression $8x^2$ means _____.

    **A.** $8 \cdot x \cdot 2$     **B.** $8 \cdot x \cdot x$     **C.** $8 + x^2$     **D.** $8x^2 \cdot 8x^2$

**2.** If $x = 2$ and $y = 1$, then the value of $xy$ is _____.

    **A.** $\dfrac{1}{2}$     **B.** $1$     **C.** $2$     **D.** $3$

**3.** The sum of 15 and a number $x$ is represented by _____.

    **A.** $15 + x$     **B.** $15 - x$     **C.** $x - 15$     **D.** $15x$

**4.** Which of the following are expressions?

    **A.** $6x = 7$     **B.** $6x + 7$     **C.** $6x - 7$     **D.** $6x - 7 = 0$

🖉 *In Exercises 5–8, give a short explanation.*

**5.** Explain why $2x^3$ is not the same as $2x \cdot 2x \cdot 2x$.

**6.** Why are "7 less than a number" and "7 is less than a number" translated differently?

**7.** When evaluating the expression $5x^2$ for $x = 4$, explain why 4 must be squared *before* multiplying by 5.

**8.** There are many pairs of values of $x$ and $y$ for which $2x + y$ will equal 6. Name two such pairs and describe how you determined them.

*Find the value for (a) $x = 4$ and (b) $x = 6$. See Example 1.*

**9.** $x + 7$      **10.** $x - 3$      **11.** $4x$      **12.** $6x$      🌐 **13.** $4x^2$

**14.** $5x^2$      **15.** $\dfrac{x + 1}{3}$      **16.** $\dfrac{x - 2}{5}$      **17.** $\dfrac{3x - 5}{2x}$      **18.** $\dfrac{4x - 1}{3x}$

**19.** $3x^2 + x$      **20.** $2x + x^2$      **21.** $6.459x$      **22.** $3.275x$

*Find the value for (a) $x = 2$ and $y = 1$ and (b) $x = 1$ and $y = 5$. See Example 2.*

🌐 **23.** $8x + 3y + 5$      **24.** $4x + 2y + 7$      **25.** $3(x + 2y)$      **26.** $2(2x + y)$

**27.** $x + \dfrac{4}{y}$      **28.** $y + \dfrac{8}{x}$      **29.** $\dfrac{x}{2} + \dfrac{y}{3}$      **30.** $\dfrac{x}{5} + \dfrac{y}{4}$

**31.** $\dfrac{2x + 4y - 6}{5y + 2}$      **32.** $\dfrac{4x + 3y - 1}{x}$      **33.** $2y^2 + 5x$      **34.** $6x^2 + 4y$

**35.** $\dfrac{3x + y^2}{2x + 3y}$      **36.** $\dfrac{x^2 + 1}{4x + 5y}$      **37.** $0.841x^2 + 0.32y^2$    **38.** $0.941x^2 + 0.25y^2$

*Write each word phrase as an algebraic expression, using $x$ as the variable. See Example 3.*

🌐 **39.** Twelve times a number      **40.** Fifteen times a number

**41.** Nine added to a number      **42.** Six added to a number

**43.** Four subtracted from a number      **44.** Seven subtracted from a number

**45.** A number subtracted from seven      **46.** A number subtracted from four

**47.** The difference between a number and 8      **48.** The difference between 8 and a number

**49.** 18 divided by a number      **50.** A number divided by 18

**51.** The product of 6 and four less than a number      **52.** The product of 9 and five more than a number

**53.** Suppose that the directions on a test read "*Solve the following expressions*." How would you politely correct the person who wrote these directions?

**54.** Suppose that, for the equation $3x - y = 9$, the value of $x$ is given as 4. What would be the corresponding value of $y$? How do you know this?

*Decide whether the given number is a solution of the equation.* ***See Example 4.***

**55.** $4m + 2 = 6; \quad 1$

**56.** $2r + 6 = 8; \quad 1$

**57.** $2y + 3(y - 2) = 14; \quad 3$

**58.** $6x + 2(x + 3) = 14; \quad 2$

**59.** $6p + 4p + 9 = 11; \quad \dfrac{1}{5}$

**60.** $2x + 3x + 8 = 20; \quad \dfrac{12}{5}$

**61.** $3r^2 - 2 = 46; \quad 4$

**62.** $2x^2 + 1 = 19; \quad 3$

**63.** $\dfrac{3}{8}x + \dfrac{1}{4} = 1; \quad 2$

**64.** $\dfrac{7}{10}x + \dfrac{1}{2} = 4; \quad 5$

**65.** $0.5(x - 4) = 80; \quad 20$

**66.** $0.2(x - 5) = 70; \quad 40$

*Write each word statement as an equation. Use x as the variable. Find all solutions from the set $\{2, 4, 6, 8, 10\}$.* ***See Example 5.***

**67.** The sum of a number and 8 is 18.

**68.** A number minus three equals 1.

**69.** Sixteen minus three-fourths of a number is 13.

**70.** The sum of six-fifths of a number and 2 is 14.

**71.** One more than twice a number is 5.

**72.** The product of a number and 3 is 6.

**73.** Three times a number is equal to 8 more than twice the number.

**74.** Twelve divided by a number equals $\frac{1}{3}$ times that number.

*Identify each as an* expression *or an* equation. ***See Example 6.***

**75.** $3x + 2(x - 4)$

**76.** $8y - (3y + 5)$

**77.** $7t + 2(t + 1) = 4$

**78.** $9r + 3(r - 4) = 2$

**79.** $x + y = 9$

**80.** $x + y - 9$

*A **mathematical model** is an equation that describes the relationship between two quantities. For example, the life expectancy at birth of Americans can be approximated by the equation*

$$y = 0.212x - 347,$$

*where x is a year between 1943 and 2005 and y is age in years. (Source: Centers for Disease Control and Prevention.)*
    *Use this model to approximate life expectancy (to the nearest tenth of a year) in each of the following years.*

**81.** 1943

**82.** 1960

**83.** 1985

**84.** 2005

**85.** How has the life expectancy at birth of Americans changed in the years from 1943 to 2005?

## 1.4 Real Numbers and the Number Line

**OBJECTIVES**

1. Classify numbers and graph them on number lines.
2. Tell which of two real numbers is less than the other.
3. Find the additive inverse of a real number.
4. Find the absolute value of a real number.
5. Interpret the meanings of real numbers from a table of data.

**OBJECTIVE 1** Classify numbers and graph them on number lines. In **Section 1.1,** we introduced the set of *natural numbers* and the set of *whole numbers*.

### Natural Numbers

$\{1, 2, 3, 4, \ldots\}$ is the set of **natural numbers** (or **counting numbers**).

### Whole Numbers

$\{0, 1, 2, 3, 4, \ldots\}$ is the set of **whole numbers.**

**NOTE** The three dots ( ... ) show that the list of numbers continues in the same way indefinitely.

We can represent numbers on a **number line** like the one in **FIGURE 3**.

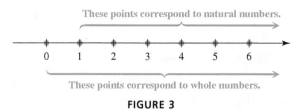

To draw a number line, choose any point on the line and label it 0. Then choose any point to the right of 0 and label it 1. Use the distance between 0 and 1 as the scale to locate, and then label, other points.

**FIGURE 3**

The natural numbers are located to the right of 0 on the number line. For each natural number, we can place a corresponding number to the left of 0, labeling the points $-1$, $-2$, $-3$, and so on, as shown in **FIGURE 4**. Each is the **opposite,** or **negative,** of a natural number. The natural numbers, their opposites, and 0 form the set of *integers*.

### Integers

$\{\ldots, -3, -2, -1, 0, 1, 2, 3, \ldots\}$ is the set of **integers.**

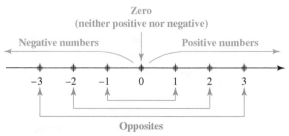

**FIGURE 4**

*Positive numbers* and *negative numbers* are called **signed numbers.**

NOW TRY
EXERCISE 1

Use an integer to express the number in boldface italics in the following statement.

At its deepest point, the floor of West Okoboji Lake sits *136* ft below the water's surface. (*Source:* www.watersafetycouncil.org)

---

**EXAMPLE 1**  Using Negative Numbers in Applications

Use an integer to express the number in boldface italics in each application.

**(a)** The lowest Fahrenheit temperature ever recorded was *129°* below zero at Vostok, Antarctica, on July 21, 1983. (*Source: World Almanac and Book of Facts.*)
Use $-129$ because "below zero" indicates a negative number.

**(b)** General Motors had a loss of about $*31* billion in 2008. (*Source: The Wall Street Journal.*)
Here, a loss indicates a negative "profit," $-31$.

NOW TRY

Fractions, introduced in **Section 1.1,** are examples of *rational numbers.*

---

### Rational Numbers

$\{x \,|\, x$ is a quotient of two integers, with denominator not 0\} is the set of **rational numbers.**

(Read the part in the braces as "the set of all numbers $x$ such that $x$ is a quotient of two integers, with denominator not 0.")

---

**NOTE**  The set symbolism used in the definition of rational numbers,

$$\{x \,|\, x \text{ has a certain property}\},$$

is called **set-builder notation.** We use this notation when it is not possible to list all the elements of a set.

---

Since any number that can be written as the quotient of two integers (that is, as a fraction) is a rational number, ***all integers, mixed numbers, terminating (or ending) decimals, and repeating decimals are rational.*** The table gives examples.

| Rational Number | Equivalent Quotient of Two Integers |
|---|---|
| $-5$ | $\frac{-5}{1}$ (means $-5 \div 1$) |
| $1\frac{3}{4}$ | $\frac{7}{4}$ (means $7 \div 4$) |
| $0.23$ (terminating decimal) | $\frac{23}{100}$ (means $23 \div 100$) |
| $0.3333\ldots$, or $0.\overline{3}$ (repeating decimal) | $\frac{1}{3}$ (means $1 \div 3$) |
| $4.7$ | $\frac{47}{10}$ (means $47 \div 10$) |

To **graph** a number, we place a dot on the number line at the point that corresponds to the number. The number is called the **coordinate** of the point. See **FIGURE 5.**

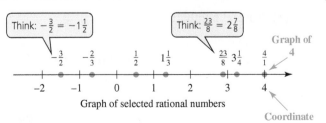

Think of the graph of a set of numbers as a picture of the set.

**FIGURE 5**

NOW TRY ANSWER
1. $-136$

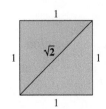

This square has diagonal of length $\sqrt{2}$. The number $\sqrt{2}$ is an irrational number.

**FIGURE 6**

Not all numbers are rational. For example, the square root of 2, written $\sqrt{2}$, cannot be written as a quotient of two integers. Because of this, $\sqrt{2}$ is an *irrational number*. (See **FIGURE 6**.)

### Irrational Numbers

$\{x \mid x \text{ is a nonrational number represented by a point on the number line}\}$ is the set of **irrational numbers.**

The decimal form of an irrational number neither terminates nor repeats.

Both rational and irrational numbers can be represented by points on the number line and together form the set of *real numbers*.

### Real Numbers

$\{x \mid x \text{ is a rational or an irrational number}\}$ is the set of **real numbers.** *

The relationships among the various sets of numbers are shown in **FIGURE 7**.

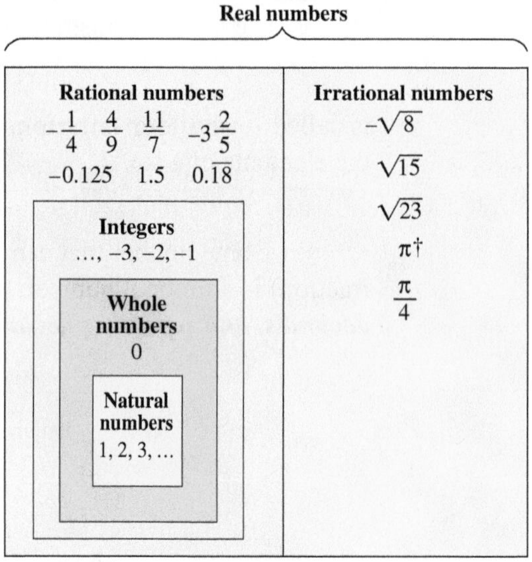

**Real numbers**

**Rational numbers**
$-\dfrac{1}{4} \quad \dfrac{4}{9} \quad \dfrac{11}{7} \quad -3\dfrac{2}{5}$
$-0.125 \quad 1.5 \quad 0.\overline{18}$

**Integers**
..., −3, −2, −1

**Whole numbers**
0

**Natural numbers**
1, 2, 3, ...

**Irrational numbers**
$-\sqrt{8}$
$\sqrt{15}$
$\sqrt{23}$
$\pi$†
$\dfrac{\pi}{4}$

**FIGURE 7**

### EXAMPLE 2 Determining Whether a Number Belongs to a Set

List the numbers in the following set that belong to each set of numbers.

$$\left\{ -5, -\frac{2}{3}, 0, 0.\overline{6}, \sqrt{2}, 3\frac{1}{4}, 5, 5.8 \right\}$$

**(a)** Natural numbers:    5

**(b)** Whole numbers:    0 and 5
    The whole numbers consist of the natural (counting) numbers and 0.

---

*An example of a number that is not a real number is the square root of a negative number, such as $\sqrt{-5}$.

†The value of $\pi$ (pi) is approximately 3.141592654. The decimal digits continue forever with no repeated pattern.

NOW TRY
EXERCISE 2

List the numbers in the following set that belong to each set of numbers.

$$\left\{-7, -\tfrac{4}{5}, 0, \sqrt{3}, 2.7, \pi, 13\right\}$$

**(a)** Whole numbers

**(b)** Integers

**(c)** Rational numbers

**(d)** Irrational numbers

**(c)** Integers:    $-5, 0,$ and $5$

**(d)** Rational numbers:    $-5, -\tfrac{2}{3}, 0, 0.\overline{6} \left(\text{or } \tfrac{2}{3}\right), 3\tfrac{1}{4} \left(\text{or } \tfrac{13}{4}\right), 5,$ and $5.8 \left(\text{or } \tfrac{58}{10}\right)$

   Each of these numbers can be written as the quotient of two integers.

**(e)** Irrational numbers:    $\sqrt{2}$

**(f)** Real numbers:    All the numbers in the set are real numbers.    *NOW TRY*

**OBJECTIVE 2** **Tell which of two real numbers is less than the other.** Given any two positive integers, you probably can tell which number is less than the other. Positive numbers decrease as the corresponding points on the number line go to the left. For example, $8 < 12$ because 8 is to the left of 12 on the number line. This ordering is extended to all real numbers by definition.

---

### Ordering of Real Numbers

For any two real numbers $a$ and $b$, **$a$ is less than $b$** if $a$ lies to the left of $b$ on the number line. See **FIGURE 8**.

---

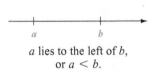

$a$ lies to the left of $b$,
or $a < b$.

**FIGURE 8**

This means that any negative number is less than 0, and any negative number is less than any positive number. Also, 0 is less than any positive number.

NOW TRY
EXERCISE 3

Determine whether the statement is *true* or *false*.

$$-8 \le -9$$

**EXAMPLE 3**   Determining the Order of Real Numbers

Is the statement $-3 < -1$ *true* or *false*?

   Locate $-3$ and $-1$ on a number line, as shown in **FIGURE 9**. Since $-3$ lies to the left of $-1$ on the number line, $-3$ is less than $-1$. The statement $-3 < -1$ is true.

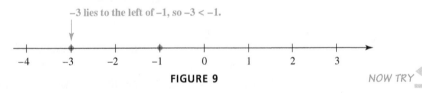

**FIGURE 9**    *NOW TRY*

We can also say that, for any two real numbers $a$ and $b$, **$a$ is greater than $b$** if $a$ lies to the right of $b$ on the number line. See **FIGURE 10**.

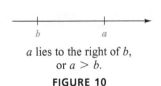

$a$ lies to the right of $b$,
or $a > b$.

**FIGURE 10**

**OBJECTIVE 3** **Find the additive inverse of a real number.** By a property of the real numbers, for any real number $x$ (except 0), there is exactly one number on the number line the same distance from 0 as $x$, but on the *opposite* side of 0. See **FIGURE 11**. Such pairs of numbers are called *additive inverses,* or *opposites,* of each other.

NOW TRY ANSWERS
**2.** **(a)** $0, 13$   **(b)** $-7, 0, 13$
   **(c)** $-7, -\tfrac{4}{5}, 0, 2.7, 13$
   **(d)** $\sqrt{3}, \pi$
**3.** false

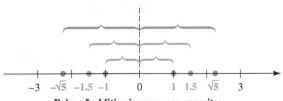

**Pairs of additive inverses, or opposites**

**FIGURE 11**

### Additive Inverse

The **additive inverse** of a number $x$ is the number that is the same distance from 0 on the number line as $x$, but on the *opposite* side of 0.

We indicate the additive inverse of a number by writing the symbol $-$ in front of the number. For example, the additive inverse of 7 is written $-7$. We could write the additive inverse of $-3$ as $-(-3)$, but we know that 3 is the additive inverse of $-3$. Since a number can have only one additive inverse, 3 and $-(-3)$ must represent the same number, so

$$-(-3) = 3.$$

This idea can be generalized.

| Number | Additive Inverse |
|--------|------------------|
| 7 | $-7$ |
| $-3$ | $-(-3)$, or 3 |
| 0 | 0 |
| 19 | $-19$ |
| $-\frac{2}{3}$ | $\frac{2}{3}$ |
| 0.52 | $-0.52$ |

*The additive inverse of a nonzero number is found by changing the sign of the number.*

### Double Negative Rule

For any real number $x$,     $-(-x) = x.$

The table in the margin shows several numbers and their additive inverses.

**OBJECTIVE 4** **Find the absolute value of a real number.** Because additive inverses are the same distance from 0 on a number line, a number and its additive inverse have the same *absolute value*. The **absolute value** of a real number $x$, written $|x|$ and read **"the absolute value of $x$,"** can be defined as the distance between 0 and the number on a number line. For example,

$|2| = 2,$     The distance between 2 and 0 on a number line is 2 units.

$|-2| = 2.$     The distance between $-2$ and 0 on a number line is also 2 units.

Distance is a physical measurement, which is never negative. *Therefore, the absolute value of a number is never negative.*

In symbols, the absolute value of $x$ is defined as follows.

### Absolute Value

For any real number $x$,

$$|x| = \begin{cases} x & \text{if } x \geq 0 \\ -x & \text{if } x < 0. \end{cases}$$

*By this definition, if $x$ is a positive number or 0, then its absolute value is $x$ itself.* For example, since 8 is a positive number,

$$|8| = 8.$$

*If $x$ is a negative number, then its absolute value is the additive inverse of $x$.*

$$|-8| = -(-8) = 8$$     The additive inverse of $-8$ is 8.

⚠ **CAUTION**  The "−x" in the second part of the definition of absolute value does **NOT** represent a negative number. Since x is negative in the second part, −x represents the opposite of a negative number—that is, a positive number. ***The absolute value of a number is never negative.***

⌐ *NOW TRY*
  *EXERCISE 4*
Simplify by finding the absolute value.

**(a)** $|4|$  **(b)** $|-4|$  **(c)** $-|-4|$

**EXAMPLE 4**  Finding the Absolute Value

Simplify by finding the absolute value.

**(a)** $|0| = 0$    **(b)** $|5| = 5$    **(c)** $|-5| = -(-5) = 5$

**(d)** $-|5| = -(5) = -5$    **(e)** $-|-5| = -(5) = -5$

**(f)** $|8 - 2| = |6| = 6$    **(g)** $-|8 - 2| = -|6| = -6$

Parts (f) and (g) show that absolute value bars are grouping symbols. We perform any operations inside absolute value symbols *before* finding the absolute value.

*NOW TRY* ⟳

**OBJECTIVE 5**  Interpret the meanings of real numbers from a table of data.

⌐ *NOW TRY*
  *EXERCISE 5*
In the table for **Example 5**, which category represents a decrease for both years?

**EXAMPLE 5**  Interpreting Data

The Consumer Price Index (CPI) measures the average change in prices of goods and services purchased by urban consumers in the United States.

The table shows the percent change in the Consumer Price Index for selected categories of goods and services from 2005 to 2006 and from 2006 to 2007. Use the table to answer each question.

| Category | Change from 2005 to 2006 | Change from 2006 to 2007 |
|---|---|---|
| Education | 6.2 | 5.7 |
| Food | 3.2 | 2.8 |
| Gasoline | 12.9 | 8.2 |
| Medical care | 4.0 | 4.4 |
| New cars | −0.2 | −1.0 |

*Source:* U.S. Bureau of Labor Statistics.

**(a)** What category in which year represents the greatest percent decrease?

We must find the negative number with the greatest absolute value. The number that satisfies this condition is −1.0, so the greatest percent decrease was shown by new cars from 2006 to 2007.

**(b)** Which category in which year represents the least change?

We must find the number (either positive, negative, or zero) with the least absolute value. From 2005 to 2006, new cars showed the least change, a decrease of 0.2%.

*NOW TRY* ⟳

*NOW TRY ANSWERS*
**4. (a)** 4  **(b)** 4  **(c)** −4
**5.** new cars

**1.4 EXERCISES** *MyMathLab* Math XL PRACTICE  WATCH  DOWNLOAD  READ  REVIEW

🌐 *Complete solution available on the Video Resources on DVD*

*In Exercises 1–4, use an integer to express each number in boldface italics representing a change. In Exercises 5–8, use a rational number.* **See Example 1.**

1. Between July 1, 2006, and July 1, 2007, the population of the United States increased by approximately **2,866,000**. (*Source:* U.S. Census Bureau.)

2. Between 2006 and 2007, the number of movie screens in the United States increased by **409**. (*Source:* Motion Picture Association of America.)

3. From 2006 to 2007, attendance at the World Series went from 225,000 to 173,000, a decrease of **52,000**. (*Source:* Major League Baseball.)

4. In 1935, there were 15,295 banks in the United States. By 2008, the number was 8441, representing a decrease of **6854** banks. (*Source:* Federal Deposit Insurance Corporation.)

5. The number of bachelor's degrees in computer and information sciences in the United States declined **11.2**% from the 2005–2006 academic year to the 2006–2007 year, while the number of bachelor's degrees in biological and biomedical sciences rose **8.6**%. (*Source:* National Center for Education Statistics.)

6. Between 2006 and 2007, print advertising revenue in the United States declined **9.4**%, while online advertising rose **18.8**%. (*Source:* Newspaper Association of America.)

7. On Tuesday, August 18, 2009, the Dow Jones Industrial Average (DJIA) closed at 9217.94. On the previous day it had closed at 9135.34. Thus, on Tuesday, it closed up **82.60** points. (*Source: The Washington Post.*)

8. On Monday, August 17, 2009, the NASDAQ closed at 1930.84. On the previous Friday, it had closed at 1985.52. Thus, on Monday, it closed down **54.68** points. (*Source: The Washington Post.*)

*Concept Check* *In Exercises 9–14, give a number that satisfies the given condition.*

9. An integer between 3.6 and 4.6

10. A rational number between 2.8 and 2.9

11. A whole number that is not positive and is less than 1

12. A whole number greater than 3.5

13. An irrational number that is between $\sqrt{12}$ and $\sqrt{14}$

14. A real number that is neither negative nor positive

*Concept Check* *In Exercises 15–20, decide whether each statement is* true *or* false.

15. Every natural number is positive.

16. Every whole number is positive.

17. Every integer is a rational number.

18. Every rational number is a real number.

19. Some numbers are both rational and irrational.

20. Every terminating decimal is a rational number.

*Concept Check* *Give three numbers between* −6 *and* 6 *that satisfy each given condition.*

21. Positive real numbers but not integers

22. Real numbers but not positive numbers

23. Real numbers but not whole numbers

24. Rational numbers but not integers

25. Real numbers but not rational numbers

26. Rational numbers but not negative numbers

*For Exercises 27 and 28,* **see Example 2.** *List all numbers from each set that are*

(a) *natural numbers*   (b) *whole numbers*   (c) *integers*
(d) *rational numbers*   (e) *irrational numbers*   (f) *real numbers.*

**27.** $\left\{ -9, -\sqrt{7}, -1\frac{1}{4}, -\frac{3}{5}, 0, 0.\overline{1}, \sqrt{5}, 3, 5.9, 7 \right\}$

**28.** $\left\{ -5.3, -5, -\sqrt{3}, -1, -\frac{1}{9}, 0, 0.\overline{27}, 1.2, 1.8, 3, \sqrt{11} \right\}$

*Graph each group of numbers on a number line. See* **FIGURE 4** *and* **FIGURE 5.**

**29.** $0, 3, -5, -6$    **30.** $2, 6, -2, -1$    **31.** $-2, -6, -4, 3, 4$

**32.** $-5, -3, -2, 0, 4$    **33.** $\frac{1}{4}, 2\frac{1}{2}, -3\frac{4}{5}, -4, -1\frac{5}{8}$    **34.** $5\frac{1}{4}, 4\frac{5}{9}, -2\frac{1}{3}, 0, -3\frac{2}{5}$

**35.** *Concept Check*  Match each expression in Column I with its value in Column II. Choices in Column II may be used once, more than once, or not at all.

|  I  |  II  |
| --- | --- |
| (a) $\lvert -9 \rvert$ | A. 9 |
| (b) $-(-9)$ | B. $-9$ |
| (c) $-\lvert -9 \rvert$ | C. Neither A nor B |
| (d) $-\lvert -(-9) \rvert$ | D. Both A and B |

**36.** *Concept Check*  Fill in the blanks with the correct values: The opposite of $-5$ is _____, while the absolute value of $-5$ is _____. The additive inverse of $-5$ is _____, while the additive inverse of the absolute value of $-5$ is _____.

*Find* (a) *the opposite (or additive inverse) of each number and* (b) *the absolute value of each number.* **See Objective 3 and Example 4.**

**37.** $-7$    **38.** $-4$    **39.** $8$    **40.** $10$    **41.** $-\frac{3}{4}$    **42.** $-\frac{2}{5}$

*Simplify by finding the absolute value.* **See Example 4.**

**43.** $\lvert -6 \rvert$    **44.** $\lvert -14 \rvert$    **45.** $-\lvert 12 \rvert$    **46.** $-\lvert 19 \rvert$

**47.** $-\left\lvert -\frac{2}{3} \right\rvert$    **48.** $-\left\lvert -\frac{4}{5} \right\rvert$    **49.** $\lvert 6 - 3 \rvert$    **50.** $-\lvert 6 - 3 \rvert$

**51.** Students often say "Absolute value is always positive." Is this true? Explain.

**52.** *Concept Check*  *True* or *false:*  If $a$ is negative, then $\lvert a \rvert = -a$.

*Select the lesser of the two given numbers.* **See Examples 3 and 4.**

**53.** $-11, -3$    **54.** $-8, -13$    **55.** $-7, -6$

**56.** $-16, -17$    **57.** $4, \lvert -5 \rvert$    **58.** $4, \lvert -3 \rvert$

**59.** $\lvert -3.5 \rvert, \lvert -4.5 \rvert$    **60.** $\lvert -8.9 \rvert, \lvert -9.8 \rvert$    **61.** $-\lvert -6 \rvert, -\lvert -4 \rvert$

**62.** $-\lvert -2 \rvert, -\lvert -3 \rvert$    **63.** $\lvert 5 - 3 \rvert, \lvert 6 - 2 \rvert$    **64.** $\lvert 7 - 2 \rvert, \lvert 8 - 1 \rvert$

*Decide whether each statement is true or false.* **See Examples 3 and 4.**

**65.** $-5 < -2$    **66.** $-8 > -2$    **67.** $-4 \leq -(-5)$

**68.** $-6 \leq -(-3)$    **69.** $\lvert -6 \rvert < \lvert -9 \rvert$    **70.** $\lvert -12 \rvert < \lvert -20 \rvert$

**71.** $-\lvert 8 \rvert > \lvert -9 \rvert$    **72.** $-\lvert 12 \rvert > \lvert -15 \rvert$    **73.** $-\lvert -5 \rvert \geq -\lvert -9 \rvert$

**74.** $-\lvert -12 \rvert \leq -\lvert -15 \rvert$    **75.** $\lvert 6 - 5 \rvert \geq \lvert 6 - 2 \rvert$    **76.** $\lvert 13 - 8 \rvert \leq \lvert 7 - 4 \rvert$

*The table shows the percent change in the Consumer Price Index (CPI) for selected categories of goods and services from 2004 to 2005 and from 2006 to 2007. Use the table to answer Exercises 77–80.* ***See Example 5.***

**77.** Which category in which year represents the greatest percentage increase?

**78.** Which category in which year represents the greatest percentage decrease?

**79.** Which category in which year represents the least change?

**80.** Which categories represent a decrease for both years?

| Category | Change from 2004 to 2005 | Change from 2006 to 2007 |
|---|---|---|
| Shelter | 2.6 | 3.7 |
| Apparel and upkeep | −0.7 | −0.4 |
| Fuel and other utilities | 10.6 | 3.0 |
| Medical care | 4.0 | 4.4 |
| Public transportation | 3.9 | 1.5 |

*Source:* U.S. Bureau of Labor Statistics.

## STUDY SKILLS

## Tackling Your Homework

You are ready to do your homework **AFTER** you have read the corresponding textbook section and worked through the examples and Now Try exercises.

### Homework Tips

▶ **Work problems neatly.** Use pencil and write legibly, so others can read your work. Skip lines between steps. Clearly separate problems from each other.

▶ **Show all your work.** It is tempting to take shortcuts. Include ALL steps.

▶ **Check your work frequently to make sure you are on the right track.** It is hard to unlearn a mistake. For all odd-numbered problems, answers are given in the back of the book.

▶ **If you have trouble with a problem, refer to the corresponding worked example in the section.** The exercise directions will often reference specific examples to review. Pay attention to every line of the worked example to see how to get from step to step.

▶ **If you are having trouble with an even-numbered problem, work the corresponding odd-numbered problem.** Check your answer in the back of the book, and apply the same steps to work the even-numbered problem.

▶ **Mark any problems you don't understand.** Ask your instructor about them.

*Select several homework tips to try this week.*

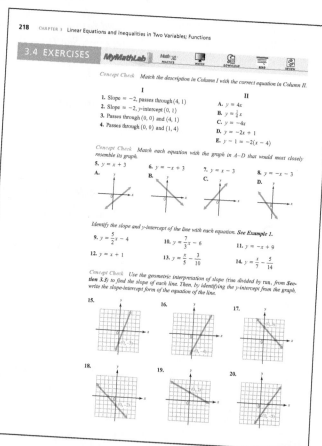

# 1.5 Adding and Subtracting Real Numbers

**OBJECTIVE 1** **Add two numbers with the same sign.** Recall that the answer to an addition problem is called a **sum.** A number line can be used to add real numbers.

**EXAMPLE 1**  Adding Numbers on a Number Line

Use a number line to find each sum.

**(a)** $2 + 3$

*Step 1*  Start at 0 and draw an arrow 2 units to the *right*. See **FIGURE 12**.

*Step 2*  From the right end of that arrow, draw another arrow 3 units to the right.

The number below the end of this second arrow is 5, so $2 + 3 = 5$.

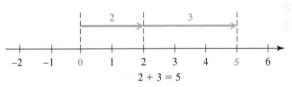

$2 + 3 = 5$

**FIGURE 12**

**(b)** $-2 + (-4)$

(We put parentheses around $-4$ due to the $+$ and $-$ next to each other.)

*Step 1*  Start at 0 and draw an arrow 2 units to the *left*. See **FIGURE 13**.

*Step 2*  From the left end of the first arrow, draw a second arrow 4 units to the *left* to represent the addition of a *negative* number.

The number below the end of this second arrow is $-6$, so $-2 + (-4) = -6$.

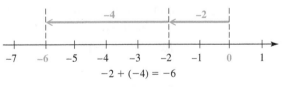

$-2 + (-4) = -6$

**FIGURE 13**                                          NOW TRY ↻

In **Example 1(b),** the sum of the two negative numbers $-2$ and $-4$ is a negative number whose distance from 0 is the sum of the distance of $-2$ from 0 and the distance of $-4$ from 0. ***That is, the sum of two negative numbers is the negative of the sum of their absolute values.***

$$-2 + (-4) = -(|-2| + |-4|) = -(2 + 4) = -6$$

↻ *NOW TRY*
*EXERCISE 1*

Use a number line to find each sum.

**(a)** $3 + 5$   **(b)** $-1 + (-3)$

*NOW TRY ANSWERS*
**1. (a)** 8  **(b)** $-4$

### Adding Numbers with the Same Sign

To add two numbers with the *same* sign, add the absolute values of the numbers. The sum has the same sign as the numbers being added.

*Example:* $-4 + (-3) = -7$

 **NOW TRY EXERCISE 2**

Find the sum.

$$-6 + (-11)$$

**EXAMPLE 2** Adding Two Negative Numbers

Find each sum.

**(a)** $-2 + (-9) = -(|-2| + |-9|) = -(2 + 9) = -11$

**(b)** $-8 + (-12) = -20$      **(c)** $-15 + (-3) = -18$    *NOW TRY*

**OBJECTIVE 2** Add two numbers with different signs.

**NOW TRY EXERCISE 3**

Use a number line to find the sum.

$$4 + (-8)$$

**EXAMPLE 3** Adding Numbers with Different Signs

Use a number line to find the sum $-2 + 5$.

*Step 1* Start at 0 and draw an arrow 2 units to the left. See **FIGURE 14**.

*Step 2* From the left end of this arrow, draw a second arrow 5 units to the right.

The number below the end of the second arrow is 3, so $-2 + 5 = 3$.

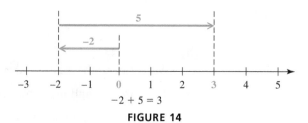

**FIGURE 14**    *NOW TRY*

### Adding Numbers with Different Signs

To add two numbers with *different* signs, find the absolute values of the numbers and subtract the lesser absolute value from the greater. Give the answer the same sign as the number having the greater absolute value.

*Example:* $-12 + 6 = -6$

**NOW TRY EXERCISE 4**

Find the sum.

$$8 + (-17)$$

**EXAMPLE 4** Adding Numbers with Different Signs

Find the sum $-12 + 5$.

Find the absolute value of each number.

$$|-12| = 12 \quad \text{and} \quad |5| = 5$$

Then find the difference between these absolute values: $12 - 5 = 7$. The sum will be negative, since $|-12| > |5|$.

$$-12 + 5 = -7 \quad\quad \textit{NOW TRY}$$

**NOW TRY ANSWERS**
**2.** $-17$   **3.** $-4$   **4.** $-9$

NOW TRY
EXERCISE 5

Check each answer.

**(a)** $\dfrac{2}{3} + \left(-2\dfrac{1}{9}\right) = -1\dfrac{4}{9}$

**(b)** $3.7 + (-5.7) = -2$

**EXAMPLE 5**   Adding Mentally

Check each answer by adding mentally. If necessary, use a number line.

**(a)** $7 + (-4) = 3$ **(b)** $-8 + 12 = 4$

**(c)** $-\dfrac{1}{2} + \dfrac{1}{8} = -\dfrac{4}{8} + \dfrac{1}{8} = -\dfrac{3}{8}$

Find a common denominator.

**(d)** $\dfrac{5}{6} + \left(-1\dfrac{1}{3}\right) = \dfrac{5}{6} + \left(-\dfrac{4}{3}\right) = \dfrac{5}{6} + \left(-\dfrac{8}{6}\right) = -\dfrac{3}{6} = -\dfrac{1}{2}$

**(e)** $-4.6 + 8.1 = 3.5$    **(f)** $-16 + 16 = 0$    **(g)** $42 + (-42) = 0$

Notice in parts (f) and (g) that ***when additive inverses are added, the sum is 0.***

NOW TRY

The rules for adding signed numbers are summarized as follows.

---

**Adding Signed Numbers**

***Same sign***   Add the absolute values of the numbers. The sum has the same sign as the given numbers being added.

***Different signs***   Find the absolute values of the numbers and subtract the lesser absolute value from the greater. Give the answer the same sign as the number having the greater absolute value.

---

**OBJECTIVE 3**   **Use the definition of subtraction.** Recall that the answer to a subtraction problem is called a **difference.** In the subtraction $x - y$, $x$ is called the **minuend** and $y$ is called the **subtrahend.**

To illustrate subtracting 4 from 7, written $7 - 4$, with a number line, we begin at 0 and draw an arrow 7 units to the right. See **FIGURE 15**. From the right end of this arrow, we draw an arrow 4 units to the *left*. The number at the end of the second arrow shows that $7 - 4 = 3$.

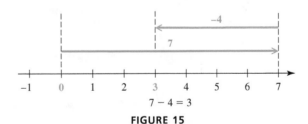

$7 - 4 = 3$

**FIGURE 15**

The procedure used to find the difference $7 - 4$ is exactly the same procedure that would be used to find the sum $7 + (-4)$, so

$$7 - 4 = 7 + (-4).$$

This equation suggests that *subtracting* a positive number from a greater positive number is the same as *adding* the additive inverse of the lesser number to the greater. This result leads to the definition of subtraction for all real numbers.

NOW TRY ANSWER
**5.** Both are correct.

**Definition of Subtraction**

For any real numbers $x$ and $y$,

$$x - y = x + (-y).$$

***To subtract y from x, add the additive inverse (or opposite) of y to x.*** That is, change the subtrahend to its opposite and add.

*Example:* $4 - 9 = 4 + (-9) = -5$

NOW TRY EXERCISE 6

Subtract.

**(a)** $-5 - (-11)$

**(b)** $4 - 15$

**(c)** $-\frac{5}{7} - \frac{1}{3}$

**EXAMPLE 6** Using the Definition of Subtraction

Subtract.

Change − to +. No change. Additive inverse of 3

**(a)** $12 - 3 = 12 + (-3) = 9$

**(b)** $5 - 7 = 5 + (-7) = -2$ **(c)** $-6 - 9 = -6 + (-9) = -15$

Change − to +. No change. Additive inverse of −5

**(d)** $-3 - (-5) = -3 + (5) = 2$

**(e)** $\frac{4}{3} - \left(-\frac{1}{2}\right) = \frac{4}{3} + \frac{1}{2} = \frac{8}{6} + \frac{3}{6} = \frac{11}{6}$, or $1\frac{5}{6}$

NOW TRY

**Uses of the Symbol −**

We use the symbol − for three purposes:

1. ***to represent subtraction,*** as in $9 - 5 = 4$;
2. ***to represent negative numbers,*** such as $-10$, $-2$, and $-3$;
3. ***to represent the opposite (or negative) of a number,*** as in "the opposite (or negative) of 8 is $-8$."

We may see more than one use of − in the same expression, such as $-6 - (-9)$, where $-9$ is subtracted from $-6$. The meaning of the − symbol depends on its position in the expression.

**OBJECTIVE 4** **Use the rules for order of operations with real numbers.**

**EXAMPLE 7** Adding and Subtracting with Grouping Symbols

Perform each indicated operation.

**(a)** $-6 - [2 - (8 + 3)]$ Start within the innermost parentheses.

$= -6 - [2 - 11]$ Add.

$= -6 - [2 + (-11)]$ Definition of subtraction

$= -6 - [-9]$ Add.

$= -6 + (9)$ Definition of subtraction

$= 3$ Add.

NOW TRY ANSWERS

6. (a) 6 (b) −11
(c) $-\frac{22}{21}$, or $-1\frac{1}{21}$

NOW TRY
EXERCISE 7

Perform each indicated
operation.

**(a)** $8 - [(-3 + 7) - (3 - 9)]$

**(b)** $3|6 - 9| - |4 - 12|$

**(b)** $5 + [(-3 - 2) - (4 - 1)]$   Work within each set of parentheses
   inside the brackets.

$= 5 + [(-3 + (-2)) - 3]$

$= 5 + [(-5) - 3]$

$= 5 + [(-5) + (-3)]$   Show all steps to
   avoid sign errors.

$= 5 + [-8]$

$= -3$

**(c)** $\dfrac{2}{3} - \left[\dfrac{1}{12} - \left(-\dfrac{1}{4}\right)\right]$

$= \dfrac{8}{12} - \left[\dfrac{1}{12} - \left(-\dfrac{3}{12}\right)\right]$   Find a common denominator.

$= \dfrac{8}{12} - \left[\dfrac{1}{12} + \dfrac{3}{12}\right]$   Definition of subtraction

$= \dfrac{8}{12} - \dfrac{4}{12}$   Add.

$= \dfrac{4}{12}, \quad \text{or} \quad \dfrac{1}{3}$   Subtract. Write in lowest terms.

**(d)**    $|4 - 7| + 2|6 - 3|$

$= |-3| + 2|3|$   Work within absolute value bars.

$= 3 + 2 \cdot 3$   Evaluate absolute values.

$= 3 + 6$   Multiply.

Be careful!
Multiply first.

$= 9$   Add.   NOW TRY

---

**OBJECTIVE 5**  **Translate words and phrases involving addition and subtraction.**  The table lists words and phrases that indicate addition.

| Word or Phrase | Example | Numerical Expression and Simplification |
|---|---|---|
| Sum of | The *sum of* −3 and 4 | −3 + 4, or 1 |
| Added to | 5 *added to* −8 | −8 + 5, or −3 |
| More than | 12 *more than* −5 | −5 + 12, or 7 |
| Increased by | −6 *increased by* 13 | −6 + 13, or 7 |
| Plus | 3 *plus* 14 | 3 + 14, or 17 |

NOW TRY
EXERCISE 8

Write a numerical expression
for the phrase, and simplify
the expression.

The sum of −3 and 7,
increased by 10

NOW TRY ANSWERS

**7. (a)** −2  **(b)** 1

**8.** (−3 + 7) + 10; 14

**EXAMPLE 8**  **Translating Words and Phrases (Addition)**

Write a numerical expression for each phrase, and simplify the expression.

**(a)** The sum of −8 and 4 and 6

$-8 + 4 + 6$   simplies to   $-4 + 6$,   or   2.

Add in order from left to right.

**(b)** 3 more than −5, increased by 12

$(-5 + 3) + 12$   simplifies to   $-2 + 12$,   or   10.   NOW TRY

The table lists words and phrases that indicate subtraction in problem solving.

| Word, Phrase, or Sentence | Example | Numerical Expression and Simplification |
|---|---|---|
| Difference between | The *difference between* −3 and −8 | −3 − (−8) simplifies to −3 + 8, or 5 |
| Subtracted from* | 12 *subtracted from* 18 | 18 − 12, or 6 |
| From..., subtract.... | From 12, subtract 8. | 12 − 8 simplifies to 12 + (−8), or 4 |
| Less | 6 *less* 5 | 6 − 5, or 1 |
| Less than* | 6 *less than* 5 | 5 − 6 simplifies to 5 + (−6), or −1 |
| Decreased by | 9 *decreased by* −4 | 9 − (−4) simplifies to 9 + 4, or 13 |
| Minus | 8 *minus* 5 | 8 − 5, or 3 |

*Be careful with order when translating.

⚠ **CAUTION**   When subtracting two numbers, be careful to write them in the correct order, because, in general,

$$x - y \neq y - x.$$

For example, $5 - 3 \neq 3 - 5$. ***Think carefully before interpreting an expression involving subtraction.***

⌐ NOW TRY
  EXERCISE 9
Write a numerical expression for each phrase, and simplify the expression.

**(a)** The difference between 5 and −8, decreased by 4

**(b)** 7 less than −2

**EXAMPLE 9**   Translating Words and Phrases (Subtraction)

Write a numerical expression for each phrase, and simplify the expression.

**(a)** The difference between −8 and 5
When "difference between" is used, write the numbers in the order given.*

$$-8 - 5 \quad \text{simplifies to} \quad -8 + (-5), \quad \text{or} \quad -13.$$

**(b)** 4 subtracted from the sum of 8 and −3
First, add 8 and −3. Next, subtract 4 from this sum.

$$[8 + (-3)] - 4 \quad \text{simplifies to} \quad 5 - 4, \quad \text{or} \quad 1.$$

**(c)** 4 less than −6
Here, 4 must be taken *from* −6, so write −6 first.

Be careful with order. → $-6 - 4 \quad \text{simplifies to} \quad -6 + (-4), \quad \text{or} \quad -10.$

Notice that "4 less than −6" differs from "4 *is less than* −6." The second of these is symbolized $4 < -6$ (which is a false statement).

**(d)** 8, decreased by 5 less than 12
First, write "5 less than 12" as $12 - 5$. Next, subtract $12 - 5$ from 8.

$$8 - (12 - 5) \quad \text{simplifies to} \quad 8 - 7, \quad \text{or} \quad 1. \qquad \text{NOW TRY} ↻$$

*NOW TRY ANSWERS*
**9. (a)** $[5 - (-8)] - 4$; 9
   **(b)** $-2 - 7$; −9

*In some cases, people interpret "the difference between" (at least for two positive numbers) to represent the larger minus the smaller. However, we will not do so in this book.

*NOW TRY*
*EXERCISE 10*

Find the difference between a gain of 226 yd on the football field by the Chesterfield Bears and a loss of 7 yd by the New London Wildcats.

**EXAMPLE 10** Solving a Problem Involving Subtraction

The record-high temperature in the United States is 134°F, recorded at Death Valley, California, in 1913. The record low is −80°F, at Prospect Creek, Alaska, in 1971. See **FIGURE 16**. What is the difference between these highest and lowest temperatures? (*Source: National Climatic Data Center.*)

We must subtract the lowest temperature from the highest temperature.

Order of numbers matters in subtraction.

$$134 - (-80)$$
$$= 134 + 80 \qquad \text{Definition of subtraction}$$
$$= 214 \qquad \text{Add.}$$

The difference between the two temperatures is 214°F.

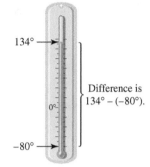

Difference is 134° − (−80°).

**FIGURE 16**

*NOW TRY*

**OBJECTIVE 6  Use signed numbers to interpret data.**

*NOW TRY*
*EXERCISE 11*

Refer to **FIGURE 17** and use a signed number to represent the change in the CPI from 2003 to 2004.

**EXAMPLE 11** Using a Signed Number to Interpret Data

The bar graph in **FIGURE 17** gives the Consumer Price Index (CPI) for footwear between 2002 and 2007.

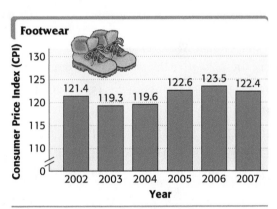

*Source:* U.S. Bureau of Labor Statistics.
**FIGURE 17**

**(a)** Use a signed number to represent the change in the CPI from 2005 to 2006.
Start with the index number for 2006. Subtract from it the index number for 2005.

$$\underbrace{123.5}_{\text{2006 index}} - \underbrace{122.6}_{\text{2005 index}} = \underbrace{+0.9}_{\substack{\text{A positive number} \\ \text{indicates an increase.}}}$$

**(b)** Use a signed number to represent the change in the CPI from 2006 to 2007.

$$\underbrace{122.4}_{\text{2007 index}} - \underbrace{123.5}_{\text{2006 index}} = 122.4 + (-123.5) = \underbrace{-1.1}_{\substack{\text{A negative number} \\ \text{indicates a decrease.}}}$$

*NOW TRY*

*NOW TRY ANSWERS*
**10.** 233 yd
**11.** 0.3

**1.5 EXERCISES** **MyMathLab**  Math XL PRACTICE  WATCH  DOWNLOAD READ  REVIEW

🌐 *Complete solution available on the Video Resources on DVD*

*Concept Check* *Fill in each blank with the correct response.*

🌐 **1.** The sum of two negative numbers will always be a _____ number.
(positive/negative)

Give a number-line illustration using the sum $-2 + (-3)$.

**2.** The sum of a number and its opposite will always be _____.

🌐 **3.** When adding a positive number and a negative number, where the negative number has the greater absolute value, the sum will be a _____ number. Give
(positive/negative)

a number-line illustration using the sum $-4 + 2$.

**4.** To simplify the expression $8 + [-2 + (-3 + 5)]$, one should begin by adding _____ and _____, according to the rule for order of operations.

**5.** By the definition of subtraction, in order to perform the subtraction $-6 - (-8)$, we must add the opposite of _____ to _____ to get _____.

**6.** "The difference between 7 and 12" translates as _____, while "the difference between 12 and 7" translates as _____.

*Concept Check* *In Exercises 7–10, suppose that x represents a positive number and y represents a negative number. Determine whether the given expression must represent a positive number or a negative number.*

**7.** $x - y$      **8.** $y - x$      **9.** $y - |x|$      **10.** $x + |y|$

*Find each sum.* *See Examples 1–7.*

🌐 **11.** $-6 + (-2)$      **12.** $-9 + (-2)$      **13.** $-5 + (-7)$

**14.** $-11 + (-5)$      **15.** $6 + (-4)$      **16.** $11 + (-8)$

**17.** $4 + (-6)$      **18.** $3 + (-7)$      **19.** $-3.5 + 12.4$

**20.** $-12.5 + 21.3$      **21.** $4 + [13 + (-5)]$      **22.** $6 + [2 + (-13)]$

**23.** $8 + [-2 + (-1)]$      **24.** $12 + [-3 + (-4)]$      **25.** $-2 + [5 + (-1)]$

**26.** $-8 + [9 + (-2)]$      **27.** $-6 + [6 + (-9)]$      **28.** $-3 + [3 + (-8)]$

**29.** $[(-9) + (-3)] + 12$      **30.** $[(-8) + (-6)] + 14$      🌐 **31.** $-\dfrac{1}{6} + \dfrac{2}{3}$

**32.** $-\dfrac{6}{25} + \dfrac{19}{20}$      **33.** $\dfrac{5}{8} + \left(-\dfrac{17}{12}\right)$      **34.** $\dfrac{9}{10} + \left(-\dfrac{3}{5}\right)$

**35.** $2\dfrac{1}{2} + \left(-3\dfrac{1}{4}\right)$      **36.** $-4\dfrac{3}{8} + 6\dfrac{1}{2}$

**37.** $-6.1 + [3.2 + (-4.8)]$      **38.** $-9.4 + [-5.8 + (-1.4)]$

**39.** $[-3 + (-4)] + [5 + (-6)]$      **40.** $[-8 + (-3)] + [-7 + (-6)]$

**41.** $[-4 + (-3)] + [8 + (-1)]$      **42.** $[-5 + (-9)] + [16 + (-21)]$

**43.** $[-4 + (-6)] + [(-3) + (-8)] + [12 + (-11)]$

**44.** $[-2 + (-11)] + [12 + (-2)] + [18 + (-6)]$

*Find each difference.* *See Examples 1–7.*

**45.** $4 - 7$      **46.** $8 - 13$      🌐 **47.** $5 - 9$      **48.** $6 - 11$

**49.** $-7 - 1$      **50.** $-9 - 4$      **51.** $-8 - 6$      **52.** $-9 - 5$

**53.** $7 - (-2)$      **54.** $9 - (-2)$      **55.** $-6 - (-2)$      **56.** $-7 - (-5)$

**57.** $2 - (3 - 5)$         **58.** $-3 - (4 - 11)$         **59.** $\dfrac{1}{2} - \left(-\dfrac{1}{4}\right)$

**60.** $\dfrac{1}{3} - \left(-\dfrac{4}{3}\right)$         **61.** $-\dfrac{3}{4} - \dfrac{5}{8}$         **62.** $-\dfrac{5}{6} - \dfrac{1}{2}$

**63.** $\dfrac{5}{8} - \left(-\dfrac{1}{2} - \dfrac{3}{4}\right)$         **64.** $\dfrac{9}{10} - \left(\dfrac{1}{8} - \dfrac{3}{10}\right)$         **65.** $3.4 - (-8.2)$

**66.** $5.7 - (-11.6)$         **67.** $-6.4 - 3.5$         **68.** $-4.4 - 8.6$

*Perform each indicated operation. **See Examples 1–7.***

**69.** $(4 - 6) + 12$         **70.** $(3 - 7) + 4$         **71.** $(8 - 1) - 12$

**72.** $(9 - 3) - 15$         **73.** $6 - (-8 + 3)$         **74.** $8 - (-9 + 5)$

**75.** $2 + (-4 - 8)$         **76.** $6 + (-9 - 2)$         **77.** $|-5 - 6| + |9 + 2|$

**78.** $|-4 + 8| + |6 - 1|$     **79.** $|-8 - 2| - |-9 - 3|$     **80.** $|-4 - 2| - |-8 - 1|$

**81.** $\left(-\dfrac{3}{4} - \dfrac{5}{2}\right) - \left(-\dfrac{1}{8} - 1\right)$         **82.** $\left(-\dfrac{3}{8} - \dfrac{2}{3}\right) - \left(-\dfrac{9}{8} - 3\right)$

**83.** $\left(-\dfrac{1}{2} + 0.25\right) - \left(-\dfrac{3}{4} + 0.75\right)$         **84.** $\left(-\dfrac{3}{2} - 0.75\right) - \left(0.5 - \dfrac{1}{2}\right)$

**85.** $-9 + [(3 - 2) - (-4 + 2)]$         **86.** $-8 - [(-4 - 1) + (9 - 2)]$

**87.** $-3 + [(-5 - 8) - (-6 + 2)]$         **88.** $-4 + [(-12 + 1) - (-1 - 9)]$

**89.** $-9.1237 + [(-4.8099 - 3.2516) + 11.27903]$

**90.** $-7.6247 - [(-3.9928 + 1.42773) - (-2.80981)]$

*Write a numerical expression for each phrase and simplify. **See Examples 8 and 9.***

**91.** The sum of $-5$ and 12 and 6
**92.** The sum of $-3$ and 5 and $-12$

**93.** 14 added to the sum of $-19$ and $-4$
**94.** $-2$ added to the sum of $-18$ and 11

**95.** The sum of $-4$ and $-10$, increased by 12
**96.** The sum of $-7$ and $-13$, increased by 14

**97.** $\dfrac{2}{7}$ more than the sum of $\dfrac{5}{7}$ and $-\dfrac{9}{7}$
**98.** 1.85 more than the sum of $-1.25$ and $-4.75$

**99.** The difference between 4 and $-8$
**100.** The difference between 7 and $-14$

**101.** 8 less than $-2$
**102.** 9 less than $-13$

**103.** The sum of 9 and $-4$, decreased by 7
**104.** The sum of 12 and $-7$, decreased by 14

**105.** 12 less than the difference between 8 and $-5$
**106.** 19 less than the difference between 9 and $-2$

*Solve each problem. **See Example 10.***

**107.** Based on 2020 population projections, New York will lose 5 seats in the U.S. House of Representatives, Pennsylvania will lose 4 seats, and Ohio will lose 3. Write a signed number that represents the total number of seats these three states are projected to lose. (*Source:* Population Reference Bureau.)

**108.** Michigan is projected to lose 3 seats in the U.S. House of Representatives and Illinois 2 in 2020. The states projected to gain the most seats are California with 9, Texas with 5, Florida with 3, Georgia with 2, and Arizona with 2. Write a signed number that represents the algebraic sum of these changes. (*Source:* Population Reference Bureau.)

**109.** The largest change in temperature ever recorded within a 24-hr period occurred in Montana, on January 23–24, 1916. The temperature fell 100°F from a starting temperature of 44°F. What was the low temperature during this period? (*Source: Guinness World Records.*)

**110.** The lowest temperature ever recorded in Tennessee was −32°F. The highest temperature ever recorded there was 145°F more than the lowest. What was this highest temperature? (*Source:* National Climatic Data Center.)

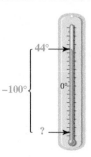

**111.** The lowest temperature ever recorded in Illinois was −36°F on January 5, 1999. The lowest temperature ever recorded in Utah was on February 1, 1985, and was 33°F lower than Illinois's record low. What is the record low temperature for Utah? (*Source:* National Climatic Data Center.)

**112.** The top of Mt. Whitney, visible from Death Valley, has an altitude of 14,494 ft above sea level. The bottom of Death Valley is 282 ft below sea level. Using 0 as sea level, find the difference between these two elevations. (*Source: World Almanac and Book of Facts.*)

**113.** The surface, or rim, of a canyon is at altitude 0. On a hike down into the canyon, a party of hikers stops for a rest at 130 m below the surface. The hikers then descend another 54 m. Write the new altitude as a signed number.

**114.** A pilot announces to the passengers that the current altitude of their plane is 34,000 ft. Because of turbulence, the pilot is forced to descend 2100 ft. Write the new altitude as a signed number.

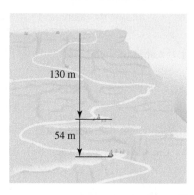

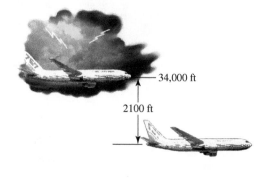

**115.** In 2005, Americans saved −0.5% of their after-tax incomes. In May 2009, they saved 6.9%. (*Source:* U.S. Bureau of Economic Analysis.)

   **(a)** Find the difference between the 2009 and the 2005 amounts.

   **(b)** How could Americans have a negative personal savings rate in 2005?

**116.** In 2000, the U.S. federal budget had a surplus of $236 billion. In 2008, the federal budget had a deficit of $455 billion. Find the difference between the 2008 and the 2000 amounts. (*Source:* U.S. Treasury Department.)

**117.** In 1998, undergraduate college students had an average (mean) credit card balance of $1879. The average balance increased $869 by 2000, then dropped $579 by 2004, and then increased $1004 by 2008. What was the average credit card balance of undergraduate college students in 2008? (*Source:* Sallie Mae.)

**118.** Among entertainment expenditures, the average annual spending per U.S. household on fees and admissions was $526 in 2001. This amount decreased $32 by 2003 and then increased $112 by 2006. What was the average household expenditure for fees and admissions in 2006? (*Source:* U.S. Bureau of Labor Statistics.)

**119.** Nadine Blackwood enjoys playing Triominoes every Wednesday night. Last Wednesday, on four successive turns, her scores were $-19, 28, -5,$ and $13$. What was her final score for the four turns?

**120.** Bruce Buit also enjoys playing Triominoes. On five successive turns, his scores were $-13, 15, -12, 24,$ and $14$. What was his total score for the five turns?

**121.** In August, Susan Goodman began with a checking account balance of $904.89. Her checks and deposits for August are as follows:

| Checks | Deposits |
|--------|----------|
| $35.84 | $85.00 |
| $26.14 | $120.76 |
| $3.12 | |

Assuming no other transactions, what was her account balance at the end of August?

**122.** In September, Jeffery Cooper began with a checking account balance of $904.89. His checks and deposits for September are as follows:

| Checks | Deposits |
|--------|----------|
| $41.29 | $80.59 |
| $13.66 | $276.13 |
| $84.40 | |

Assuming no other transactions, what was his account balance at the end of September?

**123.** Linda Des Jardines owes $870.00 on her MasterCard account. She returns two items costing $35.90 and $150.00 and receives credit for these on the account. Next, she makes a purchase of $82.50 and then two more purchases of $10.00 each. She makes a payment of $500.00. She then incurs a finance charge of $37.23. How much does she still owe?

**124.** Marcial Echenique owes $679.00 on his Visa account. He returns three items costing $36.89, $29.40, and $113.55 and receives credit for these on the account. Next, he makes purchases of $135.78 and $412.88 and two purchases of $20.00 each. He makes a payment of $400. He then incurs a finance charge of $24.57. How much does he still owe?

*The bar graph shows federal budget outlays for the U.S. Department of Homeland Security for the years 2005 through 2008. In Exercises 125–128, use a signed number to represent the change in outlay for each period.* ***See Example 11.***

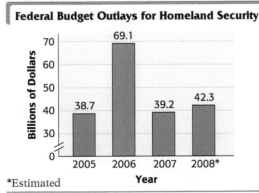

*Source:* U.S. Department of Management and Budget.

**125.** 2005 to 2006

**126.** 2006 to 2007

**127.** 2007 to 2008

**128.** 2005 to 2008

*The two tables show the heights of some selected mountains and the depths of some selected trenches. Use the information given to answer Exercises 129–134.*

| Mountain | Height (in feet) |
|----------|-----------------|
| Foraker | 17,400 |
| Wilson | 14,246 |
| Pikes Peak | 14,110 |

| Trench | Depth (in feet, as a negative number) |
|--------|--------------------------------------|
| Philippine | −32,995 |
| Cayman | −24,721 |
| Java | −23,376 |

*Source: World Almanac and Book of Facts.*

**129.** What is the difference between the height of Mt. Foraker and the depth of the Philippine Trench?

**130.** What is the difference between the height of Pikes Peak and the depth of the Java Trench?

**131.** How much deeper is the Cayman Trench than the Java Trench?

**132.** How much deeper is the Philippine Trench than the Cayman Trench?

**133.** How much higher is Mt. Wilson than Pikes Peak?

**134.** If Mt. Wilson and Pikes Peak were stacked one on top of the other, how much higher would they be than Mt. Foraker?

## STUDY SKILLS

## Using Study Cards

You may have used "flash cards" in other classes. In math, "study cards" can help you remember terms and definitions, procedures, and concepts. Use study cards to

▶ Quickly review when you have a few minutes;

▶ Review before a quiz or test.

***One of the advantages of study cards is that you learn while you are making them.***

### Vocabulary Cards

Put the word and a page reference on the front of the card. On the back, write the definition, an example, any related words, and a sample problem (if appropriate).

### Procedure ("Steps") Cards

Write the name of the procedure on the front of the card. Then write each step in words. On the back of the card, put an example showing each step.

*Make a vocabulary card and a procedure card for material you are learning now.*

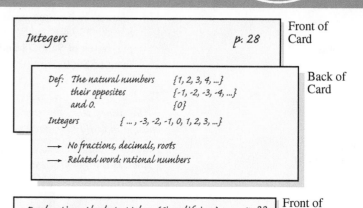

Front of Card

Back of Card

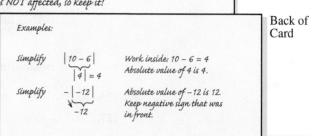

Front of Card

Back of Card

## 1.6   Multiplying and Dividing Real Numbers

The result of multiplication is called the **product.** We know that the product of two positive numbers is positive. We also know that the product of 0 and any positive number is 0, so we extend that property to all real numbers.

**Multiplication by Zero**

For any real number $x$,    $x \cdot 0 = 0.$

**OBJECTIVE 1** Find the product of a positive number and a negative number. Look at the following pattern.

$$3 \cdot 5 = 15$$
$$3 \cdot 4 = 12$$
$$3 \cdot 3 = 9$$
$$3 \cdot 2 = 6$$
$$3 \cdot 1 = 3$$
$$3 \cdot 0 = 0$$
$$3 \cdot (-1) = ?$$

The products decrease by 3.

What should $3(-1)$ equal? The product $3(-1)$ represents the sum

$$-1 + (-1) + (-1) = -3,$$

so the product should be $-3$. Also,

$$3(-2) = -2 + (-2) + (-2) = -6$$

and $$3(-3) = -3 + (-3) + (-3) = -9.$$

These results maintain the pattern in the list, which suggests the following rule.

**Multiplying Numbers with Different Signs**

For any positive real numbers $x$ and $y$,

$$x(-y) = -(xy) \quad \text{and} \quad (-x)y = -(xy).$$

That is, the product of two numbers with opposite signs is negative.

*Examples:*   $6(-3) = -18$   and   $(-6)3 = -18$

**NOW TRY**
**EXERCISE 1**
Find each product.
**(a)** $-11(9)$   **(b)** $3.1(-2.5)$

**EXAMPLE 1** Multiplying a Positive Number and a Negative Number
Find each product, using the multiplication rule given in the box.

**(a)** $8(-5) = -(8 \cdot 5) = -40$        **(b)** $(-5)4 = -(5 \cdot 4) = -20$

**(c)** $-9\left(\dfrac{1}{3}\right) = -\left(9 \cdot \dfrac{1}{3}\right) = -3$        **(d)** $6.2(-4.1) = -(6.2 \cdot 4.1) = -25.42$

**NOW TRY ANSWERS**
**1. (a)** $-99$   **(b)** $-7.75$

NOW TRY

**OBJECTIVE 2** Find the product of two negative numbers. Look at another pattern.

$$-5(4) = -20$$
$$-5(3) = -15$$
$$-5(2) = -10 \quad \text{The products}$$
$$-5(1) = -5 \quad \text{increase by 5.}$$
$$-5(0) = 0$$
$$-5(-1) = ?$$

The numbers in color on the left of the equals symbol decrease by 1 for each step down the list. The products on the right increase by 5 for each step down the list. To maintain this pattern, $-5(-1)$ should be 5 more than $-5(0)$, or 5 more than 0, so

$$-5(-1) = 5.$$

The pattern continues with

$$-5(-2) = 10$$
$$-5(-3) = 15$$
$$-5(-4) = 20$$
$$-5(-5) = 25,$$

and so on, which suggests the next rule.

---

**Multiplying Two Negative Numbers**

For any positive real numbers $x$ and $y$,

$$-x(-y) = xy.$$

That is, the product of two negative numbers is positive.

*Example:* $-5(-4) = 20$

---

> **NOW TRY**
> **EXERCISE 2**
> Find the product.
> $$-\frac{1}{7}\left(-\frac{5}{2}\right)$$

**EXAMPLE 2** Multiplying Two Negative Numbers

Find each product, using the multiplication rule given in the box.

**(a)** $-9(-2) = 9 \cdot 2 = 18$  **(b)** $-6(-12) = 6 \cdot 12 = 72$

**(c)** $-8(-1) = 8 \cdot 1 = 8$  **(d)** $-\frac{2}{3}\left(-\frac{3}{2}\right) = \frac{2}{3} \cdot \frac{3}{2} = 1$  NOW TRY

The following box summarizes multiplying signed numbers.

---

**Multiplying Signed Numbers**

The product of two numbers having the *same* sign is *positive*.

The product of two numbers having *different* signs is *negative*.

---

**OBJECTIVE 3** Identify factors of integers. The definition of **factor** from **Section 1.1** can be extended to integers. If the product of two integers is a third integer, then each of the two integers is a *factor* of the third. The table on the next page shows examples.

> **NOW TRY ANSWER**
> 2. $\frac{5}{14}$

| Integer | 18 | 20 | 15 | 7 | 1 |
|---------|----|----|----|----|----|
| | 1, 18 | 1, 20 | 1, 15 | 1, 7 | 1, 1 |
| | 2, 9 | 2, 10 | 3, 5 | −1, −7 | −1, −1 |
| Pairs of factors | 3, 6 | 4, 5 | −1, −15 | | |
| | −1, −18 | −1, −20 | −3, −5 | | |
| | −2, −9 | −2, −10 | | | |
| | −3, −6 | −4, −5 | | | |

| Number | Multiplicative Inverse (Reciprocal) |
|--------|-------------------------------------|
| 4 | $\frac{1}{4}$ |
| 0.3, or $\frac{3}{10}$ | $\frac{10}{3}$ |
| −5 | $\frac{1}{-5}$, or $-\frac{1}{5}$ |
| $-\frac{5}{8}$ | $-\frac{8}{5}$ |

*A number and its multiplicative inverse have a product of* **1.** For example,

$$4 \cdot \frac{1}{4} = \frac{4}{4} = 1.$$

**OBJECTIVE 4** Use the reciprocal of a number to apply the definition of division. Recall that the result of division is called the **quotient.** The quotient of two numbers is found by multiplying by the *reciprocal,* or *multiplicative inverse,* of the second number.

### Reciprocal or Multiplicative Inverse

Pairs of numbers whose product is 1 are called **reciprocals,** or **multiplicative inverses,** of each other.

The table in the margin shows several numbers and their multiplicative inverses.

### Definition of Division

For any real numbers $x$ and $y$, with $y \neq 0$, $\qquad \dfrac{x}{y} = x \cdot \dfrac{1}{y}.$

That is, to divide two numbers, multiply the first by the reciprocal, or multiplicative inverse, of the second.

*Example:* $\quad \dfrac{-8}{4} = -8 \cdot \dfrac{1}{4} = 2$

**NOTE** Recall that an equivalent form of $\frac{x}{y}$ is $x \div y$, where $x$ is called the **dividend** and $y$ is called the **divisor.** For example, $\frac{-8}{4} = -8 \div 4$.

Since division is defined in terms of multiplication, all the rules for multiplying signed numbers also apply to dividing them.

**NOW TRY**
**EXERCISE 3**

Find each quotient, using the definition of division.

(a) $\dfrac{15}{-3}$ (b) $\dfrac{9.81}{-0.9}$

(c) $-\dfrac{5}{6} \div \dfrac{17}{9}$

### EXAMPLE 3 Using the Definition of Division

Find each quotient, using the definition of division.

(a) $\dfrac{12}{3} = 12 \cdot \dfrac{1}{3} = 4 \quad \frac{x}{y} = x \cdot \frac{1}{y}$

(b) $\dfrac{-10}{2} = -10 \cdot \dfrac{1}{2} = -5$ 

Remember to write in lowest terms.

(c) $\dfrac{-1.47}{-7} = -1.47\left(-\dfrac{1}{7}\right) = 0.21$

(d) $-\dfrac{2}{3} \div \left(-\dfrac{4}{5}\right) = -\dfrac{2}{3} \cdot \left(-\dfrac{5}{4}\right) = \dfrac{5}{6}$

**NOW TRY ANSWERS**

3. (a) −5 (b) −10.9 (c) $-\frac{15}{34}$

**NOW TRY**

We can use multiplication to check a division problem. Consider **Example 3(a).**

$$\frac{12}{3} = 4, \quad \text{since} \quad 4 \cdot 3 = 12.$$ Multiply to check a division problem.

This relationship between multiplication and division allows us to investigate division by 0. Consider the quotient $\frac{0}{3}$.

$$\frac{0}{3} = 0, \quad \text{since} \quad 0 \cdot 3 = 0.$$

Now consider $\frac{3}{0}$.

$$\frac{3}{0} = ?$$

We need to find a number that when multiplied by 0 will equal 3, that is, $? \cdot 0 = 3$. *No* real number satisfies this equation, since the product of any real number and 0 must be 0. Thus,

$\frac{x}{0}$ **is not a number, and** *division by 0 is undefined.* **If a division problem involves division by 0, write "undefined."**

---

### Division Involving 0

For any real number $x$, with $x \neq 0$,

$$\frac{0}{x} = 0 \quad \text{and} \quad \frac{x}{0} \text{ is undefined.}$$

*Examples:* $\quad \dfrac{0}{-10} = 0 \quad$ and $\quad \dfrac{-10}{0}$ is undefined.

---

When dividing fractions, multiplying by the reciprocal works well. However, using the definition of division directly with integers may be awkward. It is easier to divide in the usual way and then determine the sign of the answer.

---

### Dividing Signed Numbers

The quotient of two numbers having the *same* sign is *positive.*

The quotient of two numbers having *different* signs is *negative.*

*Examples:* $\quad \dfrac{15}{5} = 3, \quad \dfrac{-15}{-5} = 3, \quad \dfrac{15}{-5} = -3, \quad$ and $\quad \dfrac{-15}{5} = -3$

---

NOW TRY
EXERCISE 4

Find each quotient.

(a) $\dfrac{-10}{5}$  (b) $\dfrac{-1.44}{-0.12}$

(c) $-\dfrac{3}{8} \div \dfrac{7}{10}$

**EXAMPLE 4** Dividing Signed Numbers

Find each quotient.

(a) $\dfrac{8}{-2} = -4$  (b) $\dfrac{-100}{5} = -20$  (c) $\dfrac{-4.5}{-0.09} = 50$

(d) $-\dfrac{1}{8} \div \left(-\dfrac{3}{4}\right) = -\dfrac{1}{8} \cdot \left(-\dfrac{4}{3}\right) = \dfrac{1}{6}$ Remember to write in lowest terms.

NOW TRY

NOW TRY ANSWERS

4. (a) $-2$  (b) 12  (c) $-\frac{15}{28}$

From the definitions of multiplication and division of real numbers,

$$\frac{-40}{8} = -40 \cdot \frac{1}{8} = -5 \quad \text{and} \quad \frac{40}{-8} = 40\left(\frac{1}{-8}\right) = -5, \quad \text{so} \quad \frac{-40}{8} = \frac{40}{-8}.$$

Based on this example, the quotient of a positive and a negative number can be expressed in any of the following three forms.

---

**Equivalent Forms**

For any positive real numbers $x$ and $y$, $\quad \dfrac{-x}{y} = \dfrac{x}{-y} = -\dfrac{x}{y}.$

---

Similarly, the quotient of two negative numbers can be expressed as a quotient of two positive numbers.

---

**Equivalent Forms**

For any positive real numbers $x$ and $y$, $\quad \dfrac{-x}{-y} = \dfrac{x}{y}.$

---

**OBJECTIVE 5**  Use the rules for order of operations when multiplying and dividing signed numbers.

NOW TRY
EXERCISE 5

Perform each indicated operation.

**(a)** $-4(6) - (-5)(5)$

**(b)** $\dfrac{12(-4) - 6(-3)}{-4(7 - 16)}$

**EXAMPLE 5**  Using the Rules for Order of Operations

Perform each indicated operation.

**(a)** $-9(2) - (-3)(2)$

$= -18 - (-6) \qquad$ Multiply.

$= -18 + 6 \qquad$ Definition of subtraction

$= -12 \qquad$ Add.

**(b)** $-5(-2 - 3)$

$= -5(-5) \qquad$ Work inside the parentheses.

$= 25 \qquad$ Multiply.

**(c)** $\qquad -6 + 2(3 - 5) \quad \longleftarrow$ Begin inside the parentheses.

Do *not* add first.

$= -6 + 2(-2) \qquad$ Subtract inside the parentheses.

$= -6 + (-4) \qquad$ Multiply.

$= -10 \qquad$ Add.

**(d)** $\dfrac{5(-2) - 3(4)}{2(1 - 6)}$

$= \dfrac{-10 - 12}{2(-5)} \qquad$ Simplify the numerator and denominator separately.

$= \dfrac{-22}{-10}, \quad \text{or} \quad \dfrac{11}{5} \qquad$ Subtract in the numerator. Multiply in the denominator. Write in lowest terms.

NOW TRY

NOW TRY ANSWERS
5. **(a)** 1  **(b)** $-\frac{5}{6}$

**OBJECTIVE 6**   Evaluate expressions involving variables.

**NOW TRY
EXERCISE 6**

Evaluate $\dfrac{3x^2 - 12}{y}$ for $x = -4$ and $y = -3$.

**EXAMPLE 6**   Evaluating Expressions for Numerical Values

Evaluate each expression for $x = -1$, $y = -2$, and $m = -3$.

**(a)** $(3x + 4y)(-2m)$    *Use parentheses around substituted negative values to avoid errors.*

$= [3(-1) + 4(-2)][-2(-3)]$    Substitute the given values for the variables.

$= [-3 + (-8)][6]$    Multiply.

$= [-11]6$    Add inside the brackets.

$= -66$    Multiply.

**(b)**      $2x^2 - 3y^2$    *Think: $(-2)^2 = -2(-2) = 4$*

$= 2(-1)^2 - 3(-2)^2$    Substitute.

*Think: $(-1)^2 = -1(-1) = 1$*   $= 2(1) - 3(4)$    Apply the exponents.

$= 2 - 12$    Multiply.

$= -10$    Subtract.

**(c)** $\dfrac{4y^2 + x}{m}$

$= \dfrac{4(-2)^2 + (-1)}{-3}$    Substitute.

$= \dfrac{4(4) + (-1)}{-3}$    Apply the exponent.

$= \dfrac{16 + (-1)}{-3}$    Multiply.

$= \dfrac{15}{-3}, \quad \text{or} \quad -5$    Add, and then divide.    *NOW TRY*

**OBJECTIVE 7**   **Translate words and phrases involving multiplication and division.** The table gives words and phrases that indicate multiplication.

| Word or Phrase | Example | Numerical Expression and Simplification |
|---|---|---|
| Product of | The *product of* −5 and −2 | −5(−2), or 10 |
| Times | 13 *times* −4 | 13(−4), or −52 |
| Twice (meaning "2 times") | *Twice* 6 | 2(6), or 12 |
| Of (used with fractions) | $\frac{1}{2}$ *of* 10 | $\frac{1}{2}$(10), or 5 |
| Percent of | 12% *of* −16 | 0.12(−16), or −1.92 |
| As much as | $\frac{2}{3}$ *as much as* 30 | $\frac{2}{3}$(30), or 20 |

**EXAMPLE 7**   Translating Words and Phrases (Multiplication)

Write a numerical expression for each phrase, and simplify the expression.

**(a)** The product of 12 and the sum of 3 and −6

$$12[3 + (-6)] \quad \text{simplifies to} \quad 12[-3], \quad \text{or} \quad -36.$$

**(b)** Twice the difference between 8 and −4

$$2[8 - (-4)] \quad \text{simplifies to} \quad 2[12], \quad \text{or} \quad 24.$$

*NOW TRY ANSWER*
**6.** −12

NOW TRY
EXERCISE 7

Write a numerical expression
for each phrase, and simplify
the expression.

**(a)** Twice the sum of $-10$
and 7

**(b)** 40% of the difference
between 45 and 15

**(c)** Two-thirds of the sum of $-5$ and $-3$

$$\frac{2}{3}[-5 + (-3)] \quad \text{simplifies to} \quad \frac{2}{3}[-8], \quad \text{or} \quad -\frac{16}{3}.$$

**(d)** 15% of the difference between 14 and $-2$

Remember that
15% = 0.15.    $0.15[14 - (-2)] \quad \text{simplifies to} \quad 0.15[16], \quad \text{or} \quad 2.4.$

**(e)** Double the product of 3 and 4

$$2 \cdot (3 \cdot 4) \quad \text{simplifies to} \quad 2(12), \quad \text{or} \quad 24. \qquad \text{NOW TRY}$$

In algebra, quotients are usually represented with a fraction bar. The symbol $\div$ is seldom used. The table gives some phrases associated with division.

| Phrase | Example | Numerical Expression and Simplification |
|---|---|---|
| Quotient of | The *quotient of* $-24$ and 3 | $\frac{-24}{3}$, or $-8$ |
| Divided by | $-16$ *divided by* $-4$ | $\frac{-16}{-4}$, or 4 |
| Ratio of | The *ratio of* 2 to 3 | $\frac{2}{3}$ |

***When translating a phrase involving division, we write the first number named as the numerator and the second as the denominator.***

NOW TRY
EXERCISE 8

Write a numerical expression
for the phrase, and simplify
the expression.

The quotient of 21 and the
sum of 10 and $-7$

**EXAMPLE 8** Interpreting Words and Phrases Involving Division

Write a numerical expression for each phrase, and simplify the expression.

**(a)** The quotient of 14 and the sum of $-9$ and 2

"Quotient"
indicates division.    $\dfrac{14}{-9 + 2} \quad \text{simplifies to} \quad \dfrac{14}{-7}, \quad \text{or} \quad -2.$

**(b)** The product of 5 and $-6$, divided by the difference between $-7$ and 8

$$\frac{5(-6)}{-7 - 8} \quad \text{simplifies to} \quad \frac{-30}{-15}, \quad \text{or} \quad 2. \qquad \text{NOW TRY}$$

**OBJECTIVE 8** Translate simple sentences into equations.

**EXAMPLE 9** Translating Sentences into Equations

Write each sentence as an equation, using $x$ as the variable. Then find the solution from the list of integers between $-12$ and 12, inclusive.

**(a)** Three times a number is $-18$.

The word *times*        The word *is*
indicates multiplication.    translates as =.

$$\downarrow \qquad \downarrow$$
$$3 \cdot x = -18, \quad \text{or} \quad 3x = -18 \qquad {\scriptstyle 3 \,\cdot\, x \,=\, 3x}$$

The integer between $-12$ and 12, inclusive, that makes this statement true is $-6$, since $3(-6) = -18$. The solution of the equation is $-6$.

NOW TRY ANSWERS

**7. (a)** $2(-10 + 7)$; $-6$
  **(b)** $0.40(45 - 15)$; 12

**8.** $\frac{21}{10 + (-7)}$; 7

NOW TRY
EXERCISE 9

Write each sentence as an equation, using $x$ as the variable. Then find the solution from the list of integers between $-12$ and $12$, inclusive.

**(a)** The sum of a number and $-4$ is 7.

**(b)** The difference between $-8$ and a number is $-11$.

**(b)** The sum of a number and 9 is 12.

$$x + 9 = 12$$

Since $3 + 9 = 12$, the solution of this equation is 3.

**(c)** The difference between a number and 5 is 0.

$$x - 5 = 0$$

Since $5 - 5 = 0$, the solution of this equation is 5.

**(d)** The quotient of 24 and a number is $-2$.

$$\frac{24}{x} = -2$$

Here, $x$ must be a negative number, since the numerator is positive and the quotient is negative. Since $\frac{24}{-12} = -2$, the solution is $-12$. NOW TRY

---

⚠ **CAUTION** In **Examples 7 and 8,** the *phrases* translate as *expressions,* while in **Example 9,** the *sentences* translate as *equations.* ***An expression is a phrase. An equation is a sentence with something on the left side, an $=$ symbol, and something on the right side.***

$$\frac{5(-6)}{-7 - 8} \qquad 3x = -18$$

Expression      Equation

---

NOW TRY ANSWERS
9. **(a)** $x + (-4) = 7; 11$
   **(b)** $-8 - x = -11; 3$

---

## 1.6 EXERCISES

 MyMathLab  Math XL PRACTICE  WATCH  DOWNLOAD  READ  REVIEW

🌐 *Complete solution available on the Video Resources on DVD*

*Concept Check  Fill in each blank with one of the following:* greater than 0, less than 0, equal to 0.

1. The product or the quotient of two numbers with the same sign is _____.

2. The product or the quotient of two numbers with different signs is _____.

3. If three negative numbers are multiplied, the product is _____.

4. If two negative numbers are multiplied and then their product is divided by a negative number, the result is _____.

5. If a negative number is squared and the result is added to a positive number, the result is _____.

6. The reciprocal of a negative number is _____.

7. If three positive numbers, five negative numbers, and zero are multiplied, the product is _____.

8. The cube of a negative number is _____.

🌐 9. *Concept Check*  Complete this statement:   The quotient formed by any nonzero number divided by 0 is _____, and the quotient formed by 0 divided by any nonzero number is _____. Give an example of each quotient.

10. *Concept Check*  Which expression is undefined?

   **A.** $\dfrac{4 + 4}{4 + 4}$   **B.** $\dfrac{4 - 4}{4 + 4}$   **C.** $\dfrac{4 - 4}{4 - 4}$   **D.** $\dfrac{4 - 4}{4}$

*Find each product. **See Examples 1 and 2.***

**11.** $5(-6)$  **12.** $-3(4)$  **13.** $-5(-6)$  **14.** $-3(-4)$  **15.** $-10(-12)$

**16.** $-9(-5)$  **17.** $3(-11)$  **18.** $3(-15)$  **19.** $-0.5(0)$  **20.** $-0.3(0)$

**21.** $-6.8(0.35)$  **22.** $-4.6(0.24)$  **23.** $-\dfrac{3}{8} \cdot \left(-\dfrac{10}{9}\right)$  **24.** $-\dfrac{5}{4} \cdot \left(-\dfrac{5}{8}\right)$

**25.** $\dfrac{2}{15}\left(-1\dfrac{1}{4}\right)$  **26.** $\dfrac{3}{7}\left(-1\dfrac{5}{9}\right)$  **27.** $-8\left(-\dfrac{3}{4}\right)$  **28.** $-6\left(-\dfrac{5}{3}\right)$

*Find all integer factors of each number. **See Objective 3.***

**29.** 32  **30.** 36  💿 **31.** 40  **32.** 50  **33.** 31  **34.** 17

*Find each quotient. **See Examples 3 and 4.***

💿 **35.** $\dfrac{15}{5}$  **36.** $\dfrac{35}{5}$  **37.** $\dfrac{-42}{6}$  **38.** $\dfrac{-28}{7}$

**39.** $\dfrac{-32}{-4}$  **40.** $\dfrac{-35}{-5}$  💿 **41.** $\dfrac{96}{-16}$  **42.** $\dfrac{38}{-19}$

**43.** $-\dfrac{4}{3} \div \left(-\dfrac{1}{8}\right)$  **44.** $-\dfrac{6}{5} \div \left(-\dfrac{1}{3}\right)$  **45.** $\dfrac{-8.8}{2.2}$  **46.** $\dfrac{-4.6}{0.23}$

**47.** $\dfrac{0}{-5}$  **48.** $\dfrac{0}{-9}$  **49.** $\dfrac{11.5}{0}$  **50.** $\dfrac{15.2}{0}$

*Perform each indicated operation. **See Example 5.***

**51.** $7 - 3 \cdot 6$  **52.** $8 - 2 \cdot 5$  **53.** $-10 - (-4)(2)$

**54.** $-11 - (-3)(6)$  💿 **55.** $-7(3 - 8)$  **56.** $-5(4 - 7)$

**57.** $7 + 2(4 - 1)$  **58.** $5 + 3(6 - 4)$  **59.** $-4 + 3(2 - 8)$

**60.** $-8 + 4(5 - 7)$  **61.** $(12 - 14)(1 - 4)$  **62.** $(8 - 9)(4 - 12)$

**63.** $(7 - 10)(10 - 4)$  **64.** $(5 - 12)(19 - 4)$  **65.** $(-2 - 8)(-6) + 7$

**66.** $(-9 - 4)(-2) + 10$  **67.** $3(-5) + |3 - 10|$  **68.** $4(-8) + |4 - 15|$

**69.** $\dfrac{-5(-6)}{9 - (-1)}$  **70.** $\dfrac{-12(-5)}{7 - (-5)}$  **71.** $\dfrac{-21(3)}{-3 - 6}$

**72.** $\dfrac{-40(3)}{-2 - 3}$  **73.** $\dfrac{-10(2) + 6(2)}{-3 - (-1)}$  **74.** $\dfrac{-12(4) + 5(3)}{-14 - (-3)}$

**75.** $\dfrac{3^2 - 4^2}{7(-8 + 9)}$  **76.** $\dfrac{5^2 - 7^2}{2(3 + 3)}$  **77.** $\dfrac{8(-1) - |(-4)(-3)|}{-6 - (-1)}$

**78.** $\dfrac{-27(-2) - |6 \cdot 4|}{-2(3) - 2(2)}$  **79.** $\dfrac{-13(-4) - (-8)(-2)}{(-10)(2) - 4(-2)}$  **80.** $\dfrac{-5(2) + [3(-2) - 4]}{-3 - (-1)}$

*Evaluate each expression for $x = 6$, $y = -4$, and $a = 3$. **See Example 6.***

**81.** $5x - 2y + 3a$  **82.** $6x - 5y + 4a$

💿 **83.** $(2x + y)(3a)$  **84.** $(5x - 2y)(-2a)$

**85.** $\left(\dfrac{1}{3}x - \dfrac{4}{5}y\right)\left(-\dfrac{1}{5}a\right)$  **86.** $\left(\dfrac{5}{6}x + \dfrac{3}{2}y\right)\left(-\dfrac{1}{3}a\right)$

**87.** $(-5 + x)(-3 + y)(3 - a)$  **88.** $(6 - x)(5 + y)(3 + a)$

**89.** $-2y^2 + 3a$  **90.** $5x - 4a^2$

**91.** $\dfrac{2y^2 - x}{a + 10}$  **92.** $\dfrac{xy + 8a}{x - y}$

*Write a numerical expression for each phrase and simplify.* ***See Examples 7 and 8.***

**93.** The product of −9 and 2, added to 9

**94.** The product of 4 and −7, added to −12

**95.** Twice the product of −1 and 6, subtracted from −4

**96.** Twice the product of −8 and 2, subtracted from −1

**97.** Nine subtracted from the product of 1.5 and −3.2

**98.** Three subtracted from the product of 4.2 and −8.5

**99.** The product of 12 and the difference between 9 and −8

**100.** The product of −3 and the difference between 3 and −7

**101.** The quotient of −12 and the sum of −5 and −1

**102.** The quotient of −20 and the sum of −8 and −2

**103.** The sum of 15 and −3, divided by the product of 4 and −3

**104.** The sum of −18 and −6, divided by the product of 2 and −4

**105.** Two-thirds of the difference between 8 and −1

**106.** Three-fourths of the sum of −8 and 12

**107.** 20% of the product of −5 and 6

**108.** 30% of the product of −8 and 5

**109.** The sum of $\frac{1}{2}$ and $\frac{5}{8}$, times the difference between $\frac{3}{5}$ and $\frac{1}{3}$

**110.** The sum of $\frac{3}{4}$ and $\frac{1}{2}$, times the difference between $\frac{2}{3}$ and $\frac{1}{6}$

**111.** The product of $-\frac{1}{2}$ and $\frac{3}{4}$, divided by $-\frac{2}{3}$

**112.** The product of $-\frac{2}{3}$ and $-\frac{1}{5}$, divided by $\frac{1}{7}$

*Write each sentence as an equation, using x as the variable. Then find the solution from the set of integers between −12 and 12, inclusive.* ***See Example 9.***

**113.** The quotient of a number and 3 is −3.

**114.** The quotient of a number and 4 is −1.

**115.** 6 less than a number is 4.

**116.** 7 less than a number is 2.

**117.** When 5 is added to a number, the result is −5.

**118.** When 6 is added to a number, the result is −3.

*To find the **average (mean)** of a group of numbers, we add the numbers and then divide the sum by the number of terms added. For example, to find the average of* 14, 8, 3, 9, *and* 1, *we add them and then divide by* 5.

$$\frac{14 + 8 + 3 + 9 + 1}{5} = \frac{35}{5} = 7 \leftarrow \text{Average}$$

*Find the average of each group of numbers.*

**119.** 23, 18, 13, −4, and −8

**120.** 18, 12, 0, −4, and −10

**121.** −15, 29, 8, −6

**122.** −17, 34, 9, −2

**123.** All integers between −10 and 14, inclusive

**124.** All even integers between −18 and 4, inclusive

*The operation of division is used in **divisibility tests**. A divisibility test allows us to determine whether a given number is divisible (without remainder) by another number.*

**125.** An integer is divisible by 2 if its last digit is divisible by 2, and not otherwise. Show that

**(a)** 3,473,986 is divisible by 2   and   **(b)** 4,336,879 is not divisible by 2.

**126.** An integer is divisible by 3 if the sum of its digits is divisible by 3, and not otherwise. Show that

**(a)** 4,799,232 is divisible by 3   and   **(b)** 2,443,871 is not divisible by 3.

**127.** An integer is divisible by 4 if its last two digits form a number divisible by 4, and not otherwise. Show that

(a) 6,221,464 is divisible by 4   and   (b) 2,876,335 is not divisible by 4.

**128.** An integer is divisible by 5 if its last digit is divisible by 5, and not otherwise. Show that

(a) 3,774,595 is divisible by 5   and   (b) 9,332,123 is not divisible by 5.

**129.** An integer is divisible by 6 if it is divisible by both 2 and 3, and not otherwise. Show that

(a) 1,524,822 is divisible by 6   and   (b) 2,873,590 is not divisible by 6.

**130.** An integer is divisible by 8 if its last three digits form a number divisible by 8, and not otherwise. Show that

(a) 2,923,296 is divisible by 8   and   (b) 7,291,623 is not divisible by 8.

**131.** An integer is divisible by 9 if the sum of its digits is divisible by 9, and not otherwise. Show that

(a) 4,114,107 is divisible by 9   and   (b) 2,287,321 is not divisible by 9.

**132.** An integer is divisible by 12 if it is divisible by both 3 and 4, and not otherwise. Show that

(a) 4,253,520 is divisible by 12   and   (b) 4,249,474 is not divisible by 12.

## *SUMMARY EXERCISES* on Operations with Real Numbers

### Operations with Signed Numbers

#### Addition

***Same sign***   Add the absolute values of the numbers. The sum has the same sign as the numbers being added.

***Different signs***   Find the absolute values of the numbers, and subtract the lesser absolute value from the greater. Give the answer the same sign as the number having the greater absolute value.

#### Subtraction

Add the additive inverse (or opposite) of the subtrahend to the minuend.

#### Multiplication and Division

***Same sign***   The product or quotient of two numbers with the same sign is positive.

***Different signs***   The product or quotient of two numbers with different signs is negative.

***Division by 0 is undefined.***

*Perform each indicated operation.*

**1.** $14 - 3 \cdot 10$

**2.** $-3(8) - 4(-7)$

**3.** $(3 - 8)(-2) - 10$

**4.** $-6(7 - 3)$

**5.** $7 + 3(2 - 10)$

**6.** $-4[(-2)(6) - 7]$

**7.** $(-4)(7) - (-5)(2)$

**8.** $-5[-4 - (-2)(-7)]$

**9.** $40 - (-2)[8 - 9]$

(continued)

**10.** $\dfrac{5(-4)}{-7-(-2)}$     **11.** $\dfrac{-3-(-9+1)}{-7-(-6)}$     **12.** $\dfrac{5(-8+3)}{13(-2)+(-7)(-3)}$

**13.** $\dfrac{6^2-8}{-2(2)+4(-1)}$     **14.** $\dfrac{16(-8+5)}{15(-3)+(-7-4)(-3)}$     **15.** $\dfrac{9(-6)-3(8)}{4(-7)+(-2)(-11)}$

**16.** $\dfrac{2^2+4^2}{5^2-3^2}$     **17.** $\dfrac{(2+4)^2}{(5-3)^2}$     **18.** $\dfrac{4^3-3^3}{-5(-4+2)}$

**19.** $\dfrac{-9(-6)+(-2)(27)}{3(8-9)}$     **20.** $|-4(9)|-|-11|$     **21.** $\dfrac{6(-10+3)}{15(-2)-3(-9)}$

**22.** $\dfrac{3^2-5^2}{(-9)^2-9^2}$     **23.** $\dfrac{(-10)^2+10^2}{-10(5)}$     **24.** $-\dfrac{3}{4}\div\left(-\dfrac{5}{8}\right)$

**25.** $\dfrac{1}{2}\div\left(-\dfrac{1}{2}\right)$     **26.** $\dfrac{8^2-12}{(-5)^2+2(6)}$     **27.** $\left[\dfrac{5}{8}-\left(-\dfrac{1}{16}\right)\right]+\dfrac{3}{8}$

**28.** $\left(\dfrac{1}{2}-\dfrac{1}{3}\right)-\dfrac{5}{6}$     **29.** $-0.9(-3.7)$     **30.** $-5.1(-0.2)$

**31.** $-3^2-2^2$     **32.** $|-2(3)+4|-|-2|$     **33.** $40+2(-5-3)$

*Evaluate each expression for $x=-2$, $y=3$, and $a=4$.*

**34.** $-x+y-3a$     **35.** $(x+6)^3-y^3$     **36.** $(x-y)-(a-2y)$

**37.** $\left(\dfrac{1}{2}x+\dfrac{2}{3}y\right)\left(-\dfrac{1}{4}a\right)$     **38.** $\dfrac{2x+3y}{a-xy}$     **39.** $\dfrac{x^2-y^2}{x^2+y^2}$

**40.** $-x^2+3y$     **41.** $\left(\dfrac{x}{y}\right)^3$     **42.** $\left(\dfrac{a}{x}\right)^2$

## 1.7   Properties of Real Numbers

**OBJECTIVES**

**1** Use the commutative properties.

**2** Use the associative properties.

**3** Use the identity properties.

**4** Use the inverse properties.

**5** Use the distributive property.

In the basic properties covered in this section, $a$, $b$, and $c$ represent real numbers.

**OBJECTIVE 1**   **Use the commutative properties.** The word *commute* means to go back and forth. Many people commute to work or to school. If you travel from home to work and follow the same route from work to home, you travel the same distance each time.

The **commutative properties** say that if two numbers are added or multiplied in any order, the result is the same.

**Commutative Properties**

$$a+b=b+a \qquad \text{Addition}$$
$$ab=ba \qquad \text{Multiplication}$$

NOW TRY
EXERCISE 1

Use a commutative property
to complete each statement.

**(a)** $7 + (-3) = -3 + $ _____

**(b)** $(-5)4 = 4 \cdot $ _____

---

**EXAMPLE 1**  Using the Commutative Properties

Use a commutative property to complete each statement.

**(a)** $-8 + 5 = 5 + \underline{\ ?\ }$     Notice that the "order" changed.

$-8 + 5 = 5 + (-8)$     Commutative property of addition

**(b)** $(-2)7 = \underline{\ ?\ } (-2)$

$-2(7) = 7(-2)$     Commutative property of multiplication

NOW TRY

---

**OBJECTIVE 2**  **Use the associative properties.**  When we *associate* one object with another, we think of those objects as being grouped together.

The **associative properties** say that when we add or multiply three numbers, we can group the first two together or the last two together and get the same answer.

**Associative Properties**

$$(a + b) + c = a + (b + c) \quad \text{Addition}$$
$$(ab)c = a(bc) \quad \text{Multiplication}$$

---

NOW TRY
EXERCISE 2

Use an associative property to
complete each statement.

**(a)** $-9 + (3 + 7) = $ _____

**(b)** $5[(-4) \cdot 9] = $ _____

---

**EXAMPLE 2**  Using the Associative Properties

Use an associative property to complete each statement.

**(a)** $-8 + (1 + 4) = (-8 + \underline{\ ?\ }) + 4$     The "order" is the same.
The "grouping" changed.

$-8 + (1 + 4) = (-8 + 1) + 4$     Associative property of addition

**(b)** $[2 \cdot (-7)] \cdot 6 = 2 \cdot \underline{\ ?\ }$

$[2 \cdot (-7)] \cdot 6 = 2 \cdot [(-7) \cdot 6]$     Associative property of multiplication

NOW TRY

---

By the associative property, the sum (or product) of three numbers will be the same no matter how the numbers are "associated" in groups. Parentheses can be left out if a problem contains only addition (or multiplication). For example,

$$(-1 + 2) + 3 \quad \text{and} \quad -1 + (2 + 3) \quad \text{can be written as} \quad -1 + 2 + 3.$$

---

**EXAMPLE 3**  Distinguishing Between Properties

Is each statement an example of the associative or the commutative property?

**(a)** $(2 + 4) + 5 = 2 + (4 + 5)$

The order of the three numbers is the same on both sides of the equals symbol. The only change is in the *grouping,* or association, of the numbers. This is an example of the associative property.

**(b)** $6 \cdot (3 \cdot 10) = 6 \cdot (10 \cdot 3)$

The same numbers, 3 and 10, are grouped on each side. On the left, the 3 appears first, but on the right, the 10 appears first. Since the only change involves the *order* of the numbers, this is an example of the commutative property.

NOW TRY ANSWERS
**1. (a)** 7  **(b)** $-5$
**2. (a)** $(-9 + 3) + 7$
  **(b)** $[5 \cdot (-4)] \cdot 9$

NOW TRY
EXERCISE 3

Is $5 + (7 + 6) = 5 + (6 + 7)$ an example of the associative property or the commutative property?

NOW TRY
EXERCISE 4

Find each sum or product.

**(a)** $8 + 54 + 7 + 6 + 32$

**(b)** $5(37)(20)$

**(c)** $(8 + 1) + 7 = 8 + (7 + 1)$

Both the order and the grouping are changed. On the left, the order of the three numbers is 8, 1, and 7. On the right, it is 8, 7, and 1. On the left, the 8 and 1 are grouped. On the right, the 7 and 1 are grouped. Therefore, *both* properties are used.

NOW TRY

**EXAMPLE 4** Using the Commutative and Associative Properties

Find each sum or product.

**(a)** $23 + 41 + 2 + 9 + 25$

$= (41 + 9) + (23 + 2) + 25$

$= 50 + 25 + 25$

$= 100$

Use the commutative and associative properties.

**(b)** $25(69)(4)$

$= 25(4)(69)$

$= 100(69)$

$= 6900$

NOW TRY

**OBJECTIVE 3** **Use the identity properties.** If a child wears a costume on Halloween, the child's appearance is changed, but his or her *identity* is unchanged. The identity of a real number is left unchanged when identity properties are applied.

The **identity properties** say that the sum of 0 and any number equals that number, and the product of 1 and any number equals that number.

### Identity Properties

| | | |
|---|---|---|
| $a + 0 = a$ and | $0 + a = a$ | Addition |
| $a \cdot 1 = a$ and | $1 \cdot a = a$ | Multiplication |

The number 0 leaves the identity, or value, of any real number unchanged by addition, so 0 is called the **identity element for addition,** or the **additive identity.** Since multiplication by 1 leaves any real number unchanged, 1 is the **identity element for multiplication,** or the **multiplicative identity.**

NOW TRY
EXERCISE 5

Use an identity property to complete each statement.

**(a)** $\dfrac{2}{5} \cdot$ _____ $= \dfrac{2}{5}$

**(b)** $8 +$ _____ $= 8$

**EXAMPLE 5** Using the Identity Properties

Use an identity property to complete each statement.

**(a)** $-3 + \underline{\ ?\ } = -3$

$-3 + 0 = -3$

Identity property of addition

**(b)** $\underline{\ ?\ } \cdot \dfrac{1}{2} = \dfrac{1}{2}$

$1 \cdot \dfrac{1}{2} = \dfrac{1}{2}$

Identity property of multiplication

NOW TRY

NOW TRY ANSWERS
3. commutative
4. (a) 107   (b) 3700
5. (a) 1   (b) 0

NOW TRY
EXERCISE 6
Simplify.

(a) $\dfrac{16}{20}$   (b) $\dfrac{2}{5} + \dfrac{3}{20}$

**EXAMPLE 6** Using the Identity Property to Simplify Expressions

Simplify.

(a) $\dfrac{49}{35}$

$= \dfrac{7 \cdot 7}{5 \cdot 7}$    Factor.

$= \dfrac{7}{5} \cdot \dfrac{7}{7}$    Write as a product.

$= \dfrac{7}{5} \cdot 1$    Divide.

$= \dfrac{7}{5}$    Identity property

(b) $\dfrac{3}{4} + \dfrac{5}{24}$

$= \dfrac{3}{4} \cdot 1 + \dfrac{5}{24}$    Identity property

$= \dfrac{3}{4} \cdot \dfrac{6}{6} + \dfrac{5}{24}$    Use $1 = \frac{6}{6}$ to get a common denominator.

$= \dfrac{18}{24} + \dfrac{5}{24}$    Multiply.

$= \dfrac{23}{24}$    Add.

NOW TRY

**OBJECTIVE 4** **Use the inverse properties.** Each day before you go to work or school, you probably put on your shoes. Before you go to sleep at night, you probably take them off, and this leads to the same situation that existed before you put them on. These operations from everyday life are examples of *inverse* operations.

The **inverse properties** of addition and multiplication lead to the additive and multiplicative identities, respectively. Recall that $-a$ is the **additive inverse,** or **opposite,** of $a$ and $\frac{1}{a}$ is the **multiplicative inverse,** or **reciprocal,** of the nonzero number $a$. The sum of the numbers $a$ and $-a$ is 0, and the product of the nonzero numbers $a$ and $\frac{1}{a}$ is 1.

**Inverse Properties**

$$a + (-a) = 0 \quad \text{and} \quad -a + a = 0 \qquad \text{Addition}$$

$$a \cdot \frac{1}{a} = 1 \quad \text{and} \quad \frac{1}{a} \cdot a = 1 \quad (a \neq 0) \qquad \text{Multiplication}$$

NOW TRY
EXERCISE 7

Use an inverse property to complete each statement.

(a) $10 + \underline{\quad\quad} = 0$

(b) $-9 \cdot \underline{\quad\quad} = 1$

**EXAMPLE 7** Using the Inverse Properties

Use an inverse property to complete each statement.

(a) $\underline{\ ?\ } + \dfrac{1}{2} = 0$

$-\dfrac{1}{2} + \dfrac{1}{2} = 0$

(b) $4 + \underline{\ ?\ } = 0$

$4 + (-4) = 0$

(c) $-0.75 + \dfrac{3}{4} = \underline{\ ?\ }$

$-0.75 + \dfrac{3}{4} = 0$

The inverse property of addition is used in parts (a)–(c).

(d) $\underline{\ ?\ } \cdot \dfrac{5}{2} = 1$

$\dfrac{2}{5} \cdot \dfrac{5}{2} = 1$

(e) $-5(\underline{\ ?\ }) = 1$

$-5\left(-\dfrac{1}{5}\right) = 1$

(f) $4(0.25) = \underline{\ ?\ }$

$4(0.25) = 1$

The inverse property of multiplication is used in parts (d)–(f).

NOW TRY

NOW TRY ANSWERS
6. (a) $\frac{4}{5}$   (b) $\frac{11}{20}$
7. (a) $-10$   (b) $-\frac{1}{9}$

NOW TRY
EXERCISE 8
Simplify.

$$-\frac{1}{3}x + 7 + \frac{1}{3}x$$

**EXAMPLE 8** Using Properties to Simplify an Expression

Simplify.

$$-2x + 10 + 2x$$

$= (-2x + 10) + 2x$      Order of operations

$= [10 + (-2x)] + 2x$      Commutative property

$= 10 + [(-2x) + 2x]$      Associative property

For *any* value of $x$, $-2x$ and $2x$ are additive inverses.

$= 10 + 0$      Inverse property

$= 10$      Identity property     NOW TRY

**NOTE** The steps of **Example 8** may be skipped when we actually do the simplification.

**OBJECTIVE 5** **Use the distributive property.** The word *distribute* means "to give out from one to several." Look at the value of the following expressions:

$2(5 + 8)$,   which equals   $2(13)$,   or   26

$2(5) + 2(8)$,   which equals   $10 + 16$,   or   26.

Since both expressions equal 26,

$$2(5 + 8) = 2(5) + 2(8).$$

This result is an example of the *distributive property of multiplication with respect to addition,* the only property involving *both* addition and multiplication. With this property, a product can be changed to a sum or difference. This idea is illustrated in **FIGURE 18.**

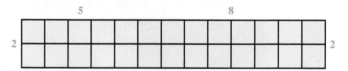

The area of the left part is $2(5) = 10$.
The area of the right part is $2(8) = 16$.
The total area is $2(5 + 8) = 2(13) = 26$,
or the total area is $2(5) + 2(8) = 10 + 16 = 26$.
Thus, $2(5 + 8) = 2(5) + 2(8)$.

**FIGURE 18**

The **distributive property** says that multiplying a number *a* by a sum of numbers $b + c$ gives the same result as multiplying *a* by *b* and *a* by *c* and then adding the two products.

**Distributive Property**

$$a(b + c) = ab + ac \quad \text{and} \quad (b + c)a = ba + ca$$

As the arrows show, the *a* outside the parentheses is "distributed" over the *b* and *c* inside. The distributive property is also valid for multiplication over subtraction.

$$a(b - c) = ab - ac \quad \text{and} \quad (b - c)a = ba - ca$$

The distributive property can be extended to more than two numbers.

$$a(b + c + d) = ab + ac + ad$$

The distributive property can also be used "in reverse."

$$ac + bc = (a + b)c$$

NOW TRY ANSWER
8. 7

**NOW TRY
EXERCISE 9**

Use the distributive property
to rewrite each expression.

**(a)** $-5(4x + 1)$

**(b)** $6(2r + t - 5z)$

**(c)** $5x - 5y$

**EXAMPLE 9**   Using the Distributive Property

Use the distributive property to rewrite each expression.

**(a)**     $5(9 + 6)$

$\qquad = 5 \cdot 9 + 5 \cdot 6$     Distributive property

$\qquad = 45 + 30$     Multiply.

[Multiply first.] $= 75$     Add.

**(b)** $4(x + 5 + y)$

$\qquad = 4x + 4 \cdot 5 + 4y$     Distributive property

$\qquad = 4x + 20 + 4y$     Multiply.

**(c)** $-\dfrac{1}{2}(4x + 3)$     [Think: $-\frac{1}{2}(4x) = \left(-\frac{1}{2} \cdot 4\right)x = \left(-\frac{1}{2} \cdot \frac{4}{1}\right)x$]

$\qquad = -\dfrac{1}{2}(4x) + \left(-\dfrac{1}{2}\right)(3)$     Distributive property

$\qquad = -2x - \dfrac{3}{2}$     Multiply.

**(d)** $3(k - 9)$

$\qquad = 3[k + (-9)]$     Definition of subtraction

$\qquad = 3k + 3(-9)$     Distributive property

$\qquad = 3k - 27$     Multiply.

**(e)** $8(3r + 11t + 5z)$

$\qquad = 8(3r) + 8(11t) + 8(5z)$     Distributive property

$\qquad = (8 \cdot 3)r + (8 \cdot 11)t + (8 \cdot 5)z$     Associative property

$\qquad = 24r + 88t + 40z$     Multiply.

**(f)** $6 \cdot 8 + 6 \cdot 2$

$\qquad = 6(8 + 2)$     Distributive property in reverse

$\qquad = 6(10)$     Add.

$\qquad = 60$     Multiply.

**(g)** $4x - 4m$

$\qquad = 4(x - m)$     Distributive property in reverse

**(h)** $6x - 12$

$\qquad = 6 \cdot x - 6 \cdot 2$

$\qquad = 6(x - 2)$     Distributive property in reverse     NOW TRY

---

⚠ **CAUTION**   In practice, we often omit the first step in **Example 9(d),** where we
rewrote the subtraction as addition of the additive inverse.

$\qquad 3(k - 9)$

$\qquad = 3k - 3(9)$     Be careful not to make a sign error.

$\qquad = 3k - 27$     Multiply.

---

**NOW TRY ANSWERS**
**9. (a)** $-20x - 5$
   **(b)** $12r + 6t - 30z$
   **(c)** $5(x - y)$

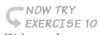

NOW TRY
EXERCISE 10

Write each expression without parentheses.

(a) $-(2 - r)$

(b) $-(2x - 5y - 7)$

The symbol $-a$ may be interpreted as $-1 \cdot a$. Using this result and the distributive property, we can remove (or clear) parentheses from some expressions.

**EXAMPLE 10** Using the Distributive Property to Remove (Clear) Parentheses

Write each expression without parentheses.

**(a)** $-(2y + 3)$

> The $-$ symbol indicates a factor of $-1$.

$= -1 \cdot (2y + 3)$    $-a = -1 \cdot a$

$= -1 \cdot 2y + (-1) \cdot 3$    Distributive property

$= -2y - 3$    Multiply.

**(b)** $-(-9w - 2)$

$= -1(-9w - 2)$

$= -1(-9w) - 1(-2)$

$= 9w + 2$

We can also interpret the negative sign in front of the parentheses to mean the *opposite* of each of the terms within the parentheses.

**(c)** $-(-x - 3y + 6z)$

$= -1(-1x - 3y + 6z)$

> Be careful with signs.

$= -1(-1x) - 1(-3y) - 1(6z)$

$= x + 3y - 6z$    $-1(-1x) = 1x = x$    NOW TRY

Here is a summary of the properties of real numbers discussed in this section.

| **Properties of Addition and Multiplication** | | |
|---|---|---|

For any real numbers $a$, $b$, and $c$, the following properties hold.

**Commutative Properties**    $a + b = b + a$    $ab = ba$

**Associative Properties**    $(a + b) + c = a + (b + c)$

$(ab)c = a(bc)$

**Identity Properties**    There is a real number 0 such that

$a + 0 = a$    and    $0 + a = a.$

There is a real number 1 such that

$a \cdot 1 = a$    and    $1 \cdot a = a.$

**Inverse Properties**    For each real number $a$, there is a single real number $-a$ such that

$a + (-a) = 0$    and    $(-a) + a = 0.$

For each nonzero real number $a$, there is a single real number $\frac{1}{a}$ such that

$a \cdot \frac{1}{a} = 1$    and    $\frac{1}{a} \cdot a = 1.$

**Distributive Properties**    $a(b + c) = ab + ac$    $(b + c)a = ba + ca$

NOW TRY ANSWERS
10. (a) $-2 + r$
    (b) $-2x + 5y + 7$

**1.7 EXERCISES** *MyMathLab*  Math XL PRACTICE  WATCH  DOWNLOAD  READ REVIEW

*Complete solution available on the Video Resources on DVD*

**1.** *Concept Check*   Match each item in Column I with the correct choice(s) from Column II. Choices may be used once, more than once, or not at all.

| I | II |
|---|---|
| **(a)** Identity element for addition | **A.** $(5 \cdot 4) \cdot 3 = 5 \cdot (4 \cdot 3)$ |
| **(b)** Identity element for multiplication | **B.** 0 |
| **(c)** Additive inverse of $a$ | **C.** $-a$ |
| **(d)** Multiplicative inverse, or reciprocal, of the nonzero number $a$ | **D.** $-1$ |
| **(e)** The number that is its own additive inverse | **E.** $5 \cdot 4 \cdot 3 = 60$ |
| **(f)** The two numbers that are their own multiplicative inverses | **F.** 1 |
| **(g)** The only number that has no multiplicative inverse | **G.** $(5 \cdot 4) \cdot 3 = 3 \cdot (5 \cdot 4)$ |
| **(h)** An example of the associative property | **H.** $5(4 + 3) = 5 \cdot 4 + 5 \cdot 3$ |
| **(i)** An example of the commutative property | **I.** $\dfrac{1}{a}$ |
| **(j)** An example of the distributive property | |

**2.** *Concept Check*   Fill in the blanks:   The commutative property allows us to change the _____ of the terms in a sum or the factors in a product. The associative property allows us to change the _____ of the terms in a sum or the factors in a product.

*Concept Check*   *Tell whether or not the following everyday activities are commutative.*

**3.** Washing your face and brushing your teeth

**4.** Putting on your left sock and putting on your right sock

**5.** Preparing a meal and eating a meal

**6.** Starting a car and driving away in a car

**7.** Putting on your socks and putting on your shoes

**8.** Getting undressed and taking a shower

**9.** *Concept Check*   Use parentheses to show how the associative property can be used to give two different meanings to the phrase "foreign sales clerk."

**10.** *Concept Check*   Use parentheses to show how the associative property can be used to give two different meanings to the phrase "defective merchandise counter."

*Use the commutative or the associative property to complete each statement. State which property is used.* **See Examples 1 and 2.**

**11.** $-15 + 9 = 9 + $ _____

**12.** $6 + (-2) = -2 + $ _____

**13.** $-8 \cdot 3 = $ _____ $\cdot (-8)$

**14.** $-12 \cdot 4 = 4 \cdot $ _____

**15.** $(3 + 6) + 7 = 3 + ($ _____ $+ 7)$

**16.** $(-2 + 3) + 6 = -2 + ($ _____ $+ 6)$

**17.** $7 \cdot (2 \cdot 5) = ($ _____ $\cdot 2) \cdot 5$

**18.** $8 \cdot (6 \cdot 4) = (8 \cdot $ _____ $) \cdot 4$

**19.** *Concept Check*   Evaluate $25 - (6 - 2)$ and evaluate $(25 - 6) - 2$. Do you think subtraction is associative?

**20.** *Concept Check*   Evaluate $180 \div (15 \div 3)$ and evaluate $(180 \div 15) \div 3$. Do you think division is associative?

**21.** *Concept Check* Complete the table and the statement beside it.

| Number | Additive Inverse | Multiplicative Inverse |
|--------|------------------|------------------------|
| 5 | | |
| −10 | | |
| $-\frac{1}{2}$ | | |
| $\frac{3}{8}$ | | |
| $x$ | | $(x \neq 0)$ |
| $-y$ | | $(y \neq 0)$ |

In general, a number and its additive inverse have _____ signs.
(the same/opposite)

A number and its multiplicative inverse have _____ signs.
(the same/opposite)

**22.** *Concept Check* The following conversation actually took place between one of the authors of this book and his son, Jack, when Jack was 4 years old:

> DADDY: "Jack, what is 3 + 0?"
> JACK: "3."
> DADDY: "Jack, what is 4 + 0?"
> JACK: "4. And Daddy, *string* plus zero equals *string*!"

What property of addition did Jack recognize?

*Decide whether each statement is an example of the* commutative, associative, identity, inverse, *or* distributive property. ***See Examples 1, 2, 3, 5, 6, 7, and 9.***

**23.** $4 + 15 = 15 + 4$

**24.** $3 + 12 = 12 + 3$

**25.** $5 \cdot (13 \cdot 7) = (5 \cdot 13) \cdot 7$

**26.** $-4 \cdot (2 \cdot 6) = (-4 \cdot 2) \cdot 6$

**27.** $-6 + (12 + 7) = (-6 + 12) + 7$

**28.** $(-8 + 13) + 2 = -8 + (13 + 2)$

**29.** $-9 + 9 = 0$

**30.** $1 + (-1) = 0$

**31.** $\frac{2}{3}\left(\frac{3}{2}\right) = 1$

**32.** $\frac{5}{8}\left(\frac{8}{5}\right) = 1$

**33.** $1.75 + 0 = 1.75$

**34.** $-8.45 + 0 = -8.45$

**35.** $(4 + 17) + 3 = 3 + (4 + 17)$

**36.** $(-8 + 4) + 12 = 12 + (-8 + 4)$

**37.** $2(x + y) = 2x + 2y$

**38.** $9(t + s) = 9t + 9s$

**39.** $-\frac{5}{9} = -\frac{5}{9} \cdot \frac{3}{3} = -\frac{15}{27}$

**40.** $-\frac{7}{12} = -\frac{7}{12} \cdot \frac{7}{7} = -\frac{49}{84}$

**41.** $4(2x) + 4(3y) = 4(2x + 3y)$

**42.** $6(5t) - 6(7r) = 6(5t - 7r)$

*Find each sum or product.* ***See Example 4.***

**43.** $97 + 13 + 3 + 37$

**44.** $49 + 199 + 1 + 1$

**45.** $1999 + 2 + 1 + 8$

**46.** $2998 + 3 + 2 + 17$

**47.** $159 + 12 + 141 + 88$

**48.** $106 + 8 + (-6) + (-8)$

**49.** $843 + 627 + (-43) + (-27)$

**50.** $1846 + 1293 + (-46) + (-93)$

**51.** $5(47)(2)$

**52.** $2(79)5$

**53.** $-4 \cdot 5 \cdot 93 \cdot 5$

**54.** $2 \cdot 25 \cdot 67 \cdot (-2)$

*Simplify each expression.* ***See Examples 7 and 8.***

**55.** $6t + 8 - 6t + 3$

**56.** $9r + 12 - 9r + 1$

**57.** $\frac{2}{3}x - 11 + 11 - \frac{2}{3}x$

**58.** $\frac{1}{5}y + 4 - 4 - \frac{1}{5}y$

**59.** $\left(\frac{9}{7}\right)(-0.38)\left(\frac{7}{9}\right)$

**60.** $\left(\frac{4}{5}\right)(-0.73)\left(\frac{5}{4}\right)$

**61.** $t + (-t) + \frac{1}{2}(2)$

**62.** $w + (-w) + \frac{1}{4}(4)$

**63.** *Concept Check* Suppose that a student simplifies the expression $-3(4 - 6)$ as shown.

$$-3(4 - 6)$$
$$= -3(4) - 3(6)$$
$$= -12 - 18$$
$$= -30$$

*WHAT WENT WRONG?* Work the problem correctly.

**64.** Explain how the procedure of changing $\frac{3}{4}$ to $\frac{9}{12}$ requires the use of the multiplicative identity element, 1.

*Use the distributive property to rewrite each expression. Simplify if possible.* **See Example 9.**

**65.** $5(9 + 8)$       **66.** $6(11 + 8)$       **67.** $4(t + 3)$

**68.** $5(w + 4)$       **69.** $7(z - 8)$       **70.** $8(x - 6)$

**71.** $-8(r + 3)$       **72.** $-11(x + 4)$       **73.** $-\frac{1}{4}(8x + 3)$

**74.** $-\frac{1}{3}(9x + 5)$       **75.** $-5(y - 4)$       **76.** $-9(g - 4)$

**77.** $-\frac{4}{3}(12y + 15z)$       **78.** $-\frac{2}{5}(10b + 20a)$       **79.** $8z + 8w$

**80.** $4s + 4r$       **81.** $7(2v) + 7(5r)$       **82.** $13(5w) + 13(4p)$

**83.** $8(3r + 4s - 5y)$       **84.** $2(5u - 3v + 7w)$       **85.** $-3(8x + 3y + 4z)$

**86.** $-5(2x - 5y + 6z)$       **87.** $5x + 15$       **88.** $9p + 18$

*Write each expression without parentheses.* **See Example 10.**

**89.** $-(4t + 3m)$       **90.** $-(9x + 12y)$       **91.** $-(-5c - 4d)$

**92.** $-(-13x - 15y)$       **93.** $-(-q + 5r - 8s)$       **94.** $-(-z + 5w - 9y)$

## 1.8 Simplifying Expressions

### OBJECTIVES

1. Simplify expressions.
2. Identify terms and numerical coefficients.
3. Identify like terms.
4. Combine like terms.
5. Simplify expressions from word phrases.

**OBJECTIVE 1** Simplify expressions. We use the properties of **Section 1.7** to do this.

**EXAMPLE 1** Simplifying Expressions

Simplify each expression.

**(a)** $4x + 8 + 9$ simplifies to $4x + 17$.

**(b)** $4(3m - 2n)$    To simplify, we clear the parentheses.

$= 4(3m) - 4(2n)$      Distributive property

$= (4 \cdot 3)m - (4 \cdot 2)n$      Associative property

$= 12m - 8n$      Multiply.

NOW TRY
EXERCISE 1
Simplify each expression.

(a) $3(2x - 4y)$

(b) $-4 - (-3y + 5)$

(c)     $6 + 3(4k + 5)$

$= 6 + 3(4k) + 3(5)$     Distributive property

$= 6 + (3 \cdot 4)k + 3(5)$     Associative property

*Don't start by adding!*

$= 6 + 12k + 15$     Multiply.

$= 6 + 15 + 12k$     Commutative property

$= 21 + 12k$     Add.

(d)     $5 - (2y - 8)$

$= 5 - 1(2y - 8)$     $-a = -1 \cdot a$

$= 5 - 1(2y) - 1(-8)$     Distributive property

*Be careful with signs.*

$= 5 - 2y + 8$     Multiply.

$= 5 + 8 - 2y$     Commutative property

$= 13 - 2y$     Add.     NOW TRY

**NOTE** The steps using the commutative and associative properties will not be shown in the rest of the examples. However, be aware that they are usually involved.

| Term | Numerical Coefficient |
|---|---|
| 8 | 8 |
| $-7y$ | $-7$ |
| $34r^3$ | 34 |
| $-26x^5yz^4$ | $-26$ |
| $-k$, or $-1k$ | $-1$ |
| $r$, or $1r$ | 1 |
| $\frac{3x}{8} = \frac{3}{8}x$ | $\frac{3}{8}$ |
| $\frac{x}{3} = \frac{1x}{3} = \frac{1}{3}x$ | $\frac{1}{3}$ |

**OBJECTIVE 2   Identify terms and numerical coefficients.** A **term** is a number, a variable, or a product or quotient of numbers and variables raised to powers, such as

$$9x, \quad 15y^2, \quad -3, \quad -8m^2n, \quad \frac{2}{p}, \quad \text{and} \quad k. \quad \text{Terms}$$

In the term $9x$, the **numerical coefficient,** or simply **coefficient,** of the variable $x$ is $9$. Additional examples are shown in the table in the margin.

⚠ **CAUTION** It is important to be able to distinguish between **terms** and **factors.** Consider the following expressions.

$8x^3 + 12x^2$     This expression has **two terms,** $8x^3$ and $12x^2$.
Terms are separated by a $+$ or $-$ symbol.

$(8x^3)(12x^2)$     This is a **one-term** expression.
The **factors** $8x^3$ and $12x^2$ are multiplied.

**OBJECTIVE 3   Identify like terms.** Terms with exactly the same variables that have the same exponents are **like terms.** Here are some examples.

| Like Terms | Unlike Terms | |
|---|---|---|
| $9t$ and $4t$ | $4y$ and $7t$ | Different variables |
| $6x^2$ and $-5x^2$ | $17x$ and $-8x^2$ | Different exponents |
| $-2pq$ and $11pq$ | $4xy^2$ and $4xy$ | Different exponents |
| $3x^2y$ and $5x^2y$ | $-7wz^3$ and $2xz^3$ | Different variables |

NOW TRY ANSWERS
**1. (a)** $6x - 12y$ **(b)** $3y - 9$

**OBJECTIVE 4**  **Combine like terms.**  Recall that the distributive property

$$a(b + c) = ab + ac \quad \text{can be written "in reverse" as} \quad ab + ac = a(b + c).$$

This last form, which may be used to find the sum or difference of like terms, provides justification for **combining like terms.**

**NOW TRY
EXERCISE 2**
Combine like terms in each expression.
**(a)** $4x + 6x - 7x$  **(b)** $z + z$
**(c)** $4p^2 - 3p^2$

**EXAMPLE 2**  Combining Like Terms

Combine like terms in each expression.

**(a)** $-9m + 5m$

$$= (-9 + 5)m$$

$$= -4m$$

**(b)** $6r + 3r + 2r$

$$= (6 + 3 + 2)r$$

$$= 11r$$

**(c)** $4x + x$

$$= 4x + 1x \qquad x = 1x$$

$$= (4 + 1)x$$

$$= 5x$$

**(d)** $16y^2 - 9y^2$

$$= (16 - 9)y^2$$

$$= 7y^2$$

**(e)** $32y + 10y^2$    These unlike terms cannot be combined.    NOW TRY

⚠ **CAUTION**  *Remember that only like terms may be combined.*

**EXAMPLE 3**  Simplifying Expressions Involving Like Terms

Simplify each expression.

**(a)** $14y + 2(6 + 3y)$

$$= 14y + 2(6) + 2(3y) \qquad \text{Distributive property}$$

$$= 14y + 12 + 6y \qquad \text{Multiply.}$$

$$= 20y + 12 \qquad \text{Combine like terms.}$$

**(b)**  $9k - 6 - 3(2 - 5k)$  Be careful with signs.

$$= 9k - 6 - 3(2) - 3(-5k) \qquad \text{Distributive property}$$

$$= 9k - 6 - 6 + 15k \qquad \text{Multiply.}$$

$$= 24k - 12 \qquad \text{Combine like terms.}$$

**(c)**  $-(2 - r) + 10r$

$$= -1(2 - r) + 10r \qquad -a = -1 \cdot a$$

$$= -1(2) - 1(-r) + 10r \qquad \text{Distributive property}$$

Be careful with signs.  $$= -2 + 1r + 10r \qquad \text{Multiply.}$$

$$= -2 + 11r \qquad \text{Combine like terms.}$$

**(d)** $100[0.03(x + 4)]$

$$= [(100)(0.03)](x + 4) \qquad \text{Associative property}$$

$$= 3(x + 4) \qquad \text{Multiply.}$$

$$= 3x + 12 \qquad \text{Distributive property}$$

**NOW TRY ANSWERS**
**2. (a)** $3x$  **(b)** $2z$  **(c)** $p^2$

NOW TRY
EXERCISE 3

Simplify each expression.

**(a)** $5k - 6 - (3 - 4k)$

**(b)** $\frac{1}{4}x - \frac{2}{3}(x - 9)$

**(e)** $5(2a - 6) - 3(4a - 9)$

$\quad = 10a - 30 - 12a + 27$  　Distributive property

$\quad = -2a - 3$  　　　　　　Combine like terms.

**(f)** $-\frac{2}{3}(x - 6) - \frac{1}{6}x$

$\quad = -\frac{2}{3}x - \frac{2}{3}(-6) - \frac{1}{6}x$  　Distributive property

$\quad = -\frac{2}{3}x + 4 - \frac{1}{6}x$  　　Multiply.

$\quad = -\frac{4}{6}x + 4 - \frac{1}{6}x$  　　Get a common denominator.

$\quad = -\frac{5}{6}x + 4$  　　　　Combine like terms.　　NOW TRY

---

**NOTE** **Examples 2 and 3** suggest that like terms may be combined by adding or subtracting the coefficients of the terms and keeping the same variable factors.

---

**OBJECTIVE 5** Simplify expressions from word phrases.

NOW TRY
EXERCISE 4

Translate the phrase into a mathematical expression and simplify.

Twice a number, subtracted from the sum of the number and 5

**NOW TRY ANSWERS**

3. **(a)** $9k - 9$  **(b)** $-\frac{5}{12}x + 6$
4. $(x + 5) - 2x; -x + 5$

**EXAMPLE 4** Translating Words into a Mathematical Expression

Translate the phrase into a mathematical expression and simplify.

The sum of 9, five times a number,
four times the number, and
six times the number

The word "sum" indicates that the terms should be added. Use $x$ for the number.

$9 + 5x + 4x + 6x$  simplifies to  $9 + 15x$.  　Combine like terms.

This is an expression to be simplified, *not* an equation to be solved.

NOW TRY

---

**1.8 EXERCISES**   PRACTICE　WATCH　DOWNLOAD　READ　REVIEW

🌐 *Complete solution available on the Video Resources on DVD*

*Concept Check* In Exercises 1–4, choose the letter of the correct response.

**1.** Which expression is a simplified form of $-(6x - 3)$?

　**A.** $-6x - 3$　**B.** $-6x + 3$　**C.** $6x - 3$　**D.** $6x + 3$

**2.** Which is an example of a term with numerical coefficient 5?

　**A.** $5x^3y^7$　**B.** $x^5$　**C.** $\frac{x}{5}$　**D.** $5^2xy^3$

**3.** Which is an example of a pair of like terms?

   **A.** $6t, 6w$      **B.** $-8x^2y, 9xy^2$      **C.** $5ry, 6yr$      **D.** $-5x^2, 2x^3$

**4.** Which is a correct translation for "six times a number, subtracted from the product of eleven and the number" (if $x$ represents the number)?

   **A.** $6x - 11x$      **B.** $11x - 6x$      **C.** $(11 + x) - 6x$      **D.** $6x - (11 + x)$

*Simplify each expression.* ***See Example 1.***

   **5.** $4r + 19 - 8$

   **6.** $7t + 18 - 4$

   **7.** $5 + 2(x - 3y)$

   **8.** $8 + 3(s - 6t)$

   **9.** $-2 - (5 - 3p)$

   **10.** $-10 - (7 - 14r)$

   **11.** $6 + (4 - 3x) - 8$

   **12.** $-12 + (7 - 8x) + 6$

*In each term, give the numerical coefficient of the variable(s).* ***See Objective 2.***

   **13.** $-12k$      **14.** $-11y$      **15.** $3m^2$      **16.** $9n^6$

   **17.** $xw$      **18.** $pq$      **19.** $-x$      **20.** $-t$

   **21.** $\dfrac{x}{2}$      **22.** $\dfrac{x}{6}$      **23.** $\dfrac{2x}{5}$

   **24.** $\dfrac{8x}{9}$      **25.** $10$      **26.** $15$

*Identify each group of terms as* like *or* unlike. ***See Objective 3.***

   **27.** $8r, -13r$      **28.** $-7x, 12x$      **29.** $5z^4, 9z^3$      **30.** $8x^5, -10x^3$

   **31.** $4, 9, -24$      **32.** $7, 17, -83$      **33.** $x, y$      **34.** $t, s$

**35.** *Concept Check*  A student simplified the expression $7x - 2(3 - 2x)$ as shown.

$$7x - 2(3 - 2x)$$
$$= 7x - 2(3) - 2(2x)$$
$$= 7x - 6 - 4x$$
$$= 3x - 6$$

*WHAT WENT WRONG?*  Find the correct simplified answer.

**36.** *Concept Check*  A student simplified the expression $3 + 2(4x - 5)$ as shown.

$$3 + 2(4x - 5)$$
$$= 5(4x - 5)$$
$$= 20x - 25$$

*WHAT WENT WRONG?*  Find the correct simplified answer.

*Simplify each expression.* ***See Examples 1–3.***

   **37.** $7y + 6y$      **38.** $5m + 2m$      **39.** $-6x - 3x$

   **40.** $-4z - 8z$      **41.** $12b + b$      **42.** $19x + x$

   **43.** $3k + 8 + 4k + 7$      **44.** $1 + 15z + 2 + 4z$

   **45.** $-5y + 3 - 1 + 5 + y - 7$      **46.** $2k - 7 - 5k + 7k - 3 - k$

   **47.** $-2x + 3 + 4x - 17 + 20$      **48.** $r - 6 - 12r - 4 + 6r$

   **49.** $16 - 5m - 4m - 2 + 2m$      **50.** $6 - 3z - 2z - 5 + z - 3z$

   **51.** $-10 + x + 4x - 7 - 4x$      **52.** $-p + 10p - 3p - 4 - 5p$

   **53.** $1 + 7x + 11x - 1 + 5x$      **54.** $-r + 2 - 5r + 3 + 4r$

   **55.** $-\dfrac{4}{3} + 2t + \dfrac{1}{3}t - 8 - \dfrac{8}{3}t$      **56.** $-\dfrac{5}{6} + 8x + \dfrac{1}{6}x - 7 - \dfrac{7}{6}$

   **57.** $6y^2 + 11y^2 - 8y^2$      **58.** $-9m^3 + 3m^3 - 7m^3$

**59.** $2p^2 + 3p^2 - 8p^3 - 6p^3$

**60.** $5y^3 + 6y^3 - 3y^2 - 4y^2$

**61.** $2(4x + 6) + 3$

**62.** $4(6y - 9) + 7$

**63.** $100[0.05(x + 3)]$

**64.** $100[0.06(x + 5)]$

**65.** $-6 - 4(y - 7)$

**66.** $-4 - 5(t - 13)$

**67.** $-\dfrac{4}{3}(y - 12) - \dfrac{1}{6}y$

**68.** $-\dfrac{7}{5}(t - 15) - \dfrac{1}{2}t$

**69.** $-5(5y - 9) + 3(3y + 6)$

**70.** $-3(2t + 4) + 8(2t - 4)$

**71.** $-3(2r - 3) + 2(5r + 3)$

**72.** $-4(5y - 7) + 3(2y - 5)$

**73.** $8(2k - 1) - (4k - 3)$

**74.** $6(3p - 2) - (5p + 1)$

**75.** $-2(-3k + 2) - (5k - 6) - 3k - 5$

**76.** $-2(3r - 4) - (6 - r) + 2r - 5$

**77.** $-4(-3x + 3) - (6x - 4) - 2x + 1$

**78.** $-5(8x + 2) - (5x - 3) - 3x + 17$

**79.** $-7.5(2y + 4) - 2.9(3y - 6)$

**80.** $8.4(6t - 6) + 2.4(9 - 3t)$

*Translate each phrase into a mathematical expression. Use x as the variable. Combine like terms when possible.* ***See Example 4.***

**81.** Five times a number, added to the sum of the number and three

**82.** Six times a number, added to the sum of the number and six

**83.** A number multiplied by $-7$, subtracted from the sum of 13 and six times the number

**84.** A number multiplied by 5, subtracted from the sum of 14 and eight times the number

**85.** Six times a number added to $-4$, subtracted from twice the sum of three times the number and 4 (*Hint: Twice* means two times.)

**86.** Nine times a number added to 6, subtracted from triple the sum of 12 and 8 times the number (*Hint: Triple* means three times.)

---

**RELATING CONCEPTS** EXERCISES 87–90

**FOR INDIVIDUAL OR GROUP WORK**

*A manufacturer has fixed costs of* $1000 *to produce widgets. Each widget costs* $5 *to make. The fixed cost to produce gadgets is* $750, *and each gadget costs* $3 *to make.* **Work Exercises 87–90 in order.**

**87.** Write an expression for the cost to make $x$ widgets. (*Hint:* The cost will be the sum of the fixed cost and the cost per item times the number of items.)

**88.** Write an expression for the cost to make $y$ gadgets.

**89.** Use your answers from **Exercises 87 and 88** to write an expression for the total cost to make $x$ widgets and $y$ gadgets.

**90.** Simplify the expression you wrote in **Exercise 89.**

# Reviewing a Chapter

Your textbook provides material to help you prepare for quizzes or tests in this course. Refer to a **Chapter Summary** as you read through the following techniques.

## Chapter Reviewing Techniques

▶ **Review the Key Terms.** Make a study card for each. Include a definition, an example, a sketch (if appropriate), and a section or page reference.

▶ **Take the Test Your Word Power quiz** to check your understanding of new vocabulary. The answers immediately follow.

▶ **Read the Quick Review.** Pay special attention to the headings. Study the explanations and examples given for each concept. Try to think about the whole chapter.

▶ **Reread your lecture notes.** Focus on what your instructor has emphasized in class, and review that material in your text.

▶ **Work the Review Exercises.** They are grouped by section.
  ✓ Pay attention to direction words, such as *simplify*, *solve*, and *estimate*.
  ✓ After you've done each section of exercises, check your answers in the answer section.
  ✓ Are your answers exact and complete? Did you include the correct labels, such as $, cm², ft, etc.?
  ✓ Make study cards for difficult problems.

▶ **Work the Mixed Review Exercises.** They are in mixed-up order. Check your answers in the answer section.

▶ **Take the Chapter Test under test conditions.**
  ✓ Time yourself.
  ✓ Use a calculator or notes (if your instructor permits them on tests).
  ✓ Take the test in one sitting.
  ✓ Show all your work.
  ✓ Check your answers in the back of the book. Section references are provided.

*Reviewing a chapter will take some time.* Avoid rushing through your review in one night. Use the suggestions over a few days or evenings to better understand the material and remember it longer.

*Follow these reviewing techniques for your next test. Evaluate how they worked for you.*

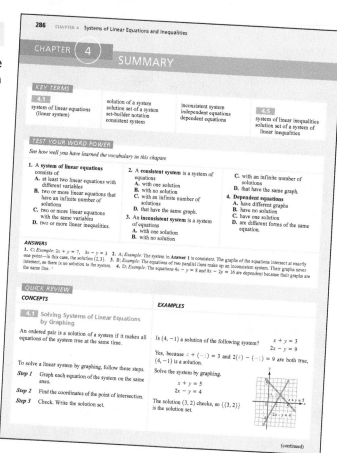

# CHAPTER ( 1 )  SUMMARY

## KEY TERMS

### 1.1

natural (counting) numbers
whole numbers
fractions
numerator
denominator
proper fraction
improper fraction
mixed number
factor
product
prime number
composite number
prime factors
basic principle of fractions
lowest terms
greatest common factor
reciprocal
quotient
sum

least common
  denominator (LCD)
difference

### 1.2

exponent (power)
base
exponential expression
grouping symbols
order of operations
inequality

### 1.3

variable
algebraic expression
equation
solution
set
element

### 1.4

number line
integers
signed numbers
rational numbers
set-builder notation
graph
coordinate
irrational numbers
real numbers
additive inverse (opposite)
absolute value

### 1.5

minuend
subtrahend

### 1.6

multiplicative inverse
  (reciprocal)

dividend
divisor

### 1.7

commutative property
associative property
identity property
identity element for addition
  (additive identity)
identity element for
  multiplication
  (multiplicative identity)
inverse property
distributive property

### 1.8

term
numerical coefficient
like terms
unlike terms
combining like terms

## NEW SYMBOLS

$a^n$    $n$ factors of $a$
[  ]    brackets
$=$    is equal to
$\neq$    is not equal to
$<$    is less than
$>$    is greater than

$\leq$    is less than or equal to
$\geq$    is greater than or
       equal to
{  }    set braces
$\{x \mid x \text{ has a certain}$
       $\textbf{property}\}$
       set-builder notation

$-x$    the additive inverse,
       or opposite, of $x$
$|x|$    absolute value of $x$
$\dfrac{1}{x}$    the multiplicative
       inverse, or reciprocal,
       of the nonzero
       number $x$

$a(b), (a)b, (a)(b), a \cdot b,$
  or $ab$    $a$ times $b$

$a \div b, \dfrac{a}{b}, a/b,$ or $b\overline{)a}$

    $a$ divided by $b$

## TEST YOUR WORD POWER

*See how well you have learned the vocabulary in this chapter.*

1. A **factor** is
   A. the answer in an addition
      problem
   B. the answer in a multiplication
      problem
   C. one of two or more numbers
      that are added to get another
      number
   D. one of two or more numbers that
      are multiplied to get another
      number.

2. A number is **prime** if
   A. it cannot be factored
   B. it has just one factor
   C. it has only itself and 1 as
      factors
   D. it has at least two different
      factors.

3. An **exponent** is
   A. a symbol that tells how many
      numbers are being multiplied
   B. a number raised to a power

   C. a number that tells how many
      times a factor is repeated
   D. one of two or more numbers that
      are multiplied.

4. A **variable** is
   A. a symbol used to represent an
      unknown number
   B. a value that makes an equation
      true
   C. a solution of an equation
   D. the answer in a division problem.

(continued)

**5.** An **integer** is
  **A.** a positive or negative number
  **B.** a natural number, its opposite, or zero
  **C.** any number that can be graphed on a number line
  **D.** the quotient of two numbers.

**6.** The **absolute value** of a number is
  **A.** the graph of the number
  **B.** the reciprocal of the number

**C.** the opposite of the number
**D.** the distance between 0 and the number on a number line.

**7.** A **term** is
  **A.** a numerical factor
  **B.** a number, a variable, or a product or quotient of numbers and variables raised to powers
  **C.** one of several variables with the same exponents

**D.** a sum of numbers and variables raised to powers.

**8.** A **numerical coefficient** is
  **A.** the numerical factor of the variable(s) in a term
  **B.** the number of terms in an expression
  **C.** a variable raised to a power
  **D.** the variable factor in a term.

**ANSWERS**

**1.** D; *Example:* Since $2 \times 5 = 10$, the numbers 2 and 5 are factors of 10. Other factors of 10 are $-10, -5, -2, -1, 1,$ and 10. **2.** C; *Examples:* 2, 3, 11, 41, 53 **3.** C; *Example:* In $2^3$, the number 3 is the exponent (or power), so 2 is a factor three times, and $2^3 = 2 \cdot 2 \cdot 2 = 8$. **4.** A; *Examples:* $a, b, c$ **5.** B; *Examples:* $-9, 0, 6$ **6.** D; *Examples:* $|2| = 2$ and $|-2| = 2$ **7.** B; *Examples:* $6, \frac{x}{2}, -4ab^2$ **8.** A; *Examples:* The term 3 has numerical coefficient 3, $8z$ has numerical coefficient 8, and $-10x^4y$ has numerical coefficient $-10$.

## QUICK REVIEW

| CONCEPTS | EXAMPLES |
|---|---|

### 1.1 Fractions

**Operations with Fractions**
*Addition/Subtraction*
**1.** *Same denominator:* Add/subtract the numerators and keep the same denominator.
**2.** *Different denominators:* Find the LCD, and write each fraction with this LCD. Then follow the procedure above.

*Multiplication:* Multiply numerators and multiply denominators.

*Division:* Multiply the first fraction by the reciprocal of the second fraction.

Perform each operation.

$$\frac{2}{5} + \frac{7}{5} = \frac{2+7}{5} = \frac{9}{5}, \text{ or } 1\frac{4}{5}$$

$$\frac{2}{3} - \frac{1}{2} = \frac{4}{6} - \frac{3}{6} \qquad \text{6 is the LCD.}$$

$$= \frac{4-3}{6} = \frac{1}{6}$$

$$\frac{4}{3} \cdot \frac{5}{6} = \frac{20}{18} = \frac{10}{9}, \text{ or } 1\frac{1}{9}$$

$$\frac{6}{5} \div \frac{1}{4} = \frac{6}{5} \cdot \frac{4}{1} = \frac{24}{5}, \text{ or } 4\frac{4}{5}$$

### 1.2 Exponents, Order of Operations, and Inequality

**Order of Operations**
Simplify within any parentheses or brackets and above and below fraction bars first. Always follow this order.

*Step 1* Apply all exponents.

*Step 2* Do any multiplications or divisions from left to right.

*Step 3* Do any additions or subtractions from left to right.

Simplify $36 - 4(2^2 + 3)$.

$$36 - 4(2^2 + 3)$$
$$= 36 - 4(4 + 3) \qquad \text{Apply the exponent.}$$
$$= 36 - 4(7) \qquad \text{Add inside the parentheses.}$$
$$= 36 - 28 \qquad \text{Multiply.}$$
$$= 8 \qquad \text{Subtract.}$$

### 1.3 Variables, Expressions, and Equations

Evaluate an expression with a variable by substituting a given number for the variable.

Evaluate $2x + y^2$ for $x = 3$ and $y = -4$.

$$2x + y^2$$
$$= 2(3) + (-4)^2 \qquad \text{Substitute.}$$
$$= 6 + 16 \qquad \text{Multiply. Apply the exponent.}$$
$$= 22 \qquad \text{Add.}$$

*(continued)*

| CONCEPTS | EXAMPLES |
|---|---|
| Values of a variable that make an equation true are solutions of the equation. | Is 2 a solution of $5x + 3 = 18$?<br>$5(2) + 3 \stackrel{?}{=} 18$     Let $x = 2$.<br>$13 = 18$     False<br>2 is not a solution. |

### 1.4 Real Numbers and the Number Line

**Ordering Real Numbers**
$a$ is less than $b$ if $a$ is to the left of $b$ on the number line.

The additive inverse of $x$ is $-x$.

The absolute value of $x$, written $|x|$, is the distance between $x$ and 0 on the number line.

Graph $-2$, 0, and 3.

$-2 < 3$     $3 > 0$     $0 < 3$

$-(5) = -5$     $-(-7) = 7$     $-0 = 0$

$|13| = 13$     $|0| = 0$     $|-5| = 5$

### 1.5 Adding and Subtracting Real Numbers

**Adding Two Signed Numbers**
**Same sign** Add their absolute values. The sum has that same sign.

**Different signs** Subtract their absolute values. The sum has the sign of the number with greater absolute value.

**Definition of Subtraction**
$$x - y = x + (-y)$$

Add.
$$9 + 4 = 13$$
$$-8 + (-5) = -13$$
$$7 + (-12) = -5$$
$$-5 + 13 = 8$$

Subtract.
$$-3 - 4 = -3 + (-4) = -7$$
$$-2 - (-6) = -2 + 6 = 4$$
$$13 - (-8) = 13 + 8 = 21$$

### 1.6 Multiplying and Dividing Real Numbers

**Multiplying and Dividing Two Signed Numbers**
**Same sign** The product (or quotient) is *positive*.
**Different signs** The product (or quotient) is *negative*.

Multiply or divide.

$$6 \cdot 5 = 30 \quad -7(-8) = 56 \quad \frac{20}{4} = 5$$

$$\frac{-24}{-6} = 4 \quad -6(5) = -30 \quad 6(-5) = -30$$

$$\frac{-18}{9} = -2 \quad \frac{49}{-7} = -7$$

**Definition of Division**
$$\frac{x}{y} = x \cdot \frac{1}{y}, \quad y \neq 0$$

$$\frac{10}{2} = 10 \cdot \frac{1}{2} = 5$$

**0 divided by a nonzero number equals 0.**
**Division by 0 is undefined.**

$$\frac{0}{5} = 0 \qquad \frac{5}{0} \text{ is undefined.}$$

### 1.7 Properties of Real Numbers

**Commutative Properties**
$$a + b = b + a$$
$$ab = ba$$

$$7 + (-1) = -1 + 7$$
$$5(-3) = (-3)5$$

**Associative Properties**
$$(a + b) + c = a + (b + c)$$
$$(ab)c = a(bc)$$

$$(3 + 4) + 8 = 3 + (4 + 8)$$
$$[-2(6)]4 = -2[(6)4]$$

**Identity Properties**
$$a + 0 = a \qquad 0 + a = a$$
$$a \cdot 1 = a \qquad 1 \cdot a = a$$

$$-7 + 0 = -7 \qquad 0 + (-7) = -7$$
$$9 \cdot 1 = 9 \qquad 1 \cdot 9 = 9$$

(continued)

| CONCEPTS | EXAMPLES |
|---|---|
| **Inverse Properties** | |
| $a + (-a) = 0 \qquad -a + a = 0$ | $7 + (-7) = 0 \qquad -7 + 7 = 0$ |
| $a \cdot \dfrac{1}{a} = 1 \qquad \dfrac{1}{a} \cdot a = 1 \quad (a \neq 0)$ | $-2\left(-\dfrac{1}{2}\right) = 1 \quad -\dfrac{1}{2}(-2) = 1$ |
| **Distributive Properties** | |
| $a(b + c) = ab + ac$ | $5(4 + 2) = 5(4) + 5(2)$ |
| $(b + c)a = ba + ca$ | $(4 + 2)5 = 4(5) + 2(5)$ |
| $a(b - c) = ab - ac$ | $9(5 - 4) = 9(5) - 9(4)$ |

| **1.8** Simplifying Expressions | $-3y^2 + 6y^2 + 14y^2$ | $4(3 + 2x) - 6(5 - x)$ |
|---|---|---|
| ***Only like terms may be combined.*** We use the distributive property to combine like terms. | $= (-3 + 6 + 14)y^2$ $\quad$ $= 17y^2$ | $= 4(3) + 4(2x) - 6(5) - 6(-x)$ $= 12 + 8x - 30 + 6x$ $= 14x - 18$ |

# CHAPTER 1 REVIEW EXERCISES

**1.1** *Perform each indicated operation.*

**1.** $\dfrac{8}{5} \div \dfrac{32}{15}$ **2.** $2\dfrac{4}{5} \cdot 1\dfrac{1}{4}$ **3.** $\dfrac{5}{8} - \dfrac{1}{6}$ **4.** $\dfrac{3}{8} + 3\dfrac{1}{2} - \dfrac{3}{16}$

*The circle graph indicates the fraction of cars in different size categories sold in the United States in 2007. There were approximately 7618 thousand cars sold that year.*

**5.** About how many luxury cars, to the nearest thousand, were sold?

**6.** To the nearest thousand, how many of the cars sold were *not* small cars?

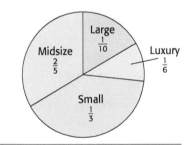

**U.S. Car Sales by Size, 2007**

**Source:** *World Almanac and Book of Facts.*

**1.2** *Find the value of each exponential expression.*

**7.** $5^4$ **8.** $\left(\dfrac{3}{5}\right)^3$ **9.** $(0.02)^2$ **10.** $(0.1)^3$

*Find the value of each expression.*

**11.** $8 \cdot 5 - 13$ **12.** $16 + 12 \div 4 - 2$ **13.** $20 - 2(5 + 3)$

**14.** $7[3 + 6(3^2)]$ **15.** $\dfrac{9(4^2 - 3)}{4 \cdot 5 - 17}$ **16.** $\dfrac{6(5 - 4) + 2(4 - 2)}{3^2 - (4 + 3)}$

*Tell whether each statement is* true *or* false.

**17.** $12 \cdot 3 - 6 \cdot 6 \le 0$        **18.** $3[5(2) - 3] > 20$        **19.** $9 \le 4^2 - 8$

*Write each word statement in symbols.*

**20.** Thirteen is less than seventeen.        **21.** Five plus two is not equal to ten.

**22.** Two-thirds is greater than or equal to four-sixths.

  **1.3**   *Evaluate each expression for $x = 6$ and $y = 3$.*

**23.** $2x + 6y$      **24.** $4(3x - y)$      **25.** $\dfrac{x}{3} + 4y$      **26.** $\dfrac{x^2 + 3}{3y - x}$

*Write each word phrase as an algebraic expression, using $x$ as the variable.*

**27.** Six added to a number        **28.** A number subtracted from eight

**29.** Nine subtracted from six times a number    **30.** Three-fifths of a number added to 12

*Decide whether the given number is a solution of the given equation.*

**31.** $5x + 3(x + 2) = 22;$   2        **32.** $\dfrac{t + 5}{3t} = 1;$   6

*Write each word statement as an equation. Use $x$ as the variable. Then find the solution from the set $\{0, 2, 4, 6, 8, 10\}$.*

**33.** Six less than twice a number is 10.        **34.** The product of a number and 4 is 8.

  **1.4**   *Graph each group of numbers on a number line.*

**35.** $-4, -\dfrac{1}{2}, 0, 2.5, 5$            **36.** $-2, |-3|, -3, |-1|$

*Classify each number, using the sets* natural numbers, whole numbers, integers, rational numbers, irrational numbers, *and* real numbers.

**37.** $\dfrac{4}{3}$        **38.** $0.\overline{63}$        **39.** 19        **40.** $\sqrt{6}$

*Select the lesser number in each pair.*

**41.** $-10, 5$      **42.** $-8, -9$      **43.** $-\dfrac{2}{3}, -\dfrac{3}{4}$      **44.** $0, -|23|$

*Decide whether each statement is* true *or* false.

**45.** $12 > -13$      **46.** $0 > -5$      **47.** $-9 < -7$      **48.** $-13 \ge -13$

*For each number, **(a)** find the opposite of the number and **(b)** find the absolute value of the number.*

**49.** $-9$      **50.** 0      **51.** 6      **52.** $-\dfrac{5}{7}$

*Simplify.*

**53.** $|-12|$      **54.** $-|3|$      **55.** $-|-19|$      **56.** $-|9 - 2|$

  **1.5**   *Perform each indicated operation.*

**57.** $-10 + 4$        **58.** $14 + (-18)$        **59.** $-8 + (-9)$

**60.** $\dfrac{4}{9} + \left(-\dfrac{5}{4}\right)$        **61.** $-13.5 + (-8.3)$        **62.** $(-10 + 7) + (-11)$

**63.** $[-6 + (-8) + 8] + [9 + (-13)]$      **64.** $(-4 + 7) + (-11 + 3) + (-15 + 1)$

**65.** $-7 - 4$

**66.** $-12 - (-11)$

**67.** $5 - (-2)$

**68.** $-\dfrac{3}{7} - \dfrac{4}{5}$

**69.** $2.56 - (-7.75)$

**70.** $(-10 - 4) - (-2)$

**71.** $(-3 + 4) - (-1)$

**72.** $-(-5 + 6) - 2$

*Write a numerical expression for each phrase, and simplify the expression.*

**73.** 19 added to the sum of $-31$ and 12

**74.** 13 more than the sum of $-4$ and $-8$

**75.** The difference between $-4$ and $-6$

**76.** Five less than the sum of 4 and $-8$

*Find the solution of each equation from the set $\{-3, -2, -1, 0, 1, 2, 3\}$.*

**77.** $x + (-2) = -4$

**78.** $12 + x = 11$

*Solve each problem.*

**79.** George Fagley found that his checkbook balance was $-\$23.75$, so he deposited $\$50.00$. What is his new balance?

**80.** The low temperature in Yellowknife, in the Canadian Northwest Territories, one January day was $-26°$F. It rose $16°$ that day. What was the high temperature?

**81.** Reginald Fulwood owed a friend $\$28$. He repaid $\$13$, but then borrowed another $\$14$. What positive or negative amount represents his present financial status?

**82.** If the temperature drops $7°$ below its previous level of $-3°$, what is the new temperature?

**83.** Mark Sanchez of the New York Jets passed for a gain of 8 yd, was sacked for a loss of 12 yd, and then threw a 42 yd touchdown pass. What positive or negative number represents the total net yardage for the plays?

**84.** On Monday, August 31, 2009, the Dow Jones Industrial Average closed at 9496.28, down 47.92 from the previous Friday. What was the closing value the previous Friday? (*Source: The Washington Post.*)

**1.6**  *Perform each indicated operation.*

**85.** $(-12)(-3)$

**86.** $15(-7)$

**87.** $-\dfrac{4}{3}\left(-\dfrac{3}{8}\right)$

**88.** $(-4.8)(-2.1)$

**89.** $5(8 - 12)$

**90.** $(5 - 7)(8 - 3)$

**91.** $2(-6) - (-4)(-3)$

**92.** $3(-10) - 5$

**93.** $\dfrac{-36}{-9}$

**94.** $\dfrac{220}{-11}$

**95.** $-\dfrac{1}{2} \div \dfrac{2}{3}$

**96.** $-33.9 \div (-3)$

**97.** $\dfrac{-5(3) - 1}{8 - 4(-2)}$

**98.** $\dfrac{5(-2) - 3(4)}{-2[3 - (-2)] - 1}$

**99.** $\dfrac{10^2 - 5^2}{8^2 + 3^2 - (-2)}$

**100.** $\dfrac{(0.6)^2 + (0.8)^2}{(-1.2)^2 - (-0.56)}$

*Evaluate each expression if $x = -5$, $y = 4$, and $z = -3$.*

**101.** $6x - 4z$

**102.** $5x + y - z$

**103.** $5x^2$

**104.** $z^2(3x - 8y)$

*Write a numerical expression for each phrase, and simplify the expression.*

**105.** Nine less than the product of $-4$ and 5

**106.** Five-sixths of the sum of 12 and $-6$

**107.** The quotient of 12 and the sum of 8 and $-4$

**108.** The product of $-20$ and 12, divided by the difference between 15 and $-15$

*Write each sentence in symbols, using x as the variable, and find the solution from the list of integers between −12 and 12.*

**109.** 8 times a number is −24.

**110.** The quotient of a number and 3 is −2.

*Find the average of each group of numbers.*

**111.** 26, 38, 40, 20, 4, 14, 96, 18

**112.** −12, 28, −36, 0, 12, −10

**1.7** *Decide whether each statement is an example of the* commutative, associative, identity, inverse, *or* distributive *property.*

**113.** $6 + 0 = 6$

**114.** $5 \cdot 1 = 5$

**115.** $-\dfrac{2}{3}\left(-\dfrac{3}{2}\right) = 1$

**116.** $17 + (-17) = 0$

**117.** $5 + (-9 + 2) = [5 + (-9)] + 2$

**118.** $w(xy) = (wx)y$

**119.** $3x + 3y = 3(x + y)$

**120.** $(1 + 2) + 3 = 3 + (1 + 2)$

*Use the distributive property to rewrite each expression. Simplify if possible.*

**121.** $7y + 14$

**122.** $-12(4 - t)$

**123.** $3(2s) + 3(5y)$

**124.** $-(-4r + 5s)$

**1.8** *Combine like terms whenever possible.*

**125.** $2m + 9m$

**126.** $15p^2 - 7p^2 + 8p^2$

**127.** $5p^2 - 4p + 6p + 11p^2$

**128.** $-2(3k - 5) + 2(k + 1)$

**129.** $7(2m + 3) - 2(8m - 4)$

**130.** $-(2k + 8) - (3k - 7)$

*Translate each phrase into a mathematical expression. Use x to represent the number, and combine like terms when possible.*

**131.** Seven times a number, subtracted from the product of −2 and three times the number

**132.** A number multiplied by 8, added to the sum of 5 and four times the number

## MIXED REVIEW EXERCISES*

*Perform each indicated operation.*

**133.** $\dfrac{6(-4) + 2(-12)}{5(-3) + (-3)}$

**134.** $\dfrac{3}{8} - \dfrac{5}{12}$

**135.** $\dfrac{8^2 + 6^2}{7^2 + 1^2}$

**136.** $-\dfrac{12}{5} \div \dfrac{9}{7}$

**137.** $2\dfrac{5}{6} - 4\dfrac{1}{3}$

**138.** $\left(-\dfrac{5}{6}\right)^2$

**139.** $[(-2) + 7 - (-5)] + [-4 - (-10)]$

**140.** $-16(-3.5) - 7.2(-3)$

**141.** $-8 + [(-4 + 17) - (-3 - 3)]$

**142.** $-4(2t + 1) - 8(-3t + 4)$

**143.** $5x^2 - 12y^2 + 3x^2 - 9y^2$

**144.** $(-8 - 3) - 5(2 - 9)$

**145.** Write a sentence or two explaining the special considerations involving 0 in division.

**146.** The highest temperature ever recorded in Iowa was 118°F at Keokuk on July 20, 1934. The lowest temperature ever recorded in the state was at Elkader on February 3, 1996, and was 165° lower than the highest temperature. What is the record low temperature for Iowa? (*Source:* National Climatic Data Center.)

---

*The order of exercises in this final group does not correspond to the order in which topics occur in the chapter. This random ordering should help you prepare for the chapter test in yet another way.

(continued)

The bar graph shows public high school (grades 9–12) enrollment in millions for selected years from 1980 to 2005 in the United States. Use a signed number to represent the change in enrollment for each period.

**147.** 1980 to 1985

**148.** 1985 to 1990

**149.** 1995 to 2000

**150.** 2000 to 2005

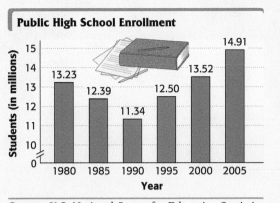

**Public High School Enrollment**

*Source:* U.S. National Center for Education Statistics.

---

# CHAPTER ( 1 )

# TEST

*View the complete solutions to all Chapter Test exercises on the Video Resources on DVD.*

**1.** Write $\frac{63}{99}$ in lowest terms.  **2.** Add: $\frac{5}{8} + \frac{11}{12} + \frac{7}{15}$.  **3.** Divide: $\frac{19}{15} \div \frac{6}{5}$.

**4.** *True* or *false*? $4[-20 + 7(-2)] \le 135$

**5.** Graph the group of numbers $-1, -3, |-4|, |-1|$ on a number line.

**6.** To which of the following sets does $-\frac{2}{3}$ belong: natural numbers, whole numbers, integers, rational numbers, irrational numbers, real numbers?

**7.** Explain how a number line can be used to show that $-8$ is less than $-1$.

**8.** Write in symbols: The quotient of $-6$ and the sum of 2 and $-8$. Simplify the expression.

*Perform each indicated operation.*

**9.** $-2 - (5 - 17) + (-6)$

**10.** $-5\frac{1}{2} + 2\frac{2}{3}$

**11.** $-6 - [-7 + (2 - 3)]$

**12.** $4^2 + (-8) - (2^3 - 6)$

**13.** $(-5)(-12) + 4(-4) + (-8)^2$

**14.** $\dfrac{30(-1 - 2)}{-9[3 - (-2)] - 12(-2)}$

*Find the solution of each equation from the set $\{-6, -4, -2, 0, 2, 4, 6\}$.*

**15.** $-x + 3 = -3$

**16.** $-3x = -12$

*Evaluate each expression, given $x = -2$ and $y = 4$.*

**17.** $3x - 4y^2$

**18.** $\dfrac{5x + 7y}{3(x + y)}$

*Solve each problem.*

**19.** The highest elevation in Argentina is Mt. Aconcagua, which is 6960 m above sea level. The lowest point in Argentina is the Valdés Peninsula, 40 m below sea level. Find the difference between the highest and lowest elevations.

**20.** For a certain system of rating relief pitchers, 3 points are awarded for a save, 3 points are awarded for a win, 2 points are subtracted for a loss, and 2 points are subtracted for a blown save. If Brad Lidge of the Philadelphia Phillies has 4 saves, 3 wins, 2 losses, and 1 blown save, how many points does he have?

**21.** For 2009, the U.S. federal government collected $2.10 trillion in revenues, but spent $3.52 trillion. Write the federal budget deficit as a signed number. (*Source: The Gazette.*)

*Match each property in Column I with the example of it in Column II.*

| I | II |
|---|---|
| **22.** Commutative property | **A.** $3x + 0 = 3x$ |
| **23.** Associative property | **B.** $(5 + 2) + 8 = 8 + (5 + 2)$ |
| **24.** Inverse property | **C.** $-3(x + y) = -3x + (-3y)$ |
| **25.** Identity property | **D.** $-5 + (3 + 2) = (-5 + 3) + 2$ |
| **26.** Distributive property | **E.** $-\dfrac{5}{3}\left(-\dfrac{3}{5}\right) = 1$ |

**27.** What property is used to clear parentheses and write $3(x + 1)$ as $3x + 3$?

**28.** Consider the expression $-6[5 + (-2)]$.

**(a)** Evaluate it by first working within the brackets.

**(b)** Evaluate it by using the distributive property.

**(c)** Why must the answers in parts (a) and (b) be the same?

*Simplify by combining like terms.*

**29.** $8x + 4x - 6x + x + 14x$

**30.** $5(2x - 1) - (x - 12) + 2(3x - 5)$

# Linear Equations and Inequalities in One Variable

In 1924, 258 competitors gathered in Chamonix, France, for the 16 events of the first Olympic Winter Games. This small, mainly European, sports competition has become the world's largest global sporting event. The XXI Olympic Winter Games, hosted in 2010 by Vancouver, British Columbia, attracted 2500 athletes, who competed in 86 events. First introduced at the 1920 Games in Antwerp, Belgium, the five interlocking rings on the Olympic flag symbolize unity among the nations of Africa, the Americas, Asia, Australia, and Europe. (*Source:* www.olympic.org)

Throughout this chapter we use *linear equations* to solve applications about the Olympics.

## 2.1  The Addition Property of Equality

**OBJECTIVES**

**1** Identify linear equations.

**2** Use the addition property of equality.

**3** Simplify, and then use the addition property of equality.

An **equation** is a statement asserting that two algebraic expressions are equal.

---

⚠ **CAUTION**  *Remember that an equation includes an equals symbol.*

Equation (to solve)        Expression (to simplify or evaluate)

$$x - 5 = 2 \qquad\qquad x - 5$$

Left side   Right side

---

**OBJECTIVE 1** **Identify linear equations.** The simplest type of equation is a *linear equation.*

**Linear Equation in One Variable**

A **linear equation in one variable** can be written in the form

$$Ax + B = C,$$

where $A$, $B$, and $C$ are real numbers, and $A \neq 0$.

$$4x + 9 = 0, \quad 2x - 3 = 5, \quad \text{and} \quad x = 7 \qquad \text{Linear equations}$$

$$x^2 + 2x = 5, \quad \frac{1}{x} = 6, \quad \text{and} \quad |2x + 6| = 0 \qquad \textit{Nonlinear equations}$$

A **solution** of an equation is a number that makes the equation true when it replaces the variable. An equation is solved by finding its **solution set,** the set of all solutions. Equations with exactly the same solution sets are **equivalent equations.**

A linear equation in $x$ is solved by using a series of steps to produce a simpler equivalent equation of the form

$$x = \text{a number} \qquad \text{or} \qquad \text{a number} = x.$$

**OBJECTIVE 2** **Use the addition property of equality.** In the linear equation $x - 5 = 2$, both $x - 5$ and 2 represent the same number because that is the meaning of the equals symbol. To solve the equation, we change the left side from $x - 5$ to just $x$, as follows.

| | |
|---|---|
| $x - 5 = 2$ | Given equation |
| $x - 5 + 5 = 2 + 5$ | Add 5 to *each* side to keep them equal. |
| $x + 0 = 7$ | Additive inverse property |
| $x = 7$ | Additive identity property |

Add 5. It is the opposite (additive inverse) of $-5$, and $-5 + 5 = 0$.

The solution is 7. We check by replacing $x$ with 7 in the original equation.

| CHECK | | |
|---|---|---|
| | $x - 5 = 2$ | Original equation |
| | $7 - 5 \stackrel{?}{=} 2$ | Let $x = 7$. |
| | $2 = 2$ ✓ | True |

The left side equals the right side.

Since the final equation is true, 7 checks as the solution and $\{7\}$ is the solution set.

To solve the equation $x - 5 = 2$, we used the **addition property of equality.**

### Addition Property of Equality

If $A$, $B$, and $C$ represent real numbers, then the equations

$$A = B \quad \text{and} \quad A + C = B + C$$

are equivalent equations.

That is, we can add the same number to each side of an equation without changing the solution.

In this property, $C$ represents a real number. Any quantity that represents a real number can be added to each side of an equation to obtain an equivalent equation.

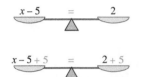

**FIGURE 1**

**NOTE** Equations can be thought of in terms of a balance. Thus, adding the same quantity to each side does not affect the balance. See **FIGURE 1**.

NOW TRY
EXERCISE 1
Solve $x - 13 = 4$.

**EXAMPLE 1** Applying the Addition Property of Equality

Solve $x - 16 = 7$.

Our goal is to get an equivalent equation of the form $x = $ a number.

$$x - 16 = 7$$
$$x - 16 + 16 = 7 + 16 \qquad \text{Add 16 to each side.}$$
$$x = 23 \qquad \text{Combine like terms.}$$

CHECK    Substitute 23 for $x$ in the *original* equation.

$$x - 16 = 7 \qquad \text{Original equation}$$
$$23 - 16 \overset{?}{=} 7 \qquad \text{Let } x = 23.$$

7 is *not* the solution.

$$7 = 7 \ \checkmark \qquad \text{True}$$

Since a true statement results, $23$ is the solution and $\{23\}$ is the solution set.

NOW TRY

⚠ **CAUTION** *The final line of the check does **not** give the solution to the problem,* only a confirmation that the solution found is correct.

NOW TRY
EXERCISE 2
Solve $t - 5.7 = -7.2$.

**EXAMPLE 2** Applying the Addition Property of Equality

Solve $x - 2.9 = -6.4$.

Our goal is to isolate $x$.

$$x - 2.9 = -6.4$$
$$x - 2.9 + 2.9 = -6.4 + 2.9 \qquad \text{Add 2.9 to each side.}$$
$$x = -3.5$$

CHECK
$$x - 2.9 = -6.4 \qquad \text{Original equation}$$
$$-3.5 - 2.9 \overset{?}{=} -6.4 \qquad \text{Let } x = -3.5.$$
$$-6.4 = -6.4 \ \checkmark \qquad \text{True}$$

NOW TRY ANSWERS
**1.** $\{17\}$  **2.** $\{-1.5\}$

Since a true statement results, the solution set is $\{-3.5\}$.    NOW TRY

The addition property of equality says that the same number may be *added* to each side of an equation. In **Section 1.5,** subtraction was defined as addition of the opposite. Thus, we can also use the following rule when solving an equation.

> **The same number may be *subtracted* from each side of an equation without changing the solution.**

NOW TRY
EXERCISE 3
Solve $-15 = x + 12$.

**EXAMPLE 3** Applying the Addition Property of Equality

Solve $-7 = x + 22$.

Here, the variable $x$ is on the right side of the equation.

$$-7 = x + 22$$ The variable can be isolated on *either* side.

$$-7 - 22 = x + 22 - 22$$ Subtract 22 from each side.

$$-29 = x, \quad \text{or} \quad x = -29$$ Rewrite; a number = x, or x = a number.

CHECK

$$-7 = x + 22$$ Original equation

$$-7 \stackrel{?}{=} -29 + 22$$ Let x = -29.

$$-7 = -7 \checkmark$$ True

The check confirms that the solution set is $\{-29\}$.

NOW TRY

---

**NOTE** In **Example 3,** what happens if we subtract $-7 - 22$ incorrectly, obtaining $x = -15$, instead of $x = -29$, as the last line of the solution? A check should indicate an error.

CHECK

$$-7 = x + 22$$ Original equation from **Example 3**

The left side does *not* equal the right side.

$$-7 \stackrel{?}{=} -15 + 22$$ Let x = -15.

$$-7 = 7$$ False

The false statement indicates that $-15$ is *not* a solution of the equation. If this happens, rework the problem.

---

NOW TRY
EXERCISE 4
Solve $\frac{2}{3}x - 4 = \frac{5}{3}x$.

**EXAMPLE 4** Subtracting a Variable Expression

Solve $\frac{3}{5}x + 17 = \frac{8}{5}x$.

$$\frac{3}{5}x + 17 = \frac{8}{5}x$$ Original equation

$$\frac{3}{5}x + 17 - \frac{3}{5}x = \frac{8}{5}x - \frac{3}{5}x$$ Subtract $\frac{3}{5}x$ from each side.

From now on we will skip this step.

$$17 = 1x$$ $\frac{3}{5}x - \frac{3}{5}x = 0; \frac{8}{5}x - \frac{3}{5}x = \frac{5}{5}x = 1x$

$$17 = x$$ Multiplicative identity property

Check by replacing $x$ with 17 in the original equation. The solution set is $\{17\}$.

NOW TRY

NOW TRY ANSWERS
3. $\{-27\}$  4. $\{-4\}$

What happens in **Example 4** if we start by subtracting $\frac{8}{5}x$ from each side?

$$\frac{3}{5}x + 17 = \frac{8}{5}x \qquad \text{Original equation from \textbf{Example 4}}$$

$$\frac{3}{5}x + 17 - \frac{8}{5}x = \frac{8}{5}x - \frac{8}{5}x \qquad \text{Subtract } \tfrac{8}{5}x \text{ from each side.}$$

$$17 - x = 0 \qquad \tfrac{3}{5}x - \tfrac{8}{5}x = -\tfrac{5}{5}x = -1x = -x;\ \tfrac{8}{5}x - \tfrac{8}{5}x = 0$$

$$17 - x - 17 = 0 - 17 \qquad \text{Subtract 17 from each side.}$$

$$-x = -17 \qquad \text{Combine like terms; additive inverse}$$

This result gives the value of $-x$, but not of $x$ itself. However, it does say that the additive inverse of $x$ is $-17$, which means that $x$ must be 17.

$$x = 17 \qquad \text{Same result as in \textbf{Example 4}}$$

We can make the following generalization:

**If $a$ is a number and $-x = a$, then $x = -a$.**

NOW TRY
EXERCISE 5
Solve $6x - 8 = 12 + 5x$.

> **EXAMPLE 5** Applying the Addition Property of Equality Twice

Solve $8 - 6p = -7p + 5$.

$$8 - 6p = -7p + 5$$

$$8 - 6p + 7p = -7p + 5 + 7p \qquad \text{Add } 7p \text{ to each side.}$$

$$8 + p = 5 \qquad \text{Combine like terms.}$$

$$8 + p - 8 = 5 - 8 \qquad \text{Subtract 8 from each side.}$$

$$p = -3 \qquad \text{Combine like terms.}$$

CHECK

$$8 - 6p = -7p + 5 \qquad \text{Original equation}$$

$$8 - 6(-3) \overset{?}{=} -7(-3) + 5 \qquad \text{Let } p = -3.$$

> Use parentheses when substituting to avoid errors.

$$8 + 18 \overset{?}{=} 21 + 5 \qquad \text{Multiply.}$$

$$26 = 26 \ \checkmark \qquad \text{True}$$

The check results in a true statement, so the solution set is $\{-3\}$. NOW TRY

---

**NOTE** *There are often several correct ways to solve an equation.* In **Example 5**, we could begin by adding $6p$ to each side. Combining like terms and subtracting 5 from each side gives $3 = -p$. (Try this.) If $3 = -p$, then $-3 = p$, and the variable has been isolated on the right side of equation. The same solution results.

---

**OBJECTIVE 3** Simplify, and then use the addition property of equality.

> **EXAMPLE 6** Combining Like Terms When Solving

Solve $3t - 12 + t + 2 = 5 + 3t + 2$.

$$3t - 12 + t + 2 = 5 + 3t + 2$$

$$4t - 10 = 7 + 3t \qquad \text{Combine like terms.}$$

$$4t - 10 - 3t = 7 + 3t - 3t \qquad \text{Subtract } 3t \text{ from each side.}$$

$$t - 10 = 7 \qquad \text{Combine like terms.}$$

$$t - 10 + 10 = 7 + 10 \qquad \text{Add 10 to each side.}$$

$$t = 17 \qquad \text{Combine like terms.}$$

NOW TRY ANSWER
5. $\{20\}$

NOW TRY
EXERCISE 6

Solve.

$5x - 10 - 12x$
$= 4 - 8x - 9$

CHECK

| | | |
|---|---|---|
| $3t - 12 + t + 2 = 5 + 3t + 2$ | Original equation |
| $3(17) - 12 + 17 + 2 \stackrel{?}{=} 5 + 3(17) + 2$ | Let $t = 17$. |
| $51 - 12 + 17 + 2 \stackrel{?}{=} 5 + 51 + 2$ | Multiply. |
| $58 = 58$ ✓ | True |

The check results in a true statement, so the solution set is $\{17\}$.　NOW TRY

NOW TRY
EXERCISE 7

Solve.

$4(3x - 2) - (11x - 4) = 3$

**EXAMPLE 7** Using the Distributive Property When Solving

Solve $3(2 + 5x) - (1 + 14x) = 6$.

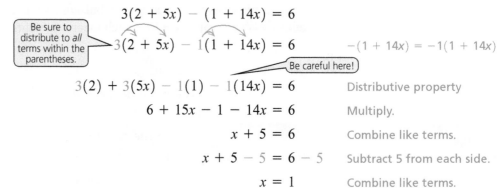

Be sure to distribute to *all* terms within the parentheses.

$3(2 + 5x) - 1(1 + 14x) = 6$　$-(1 + 14x) = -1(1 + 14x)$

Be careful here!

| | |
|---|---|
| $3(2) + 3(5x) - 1(1) - 1(14x) = 6$ | Distributive property |
| $6 + 15x - 1 - 14x = 6$ | Multiply. |
| $x + 5 = 6$ | Combine like terms. |
| $x + 5 - 5 = 6 - 5$ | Subtract 5 from each side. |
| $x = 1$ | Combine like terms. |

Check by substituting 1 for $x$ in the original equation. The solution set is $\{1\}$.

NOW TRY

NOW TRY ANSWERS
6. $\{5\}$　7. $\{7\}$

⚠ **CAUTION** *Be careful to apply the distributive property correctly* in a problem like that in **Example 7,** or a sign error may result.

---

## 2.1 EXERCISES

*MyMathLab* | Math XL PRACTICE | WATCH | DOWNLOAD | READ | REVIEW

🌐 *Complete solution available on the Video Resources on DVD*

**1.** *Concept Check* Decide whether each of the following is an *expression* or an *equation*. If it is an expression, simplify it. If it is an equation, solve it.

   **(a)** $5x + 8 - 4x + 7$　　　　　　**(b)** $-6y + 12 + 7y - 5$

   **(c)** $5x + 8 - 4x = 7$　　　　　　**(d)** $-6y + 12 + 7y = -5$

**2.** *Concept Check* Which pairs of equations are equivalent equations?

   **A.** $x + 2 = 6$ and $x = 4$　　　　　**B.** $10 - x = 5$ and $x = -5$

   **C.** $x + 3 = 9$ and $x = 6$　　　　　**D.** $4 + x = 8$ and $x = -4$

**3.** *Concept Check* Which of the following are *not* linear equations in one variable?

   **A.** $x^2 - 5x + 6 = 0$　　**B.** $x^3 = x$　　**C.** $3x - 4 = 0$　　**D.** $7x - 6x = 3 + 9x$

📝 **4.** Explain how to check a solution of an equation.

*Solve each equation, and check your solution.* **See Examples 1–5.**

   **5.** $x - 3 = 9$　　　　　　**6.** $x - 9 = 8$　　　　🌐 **7.** $x - 12 = 19$

   **8.** $x - 18 = 22$　　　　　**9.** $x - 6 = -9$　　　　**10.** $x - 5 = -7$

**11.** $r + 8 = 12$

**12.** $x + 7 = 11$

**13.** $x + 28 = 19$

**14.** $x + 47 = 26$

**15.** $x + \dfrac{1}{4} = -\dfrac{1}{2}$

**16.** $x + \dfrac{2}{3} = -\dfrac{1}{6}$

**17.** $7 + r = -3$

**18.** $8 + k = -4$

🌐 **19.** $2 = p + 15$

**20.** $5 = z + 19$

**21.** $-4 = x - 14$

**22.** $-7 = x - 22$

**23.** $-\dfrac{1}{3} = x - \dfrac{3}{5}$

**24.** $-\dfrac{1}{4} = x - \dfrac{2}{3}$

🌐 **25.** $x - 8.4 = -2.1$

**26.** $x - 15.5 = -5.1$

**27.** $t + 12.3 = -4.6$

**28.** $x + 21.5 = -13.4$

**29.** $3x = 2x + 7$

**30.** $5x = 4x + 9$

**31.** $10x + 4 = 9x$

**32.** $8t + 5 = 7t$

**33.** $3x + 7 = 2x + 4$

**34.** $9x + 1 = 8x + 4$

**35.** $8t + 6 = 7t + 6$

**36.** $13t + 9 = 12t + 9$

**37.** $-4x + 7 = -5x + 9$

**38.** $-6x + 3 = -7x + 10$   🌐 **39.** $\dfrac{2}{5}w - 6 = \dfrac{7}{5}w$

**40.** $\dfrac{2}{7}z - 2 = \dfrac{9}{7}z$

**41.** $5.6x + 2 = 4.6x$

**42.** $9.1x + 5 = 8.1x$

**43.** $1.4x - 3 = 0.4x$

**44.** $1.9t - 6 = 0.9t$

**45.** $5p = 4p$

**46.** $8z = 7z$

**47.** $1.2y - 4 = 0.2y - 4$

**48.** $7.7r - 6 = 6.7r - 6$

**49.** $\dfrac{1}{2}x + 5 = -\dfrac{1}{2}x$

**50.** $\dfrac{1}{5}x + 7 = -\dfrac{4}{5}x$

**51.** $3x + 7 - 2x = 0$

**52.** $5x + 4 - 4x = 0$

*Solve each equation, and check your solution.* **See Examples 6 and 7.**

**53.** $5t + 3 + 2t - 6t = 4 + 12$

**54.** $4x + 3x - 6 - 6x = 10 + 3$

🌐 **55.** $6x + 5 + 7x + 3 = 12x + 4$

**56.** $4x - 3 - 8x + 1 = -5x + 9$

**57.** $5.2q - 4.6 - 7.1q = -0.9q - 4.6$

**58.** $-4.0x + 2.7 - 1.6x = -4.6x + 2.7$

**59.** $\dfrac{5}{7}x + \dfrac{1}{3} = \dfrac{2}{5} - \dfrac{2}{7}x + \dfrac{2}{5}$

**60.** $\dfrac{6}{7}s - \dfrac{3}{4} = \dfrac{4}{5} - \dfrac{1}{7}s + \dfrac{1}{6}$

**61.** $(5y + 6) - (3 + 4y) = 10$

**62.** $(8r - 3) - (7r + 1) = -6$

🌐 **63.** $2(p + 5) - (9 + p) = -3$

**64.** $4(k - 6) - (3k + 2) = -5$

**65.** $-6(2b + 1) + (13b - 7) = 0$

**66.** $-5(3w - 3) + (1 + 16w) = 0$

**67.** $10(-2x + 1) = -19(x + 1)$

**68.** $2(2 - 3r) = -5(r - 3)$

*Brain Busters*   *Solve each equation, and check your solution.* **See Examples 6 and 7.**

**69.** $-2(8p + 2) - 3(2 - 7p) - 2(4 + 2p) = 0$

**70.** $-5(1 - 2z) + 4(3 - z) - 7(3 + z) = 0$

**71.** $4(7x - 1) + 3(2 - 5x) - 4(3x + 5) = -6$

**72.** $9(2m - 3) - 4(5 + 3m) - 5(4 + m) = -3$

**73.** *Concept Check*   Write an equation that requires the use of the addition property of equality, in which 6 must be added to each side to solve the equation and the solution is a negative number.

**74.** *Concept Check*   Write an equation that requires the use of the addition property of equality, in which $\frac{1}{2}$ must be subtracted from each side and the solution is a positive number.

*Write an equation using the information given in the problem. Use x as the variable. Then solve the equation.*

**75.** Three times a number is 17 more than twice the number. Find the number.

**76.** One added to three times a number is three less than four times the number. Find the number.

**77.** If six times a number is subtracted from seven times the number, the result is $-9$. Find the number.

**78.** If five times a number is added to three times the number, the result is the sum of seven times the number and 9. Find the number.

**"Preview Exercises"** are designed to *review* ideas introduced earlier, as well as *preview* ideas needed for the next section.

**PREVIEW EXERCISES**

*Simplify each expression.* ***See Section 1.8.***

**79.** $\dfrac{2}{3}\left(\dfrac{3}{2}\right)$   **80.** $\dfrac{5}{6}\left(\dfrac{6}{5}\right)$   **81.** $-\dfrac{5}{4}\left(-\dfrac{4}{5}x\right)$

**82.** $-\dfrac{9}{7}\left(-\dfrac{7}{9}x\right)$   **83.** $9\left(\dfrac{r}{9}\right)$   **84.** $6\left(\dfrac{t}{6}\right)$

---

## 2.2   The Multiplication Property of Equality

**OBJECTIVES**

**1** Use the multiplication property of equality.

**2** Simplify, and then use the multiplication property of equality.

**OBJECTIVE 1**  **Use the multiplication property of equality.** The addition property of equality from **Section 2.1** is not enough to solve some equations, such as $3x + 2 = 17$.

$$3x + 2 = 17$$
$$3x + 2 - 2 = 17 - 2 \qquad \text{Subtract 2 from each side.}$$
$$3x = 15 \qquad \text{Combine like terms.}$$

The coefficient of $x$ is 3, not 1 as desired. Another property, the **multiplication property of equality,** is needed to change $3x = 15$ to an equation of the form

$$x = \text{a number.}$$

Since $3x = 15$, both $3x$ and 15 must represent the same number. Multiplying both $3x$ and 15 by the same number will also result in an equality.

**Multiplication Property of Equality**

If $A$, $B$, and $C$ ($C \neq 0$) represent real numbers, then the equations

$$A = B \qquad \text{and} \qquad AC = BC$$

are equivalent equations.

That is, we can multiply each side of an equation by the same nonzero number without changing the solution.

In $3x = 15$, we must change $3x$ to $1x$, or $x$. To do this, we multiply each side of the equation by $\frac{1}{3}$, the reciprocal of 3, because $\frac{1}{3} \cdot 3 = \frac{3}{3} = 1$.

$$3x = 15$$

$$\frac{1}{3}(3x) = \frac{1}{3} \cdot 15 \qquad \text{Multiply each side by } \tfrac{1}{3}.$$

$$\left(\frac{1}{3} \cdot 3\right)x = \frac{1}{3} \cdot 15 \qquad \text{Associative property}$$

The product of a number and its reciprocal is 1.

$$1x = 5 \qquad \text{Multiplicative inverse property}$$

$$x = 5 \qquad \text{Multiplicative identity property}$$

The solution is 5. We can check this result in the original equation.

Just as the addition property of equality permits *subtracting* the same number from each side of an equation, the multiplication property of equality permits *dividing* each side of an equation by the same nonzero number.

$$3x = 15$$

$$\frac{3x}{3} = \frac{15}{3} \qquad \text{Divide each side by 3.}$$

$$x = 5 \qquad \text{Same result as above}$$

We can divide each side of an equation by the same nonzero number without changing the solution. ***Do not, however, divide each side by a variable, since the variable might be equal to 0.***

**NOTE** In practice, it is usually easier to multiply on each side if the coefficient of the variable is a fraction, and divide on each side if the coefficient is an integer. For example, to solve

$$\frac{3}{4}x = 12, \quad \text{it is easier to multiply by } \tfrac{4}{3} \text{ than to divide by } \tfrac{3}{4}.$$

On the other hand, to solve

$$5x = 20, \quad \text{it is easier to divide by 5 than to multiply by } \tfrac{1}{5}.$$

**NOW TRY
EXERCISE 1**
Solve $8x = 80$.

**EXAMPLE 1** Applying the Multiplication Property of Equality

Solve $5x = 60$.

$$5x = 60 \qquad \text{Our goal is to isolate } x.$$

Dividing by 5 is the same as multiplying by $\frac{1}{5}$.

$$\frac{5x}{5} = \frac{60}{5} \qquad \text{Divide each side by 5, the coefficient of } x.$$

$$x = 12 \qquad \tfrac{5x}{5} = \tfrac{5}{5}x = 1x = x$$

**CHECK** Substitute 12 for $x$ in the original equation.

$$5x = 60 \qquad \text{Original equation}$$

$$5(12) \stackrel{?}{=} 60 \qquad \text{Let } x = 12.$$

$$60 = 60 \ \checkmark \quad \text{True}$$

**NOW TRY ANSWER**
**1.** $\{10\}$

Since a true statement results, the solution set is $\{12\}$.

*NOW TRY*

NOW TRY
EXERCISE 2
Solve $10x = -24$.

**EXAMPLE 2** Applying the Multiplication Property of Equality

Solve $25x = -30$.

$$25x = -30$$

$$\frac{25x}{25} = \frac{-30}{25} \qquad \text{Divide each side by 25, the coefficient of } x.$$

$$x = \frac{-30}{25} = -\frac{6}{5} \qquad \frac{-a}{b} = -\frac{a}{b}; \text{ Write in lowest terms.}$$

CHECK $\qquad\qquad 25x = -30 \qquad$ Original equation

$$\frac{25}{1}\left(-\frac{6}{5}\right) \overset{?}{=} -30 \qquad \text{Let } x = -\frac{6}{5}.$$

$$-30 = -30 \;\checkmark \qquad \text{True}$$

The check confirms that the solution set is $\left\{-\frac{6}{5}\right\}$. $\qquad$ NOW TRY

NOW TRY
EXERCISE 3
Solve $-1.3x = 7.02$.

**EXAMPLE 3** Solving an Equation with Decimals

Solve $-2.1x = 6.09$.

$$-2.1x = 6.09$$

$$\frac{-2.1x}{-2.1} = \frac{6.09}{-2.1} \qquad \text{Divide each side by } -2.1.$$

$$x = -2.9 \qquad \text{Divide.}$$

Check by replacing $x$ with $-2.9$ in the original equation. The solution set is $\{-2.9\}$.

NOW TRY

NOW TRY
EXERCISE 4
Solve $\frac{x}{5} = -7$.

**EXAMPLE 4** Applying the Multiplication Property of Equality

Solve $\frac{x}{4} = 3$.

$$\frac{x}{4} = 3$$

$$\frac{1}{4}x = 3 \qquad \frac{x}{4} = \frac{1x}{4} = \frac{1}{4}x$$

$$4 \cdot \frac{1}{4}x = 4 \cdot 3 \qquad \text{Multiply each side by 4, the reciprocal of } \frac{1}{4}.$$

$\boxed{4 \cdot \frac{1}{4}x = 1x = x} \longrightarrow x = 12 \qquad$ Multiplicative inverse property; multiplicative identity property

CHECK $\qquad\qquad \dfrac{x}{4} = 3 \qquad$ Original equation

$$\frac{12}{4} \overset{?}{=} 3 \qquad \text{Let } x = 12.$$

$$3 = 3 \;\checkmark \qquad \text{True}$$

NOW TRY ANSWERS
2. $\left\{-\frac{12}{5}\right\}$  3. $\{-5.4\}$
4. $\{-35\}$

Since a true statement results, the solution set is $\{12\}$. $\qquad$ NOW TRY

NOW TRY
EXERCISE 5
Solve $\frac{4}{7}z = -16$.

### EXAMPLE 5 Applying the Multiplication Property of Equality

Solve $\frac{3}{4}w = 6$.

$$\frac{3}{4}w = 6$$

$$\frac{4}{3} \cdot \frac{3}{4}w = \frac{4}{3} \cdot 6 \qquad \text{Multiply each side by } \frac{4}{3}, \text{ the reciprocal of } \frac{3}{4}.$$

$$1 \cdot w = \frac{4}{3} \cdot \frac{6}{1} \qquad \text{Multiplicative inverse property}$$

$$w = 8 \qquad \text{Multiplicative identity property; multiply fractions.}$$

Check to confirm that the solution set is $\{8\}$. NOW TRY

In **Section 2.1,** we obtained $-x = -17$ in our alternative solution to **Example 4.** We reasoned that since the additive inverse (or opposite) of $x$ is $-17$, then $x$ must equal 17. We can use the multiplication property of equality to obtain the same result.

NOW TRY
EXERCISE 6
Solve $-x = 9$.

### EXAMPLE 6 Applying the Multiplication Property of Equality

Solve $-x = -17$.

$$-x = -17$$

$$-1x = -17 \qquad -x = -1x$$

$$-1(-1x) = -1(-17) \qquad \text{Multiply each side by } -1.$$

$$[-1(-1)]x = 17 \qquad \text{Associative property; multiply.}$$

These steps are usually omitted.

$$1x = 17 \qquad \text{Multiplicative inverse property}$$

$$x = 17 \qquad \text{Multiplicative identity property}$$

CHECK

$$-x = -17 \qquad \text{Original equation}$$

$$-(17) \overset{?}{=} -17 \qquad \text{Let } x = 17.$$

$$-17 = -17 \checkmark \qquad \text{True}$$

The solution, 17, checks, so $\{17\}$ is the solution set. NOW TRY

**OBJECTIVE 2** Simplify, and then use the multiplication property of equality.

NOW TRY
EXERCISE 7
Solve $9n - 6n = 21$.

### EXAMPLE 7 Combining Like Terms When Solving

Solve $5m + 6m = 33$.

$$5m + 6m = 33$$

$$11m = 33 \qquad \text{Combine like terms.}$$

$$\frac{11m}{11} = \frac{33}{11} \qquad \text{Divide by 11.}$$

$$m = 3 \qquad \text{Multiplicative identity property; divide.}$$

CHECK

$$5m + 6m = 33 \qquad \text{Original equation}$$

$$5(3) + 6(3) \overset{?}{=} 33 \qquad \text{Let } m = 3.$$

$$15 + 18 \overset{?}{=} 33 \qquad \text{Multiply.}$$

$$33 = 33 \checkmark \qquad \text{True}$$

NOW TRY ANSWERS
**5.** $\{-28\}$ **6.** $\{-9\}$ **7.** $\{7\}$

Since a true statement results, the solution set is $\{3\}$. NOW TRY

## 2.2 EXERCISES

🌐 *Complete solution available on the Video Resources on DVD*

**1.** *Concept Check* Tell whether you would use the addition or multiplication property of equality to solve each equation. *Do not actually solve.*

**(a)** $3x = 12$　　**(b)** $3 + x = 12$　　**(c)** $-x = 4$　　**(d)** $-12 = 6 + x$

**2.** *Concept Check* Which equation does *not* require the use of the multiplication property of equality?

**A.** $3x - 5x = 6$　　**B.** $-\dfrac{1}{4}x = 12$　　**C.** $5x - 4x = 7$　　**D.** $\dfrac{x}{3} = -2$

**3.** How would you find the solution of a linear equation with next-to-last step "$-x = 5$?"

**4.** In the statement of the multiplication property of equality in this section, there is a restriction that $C \neq 0$. What would happen if you multiplied each side of an equation by 0?

*Concept Check* *By what number is it necessary to multiply both sides of each equation to isolate x on the left side? Do not actually solve.*

**5.** $\dfrac{4}{5}x = 8$　　**6.** $\dfrac{2}{3}x = 6$　　**7.** $\dfrac{x}{10} = 5$　　**8.** $\dfrac{x}{100} = 10$

**9.** $-\dfrac{9}{2}x = -4$　　**10.** $-\dfrac{8}{3}x = -11$　　**11.** $-x = 0.75$　　**12.** $-x = 0.48$

*Concept Check* *By what number is it necessary to divide both sides of each equation to isolate x on the left side? Do not actually solve.*

**13.** $6x = 5$　　**14.** $7x = 10$　　**15.** $-4x = 16$　　**16.** $-13x = 26$

**17.** $0.12x = 48$　　**18.** $0.21x = 63$　　**19.** $-x = 25$　　**20.** $-x = 50$

*Solve each equation, and check your solution.* **See Examples 1–6.**

**21.** $6x = 36$　　**22.** $8x = 64$　　**23.** $2m = 15$　　**24.** $3m = 10$

**25.** $4x = -20$　　**26.** $5x = -60$　　**27.** $-7x = 28$　　**28.** $-9x = 36$

🌐 **29.** $10t = -36$　　**30.** $10s = -54$　　**31.** $-6x = -72$　　**32.** $-4x = -64$

**33.** $4r = 0$　　**34.** $7x = 0$　　🌐 **35.** $-x = 12$　　**36.** $-t = 14$

**37.** $-x = -\dfrac{3}{4}$　　**38.** $-x = -\dfrac{1}{2}$　　**39.** $0.2t = 8$　　**40.** $0.9x = 18$

🌐 **41.** $-2.1m = 25.62$　　**42.** $-3.9x = 32.76$　　**43.** $\dfrac{1}{4}x = -12$　　**44.** $\dfrac{1}{5}p = -3$

🌐 **45.** $\dfrac{z}{6} = 12$　　**46.** $\dfrac{x}{5} = 15$　　**47.** $\dfrac{x}{7} = -5$　　**48.** $\dfrac{r}{8} = -3$

🌐 **49.** $\dfrac{2}{7}p = 4$　　**50.** $\dfrac{3}{8}x = 9$　　**51.** $-\dfrac{5}{6}t = -15$　　**52.** $-\dfrac{3}{4}z = -21$

**53.** $-\dfrac{7}{9}x = \dfrac{3}{5}$　　**54.** $-\dfrac{5}{6}x = \dfrac{4}{9}$　　**55.** $-0.3x = 9$　　**56.** $-0.5x = 20$

*Solve each equation, and check your solution.* **See Example 7.**

🌐 **57.** $4x + 3x = 21$　　**58.** $8x + 3x = 121$　　**59.** $6r - 8r = 10$

**60.** $3p - 7p = 24$　　**61.** $\dfrac{2}{5}x - \dfrac{3}{10}x = 2$　　**62.** $\dfrac{2}{3}x - \dfrac{5}{9}x = 4$

**63.** $7m + 6m - 4m = 63$　　**64.** $9r + 2r - 7r = 68$　　**65.** $-6x + 4x - 7x = 0$

**66.** $-5x + 4x - 8x = 0$   **67.** $8w - 4w + w = -3$   **68.** $9x - 3x + x = -4$

**69.** $\dfrac{1}{3}x - \dfrac{1}{4}x + \dfrac{1}{12}x = 3$   **70.** $\dfrac{2}{5}x + \dfrac{1}{10}x - \dfrac{1}{20}x = 18$

**71.** *Concept Check*   Write an equation that requires the use of the multiplication property of equality, where each side must be multiplied by $\frac{2}{3}$ and the solution is a negative number.

**72.** *Concept Check*   Write an equation that requires the use of the multiplication property of equality, where each side must be divided by 100 and the solution is not an integer.

*Write an equation using the information given in the problem. Use x as the variable. Then solve the equation.*

**73.** When a number is multiplied by 4, the result is 6. Find the number.

**74.** When a number is multiplied by $-4$, the result is 10. Find the number.

**75.** When a number is divided by $-5$, the result is 2. Find the number.

**76.** If twice a number is divided by 5, the result is 4. Find the number.

### PREVIEW EXERCISES

*Simplify each expression.* **See Section 1.8.**

**77.** $-(3m + 5)$

**78.** $-4(-1 + 6x)$

**79.** $4(-5 + 2p) - 3(p - 4)$

**80.** $2(4k - 7) - 4(-k + 3)$

*Solve each equation.* **See Section 2.1.**

**81.** $4x + 5 + 2x = 7x$

**82.** $2x + 5x - 3x + 4 = 3x + 2$

## 2.3  More on Solving Linear Equations

### OBJECTIVES

1. Learn and use the four steps for solving a linear equation.
2. Solve equations with fractions or decimals as coefficients.
3. Solve equations with no solution or infinitely many solutions.
4. Write expressions for two related unknown quantities.

**OBJECTIVE 1**   **Learn and use the four steps for solving a linear equation.** We now apply *both* properties of equality to solve linear equations.

**Solving a Linear Equation**

*Step 1*   **Simplify each side separately.** Clear (eliminate) parentheses, fractions, and decimals, using the distributive property as needed, and combine like terms.

*Step 2*   **Isolate the variable term on one side.** Use the addition property if necessary so that the variable term is on one side of the equation and a number is on the other.

*Step 3*   **Isolate the variable.** Use the multiplication property if necessary to get the equation in the form $x = $ a number, or a number $= x$. (Other letters may be used for variables.)

*Step 4*   **Check.** Substitute the proposed solution into the *original* equation to see if a true statement results. If not, rework the problem.

*Remember that when we solve an equation, our primary goal is to isolate the variable on one side of the equation.*

NOW TRY
EXERCISE 1
Solve $7 + 2m = -3$.

**EXAMPLE 1** Applying Both Properties of Equality to Solve an Equation

Solve $-6x + 5 = 17$.

**Step 1** There are no parentheses, fractions, or decimals in this equation, so this step is not necessary.

Our goal is to isolate $x$.
$$-6x + 5 = 17$$

**Step 2**
$$-6x + 5 - 5 = 17 - 5 \qquad \text{Subtract 5 from each side.}$$
$$-6x = 12 \qquad \text{Combine like terms.}$$

**Step 3**
$$\frac{-6x}{-6} = \frac{12}{-6} \qquad \text{Divide each side by } -6.$$
$$x = -2$$

**Step 4** Check by substituting $-2$ for $x$ in the original equation.

CHECK
$$-6x + 5 = 17 \qquad \text{Original equation}$$
$$-6(-2) + 5 \stackrel{?}{=} 17 \qquad \text{Let } x = -2.$$
$$12 + 5 \stackrel{?}{=} 17 \qquad \text{Multiply.}$$
$$17 = 17 \ \checkmark \qquad \text{True}$$

The solution, $-2$, checks, so the solution set is $\{-2\}$.

NOW TRY

NOW TRY
EXERCISE 2
Solve $2q + 3 = 4q - 9$.

**EXAMPLE 2** Applying Both Properties of Equality to Solve an Equation

Solve $3x + 2 = 5x - 8$.

**Step 1** There are no parentheses, fractions, or decimals in the equation.

Our goal is to isolate $x$.
$$3x + 2 = 5x - 8$$

**Step 2**
$$3x + 2 - 5x = 5x - 8 - 5x \qquad \text{Subtract } 5x \text{ from each side.}$$
$$-2x + 2 = -8 \qquad \text{Combine like terms.}$$
$$-2x + 2 - 2 = -8 - 2 \qquad \text{Subtract 2 from each side.}$$
$$-2x = -10 \qquad \text{Combine like terms.}$$

**Step 3**
$$\frac{-2x}{-2} = \frac{-10}{-2} \qquad \text{Divide each side by } -2.$$
$$x = 5$$

**Step 4** Check by substituting 5 for $x$ in the original equation.

CHECK
$$3x + 2 = 5x - 8 \qquad \text{Original equation}$$
$$3(5) + 2 \stackrel{?}{=} 5(5) - 8 \qquad \text{Let } x = 5.$$
$$15 + 2 \stackrel{?}{=} 25 - 8 \qquad \text{Multiply.}$$
$$17 = 17 \ \checkmark \qquad \text{True}$$

The solution, 5, checks, so the solution set is $\{5\}$.

NOW TRY

NOW TRY ANSWERS
**1.** $\{-5\}$ **2.** $\{6\}$

**NOTE** *Remember that the variable can be isolated on either side of the equation.* In **Example 2,** *x* will be isolated on the right if we begin by subtracting $3x$.

| | |
|---|---|
| $3x + 2 = 5x - 8$ | Equation from **Example 2** |
| $3x + 2 - 3x = 5x - 8 - 3x$ | Subtract $3x$ from each side. |
| $2 = 2x - 8$ | Combine like terms. |
| $2 + 8 = 2x - 8 + 8$ | Add 8 to each side. |
| $10 = 2x$ | Combine like terms. |
| $\dfrac{10}{2} = \dfrac{2x}{2}$ | Divide each side by 2. |
| $5 = x$ | The same solution results. |

*There are often several equally correct ways to solve an equation.*

NOW TRY
EXERCISE 3
Solve.

$3(z - 6) - 5z = -7z + 7$

**EXAMPLE 3** Using the Four Steps to Solve an Equation

Solve $4(k - 3) - k = k - 6$.

*Step 1* Clear parentheses using the distributive property.

| | |
|---|---|
| $4(k - 3) - k = k - 6$ | |
| $4(k) + 4(-3) - k = k - 6$ | Distributive property |
| $4k - 12 - k = k - 6$ | Multiply. |
| $3k - 12 = k - 6$ | Combine like terms. |
| *Step 2*  $3k - 12 - k = k - 6 - k$ | Subtract $k$. |
| $2k - 12 = -6$ | Combine like terms. |
| $2k - 12 + 12 = -6 + 12$ | Add 12. |
| $2k = 6$ | Combine like terms. |
| *Step 3*  $\dfrac{2k}{2} = \dfrac{6}{2}$ | Divide by 2. |
| $k = 3$ | |

*Step 4*  CHECK

| | |
|---|---|
| $4(k - 3) - k = k - 6$ | Original equation |
| $4(3 - 3) - 3 \stackrel{?}{=} 3 - 6$ | Let $k = 3$. |
| $4(0) - 3 \stackrel{?}{=} 3 - 6$ | Work inside the parentheses. |
| $-3 = -3$ ✓ | True |

The solution set of the equation is $\{3\}$.   NOW TRY

**EXAMPLE 4** Using the Four Steps to Solve an Equation

Solve $8z - (3 + 2z) = 3z + 1$.

| | |
|---|---|
| *Step 1*      $8z - (3 + 2z) = 3z + 1$ | |
| $8z - 1(3 + 2z) = 3z + 1$ | Multiplicative identity property |
| $8z - 3 - 2z = 3z + 1$ | Distributive property |
| $6z - 3 = 3z + 1$ | Combine like terms. |

Be careful with signs.

NOW TRY ANSWER
**3.** $\{5\}$

NOW TRY
EXERCISE 4
Solve.

$$5x - (x + 9) = x - 4$$

**Step 2**   $6z - 3 - 3z = 3z + 1 - 3z$   Subtract $3z$.

$$3z - 3 = 1$$   Combine like terms.

$$3z - 3 + 3 = 1 + 3$$   Add 3.

$$3z = 4$$   Combine like terms.

**Step 3**   $\dfrac{3z}{3} = \dfrac{4}{3}$   Divide by 3.

$$z = \dfrac{4}{3}$$

**Step 4**   Check that $\left\{\dfrac{4}{3}\right\}$ is the solution set.   NOW TRY

---

⚠ **CAUTION**   In an expression such as $8z - (3 + 2z)$ in **Example 4,** the $-$ sign acts like a factor of $-1$ and affects the sign of *every* term within the parentheses.

$$8z - (3 + 2z)$$
$$= 8z - 1(3 + 2z)$$
$$= 8z + (-1)(3 + 2z)$$
$$= 8z - 3 - 2z$$

Change to $-$ in *both* terms.

---

NOW TRY
EXERCISE 5
Solve.

$$24 - 4(7 - 2t) = 4(t - 1)$$

**EXAMPLE 5**   Using the Four Steps to Solve an Equation

Solve $4(4 - 3x) = 32 - 8(x + 2)$.

**Step 1**   $4(4 - 3x) = 32 - 8(x + 2)$   Be careful with signs.

$$16 - 12x = 32 - 8x - 16$$   Distributive property

$$16 - 12x = 16 - 8x$$   Combine like terms.

**Step 2**   $16 - 12x + 8x = 16 - 8x + 8x$   Add $8x$.

$$16 - 4x = 16$$   Combine like terms.

$$16 - 4x - 16 = 16 - 16$$   Subtract 16.

$$-4x = 0$$   Combine like terms.

**Step 3**   $\dfrac{-4x}{-4} = \dfrac{0}{-4}$   Divide by $-4$.

$$x = 0$$

**Step 4**   CHECK   $4(4 - 3x) = 32 - 8(x + 2)$   Original equation

$$4[4 - 3(0)] \stackrel{?}{=} 32 - 8(0 + 2)$$   Let $x = 0$.

$$4(4 - 0) \stackrel{?}{=} 32 - 8(2)$$   Multiply and add.

$$4(4) \stackrel{?}{=} 32 - 16$$   Subtract and multiply.

$$16 = 16 ✓$$   True

Since the solution 0 checks, the solution set is $\{0\}$.   NOW TRY

**OBJECTIVE 2**   Solve equations with fractions or decimals as coefficients.

To avoid messy computations, we clear an equation of fractions by multiplying each side by the least common denominator (LCD) of all the fractions in the equation.

NOW TRY ANSWERS
4. $\left\{\dfrac{5}{3}\right\}$   5. $\{0\}$

⚠ **CAUTION**   *When clearing an equation of fractions, be sure to multiply every term on each side of the equation by the LCD.*

◠ *NOW TRY*
↳ *EXERCISE 6*

Solve.

$$\frac{1}{2}x + \frac{5}{8}x = \frac{3}{4}x - 6$$

**EXAMPLE 6**   Solving an Equation with Fractions as Coefficients

Solve $\frac{2}{3}x - \frac{1}{2}x = -\frac{1}{6}x - 2$.

**Step 1**   The LCD of all the fractions in the equation is 6.

$$\frac{2}{3}x - \frac{1}{2}x = -\frac{1}{6}x - 2$$   Pay particular attention here.

$$6\left(\frac{2}{3}x - \frac{1}{2}x\right) = 6\left(-\frac{1}{6}x - 2\right)$$   Multiply each side by 6, the LCD.

$$6\left(\frac{2}{3}x\right) + 6\left(-\frac{1}{2}x\right) = 6\left(-\frac{1}{6}x\right) + 6(-2)$$   Distributive property; multiply *each* term inside the parentheses by 6.

The fractions have been cleared. → $$4x - 3x = -x - 12$$   Multiply.

$$x = -x - 12$$   Combine like terms.

**Step 2**   $$x + x = -x - 12 + x$$   Add x.

$$2x = -12$$   Combine like terms.

**Step 3**   $$\frac{2x}{2} = \frac{-12}{2}$$   Divide by 2.

$$x = -6$$

**Step 4**   CHECK   $$\frac{2}{3}x - \frac{1}{2}x = -\frac{1}{6}x - 2$$   Original equation

$$\frac{2}{3}(-6) - \frac{1}{2}(-6) \stackrel{?}{=} -\frac{1}{6}(-6) - 2$$   Let x = -6.

$$-4 + 3 \stackrel{?}{=} 1 - 2$$   Multiply.

$$-1 = -1 \ ✓$$   True

The solution, -6, checks, so the solution set is $\{-6\}$.   NOW TRY ↻

**EXAMPLE 7**   Solving an Equation with Fractions as Coefficients

Solve $\frac{1}{3}(x + 5) - \frac{3}{5}(x + 2) = 1$.

**Step 1**   $$\frac{1}{3}(x + 5) - \frac{3}{5}(x + 2) = 1$$

$$15\left[\frac{1}{3}(x + 5) - \frac{3}{5}(x + 2)\right] = 15(1)$$   Clear the fractions. Multiply by 15, the LCD.

$$15\left[\frac{1}{3}(x + 5)\right] + 15\left[-\frac{3}{5}(x + 2)\right] = 15(1)$$   Distributive property

$$5(x + 5) - 9(x + 2) = 15$$   Multiply.

$15[\frac{1}{3}(x + 5)]$
$= 15 \cdot \frac{1}{3} \cdot (x + 5)$
$= 5(x + 5)$

$$5x + 25 - 9x - 18 = 15$$   Distributive property

$$-4x + 7 = 15$$   Combine like terms.

*NOW TRY ANSWER*
**6.** $\{-16\}$

NOW TRY
EXERCISE 7
Solve.

$\dfrac{2}{3}(x + 2) - \dfrac{1}{2}(3x + 4) = -4$

***Step 2***

$$-4x + 7 - 7 = 15 - 7 \qquad \text{Subtract 7.}$$

$$-4x = 8 \qquad \text{Combine like terms.}$$

***Step 3***

$$\dfrac{-4x}{-4} = \dfrac{8}{-4} \qquad \text{Divide by } -4.$$

$$x = -2$$

***Step 4*** Check to confirm that $\{-2\}$ is the solution set.    NOW TRY

---

⚠ **CAUTION**   Be sure you understand how to multiply by the LCD to clear an equation of fractions. ***Study Step 1 in Examples 6 and 7 carefully.***

---

NOW TRY
EXERCISE 8
Solve.

$0.05(13 - t) - 0.2t = 0.08(30)$

**EXAMPLE 8**   Solving an Equation with Decimals as Coefficients

Solve $0.1t + 0.05(20 - t) = 0.09(20)$.

***Step 1***   The decimals here are expressed as tenths $(0.1)$ and hundredths $(0.05$ and $0.09)$. We choose the least exponent on 10 needed to eliminate the decimals. Here, we use $10^2 = 100$.

$$0.1t + 0.05(20 - t) = 0.09(20)$$

$$0.10t + 0.05(20 - t) = 0.09(20) \qquad 0.1 = 0.10$$

$$100[0.10t + 0.05(20 - t)] = 100[0.09(20)] \qquad \text{Multiply by 100.}$$

$$100(0.10t) + 100[0.05(20 - t)] = 100[0.09(20)] \qquad \text{Distributive property}$$

$$10t + 5(20 - t) = 9(20) \qquad \text{Multiply.}$$

$$10t + 5(20) + 5(-t) = 180 \qquad \text{Distributive property}$$

$$10t + 100 - 5t = 180 \qquad \text{Multiply.}$$

$$5t + 100 = 180 \qquad \text{Combine like terms.}$$

***Step 2***

$$5t + 100 - 100 = 180 - 100 \qquad \text{Subtract 100.}$$

$$5t = 80 \qquad \text{Combine like terms.}$$

***Step 3***

$$\dfrac{5t}{5} = \dfrac{80}{5} \qquad \text{Divide by 5.}$$

$$t = 16$$

***Step 4***   Check to confirm that $\{16\}$ is the solution set.    NOW TRY

---

**NOTE**   In **Example 8,** multiplying by 100 is the same as moving the decimal point two places to the right.

$$0.10t + 0.05(20 - t) = 0.09(20)$$

$$10t + 5(20 - t) = 9(20) \qquad \text{Multiply by 100.}$$

---

**OBJECTIVE 3**   Solve equations with no solution or infinitely many solutions. Each equation so far has had exactly one solution. An equation with exactly one solution is a **conditional equation** because it is only true under certain conditions. Some equations may have no solution or infinitely many solutions.

NOW TRY ANSWERS
7. $\{4\}$   8. $\{-7\}$

⌐ *NOW TRY*
  *EXERCISE 9*
Solve.

$$-3(x - 7) = 2x - 5x + 21$$

**EXAMPLE 9**  Solving an Equation That Has Infinitely Many Solutions

Solve $5x - 15 = 5(x - 3)$.

$$5x - 15 = 5(x - 3)$$

$$5x - 15 = 5x - 15 \qquad \text{Distributive property}$$

$$5x - 15 - 5x = 5x - 15 - 5x \qquad \text{Subtract } 5x.$$

Notice that the variable "disappeared."  $\quad -15 = -15 \qquad \text{Combine like terms.}$

$$-15 + 15 = -15 + 15 \qquad \text{Add 15.}$$

$$0 = 0 \qquad \text{True}$$

**Solution set:   {all real numbers}**

Since the last statement $(0 = 0)$ is true, *any* real number is a solution. We could have predicted this from the second line in the solution,

$$5x - 15 = 5x - 15. \leftarrow \text{This is true for } \textit{any} \text{ value of } x.$$

Try several values for $x$ in the original equation to see that they all satisfy it.

An equation with both sides exactly the same, like $0 = 0$, is called an **identity.** An identity is true for all replacements of the variables. As shown above, we write the solution set as **{all real numbers}.**  *NOW TRY* ⤺

---

⚠ CAUTION   In **Example 9,** do not write $\{0\}$ as the solution set. While 0 is a solution, there are infinitely many other solutions. *For $\{0\}$ to be the solution set, the last line must include a variable, such as x, and read x = 0, not 0 = 0.*

---

⌐ *NOW TRY*
  *EXERCISE 10*
Solve.

$$-4x + 12 = 3 - 4(x - 3)$$

**EXAMPLE 10**  Solving an Equation That Has No Solution

Solve $2x + 3(x + 1) = 5x + 4$.

$$2x + 3(x + 1) = 5x + 4$$

$$2x + 3x + 3 = 5x + 4 \qquad \text{Distributive property}$$

$$5x + 3 = 5x + 4 \qquad \text{Combine like terms.}$$

$$5x + 3 - 5x = 5x + 4 - 5x \qquad \text{Subtract } 5x.$$

Again, the variable "disappeared."  $\quad 3 = 4 \qquad \text{False}$

**There is no solution.   Solution set:  ∅**

A false statement $(3 = 4)$ results. The original equation, called a **contradiction,** has no solution. Its solution set is the **empty set,** or **null set,** symbolized **∅.**  *NOW TRY* ⤺

---

⚠ CAUTION   **DO NOT** write $\{∅\}$ to represent the empty set.

---

The table summarizes the solution sets of the equations in this section.

| Type of Equation | Final Equation in Solution | Number of Solutions | Solution Set |
|---|---|---|---|
| Conditional (See Examples 1–8.) | $x$ = a number | One | {a number} |
| Identity (See Example 9.) | A true statement with no variable, such as $0 = 0$ | Infinite | {all real numbers} |
| Contradiction (See Example 10.) | A false statement with no variable, such as $3 = 4$ | None | ∅ |

*NOW TRY ANSWERS*
**9.** {all real numbers}  **10.** ∅

**OBJECTIVE 4** Write expressions for two related unknown quantities.

*NOW TRY*
*EXERCISE 11*

Two numbers have a sum of 18. If one of the numbers is represented by $m$, find an expression for the other number.

**EXAMPLE 11** Translating a Phrase into an Algebraic Expression

Perform each translation.

**(a)** Two numbers have a sum of 23. If one of the numbers is represented by $x$, find an expression for the other number.

First, suppose that the sum of two numbers is 23, and one of the numbers is 10. How would you find the other number? You would subtract 10 from 23.

$$23 - 10 \leftarrow \text{This gives 13 as the other number.}$$

Instead of using 10 as one of the numbers, use $x$. The other number would be obtained in the same way—by subtracting $x$ from 23.

$$23 - x. \quad \boxed{x - 23 \text{ is not correct.}}$$

To check, find the sum of the two numbers:

$$x + (23 - x) = 23, \quad \text{as required.}$$

**(b)** Two numbers have a product of 24. If one of the numbers is represented by $x$, find an expression for the other number.

Suppose that one of the numbers is 4. To find the other number, we would divide 24 by 4.

$$\frac{24}{4} \leftarrow \begin{array}{l}\text{This gives 6 as the other number.}\\ \text{The product } 6 \cdot 4 \text{ is 24.}\end{array}$$

In the same way, if $x$ is one of the numbers, then we divide 24 by $x$ to find the other number.

*NOW TRY ANSWER*
**11.** $18 - m$

$$\frac{24}{x} \leftarrow \text{The other number} \qquad \text{NOW TRY}$$

---

## 2.3 EXERCISES

**MyMathLab**    Math XL PRACTICE   WATCH   DOWNLOAD    READ    REVIEW

🌐 *Complete solution available on the Video Resources on DVD*

📝 *Using the methods of this section, what should we do first when solving each equation? Do not actually solve.*

**1.** $7x + 8 = 1$     **2.** $7x - 5x + 15 = 8 + x$     **3.** $3(2t - 4) = 20 - 2t$

**4.** $\frac{3}{4}z = -15$     **5.** $\frac{2}{3}x - \frac{1}{6} = \frac{3}{2}x + 1$     **6.** $0.9x + 0.3(x + 12) = 6$

**7.** *Concept Check* Which equation does *not* have {all real numbers} as its solution set?

   **A.** $5x = 4x + x$     **B.** $2(x + 6) = 2x + 12$     **C.** $\frac{1}{2}x = 0.5x$     **D.** $3x = 2x$

**8.** *Concept Check* The expression $100[0.03(x - 10)]$ is equivalent to which of the following?

   **A.** $0.03x - 0.3$     **B.** $3x - 3$     **C.** $3x - 10$     **D.** $3x - 30$

*Solve each equation, and check your solution. **See Examples 1–5, 9, and 10.***

**9.** $3x + 2 = 14$     **10.** $4x + 3 = 27$     **11.** $-5z - 4 = 21$

**12.** $-7w - 4 = 10$     **13.** $4p - 5 = 2p$     **14.** $6q - 2 = 3q$

**15.** $2x + 9 = 4x + 11$    **16.** $7p + 8 = 9p - 2$    **17.** $5m + 8 = 7 + 3m$

**18.** $4r + 2 = r - 6$    **19.** $-12x - 5 = 10 - 7x$    **20.** $-16w - 3 = 13 - 8w$

**21.** $12h - 5 = 11h + 5 - h$    **22.** $-4x - 1 = -5x + 1 + 3x$

**23.** $7r - 5r + 2 = 5r + 2 - r$    **24.** $9p - 4p + 6 = 7p + 6 - 3p$

**25.** $3(4x + 2) + 5x = 30 - x$    **26.** $5(2m + 3) - 4m = 2m + 25$

**27.** $-2p + 7 = 3 - (5p + 1)$    **28.** $4x + 9 = 3 - (x - 2)$

**29.** $6(3w + 5) = 2(10w + 10)$    **30.** $4(2x - 1) = -6(x + 3)$

**31.** $-(4x + 2) - (-3x - 5) = 3$    **32.** $-(6k - 5) - (-5k + 8) = -3$

**33.** $6(4x - 1) = 12(2x + 3)$    **34.** $6(2x + 8) = 4(3x - 6)$

**35.** $3(2x - 4) = 6(x - 2)$    **36.** $3(6 - 4x) = 2(-6x + 9)$

**37.** $11x - 5(x + 2) = 6x + 5$    **38.** $6x - 4(x + 1) = 2x + 4$

*Solve each equation, and check your solution.* ***See Examples 6–8.***

**39.** $\dfrac{3}{5}t - \dfrac{1}{10}t = t - \dfrac{5}{2}$    **40.** $-\dfrac{2}{7}r + 2r = \dfrac{1}{2}r + \dfrac{17}{2}$

**41.** $\dfrac{3}{4}x - \dfrac{1}{3}x + 5 = \dfrac{5}{6}x$    **42.** $\dfrac{1}{5}x - \dfrac{2}{3}x - 2 = -\dfrac{2}{5}x$

**43.** $\dfrac{1}{7}(3x + 2) - \dfrac{1}{5}(x + 4) = 2$    **44.** $\dfrac{1}{4}(3x - 1) + \dfrac{1}{6}(x + 3) = 3$

**45.** $-\dfrac{1}{4}(x - 12) + \dfrac{1}{2}(x + 2) = x + 4$    **46.** $\dfrac{1}{9}(p + 18) + \dfrac{1}{3}(2p + 3) = p + 3$

**47.** $\dfrac{2}{3}k - \left(k - \dfrac{1}{2}\right) = \dfrac{1}{6}(k - 51)$    **48.** $-\dfrac{5}{6}q - (q - 1) = \dfrac{1}{4}(-q + 80)$

**49.** $0.2(60) + 0.05x = 0.1(60 + x)$    **50.** $0.3(30) + 0.15x = 0.2(30 + x)$

**51.** $1.00x + 0.05(12 - x) = 0.10(63)$    **52.** $0.92x + 0.98(12 - x) = 0.96(12)$

**53.** $0.6(10{,}000) + 0.8x = 0.72(10{,}000 + x)$    **54.** $0.2(5000) + 0.3x = 0.25(5000 + x)$

*Solve each equation, and check your solution.* ***See Examples 1–10.***

**55.** $10(2x - 1) = 8(2x + 1) + 14$    **56.** $9(3k - 5) = 12(3k - 1) - 51$

**57.** $\dfrac{1}{2}(x + 2) + \dfrac{3}{4}(x + 4) = x + 5$    **58.** $\dfrac{1}{3}(x + 3) + \dfrac{1}{6}(x - 6) = x + 3$

**59.** $0.1(x + 80) + 0.2x = 14$    **60.** $0.3(x + 15) + 0.4(x + 25) = 25$

**61.** $4(x + 8) = 2(2x + 6) + 20$    **62.** $4(x + 3) = 2(2x + 8) - 4$

**63.** $9(v + 1) - 3v = 2(3v + 1) - 8$    **64.** $8(t - 3) + 4t = 6(2t + 1) - 10$

*Write the answer to each problem in terms of the variable.* ***See Example 11.***

**65.** Two numbers have a sum of 11. One of the numbers is $q$. What expression represents the other number?

**66.** Two numbers have a sum of 34. One of the numbers is $r$. What expression represents the other number?

**67.** The product of two numbers is 9. One of the numbers is $x$. What expression represents the other number?

**68.** The product of two numbers is $-6$. One of the numbers is $m$. What expression represents the other number?

**69.** A football player gained $x$ yards rushing. On the next down, he gained 9 yd. What expression represents the number of yards he gained altogether?

**70.** A football player gained $y$ yards on a punt return. On the next return, he gained 6 yd. What expression represents the number of yards he gained altogether?

**71.** A baseball player got 65 hits one season. He got $h$ of the hits in one game. What expression represents the number of hits he got in the rest of the games?

**72.** A hockey player scored 42 goals in one season. He scored $n$ goals in one game. What expression represents the number of goals he scored in the rest of the games?

**73.** Monica is $x$ years old. What expression represents her age 15 yr from now? 5 yr ago?

**74.** Chandler is $y$ years old. What expression represents his age 4 yr ago? 11 yr from now?

**75.** Cliff has $r$ quarters. Express the value of the quarters in cents.

**76.** Claire has $y$ dimes. Express the value of the dimes in cents.

**77.** A bank teller has $t$ dollars, all in \$5 bills. What expression represents the number of \$5 bills the teller has?

**78.** A clerk has $v$ dollars, all in \$10 bills. What expression represents the number of \$10 bills the clerk has?

**79.** A plane ticket costs $x$ dollars for an adult and $y$ dollars for a child. Find an expression that represents the total cost for 3 adults and 2 children.

**80.** A concert ticket costs $p$ dollars for an adult and $q$ dollars for a child. Find an expression that represents the total cost for 4 adults and 6 children.

### PREVIEW EXERCISES

*Write each phrase as a mathematical expression using x as the variable.* **See Sections 1.3, 1.5, 1.6, and 1.8.**

**81.** A number added to $-6$

**82.** A number decreased by 9

**83.** The difference between $-5$ and a number

**84.** The quotient of $-6$ and a nonzero number

**85.** The product of 12 and the difference between a number and 9

**86.** The quotient of 9 more than a number and 6 less than the number

### SUMMARY EXERCISES on Solving Linear Equations

*This section provides practice in solving all the types of linear equations introduced in* **Sections 2.1–2.3.**

*Solve each equation, and check your solution.*

**1.** $x + 2 = -3$      **2.** $2m + 8 = 16$      **3.** $12.5x = -63.75$

**4.** $-x = -12$      **5.** $\dfrac{4}{5}x = -20$      **6.** $7m - 5m = -12$

**7.** $5x - 9 = 3(x - 3)$      **8.** $\dfrac{x}{-2} = 8$      **9.** $-x = 6$

**10.** $\dfrac{2}{3}x + 8 = \dfrac{1}{4}x$      **11.** $4x + 2(3 - 2x) = 6$      **12.** $-6z = -14$

13. $-3(m - 4) + 2(5 + 2m) = 29$

14. $-0.3x + 2.1(x - 4) = -6.6$

15. $0.08x + 0.06(x + 9) = 1.24$

16. $x - 16.2 = 7.5$

17. $7m - (2m - 9) = 39$

18. $7(p - 2) + p = 2(p + 2)$

19. $-2t + 5t - 9 = 3(t - 4) - 5$

20. $3(m + 5) - 1 + 2m = 5(m + 2)$

21. $0.2(50) + 0.8r = 0.4(50 + r)$

22. $2.3x + 13.7 = 1.3x + 2.9$

23. $2(3 + 7x) - (1 + 15x) = 2$

24. $6q - 9 = 12 + 3q$

25. $2(4 + 3r) = 3(r + 1) + 11$

26. $r + 9 + 7r = 4(3 + 2r) - 3$

27. $\frac{1}{4}x - 4 = \frac{3}{2}x + \frac{3}{4}x$

28. $0.6(100 - x) + 0.4x = 0.5(92)$

29. $\frac{3}{4}(z - 2) - \frac{1}{3}(5 - 2z) = -2$

30. $2 - (m + 4) = 3m - 2$

# STUDY SKILLS

## Using Study Cards Revisited

We introduced study cards on **page 48.** Another type of study card follows.

### Practice Quiz Cards

Write a problem with direction words (like *solve, simplify*) on the front of the card, and work the problem on the back. Make one for each type of problem you learn.

Solve $4(3x - 4) = 2(6x - 9) + 2$.     *p. 103*    Front of Card

Back of Card

$4(3x - 4) = 2(6x - 9) + 2$

$12x - 16 = 12x - 18 + 2$    Distributive property

$12x - 16 = 12x - 16$    Combine like terms.

$12x - 16 + 16 = 12x - 16 + 16$    Add 16.

$12x = 12x$    Combine like terms.

$12x - 12x = 12x - 12x$    Subtract 12x.

$0 = 0$    True

When both sides of an equation are the same, it is called an identity.

Any real number will work, so the solution set is {all real numbers} (not just {0}).

*Make a practice quiz card for material you are learning now.*

## 2.4 An Introduction to Applications of Linear Equations

**OBJECTIVES**

1. Learn the six steps for solving applied problems.
2. Solve problems involving unknown numbers.
3. Solve problems involving sums of quantities.
4. Solve problems involving consecutive integers.
5. Solve problems involving supplementary and complementary angles.

**OBJECTIVE 1** **Learn the six steps for solving applied problems.** To solve applied problems, the following six-step method is often applicable.

**Solving an Applied Problem**

*Step 1* **Read** the problem carefully. What information is given? What are you asked to find?

*Step 2* **Assign a variable** to represent the unknown value. Use a sketch, diagram, or table, as needed. If necessary, express any other unknown values in terms of the variable.

*Step 3* **Write an equation** using the variable expression(s).

*Step 4* **Solve** the equation.

*Step 5* **State the answer.** Label it appropriately. Does it seem reasonable?

*Step 6* **Check** the answer in the words of the *original* problem.

**OBJECTIVE 2** Solve problems involving unknown numbers.

**NOW TRY**
**EXERCISE 1**

If 5 is added to a number, the result is 7 less than 3 times the number. Find the number.

**EXAMPLE 1** Finding the Value of an Unknown Number

If 4 is multiplied by a number decreased by 7, the product is 100. Find the number.

*Step 1* **Read** the problem carefully. We are asked to find a number.

*Step 2* **Assign a variable** to represent the unknown quantity.

$$\text{Let } x = \text{the number.}$$

*Step 3* **Write an equation.**

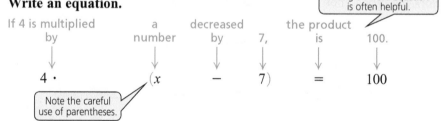

Writing a "word equation" is often helpful.

Note the careful use of parentheses.

*Step 4* **Solve** the equation.

| | |
|---|---|
| $4(x - 7) = 100$ | Equation from Step 3 |
| $4x - 28 = 100$ | Distributive property |
| $4x - 28 + 28 = 100 + 28$ | Add 28. |
| $4x = 128$ | Combine like terms. |
| $\dfrac{4x}{4} = \dfrac{128}{4}$ | Divide by 4. |
| $x = 32$ | |

*Step 5* **State the answer.** The number is 32.

**NOW TRY ANSWER**
1. 6

*Step 6* **Check.** When 32 is decreased by 7, we get $32 - 7 = 25$. If 4 is multiplied by 25, we get 100, as required. The answer, 32, is correct. **NOW TRY**

**OBJECTIVE 3**  Solve problems involving sums of quantities.

**PROBLEM-SOLVING HINT**

To solve problems involving sums of quantities, choose a variable to represent one of the unknowns. *Then represent the other quantity in terms of the same variable.* (See **Example 11** in **Section 2.3.**)

**NOW TRY**
**EXERCISE 2**

In the 2006 Winter Olympics in Torino, Italy, Russia won 7 fewer medals than Germany. The two countries won a total of 51 medals. How many medals did each country win? (*Source:* U.S. Olympic Committee.)

**EXAMPLE 2**  Finding Numbers of Olympic Medals

In the 2006 Winter Olympics in Torino, Italy, the United States won 11 more medals than Sweden. The two countries won a total of 39 medals. How many medals did each country win? (*Source:* U.S. Olympic Committee.)

*Step 1*  **Read** the problem carefully. We are given information about the total number of medals and asked to find the number each country won.

*Step 2*  **Assign a variable.**

Let $x$ = the number of medals Sweden won.

Then $x + 11$ = the number of medals the United States won.

*Step 3*  **Write an equation.**

| The total | is | the number of medals Sweden won | plus | the number of medals the United States won. |
| --- | --- | --- | --- | --- |
| ↓ | ↓ | ↓ | ↓ | ↓ |
| 39 | = | $x$ | + | $(x + 11)$ |

*Step 4*  **Solve the equation.**

$$39 = 2x + 11 \qquad \text{Combine like terms.}$$
$$39 - 11 = 2x + 11 - 11 \qquad \text{Subtract 11.}$$
$$28 = 2x \qquad \text{Combine like terms.}$$
$$\frac{28}{2} = \frac{2x}{2} \qquad \text{Divide by 2.}$$
$$14 = x, \quad \text{or} \quad x = 14$$

*Step 5*  **State the answer.** The variable $x$ represents the number of medals Sweden won, so Sweden won 14 medals. The number of medals the United States won is

$$x + 11 = 14 + 11 = 25.$$

*Step 6*  **Check.** Since the United States won 25 medals and Sweden won 14, the total number of medals was $25 + 14 = 39$. Because $25 - 14 = 11$, the United States won 11 more medals than Sweden. This information agrees with what is given in the problem, so the answer checks.  *NOW TRY*

**NOW TRY ANSWER**
**2.** Germany: 29 medals;
Russia: 22 medals

**NOTE** The problem in **Example 2** could also be solved by letting $x$ represent the number of medals the United States won. Then $x - 11$ would represent the number of medals Sweden won. The equation would be different.

$$39 = x + (x - 11)$$

The solution of this equation is 25, which is the number of U.S. medals. The number of Swedish medals would be $25 - 11 = 14$. *The answers are the same,* whichever approach is used, even though the equation and its solution are different.

NOW TRY
EXERCISE 3

In one week, the owner of Carly's Coffeehouse found that the number of orders for bagels was $\frac{2}{3}$ the number of orders for chocolate scones. If the total number of orders for the two items was 525, how many orders were placed for bagels?

**EXAMPLE 3** Finding the Number of Orders for Tea

The owner of Terry's Coffeehouse found that on one day the number of orders for tea was $\frac{1}{3}$ the number of orders for coffee. If the total number of orders for the two drinks was 76, how many orders were placed for tea?

*Step 1* **Read** the problem. It asks for the number of orders for tea.

*Step 2* **Assign a variable.** Because of the way the problem is stated, let the variable represent the number of orders for coffee.

Let $x$ = the number of orders for coffee.

Then $\frac{1}{3}x$ = the number of orders for tea.

*Step 3* **Write an equation.** Use the fact that the total number of orders was 76.

| The total | is | orders for coffee | plus | orders for tea. |
|:---:|:---:|:---:|:---:|:---:|
| ↓ | ↓ | ↓ | ↓ | ↓ |
| 76 | = | $x$ | + | $\frac{1}{3}x$ |

*Step 4* **Solve.**

$$76 = \frac{4}{3}x \qquad \text{$x = 1x = \frac{3}{3}x$; Combine like terms.}$$

$$\frac{3}{4}(76) = \frac{3}{4}\left(\frac{4}{3}x\right) \qquad \text{Multiply by } \tfrac{3}{4}.$$

Be careful! This is *not* the answer.

$$57 = x$$

*Step 5* **State the answer.** In this problem, *x does not represent the quantity that we are asked to find.* The number of orders for tea was $\frac{1}{3}x$. So $\frac{1}{3}(57) = 19$ is the number of orders for tea.

*Step 6* **Check.** The number of orders for tea, 19, is one-third the number of orders for coffee, 57, and $19 + 57 = 76$. Since this agrees with the information given in the problem, the answer is correct.

NOW TRY

**PROBLEM-SOLVING HINT**

In **Example 3**, it was easier to let the variable represent the quantity that was *not* specified. This required extra work in Step 5 to find the number of orders for tea. In some cases, this approach is easier than letting the variable represent the quantity that we are asked to find.

NOW TRY ANSWER
3. 210 bagel orders

NOW TRY
EXERCISE 4
At the Sherwood Estates pool party, each resident brought four guests. If a total of 175 people visited the pool that day, how many were residents and how many were guests?

**EXAMPLE 4**   Analyzing a Gasoline-Oil Mixture

A lawn trimmer uses a mixture of gasoline and oil. The mixture contains 16 oz of gasoline for each 1 ounce of oil. If the tank holds 68 oz of the mixture, how many ounces of oil and how many ounces of gasoline does it require when it is full?

*Step 1*   **Read** the problem. We must find how many ounces of oil and gasoline are needed to fill the tank.

*Step 2*   **Assign a variable.**

Let          $x$ = the number of ounces of oil required.

Then       $16x$ = the number of ounces of gasoline required.

A diagram like the following is sometimes helpful.

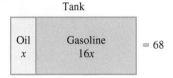

Tank

| Oil $x$ | Gasoline $16x$ | = 68 |

*Step 3*   **Write an equation.**

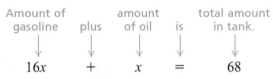

| Amount of gasoline | plus | amount of oil | is | total amount in tank. |

$$16x \quad + \quad x \quad = \quad 68$$

*Step 4*   **Solve.**                                   $17x = 68$   Combine like terms.

$$\frac{17x}{17} = \frac{68}{17}$$   Divide by 17.

$$x = 4$$

*Step 5*   **State the answer.** The lawn trimmer requires 4 oz of oil, and $16(4) = 64$ oz of gasoline when full.

*Step 6*   **Check.** Since $4 + 64 = 68$, and 64 is 16 times 4, the answer checks.

NOW TRY

**PROBLEM-SOLVING HINT**

Sometimes we must find three unknown quantities. When the three unknowns are compared in *pairs*, *let the variable represent the unknown found in both pairs.*

**EXAMPLE 5**   Dividing a Board into Pieces

A project calls for three pieces of wood. The longest piece must be twice the length of the middle-sized piece. The shortest piece must be 10 in. shorter than the middle-sized piece. If a board 70 in. long is to be used, how long can each piece be?

*Step 1*   **Read** the problem. There will be three answers.

*Step 2*   **Assign a variable.** Since the middle-sized piece appears in both pairs of comparisons, let $x$ represent the length, in inches, of the middle-sized piece.

Let          $x$ = the length of the middle-sized piece.

Then       $2x$ = the length of the longest piece,

and        $x - 10$ = the length of the shortest piece.

NOW TRY ANSWER
**4.** 35 residents; 140 guests

NOW TRY
EXERCISE 5

A basketball player spent 6 hr watching game films, practicing free throws, and lifting weights. He spent twice as much time lifting weights as practicing free throws and 2 hr longer watching game films than practicing free throws. How many hours did he spend on each task?

A sketch is helpful here. See **FIGURE 2**.

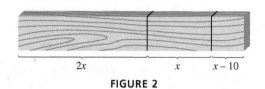

**FIGURE 2**

**Step 3**  **Write an equation.**

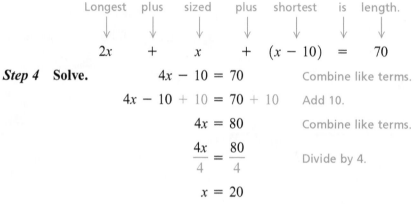

**Step 4**  **Solve.**

$$4x - 10 = 70 \qquad \text{Combine like terms.}$$

$$4x - 10 + 10 = 70 + 10 \qquad \text{Add 10.}$$

$$4x = 80 \qquad \text{Combine like terms.}$$

$$\frac{4x}{4} = \frac{80}{4} \qquad \text{Divide by 4.}$$

$$x = 20$$

**Step 5**  **State the answer.** The middle-sized piece is 20 in. long, the longest piece is $2(20) = 40$ in. long, and the shortest piece is $20 - 10 = 10$ in. long.

**Step 6**  **Check.** The lengths sum to 70 in. All problem conditions are satisfied.

NOW TRY

Consecutive integers

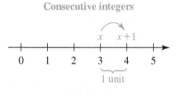

**FIGURE 3**

**OBJECTIVE 4**  **Solve problems involving consecutive integers.** Two integers that differ by 1 are called **consecutive integers.** For example, 3 and 4, 6 and 7, and $-2$ and $-1$ are pairs of consecutive integers. See **FIGURE 3**.

> *In general, if x represents an integer, x + 1 represents the next greater consecutive integer.*

**EXAMPLE 6**  Finding Consecutive Integers

Two pages that face each other in this book have 225 as the sum of their page numbers. What are the page numbers?

**Step 1**  **Read** the problem. Because the two pages face each other, they must have page numbers that are consecutive integers.

**Step 2**  **Assign a variable.**

Let $\quad x =$ the lesser page number.

Then $\quad x + 1 =$ the greater page number.

**Step 3**  **Write an equation.** The sum of the page numbers is 225.

$$x + (x + 1) = 225$$

**Step 4**  **Solve.**

$$2x + 1 = 225 \qquad \text{Combine like terms.}$$

$$2x = 224 \qquad \text{Subtract 1.}$$

$$x = 112 \qquad \text{Divide by 2.}$$

**NOW TRY ANSWER**
**5.** practicing free throws: 1 hr;
  lifting weights: 2 hr;
  watching game films: 3 hr

NOW TRY
EXERCISE 6

Two pages that face each other have 593 as the sum of their page numbers. What are the page numbers?

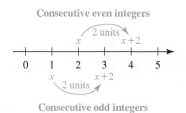

Consecutive even integers

Consecutive odd integers

**FIGURE 4**

NOW TRY
EXERCISE 7

Find two consecutive odd integers such that the sum of twice the lesser and three times the greater is 191.

*Step 5* **State the answer.** The lesser page number is 112, and the greater page number is $112 + 1 = 113$. (Your book is opened to these two pages.)

*Step 6* **Check.** The sum of 112 and 113 is 225. The answer is correct.

NOW TRY

Consecutive *even* **integers,** such as 8 and 10, differ by 2. Similarly, **consecutive** *odd* **integers,** such as 9 and 11, also differ by 2. See **FIGURE 4.**

*In general, if x represents an even or odd integer, x + 2 represents the next greater consecutive even or odd integer, respectively.*

In this book, we list consecutive integers in increasing order.

**PROBLEM-SOLVING HINT**

If $x$ = the lesser integer, then, for any

| two consecutive integers, use | $x, \ x + 1;$ |
| two consecutive *even* integers, use | $x, \ x + 2;$ |
| two consecutive *odd* integers, use | $x, \ x + 2.$ |

**EXAMPLE 7** Finding Consecutive Odd Integers

If the lesser of two consecutive odd integers is doubled, the result is 7 more than the greater of the two integers. Find the two integers.

Let $x$ be the lesser integer. Since the two numbers are consecutive *odd* integers, then $x + 2$ is the greater. Now we write an equation.

If the lesser is doubled, the result is 7 more than the greater.

$$2x \qquad = \qquad 7 \ + \ (x + 2)$$

$$2x = 9 + x \qquad \text{Combine like terms.}$$

$$x = 9 \qquad \text{Subtract } x.$$

The lesser integer is 9 and the greater is $9 + 2 = 11$. As a check, when 9 is doubled, we get 18, which is 7 more than the greater odd integer, 11. The answers are correct.

NOW TRY

**OBJECTIVE 5** **Solve problems involving supplementary and complementary angles.** An angle can be measured by a unit called the **degree** (°), which is $\frac{1}{360}$ of a complete rotation. Two angles whose sum is 90° are said to be **complementary,** or *complements* of each other. An angle that measures 90° is a **right angle.** Two angles whose sum is 180° are said to be **supplementary,** or *supplements* of each other. One angle *supplements* the other to form a **straight angle** of 180°. See **FIGURE 5.**

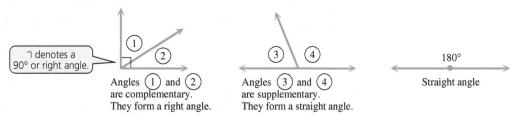

**FIGURE 5**

NOW TRY ANSWERS
**6.** 296, 297 **7.** 37, 39

> PROBLEM-SOLVING HINT
>
> If $x$ represents the degree measure of an angle, then
>
> **$90 - x$** represents the degree measure of its complement.
>
> **$180 - x$** represents the degree measure of its supplement.

NOW TRY
EXERCISE 8
Find the measure of an angle whose complement is twice its measure.

> EXAMPLE 8  Finding the Measure of an Angle

Find the measure of an angle whose complement is five times its measure.

*Step 1* **Read** the problem. We must find the measure of an angle, given information about the measure of its complement.

*Step 2* **Assign a variable.**

Let $\qquad x =$ the degree measure of the angle.

Then $\quad 90 - x =$ the degree measure of its complement.

*Step 3* **Write an equation.**

| Measure of the complement | is | 5 times the measure of the angle. |
|:---:|:---:|:---:|
| ↓ | ↓ | ↓ |
| $90 - x$ | $=$ | $5x$ |

*Step 4* **Solve.**

$$90 - x + x = 5x + x \qquad \text{Add } x.$$
$$90 = 6x \qquad \text{Combine like terms.}$$
$$\frac{90}{6} = \frac{6x}{6} \qquad \text{Divide by 6.}$$
$$15 = x, \quad \text{or} \quad x = 15$$

*Step 5* **State the answer.** The measure of the angle is $15°$.

*Step 6* **Check.** If the angle measures $15°$, then its complement measures $90° - 15° = 75°$, which is equal to five times $15°$, as required.

NOW TRY

> EXAMPLE 9  Finding the Measure of an Angle

Find the measure of an angle whose supplement is $10°$ more than twice its complement.

*Step 1* **Read** the problem. We are to find the measure of an angle, given information about its complement and its supplement.

*Step 2* **Assign a variable.**

Let $\qquad x =$ the degree measure of the angle.

Then $\quad 90 - x =$ the degree measure of its complement,

and $\quad 180 - x =$ the degree measure of its supplement.

We can visualize this information using a sketch. See **FIGURE 6**.

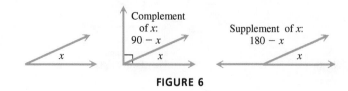

**FIGURE 6**

NOW TRY
EXERCISE 9

Find the measure of an angle whose supplement is 46° less than three times its complement.

*Step 3*   **Write an equation.**

Supplement    is    10    more than    twice    its complement.

$$180 - x = 10 + 2 \cdot (90 - x)$$

Be sure to use parentheses here.

*Step 4*   **Solve.**

| $180 - x = 10 + 180 - 2x$ | Distributive property |
| $180 - x = 190 - 2x$ | Combine like terms. |
| $180 - x + 2x = 190 - 2x + 2x$ | Add $2x$. |
| $180 + x = 190$ | Combine like terms. |
| $180 + x - 180 = 190 - 180$ | Subtract 180. |
| $x = 10$ | |

*Step 5*   **State the answer.** The measure of the angle is 10°.

*Step 6*   **Check.** The complement of 10° is 80° and the supplement of 10° is 170°. 170° is equal to 10° more than twice 80° (that is, $170 = 10 + 2(80)$ is true). Therefore, the answer is correct.

NOW TRY

NOW TRY ANSWER
9. 22°

---

## 2.4 EXERCISES

MyMathLab   Math XL PRACTICE   WATCH   DOWNLOAD   READ   REVIEW

*Complete solution available on the Video Resources on DVD*

**1.** *Concept Check*   A problem requires finding the number of cars on a dealer's lot. Which would *not* be a reasonable answer? Justify your response.

   **A.** 0        **B.** 45        **C.** 1        **D.** $6\frac{1}{2}$

**2.** *Concept Check*   A problem requires finding the number of hours a lightbulb is on during a day. Which would *not* be a reasonable answer? Justify your response.

   **A.** 0        **B.** 4.5        **C.** 13        **D.** 25

**3.** *Concept Check*   A problem requires finding the distance traveled in miles. Which would *not* be a reasonable answer? Justify your response.

   **A.** $-10$        **B.** 1.8        **C.** $10\frac{1}{2}$        **D.** 50

**4.** *Concept Check*   A problem requires finding the time in minutes. Which would *not* be a reasonable answer? Justify your response.

   **A.** 0        **B.** 10.5        **C.** $-5$        **D.** 90

*Solve each problem.* **See Example 1.**

**5.** The product of 8, and a number increased by 6, is 104. What is the number?

**6.** The product of 5, and 3 more than twice a number, is 85. What is the number?

**7.** If 2 is added to five times a number, the result is equal to 5 more than four times the number. Find the number.

**8.** If four times a number is added to 8, the result is three times the number, added to 5. Find the number.

**9.** If 2 is subtracted from a number and this difference is tripled, the result is 6 more than the number. Find the number.

**10.** If 3 is added to a number and this sum is doubled, the result is 2 more than the number. Find the number.

**11.** The sum of three times a number and 7 more than the number is the same as the difference between $-11$ and twice the number. What is the number?

**12.** If 4 is added to twice a number and this sum is multiplied by 2, the result is the same as if the number is multiplied by 3 and 4 is added to the product. What is the number?

*Solve each problem.* ***See Example 2.***

**13.** Pennsylvania and Ohio were the states with the most remaining drive-in movie screens in the United States in 2007. Pennsylvania had 2 more screens than Ohio, and there were 68 screens total in the two states. How many drive-in movie screens remained in each state? (*Source:* www.drive-ins.com)

**14.** As of 2008, the two most highly watched episodes in the history of television were the final episode of *M\*A\*S\*H* and the final episode of *Cheers*. The number of viewers for these original broadcasts in 1983 was about 92 million, with 8 million more people watching the *M\*A\*S\*H* episode than the *Cheers* episode. How many people watched each show? (*Source:* Nielsen Media Research.)

**15.** In August 2009, the U.S. Senate had a total of 98 Democrats and Republicans. There were 18 more Democrats than Republicans. How many members of each party were there? (*Source:* www.thegreenpapers.com)

**16.** In August 2009, the total number of Democrats and Republicans in the U.S. House of Representatives was 434. There were 78 more Democrats than Republicans. How many members of each party were there? (*Source:* www.thegreenpapers.com)

**17.** Bon Jovi and Bruce Springsteen had the two top-grossing North American concert tours for 2008, together generating $415.3 million in ticket sales. If Bruce Springsteen took in $6.1 million less than Bon Jovi, how much did each tour generate? (*Source:* www.billboard.com)

**18.** The Toyota Camry was the top-selling passenger car in the United States in 2007, followed by the Honda Accord. Accord sales were 81 thousand less than Camry sales, and 865 thousand of the two types of cars were sold. How many of each make of car were sold? (*Source: World Almanac and Book of Facts.*)

**19.** In the 2008–2009 NBA regular season, the Boston Celtics won two more than three times as many games as they lost. The Celtics played 82 games. How many wins and losses did the team have? (*Source:* www.NBA.com)

**20.** In the 2008 regular baseball season, the Tampa Bay Rays won 33 fewer than twice as many games as they lost. They played 162 regular-season games. How many wins and losses did the team have? (*Source:* www.MLB.com)

**21.** A one-cup serving of orange juice contains 3 mg less than four times the amount of vitamin C as a one-cup serving of pineapple juice. Servings of the two juices contain a total of 122 mg of vitamin C. How many milligrams of vitamin C are in a serving of each type of juice? (*Source:* U.S. Agriculture Department.)

**22.** A one-cup serving of pineapple juice has 9 more than three times as many calories as a one-cup serving of tomato juice. Servings of the two juices contain a total of 173 calories. How many calories are in a serving of each type of juice? (*Source:* U.S. Agriculture Department.)

*Solve each problem.* ***See Examples 3 and 4.***

💿 **23.** In one day, a store sold $\frac{8}{5}$ as many DVDs as CDs. The total number of DVDs and CDs sold that day was 273. How many DVDs were sold?

**24.** A workout that combines weight training and aerobics burns a total of 374 calories. If doing aerobics burns $\frac{12}{5}$ as many calories as weight training, how many calories does each activity burn?

**25.** The world's largest taco contained approximately 1 kg of onion for every 6.6 kg of grilled steak. The total weight of these two ingredients was 617.6 kg. To the nearest tenth of a kilogram, how many kilograms of each ingredient were used to make the taco? (*Source: Guinness World Records.*)

**26.** As of 2005, the combined population of China and India was estimated at 2.4 billion. If there were about 0.8 as many people living in India as China, what was the population of each country, to the nearest tenth of a billion? (*Source:* U.S. Census Bureau.)

**27.** The value of a "Mint State-63" (uncirculated) 1950 Jefferson nickel minted at Denver is twice the value of a 1945 nickel in similar condition minted at Philadelphia. Together, the total value of the two coins is $24.00. What is the value of each coin? (*Source:* Yeoman, R., *A Guide Book of United States Coins,* 62nd edition, 2009.)

**28.** U.S. five-cent coins are made from a combination of two metals: nickel and copper. For every 1 pound of nickel, 3 lb of copper are used. How many pounds of copper would be needed to make 560 lb of five-cent coins? (*Source:* The United States Mint.)

💿 **29.** A recipe for whole-grain bread calls for 1 oz of rye flour for every 4 oz of whole-wheat flour. How many ounces of each kind of flour should be used to make a loaf of bread weighing 32 oz?

**30.** A medication contains 9 mg of active ingredients for every 1 mg of inert ingredients. How much of each kind of ingredient would be contained in a single 250-mg caplet?

*Solve each problem.* ***See Example 5.***

**31.** An office manager booked 55 airline tickets, divided among three airlines. He booked 7 more tickets on American Airlines than United Airlines. On Southwest Airlines, he booked 4 more than twice as many tickets as on United. How many tickets did he book on each airline?

**32.** A mathematics textbook editor spent 7.5 hr making telephone calls, writing e-mails, and attending meetings. She spent twice as much time attending meetings as making telephone calls and 0.5 hr longer writing e-mails than making telephone calls. How many hours did she spend on each task?

**33.** A party-length submarine sandwich that is 59 in. long is cut into three pieces. The middle piece is 5 in. longer than the shortest piece, and the shortest piece is 9 in. shorter than the longest piece. How long is each piece?

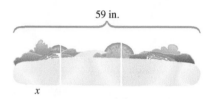

**34.** China earned a total of 100 medals at the 2008 Beijing Summer Olympics. The number of gold medals earned was 23 more than the number of bronze medals. The number of bronze medals earned was 7 more than the number of silver medals. How many of each kind of medal did China earn? (*Source: World Almanac and Book of Facts.*)

**35.** Venus is 31.2 million mi farther from the sun than Mercury, while Earth is 57 million mi farther from the sun than Mercury. If the total of the distances from these three planets to the sun is 196.2 million mi, how far away from the sun is Mercury? (All distances given here are *mean* (*average*) distances.) (*Source: The New York Times Almanac.*)

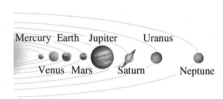

**36.** Together, Saturn, Jupiter, and Uranus have a total of 137 known satellites (moons). Jupiter has 16 more satellites than Saturn, and Uranus has 20 fewer satellites than Saturn. How many known satellites does Uranus have? (*Source: The New York Times Almanac.*)

**37.** The sum of the measures of the angles of any triangle is 180°. In triangle *ABC*, angles *A* and *B* have the same measure, while the measure of angle *C* is 60° greater than each of *A* and *B*. What are the measures of the three angles?

**38.** In triangle *ABC*, the measure of angle *A* is 141° more than the measure of angle *B*. The measure of angle *B* is the same as the measure of angle *C*. Find the measure of each angle. (*Hint:* **See Exercise 37.**)

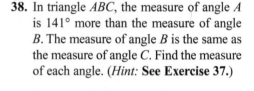

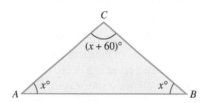

*Solve each problem.* ***See Examples 6 and 7.***

**39.** The numbers on two consecutively numbered gym lockers have a sum of 137. What are the locker numbers?

**40.** The numbers on two consecutive checkbook checks have a sum of 357. What are the numbers?

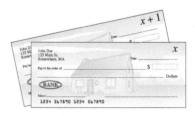

**41.** Two pages that are back-to-back in this book have 203 as the sum of their page numbers. What are the page numbers?

**42.** Two apartments have numbers that are consecutive integers. The sum of the numbers is 59. What are the two apartment numbers?

**43.** Find two consecutive even integers such that the lesser added to three times the greater gives a sum of 46.

**44.** Find two consecutive odd integers such that twice the greater is 17 more than the lesser.

**45.** When the lesser of two consecutive integers is added to three times the greater, the result is 43. Find the integers.

**46.** If five times the lesser of two consecutive integers is added to three times the greater, the result is 59. Find the integers.

*Brain Busters*   *Solve each problem.*

**47.** If the sum of three consecutive even integers is 60, what is the first of the three even integers? (*Hint:* If $x$ and $x + 2$ represent the first two consecutive even integers, how would you represent the third consecutive even integer?)

**48.** If the sum of three consecutive odd integers is 69, what is the third of the three odd integers?

**49.** If 6 is subtracted from the third of three consecutive odd integers and the result is multiplied by 2, the answer is 23 less than the sum of the first and twice the second of the integers. Find the integers.

**50.** If the first and third of three consecutive even integers are added, the result is 22 less than three times the second integer. Find the integers.

*Solve each problem.* **See Examples 8 and 9.**

**51.** Find the measure of an angle whose complement is four times its measure.

**52.** Find the measure of an angle whose complement is five times its measure.

**53.** Find the measure of an angle whose supplement is eight times its measure.

**54.** Find the measure of an angle whose supplement is three times its measure.

**55.** Find the measure of an angle whose supplement measures 39° more than twice its complement.

**56.** Find the measure of an angle whose supplement measures 38° less than three times its complement.

**57.** Find the measure of an angle such that the difference between the measures of its supplement and three times its complement is 10°.

**58.** Find the measure of an angle such that the sum of the measures of its complement and its supplement is 160°.

### PREVIEW EXERCISES

*Use the given values to evaluate each expression.* **See Section 1.3.**

**59.** $LW$;   $L = 6, W = 4$

**60.** $rt$;   $r = 25, t = 4.5$

**61.** $2L + 2W$;   $L = 8, W = 2$

**62.** $\frac{1}{2}h(b + B)$;   $h = 10, b = 4, B = 12$

### 2.5 Formulas and Additional Applications from Geometry

**OBJECTIVES**

1 Solve a formula for one variable, given values of the other variables.

2 Use a formula to solve an applied problem.

3 Solve problems involving vertical angles and straight angles.

4 Solve a formula for a specified variable.

A **formula** is an equation in which variables are used to describe a relationship. For example, formulas exist for finding perimeters and areas of geometric figures, calculating money earned on bank savings, and converting among measurements.

$$P = 4s, \quad \mathscr{A} = \pi r^2, \quad I = prt, \quad F = \frac{9}{5}C + 32 \qquad \text{Formulas}$$

*Many of the formulas used in this book are given on the inside covers.*

**OBJECTIVE 1** Solve a formula for one variable, given values of the other variables. In **Example 1,** we use the idea of *area*. The **area** of a plane (two-dimensional) geometric figure is a measure of the surface covered by the figure.

**EXAMPLE 1** Using Formulas to Evaluate Variables

Find the value of the remaining variable in each formula.

**(a)** $\mathscr{A} = LW; \quad \mathscr{A} = 64, L = 10$

As shown in **FIGURE 7**, this formula gives the area $\mathscr{A}$ of a rectangle with length $L$ and width $W$. Substitute the given values into the formula.

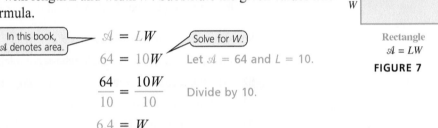

In this book, $\mathscr{A}$ denotes area.

$$\mathscr{A} = LW \qquad \text{(Solve for } W.\text{)}$$

$$64 = 10W \qquad \text{Let } \mathscr{A} = 64 \text{ and } L = 10.$$

$$\frac{64}{10} = \frac{10W}{10} \qquad \text{Divide by 10.}$$

$$6.4 = W$$

Rectangle
$\mathscr{A} = LW$

**FIGURE 7**

The width is $6.4$. Since $10(6.4) = 64$, the given area, the answer checks.

**(b)** $\mathscr{A} = \frac{1}{2}h(b + B); \quad \mathscr{A} = 210, B = 27, h = 10$

This formula gives the area of a trapezoid. See **FIGURE 8**.

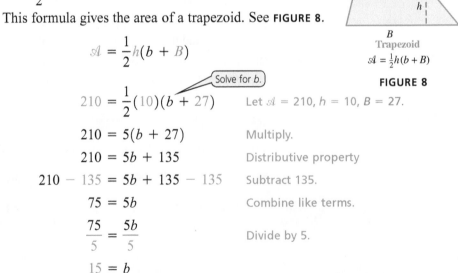

$$\mathscr{A} = \frac{1}{2}h(b + B)$$

$$210 = \frac{1}{2}(10)(b + 27) \qquad \text{(Solve for } b.\text{)} \quad \text{Let } \mathscr{A} = 210, h = 10, B = 27.$$

$$210 = 5(b + 27) \qquad \text{Multiply.}$$

$$210 = 5b + 135 \qquad \text{Distributive property}$$

$$210 - 135 = 5b + 135 - 135 \qquad \text{Subtract 135.}$$

$$75 = 5b \qquad \text{Combine like terms.}$$

$$\frac{75}{5} = \frac{5b}{5} \qquad \text{Divide by 5.}$$

$$15 = b$$

Trapezoid
$\mathscr{A} = \frac{1}{2}h(b + B)$

**FIGURE 8**

The length of the shorter parallel side, $b$, is $15$. This answer checks, since

$$\frac{1}{2}(10)(15 + 27) = 210, \quad \text{as required.} \qquad \text{NOW TRY}$$

NOW TRY EXERCISE 1

Find the value of the remaining variable.

$$P = 2a + 2b;$$
$$P = 78, a = 12$$

NOW TRY ANSWER
**1.** $b = 27$

**OBJECTIVE 2** Use a formula to solve an applied problem. *When solving an applied problem that involves a geometric figure, it is a good idea to draw a sketch. Examples 2 and 3 use the idea of perimeter.* The **perimeter** of a plane (two-dimensional) geometric figure is the distance around the figure. For a polygon (e.g., a rectangle, square, or triangle), it is the sum of the lengths of its sides.

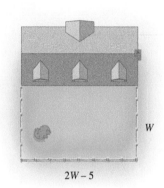

NOW TRY
EXERCISE 2

Kurt's garden is in the shape of a rectangle. The length is 10 ft less than twice the width, and the perimeter is 160 ft. Find the dimensions of the garden.

**EXAMPLE 2** Finding the Dimensions of a Rectangular Yard

Cathleen Horne's backyard is in the shape of a rectangle. The length is 5 m less than twice the width, and the perimeter is 80 m. Find the dimensions of the yard.

*Step 1* **Read** the problem. We must find the dimensions of the yard.

*Step 2* **Assign a variable.** Let $W$ = the width of the lot, in meters. Since the length is 5 meters less than twice the width, the length is $L = 2W - 5$. See **FIGURE 9**.

**FIGURE 9**

*Step 3* **Write an equation.** Use the formula for the perimeter of a rectangle.

$$P = 2L + 2W$$   Perimeter of a rectangle

Perimeter $= 2 \cdot$ Length $+ 2 \cdot$ Width

$$80 = 2(2W - 5) + 2W$$   Substitute $2W - 5$ for length $L$.

*Step 4* **Solve.**

$$80 = 4W - 10 + 2W$$   Distributive property

$$80 = 6W - 10$$   Combine like terms.

$$80 + 10 = 6W - 10 + 10$$   Add 10.

$$90 = 6W$$   Combine like terms.

$$\frac{90}{6} = \frac{6W}{6}$$   Divide by 6.

$$15 = W$$

*Step 5* **State the answer.** The width is 15 m and the length is $2(15) - 5 = 25$ m.

*Step 6* **Check.** If the width is 15 m and the length is 25 m, the perimeter is

$$2(25) + 2(15) = 50 + 30 = 80 \text{ m}, \quad \text{as required.} \quad \text{NOW TRY}$$

**EXAMPLE 3** Finding the Dimensions of a Triangle

The longest side of a triangle is 3 ft longer than the shortest side. The medium side is 1 ft longer than the shortest side. If the perimeter of the triangle is 16 ft, what are the lengths of the three sides?

*Step 1* **Read** the problem. We must find the lengths of the sides of a triangle.

*Step 2* **Assign a variable.**

Let  $s$ = the length of the shortest side, in feet,

$s + 1$ = the length of the medium side, in feet, and,

NOW TRY ANSWER
**2.** width: 30 ft; length: 50 ft

$s + 3$ = the length of the longest side in feet.

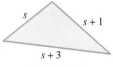

**FIGURE 10**

See **FIGURE 10**.

NOW TRY
EXERCISE 3
The perimeter of a triangle is 30 ft. The longest side is 1 ft longer than the medium side, and the shortest side is 7 ft shorter than the medium side. What are the lengths of the three sides?

*Step 3*   **Write an equation.** Use the formula for the perimeter of a triangle.

$$P = a + b + c \qquad \text{Perimeter of a triangle}$$
$$16 = s + (s + 1) + (s + 3) \qquad \text{Substitute.}$$

*Step 4*   **Solve.**   $16 = 3s + 4$   Combine like terms.
$$12 = 3s \qquad \text{Subtract 4.}$$
$$4 = s \qquad \text{Divide by 3.}$$

*Step 5*   **State the answer.** The shortest side, $s$, has length 4 ft. Then
$$s + 1 = 4 + 1 = 5 \text{ ft}, \qquad \text{Length of medium side}$$
and   $s + 3 = 4 + 3 = 7$ ft.   Length of longest side

*Step 6*   **Check.** The medium side, 5 ft, is 1 ft longer than the shortest side, and the longest side, 7 ft, is 3 ft longer than the shortest side. Futhermore, the perimeter is $4 + 5 + 7 = 16$ ft, as required.   *NOW TRY*

NOW TRY
EXERCISE 4

The area of a triangle is 77 cm². The base is 14 cm. Find the height of the triangle.

### EXAMPLE 4   Finding the Height of a Triangular Sail

The area of a triangular sail of a sailboat is $126 \text{ ft}^2$. (Recall that "$\text{ft}^2$" means "square feet.") The base of the sail is 12 ft. Find the height of the sail.

*Step 1*   **Read** the problem. We must find the height of the triangular sail.

*Step 2*   **Assign a variable.** Let $h =$ the height of the sail, in feet. See **FIGURE 11**.

*Step 3*   **Write an equation.** The formula for the area of a triangle is $\mathcal{A} = \frac{1}{2}bh$, where $\mathcal{A}$ is the area, $b$ is the base, and $h$ is the height.

**FIGURE 11**

$$\mathcal{A} = \frac{1}{2}bh \qquad \text{Area of a triangle}$$
$$126 = \frac{1}{2}(12)h \qquad \mathcal{A} = 126, b = 12$$

*Step 4*   **Solve.**   $126 = 6h$   Multiply.
$$21 = h \qquad \text{Divide by 6.}$$

*Step 5*   **State the answer.** The height of the sail is 21 ft.

*Step 6*   **Check** to see that the values $\mathcal{A} = 126$, $b = 12$, and $h = 21$ satisfy the formula for the area of a triangle.   *NOW TRY*

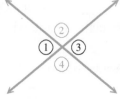

**FIGURE 12**

NOW TRY ANSWERS
**3.** 5 ft, 12 ft, 13 ft   **4.** 11 cm

**OBJECTIVE 3**   Solve problems involving vertical angles and straight angles.
**FIGURE 12** shows two intersecting lines forming angles that are numbered ①, ②, ③, and ④. Angles ① and ③ lie "opposite" each other. They are called **vertical angles**. Another pair of vertical angles is ② and ④. *Vertical angles have equal measures.*

Now look at angles ① and ②. When their measures are added, we get 180°, the measure of a straight angle. There are three other such pairs of angles:   ② and ③, ③ and ④, and ① and ④.

⌐NOW TRY
⤳ EXERCISE 5
Find the measure of each marked angle in the figure.

$(6x + 2)°$ $(8x - 8)°$

**EXAMPLE 5** Finding Angle Measures

Refer to the appropriate figure in each part.

**(a)** Find the measure of each marked angle in **FIGURE 13**.
Since the marked angles are vertical angles, they have equal measures.

$$4x + 19 = 6x - 5 \qquad \text{Set } 4x + 19 \text{ equal to } 6x - 5.$$
$$19 = 2x - 5 \qquad \text{Subtract } 4x.$$
$$24 = 2x \qquad \text{Add 5.}$$

*This is not the answer.* → $$12 = x \qquad \text{Divide by 2.}$$

Replace $x$ with 12 in the expression for the measure of each angle.

$$4x + 19 = 4(12) + 19 = 48 + 19 = 67$$
$$6x - 5 = 6(12) - 5 = 72 - 5 = 67$$

The angles have equal measures, as required.

Each angle measures $67°$.

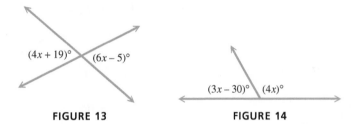

$(4x + 19)°$ $(6x - 5)°$

$(3x - 30)°$ $(4x)°$

**FIGURE 13**  **FIGURE 14**

**(b)** Find the measure of each marked angle in **FIGURE 14**.
The measures of the marked angles must add to 180° because together they form a straight angle. (They are also *supplements* of each other.)

$$(3x - 30) + 4x = 180$$
$$7x - 30 = 180 \qquad \text{Combine like terms.}$$
$$7x = 210 \qquad \text{Add 30.}$$

*Don't stop here!* → $$x = 30 \qquad \text{Divide by 7.}$$

Replace $x$ with 30 in the expression for the measure of each angle.

$$3x - 30 = 3(30) - 30 = 90 - 30 = 60$$
$$4x = 4(30) = 120$$

The measures of the angles add to 180°, as required.

The two angle measures are $60°$ and $120°$.

NOW TRY ↻

---

⚠ **CAUTION**  In **Example 5,** the answer is *not* the value of $x$. *Remember to substitute the value of the variable into the expression given for each angle.*

---

**OBJECTIVE 4** **Solve a formula for a specified variable.** Sometimes we want to rewrite a formula in terms of a *different* variable in the formula. For example, consider $\mathcal{A} = LW$, the formula for the area of a rectangle.

How can we rewrite $\mathcal{A} = LW$ in terms of $W$?

NOW TRY ANSWER
**5.** 32°, 32°

The process whereby we do this is called **solving for a specified variable,** or **solving a literal equation.**

To solve a formula for a specified variable, we use the *same* steps that we used to solve an equation with just one variable. For example, solve the following for $x$.

| | | | | |
|---|---|---|---|---|
| $3x + 4 = 13$ | | | $ax + b = c$ | |
| $3x + 4 - 4 = 13 - 4$ | Subtract 4. | | $ax + b - b = c - b$ | Subtract $b$. |
| $3x = 9$ | | | $ax = c - b$ | |
| $\dfrac{3x}{3} = \dfrac{9}{3}$ | Divide by 3. | | $\dfrac{ax}{a} = \dfrac{c - b}{a}$ | Divide by $a$. |
| $x = 3$ | Equation solved for $x$ | | $x = \dfrac{c - b}{a}$ | Formula solved for $x$ |

***When solving a formula for a specified variable, we treat the specified variable as if it were the ONLY variable, and treat the other variables as if they were numbers.***

**NOW TRY**
**EXERCISE 6**
Solve $W = Fd$ for $F$.

**EXAMPLE 6** Solving for a Specified Variable

Solve $A = LW$ for $W$.

$W$ is multiplied by $L$, so undo the multiplication by dividing each side by $L$.

$$A = LW \quad \boxed{\text{Our goal is to isolate } W.}$$

$$\frac{A}{L} = \frac{LW}{L} \qquad \text{Divide by } L.$$

$$\frac{A}{L} = W, \quad \text{or} \quad W = \frac{A}{L} \qquad \tfrac{LW}{L} = \tfrac{L}{L} \cdot W = 1 \cdot W = W \qquad \text{NOW TRY}$$

**NOW TRY**
**EXERCISE 7**
Solve $Ax + By = C$ for $A$.

**EXAMPLE 7** Solving for a Specified Variable

Solve $P = 2L + 2W$ for $L$.

$$P = 2L + 2W \quad \boxed{\text{Our goal is to isolate } L.}$$

$$P - 2W = 2L + 2W - 2W \qquad \text{Subtract } 2W.$$

$$P - 2W = 2L \qquad \text{Combine like terms.}$$

$$\frac{P - 2W}{2} = \frac{2L}{2} \qquad \text{Divide by 2.}$$

$$\frac{P - 2W}{2} = L, \quad \text{or} \quad L = \frac{P - 2W}{2} \qquad \tfrac{2L}{2} = \tfrac{2}{2} \cdot L = 1 \cdot L = L \qquad \text{NOW TRY}$$

**NOW TRY**
**EXERCISE 8**
Solve $x = u + zs$ for $z$.

**EXAMPLE 8** Solving for a Specified Variable

Solve $F = \frac{9}{5}C + 32$ for $C$.

$$\boxed{\text{Our goal is to isolate } C.} \quad F = \frac{9}{5}C + 32$$

This is the formula for converting temperatures from Celsius to Fahrenheit.

$$F - 32 = \frac{9}{5}C + 32 - 32 \qquad \text{Subtract 32.}$$

$$\boxed{\text{Be sure to use parentheses.}} \quad F - 32 = \frac{9}{5}C$$

$$\frac{5}{9}(F - 32) = \frac{5}{9} \cdot \frac{9}{5}C \qquad \text{Multiply by } \tfrac{5}{9}.$$

$$\frac{5}{9}(F - 32) = C, \quad \text{or} \quad C = \frac{5}{9}(F - 32)$$

This is the formula for converting temperatures from Fahrenheit to Celsius.

NOW TRY

**NOW TRY ANSWERS**
**6.** $F = \frac{W}{d}$ **7.** $A = \frac{C - By}{x}$
**8.** $z = \frac{x - u}{s}$

⌐ *NOW TRY*
*EXERCISE 9*

Solve $S = \frac{1}{2}(a + b + c)$ for $a$.

---

EXAMPLE 9 **Solving for a Specified Variable**

Solve $\mathcal{A} = \frac{1}{2}h(b + B)$ for $B$.

> Our goal is to isolate $B$.

$$\mathcal{A} = \frac{1}{2}h(b + B)$$

> Multiplying 2 times $\frac{1}{2}$ here is *not* an application of the distributive property.

$$2\mathcal{A} = 2 \cdot \frac{1}{2}h(b + B) \qquad \text{Multiply by 2 to clear the fraction.}$$

$$2\mathcal{A} = h(b + B) \qquad 2 \cdot \frac{1}{2} = \frac{2}{2} = 1$$

$$2\mathcal{A} = hb + hB \qquad \text{Distributive property}$$

$$2\mathcal{A} - hb = hb + hB - hb \qquad \text{Subtract } hb.$$

$$2\mathcal{A} - hb = hB \qquad \text{Combine like terms.}$$

$$\frac{2\mathcal{A} - hb}{h} = \frac{hB}{h} \qquad \text{Divide by } h.$$

$$\frac{2\mathcal{A} - hb}{h} = B, \quad \text{or} \quad B = \frac{2\mathcal{A} - hb}{h} \qquad NOW\ TRY ⟳$$

---

NOTE The result in **Example 9** can be written in a different form as follows:

$$B = \frac{2\mathcal{A} - hb}{h} = \frac{2\mathcal{A}}{h} - \frac{hb}{h} = \frac{2\mathcal{A}}{h} - b. \qquad \frac{a - b}{c} = \frac{a}{c} - \frac{b}{c}$$

NOW TRY ANSWER
**9.** $a = 2S - b - c$

---

## 2.5 EXERCISES

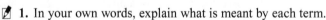

🌐 *Complete solution available on the Video Resources on DVD*

📝 **1.** In your own words, explain what is meant by each term.

   **(a)** Perimeter of a plane geometric figure

   **(b)** Area of a plane geometric figure

**2.** *Concept Check* In parts (a)–(c), choose one of the following words to make the statement true: *linear, square*, or *cubic*.

   **(a)** If the dimensions of a plane geometric figure are given in feet, then the **area** is given in _____ feet.

   **(b)** If the dimensions of a rectangle are given in yards, then the **perimeter** is given in _____ yards.

   **(c)** If the dimensions of a pyramid are given in meters, then the **volume** is given in _____ meters.

**3.** *Concept Check* The measure of a straight angle is _____. Vertical angles have _____ measures.
   (the same/different)

**4.** *Concept Check* If a formula has exactly five variables, how many values would you need to be given in order to find the value of any one variable?

*Concept Check* *Decide whether perimeter or area would be used to solve a problem concerning the measure of the quantity.*

5. Carpeting for a bedroom

6. Sod for a lawn

7. Fencing for a yard

8. Baseboards for a living room

9. Tile for a bathroom

10. Fertilizer for a garden

11. Determining the cost of replacing a linoleum floor with a wood floor

12. Determining the cost of planting rye grass in a lawn for the winter

*A formula is given along with the values of all but one of the variables. Find the value of the variable that is not given. Use 3.14 as an approximation for π (pi).* ***See Example 1.***

13. $P = 2L + 2W$ (perimeter of a rectangle); $L = 8, W = 5$

14. $P = 2L + 2W$;   $L = 6, W = 4$

15. $A = \frac{1}{2}bh$ (area of a triangle);   $b = 8, h = 16$

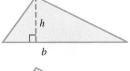

16. $A = \frac{1}{2}bh$;   $b = 10, h = 14$

17. $P = a + b + c$ (perimeter of a triangle); $P = 12, a = 3, c = 5$

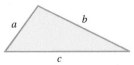

18. $P = a + b + c$;   $P = 15, a = 3, b = 7$

🌐 19. $d = rt$ (distance formula);   $d = 252, r = 45$

20. $d = rt$;   $d = 100, t = 2.5$

21. $I = prt$ (simple interest);   $p = 7500, r = 0.035, t = 6$

22. $I = prt$;   $p = 5000, r = 0.025, t = 7$

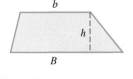

23. $A = \frac{1}{2}h(b + B)$ (area of a trapezoid); $A = 91, h = 7, b = 12$

24. $A = \frac{1}{2}h(b + B)$;   $A = 75, b = 19, B = 31$

25. $C = 2\pi r$ (circumference of a circle); $C = 16.328$

26. $C = 2\pi r$;   $C = 8.164$

27. $C = 2\pi r$;   $C = 20\pi$

28. $C = 2\pi r$;   $C = 100\pi$

29. $A = \pi r^2$ (area of a circle);   $r = 4$

30. $A = \pi r^2$;   $r = 12$

31. $S = 2\pi rh$;   $S = 120\pi, h = 10$

32. $S = 2\pi rh$;   $S = 720\pi, h = 30$

The **volume** of a three-dimensional object is a measure of the space occupied by the object. For example, we would need to know the volume of a gasoline tank in order to find how many gallons of gasoline it would take to completely fill the tank.

In the following exercises, a formula for the volume (V) of a three-dimensional object is given, along with values for the other variables. Evaluate V. (Use 3.14 as an approximation for π.) ***See Example 1.***

33. $V = LWH$ (volume of a rectangular box); $L = 10, W = 5, H = 3$

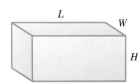

34. $V = LWH$;   $L = 12, W = 8, H = 4$

**35.** $V = \frac{1}{3}Bh$ (volume of a pyramid);   $B = 12, h = 13$

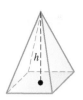

**36.** $V = \frac{1}{3}Bh$;   $B = 36, h = 4$

**37.** $V = \frac{4}{3}\pi r^3$ (volume of a sphere);   $r = 12$

**38.** $V = \frac{4}{3}\pi r^3$;   $r = 6$

*Solve each problem.* ***See Examples 2 and 3.***

**39.** The length of a rectangle is 9 in. more than the width. The perimeter is 54 in. Find the length and the width of the rectangle.

**40.** The width of a rectangle is 3 ft less than the length. The perimeter is 62 ft. Find the length and the width of the rectangle.

**41.** The perimeter of a rectangle is 36 m. The length is 2 m more than three times the width. Find the length and the width of the rectangle.

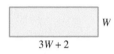

**42.** The perimeter of a rectangle is 36 yd. The width is 18 yd less than twice the length. Find the length and the width of the rectangle.

**43.** The longest side of a triangle is 3 in. longer than the shortest side. The medium side is 2 in. longer than the shortest side. If the perimeter of the triangle is 20 in., what are the lengths of the three sides?

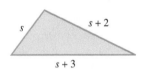

**44.** The perimeter of a triangle is 28 ft. The medium side is 4 ft longer than the shortest side, while the longest side is twice as long as the shortest side. What are the lengths of the three sides?

**45.** Two sides of a triangle have the same length. The third side measures 4 m less than twice that length. The perimeter of the triangle is 24 m. Find the lengths of the three sides.

**46.** A triangle is such that its medium side is twice as long as its shortest side and its longest side is 7 yd less than three times its shortest side. The perimeter of the triangle is 47 yd. What are the lengths of the three sides?

*Use a formula to solve each problem. (Use 3.14 as an approximation for π.)* ***Formulas are found on the inside covers of this book.*** ***See Examples 2–4.***

**47.** A prehistoric ceremonial site dating to about 3000 B.C. was discovered in southwestern England. The site is a nearly perfect circle, consisting of nine concentric rings that probably held upright wooden posts. Around this timber temple is a wide, encircling ditch enclosing an area with a diameter of 443 ft. Find this enclosed area to the nearest thousand square feet. (*Hint:* Find the radius. Then use $\mathcal{A} = \pi r^2$.) (*Source: Archaeology,* vol. 51, no. 1, Jan./Feb. 1998.)

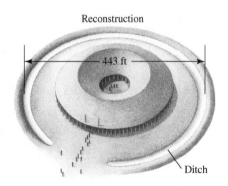

Reconstruction

443 ft

Ditch

**48.** The Rogers Centre in Toronto, Canada, is the first stadium with a hard-shell, retractable roof. The steel dome is 630 ft in diameter. To the nearest foot, what is the circumference of this dome? (*Source:* www.ballparks.com)

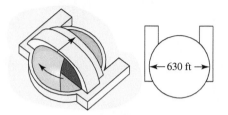

**49.** The largest fashion catalogue in the world was published in Hamburg, Germany. Each of the 212 pages in the catalogue measured 1.2 m by 1.5 m. What was the perimeter of a page? What was the area? (*Source: Guinness World Records.*)

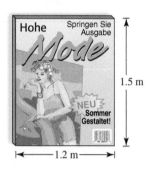

**50.** The world's largest sand painting was created by Buddhist monks in the Singapore Expo Hall in May 2004. The painting measured 12.24 m by 12.24 m. What was the perimeter of the sand painting? To the nearest hundredth of a square meter, what was the area? (*Source: Guinness World Records.*)

**51.** The area of a triangular road sign is 70 ft². If the base of the sign measures 14 ft, what is the height of the sign?

**52.** The area of a triangular advertising banner is 96 ft². If the height of the banner measures 12 ft, what is the measure of the base?

**53.** The largest drum ever constructed was made from Japanese cedar and cowhide, with diameter 15.74 ft. What was the area of the circular face of the drum? What was the circumference of the drum? Round your answers to the nearest hundredth. (*Source: Guinness World Records.*)

**54.** A drum played at the Royal Festival Hall in London had diameter 13 ft. What was the area of the circular face of the drum? What was the circumference of the drum? (*Source: Guinness World Records.*)

**55.** The survey plat depicted here shows two lots that form a trapezoid. The measures of the parallel sides are 115.80 ft and 171.00 ft. The height of the trapezoid is 165.97 ft. Find the combined area of the two lots. Round your answer to the nearest hundredth of a square foot.

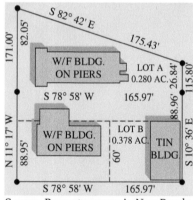

Source: Property survey in New Roads, Louisiana.

**56.** Lot A in the survey plat is in the shape of a trapezoid. The parallel sides measure 26.84 ft and 82.05 ft. The height of the trapezoid is 165.97 ft. Find the area of Lot A. Round your answer to the nearest hundredth of a square foot.

**57.** The U.S. Postal Service requires that any box sent by Priority Mail® have length plus girth (distance around) totaling no more than 108 in. The maximum volume that meets this condition is contained by a box with a square end 18 in. on each side. What is the length of the box? What is the maximum volume? (*Source:* United States Postal Service.)

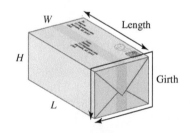

**58.** The world's largest sandwich, made by Wild Woody's Chill and Grill in Roseville, Michigan, was 12 ft long, 12 ft wide, and $17\frac{1}{2}$ in. $\left(1\frac{11}{24}\text{ ft}\right)$ thick. What was the volume of the sandwich? (*Source: Guinness World Records.*)

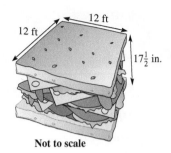

**Not to scale**

*Find the measure of each marked angle.* **See Example 5.**

**59.**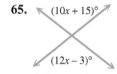

$(x + 1)°$    $(4x - 56)°$

**60.**

$(10x + 7)°$  $(7x + 3)°$

**61.**

$(8x - 1)°$

$(5x)°$

(*Hint:* These angles are *complements* of each other.)

**62.**

$(4x)°$

$(3x + 13)°$

**63.**

$(5x - 129)°$  $(2x - 21)°$

**64.**

$(3x + 45)°$    $(7x + 5)°$

**65.**  $(10x + 15)°$

$(12x - 3)°$

**66.**

$(11x - 37)°$

$(7x + 27)°$

*Solve each formula for the specified variable.* **See Examples 6–9.**

**67.** $d = rt$ for $t$

**68.** $d = rt$ for $r$

**69.** $\mathcal{A} = bh$ for $b$

**70.** $\mathcal{A} = LW$ for $L$

**71.** $C = \pi d$ for $d$

**72.** $P = 4s$ for $s$

**73.** $V = LWH$ for $H$

**74.** $V = LWH$ for $W$

**75.** $I = prt$ for $r$

**76.** $I = prt$ for $p$

**77.** $\mathcal{A} = \frac{1}{2}bh$ for $h$

**78.** $\mathcal{A} = \frac{1}{2}bh$ for $b$

**79.** $V = \frac{1}{3}\pi r^2 h$ for $h$

**80.** $V = \pi r^2 h$ for $h$

**81.** $P = a + b + c$ for $b$

**82.** $P = a + b + c$ for $a$

**83.** $P = 2L + 2W$ for $W$

**84.** $A = p + prt$ for $r$

**85.** $y = mx + b$ for $m$

**86.** $y = mx + b$ for $x$

**87.** $Ax + By = C$ for $y$

**88.** $Ax + By = C$ for $x$

**89.** $M = C(1 + r)$ for $r$

**90.** $C = \frac{5}{9}(F - 32)$ for $F$

**91.** $P = 2(a + b)$ for $a$

**92.** $P = 2(a + b)$ for $b$

**PREVIEW EXERCISES**

*Solve each equation.* **See Section 2.2.**

**93.** $0.06x = 300$

**94.** $0.4x = 80$

**95.** $\frac{3}{4}x = 21$

**96.** $-\frac{5}{6}x = 30$

**97.** $-3x = \frac{1}{4}$

**98.** $4x = \frac{1}{3}$

# 2.6 Ratio, Proportion, and Percent

**OBJECTIVE 1** **Write ratios.** A **ratio** is a comparison of two quantities using a quotient.

| Ratio |
|---|
| The ratio of the number $a$ to the number $b$ (where $b \neq 0$) is written<br><br>$\qquad$ **$a$ to $b$,** $\qquad$ **$a$:$b$,** $\qquad$ or $\qquad$ $\dfrac{a}{b}$. |

Writing a ratio as a quotient $\frac{a}{b}$ is most common in algebra.

---

**NOW TRY**
**EXERCISE 1**

Write a ratio for each word phrase.

**(a)** 7 in. to 4 in.

**(b)** 45 sec to 2 min

**EXAMPLE 1** Writing Word Phrases as Ratios

Write a ratio for each word phrase.

**(a)** 5 hr to 3 hr $\qquad \dfrac{5 \text{ hr}}{3 \text{ hr}} = \dfrac{5}{3}$

**(b)** 6 hr to 3 days

First convert 3 days to hours.

$$3 \text{ days} = 3 \cdot 24 = 72 \text{ hr} \qquad 1 \text{ day} = 24 \text{ hr}$$

Now write the ratio using the common unit of measure, hours.

$$\frac{6 \text{ hr}}{3 \text{ days}} = \frac{6 \text{ hr}}{72 \text{ hr}} = \frac{6}{72} = \frac{1}{12} \qquad \text{Write in lowest terms.} \qquad \textit{NOW TRY}$$

An application of ratios is in *unit pricing,* to see which size of an item offered in different sizes produces the best price per unit.

**EXAMPLE 2** Finding Price per Unit

A Cub Foods supermarket charges the following prices for a jar of extra crunchy peanut butter.

PEANUT BUTTER

| Size | Price |
|---|---|
| 18 oz | $1.78 |
| 28 oz | $2.97 |
| 40 oz | $3.98 |

**NOW TRY ANSWERS**
1. **(a)** $\frac{7}{4}$ **(b)** $\frac{3}{8}$

Which size is the best buy? That is, which size has the lowest unit price?

NOW TRY
EXERCISE 2

A supermarket charges the following prices for a certain brand of liquid detergent.

| Size | Price |
|------|-------|
| 150 oz | $19.97 |
| 100 oz | $13.97 |
| 75 oz | $ 8.94 |

Which size is the best buy? What is the unit cost for that size?

To find the best buy, write ratios comparing the price for each size of jar to the number of units (ounces) per jar. Then divide to obtain the price per unit (ounce).

| Size | Unit Cost (dollars per ounce) | |
|------|------|------|
| 18 oz | $\frac{\$1.78}{18} = \$0.099$ | ← The best buy |
| 28 oz | $\frac{\$2.97}{28} = \$0.106$ | (Results are rounded to the nearest thousandth.) |
| 40 oz | $\frac{\$3.98}{40} = \$0.100$ | |

Because the 18-oz size produces the lowest unit cost, it is the best buy. This example shows that buying the largest size does not always provide the best buy.

NOW TRY

**OBJECTIVE 2  Solve proportions.** A ratio is used to compare two numbers or amounts. A **proportion** says that two ratios are equal. For example, the proportion

$$\frac{3}{4} = \frac{15}{20}$$

[A proportion is a special type of equation.]

says that the ratios $\frac{3}{4}$ and $\frac{15}{20}$ are equal. In the proportion

$$\frac{a}{b} = \frac{c}{d} \quad (\text{where } b, d \neq 0),$$

$a$, $b$, $c$, and $d$ are the **terms** of the proportion. The terms $a$ and $d$ are called the **extremes,** and the terms $b$ and $c$ are called the **means.** We read the proportion $\frac{a}{b} = \frac{c}{d}$ as "*a* **is to** *b* **as** *c* **is to** *d*." Multiplying each side of this proportion by the common denominator, $bd$, gives the following.

$$bd \cdot \frac{a}{b} = bd \cdot \frac{c}{d} \qquad \text{Multiply each side by } bd.$$

$$\frac{b}{b}(d \cdot a) = \frac{d}{d}(b \cdot c) \qquad \text{Associative and commutative properties}$$

$$ad = bc \qquad \text{Commutative and identity properties}$$

We can also find the products $ad$ and $bc$ by multiplying diagonally.

$$ad = bc$$
$$\frac{a}{b} = \frac{c}{d}$$

For this reason, $ad$ and $bc$ are called **cross products.**

**Cross Products**

If $\frac{a}{b} = \frac{c}{d}$, then the cross products $ad$ and $bc$ are equal—that is, ***the product of the extremes equals the product of the means.***

Also, if $ad = bc$, then $\frac{a}{b} = \frac{c}{d}$ (where $b, d \neq 0$).

NOW TRY ANSWER
**2.** 75 oz; $0.119 per oz

**NOTE** If $\frac{a}{c} = \frac{b}{d}$, then $ad = cb$, or $ad = bc$. This means that the two proportions are equivalent, and the proportion

$$\frac{a}{b} = \frac{c}{d} \quad \text{can also be written as} \quad \frac{a}{c} = \frac{b}{d} \quad (\text{where } c, d \neq 0).$$

Sometimes one form is more convenient to work with than the other.

*NOW TRY*
*EXERCISE 3*

Decide whether each proportion is *true* or *false*.

**(a)** $\frac{1}{3} = \frac{33}{100}$ **(b)** $\frac{4}{13} = \frac{16}{52}$

**EXAMPLE 3** Deciding Whether Proportions Are True

Decide whether each proportion is *true* or *false*.

**(a)** $\frac{3}{4} = \frac{15}{20}$

Check to see whether the cross products are equal.

$$3 \cdot 20 = 60 \qquad 4 \cdot 15 = 60$$

$$\frac{3}{4} = \frac{15}{20}$$

The cross products are equal, so the proportion is true.

**(b)** $\frac{6}{7} = \frac{30}{32}$

The cross products, $6 \cdot 32 = 192$ and $7 \cdot 30 = 210$, are not equal, so the proportion is false.

*NOW TRY*

Four numbers are used in a proportion. If any three of these numbers are known, the fourth can be found.

*NOW TRY*
*EXERCISE 4*

Solve the proportion.

$$\frac{9}{7} = \frac{x}{56}$$

**EXAMPLE 4** Finding an Unknown in a Proportion

Solve the proportion $\frac{5}{9} = \frac{x}{63}$.

$$\frac{5}{9} = \frac{x}{63} \qquad \boxed{\text{Solve for } x.}$$

$$5 \cdot 63 = 9 \cdot x \qquad \text{Cross products must be equal.}$$

$$315 = 9x \qquad \text{Multiply.}$$

$$\frac{315}{9} = \frac{9x}{9} \qquad \text{Divide by 9.}$$

$$35 = x$$

Check by substituting 35 for $x$ in the proportion. The solution set is $\{35\}$.

*NOW TRY*

⚠ **CAUTION** *The cross-product method cannot be used directly if there is more than one term on either side of the equals symbol.*

NOW TRY
EXERCISE 5

Solve the equation.

$$\frac{k - 3}{6} = \frac{3k + 2}{4}$$

**EXAMPLE 5**  Solving an Equation by Using Cross Products

Solve the equation $\frac{m - 2}{5} = \frac{m + 1}{3}$.

$$\frac{m - 2}{5} = \frac{m + 1}{3}$$     *Be sure to use parentheses.*

$$3(m - 2) = 5(m + 1)$$    Cross products

$$3m - 6 = 5m + 5$$    Distributive property

$$3m = 5m + 11$$    Add 6.

$$-2m = 11$$    Subtract 5m.

$$m = -\frac{11}{2}$$    Divide by $-2$.

The solution set is $\left\{ -\frac{11}{2} \right\}$.     *NOW TRY*

---

**NOTE**  When you set cross products equal to each other, you are really multiplying each ratio in the proportion by a common denominator.

---

**OBJECTIVE 3**  Solve applied problems by using proportions.

NOW TRY
EXERCISE 6

Twenty gallons of gasoline costs $49.80. How much would 27 gal of the same gasoline cost?

**EXAMPLE 6**  Applying Proportions

After Lee Ann Spahr had pumped 5.0 gal of gasoline, the display showing the price read $16.60. When she finished pumping the gasoline, the price display read $48.14. How many gallons did she pump?

To solve this problem, set up a proportion, with prices in the numerators and gallons in the denominators. Let $x =$ the number of gallons she pumped.

Price ⟶ $$\frac{\$16.60}{5.0} = \frac{\$48.14}{x}$$ ⟵ Price
Gallons ⟶         ⟵ Gallons

*Be sure that numerators represent the same quantities and denominators represent the same quantities.*

$$16.60x = 5.0(48.14)$$    Cross products

$$16.60x = 240.70$$    Multiply.

$$x = 14.5$$    Divide by 16.60.

She pumped 14.5 gal. Check this answer. (Using a calculator reduces the possibility of error.) Notice that the way the proportion was set up uses the fact that the unit price is the same, no matter how many gallons are purchased.    *NOW TRY*

---

**OBJECTIVE 4**  Find percents and percentages.  ***A percent is a ratio where the second number is always 100.*** For example,

50% represents the ratio of 50 to 100, that is, $\frac{50}{100}$, or, as a decimal, 0.50.

27% represents the ratio of 27 to 100, that is, $\frac{27}{100}$, or, as a decimal, 0.27.

Since the word **percent** means **"per 100,"** one percent means "one per one hundred."

$$1\% = 0.01, \quad \text{or} \quad 1\% = \frac{1}{100}$$

NOW TRY ANSWERS
**5.** $\left\{ -\frac{12}{7} \right\}$   **6.** $67.23

**NOW TRY
EXERCISE 7**

Convert.

**(a)** 16% to a decimal

**(b)** 1.5 to a percent

**EXAMPLE 7** Converting Between Decimals and Percents

**(a)** Write 75% as a decimal.

$$75\% = 75 \cdot 1\% = 75 \cdot 0.01 = 0.75$$

The fraction form $1\% = \frac{1}{100}$ can also be used to convert 75% to a decimal.

$$75\% = 75 \cdot 1\% = 75 \cdot \frac{1}{100} = \frac{75}{100} = 0.75$$

**(b)** Write 3% as a decimal.

$$3\% = 3 \cdot 1\% = 3 \cdot 0.01 = 0.03$$

**(c)** Write 0.375 as a percent.

$$0.375 = 37.5 \cdot 0.01 = 37.5 \cdot 1\% = 37.5\%$$

**(d)** Write 2.63 as a percent.

$$2.63 = 263 \cdot 0.01 = 263 \cdot 1\% = 263\%$$      *NOW TRY*

We can solve a percent problem involving $x\%$ by writing it as the proportion

$$\frac{\textit{amount}}{\textit{base}} = \frac{x}{100}.$$

The amount, or **percentage,** is compared to the **base** (the whole amount). Another way to write this proportion is

$$\frac{\text{amount}}{\text{base}} = \text{percent (as a decimal)}$$

**amount = percent (as a decimal) · base.**      Basic percent equation

**EXAMPLE 8** Solving Percent Equations

Solve each problem.

**(a)** What is 15% of 600?

Let $n$ = the number. The word *of* indicates multiplication.

What    is    15%    of    600?      *Translate each word or phrase to write the equation.*

$n$    =    0.15    ·    600      Write the percent equation.

$n = 90$      *Write 15% as a decimal.*      Multiply.

Thus, 90 is 15% of 600.

**(b)** 32% of what number is 64?

32%    of    what number    is    64?

0.32    ·      $n$      =    64      Write the percent equation.

*Write 32% as a decimal.*      $n = \dfrac{64}{0.32}$      Divide by 0.32.

$n = 200$      Simplify. Use a calculator.

32% of 200 is 64.

*NOW TRY ANSWERS*
**7. (a)** 0.16   **(b)** 150%

NOW TRY
EXERCISE 8

Solve each problem.

**(a)** What is 20% of 70?

**(b)** 40% of what number is 130?

**(c)** 121 is what percent of 484?

**(c)** 90 is what percent of 360?

$$\begin{array}{ccccc} 90 & \text{is} & \text{what percent} & \text{of} & 360? \\ \downarrow & \downarrow & \downarrow & \downarrow & \downarrow \\ 90 & = & p & \cdot & 360 \end{array}$$    Write the percent equation.

$$\frac{90}{360} = p$$    Divide by 360.

$$0.25 = p, \quad \text{or} \quad 25\% = p$$    Simplify. Write 0.25 as a percent.

Thus, 90 is 25% of 360.                                    NOW TRY

NOW TRY
EXERCISE 9

A winter coat is on a clearance sale for $48. The regular price is $120. What percent of the regular price is the savings?

EXAMPLE 9  Solving Applied Percent Problems

Solve each problem.

**(a)** A DVD with a regular price of $18 is on sale this week at 22% off. Find the amount of the discount and the sale price of the disc.

The discount is 22% of 18, so we must find the number that is 22% of 18.

$$\begin{array}{ccccc} \text{What number} & \text{is} & 22\% & \text{of} & 18? \\ \downarrow & \downarrow & \downarrow & \downarrow & \downarrow \\ n & = & 0.22 & \cdot & 18 \end{array}$$   Write the percent equation.

$$n = 3.96$$    Multiply.

The discount is $3.96, so the sale price is found by subtracting.

$$\$18.00 - \$3.96 = \$14.04$$    Original price − discount = sales price

**(b)** A newspaper ad offered a set of tires at a sales price of $258. The regular price was $300. What percent of the regular price was the savings?

The savings amounted to $300 − $258 = $42. We can now restate the problem:   What percent of 300 is 42?

$$\begin{array}{ccccc} \text{What percent} & \text{of} & 300 & \text{is} & 42? \\ \downarrow & & \downarrow & \downarrow & \downarrow \\ p & \cdot & 300 & = & 42 \end{array}$$   Write the percent equation.

$$p = \frac{42}{300}$$    Divide by 300.

NOW TRY ANSWERS

**8. (a)** 14  **(b)** 325  **(c)** 25%

**9.** 60%

$$p = 0.14, \quad \text{or} \quad 14\%$$    Simplify. Write 0.14 as a percent.

The sale price represents a 14% savings.                  NOW TRY

---

**2.6 EXERCISES**   **MyMathLab**   Math XL PRACTICE    WATCH    DOWNLOAD    READ    REVIEW

⊙ *Complete solution available on the Video Resources on DVD*

**1.** *Concept Check*  Match each ratio in Column I with the ratio equivalent to it in Column II.

|  I |  II |
|---|---|
| **(a)** 75 to 100 | **A.** 80 to 100 |
| **(b)** 5 to 4 | **B.** 50 to 100 |
| **(c)** $\frac{1}{2}$ | **C.** 3 to 4 |
| **(d)** 4 to 5 | **D.** 15 to 12 |

**2.** Which one of the following represents a ratio of 3 days to 2 weeks?

**A.** $\frac{3}{2}$   **B.** $\frac{3}{7}$

**C.** $\frac{1.5}{1}$   **D.** $\frac{3}{14}$

*Write a ratio for each word phrase. Write fractions in lowest terms.* ***See Example 1.***

🌐 **3.** 40 mi to 30 mi            **4.** 60 ft to 70 ft

    **5.** 120 people to 90 people         **6.** 72 dollars to 220 dollars

🌐 **7.** 20 yd to 8 ft       **8.** 30 in. to 8 ft       **9.** 24 min to 2 hr

   **10.** 16 min to 1 hr      **11.** 60 in. to 2 yd      **12.** 5 days to 40 hr

*Find the best buy for each item. Give the unit price to the nearest thousandth.* ***See Example 2.***
(*Source:* Cub Foods.)

**13.** GRANULATED SUGAR

| Size | Price |
|------|-------|
| 4 lb | $1.78 |
| 10 lb | $4.29 |

**14.** GROUND COFFEE

| Size | Price |
|------|-------|
| 15 oz | $3.43 |
| 34.5 oz | $6.98 |

🌐 **15.** SALAD DRESSING

| Size | Price |
|------|-------|
| 16 oz | $2.44 |
| 32 oz | $2.98 |
| 48 oz | $4.95 |

**16.** BLACK PEPPER

| Size | Price |
|------|-------|
| 2 oz | $2.23 |
| 4 oz | $2.49 |
| 8 oz | $6.59 |

**17.** VEGETABLE OIL

| Size | Price |
|------|-------|
| 16 oz | $1.66 |
| 32 oz | $2.59 |
| 64 oz | $4.29 |
| 128 oz | $6.49 |

**18.** MOUTHWASH

| Size | Price |
|------|-------|
| 8.5 oz | $0.99 |
| 16.9 oz | $1.87 |
| 33.8 oz | $2.49 |
| 50.7 oz | $2.99 |

**19.** TOMATO KETCHUP

| Size | Price |
|------|-------|
| 14 oz | $1.39 |
| 24 oz | $1.55 |
| 36 oz | $1.78 |
| 64 oz | $3.99 |

**20.** GRAPE JELLY

| Size | Price |
|------|-------|
| 12 oz | $1.05 |
| 18 oz | $1.73 |
| 32 oz | $1.84 |
| 48 oz | $2.88 |

**21.** LAUNDRY DETERGENT

| Size | Price |
|------|-------|
| 87 oz | $7.88 |
| 131 oz | $10.98 |
| 263 oz | $19.96 |

**22.** SPAGHETTI SAUCE

| Size | Price |
|------|-------|
| 15.5 oz | $1.19 |
| 32 oz | $1.69 |
| 48 oz | $2.69 |

*Decide whether each proportion is* true *or* false. ***See Example 3.***

🌐 **23.** $\dfrac{5}{35} = \dfrac{8}{56}$        **24.** $\dfrac{4}{12} = \dfrac{7}{21}$        **25.** $\dfrac{120}{82} = \dfrac{7}{10}$

   **26.** $\dfrac{27}{160} = \dfrac{18}{110}$        **27.** $\dfrac{\frac{1}{2}}{5} = \dfrac{1}{10}$        **28.** $\dfrac{\frac{1}{3}}{6} = \dfrac{1}{18}$

*Solve each equation.* ***See Examples 4 and 5.***

🌐 **29.** $\dfrac{k}{4} = \dfrac{175}{20}$    **30.** $\dfrac{x}{6} = \dfrac{18}{4}$    **31.** $\dfrac{49}{56} = \dfrac{z}{8}$    **32.** $\dfrac{20}{100} = \dfrac{z}{80}$

   **33.** $\dfrac{x}{24} = \dfrac{15}{16}$    **34.** $\dfrac{x}{4} = \dfrac{12}{30}$    **35.** $\dfrac{z}{2} = \dfrac{z+1}{3}$    **36.** $\dfrac{m}{5} = \dfrac{m-2}{2}$

🌐 **37.** $\dfrac{3y-2}{5} = \dfrac{6y-5}{11}$    **38.** $\dfrac{2r+8}{4} = \dfrac{3r-9}{3}$    **39.** $\dfrac{5k+1}{6} = \dfrac{3k-2}{3}$

   **40.** $\dfrac{x+4}{6} = \dfrac{x+10}{8}$    **41.** $\dfrac{2p+7}{3} = \dfrac{p-1}{4}$    **42.** $\dfrac{3m-2}{5} = \dfrac{4-m}{3}$

*Solve each problem. (Assume that all items are equally priced.) (In Exercises 53–56, round answers to the nearest tenth.)* ***See Example 6.***

**43.** If 16 candy bars cost $20.00, how much do 24 candy bars cost?

**44.** If 12 ring tones cost $30.00, how much do 8 ring tones cost?

**45.** Eight quarts of oil cost $14.00. How much do 5 qt of oil cost?

**46.** Four tires cost $398.00. How much do 7 tires cost?

**47.** If 9 pairs of jeans cost $121.50, find the cost of 5 pairs.

**48.** If 7 shirts cost $87.50, find the cost of 11 shirts.

**49.** If 6 gal of premium unleaded gasoline costs $19.56, how much would it cost to completely fill a 15-gal tank?

**50.** If sales tax on a $16.00 DVD is $1.32, find the sales tax on a $120.00 DVD player.

**51.** The distance between Kansas City, Missouri, and Denver is 600 mi. On a certain wall map, this is represented by a length of 2.4 ft. On the map, how many feet would there be between Memphis and Philadelphia, two cities that are actually 1000 mi apart?

**52.** The distance between Singapore and Tokyo is 3300 mi. On a certain wall map, this distance is represented by 11 in. The actual distance between Mexico City and Cairo is 7700 mi. How far apart are they on the same map?

**53.** A wall map of the United States has a distance of 8.5 in. between Memphis and Denver, two cities that are actually 1040 mi apart. The actual distance between St. Louis and Des Moines is 333 mi. How far apart are St. Louis and Des Moines on the map?

**54.** A wall map of the United States has a distance of 8.0 in. between New Orleans and Chicago, two cities that are actually 912 mi apart. The actual distance between Milwaukee and Seattle is 1940 mi. How far apart are Milwaukee and Seattle on the map?

**55.** On a world globe, the distance between Capetown and Bangkok, two cities that are actually 10,080 km apart, is 12.4 in. The actual distance between Moscow and Berlin is 1610 km. How far apart are Moscow and Berlin on this globe?

**56.** On a world globe, the distance between Rio de Janeiro and Hong Kong, two cities that are actually 17,615 km apart, is 21.5 in. The actual distance between Paris and Stockholm is 1605 km. How far apart are Paris and Stockholm on this globe?

**57.** According to the directions on a bottle of Armstrong® Concentrated Floor Cleaner, for routine cleaning, $\frac{1}{4}$ cup of cleaner should be mixed with 1 gal of warm water. How much cleaner should be mixed with $10\frac{1}{2}$ gal of water?

**58.** The directions on the bottle mentioned in **Exercise 57** also specify that, for extra-strength cleaning, $\frac{1}{2}$ cup of cleaner should be used for each gallon of water. For extra-strength cleaning, how much cleaner should be mixed with $15\frac{1}{2}$ gal of water?

**59.** The euro is the common currency used by most European countries, including Italy. On August 15, 2009, the exchange rate between euros and U.S. dollars was 1 euro to $1.4294. Ashley went to Rome and exchanged her U.S. currency for euros, receiving 300 euros. How much in U.S. dollars did she exchange? (*Source:* www.xe.com/ucc)

**60.** If 8 U.S. dollars can be exchanged for 103.0 Mexican pesos, how many pesos can be obtained for $65? (Round to the nearest tenth.)

**61.** Biologists tagged 500 fish in North Bay on August 20. At a later date, they found 7 tagged fish in a sample of 700. Estimate the total number of fish in North Bay to the nearest hundred.

**62.** On June 13, researchers at West Okoboji Lake tagged 840 fish. A few weeks later, a sample of 1000 fish contained 18 that were tagged. Approximate the fish population to the nearest hundred.

Two triangles are **similar** if they have the same shape (but not necessarily the same size). Similar triangles have sides that are proportional. The figure shows two similar triangles. Notice that the ratios of the corresponding sides all equal $\frac{3}{2}$:

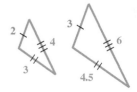

$$\frac{3}{2} = \frac{3}{2}, \qquad \frac{4.5}{3} = \frac{3}{2}, \qquad \frac{6}{4} = \frac{3}{2}.$$

If we know that two triangles are similar, we can set up a proportion to solve for the length of an unknown side.

Use a proportion to find the lengths x and y in each pair of similar triangles.

**63.**

**64.**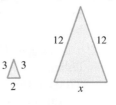

**65.**

**66.**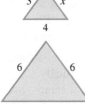

**67.**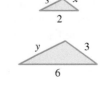

**68.**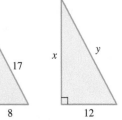

For Exercises 69 and 70, **(a)** draw a sketch consisting of two right triangles depicting the situation described, and **(b)** solve the problem. (Source: Guinness World Records.)

**69.** An enlarged version of the chair used by George Washington at the Constitutional Convention casts a shadow 18 ft long at the same time a vertical pole 12 ft high casts a shadow 4 ft long. How tall is the chair?

**70.** One of the tallest candles ever constructed was exhibited at the 1897 Stockholm Exhibition. If it cast a shadow 5 ft long at the same time a vertical pole 32 ft high cast a shadow 2 ft long, how tall was the candle?

The Consumer Price Index (CPI) provides a means of determining the purchasing power of the U.S. dollar from one year to the next. Using the period from 1982 to 1984 as a measure of 100.0, the CPI for selected years from 1995 through 2007 is shown in the table. To use the CPI to predict a price in a particular year, we set up a proportion and compare it with a known price in another year:

| Year | Consumer Price Index |
|------|----------------------|
| 1995 | 152.4 |
| 1997 | 160.5 |
| 1999 | 166.6 |
| 2001 | 177.1 |
| 2003 | 184.0 |
| 2005 | 195.3 |
| 2007 | 207.3 |

Source: Bureau of Labor Statistics.

$$\frac{\text{price in year } A}{\text{index in year } A} = \frac{\text{price in year } B}{\text{index in year } B}.$$

Use the CPI figures in the table to find the amount that would be charged for using the same amount of electricity that cost $225 in 1995. Give your answer to the nearest dollar.

**71.** in 1997      **72.** in 1999      **73.** in 2003      **74.** in 2007

Convert each percent to a decimal. **See Examples 7(a) and 7(b).**

**75.** 53%      **76.** 38%      **77.** 96%      **78.** 11%

**79.** 9%      **80.** 7%      **81.** 129%      **82.** 174%

*Convert each decimal to a percent. **See Examples 7(c) and 7(d).***

**83.** 0.80      **84.** 0.75      **85.** 0.02      **86.** 0.06

**87.** 0.125      **88.** 0.983      **89.** 2.2      **90.** 1.4

*Solve each problem. **See Examples 8 and 9.***

**91.** What is 14% of 780?      **92.** What is 26% of 480?

**93.** 42% of what number is 294?      **94.** 18% of what number is 108?

**95.** 120% of what number is 510?      **96.** 140% of what number is 315?

**97.** 4 is what percent of 50?      **98.** 8 is what percent of 64?

**99.** What percent of 30 is 36?      **100.** What percent of 48 is 96?

**101.** Find the discount on a leather recliner with a regular price of $795 if the recliner is 15% off. What is the sale price of the recliner?

**102.** A laptop computer with a regular price of $597 is on sale at 20% off. Find the amount of the discount and the sale price of the computer.

**103.** Clayton earned 48 points on a 60-point geometry project. What percent of the total points did he earn?

**104.** On a 75-point algebra test, Grady scored 63 points. What percent of the total points did he score?

**105.** Anna saved $1950, which was 65% of the amount she needed for a used car. What was the total amount she needed for the car?

**106.** Bryn had $525, which was 70% of the total amount she needed for a deposit on an apartment. What was the total deposit she needed?

### PREVIEW EXERCISES

*Solve each equation. **See Section 2.3.***

**107.** $0.15x + 0.30(3) = 0.20(3 + x)$      **108.** $0.20(60) + 0.05x = 0.10(60 + x)$

**109.** $0.92x + 0.98(12 - x) = 0.96(12)$      **110.** $0.10(7) + 1.00x = 0.30(7 + x)$

## 2.7   Further Applications of Linear Equations

**OBJECTIVES**

1. Use percent in solving problems involving rates.
2. Solve problems involving mixtures.
3. Solve problems involving simple interest.
4. Solve problems involving denominations of money.
5. Solve problems involving distance, rate, and time.

**OBJECTIVE 1** Use percent in solving problems involving rates. Recall from **Section 2.6** that the word "percent" means "per 100."

$$1\% = 0.01, \quad \text{or} \quad 1\% = \frac{1}{100}$$

**PROBLEM-SOLVING HINT**

Mixing different concentrations of a substance or different interest rates involves percents. To get the amount of pure substance or the interest, we multiply.

| Mixture Problems | Interest Problems (annual) |
|:---:|:---:|
| base × rate (%) = percentage | principal × rate (%) = interest |
| $b \times r = p$ | $p \times r = I$ |

*In an equation, percent is always written as a decimal or a fraction.*

*NOW TRY*
*EXERCISE 1*

**(a)** How much pure alcohol is in 70 L of a 20% alcohol solution?

**(b)** Find the annual simple interest if $3200 is invested at 2%.

---

**EXAMPLE 1**    Using Percents to Find Percentages

**(a)** If a chemist has 40 L of a 35% acid solution, then the amount of pure acid in the solution is

> Write 35% as a decimal.

$$40 \text{ L} \qquad \times \qquad 0.35 \qquad = \qquad 14 \text{ L}.$$

Amount of solution        Rate of concentration        Amount of pure acid

**(b)** If $1300 is invested for one year at 7% simple interest, the amount of interest earned in the year is

$$\$1300 \quad \times \quad 0.07 \quad = \quad \$91.$$

Principal        Interest rate        Interest earned        *NOW TRY*

---

**OBJECTIVE 2**    Solve problems involving mixtures.

**PROBLEM-SOLVING HINT**

Using a table helps organize the information in a problem and more easily set up an equation, which is usually the most difficult step.

---

**EXAMPLE 2**    Solving a Mixture Problem

A chemist needs to mix 20 L of a 40% acid solution with some 70% acid solution to obtain a mixture that is 50% acid. How many liters of the 70% acid solution should be used?

*Step 1*    **Read** the problem. Note the percent of each solution and of the mixture.

*Step 2*    **Assign a variable.**

Let $x$ = the number of liters of 70% acid solution needed.

Recall from **Example 1(a)** that the amount of pure acid in this solution is the product of the percent of strength and the number of liters of solution, or

$$0.70x. \qquad \text{Liters of pure acid in } x \text{ liters of 70\% solution}$$

The amount of pure acid in the 20 L of 40% solution is

$$0.40(20) = 8. \qquad \text{Liters of pure acid in the 40\% solution}$$

The new solution will contain $(x + 20)$ liters of 50% solution. The amount of pure acid in this solution is

$$0.50(x + 20). \qquad \text{Liters of pure acid in the 50\% solution}$$

**FIGURE 15** illustrates this information, which is summarized in the table.

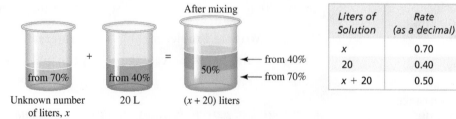

| Liters of Solution | Rate (as a decimal) | Liters of Pure Acid |
|---|---|---|
| $x$ | 0.70 | $0.70x$ |
| 20 | 0.40 | $0.40(20) = 8$ |
| $x + 20$ | 0.50 | $0.50(x + 20)$ |

*NOW TRY ANSWERS*

**1. (a)** 14 L   **(b)** $64

**FIGURE 15**

*NOW TRY*
*EXERCISE 2*

A certain seasoning is 70% salt. How many ounces of this seasoning must be mixed with 30 oz of dried herbs containing 10% salt to obtain a seasoning that is 50% salt?

*Step 3*  **Write an equation.** The number of liters of pure acid in the 70% solution added to the number of liters of pure acid in the 40% solution will equal the number of liters of pure acid in the final mixture.

| Pure acid in 70% | plus | pure acid in 40% | is | pure acid in 50%. |
|:---:|:---:|:---:|:---:|:---:|
| ↓ | ↓ | ↓ | ↓ | ↓ |
| $0.70x$ | $+$ | $0.40(20)$ | $=$ | $0.50(x + 20)$ |

*Step 4*  **Solve** the equation.

$$0.70x + 0.40(20) = 0.50x + 0.50(20) \qquad \text{Distributive property}$$
$$70x + 40(20) = 50x + 50(20) \qquad \text{Multiply by 100.}$$
$$70x + 800 = 50x + 1000 \qquad \text{Multiply.}$$
$$20x + 800 = 1000 \qquad \text{Subtract } 50x.$$
$$20x = 200 \qquad \text{Subtract 800.}$$
$$x = 10 \qquad \text{Divide by 20.}$$

*Step 5*  **State the answer.** The chemist needs to use $10$ L of 70% solution.

*Step 6*  **Check.** The answer checks, since

$$0.70(10) + 0.40(20) = 7 + 8 = 15 \qquad \text{Sum of two solutions}$$

and

$$0.50(10 + 20) = 0.50(30) = 15. \qquad \text{Mixture} \qquad \text{NOW TRY}$$

---

**NOTE**  In a mixture problem, the concentration of the final mixture must be *between* the concentrations of the two solutions making up the mixture.

---

**OBJECTIVE 3**  **Solve problems involving simple interest.**  The formula for simple interest, $I = prt$, becomes $I = pr$ when time $t = 1$ (for annual interest), as shown in the Problem-Solving Hint at the beginning of this section. Multiplying the total amount (principal) by the rate (rate of interest) gives the percentage (amount of interest).

**EXAMPLE 3**  Solving a Simple Interest Problem

Susan Grody plans to invest some money at 6% and $2000 more than this amount at 7%. To earn $790 per year in interest, how much should she invest at each rate?

*Step 1*  **Read** the problem again. There will be two answers.

*Step 2*  **Assign a variable.**

Let $x =$ the amount invested at 6% (in dollars).

Then $x + 2000 =$ the amount invested at 7% (in dollars).

| Amount Invested in Dollars | Rate of Interest | Interest for One Year |
|:---:|:---:|:---:|
| $x$ | 0.06 | 0.06x |
| $x + 2000$ | 0.07 | 0.07(x + 2000) |

Use a table to arrange the given information.

*NOW TRY ANSWER*
**2.**  60 oz

NOW TRY
EXERCISE 3
A financial advisor invests some money in a municipal bond paying 3% annual interest and $5000 more than that amount in a certificate of deposit paying 4% annual interest. To earn $410 per year in interest, how much should he invest at each rate?

*Step 3* **Write an equation.** Multiply amount by rate to get the interest earned.

| Interest at 6% | plus | interest at 7% | is | total interest. |
|---|---|---|---|---|
| ↓ | ↓ | ↓ | ↓ | ↓ |
| $0.06x$ | $+$ | $0.07(x + 2000)$ | $=$ | $790$ |

*Step 4* **Solve.**

$$0.06x + 0.07x + 0.07(2000) = 790 \quad \text{Distributive property}$$
$$6x + 7x + 7(2000) = 79{,}000 \quad \text{Multiply by 100.}$$
$$6x + 7x + 14{,}000 = 79{,}000 \quad \text{Multiply.}$$
$$13x + 14{,}000 = 79{,}000 \quad \text{Combine like terms.}$$
$$13x = 65{,}000 \quad \text{Subtract 14,000.}$$
$$x = 5000 \quad \text{Divide by 13.}$$

*Step 5* **State the answer.** She should invest $5000 at 6% and $5000 + $2000 = $7000 at 7%.

*Step 6* **Check.** Investing $5000 at 6% and $7000 at 7% gives total interest of

$$0.06(\$5000) + 0.07(\$7000) = \$300 + \$490 = \$790, \quad \text{as required.}$$

NOW TRY

---

**OBJECTIVE 4** **Solve problems involving denominations of money.**

**PROBLEM-SOLVING HINT**

To get the total value in problems that involve different denominations of money or items with different monetary values, we multiply.

**Money Denominations Problems**

**number × value of one item = total value**

For example, 30 dimes have a monetary value of $30(\$0.10) = \$3$. Fifteen $5 bills have a value of $15(\$5) = \$75$. A table is also helpful for these problems.

---

**EXAMPLE 4** Solving a Money Denominations Problem

A bank teller has 25 more $5 bills than $10 bills. The total value of the money is $200. How many of each denomination of bill does she have?

*Step 1* **Read** the problem. We must find the number of each denomination of bill.

*Step 2* **Assign a variable.**

Let $x$ = the number of $10 bills.

Then $x + 25$ = the number of $5 bills.

| Number of Bills | Denomination | Total Value |
|---|---|---|
| $x$ | 10 | $10x$ |
| $x + 25$ | 5 | $5(x + 25)$ |

Organize the given information in a table.

NOW TRY ANSWER
**3.** $3000 at 3%; $8000 at 4%

NOW TRY
EXERCISE 4

Clayton has saved $5.65 in dimes and quarters. He has 10 more quarters than dimes. How many of each denomination of coin does he have?

*Step 3* **Write an equation.** Multiplying the number of bills by the denomination gives the monetary value. The value of the tens added to the value of the fives must be $200.

Value of
tens     plus     value of
fives     is     $200.

$$10x \quad + \quad 5(x + 25) \quad = \quad 200$$

*Step 4* **Solve.**

| $10x + 5x + 125 = 200$ | Distributive property |
| $15x + 125 = 200$ | Combine like terms. |
| $15x = 75$ | Subtract 125. |
| $x = 5$ | Divide by 15. |

*Step 5* **State the answer.** The teller has 5 tens and $5 + 25 = 30$ fives.

*Step 6* **Check.** The teller has $30 - 5 = 25$ more fives than tens. The value of the money is

$$5(\$10) + 30(\$5) = \$200, \quad \text{as required.} \quad \text{NOW TRY}$$

**OBJECTIVE 5** **Solve problems involving distance, rate, and time.** If your car travels at an average rate of 50 mph for 2 hr, then it travels $50 \times 2 = 100$ mi. This is an example of the basic relationship between distance, rate, and time,

**distance = rate × time,**

given by the formula $d = rt$. By solving, in turn, for $r$ and $t$ in the formula, we obtain two other equivalent forms of the formula. The three forms are given here.

**Distance, Rate, and Time Relationship**

$$d = rt \qquad r = \frac{d}{t} \qquad t = \frac{d}{r}$$

**EXAMPLE 5** Finding Distance, Rate, or Time

Solve each problem using a form of the distance formula.

**(a)** The speed of sound is 1088 ft per sec at sea level at 32°F. Find the distance sound travels in 5 sec under these conditions.

We must find distance, given rate and time, using $d = rt$ (or $rt = d$).

$$1088 \quad \times \quad 5 \quad = \quad 5440 \text{ ft}$$

Rate   × Time   =   Distance

**(b)** The winner of the first Indianapolis 500 race (in 1911) was Ray Harroun, driving a Marmon Wasp at an average rate (speed) of 74.59 mph. (*Source: Universal Almanac.*) How long did it take him to complete the 500 mi?

We must find time, given rate and distance, using $t = \frac{d}{r} \left( \text{or } \frac{d}{r} = t \right)$.

Distance → $\dfrac{500}{74.59}$ = 6.70 hr   (rounded) ← Time
Rate →

To convert 0.70 hr to minutes, we multiply by 60 to get $0.70(60) = 42$. It took Harroun about 6 hr, 42 min, to complete the race.

NOW TRY ANSWER
**4.** dimes: 9; quarters: 19

NOW TRY EXERCISE 5

It took a driver 6 hr to travel from St. Louis to Fort Smith, a distance of 400 mi. What was the driver's rate, to the nearest hundredth?

 NOW TRY EXERCISE 6

From a point on a straight road, two bicyclists ride in the same direction. One travels at a rate of 18 mph, the other at a rate of 20 mph. In how many hours will they be 5 mi apart?

**(c)** At the 2008 Olympic Games, Australian swimmer Leisel Jones set an Olympic record of 65.17 sec in the women's 100-m breaststroke swimming event. (*Source: World Almanac and Book of Facts.*) Find her rate.

We must find rate, given distance and time, using $r = \frac{d}{t}$ $\left(\text{or } \frac{d}{t} = r\right)$.

$$\text{Distance} \rightarrow \frac{100}{65.17} = 1.53 \text{ m per sec (rounded)} \leftarrow \text{Rate} \quad \text{NOW TRY}$$
$$\text{Time} \rightarrow$$

---

**EXAMPLE 6** Solving a Motion Problem

Two cars leave Iowa City, Iowa, at the same time and travel east on Interstate 80. One travels at a constant rate of 55 mph. The other travels at a constant rate of 63 mph. In how many hours will the distance between them be 24 mi?

*Step 1* **Read** the problem. We must find the time it will take for the distance between the cars to be 24 mi.

*Step 2* **Assign a variable.** We are looking for time.

Let $t$ = the number of hours until the distance between them is 24 mi.

The sketch in **FIGURE 16** shows what is happening in the problem.

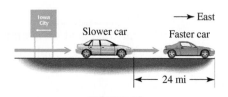

**FIGURE 16**

To construct a table, we fill in the information given in the problem, using $t$ for the time traveled by each car. We multiply rate by time to get the expressions for distances traveled.

| | Rate | Time | Distance |
|---|---|---|---|
| Faster Car | 63 | $t$ | $63t$ |
| Slower Car | 55 | $t$ | $55t$ |

The quantities $63t$ and $55t$ represent the two distances. The *difference* between the larger distance and the smaller distance is 24 mi.

*Step 3* **Write an equation.**

$$63t - 55t = 24$$

*Step 4* **Solve.**
$$8t = 24 \quad \text{Combine like terms.}$$
$$t = 3 \quad \text{Divide by 8.}$$

*Step 5* **State the answer.** It will take the cars 3 hr to be 24 mi apart.

*Step 6* **Check.** After 3 hr, the faster car will have traveled $63 \times 3 = 189$ mi and the slower car will have traveled $55 \times 3 = 165$ mi. The difference is

$$189 - 165 = 24, \quad \text{as required.} \quad \text{NOW TRY}$$

---

**PROBLEM-SOLVING HINT**

In motion problems, once we have filled in two pieces of information in each row of the table, we can automatically fill in the third piece of information, using the appropriate form of the distance formula. Then we set up the equation based on our sketch and the information in the table.

NOW TRY ANSWERS
**5.** 66.67 mph   **6.** 2.5 hr

*NOW TRY*
*EXERCISE 7*

Two cars leave a parking lot at the same time, one traveling east and the other traveling west. The westbound car travels 6 mph faster than the eastbound car. In $\frac{1}{4}$ hr, they are 35 mi apart. What are their rates?

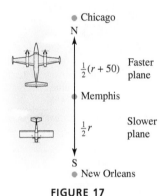

FIGURE 17

**EXAMPLE 7** Solving a Motion Problem

Two planes leave Memphis at the same time. One heads south to New Orleans. The other heads north to Chicago. The Chicago plane flies 50 mph faster than the New Orleans plane. In $\frac{1}{2}$ hr, the planes are 275 mi apart. What are their rates?

*Step 1* **Read** the problem carefully.

*Step 2* **Assign a variable.**

Let $r$ = the rate of the slower plane.

Then $r + 50$ = the rate of the faster plane.

|  | Rate | Time | Distance |
|---|---|---|---|
| Slower plane | $r$ | $\frac{1}{2}$ | $\frac{1}{2}r$ |
| Faster plane | $r + 50$ | $\frac{1}{2}$ | $\frac{1}{2}(r + 50)$ |

Sum is 275 mi.

*Step 3* **Write an equation.** As **FIGURE 17** shows, the planes are headed in *opposite* directions. The *sum* of their distances equals 275 mi.

$$\frac{1}{2}r + \frac{1}{2}(r + 50) = 275$$

*Step 4* **Solve.**

$$r + (r + 50) = 550 \quad \text{Multiply by 2.}$$
$$2r + 50 = 550 \quad \text{Combine like terms.}$$
$$2r = 500 \quad \text{Subtract 50.}$$
$$r = 250 \quad \text{Divide by 2.}$$

*Step 5* **State the answer.** The slower plane (headed south) has a rate of 250 mph. The rate of the faster plane is $250 + 50 = 300$ mph.

*NOW TRY ANSWER*
7. 67 mph; 73 mph

*Step 6* **Check.** Verify that $\frac{1}{2}(250) + \frac{1}{2}(300) = 275$ mi.

NOW TRY

---

## 2.7 EXERCISES

MyMathLab | Math XL PRACTICE  WATCH  DOWNLOAD  READ  REVIEW

*Complete solution available on the Video Resources on DVD*

*Answer each question.* **See Example 1 and the Problem-Solving Hint preceding Example 4.**

**1.** How much pure alcohol is in 150 L of a 30% alcohol solution?

**2.** How much pure acid is in 250 mL of a 14% acid solution?

**3.** If $25,000 is invested for 1 yr at 3% simple interest, how much interest is earned?

**4.** If $10,000 is invested for 1 yr at 3.5% simple interest, how much interest is earned?

**5.** What is the monetary value of 35 half-dollars?

**6.** What is the monetary value of 283 nickels?

*Concept Check* *Solve each percent problem. Remember that base × rate = percentage.*

**7.** The population of New Mexico in 2007 was about 1,917,000, with 44.4% Hispanic. What is the best estimate of the Hispanic population in New Mexico? (*Source:* U.S. Census Bureau.)

**A.** 850,000     **B.** 85,000     **C.** 650,000     **D.** 44,000

8. The population of Alabama in 2007 was about 4,628,000, with 26.5% represented by African-Americans. What is the best estimate of the African-American population in Alabama? (*Source:* U.S. Census Bureau.)

   **A.** 600,000     **B.** 750,000     **C.** 1,200,000     **D.** 1,500,000

9. The graph shows the breakdown, by approximate percents, of the colors chosen for new 2007 model-year full-size and intermediate cars sold in the United States. If approximately 3.8 million of these cars were sold, about how many were each color? (*Source:* Ward's Communications.)

   **(a)** White     **(b)** Silver     **(c)** Red

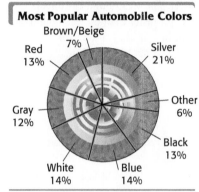

**Most Popular Automobile Colors**

Brown/Beige 7%   Silver 21%   Red 13%   Other 6%   Gray 12%   Black 13%   White 14%   Blue 14%

*Source:* DuPont Automotive Products.

10. An average middle-income family will spend $221,190 to raise a child born in 2008 from birth to age 18. The graph shows the breakdown, by approximate percents, for various expense categories. To the nearest dollar, about how much will be spent to provide the following?

    **(a)** Housing
    **(b)** Food
    **(c)** Health care

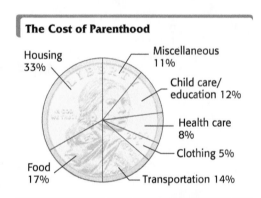

**The Cost of Parenthood**

Housing 33%   Miscellaneous 11%   Child care/education 12%   Health care 8%   Clothing 5%   Transportation 14%   Food 17%

*Source:* U.S. Department of Agriculture.

*Concept Check*   *Answer each question.*

11. Suppose that a chemist is mixing two acid solutions, one of 20% concentration and the other of 30% concentration. Which concentration could *not* be obtained?

    **A.** 22%     **B.** 24%     **C.** 28%     **D.** 32%

12. Suppose that pure alcohol is added to a 24% alcohol mixture. Which concentration could *not* be obtained?

    **A.** 22%     **B.** 26%     **C.** 28%     **D.** 30%

*Work each mixture problem.* ***See Example 2.***

13. How many liters of 25% acid solution must a chemist add to 80 L of 40% acid solution to obtain a solution that is 30% acid?

| Liters of Solution | Rate | Liters of Acid |
|---|---|---|
| $x$ | 0.25 | $0.25x$ |
| 80 | 0.40 | $0.40(80)$ |
| $x + 80$ | 0.30 | $0.30(x + 80)$ |

14. How many gallons of 50% antifreeze must be mixed with 80 gal of 20% antifreeze to obtain a mixture that is 40% antifreeze?

| Gallons of Mixture | Rate | Gallons of Antifreeze |
|---|---|---|
| $x$ | 0.50 | $0.50x$ |
| 80 | 0.20 | $0.20(80)$ |
| $x + 80$ | 0.40 | $0.40(x + 80)$ |

**15.** A pharmacist has 20 L of a 10% drug solution. How many liters of 5% solution must be added to get a mixture that is 8%?

| Liters of Solution | Rate | Liters of Pure Drug |
|---|---|---|
| 20 | | 20(0.10) |
| | 0.05 | |
| | 0.08 | |

**16.** A certain metal is 20% tin. How many kilograms of this metal must be mixed with 80 kg of a metal that is 70% tin to get a metal that is 50% tin?

| Kilograms of Metal | Rate | Kilograms of Pure Tin |
|---|---|---|
| x | 0.20 | |
| | 0.70 | |
| | 0.50 | |

**17.** In a chemistry class, 12 L of a 12% alcohol solution must be mixed with a 20% solution to get a 14% solution. How many liters of the 20% solution are needed?

**18.** How many liters of a 10% alcohol solution must be mixed with 40 L of a 50% solution to get a 40% solution?

**19.** Minoxidil is a drug that has recently proven to be effective in treating male pattern baldness. Water must be added to 20 mL of a 4% minoxidil solution to dilute it to a 2% solution. How many milliliters of water should be used? (*Hint:* Water is 0% minoxidil.)

**20.** A pharmacist wishes to mix a solution that is 2% minoxidil. She has on hand 50 mL of a 1% solution, and she wishes to add some 4% solution to it to obtain the desired 2% solution. How much 4% solution should she add?

**21.** How many liters of a 60% acid solution must be mixed with a 75% acid solution to get 20 L of a 72% solution?

**22.** How many gallons of a 12% indicator solution must be mixed with a 20% indicator solution to get 10 gal of a 14% solution?

*Work each investment problem using simple interest.* ***See Example 3.***

**23.** Arlene Frank is saving money for her college education. She deposited some money in a savings account paying 5% and $1200 less than that amount in a second account paying 4%. The two accounts produced a total of $141 interest in 1 yr. How much did she invest at each rate?

**24.** Margaret Fennell won a prize for her work. She invested part of the money in a certificate of deposit at 4% and $3000 more than that amount in a bond paying 6%. Her annual interest income was $780. How much did Margaret invest at each rate?

**25.** An artist invests in a tax-free bond paying 6%, and $6000 more than three times as much in mutual funds paying 5%. Her total annual interest income from the investments is $825. How much does she invest at each rate?

**26.** With income earned by selling the rights to his life story, an actor invests some of the money at 3% and $30,000 more than twice as much at 4%. The total annual interest earned from the investments is $5600. How much is invested at each rate?

*Work each problem involving monetary values.* ***See Example 4.***

**27.** A coin collector has $1.70 in dimes and nickels. She has two more dimes than nickels. How many nickels does she have?

| Number of Coins | Denomination | Total Value |
|---|---|---|
| x | 0.05 | 0.05x |
| | 0.10 | |

**28.** A bank teller has $725 in $5 bills and $20 bills. The teller has five more twenties than fives. How many $5 bills does the teller have?

| Number of Bills | Denomination | Total Value |
|---|---|---|
| x | 5 | |
| x + 5 | 20 | |

**29.** In May 2009, U.S. first-class mail rates increased to 44 cents for the first ounce, plus 17 cents for each additional ounce. If Sabrina spent $14.40 for a total of 45 stamps of these two denominations, how many stamps of each denomination did she buy? (*Source:* U.S. Postal Service.)

**30.** A movie theater has two ticket prices: $8 for adults and $5 for children. If the box office took in $4116 from the sale of 600 tickets, how many tickets of each kind were sold?

**31.** Harriet Amato operates a coffee shop. One of her customers wants to buy two kinds of beans: Arabian Mocha and Colombian Decaf. If she wants twice as much Mocha as Colombian Decaf, how much of each can she buy for a total of $87.50? (Prices are listed on the sign.)

> Arabian Mocha .........$8.50/lb
> Chocolate Mint........ $10.50/lb
> Colombian Decaf........$8.00/lb
> French Roast...........$7.50/lb
> Guatemalan Spice.......$9.50/lb
> Hazelnut Decaf........$10.00/lb
> Italian Espresso.........$9.00/lb
> Kona Deluxe ...........$11.50/lb

**32.** Harriet's Special Blend contains a combination of French Roast and Kona Deluxe beans. How many pounds of Kona Deluxe should she mix with 12 lb of French Roast to get a blend to be sold for $10 a pound?

*Solve each problem involving distance, rate, and time.* ***See Example 5.***

**33.** *Concept Check* Which choice is the best estimate for the average rate of a bus trip of 405 mi that lasted 8.2 hr?

**A.** 50 mph **B.** 30 mph **C.** 60 mph **D.** 40 mph

**34.** Suppose that an automobile averages 45 mph and travels for 30 min. Is the distance traveled $45 \times 30 = 1350$ mi? If not, explain why not, and give the correct distance.

**35.** A driver averaged 53 mph and took 10 hr to travel from Memphis to Chicago. What is the distance between Memphis and Chicago?

**36.** A small plane traveled from Warsaw to Rome, averaging 164 mph. The trip took 2 hr. What is the distance from Warsaw to Rome?

**37.** The winner of the 2008 Indianapolis 500 (mile) race was Scott Dixon, who drove his Dellara-Honda to victory at a rate of 143.567 mph. What was his time (to the nearest thousandth of an hour)? (*Source: World Almanac and Book of Facts.*)

**38.** In 2008, Jimmie Johnson drove his Chevrolet to victory in the Brickyard 400 (mile) race at a rate of 115.117 mph. What was his time (to the nearest thousandth of an hour)? (*Source: World Almanac and Book of Facts.*)

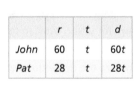

*In Exercises 39–42, find the rate on the basis of the information provided. Use a calculator and round your answers to the nearest hundredth. All events were at the 2008 Olympics. (Source: World Almanac and Book of Facts.)*

|  | Event | Participant | Distance | Time |
|---|---|---|---|---|
| **39.** | 100-m hurdles, women | Dawn Harper, USA | 100 m | 12.54 sec |
| **40.** | 400-m hurdles, women | Melanie Walker, Jamaica | 400 m | 52.64 sec |
| **41.** | 400-m hurdles, men | Angelo Taylor, USA | 400 m | 47.25 sec |
| **42.** | 400-m run, men | LaShawn Merritt, USA | 400 m | 43.75 sec |

*Solve each motion problem.* ***See Examples 6 and 7.***

**43.** Atlanta and Cincinnati are 440 mi apart. John leaves Cincinnati, driving toward Atlanta at an average rate of 60 mph. Pat leaves Atlanta at the same time, driving toward Cincinnati in her antique auto, averaging 28 mph. How long will it take them to meet?

|  | $r$ | $t$ | $d$ |
|---|---|---|---|
| John | 60 | $t$ | $60t$ |
| Pat | 28 | $t$ | $28t$ |

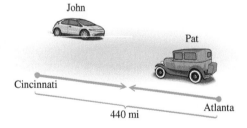

**44.** St. Louis and Portland are 2060 mi apart. A small plane leaves Portland, traveling toward St. Louis at an average rate of 90 mph. Another plane leaves St. Louis at the same time, traveling toward Portland and averaging 116 mph. How long will it take them to meet?

|  | $r$ | $t$ | $d$ |
|---|---|---|---|
| Plane Leaving Portland | 90 | $t$ | $90t$ |
| Plane Leaving St. Louis | 116 | $t$ | $116t$ |

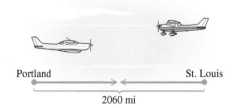

**45.** A train leaves Kansas City, Kansas, and travels north at 85 km per hr. Another train leaves at the same time and travels south at 95 km per hour. How long will it take before they are 315 km apart?

**46.** Two steamers leave a port on a river at the same time, traveling in opposite directions. Each is traveling at 22 mph. How long will it take for them to be 110 mi apart?

**47.** From a point on a straight road, Marco and Celeste ride bicycles in the same direction. Marco rides at 10 mph and Celeste rides at 12 mph. In how many hours will they be 15 mi apart?

**48.** At a given hour, two steamboats leave a city in the same direction on a straight canal. One travels at 18 mph and the other travels at 24 mph. In how many hours will the boats be 9 mi apart?

**49.** Two planes leave an airport at the same time, one flying east, the other flying west. The eastbound plane travels 150 mph slower. They are 2250 mi apart after 3 hr. Find the rate of each plane.

|  | $r$ | $t$ | $d$ |
|---|---|---|---|
| Eastbound | $x - 150$ | 3 | |
| Westbound | $x$ | 3 | |

**50.** Two trains leave a city at the same time. One travels north, and the other travels south 20 mph faster. In 2 hr, the trains are 280 mi apart. Find their rates.

|  | $r$ | $t$ | $d$ |
|---|---|---|---|
| Northbound | $x$ | 2 | |
| Southbound | $x + 20$ | 2 | |

**51.** Two cars start from towns 400 mi apart and travel toward each other. They meet after 4 hr. Find the rate of each car if one travels 20 mph faster than the other.

**52.** Two cars leave towns 230 km apart at the same time, traveling directly toward one another. One car travels 15 km per hr slower than the other. They pass one another 2 hr later. What are their rates?

*Brains Busters* Solve each problem.

**53.** Kevin is three times as old as Bob. Three years ago the sum of their ages was 22 yr. How old is each now? (*Hint:* Write an expression first for the age of each now and then for the age of each three years ago.)

**54.** A store has 39 qt of milk, some in pint cartons and some in quart cartons. There are six times as many quart cartons as pint cartons. How many quart cartons are there? (*Hint:* 1 qt = 2 pt)

**55.** A table is three times as long as it is wide. If it were 3 ft shorter and 3 ft wider, it would be square (with all sides equal). How long and how wide is the table?

**56.** Elena works for $6 an hour. A total of 25% of her salary is deducted for taxes and insurance. How many hours must she work to take home $450?

**57.** Paula received a paycheck for $585 for her weekly wages less 10% deductions. How much was she paid before the deductions were made?

**58.** At the end of a day, the owner of a gift shop had $2394 in the cash register. This amount included sales tax of 5% on all sales. Find the amount of the sales.

### PREVIEW EXERCISES

Decide whether each statement is true or false. ***See Section 1.4.***

**59.** $6 > 6$     **60.** $10 \leq 10$     **61.** $-4 \leq -3$     **62.** $-11 > -9$     **63.** $0 > -\dfrac{1}{2}$

**64.** Graph the numbers $-3, -\frac{2}{3}, 0, 2, \frac{7}{2}$ on a number line. **See Section 1.4.**

## 2.8 Solving Linear Inequalities

An **inequality** is an algebraic expression related by

$<$ "is less than," $\qquad \le$ "is less than or equal to,"

$>$ "is greater than," or $\ge$ "is greater than or equal to."

**Linear Inequality in One Variable**

A **linear inequality in one variable** can be written in the form

$$Ax + B < C, \quad Ax + B \le C, \quad Ax + B > C, \quad \text{or} \quad Ax + B \ge C,$$

where $A$, $B$, and $C$ represent real numbers, and $A \ne 0$.

Some examples of linear inequalities in one variable follow.

$$x + 5 < 2, \quad z - \frac{3}{4} \ge 5, \quad \text{and} \quad 2k + 5 \le 10 \qquad \text{Linear inequalities}$$

We solve a linear inequality by finding all real number solutions of it. For example, the solution set

$$\{x \mid x \le 2\} \qquad \text{Set-builder notation (Section 1.4)}$$

The set of all $x$ such that $x$ is less than or equal to 2

includes *all real numbers* that are less than or equal to 2, not just the *integers* less than or equal to 2.

**OBJECTIVE 1 Graph intervals on a number line.** Graphing is a good way to show the solution set of an inequality. To graph all real numbers belonging to the set $\{x \mid x \le 2\}$, we place a square bracket at 2 on a number line and draw an arrow extending from the bracket to the left (since all numbers *less than* 2 are also part of the graph). See **FIGURE 18**.

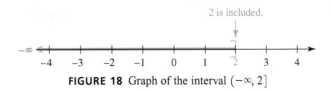

**FIGURE 18** Graph of the interval $(-\infty, 2]$

The set of numbers less than or equal to 2 is an example of an **interval** on the number line. We can write this interval using **interval notation.**

$$(-\infty, 2] \qquad \text{Interval notation}$$

The **negative infinity** symbol $-\infty$ does not indicate a number, but shows that the interval includes *all* real numbers less than 2. Again, the square bracket indicates that 2 is part of the solution.

NOW TRY
EXERCISE 1

Write each inequality in interval notation, and graph the interval.

**(a)** $x < -1$   **(b)** $-2 \le x$

**EXAMPLE 1** Graphing Intervals on a Number Line

Write each inequality in interval notation, and graph the interval.

**(a)** $x > -5$

The statement $x > -5$ says that $x$ can represent any number greater than $-5$ but cannot equal $-5$. The interval is written $(-5, \infty)$. We graph this interval by placing a parenthesis at $-5$ and drawing an arrow to the right, as in **FIGURE 19**. The parenthesis at $-5$ indicates that $-5$ is *not* part of the graph.

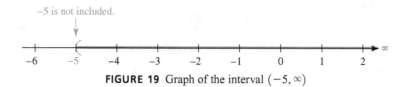

**FIGURE 19** Graph of the interval $(-5, \infty)$

**(b)** $3 > x$

The statement $3 > x$ means the same as $x < 3$. ***The inequality symbol continues to point toward the lesser number.*** The graph of $x < 3$, written in interval notation as $(-\infty, 3)$, is shown in **FIGURE 20**.

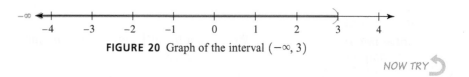

**FIGURE 20** Graph of the interval $(-\infty, 3)$

NOW TRY

***Keep the following important concepts regarding interval notation in mind:***

**1.** A parenthesis indicates that an endpoint is *not included* in a solution set.

**2.** A bracket indicates that an endpoint is *included* in a solution set.

**3.** A parenthesis is *always* used next to an infinity symbol, $-\infty$ or $\infty$.

**4.** The set of all real numbers is written in interval notation as $(-\infty, \infty)$.

**NOTE** Some texts use a solid circle ● rather than a square bracket to indicate that an endpoint is included in a number line graph. An open circle ○ is used to indicate noninclusion, rather than a parenthesis.

The table summarizes methods of expressing solution sets of linear inequalities.

NOW TRY ANSWERS

**1. (a)** $(-\infty, -1)$

-3 -2 -1 0 1 2 3

**(b)** $[-2, \infty)$

-3 -2 -1 0 1 2 3

| Set-Builder Notation | Interval Notation | Graph |
|---|---|---|
| $\{x \mid x < a\}$ | $(-\infty, a)$ | *a* |
| $\{x \mid x \le a\}$ | $(-\infty, a]$ | *a* |
| $\{x \mid x > a\}$ | $(a, \infty)$ | *a* |
| $\{x \mid x \ge a\}$ | $[a, \infty)$ | *a* |
| $\{x \mid x \text{ is a real number}\}$ | $(-\infty, \infty)$ | |

**OBJECTIVE 2** Use the addition property of inequality. Consider the true inequality $2 < 5$. If 4 is added to each side, the result is

$$2 + 4 < 5 + 4 \qquad \text{Add 4.}$$
$$6 < 9, \qquad \text{True}$$

also a true sentence. This example suggests the **addition property of inequality.**

> ### Addition Property of Inequality
>
> If $A$, $B$, and $C$ represent real numbers, then the inequalities
>
> $$A < B \qquad \text{and} \qquad A + C < B + C$$
>
> have exactly the same solutions.
> That is, the same number may be added to each side of an inequality without changing the solutions.

*As with the addition property of equality, the same number may be **subtracted** from each side of an inequality.*

*NOW TRY*
*EXERCISE 2*

Solve the inequality, and graph the solution set.

$$5 + 5x \geq 4x + 3$$

**EXAMPLE 2** Using the Addition Property of Inequality

Solve $7 + 3x \geq 2x - 5$, and graph the solution set.

$$7 + 3x \geq 2x - 5$$
$$7 + 3x - 2x \geq 2x - 5 - 2x \qquad \text{Subtract } 2x.$$
$$7 + x \geq -5 \qquad \text{Combine like terms.}$$
$$7 + x - 7 \geq -5 - 7 \qquad \text{Subtract 7.}$$
$$x \geq -12 \qquad \text{Combine like terms.}$$

The solution set is $[-12, \infty)$. Its graph is shown in **FIGURE 21**.

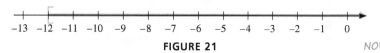

**FIGURE 21**                    NOW TRY

---

**NOTE** Because an inequality has many solutions, we cannot check all of them by substitution as we did with the single solution of an equation. To check the solutions in **Example 2,** we first substitute $-12$ for $x$ in the related *equation*.

CHECK

$$7 + 3x = 2x - 5 \qquad \text{Related equation}$$
$$7 + 3(-12) \stackrel{?}{=} 2(-12) - 5 \qquad \text{Let } x = -12.$$
$$7 - 36 \stackrel{?}{=} -24 - 5 \qquad \text{Multiply.}$$
$$-29 = -29 \ \checkmark \qquad \text{True}$$

A true statement results, so $-12$ is indeed the "boundary" point. Next we test a number other than $-12$ from the interval $[-12, \infty)$. We choose 0.

CHECK

$$7 + 3x \geq 2x - 5 \qquad \text{Original inequality}$$
$$7 + 3(0) \stackrel{?}{\geq} 2(0) - 5 \qquad \text{Let } x = 0.$$
$$7 \geq -5 \ \checkmark \qquad \text{True}$$

*0 is easy to substitute.*

*NOW TRY ANSWER*
**2.** $[-2, \infty)$

The checks confirm that solutions to the inequality are in the interval $[-12, \infty)$. Any number "outside" the interval $[-12, \infty)$, that is, any number in $(-\infty, -12)$, will give a false statement when tested. (Try this.)

**OBJECTIVE 3** Use the multiplication property of inequality. Consider the true inequality $3 < 7$. Multiply each side by the positive number 2.

$$3 < 7$$
$$2(3) < 2(7) \qquad \text{Multiply each side by 2.}$$
$$6 < 14 \qquad \text{True}$$

Now multiply each side of $3 < 7$ by the negative number $-5$.

$$3 < 7$$
$$-5(3) < -5(7) \qquad \text{Multiply each side by } -5.$$
$$-15 < -35 \qquad \text{False}$$

To get a true statement when multiplying each side by $-5$, *we must reverse the direction of the inequality symbol.*

$$3 < 7$$
$$-5(3) > -5(7) \qquad \text{Multiply by } -5. \text{ Reverse the symbol.}$$
$$-15 > -35 \qquad \text{True}$$

---

**NOTE** The above illustrations began with the inequality $3 < 7$, a true statement involving two positive numbers. Similar results occur when one or both of the numbers is negative. Verify this with

$$-3 < 7, \quad 3 > -7, \quad \text{and} \quad -7 < -3$$

by multiplying each inequality first by 2 and then by $-5$.

---

These observations suggest the **multiplication property of inequality.**

**Multiplication Property of Inequality**

If $A$, $B$, and $C$ represent real numbers, with $C \neq 0$, and

**1.** if $C$ is *positive,* then the inequalities

$$A < B \qquad \text{and} \qquad AC < BC$$

have exactly the same solutions;

**2.** if $C$ is *negative,* then the inequalities

$$A < B \qquad \text{and} \qquad AC > BC$$

have exactly the same solutions.

That is, each side of an inequality may be multiplied by the same positive number without changing the solutions. *If the multiplier is negative, we must reverse the direction of the inequality symbol.*

*As with the multiplication property of equality, the same nonzero number may be divided into each side of an inequality.*

Note the following differences for positive and negative numbers.

**1.** When each side of an inequality is multiplied or divided by a *positive number,* the direction of the inequality symbol *does not change.*

**2.** *Reverse the direction of the inequality symbol ONLY when multiplying or dividing each side of an inequality by a NEGATIVE NUMBER.*

↰ *NOW TRY*
*EXERCISE 3*
Solve the inequality, and graph the solution set.

$$-5k \geq 15$$

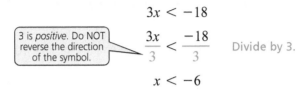

EXAMPLE 3    Using the Multiplication Property of Inequality

Solve each inequality, and graph the solution set.

**(a)** $3x < -18$

We divide each side by 3, a positive number, so the direction of the inequality symbol *does not* change. *(It does not matter that the number on the right side of the inequality is negative.)*

$$3x < -18$$

> 3 is *positive*. Do NOT reverse the direction of the symbol.

$$\frac{3x}{3} < \frac{-18}{3} \qquad \text{Divide by 3.}$$

$$x < -6$$

The solution set is $(-\infty, -6)$. The graph is shown in **FIGURE 22**.

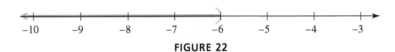

**FIGURE 22**

**(b)** $-4x \geq 8$

Here, each side of the inequality must be divided by $-4$, a negative number, which *does* require changing the direction of the inequality symbol.

$$-4x \geq 8$$

> $-4$ is *negative*. Change $\geq$ to $\leq$.

$$\frac{-4x}{-4} \leq \frac{8}{-4} \qquad \begin{array}{l}\text{Divide by } -4.\\ \text{Reverse the symbol.}\end{array}$$

$$x \leq -2$$

The solution set $(-\infty, -2]$ is graphed in **FIGURE 23**.

**FIGURE 23**                                    *NOW TRY* ↻

**OBJECTIVE 4** Solve linear inequalities by using both properties of inequality.

---

**Solving a Linear Inequality**

*Step 1*    **Simplify each side separately.** Use the distributive property to clear parentheses and combine like terms on each side as needed.

*Step 2*    **Isolate the variable terms on one side.** Use the addition property of inequality to get all terms with variables on one side of the inequality and all numbers on the other side.

*Step 3*    **Isolate the variable.** Use the multiplication property of inequality to change the inequality to the form "variable $< k$" or "variable $> k$," where $k$ is a number.

*Remember:    Reverse the direction of the inequality symbol only when multiplying or dividing each side of an inequality by a negative number.*

---

*NOW TRY ANSWER*
**3.** $(-\infty, -3]$

NOW TRY
EXERCISE 4

Solve the inequality, and graph the solution set.

$$6 - 2t + 5t \le 8t - 4$$

### EXAMPLE 4  Solving a Linear Inequality

Solve $3x + 2 - 5 > -x + 7 + 2x$, and graph the solution set.

***Step 1***  Combine like terms and simplify.

$$3x + 2 - 5 > -x + 7 + 2x$$
$$3x - 3 > x + 7$$

***Step 2***  Use the addition property of inequality.

$$3x - 3 + 3 > x + 7 + 3 \qquad \text{Add 3.}$$
$$3x > x + 10$$
$$3x - x > x + 10 - x \qquad \text{Subtract } x.$$
$$2x > 10$$

***Step 3***  Use the multiplication property of inequality.

Because 2 is positive, keep the symbol >.

$$\frac{2x}{2} > \frac{10}{2} \qquad \text{Divide by 2.}$$
$$x > 5$$

The solution set is $(5, \infty)$. Its graph is shown in **FIGURE 24**.

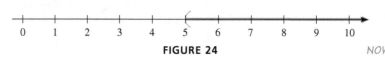

**FIGURE 24**

NOW TRY

NOW TRY
EXERCISE 5

Solve the inequality, and graph the solution set.

$$2x - 3(x - 6) < 4(x + 7)$$

### EXAMPLE 5  Solving a Linear Inequality

Solve $5(x - 3) - 7x \ge 4(x - 3) + 9$, and graph the solution set.

| | | |
|---|---|---|
| ***Step 1*** | $5(x - 3) - 7x \ge 4(x - 3) + 9$ | |
| | $5x - 15 - 7x \ge 4x - 12 + 9$ | Distributive property |
| | $-2x - 15 \ge 4x - 3$ | Combine like terms. |
| ***Step 2*** | $-2x - 15 - 4x \ge 4x - 3 - 4x$ | Subtract $4x$. |
| | $-6x - 15 \ge -3$ | Combine like terms. |
| | $-6x - 15 + 15 \ge -3 + 15$ | Add 15. |
| | $-6x \ge 12$ | Combine like terms. |

***Step 3***

Because −6 is negative, change $\ge$ to $\le$.

$$\frac{-6x}{-6} \le \frac{12}{-6} \qquad \begin{array}{l}\text{Divide by } -6.\\ \text{Reverse the symbol.}\end{array}$$
$$x \le -2$$

The solution set is $(-\infty, -2]$. Its graph is shown in **FIGURE 25**.

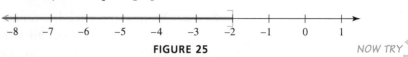

**FIGURE 25**

NOW TRY

NOW TRY ANSWERS
4. $[2, \infty)$

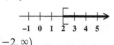

5. $(-2, \infty)$

## OBJECTIVE 5  Solve applied problems by using inequalities.

The table gives some common phrases that suggest inequality.

| Phrase/Word | Example | Inequality |
|---|---|---|
| Is more than | A number *is more than* 4 | $x > 4$ |
| Is less than | A number *is less than* −12 | $x < -12$ |
| Exceeds | A number *exceeds* 3.5 | $x > 3.5$ |
| Is at least | A number *is at least* 6 | $x \ge 6$ |
| Is at most | A number *is at most* 8 | $x \le 8$ |

⚠ **CAUTION** Do not confuse statements such as "5 is more than a number" with the phrase "5 more than a number." The first of these is expressed as $5 > x$, while the second is expressed as $x + 5$, or $5 + x$.

The next example uses the idea of finding the average of a number of scores. ***In general, to find the average of n numbers, add the numbers and divide by n.*** We use the six problem-solving steps from **Section 2.4,** changing Step 3 to "Write an inequality."

> **NOW TRY**
> **EXERCISE 6**
> Kristine has grades of 98 and 85 on her first two tests in algebra. If she wants an average of at least 90 after her third test, what score must she make on that test?

**EXAMPLE 6** Finding an Average Test Score

John Baker has grades of 86, 88, and 78 on his first three tests in geometry. If he wants an average of at least 80 after his fourth test, what are the possible scores he can make on that test?

***Step 1*** **Read** the problem again.

***Step 2*** **Assign a variable.** Let $x$ = John's score on his fourth test.

***Step 3*** **Write an inequality.**

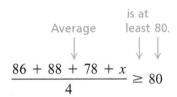

$$\frac{86 + 88 + 78 + x}{4} \geq 80 \qquad \text{To find his average after four tests, add the test scores and divide by 4.}$$

***Step 4*** **Solve.**

$$\frac{252 + x}{4} \geq 80 \qquad \text{Add in the numerator.}$$

$$4\left(\frac{252 + x}{4}\right) \geq 4(80) \qquad \text{Multiply by 4.}$$

$$252 + x \geq 320$$

$$252 + x - 252 \geq 320 - 252 \qquad \text{Subtract 252.}$$

$$x \geq 68 \qquad \text{Combine like terms.}$$

***Step 5*** **State the answer.** He must score 68 or more on the fourth test to have an average of *at least* 80.

***Step 6*** **Check.**
$$\frac{86 + 88 + 78 + 68}{4} = \frac{320}{4} = 80$$

(Also show that a score greater than 68 gives an average greater than 80.)

NOW TRY ↻

⚠ **CAUTION** In applied problems, remember that

| | at least | **translates as** | is greater than or equal to |
| and | at most | **translates as** | is less than or equal to. |

**OBJECTIVE 6** **Solve linear inequalities with three parts.** Inequalities that say that one number is *between* two other numbers are **three-part inequalities.** For example,

$$-3 < 5 < 7 \qquad \text{says that 5 is } between -3 \text{ and } 7.$$

NOW TRY ANSWER
**6.** 87 or more

*NOW TRY*
*EXERCISE 7*
Write the inequality in interval notation, and graph the interval.

$$0 \le x < 2$$

**EXAMPLE 7** Graphing a Three-Part Inequality

Write the inequality in interval notation, and graph the interval.

$$-1 \le x < 3$$

The statement is read "−1 is less than or equal to *x and x* is less than 3." We want the set of numbers *between* −1 and 3, with −1 included and 3 excluded. In interval notation, we write $[-1, 3)$, using a square bracket at −1 because −1 is part of the graph and a parenthesis at 3 because 3 is not part of the graph. See **FIGURE 26**.

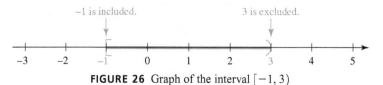

−1 is included.  3 is excluded.

**FIGURE 26** Graph of the interval $[-1, 3)$

*NOW TRY*

The three-part inequality

$$3 < x + 2 < 8$$

says that $x + 2$ is between 3 and 8. We solve this inequality as follows.

$$3 - 2 < x + 2 - 2 < 8 - 2 \qquad \text{Subtract 2 from each part.}$$
$$1 < \quad x \quad < 6$$

The idea is to get the inequality in the form

a number $< x <$ another number.

---

⚠ **CAUTION** *Three-part inequalities are written so that the symbols point in the same direction and both point toward the lesser number.* It would be *wrong* to write an inequality as $8 < x + 2 < 3$, since this would imply that $8 < 3$, a false statement.

---

**EXAMPLE 8** Solving Three-Part Inequalities

Solve each inequality, and graph the solution set.

**(a)**
$$4 < \quad 3x - 5 \quad \le 10$$
$$4 + 5 < 3x - 5 + 5 \le 10 + 5 \qquad \text{Add 5 to each part.}$$
$$9 < \quad 3x \quad \le 15$$

Remember to divide all *three* parts by 3.

$$\frac{9}{3} < \quad \frac{3x}{3} \quad \le \frac{15}{3} \qquad \text{Divide each part by 3.}$$
$$3 < \quad x \quad \le 5$$

The solution set is $(3, 5]$. Its graph is shown in **FIGURE 27**.

*NOW TRY ANSWER*
**7.** $[0, 2)$
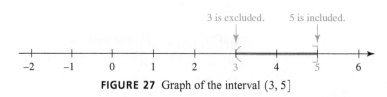

3 is excluded.  5 is included.

**FIGURE 27** Graph of the interval $(3, 5]$

NOW TRY
EXERCISE 8

Solve the inequality, and graph the solution set.

$$-4 \le \frac{3}{2}x - 1 \le 0$$

**(b)**

$$-4 \le \frac{2}{3}m - 1 < 8$$

$$3(-4) \le 3\left(\frac{2}{3}m - 1\right) < 3(8) \qquad \text{Multiply each part by 3 to clear the fraction.}$$

$$-12 \le 2m - 3 < 24 \qquad \text{Distributive property}$$

$$-12 + 3 \le 2m - 3 + 3 < 24 + 3 \qquad \text{Add 3 to each part.}$$

$$-9 \le 2m < 27$$

$$\frac{-9}{2} \le \frac{2m}{2} < \frac{27}{2} \qquad \text{Divide each part by 2.}$$

$$-\frac{9}{2} \le m < \frac{27}{2}$$

The solution set is $\left[-\frac{9}{2}, \frac{27}{2}\right)$. Its graph is shown in **FIGURE 28**.

Think: $-\frac{9}{2} = -4\frac{1}{2}$       Think: $\frac{27}{2} = 13\frac{1}{2}$

**FIGURE 28**

NOW TRY

---

**NOTE** The inequality in **Example 8(b)**, $-4 \le \frac{2}{3}m - 1 < 8$, can also be solved by first adding 1 to each part and then multiplying each part by $\frac{3}{2}$. Try this.

---

The table summarizes methods of expressing solution sets of three-part inequalities.

| Set-Builder Notation | Interval Notation | Graph |
|---|---|---|
| $\{x \mid a < x < b\}$ | $(a, b)$ | 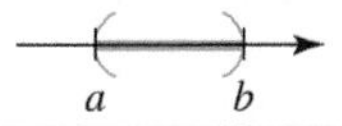 |
| $\{x \mid a < x \le b\}$ | $(a, b]$ | 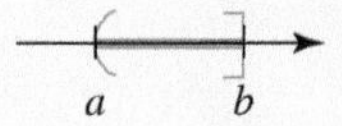 |
| $\{x \mid a \le x < b\}$ | $[a, b)$ | 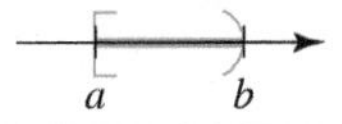 |
| $\{x \mid a \le x \le b\}$ | $[a, b]$ | 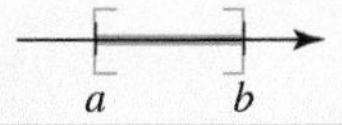 |

NOW TRY ANSWER

**8.** $\left[-2, \frac{2}{3}\right]$

---

## 2.8 EXERCISES

**MyMathLab**   Math XL PRACTICE   WATCH   DOWNLOAD   READ   REVIEW

*Concept Check* Work each problem.

**1.** When graphing an inequality, use a parenthesis if the inequality symbol is _____ or _____ . Use a square bracket if the inequality symbol is _____ or _____ .

**2.** *True* or *false*?   In interval notation, a square bracket is sometimes used next to an infinity symbol.

**3.** In interval notation, the set $\{x \mid x > 0\}$ is written _____ .

**4.** How does the graph of $x \ge -7$ differ from the graph of $x > -7$?

*Concept Check* Write an inequality involving the variable x that describes each set of numbers graphed.

**5.**
−4 −3 −2 −1 0 1 2 3

**6.**
−4 −3 −2 −1 0 1 2 3 4

**7.**
−2 −1 0 1 2 3 4 5

**8.**
−2 −1 0 1 2 3 4 5

*Write each inequality in interval notation, and graph the interval.* **See Example 1.**

**9.** $k \leq 4$    **10.** $x \leq 3$    **11.** $x < -3$    **12.** $r < -11$    **13.** $t > 4$

**14.** $m > 5$    **15.** $0 \geq x$    **16.** $1 \geq x$    **17.** $-\dfrac{1}{2} \leq x$    **18.** $-\dfrac{3}{4} \leq x$

*Solve each inequality. Write the solution set in interval notation, and graph it.* **See Example 2.**

**19.** $z - 8 \geq -7$    **20.** $p - 3 \geq -11$    **21.** $2k + 3 \geq k + 8$

**22.** $3x + 7 \geq 2x + 11$    **23.** $3n + 5 < 2n - 6$    **24.** $5x - 2 < 4x - 5$

**25.** Under what conditions must the inequality symbol be reversed when solving an inequality?

**26.** *Concept Check* If $p < q$ and $r < 0$, which one of the following statements is false?

    **A.** $pr < qr$    **B.** $pr > qr$    **C.** $p + r < q + r$    **D.** $p - r < q - r$

*Solve each inequality. Write the solution set in interval notation, and graph it.* **See Example 3.**

**27.** $3x < 18$    **28.** $5x < 35$    **29.** $2y \geq -20$

**30.** $6m \geq -24$    **31.** $-8t > 24$    **32.** $-7x > 49$

**33.** $-x \geq 0$    **34.** $-k < 0$    **35.** $-\dfrac{3}{4}r < -15$

**36.** $-\dfrac{7}{8}t < -14$    **37.** $-0.02x \leq 0.06$    **38.** $-0.03v \geq -0.12$

*Solve each inequality. Write the solution set in interval notation, and graph it.* **See Examples 4 and 5.**

**39.** $8x + 9 \leq -15$    **40.** $6x + 7 \leq -17$

**41.** $-4x - 3 < 1$    **42.** $-5x - 4 < 6$

**43.** $5r + 1 \geq 3r - 9$    **44.** $6t + 3 < 3t + 12$

**45.** $6x + 3 + x < 2 + 4x + 4$    **46.** $-4w + 12 + 9w \geq w + 9 + w$

**47.** $-x + 4 + 7x \leq -2 + 3x + 6$    **48.** $14y - 6 + 7y > 4 + 10y - 10$

**49.** $5(t - 1) > 3(t - 2)$    **50.** $7(m - 2) < 4(m - 4)$

**51.** $5(x + 3) - 6x \leq 3(2x + 1) - 4x$    **52.** $2(x - 5) + 3x < 4(x - 6) + 1$

**53.** $\dfrac{2}{3}(p + 3) > \dfrac{5}{6}(p - 4)$    **54.** $\dfrac{7}{9}(y - 4) \leq \dfrac{4}{3}(y + 5)$

**55.** $4x - (6x + 1) \leq 8x + 2(x - 3)$

**56.** $2y - (4y + 3) > 6y + 3(y + 4)$

**57.** $5(2k + 3) - 2(k - 8) > 3(2k + 4) + k - 2$

**58.** $2(3z - 5) + 4(z + 6) \geq 2(3z + 2) + 3z - 15$

**FOR INDIVIDUAL OR GROUP WORK**

***Work Exercises 59–62 in order,*** *to see how the solutions of an inequality are closely connected to the solution of the corresponding equation.*

**59.** Solve the equation $3x + 2 = 14$, and graph the solution set on a number line.

**60.** Solve the inequality $3x + 2 > 14$, and graph the solution set on a number line.

**61.** Solve the inequality $3x + 2 < 14$, and graph the solution set on a number line.

**62.** If we were to graph all the solution sets from **Exercises 59–61** on the same number line, describe the graph. (This is called the **union** of all the solution sets.)

*Concept Check*   *Translate each statement into an inequality. Use x as the variable.*

**63.** You must be at least 18 yr old to vote.

**64.** Less than 1 in. of rain fell.

**65.** Chicago received more than 5 in. of snow.

**66.** A full-time student must take at least 12 credits.

**67.** Tracy could spend at most $20 on a gift.

**68.** The car's speed exceeded 60 mph.

*Solve each problem.* ***See Example 6.***

**69.** Christy Heinrich has scores of 76 and 81 on her first two algebra tests. If she wants an average of at least 80 after her third test, what possible scores can she make on that test?

**70.** Joseph Despagne has scores of 96 and 86 on his first two geometry tests. What possible scores can he make on his third test so that his average is at least 90?

**71.** When 2 is added to the difference between six times a number and 5, the result is greater than 13 added to five times the number. Find all such numbers.

**72.** When 8 is subtracted from the sum of three times a number and 6, the result is less than 4 more than the number. Find all such numbers.

**73.** The formula for converting Fahrenheit temperature to Celsius is

$$C = \frac{5}{9}(F - 32).$$

If the Celsius temperature on a certain winter day in Minneapolis is never less than $-25°$, how would you describe the corresponding Fahrenheit temperatures? (*Source:* National Climatic Data Center.)

**74.** The formula for converting Celsius temperature to Fahrenheit is

$$F = \frac{9}{5}C + 32.$$

The Fahrenheit temperature of Phoenix has never exceeded 122°. How would you describe this using Celsius temperature? (*Source:* National Climatic Data Center.)

**75.** For what values of $x$ would the rectangle have a perimeter of at least 400?

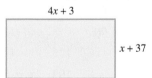

$4x + 3$

$x + 37$

**76.** For what values of $x$ would the triangle have a perimeter of at least 72?

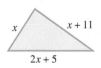

$x$   $x + 11$

$2x + 5$

**77.** For a certain provider, an international phone call costs $2.00 for the first 3 min, plus $0.30 per minute for each minute or fractional part of a minute after the first 3 min. If $x$ represents the number of minutes of the length of the call after the first 3 min, then $2 + 0.30x$ represents the cost of the call. If Alan Lebovitz has $5.60 to spend on a call, what is the maximum total time he can use the phone?

**78.** At the Speedy Gas'n Go, a car wash costs $4.50 and gasoline is selling for $3.20 per gallon. Carla Arriola has $38.10 to spend, and her car is so dirty that she must have it washed. What is the maximum number of gallons of gasoline that she can purchase?

*A company that produces DVDs has found that revenue from the sales of the DVDs is $5 per DVD, less sales costs of $100. Production costs are $125, plus $4 per DVD. Profit (P) is given by revenue (R) less cost (C), so the company must find the production level x that makes*

$$P > 0, \quad \text{that is,} \quad R - C > 0. \qquad P = R - C$$

**79.** Write an expression for revenue $R$, letting $x$ represent the production level (number of DVDs to be produced).

**80.** Write an expression for production costs $C$ in terms of $x$.

**81.** Write an expression for profit $P$, and then solve the inequality $P > 0$.

**82.** Describe the solution in terms of the problem.

*Concept Check* Write a three-part inequality involving the variable $x$ that describes each set of numbers graphed.

**83.**

**84.**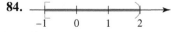

**85.** 

**86.** 

*Write each inequality in interval notation, and graph the interval.* ***See Example 7.***

**87.** $8 \le x \le 10$

**88.** $3 \le x \le 5$

**89.** $0 < y \le 10$

**90.** $-3 \le x < 0$

**91.** $4 > x > -3$

**92.** $6 \ge x \ge -4$

*Solve each inequality. Write the solution set in interval notation, and graph it.* ***See Example 8.***

**93.** $-5 \le 2x - 3 \le 9$

**94.** $-7 \le 3x - 4 \le 8$

**95.** $5 < 1 - 6m < 12$

**96.** $-1 \le 1 - 5q \le 16$

**97.** $10 < 7p + 3 < 24$

**98.** $-8 \le 3r - 1 \le -1$

**99.** $-12 \le \frac{1}{2}z + 1 \le 4$

**100.** $-6 \le 3 + \frac{1}{3}x \le 5$

**101.** $1 \le 3 + \frac{2}{3}p \le 7$

**102.** $2 < 6 + \frac{3}{4}x < 12$

**103.** $-7 \le \frac{5}{4}r - 1 \le -1$

**104.** $-12 \le \frac{3}{7}x + 2 \le -4$

**PREVIEW EXERCISES**

*Find the value of y when (**a**) $x = -2$ and (**b**) $x = 4$.* ***See Sections 1.3 and 2.3.***

**105.** $y = 5x + 3$

**106.** $y = 4 - 3x$

**107.** $6x - 2 = y$

**108.** $4x + 7y = 11$

**109.** $2x - 5y = 10$

**110.** $y + 3x = 8$

STUDY SKILLS

## Taking Math Tests

| Techniques To Improve Your Test Score | Comments |
|---|---|
| **Come prepared** with a pencil, eraser, paper, and calculator, if allowed. | Working in pencil lets you erase, keeping your work neat and readable. |
| **Scan the entire test, note the point values of different problems, and plan your time accordingly.** | To do 20 problems in 50 minutes, allow $50 \div 20 = 2.5$ minutes per problem. Spend less time on the easier problems. |
| **Do a "knowledge dump" when you get the test.** Write important notes to yourself in a corner of the test, such as formulas. | Writing down tips and things that you've memorized at the beginning allows you to relax later. |
| **Read directions carefully, and circle any significant words.** When you finish a problem, read the directions again to make sure you did what was asked. | Pay attention to announcements written on the board or made by your instructor. Ask if you don't understand. |
| **Show all your work.** Many teachers give partial credit if some steps are correct, even if the final answer is wrong. **Write neatly.** | If your teacher can't read your writing, you won't get credit for it. If you need more space to work, ask to use extra paper. |
| **Write down anything that might help solve a problem: a formula, a diagram, etc.** If you can't get it, circle the problem and come back to it later. Do *not* erase anything you wrote down. | If you know even a little bit about the problem, write it down. The answer may come to you as you work on it, or you may get partial credit. Don't spend too long on any one problem. |
| **If you can't solve a problem, make a guess.** Do not change it unless you find an obvious mistake. | Have a good reason for changing an answer. Your first guess is usually your best bet. |
| **Check that the answer to an application problem is reasonable and makes sense.** Read the problem again to make sure you've answered the question. | Use common sense. Can the father really be seven years old? Would a month's rent be $32,140? Label your answer: $, years, inches, etc. |
| **Check for careless errors. Rework the problem without looking at your previous work.** Compare the two answers. | Reworking the problem from the beginning forces you to rethink it. If possible, use a different method to solve the problem. |

*Select several tips to try when you take your next math test.*

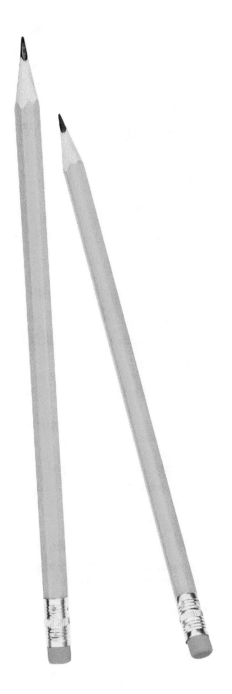

# CHAPTER ( 2 )   SUMMARY

## KEY TERMS

### 2.1
equation
linear equation in one
    variable
solution
solution set
equivalent equations

### 2.3
conditional equation
identity

contradiction
empty (null) set

### 2.4
consecutive integers
degree
complementary angles
right angle
supplementary angles
straight angle

### 2.5
formula
area
perimeter
vertical angles
volume

### 2.6
ratio
proportion
terms of a proportion

extremes
means
cross products

### 2.8
inequality
linear inequality in one
    variable
interval on a number line
interval notation
three-part inequality

## NEW SYMBOLS

$\emptyset$  empty set
$1°$  one degree

$a$ to $b$,  $a{:}b$,  or  $\dfrac{a}{b}$
        the ratio of $a$ to $b$

$\infty$        infinity
$-\infty$      negative infinity
$(-\infty, \infty)$  set of all real
              numbers

$(a, b)$  interval notation for
          $a < x < b$
$[a, b]$  interval notation for
          $a \leq x \leq b$

## TEST YOUR WORD POWER

*See how well you have learned the vocabulary in this chapter.*

1. A **solution set** is the set of numbers that
   **A.** make an expression undefined
   **B.** make an equation false
   **C.** make an equation true
   **D.** make an expression equal to 0.

2. **Complementary angles** are angles
   **A.** formed by two parallel lines
   **B.** whose sum is 90°
   **C.** whose sum is 180°
   **D.** formed by perpendicular lines.

3. **Supplementary angles** are angles
   **A.** formed by two parallel lines
   **B.** whose sum is 90°
   **C.** whose sum is 180°
   **D.** formed by perpendicular lines.

4. A **ratio**
   **A.** compares two quantities using a quotient
   **B.** says that two quotients are equal
   **C.** is a product of two quantities
   **D.** is a difference between two quantities.

5. A **proportion**
   **A.** compares two quantities using a quotient
   **B.** says that two quotients are equal
   **C.** is a product of two quantities
   **D.** is a difference between two quantities.

6. An **inequality** is
   **A.** a statement that two algebraic expressions are equal
   **B.** a point on a number line
   **C.** an equation with no solutions
   **D.** a statement with algebraic expressions related by $<, \leq, >$, or $\geq$.

### ANSWERS

**1.** C; *Example:* {8} is the solution set of $2x + 5 = 21$.   **2.** B; *Example:* Angles with measures 35° and 55° are complementary angles.
**3.** C; *Example:* Angles with measures 112° and 68° are supplementary angles.   **4.** A; *Example:* $\frac{7 \text{ in.}}{12 \text{ in.}}$, or $\frac{7}{12}$   **5.** B; *Example:* $\frac{2}{3} = \frac{8}{12}$
**6.** D; *Examples:* $x < 5, 7 + 2y \geq 11, -5 < 2z - 1 \leq 3$

| CONCEPTS | EXAMPLES |
|---|---|

### 2.1 The Addition Property of Equality

The same number may be added to (or subtracted from) each side of an equation without changing the solution.

Solve. $x - 6 = 12$

$$x - 6 + 6 = 12 + 6 \qquad \text{Add 6.}$$
$$x = 18 \qquad \text{Combine like terms.}$$

Solution set: $\{18\}$

### 2.2 The Multiplication Property of Equality

Each side of an equation may be multiplied (or divided) by the same nonzero number without changing the solution.

Solve. $\dfrac{3}{4}x = -9$

$$\frac{4}{3} \cdot \left(\frac{3}{4}x\right) = \frac{4}{3}(-9) \qquad \text{Multiply by } \tfrac{4}{3}.$$
$$x = -12$$

Solution set: $\{-12\}$

### 2.3 More on Solving Linear Equations

**Step 1** Simplify each side separately.

Solve.

$$2x + 2(x + 1) = 14 + x$$
$$2x + 2x + 2 = 14 + x \qquad \text{Distributive property}$$
$$4x + 2 = 14 + x \qquad \text{Combine like terms.}$$

**Step 2** Isolate the variable term on one side.

$$4x + 2 - x - 2 = 14 + x - x - 2 \qquad \text{Subtract } x. \text{ Subtract 2.}$$
$$3x = 12 \qquad \text{Combine like terms.}$$

**Step 3** Isolate the variable.

$$\frac{3x}{3} = \frac{12}{3} \qquad \text{Divide by 3.}$$
$$x = 4$$

**Step 4** Check.

$$CHECK \quad 2(4) + 2(4 + 1) \stackrel{?}{=} 14 + 4 \qquad \text{Let } x = 4.$$
$$18 = 18 \ \checkmark \qquad \text{True}$$

Solution set: $\{4\}$

### 2.4 An Introduction to Applications of Linear Equations

**Step 1** Read.

One number is five more than another. Their sum is 21. What are the numbers?

**Step 2** Assign a variable.

Let $x =$ the lesser number.
Then $x + 5 =$ the greater number.

**Step 3** Write an equation.

$$x + (x + 5) = 21$$

**Step 4** Solve the equation.

$$2x + 5 = 21 \qquad \text{Combine like terms.}$$
$$2x = 16 \qquad \text{Subtract 5.}$$
$$x = 8 \qquad \text{Divide by 2.}$$

**Step 5** State the answer.

The numbers are 8 and 13.

**Step 6** Check.

13 is five more than 8, and $8 + 13 = 21$. It checks.

(continued)

| CONCEPTS | EXAMPLES |
|---|---|

## 2.5 Formulas and Additional Applications from Geometry

To find the value of one of the variables in a formula, given values for the others, substitute the known values into the formula.

Find $L$ if $\mathcal{A} = LW$, given that $\mathcal{A} = 24$ and $W = 3$.

$$24 = L \cdot 3 \qquad \mathcal{A} = 24, W = 3$$

$$\frac{24}{3} = \frac{L \cdot 3}{3} \qquad \text{Divide by 3.}$$

$$8 = L$$

To solve a formula for one of the variables, isolate that variable by treating the other variables as numbers and using the steps for solving equations.

Solve $P = 2a + 2b$ for $b$.

$$P - 2a = 2a + 2b - 2a \qquad \text{Subtract } 2a.$$

$$P - 2a = 2b \qquad \text{Combine like terms.}$$

$$\frac{P - 2a}{2} = \frac{2b}{2} \qquad \text{Divide by 2.}$$

$$\frac{P - 2a}{2} = b, \quad \text{or} \quad b = \frac{P - 2a}{2}$$

## 2.6 Ratio, Proportion, and Percent

To write a ratio, express quantities in the same units.

$$4 \text{ ft to } 8 \text{ in.} = 48 \text{ in. to } 8 \text{ in.} = \frac{48}{8} = \frac{6}{1}$$

To solve a proportion, use the method of cross products.

Solve. $\dfrac{x}{12} = \dfrac{35}{60}$

$$60x = 12 \cdot 35 \qquad \text{Cross products}$$

$$60x = 420 \qquad \text{Multiply.}$$

$$x = 7 \qquad \text{Divide by 60.}$$

Solution set: $\{7\}$

To solve a percent problem, use the percent equation.

**amount = percent (as a decimal) · base**

65 is what percent of 325?

$$65 = p \cdot 325$$

$$\frac{65}{325} = p$$

$$0.2 = p, \quad \text{or} \quad 20\% = p$$

65 is 20% of 325.

## 2.7 Further Applications of Linear Equations

***Step 1*** Read.

Two cars leave from the same point, traveling in opposite directions. One travels at 45 mph and the other at 60 mph. How long will it take them to be 210 mi apart?

***Step 2*** Assign a variable. Make a table and/or draw a sketch to help solve the problem.

The three forms of the formula relating distance, rate, and time are

$$d = rt, \quad r = \frac{d}{t}, \quad \text{and} \quad t = \frac{d}{r}.$$

Let $t$ = time it takes for them to be 210 mi apart.

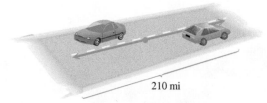

210 mi

(continued)

| CONCEPTS | EXAMPLES |
|---|---|

|  | | | Rate | Time | Distance | |
|  |---|---|---|---|---|
|  | One Car | 45 | $t$ | $45t$ |
|  | Other Car | 60 | $t$ | $60t$ |

The sum of the distances is 210 mi.

**Step 3** Write an equation.

$$45t + 60t = 210$$

**Step 4** Solve the equation.

$$105t = 210 \qquad \text{Combine like terms.}$$
$$t = 2 \qquad \text{Divide by 105.}$$

**Steps 5 and 6** State the answer and check the solution.

It will take them 2 hr to be 210 mi apart.

### 2.8 Solving Linear Inequalities

**Step 1** Simplify each side separately.

Solve the inequality, and graph the solution set.

$$3(1 - x) + 5 - 2x > 9 - 6$$
$$3 - 3x + 5 - 2x > 9 - 6 \qquad \text{Clear parentheses.}$$
$$8 - 5x > 3 \qquad \text{Combine like terms.}$$

**Step 2** Isolate the variable term on one side.

$$8 - 5x - 8 > 3 - 8 \qquad \text{Subtract 8.}$$
$$-5x > -5 \qquad \text{Combine like terms.}$$

**Step 3** Isolate the variable.

$$\frac{-5x}{-5} < \frac{-5}{-5} \qquad \begin{array}{l}\text{Divide by } -5.\\ \text{Change} > \text{to} <.\end{array}$$

*Be sure to reverse the direction of the inequality symbol when multiplying or dividing by a negative number.*

$$x < 1$$

Solution set: $(-\infty, 1)$

To solve a three-part inequality such as

$$4 < 2x + 6 < 8,$$

work with all three expressions at the same time.

Solve.

$$4 < 2x + 6 < 8$$
$$4 - 6 < 2x + 6 - 6 < 8 - 6 \qquad \text{Subtract 6.}$$
$$-2 < 2x < 2$$
$$\frac{-2}{2} < \frac{2x}{2} < \frac{2}{2} \qquad \text{Divide by 2.}$$
$$-1 < x < 1$$

Solution set: $(-1, 1)$

---

## CHAPTER 2 REVIEW EXERCISES

**2.1–2.3** *Solve each equation.*

**1.** $x - 5 = 1$

**2.** $x + 8 = -4$

**3.** $3t + 1 = 2t + 8$

**4.** $5z = 4z + \dfrac{2}{3}$

**5.** $(4r - 2) - (3r + 1) = 8$

**6.** $3(2x - 5) = 2 + 5x$

**7.** $7x = 35$

**8.** $12r = -48$

**9.** $2p - 7p + 8p = 15$

**10.** $\dfrac{x}{12} = -1$

**11.** $\dfrac{5}{8}q = 8$

**12.** $12m + 11 = 59$

**13.** $3(2x + 6) - 5(x + 8) = x - 22$      **14.** $5x + 9 - (2x - 3) = 2x - 7$

**15.** $\dfrac{1}{2}r - \dfrac{r}{3} = \dfrac{r}{6}$      **16.** $0.1(x + 80) + 0.2x = 14$

**17.** $3x - (-2x + 6) = 4(x - 4) + x$      **18.** $\dfrac{1}{2}(x + 3) - \dfrac{2}{3}(x - 2) = 3$

**2.4**   *Solve each problem.*

**19.** If 7 is added to five times a number, the result is equal to three times the number. Find the number.

**20.** In 2009, Illinois had 118 members in its House of Representatives, consisting of only Democrats and Republicans. There were 22 more Democrats than Republicans. How many representatives from each party were there? (*Source:* www.ilga.gov)

**21.** The land area of Hawaii is 5213 mi² greater than the area of Rhode Island. Together, the areas total 7637 mi². What is the area of each of the two states?

**22.** The height of Seven Falls in Colorado is $\frac{5}{2}$ the height of Twin Falls in Idaho. The sum of the heights is 420 ft. Find the height of each. (*Source: World Almanac and Book of Facts.*)

**23.** The supplement of an angle measures 10 times the measure of its complement. What is the measure of the angle?

**24.** Find two consecutive odd integers such that when the lesser is added to twice the greater, the result is 24 more than the greater integer.

**2.5**   *A formula is given along with the values for all but one of the variables. Find the value of the variable that is not given. Use 3.14 as an approximation for $\pi$.*

**25.** $\mathcal{A} = \dfrac{1}{2}bh;$   $\mathcal{A} = 44, b = 8$      **26.** $\mathcal{A} = \dfrac{1}{2}h(b + B);$   $h = 8, b = 3, B = 4$

**27.** $C = 2\pi r;$   $C = 29.83$      **28.** $V = \dfrac{4}{3}\pi r^3;$   $r = 6$

*Solve each formula for the specified variable.*

**29.** $\mathcal{A} = bh$ for $h$      **30.** $\mathcal{A} = \dfrac{1}{2}h(b + B)$ for $h$

*Find the measure of each marked angle.*

**31.**

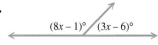

**32.**

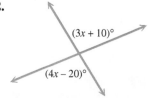

*Solve each problem.*

**33.** The perimeter of a certain rectangle is 16 times the width. The length is 12 cm more than the width. Find the width of the rectangle.

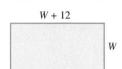

**34.** The Ziegfield Room in Reno, Nevada, has a circular turntable on which its showgirls dance. The circumference of the table is 62.5 ft. What is the diameter? What is the radius? What is the area? (Use $\pi = 3.14$.) (*Source: Guinness World Records.*)

**35.** A baseball diamond is a square with a side of 90 ft. The pitcher's mound is located 60.5 ft from home plate, as shown in the figure. Find the measures of the angles marked in the figure. (*Hint:* Recall that the sum of the measures of the angles of any triangle is 180°.)

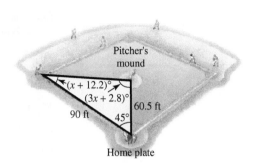

---

**2.6**  *Give a ratio for each word phrase, writing fractions in lowest terms.*

**36.** 60 cm to 40 cm  **37.** 5 days to 2 weeks  **38.** 90 in. to 10 ft

*Solve each equation.*

**39.** $\dfrac{p}{21} = \dfrac{5}{30}$

**40.** $\dfrac{5 + x}{3} = \dfrac{2 - x}{6}$

*Solve each problem.*

**41.** The tax on a $24.00 item is $2.04. How much tax would be paid on a $36.00 item?

**42.** The distance between two cities on a road map is 32 cm. The two cities are actually 150 km apart. The distance on the map between two other cities is 80 cm. How far apart are these cities?

**43.** In the 2008 Olympics in Beijing, China, Japanese athletes earned 25 medals. Two of every 5 medals were bronze. How many bronze medals did Japan earn? (*Source:* World Almanac and Book of Facts.)

**44.** Find the best buy. Give the unit price to the nearest thousandth for that size. (*Source:* Cub Foods.)

CEREAL

| Size | Price |
| --- | --- |
| 15 oz | $2.69 |
| 20 oz | $3.29 |
| 25.5 oz | $3.49 |

**45.** What is 8% of 75?

**46.** What percent of 12 is 21?

**47.** 36% of what number is 900?

**2.7**  *Solve each problem.*

**48.** A nurse must mix 15 L of a 10% solution of a drug with some 60% solution to obtain a 20% mixture. How many liters of the 60% solution will be needed?

**49.** Robert Kay invested $10,000, from which he earns an annual income of $550 per year. He invested part of the $10,000 at 5% annual interest and the remainder in bonds paying 6% interest. How much did he invest at each rate?

**50.** In 1846, the vessel *Yorkshire* traveled from Liverpool to New York, a distance of 3150 mi, in 384 hr. What was the *Yorkshire's* average rate? Round your answer to the nearest tenth.

**51.** Janet Hartnett drove from Louisville to Dallas, a distance of 819 mi, averaging 63 mph. What was her driving time?

**52.** Two planes leave St. Louis at the same time. One flies north at 350 mph and the other flies south at 420 mph. In how many hours will they be 1925 mi apart?

**2.8**  *Write each inequality in interval notation, and graph it.*

**53.** $x \geq -4$  **54.** $x < 7$  **55.** $-5 \leq x < 6$

**56.** *Concept Check*  Which inequality requires reversing the inequality symbol when it is solved?

**A.** $4x \geq -36$ **B.** $-4x \leq 36$ **C.** $4x < 36$ **D.** $4x > 36$

*Solve each inequality. Write the solution set in interval notation, and graph it.*

**57.** $x + 6 \geq 3$

**58.** $5x < 4x + 2$

**59.** $-6x \leq -18$

**60.** $8(x - 5) - (2 + 7x) \geq 4$

**61.** $4x - 3x > 10 - 4x + 7x$

**62.** $3(2x + 5) + 4(8 + 3x) < 5(3x + 7)$

**63.** $-3 \leq 2x + 1 \leq 4$

**64.** $9 < 3x + 5 \leq 20$

*Solve each problem.*

**65.** Awilda Delgado has grades of 94 and 88 on her first two calculus tests. What possible scores on a third test will give her an average of at least 90?

**66.** If nine times a number is added to 6, the result is at most 3. Find all such numbers.

---

## MIXED REVIEW EXERCISES

*Solve.*

**67.** $\dfrac{x}{7} = \dfrac{x - 5}{2}$

**68.** $I = prt$ for $r$

**69.** $-2x > -4$

**70.** $2k - 5 = 4k + 13$

**71.** $0.05x + 0.02x = 4.9$

**72.** $2 - 3(x - 5) = 4 + x$

**73.** $9x - (7x + 2) = 3x + (2 - x)$

**74.** $\dfrac{1}{3}s + \dfrac{1}{2}s + 7 = \dfrac{5}{6}s + 5 + 2$

**75.** A family of four with a monthly income of $3800 plans to spend 8% of this amount on entertainment. How much will be spent on entertainment?

**76.** Athletes in vigorous training programs can eat 50 calories per day for every 2.2 lb of body weight. To the nearest hundred, how many calories can a 175-lb athlete consume per day? (*Source: The Gazette.*)

**77.** The Golden Gate Bridge in San Francisco is 2604 ft longer than the Brooklyn Bridge. Together, their spans total 5796 ft. How long is each bridge? (*Source: World Almanac and Book of Facts.*)

**78.** Find the best buy. Give the unit price to the nearest thousandth for that size. (*Source: Cub Foods.*)

LAUNDRY DETERGENT

| Size | Price |
|---|---|
| 50 oz | $ 4.69 |
| 100 oz | $ 5.98 |
| 200 oz | $13.68 |

**79.** If 1 qt of oil must be mixed with 24 qt of gasoline, how much oil would be needed for 192 qt of gasoline?

**80.** Two trains are 390 mi apart. They start at the same time and travel toward one another, meeting 3 hr later. If the rate of one train is 30 mph more than the rate of the other train, find the rate of each train.

**81.** The perimeter of a triangle is 96 m. One side is twice as long as another, and the third side is 30 m long. What is the length of the longest side?

$P = a + b + c$

**82.** The perimeter of a certain square cannot be greater than 200 m. Find the possible values for the length of a side.

# CHAPTER 2 TEST

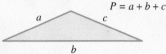

Step-by-step test solutions are found on the Chapter Test Prep Videos available via the Video Resources on DVD, in *MyMathLab*, or on YouTube (search "LialBeginningAlgebra").

*View the complete solutions to all Chapter Test exercises on the Video Resources on DVD.*

*Solve each equation.*

**1.** $5x + 9 = 7x + 21$

**2.** $-\dfrac{4}{7}x = -12$

**3.** $7 - (x - 4) = -3x + 2(x + 1)$

**4.** $0.6(x + 20) + 0.8(x - 10) = 46$

**5.** $-8(2x + 4) = -4(4x + 8)$

*Solve each problem.*

**6.** In the 2008 baseball season, the Los Angeles Angels of Anaheim won the most games of any major league team. The Angels won 24 less than twice as many games as they lost. They played 162 regular-season games. How many wins and losses did the Angels have? (*Source:* www.MLB.com)

**7.** Three islands in the Hawaiian island chain are Hawaii (the Big Island), Maui, and Kauai. Together, their areas total 5300 mi$^2$. The island of Hawaii is 3293 mi$^2$ larger than the island of Maui, and Maui is 177 mi$^2$ larger than Kauai. What is the area of each island?

**8.** Find the measure of an angle if its supplement measures 10° more than three times its complement.

**9.** The formula for the perimeter of a rectangle is $P = 2L + 2W$.

    **(a)** Solve for $W$.

    **(b)** If $P = 116$ and $L = 40$, find the value of $W$.

**10.** Find the measure of each marked angle.

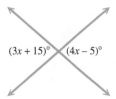

$(3x + 15)°$    $(4x - 5)°$

*Solve each equation.*

**11.** $\dfrac{z}{8} = \dfrac{12}{16}$

**12.** $\dfrac{x+5}{3} = \dfrac{x-3}{4}$

*Solve each problem.*

**13.** Find the best buy. Give the unit price to the nearest thousandth for that size.

PROCESSED
CHEESE SLICES

| Size | Price |
|------|-------|
| 8 oz | $2.79 |
| 16 oz | $4.99 |
| 32 oz | $7.99 |

**14.** The distance between Milwaukee and Boston is 1050 mi. On a certain map, this distance is represented by 42 in. On the same map, Seattle and Cincinnati are 92 in. apart. What is the actual distance between Seattle and Cincinnati?

**15.** Carlos Periu invested some money at 3% simple interest and $6000 more than that amount at 4.5% simple interest. After 1 yr, his total interest from the two accounts was $870. How much did he invest at each rate?

**16.** Two cars leave from the same point, traveling in opposite directions. One travels at a constant rate of 50 mph, while the other travels at a constant rate of 65 mph. How long will it take for them to be 460 mi apart?

*Solve each inequality. Write the solution set in interval notation, and graph it.*

**17.** $-4x + 2(x-3) \geq 4x - (3+5x) - 7$  **18.** $-10 < 3x - 4 \leq 14$

**19.** Susan Jacobson has grades of 76 and 81 on her first two algebra tests. If she wants an average of at least 80 after her third test, what score must she make on that test?

**20.** Write a short explanation of the additional (extra) rule that must be remembered when solving an inequality (as opposed to solving an equation).

## CHAPTERS 1–2  CUMULATIVE REVIEW EXERCISES

*Perform each indicated operation.*

**1.** $\dfrac{5}{6} + \dfrac{1}{4} - \dfrac{7}{15}$

**2.** $\dfrac{9}{8} \cdot \dfrac{16}{3} \div \dfrac{5}{8}$

*Translate from words to symbols. Use x as the variable.*

**3.** The difference between half a number and 18

**4.** The quotient of 6 and 12 more than a number is 2.

**5.** *True* or *false?* $\dfrac{8(7) - 5(6+2)}{3 \cdot 5 + 1} \geq 1$

*Perform each indicated operation.*

**6.** $\dfrac{-4(9)(-2)}{-3^2}$

**7.** $(-7 - 1)(-4) + (-4)$

**8.** Find the value of $\dfrac{3x^2 - y^3}{-4z}$ when $x = -2$, $y = -4$, and $z = 3$.

*Name each property illustrated.*

**9.** $7(p + q) = 7p + 7q$

**10.** $3 + (5 + 2) = 3 + (2 + 5)$

*Solve each equation, and check the solution.*

**11.** $2r - 6 = 8r$

**12.** $4 - 5(s + 2) = 3(s + 1) - 1$

**13.** $\dfrac{2}{3}x + \dfrac{3}{4}x = -17$

**14.** $\dfrac{2x + 3}{5} = \dfrac{x - 4}{2}$

**15.** Solve $3x + 4y = 24$ for $y$.

*Solve each inequality. Write the solution set in interval notation, and graph it.*

**16.** $6(r - 1) + 2(3r - 5) \le -4$

**17.** $-18 \le -9z < 9$

*Solve each problem.*

**18.** A 40-cm piece of yarn must be cut into three pieces. The longest piece is to be three times as long as the middle-sized piece, and the shortest piece is to be 5 cm shorter than the middle-sized piece. Find the length of each piece.

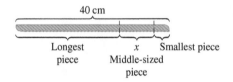

**19.** A fully inflated professional basketball has a circumference of 78 cm. What is the radius of a circular cross section through the center of the ball? (Use 3.14 as the approximation for $\pi$.) Round your answer to the nearest hundredth.

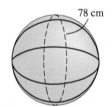

**20.** Two cars are 400 mi apart. Both start at the same time and travel toward one another. They meet 4 hr later. If the rate of one car is 20 mph faster than the other, what is the rate of each car?

# Linear Equations and Inequalities in Two Variables; Functions

In recent years, college students, like U.S. consumers as a whole, have increased their dependency on credit cards. In 2008, 84% of undergraduates had at least one credit card, up from 76% in 2004. The average (mean) outstanding balance for undergraduates grew from $946 in 2004 to a record-high $3173 in 2008, with 92% of these students using credit cards to pay direct education expenses. (*Source:* Sallie Mae.)

In **Example 7** of **Section 3.2,** we examine a *linear equation in two variables* that models credit card debt in the United States.

# Linear Equations in Two Variables; The Rectangular Coordinate System

3.1

**OBJECTIVE 1 Interpret graphs.** A line graph is used to show changes or trends in data over time. To form a **line graph,** we connect a series of points representing data with line segments.

**EXAMPLE 1** Interpreting a Line Graph

The line graph in **FIGURE 1** shows average prices of a gallon of regular unleaded gasoline in the United States for the years 2001 through 2008.

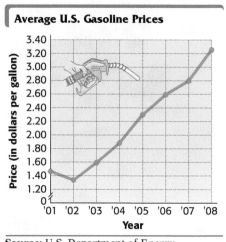

**Average U.S. Gasoline Prices**

*Source:* U.S. Department of Energy.

**FIGURE 1**

**NOW TRY EXERCISE 1**

Refer to the line graph in **FIGURE 1.**

**(a)** Estimate the average price of a gallon of gasoline in 2006.

**(b)** About how much did the average price of a gallon of gasoline increase from 2006 to 2008?

**(a)** Between which years did the average price of a gallon of gasoline decrease?

The line between 2001 and 2002 falls, so the average price of a gallon of gasoline decreased from 2001 to 2002.

**(b)** What was the general trend in the average price of a gallon of gasoline from 2002 through 2008?

The line graph rises from 2002 to 2008, so the average price of a gallon of gasoline increased over those years.

**(c)** Estimate the average price of a gallon of gasoline in 2002 and 2008. About how much did the price increase between 2002 and 2008?

Move up from 2002 on the horizontal scale to the point plotted for 2002. Looking across at the vertical scale, this point is about three-fourths of the way between the lines on the vertical scale for $1.20 and $1.40. Halfway between the lines for $1.20 and $1.40 would be $1.30. So, it cost about $1.35 for a gallon of gasoline in 2002.

Similarly, move up from 2008 on the horizontal scale to the point plotted for 2008. Then move across to the vertical scale. The price for a gallon of gasoline in 2008 was about $3.25.

Between 2002 and 2008, the average price of a gallon of gasoline increased by about

$$\$3.25 - \$1.35 = \$1.90.$$

*NOW TRY*

| Year | Average Price (in dollars per gallon) |
|------|------|
| 2001 | 1.46 |
| 2002 | 1.36 |
| 2003 | 1.59 |
| 2004 | 1.88 |
| 2005 | 2.30 |
| 2006 | 2.59 |
| 2007 | 2.80 |
| 2008 | 3.25 |

*Actual Data Source:* U.S. Department of Energy.

The line graph in **FIGURE 1** relates years to average prices for a gallon of gasoline. We can also represent these two related quantities using a table of data, as shown in the margin. In table form, we can see more precise data rather than estimating it. Trends in the data are easier to see from the graph, which gives a "picture" of the data.

We can extend these ideas to the subject of this chapter, *linear equations in two variables*. A linear equation in two variables, one for each of the quantities being related, can be used to represent the data in the table or graph. ***The graph of a linear equation in two variables is a line.***

### Linear Equation in Two Variables

A **linear equation in two variables** is an equation that can be written in the form

$$Ax + By = C,$$

where $A$, $B$, and $C$ are real numbers and $A$ and $B$ are not both 0.

Some examples of linear equations in two variables in this form, called *standard form,* are

$$3x + 4y = 9, \quad x - y = 0, \quad \text{and} \quad x + 2y = -8. \qquad \text{Linear equations in two variables}$$

**NOTE**  Other linear equations in two variables, such as

$$y = 4x + 5 \quad \text{and} \quad 3x = 7 - 2y,$$

are not written in standard form, but could be algebraically rewritten in this form. We discuss the forms of linear equations in more detail in **Section 3.4.**

**OBJECTIVE 2**  **Write a solution as an ordered pair.** Recall from **Section 1.3** that a *solution* of an equation is a number that makes the equation true when it replaces the variable. For example, the linear equation in *one* variable

$$x - 2 = 5$$

has solution 7, since replacing $x$ with 7 gives a true statement.

*A solution of a linear equation in* **two** *variables requires* **two** *numbers, one for each variable.* For example, a true statement results when we replace $x$ with 2 and $y$ with 13 in the equation $y = 4x + 5$, since

$$13 = 4(2) + 5. \qquad \text{Let } x = 2 \text{ and } y = 13.$$

The pair of numbers $x = 2$ and $y = 13$ gives a solution of the equation $y = 4x + 5$. The phrase "$x = 2$ and $y = 13$" is abbreviated

$$x\text{-value} \searrow \quad \swarrow y\text{-value}$$
$$(2, 13)$$
$$\text{Ordered pair}$$

with the $x$-value, 2, and the $y$-value, 13, given as a pair of numbers written inside parentheses. ***The x-value is always given first.*** A pair of numbers such as (2, 13) is called an **ordered pair.**

> ⚠ **CAUTION** The ordered pairs $(2, 13)$ and $(13, 2)$ are *not* the same. In the first pair, $x = 2$ and $y = 13$. In the second pair, $x = 13$ and $y = 2$. ***The order in which the numbers are written in an ordered pair is important.***

**OBJECTIVE 3** **Decide whether a given ordered pair is a solution of a given equation.** We substitute the $x$- and $y$-values of an ordered pair into a linear equation in two variables to see whether the ordered pair is a solution. An ordered pair that is a solution of an equation is said to *satisfy* the equation.

↻ NOW TRY
EXERCISE 2

Decide whether each ordered pair is a solution of the equation.

$$3x - 7y = 19$$

**(a)** $(3, 4)$  **(b)** $(-3, -4)$

**EXAMPLE 2** **Deciding Whether Ordered Pairs Are Solutions of an Equation**

Decide whether each ordered pair is a solution of the equation $2x + 3y = 12$.

**(a)** $(3, 2)$

Substitute 3 for $x$ and 2 for $y$ in the equation.

$$2x + 3y = 12$$
$$2(3) + 3(2) \stackrel{?}{=} 12 \quad \text{Let } x = 3 \text{ and } y = 2.$$
$$6 + 6 \stackrel{?}{=} 12 \quad \text{Multiply.}$$
$$12 = 12 \ \checkmark \ \text{True}$$

This result is true, so $(3, 2)$ is a solution of $2x + 3y = 12$.

**(b)** $(-2, -7)$

$$2x + 3y = 12$$
$$2(-2) + 3(-7) \stackrel{?}{=} 12 \quad \text{Let } x = -2 \text{ and } y = -7.$$

> Use parentheses to avoid errors.

$$-4 + (-21) \stackrel{?}{=} 12 \quad \text{Multiply.}$$
$$-25 = 12 \quad \text{False}$$

This result is false, so $(-2, -7)$ is *not* a solution of $2x + 3y = 12$.   NOW TRY ↻

**OBJECTIVE 4** **Complete ordered pairs for a given equation.** Substituting a number for one variable in a linear equation makes it possible to find the value of the other variable.

**EXAMPLE 3** **Completing Ordered Pairs**

Complete each ordered pair for the equation $y = 4x + 5$.

**(a)** $(7, \underline{\ \ })$

> The $x$-value always comes first.

In this ordered pair, $x = 7$. To find the corresponding value of $y$, replace $x$ with 7 in the equation.

$$y = 4x + 5$$
$$y = 4(7) + 5 \quad \text{Let } x = 7.$$
$$y = 28 + 5 \quad \text{Multiply.}$$
$$y = 33 \quad \text{Add.}$$

The ordered pair is $(7, 33)$.

**NOW TRY ANSWERS**
**2. (a)** no  **(b)** yes

*NOW TRY*
*EXERCISE 3*
Complete each ordered pair for the equation.

$$y = 3x - 12$$

**(a)** $(4, \_\_)$   **(b)** $(\_\_, 3)$

**(b)** $(\_\_, -3)$

In this ordered pair, $y = -3$. Find the corresponding value of $x$ by replacing $y$ with $-3$ in the equation.

$$y = 4x + 5$$

| | |
|---|---|
| $-3 = 4x + 5$ | Let $y = -3$. |
| $-8 = 4x$ | Subtract 5 from each side. |
| $-2 = x$ | Divide each side by 4. |

The ordered pair is $(-2, -3)$.                                    *NOW TRY*

**OBJECTIVE 5**  **Complete a table of values.** Ordered pairs are often displayed in a **table of values.** Although we usually write tables of values vertically, they may be written horizontally.

**EXAMPLE 4**   Completing Tables of Values

Complete the table of values for each equation. Write the results as ordered pairs.

**(a)** $x - 2y = 8$

| x | y |
|---|---|
| 2 | |
| 10 | |
| | 0 |
| | -2 |

To complete the first two ordered pairs, let $x = 2$ and $x = 10$, respectively, in the equation.

| | If | $x = 2,$ | | If | $x = 10,$ |
|---|---|---|---|---|---|
| | then | $x - 2y = 8$ | | then | $x - 2y = 8$ |
| | becomes | $2 - 2y = 8$ | | becomes | $10 - 2y = 8$ |
| | | $-2y = 6$ | | | $-2y = -2$ |
| | | $y = -3.$ | | | $y = 1.$ |

The first two ordered pairs are $(2, -3)$ and $(10, 1)$. Complete the last two ordered pairs by letting $y = 0$ and $y = -2$, respectively.

| | If | $y = 0,$ | | If | $y = -2,$ |
|---|---|---|---|---|---|
| | then | $x - 2y = 8$ | | then | $x - 2y = 8$ |
| | becomes | $x - 2(0) = 8$ | | becomes | $x - 2(-2) = 8$ |
| | | $x - 0 = 8$ | | | $x + 4 = 8$ |
| | | $x = 8.$ | | | $x = 4.$ |

The last two ordered pairs are $(8, 0)$ and $(4, -2)$. The completed table of values and corresponding ordered pairs follow.

| x | y | Ordered Pairs |
|---|---|---|
| 2 | -3 | $\longrightarrow$ (2, -3) |
| 10 | 1 | $\longrightarrow$ (10, 1) |
| 8 | 0 | $\longrightarrow$ (8, 0) |
| 4 | -2 | $\longrightarrow$ (4, -2) |

NOW TRY ANSWERS
**3. (a)** $(4, 0)$  **(b)** $(5, 3)$

Each ordered pair is a solution of the given equation $x - 2y = 8$.

*NOW TRY*
*EXERCISE 4*

Complete the table of values for the equation. Write the results as ordered pairs.

$$5x - 4y = 20$$

| x | y |
|---|---|
| 0 |   |
|   | 0 |
| 2 |   |

**(b)** $x = 5$

| x | y |
|---|----|
|   | -2 |
|   | 6  |
|   | 3  |

The given equation is $x = 5$. No matter which value of $y$ is chosen, the value of $x$ is always 5.

| x | y | | Ordered Pairs |
|---|----|---|---|
| 5 | -2 | ⟶ | $(5, -2)$ |
| 5 | 6  | ⟶ | $(5, 6)$ |
| 5 | 3  | ⟶ | $(5, 3)$ |

*NOW TRY*

---

**NOTE** We can think of $x = 5$ in **Example 4(b)** as an equation in two variables by rewriting $x = 5$ as $x + 0y = 5$. This form of the equation shows that, for any value of $y$, the value of $x$ is 5. Similarly, $y = 4$ can be written $0x + y = 4$.

---

**OBJECTIVE 6** **Plot ordered pairs.** In **Section 2.3**, we saw that linear equations in *one* variable had either one, zero, or an infinite number of real number solutions. These solutions could be graphed on *one* number line. For example, the linear equation in one variable $x - 2 = 5$ has solution 7, which is graphed on the number line in **FIGURE 2**.

$$\begin{array}{c} \text{number line from } 0 \text{ to } 7 \end{array}$$

**FIGURE 2**

Every linear equation in *two* variables has an infinite number of ordered pairs $(x, y)$ as solutions. To graph these solutions, we need *two* number lines, one for each variable, drawn at right angles as in **FIGURE 3**. The horizontal number line is called the **x-axis,** and the vertical line is called the **y-axis.** The point at which the $x$-axis and $y$-axis intersect is called the **origin.** Together, the $x$-axis and $y$-axis form a **rectangular coordinate system.**

The rectangular coordinate system is divided into four regions, called **quadrants.** These quadrants are numbered counterclockwise, as shown in **FIGURE 3**.

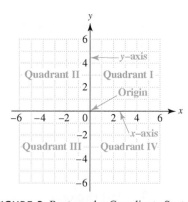

**René Descartes** (1596–1650)

The rectangular coordinate system is also called the **Cartesian coordinate system,** in honor of René Descartes, the French mathematician credited with its invention.

**FIGURE 3** Rectangular Coordinate System

The $x$-axis and $y$-axis determine a **plane**—a flat surface illustrated by a sheet of paper. By referring to the two axes, we can associate every point in the plane with an ordered pair. The numbers in the ordered pair are called the **coordinates** of the point.

*NOW TRY ANSWER*

4.

| x | y |
|---|----|
| 0 | -5 |
| 4 | 0  |
| 2 | $-\frac{5}{2}$ |

$(0, -5), (4, 0), \left(2, -\frac{5}{2}\right)$

**NOTE** In a plane, *both* numbers in the ordered pair are needed to locate a point. The ordered pair is a name for the point.

NOW TRY
EXERCISE 5

Plot the given points in a co-ordinate system.

$(-3, 1), (2, -4), (0, -1),$
$\left(\frac{5}{2}, 3\right), (-4, -3), (-4, 0)$

**EXAMPLE 5**   Plotting Ordered Pairs

Plot the given points in a coordinate system.

**(a)** $(2, 3)$ **(b)** $(-1, -4)$ **(c)** $(-2, 3)$ **(d)** $(3, -2)$ **(e)** $\left(\frac{3}{2}, 2\right)$

**(f)** $(4, -3.75)$ **(g)** $(5, 0)$ **(h)** $(0, -3)$ **(i)** $(0, 0)$

The point $(2, 3)$ from part (a) is **plotted** (graphed) in **FIGURE 4**. The other points are plotted in **FIGURE 5**.

In each case, begin at the origin. Move right or left the number of units that corresponds to the *x*-coordinate in the ordered pair—*right if the x-coordinate is positive or left if it is negative.* Then turn and move up or down the number of units that corresponds to the *y*-coordinate—*up if the y-coordinate is positive or down if it is negative.*

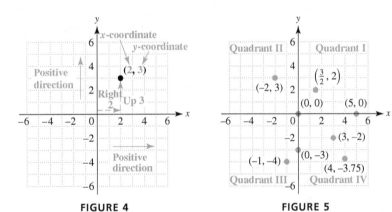

**FIGURE 4**             **FIGURE 5**

Notice the difference in the locations of the points $(-2, 3)$ and $(3, -2)$ in parts (c) and (d). The point $(-2, 3)$ is in quadrant II, whereas the point $(3, -2)$ is in quadrant IV. *The order of the coordinates is important. The x-coordinate is always given first in an ordered pair.*

To plot the point $\left(\frac{3}{2}, 2\right)$ in part (e), think of the improper fraction $\frac{3}{2}$ as the mixed number $1\frac{1}{2}$ and move $\frac{3}{2}$ $\left(\text{or } 1\frac{1}{2}\right)$ units to the right along the *x*-axis. Then turn and go 2 units up, parallel to the *y*-axis. The point $(4, -3.75)$ in part (f) is plotted similarly, by approximating the location of the decimal *y*-coordinate.

In part (g), the point $(5, 0)$ lies on the *x*-axis since the *y*-coordinate is 0. In part (h), the point $(0, -3)$ lies on the *y*-axis since the *x*-coordinate is 0. In part (i), the point $(0, 0)$ is at the origin. *Points on the axes themselves are not in any quadrant.*

NOW TRY

NOW TRY ANSWER
**5.**

Sometimes we can use a linear equation to mathematically describe, or *model,* a real-life situation, as shown in the next example.

NOW TRY
EXERCISE 6

Use the linear equation in **Example 6** to estimate the number of twin births in 2004. Interpret the results.

**EXAMPLE 6** Completing Ordered Pairs to Estimate the Number of Twin Births

The annual number of twin births in the United States from 2001 through 2006 can be closely approximated by the linear equation

Number of twin births ——↓          ↓—— Year

$$y = 3.049x - 5979.0,$$

which relates $x$, the year, and $y$, the number of twin births in thousands. (*Source:* Department of Health and Human Services.)

**(a)** Complete the table of values for the given linear equation.

| x (Year) | y (Number of Twin Births, in thousands) |
|----------|-----------------------------------------|
| 2001     |                                         |
| 2003     |                                         |
| 2006     |                                         |

To find $y$ when $x = 2001$, we substitute into the equation.

≈ means "is approximately equal to."

$$y = 3.049(2001) - 5979.0 \qquad \text{Let } x = 2001.$$
$$y \approx 122 \qquad \text{Use a calculator.}$$

This means that in 2001, there were about 122 thousand (or 122,000) twin births. We substitute the years 2003 and 2006 in the same way to complete the table.

| x (Year) | y (Number of Twin Births, in thousands) | Ordered Pairs (x, y) |
|----------|-----------------------------------------|----------------------|
| 2001     | 122                                     | ⟶ (2001, 122)        |
| 2003     | 128                                     | ⟶ (2003, 128)        |
| 2006     | 137                                     | ⟶ (2006, 137)        |

Here each year $x$ is paired with the number of twin births $y$ (in thousands).

**(b)** Graph the ordered pairs found in part (a).

The ordered pairs are graphed in **FIGURE 6**. This graph of ordered pairs of data is called a **scatter diagram.**

**NUMBER OF TWIN BIRTHS**

Notice the axes labels and scales. Each square represents 1 unit in the horizontal direction and 5 units in the vertical direction. Because the numbers in the first ordered pair are large, we show a break in the axes near the origin.

**FIGURE 6**

NOW TRY ANSWER
6. $y \approx 131$; There were approximately 131 thousand (or 131,000) twin births in the U.S. in 2004.

A scatter diagram enables us to tell whether two quantities are related to each other. In **FIGURE 6**, the plotted points could be connected to approximate a straight ***line,*** so the variables $x$ (year) and $y$ (number of twin births) have a ***linear*** relationship. The increase in the number of twin births is also reflected.

NOW TRY

⚠ CAUTION   The equation in **Example 6** is valid only for the years 2001 through 2006, because it was based on data for those years. ***Do not assume that this equation would provide reliable data for other years, since the data for those years may not follow the same pattern.***

---

## 3.1 EXERCISES

**MyMathLab**

🌐 *Complete solution available on the Video Resources on DVD*

*The line graph shows the overall unemployment rate in the U.S. civilian labor force in August of the years 2003 through 2009. Use the graph to work Exercises 1–4.* **See Example 1.**

**1.** Between which pairs of consecutive years did the unemployment rate decrease?

**2.** What was the general trend in the unemployment rate between 2007 and 2009?

**3.** Estimate the overall unemployment rate in 2003 and 2004. About how much did the unemployment rate decline between 2003 and 2004?

**4.** During which year(s)

(a) was the unemployment rate greater than 6%, but less than 7%?

(b) did the unemployment rate stay the same?

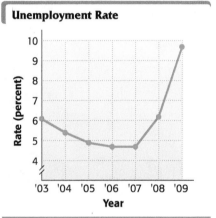

**Unemployment Rate**

*Source:* U.S. Bureau of Labor Statistics.

*Concept Check*   *Fill in each blank with the correct response.*

**5.** The symbol $(x, y)$ _____ represent an ordered pair, while the symbols $[x, y]$ and
(does/does not)

$\{x, y\}$ _____ represent ordered pairs.
(do/do not)

**6.** The ordered pair $(3, 2)$ is a solution of the equation $2x - 5y =$ _____.

**7.** The point whose graph has coordinates $(-4, 2)$ is in quadrant _____.

**8.** The point whose graph has coordinates $(0, 5)$ lies on the _____-axis.

**9.** The ordered pair $(4, \_\_)$ is a solution of the equation $y = 3$.

**10.** The ordered pair $(\_\_, -2)$ is a solution of the equation $x = 6$.

*Decide whether the given ordered pair is a solution of the given equation.* **See Example 2.**

🌐 **11.** $x + y = 8$;   $(0, 8)$     **12.** $x + y = 9$;   $(0, 9)$     **13.** $2x + y = 5$;   $(3, -1)$

**14.** $2x - y = 6$;   $(4, 2)$     **15.** $5x - 3y = 15$;   $(5, 2)$     **16.** $4x - 3y = 6$;   $(2, 1)$

**17.** $x = -4y$;   $(-8, 2)$     **18.** $y = 3x$;   $(2, 6)$     **19.** $y = 2$;   $(4, 2)$

**20.** $x = -6$;   $(-6, 5)$     **21.** $x - 6 = 0$;   $(4, 2)$     **22.** $x + 4 = 0$;   $(-6, 2)$

*Complete each ordered pair for the equation $y = 2x + 7$.* **See Example 3.**

🌐 **23.** $(5, \_\_)$      **24.** $(2, \_\_)$      **25.** $(\_\_, -3)$      **26.** $(\_\_, 0)$

*Complete each ordered pair for the equation $y = -4x - 4$.* **See Example 3.**

**27.** $(\_\_, 0)$      **28.** $(0, \_\_)$      **29.** $(\_\_, 24)$      **30.** $(\_\_, 16)$

*Complete each table of values. Write the results as ordered pairs.* **See Example 4.**

**31.** $4x + 3y = 24$

| x | y |
|---|---|
| 0 |   |
|   | 0 |
| 4 |   |

**32.** $2x + 3y = 12$

| x | y |
|---|---|
| 0 |   |
|   | 0 |
|   | 8 |

**33.** $4x - 9y = -36$

| x | y |
|---|---|
|   | 0 |
| 0 |   |
|   | 8 |

**34.** $3x - 5y = -15$

| x | y |
|---|---|
| 0 |   |
|   | 0 |
|   | -6 |

**35.** $x = 12$

| x | y |
|---|---|
|   | 3 |
|   | 8 |
|   | 0 |

**36.** $x = -9$

| x | y |
|---|---|
|   | 6 |
|   | 2 |
|   | -3 |

**37.** $y = -10$

| x | y |
|---|---|
| 4 |   |
| 0 |   |
| -4 |   |

**38.** $y = -6$

| x | y |
|---|---|
| 8 |   |
| 4 |   |
| -2 |   |

**39.** $y + 2 = 0$

| x | y |
|---|---|
| 9 |   |
| 2 |   |
| 0 |   |

**40.** $y + 6 = 0$

| x | y |
|---|---|
| 6 |   |
| 3 |   |
| 0 |   |

**41.** $x - 4 = 0$

| x | y |
|---|---|
|   | 4 |
|   | 0 |
|   | -4 |

**42.** $x - 8 = 0$

| x | y |
|---|---|
|   | 8 |
|   | 3 |
|   | 0 |

**43.** Do $(3, 4)$ and $(4, 3)$ correspond to the same point in the plane? Explain.

**44.** Do $(4, -1)$ and $(-1, 4)$ represent the same ordered pair? Explain.

**45.** Give the ordered pairs for the points labeled *A–F* in the figure. (All coordinates are integers.) Tell the quadrant in which each point is located. **See Example 5.**

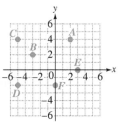

**46.** *Concept Check*  The origin is represented by the ordered pair _____.

*Plot and label each point in a rectangular coordinate system.* **See Example 5.**

**47.** $(6, 2)$     **48.** $(5, 3)$     **49.** $(-4, 2)$     **50.** $(-3, 5)$

**51.** $\left(-\dfrac{4}{5}, -1\right)$     **52.** $\left(-\dfrac{3}{2}, -4\right)$     **53.** $(3, -1.75)$     **54.** $(5, -4.25)$

**55.** $(0, 4)$     **56.** $(0, -3)$     **57.** $(4, 0)$     **58.** $(-3, 0)$

*Concept Check*  *Fill in each blank with the word* positive *or the word* negative.

The point with coordinates $(x, y)$ is in

**59.** quadrant III if $x$ is _____ and $y$ is _____.

**60.** quadrant II if $x$ is _____ and $y$ is _____.

**61.** quadrant IV if $x$ is _____ and $y$ is _____.

**62.** quadrant I if $x$ is _____ and $y$ is _____.

**63.** A point $(x, y)$ has the property that $xy < 0$. In which quadrant(s) must the point lie? Explain.

**64.** A point $(x, y)$ has the property that $xy > 0$. In which quadrant(s) must the point lie? Explain.

*Complete each table of values. Then plot and label the ordered pairs.* **See Examples 4 and 5.**

**65.** $x - 2y = 6$

| x | y |
|---|---|
| 0 |   |
|   | 0 |
| 2 |   |
|   | -1 |

**66.** $2x - y = 4$

| x | y |
|---|---|
| 0 |   |
|   | 0 |
| 1 |   |
|   | -6 |

**67.** $3x - 4y = 12$

| x | y |
|---|---|
| 0 |   |
|   | 0 |
| -4 |   |
|   | -4 |

**68.** $2x - 5y = 10$

| x | y |
|---|---|
| 0 | |
| | 0 |
| −5 | |
| | −3 |

**69.** $y + 4 = 0$

| x | y |
|---|---|
| 0 | |
| 5 | |
| −2 | |
| −3 | |

**70.** $x - 5 = 0$

| x | y |
|---|---|
| | 1 |
| | 0 |
| | 6 |
| | −4 |

**71.** Look at your graphs of the ordered pairs in **Exercises 65–70.** Describe the pattern indicated by the plotted points.

**72. (a)** A line through the plotted points in **Exercise 69** would be horizontal. What do you notice about the $y$-coordinates of the ordered pairs?

**(b)** A line through the plotted points in **Exercise 70** would be vertical. What do you notice about the $x$-coordinates of the ordered pairs?

*Solve each problem. **See Example 6.***

**73.** It costs a flat fee of $20 plus $5 per day to rent a pressure washer. Therefore, the cost to rent the pressure washer for $x$ days is given by

$$y = 5x + 20,$$

where $y$ is in dollars. Express each of the following as an ordered pair.

**(a)** When the washer is rented for 5 days, the cost is $45.

**(b)** I paid $50 when I returned the washer, so I must have rented it for 6 days.

**74.** Suppose that it costs $5000 to start up a business selling snow cones. Furthermore, it costs $0.50 per cone in labor, ice, syrup, and overhead. Then the cost to make $x$ snow cones is given by $y$ dollars, where

$$y = 0.50x + 5000.$$

Express each of the following as an ordered pair.

**(a)** When 100 snow cones are made, the cost is $5050.

**(b)** When the cost is $6000, the number of snow cones made is 2000.

**75.** The table shows the rate (in percent) at which 2-year college students (public) completed a degree within 3 years.

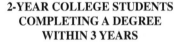

**2-YEAR COLLEGE STUDENTS COMPLETING A DEGREE WITHIN 3 YEARS**

| Year | Percent |
|------|---------|
| 2002 | 31.6 |
| 2003 | 30.1 |
| 2004 | 29.0 |
| 2005 | 27.5 |
| 2006 | 26.6 |
| 2007 | 26.9 |

*Source:* ACT.

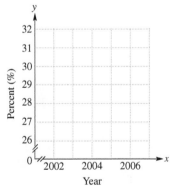

**(a)** Write the data from the table as ordered pairs $(x, y)$, where $x$ represents the year and $y$ represents the percent.

**(b)** What does the ordered pair $(2007, 26.9)$ mean in the context of this problem?

**(c)** Make a scatter diagram of the data, using the ordered pairs from part (a) and the given grid.

**(d)** Describe the pattern indicated by the points on the scatter diagram. What is happening to rates at which 2-year college students complete a degree within 3 years?

**76.** The table shows the number of U.S. students who studied abroad (in thousands) for several academic years.

| Academic Year | Number of Students (in thousands) |
|---|---|
| 2001 | 161 |
| 2002 | 175 |
| 2003 | 191 |
| 2004 | 206 |
| 2005 | 224 |
| 2006 | 242 |

*Source:* Institute of International Education.

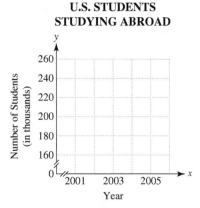

**U.S. STUDENTS STUDYING ABROAD**

**(a)** Write the data from the table as ordered pairs $(x, y)$, where $x$ represents the year and $y$ represents the number of U.S. students (in thousands) studying abroad.

**(b)** What does the ordered pair $(2006, 242)$ mean in the context of this problem?

**(c)** Make a scatter diagram of the data, using the ordered pairs from part (a) and the given grid.

**(d)** Describe the pattern indicated by the points on the scatter diagram. What was the trend in the number of U.S. students studying abroad during these years?

**77.** The maximum benefit for the heart from exercising occurs if the heart rate is in the target heart rate zone. The lower limit of this target zone can be approximated by the linear equation

$$y = -0.65x + 143,$$

where $x$ represents age and $y$ represents heartbeats per minute. (*Source: The Gazette.*)

| Age | Heartbeats (per minute) |
|---|---|
| 20 | |
| 40 | |
| 60 | |
| 80 | |

**(a)** Complete the table of values for this linear equation.

**(b)** Write the data from the table of values as ordered pairs.

**(c)** Make a scatter diagram of the data. Do the points lie in an approximately linear pattern?

**78.** (See **Exercise 77.**) The upper limit of the target heart rate zone can be approximated by the linear equation

$$y = -0.85x + 187,$$

where $x$ represents age and $y$ represents heartbeats per minute. (*Source: The Gazette.*)

| Age | Heartbeats (per minute) |
|---|---|
| 20 | |
| 40 | |
| 60 | |
| 80 | |

**(a)** Complete the table of values for this linear equation.

**(b)** Write the data from the table of values as ordered pairs.

**(c)** Make a scatter diagram of the data. Describe the pattern indicated by the data.

**79.** See **Exercises 77 and 78.** What is the target heart rate zone for age 20?    Age 40?

**80.** See **Exercises 77 and 78.** What is the target heart rate zone for age 60?    Age 80?

## PREVIEW EXERCISES

*Solve each equation.* ***See Section 2.3.***

**81.** $3x + 6 = 0$      **82.** $4 + 2x = 10$      **83.** $9 - x = -4$      **84.** $-5 + t = 3$

# Managing Your Time

Many college students juggle a difficult schedule and multiple responsibilities, including school, work, and family demands.

## Time Management Tips

▶ **Read the syllabus for each class.** Understand class policies, such as attendance, late homework, and make-up tests. Find out how you are graded.

▶ **Make a semester or quarter calendar.** Put test dates and major due dates for *all* your classes on the *same* calendar. Try using a different color pen for each class.

▶ **Make a weekly schedule.** After you fill in your classes and other regular responsibilities, block off some study periods. Aim for 2 hours of study for each 1 hour in class.

▶ **Choose a regular study time and place** (such as the campus library). Routine helps.

▶ **Make "to-do" lists.** Number tasks in order of importance. Cross off tasks as you complete them.

▶ **Break big assignments into smaller chunks.** Make deadlines for each smaller chunk so that you stay on schedule.

▶ **Take breaks when studying.** Do not try to study for hours at a time. Take a 10-minute break each hour or so.

▶ **Ask for help when you need it.** Talk with your instructor during office hours. Make use of the learning center, tutoring center, counseling office, or other resources available at your school.

*Select several tips to help manage your time this week.*

# Graphing Linear Equations in Two Variables

**OBJECTIVES**

1. Graph linear equations by plotting ordered pairs.
2. Find intercepts.
3. Graph linear equations of the form $Ax + By = 0$.
4. Graph linear equations of the form $y = k$ or $x = k$.
5. Use a linear equation to model data.

**OBJECTIVE 1    Graph linear equations by plotting ordered pairs.**  We know that infinitely many ordered pairs satisfy a linear equation in two variables. We find these ordered-pair solutions by choosing as many values of $x$ (or $y$) as we wish and then completing each ordered pair. For example, consider the equation

$$x + 2y = 7.$$

If we choose $x = 1$, then $y = 3$, so the ordered pair $(1, 3)$ is a solution.

$$1 + 2(3) = 7 \qquad \text{(1, 3) is a solution.}$$

This ordered pair and other solutions of $x + 2y = 7$ are graphed in **FIGURE 7**.

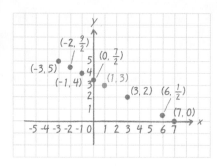

**FIGURE 7**                    **FIGURE 8**

Notice that the points plotted in **FIGURE 7** all appear to lie on a straight line, as shown in **FIGURE 8**. In fact, the following is true.

*Every point on the line represents a solution of the equation $x + 2y = 7$, and every solution of the equation corresponds to a point on the line.*

The line gives a "picture" of all the solutions of the equation $x + 2y = 7$. The line extends indefinitely in both directions, as suggested by the arrowhead on each end. The line is called the **graph** of the equation, and the process of plotting the ordered pairs and drawing the line through the corresponding points is called **graphing.**

**Graph of a Linear Equation**

The graph of any linear equation in two variables is a straight line.

Notice that the word *line* appears in the name "*line*ar equation."

**EXAMPLE 1    Graphing a Linear Equation**

Graph $4x - 5y = 20$.

At least two different points are needed to draw the graph. First let $x = 0$ and then let $y = 0$ in the equation to complete two ordered pairs.

| | | |
|---|---|---|
| $4x - 5y = 20$ | | $4x - 5y = 20$ | |
| $4(0) - 5y = 20$ | Let $x = 0$. | $4x - 5(0) = 20$ | Let $y = 0$. |
| $0 - 5y = 20$ | Multiply. | $4x - 0 = 20$ | Multiply. |
| $-5y = 20$ | Subtract. | $4x = 20$ | Subtract. |
| $y = -4$ | Divide by . | $x = 5$ | Divide by 4. |

NOW TRY
EXERCISE 1
Graph $2x - 4y = 8$.

Write each x-value first.

The ordered pairs are $(0, -4)$ and $(5, 0)$. We find a third ordered pair (as a check) by choosing some other number for $x$ or $y$. We choose $y = 2$.

$$4x - 5y = 20$$
$$4x - 5(2) = 20 \qquad \text{Let } y = 2.$$
$$4x - 10 = 20 \qquad \text{Multiply.}$$
$$4x = 30 \qquad \text{Add 10.}$$
$$x = \frac{30}{4}, \quad \text{or} \quad \frac{15}{2} \qquad \text{Divide by 4. Write in lowest terms.}$$

This gives the ordered pair $\left(\frac{15}{2}, 2\right)$, or $\left(7\frac{1}{2}, 2\right)$. We plot the three ordered pairs $(0, -4)$, $(5, 0)$, and $\left(7\frac{1}{2}, 2\right)$, and draw a line through them, as shown in **FIGURE 9**.

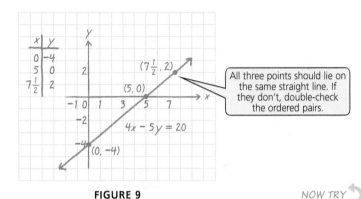

All three points should lie on the same straight line. If they don't, double-check the ordered pairs.

**FIGURE 9**

NOW TRY

**EXAMPLE 2** Graphing a Linear Equation

Graph $y = -\frac{3}{2}x + 3$.

Although this linear equation is not in standard form $(Ax + By = C)$, it *could* be written in that form. To find two different points on the graph, we first let $x = 0$ and then let $y = 0$.

$$y = -\frac{3}{2}x + 3 \qquad\qquad\qquad y = -\frac{3}{2}x + 3$$

$$y = -\frac{3}{2}(0) + 3 \quad \text{Let } x = 0. \qquad 0 = -\frac{3}{2}x + 3 \quad \text{Let } y = 0.$$

$$y = 0 + 3 \quad \text{Multiply.} \qquad \frac{3}{2}x = 3 \quad \text{Add } \frac{3}{2}x.$$

$$y = 3 \quad \text{Add.} \qquad x = 2 \quad \text{Multiply by } \frac{2}{3}.$$

This gives the ordered pairs $(0, 3)$ and $(2, 0)$. To find a third point, we let $x = -2$.

$$y = -\frac{3}{2}x + 3$$

Choosing a multiple of 2 makes multiplying by $-\frac{3}{2}$ easier.

$$y = -\frac{3}{2}(-2) + 3 \quad \text{Let } x = -2.$$

$$y = 3 + 3 \quad \text{Multiply.}$$

$$y = 6 \quad \text{Add.}$$

NOW TRY ANSWER
1.

NOW TRY
EXERCISE 2

Graph $y = \frac{1}{3}x + 1$.

This gives the ordered pair $(-2, 6)$. We plot the three ordered pairs and draw a line through them, as shown in **FIGURE 10**.

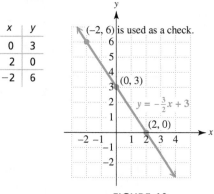

**FIGURE 10**

NOW TRY

**OBJECTIVE 2** **Find intercepts.** In **FIGURE 10**, the graph intersects (crosses) the $y$-axis at $(0, 3)$ and the $x$-axis at $(2, 0)$. For this reason, $(0, 3)$ is called the **$y$-intercept** and $(2, 0)$ is called the **$x$-intercept** of the graph. The intercepts are particularly useful for graphing linear equations.

### Finding Intercepts

To find the $x$-intercept, let $y = 0$ in the given equation and solve for $x$. Then $(x, 0)$ is the $x$-intercept.

To find the $y$-intercept, let $x = 0$ in the given equation and solve for $y$. Then $(0, y)$ is the $y$-intercept.

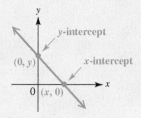

**EXAMPLE 3** Finding Intercepts

Find the intercepts for the graph of $2x + y = 4$. Then draw the graph.

To find the $y$-intercept, let $x = 0$.

$$2x + y = 4$$
$$2(0) + y = 4 \qquad \text{Let } x = 0.$$
$$0 + y = 4$$
$$y = 4 \qquad \text{$y$-intercept is } (0, 4).$$

To find the $x$-intercept, let $y = 0$.

$$2x + y = 4$$
$$2x + 0 = 4 \qquad \text{Let } y = 0.$$
$$2x = 4$$
$$x = 2 \qquad \text{$x$-intercept is } (2, 0).$$

The intercepts are $(0, 4)$ and $(2, 0)$. To find a third point, we let $x = 4$.

$$2x + y = 4$$
$$2(4) + y = 4 \qquad \text{Let } x = 4.$$
$$8 + y = 4 \qquad \text{Multiply.}$$
$$y = -4 \qquad \text{Subtract 8.}$$

NOW TRY ANSWER

2.

This gives the ordered pair $(4, -4)$. The graph, with the two intercepts in red, is shown in **FIGURE 11** on the next page.

NOW TRY
EXERCISE 3
Find the intercepts for the
graph of $x + 2y = 2$. Then
draw the graph.

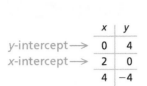

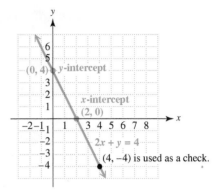

**FIGURE 11**

NOW TRY

---

⚠ **CAUTION** *When choosing x- or y-values to find ordered pairs to plot, be careful to choose so that the resulting points are not too close together.* For example, using $(-1, -1)$, $(0, 0)$, and $(1, 1)$ to graph $x - y = 0$ may result in an inaccurate line. It is better to choose points whose x-values differ by at least 2.

---

**OBJECTIVE 3** **Graph linear equations of the form Ax + By = 0.**

NOW TRY
EXERCISE 4
Graph $2x + y = 0$.

**EXAMPLE 4** Graphing an Equation with x- and y-Intercepts (0, 0)

Graph $x - 3y = 0$.

| To find the y-intercept, let $x = 0$. | To find the x-intercept, let $y = 0$. |
|---|---|
| $x - 3y = 0$ | $x - 3y = 0$ |
| $0 - 3y = 0$    Let $x = 0$. | $x - 3(0) = 0$    Let $y = 0$. |
| $-3y = 0$ | $x - 0 = 0$ |
| $y = 0$    y-intercept is $(0, 0)$. | $x = 0$    x-intercept is $(0, 0)$. |

The x- and y-intercepts are the *same* point, $(0, 0)$. We must select *two other values* for x or y to find two other points on the graph. We choose $x = 6$ and $x = -6$.

| | |
|---|---|
| $x - 3y = 0$ | $x - 3y = 0$ |
| $6 - 3y = 0$    Let $x = 6$. | $-6 - 3y = 0$    Let $x = -6$. |
| $-3y = -6$ | $-3y = 6$ |
| $y = 2$    Gives $(6, 2)$ | $y = -2$    Gives $(-6, -2)$ |

We use the ordered pairs $(-6, -2)$, $(0, 0)$, and $(6, 2)$ to draw the graph in **FIGURE 12**.

NOW TRY ANSWERS
3. x-intercept: $(2, 0)$;
   y-intercept: $(0, 1)$

4.

| x | y |
|---|---|
| 0 | 0 |
| 6 | 2 |
| -6 | -2 |

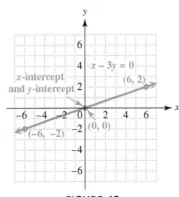

**FIGURE 12**

NOW TRY

### Line through the Origin

If $A$ and $B$ are nonzero real numbers, the graph of a linear equation of the form

$$Ax + By = 0$$

passes through the origin $(0, 0)$.

**OBJECTIVE 4** Graph linear equations of the form $y = k$ or $x = k$. Consider the following linear equations:

$$y = -4, \quad \text{which can be written} \quad 0x + y = -4;$$

$$x = 3, \quad \text{which can be written} \quad x + 0y = 3.$$

When the coefficient of $x$ or $y$ is 0, the graph of the linear equation is a horizontal or vertical line.

NOW TRY
EXERCISE 5
Graph $y = 2$.

**EXAMPLE 5** Graphing an Equation of the Form $y = k$ (Horizontal Line)

Graph $y = -4$.

For any value of $x$, $y$ is always equal to $-4$. Three ordered pairs that satisfy the equation are shown in the table of values. Drawing a line through these points gives the **horizontal line** shown in **FIGURE 13**. The $y$-intercept is $(0, -4)$. There is no $x$-intercept.

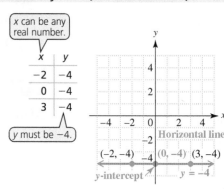

**FIGURE 13**

NOW TRY

### Horizontal Line

The graph of the linear equation $y = k$, where $k$ is a real number, is the horizontal line with $y$-intercept $(0, k)$. There is no $x$-intercept (unless the horizontal line is the $x$-axis itself).

NOW TRY
EXERCISE 6
Graph $x + 4 = 0$.

**5.**

**6.**

**EXAMPLE 6** Graphing an Equation of the Form $x = k$ (Vertical Line)

Graph $x - 3 = 0$.

First we add 3 to each side of the equation $x - 3 = 0$ to get $x = 3$. All ordered-pair solutions of this equation have $x$-coordinate 3. Any number can be used for $y$. We show three ordered pairs that satisfy the equation in the table of values. The graph is the **vertical line** shown in **FIGURE 14**. The $x$-intercept is $(3, 0)$. There is no $y$-intercept.

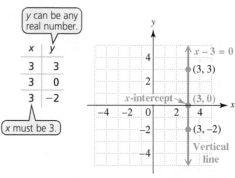

**FIGURE 14**

NOW TRY

| Vertical Line |
|---|

The graph of the linear equation $x = k$, where $k$ is a real number, is the vertical line with $x$-intercept $(k, 0)$. There is no $y$-intercept (unless the vertical line is the $y$-axis itself).

*The equation of the x-axis is the horizontal line $y = 0$, and the equation of the y-axis is the vertical line $x = 0$.*

⚠ CAUTION   The equations of horizontal and vertical lines are often confused with each other. Remember that the graph of $y = k$ is parallel to the $x$-axis and the graph of $x = k$ is parallel to the $y$-axis (for $k \neq 0$).

A summary of the forms of linear equations from this section follows.

| Graphing a Linear Equation | | |
|---|---|---|
| *Equation* | *To Graph* | *Example* |
| $y = k$ | Draw a horizontal line, through $(0, k)$. | $y = -2$ |
| $x = k$ | Draw a vertical line, through $(k, 0)$. | $x = 4$ |
| $Ax + By = 0$ | The graph passes through $(0, 0)$. To find additional points that lie on the graph, choose any value for $x$ or $y$, except 0. | $x = 2y$ |
| $Ax + By = C$ (but not of the types above) | Find any two points on the line. A good choice is to find the intercepts. Let $x = 0$, and find the corresponding value of $y$. Then let $y = 0$, and find $x$. <br><br> As a check, get a third point by choosing a value for $x$ or $y$ that has not yet been used. | $(4, 3)$ $(2, 0)$ $3x - 2y = 6$ $(0, -3)$ |

**OBJECTIVE 5** Use a linear equation to model data.

*NOW TRY*
*EXERCISE 7*
Use **(a)** the graph and **(b)** the equation in **Example 7** to approximate credit card debt in 2006.

**EXAMPLE 7** Using a Linear Equation to Model Credit Card Debt

Credit card debt in the United States increased steadily from 2000 through 2008. The amount of debt $y$ in billions of dollars can be modeled by the linear equation

$$y = 32.0x + 684,$$

where $x = 0$ represents 2000, $x = 1$ represents 2001, and so on. (*Source: The Nilson Report.*)

**(a)** Use the equation to approximate credit card debt in the years 2000, 2004, and 2008.

For 2000: $y = 32.0(0) + 684$     Replace $x$ with 0.

              $y = 684$ billion dollars

For 2004: $y = 32.0(4) + 684$     $2004 - 2000 = 4$

              $y = 812$ billion dollars    Replace $x$ with 4.

For 2008: $y = 32.0(8) + 684$     $2008 - 2000 = 8$

              $y = 940$ billion dollars    Replace $x$ with 8.

**(b)** Write the information from part (a) as three ordered pairs, and use them to graph the given linear equation.

Since $x$ represents the year and $y$ represents the debt, the ordered pairs are

$$(0, 684), \quad (4, 812), \quad \text{and} \quad (8, 940).$$

See **FIGURE 15**. (Arrowheads are not included with the graphed line, since the data are for the years 2000 to 2008 only—that is, from $x = 0$ to $x = 8$.)

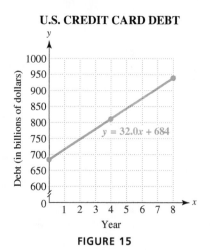

**U.S. CREDIT CARD DEBT**

$y = 32.0x + 684$

**FIGURE 15**

**(c)** Use the graph and then the equation to approximate credit card debt in 2002.

For 2002, $x = 2$. On the graph, find 2 on the horizontal axis, move up to the graphed line and then across to the vertical axis. It appears that credit card debt in 2002 was about 750 billion dollars. To use the equation, substitute 2 for $x$.

$y = 32.0x + 684$     Given linear equation

$y = 32.0(2) + 684$     Let $x = 2$.

$y = 748$ billion dollars     Multiply, and then add.

This result for 2002 is close to our estimate of 750 billion dollars from the graph.

*NOW TRY ANSWERS*
**7. (a)** about 875 billion dollars
    **(b)** 876 billion dollars

*NOW TRY*

**FIGURE 16**

## CONNECTIONS

Among the basic features of graphing calculators is their ability to graph equations. We must solve the equation for $y$ in order to enter it into the calculator. Also, we must select a "window" for the graph, determined by the minimum and maximum values of $x$ and $y$. The *standard window* is from $x = -10$ to $x = 10$ and from $y = -10$ to $y = 10$, written $[-10, 10]$, $[-10, 10]$, with the $x$-interval first.

To graph $2x + y = 4$, discussed in **Example 3**, we first solve for $y$.

$$y = -2x + 4 \qquad \text{Subtract } 2x.$$

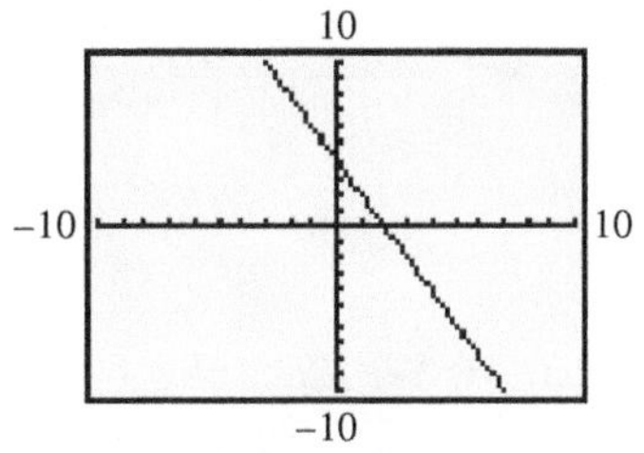

We enter this equation into the calculator and choose the standard window to get the graph in **FIGURE 16**. The line intersects the $x$-axis at $(2, 0)$, indicating that 2 is the solution of the equation

$$-2x + 4 = 0.$$

**For Discussion or Writing**

Rewrite each equation with the left side equal to 0, the form required for a graphing calculator. (It is not necessary to clear parentheses or combine like terms.)

**1.** $3x + 4 - 2x - 7 = 4x + 3$      **2.** $5x - 15 = 3(x - 2)$

---

## 3.2 EXERCISES

**MyMathLab**    Math XL PRACTICE    WATCH    DOWNLOAD    READ    REVIEW

*Complete solution available on the Video Resources on DVD*

*Use the given equation to complete the given ordered pairs. Then graph each equation by plotting the points and drawing a line through them. **See Examples 1 and 2.***

**1.** $x + y = 5$
$(0, \_\_), (\_\_, 0), (2, \_\_)$

**2.** $x - y = 2$
$(0, \_\_), (\_\_, 0), (5, \_\_)$

**3.** $y = \dfrac{2}{3}x + 1$
$(0, \_\_), (3, \_\_), (-3, \_\_)$

**4.** $y = -\dfrac{3}{4}x + 2$
$(0, \_\_), (4, \_\_), (-4, \_\_)$

**5.** $3x = -y - 6$
$(0, \_\_), (\_\_, 0), \left(-\dfrac{1}{3}, \_\_\right)$

**6.** $x = 2y + 3$
$(\_\_, 0), (0, \_\_), \left(\_\_, \dfrac{1}{2}\right)$

**7.** *Concept Check*   Match the information about each graph in Column I with the correct linear equation in Column II.

| **I** | **II** |
| --- | --- |
| **(a)** The graph of the equation has $y$-intercept $(0, -4)$. | **A.** $3x + y = -4$ |
| **(b)** The graph of the equation has $(0, 0)$ as $x$-intercept and $y$-intercept. | **B.** $x - 4 = 0$ |
| **(c)** The graph of the equation does not have an $x$-intercept. | **C.** $y = 4x$ |
| **(d)** The graph of the equation has $x$-intercept $(4, 0)$. | **D.** $y = 4$ |

**8.** *Concept Check*   Which of these equations have a graph with only one intercept?

    **A.** $x + 8 = 0$      **B.** $x - y = 3$      **C.** $x + y = 0$      **D.** $y = 4$

*Concept Check* *Find the intercepts of each graph. (All coordinates are integers.)*

9.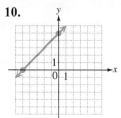

10.

11.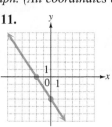

12.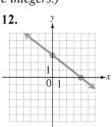

*Find the x-intercept and the y-intercept for the graph of each equation.* **See Examples 1–6.**

13. $x - y = 8$
14. $x - y = 7$
15. $5x - 2y = 20$
16. $-3x + 2y = 12$

17. $x + 6y = 0$
18. $3x + y = 0$
19. $y = -2x + 4$
20. $y = 3x + 6$

21. $y = \dfrac{1}{3}x - 2$
22. $y = \dfrac{1}{4}x - 1$
23. $2x - 3y = 0$
24. $4x - 5y = 0$

25. $x - 4 = 0$
26. $x - 5 = 0$
27. $y = 2.5$
28. $y = -1.5$

29. *Concept Check* Match each equation in (a)–(d) with its graph in A–D.

   **(a)** $x = -2$    **(b)** $y = -2$    **(c)** $x = 2$    **(d)** $y = 2$

   **A.** 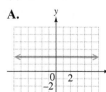    **B.** 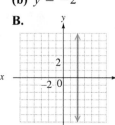    **C.** 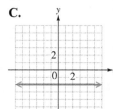    **D.**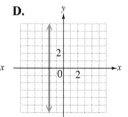

30. *Concept Check* What is the equation of the *x*-axis? What is the equation of the *y*-axis?

*Graph each linear equation.* **See Examples 1–6.**

31. $x = y + 2$
32. $x = -y + 6$
33. $x - y = 4$

34. $x - y = 5$
35. $2x + y = 6$
36. $-3x + y = -6$

37. $y = 2x - 5$
38. $y = 4x + 3$
39. $3x + 7y = 14$

40. $6x - 5y = 18$
41. $y = -\dfrac{3}{4}x + 3$
42. $y = -\dfrac{2}{3}x - 2$

43. $y - 2x = 0$
44. $y + 3x = 0$
45. $y = -6x$

46. $y = 4x$
47. $y = -1$
48. $y = 3$

49. $x + 2 = 0$
50. $x - 4 = 0$
51. $-3y = 15$

52. $-2y = 12$
53. $x + 2 = 8$
54. $x - 1 = -4$

*Concept Check* *In Exercises 55–62, describe what the graph of each linear equation will look like in the coordinate plane. (Hint: Rewrite the equation if necessary so that it is in a more recognizable form.)*

55. $3x = y - 9$
56. $2x = y - 4$
57. $x - 10 = 1$
58. $x + 4 = 3$

59. $3y = -6$
60. $5y = -15$
61. $2x = 4y$
62. $3x = 9y$

*Concept Check* *Plot each set of points, and draw a line through them. Then give the equation of the line.*

63. $(3, 5)$, $(3, 0)$, and $(3, -3)$

64. $(1, 3)$, $(1, 0)$, and $(1, -1)$

65. $(-3, -3)$, $(0, -3)$, and $(4, -3)$

66. $(-5, 5)$, $(0, 5)$, and $(3, 5)$

*Solve each problem.* ***See Example 7.***

**67.** The weight $y$ (in pounds) of a man taller than 60 in. can be approximated by the linear equation

$$y = 5.5x - 220,$$

where $x$ is the height of the man in inches.

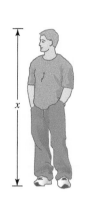

**(a)** Use the equation to approximate the weights of men whose heights are 62 in., 66 in., and 72 in.

**(b)** Write the information from part (a) as three ordered pairs.

**(c)** Graph the equation, using the data from part (b).

**(d)** Use the graph to estimate the height of a man who weighs 155 lb. Then use the equation to find the height of this man to the nearest inch.

**68.** The height $y$ (in centimeters) of a woman is related to the length of her radius bone $x$ (from the wrist to the elbow) and is approximated by the linear equation

$$y = 3.9x + 73.5.$$

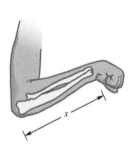

**(a)** Use the equation to approximate the heights of women with radius bone of lengths 20 cm, 26 cm, and 22 cm.

**(b)** Write the information from part (a) as three ordered pairs.

**(c)** Graph the equation, using the data from part (b).

**(d)** Use the graph to estimate the length of the radius bone in a woman who is 167 cm tall. Then use the equation to find the length of the radius bone to the nearest centimeter.

**69.** As a fundraiser, a club is selling posters. The printer charges a $25 set-up fee, plus $0.75 for each poster. The cost $y$ in dollars to print $x$ posters is given by

$$y = 0.75x + 25.$$

**(a)** What is the cost $y$ in dollars to print 50 posters?   To print 100 posters?

**(b)** Find the number of posters $x$ if the printer billed the club for costs of $175.

**(c)** Write the information from parts (a) and (b) as three ordered pairs.

**(d)** Use the data from part (c) to graph the equation.

**70.** A gas station is selling gasoline for $3.50 per gallon and charges $7 for a car wash. The cost $y$ in dollars for $x$ gallons of gasoline and a car wash is given by

$$y = 3.50x + 7.$$

**(a)** What is the cost $y$ in dollars for 9 gallons of gasoline and a car wash?   For 4 gallons of gasoline and a car wash?

**(b)** Find the number of gallons of gasoline $x$ if the cost for gasoline and a car wash is $35.

**(c)** Write the information from parts (a) and (b) as three ordered pairs.

**(d)** Use the data from part (c) to graph the equation.

**71.** The graph shows the value of a sport-utility vehicle (SUV) over the first 5 yr of ownership. Use the graph to do the following.

**(a)** Determine the initial value of the SUV.

**(b)** Find the **depreciation** (loss in value) from the original value after the first 3 yr.

**(c)** What is the annual or yearly depreciation in each of the first 5 yr?

**(d)** What does the ordered pair (5, 5000) mean in the context of this problem?

**72.** Demand for an item is often closely related to its price. As price increases, demand decreases, and as price decreases, demand increases. Suppose demand for a video game is 2000 units when the price is $40 and is 2500 units when the price is $30.

(a) Let $x$ be the price and $y$ be the demand for the game. Graph the two given pairs of prices and demands.

(b) Assume that the relationship is linear. Draw a line through the two points from part (a). From your graph, estimate the demand if the price drops to $20.

(c) Use the graph to estimate the price if the demand is 3500 units.

**73.** In the United States, sporting goods sales $y$ (in billions of dollars) from 2000 through 2006 are shown in the graph and modeled by the linear equation

$$y = 3.018x + 72.52,$$

where $x = 0$ corresponds to 2000, $x = 1$ corresponds to 2001, and so on.

**Sporting Goods Sales**

*Source:* National Sporting Goods Association.

(a) Use the equation to approximate sporting goods sales in 2000, 2004, and 2006. Round your answers to the nearest billion dollars.

(b) Use the graph to estimate sales for the same years.

(c) How do the approximations using the equation compare with the estimates from the graph?

**74.** U.S. per capita consumption of cheese increased for the years 1980 through 2005 as shown in the graph. If $x = 0$ represents 1980, $x = 5$ represents 1985, and so on, per capita consumption $y$ in pounds can be modeled by the linear equation

$$y = 0.5383x + 18.74.$$

(a) Use the equation to approximate cheese consumption (to the nearest tenth) in 1990, 2000, and 2005.

(b) Use the graph to estimate consumption for the same years.

(c) How do the approximations using the equation compare with the estimates from the graph?

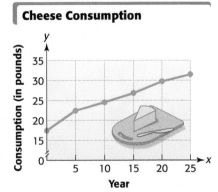

**Cheese Consumption**

*Source:* U.S. Department of Agriculture.

*Find each quotient.* ***See Section 1.8.***

**75.** $\dfrac{4-2}{8-5}$ **76.** $\dfrac{-3-5}{2-7}$ **77.** $\dfrac{-2-(-4)}{3-(-1)}$ **78.** $\dfrac{5-(-7)}{-4-(-1)}$

## 3.3 The Slope of a Line

**OBJECTIVES**

1 Find the slope of a line, given two points.

2 Find the slope from the equation of a line.

3 Use slopes to determine whether two lines are parallel, perpendicular, or neither.

An important characteristic of the lines we graphed in **Section 3.2** is their slant, or "steepness." See **FIGURE 17**.

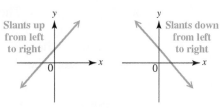

**FIGURE 17**

One way to measure the steepness of a line is to compare the vertical change in the line with the horizontal change while moving along the line from one fixed point to another. This measure of steepness is called the *slope* of the line.

**OBJECTIVE 1** **Find the slope of a line, given two points.** To find the steepness, or slope, of the line in **FIGURE 18**, we begin at point $Q$ and move to point $P$. The vertical change, or **rise,** is the change in the $y$-values, which is the difference

$$6 - 1 = 5 \text{ units.}$$

The horizontal change, or **run,** is the change in the $x$-values, which is the difference

$$5 - 2 = 3 \text{ units.}$$

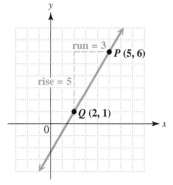

**FIGURE 18**

Remember from **Section 2.6** that one way to compare two numbers is by using a ratio. **Slope** is the ratio of the vertical change in $y$ to the horizontal change in $x$. The line in **FIGURE 18** has

$$\text{slope} = \frac{\text{vertical change in } y \text{ (rise)}}{\text{horizontal change in } x \text{ (run)}} = \frac{5}{3}.$$

To confirm this ratio, we can count grid squares. We start at point $Q$ in **FIGURE 18** and count *up* 5 grid squares to find the vertical change (rise). To find the horizontal change (run) and arrive at point $P$, we count to the *right* 3 grid squares. The slope is $\frac{5}{3}$, as found analytically.

We can summarize this discussion as follows.

*Slope is a single number that allows us to determine the direction in which a line is slanting from left to right, as well as how much slant there is to the line.*

NOW TRY
EXERCISE 1

Find the slope of the line.

### EXAMPLE 1   Finding the Slope of a Line

Find the slope of the line in **FIGURE 19**.

We use the two points shown on the line. The vertical change is the difference in the *y*-values, or $-1 - 3 = -4$, and the horizontal change is the difference in the *x*-values, or $6 - 2 = 4$. Thus, the line has

$$\text{slope} = \frac{\text{change in } y \text{ (rise)}}{\text{change in } x \text{ (run)}} = \frac{-4}{4}, \quad \text{or} \quad -1.$$

Counting grid squares, we begin at point *P* and count *down* 4 grid squares. Then we count to the *right* 4 grid squares to reach point *Q*. Because we counted down, we write the vertical change as a negative number, $-4$ here. The slope is $\frac{-4}{4}$, or $-1$.

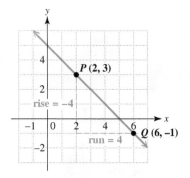

**FIGURE 19**

NOW TRY

**NOTE** *The slope of a line is the same for any two points on the line.* To see this, refer to **FIGURE 19**. Find the points $(3, 2)$ and $(5, 0)$ on the line. If we start at $(3, 2)$ and count *down* 2 units and then to the *right* 2 units, we arrive at $(5, 0)$. The slope is $\frac{-2}{2}$, or $-1$, the same slope we found in **Example 1.**

The idea of slope is used in many everyday situations. See **FIGURE 20**. A highway with a 10%, or $\frac{1}{10}$, grade (or slope) rises 1 m for every 10 m horizontally. Architects specify the pitch of a roof by using slope. A $\frac{5}{12}$ roof means that the roof rises 5 ft for every 12 ft that it runs horizontally. The slope of a stairwell indicates the ratio of the vertical rise to the horizontal run. The slope of the stairwell is $\frac{8}{12}$, or $\frac{2}{3}$.

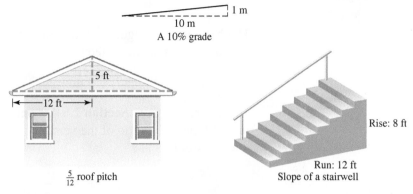

**FIGURE 20**

We can generalize the preceding discussion and find the slope of a line through two nonspecific points $(x_1, y_1)$ and $(x_2, y_2)$. (This notation is called **subscript notation.** Read $x_1$ as "*x*-sub-one" and $x_2$ as "*x*-sub-two.") See **FIGURE 21** on the next page.

NOW TRY ANSWER
1. 3

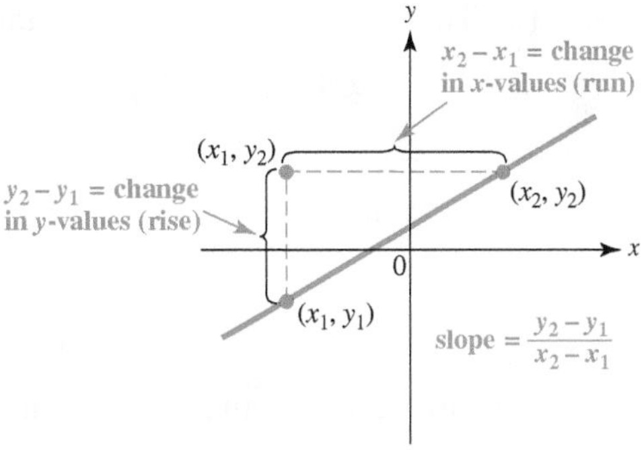

$y$

$x_2 - x_1$ = change
in $x$-values (run)

$(x_1, y_2)$

$y_2 - y_1$ = change
in $y$-values (rise)

$(x_2, y_2)$

0

$x$

$(x_1, y_1)$

slope = $\dfrac{y_2 - y_1}{x_2 - x_1}$

**FIGURE 21**

Moving along the line from the point $(x_1, y_1)$ to the point $(x_2, y_2)$, we see that $y$ changes by $y_2 - y_1$ units. This is the vertical change (rise). Similarly, $x$ changes by $x_2 - x_1$ units, which is the horizontal change (run). The slope of the line is the ratio of $y_2 - y_1$ to $x_2 - x_1$.

**NOTE**  Subscript notation is used to identify a point. It does *not* indicate any operation. Note the difference between $x_2$, a nonspecific value, and $x^2$, which means $x \cdot x$. Read $x_2$ as "$x$-sub-two," *not* "$x$ squared."

### Slope Formula

The **slope $m$** of the line through the points $(x_1, y_1)$ and $(x_2, y_2)$ is

$$m = \frac{\textbf{change in } y}{\textbf{change in } x} = \frac{y_2 - y_1}{x_2 - x_1} \qquad (\text{where } x_1 \neq x_2).$$

*The slope gives the change in y for each unit of change in x.*

### EXAMPLE 2   Finding Slopes of Lines

Find the slope of each line.

**(a)** The line through $(-4, 7)$ and $(1, -2)$

Use the slope formula. Let $(-4, 7) = (x_1, y_1)$ and $(1, -2) = (x_2, y_2)$.

$$\text{slope } m = \frac{\text{change in } y}{\text{change in } x} = \frac{y_2 - y_1}{x_2 - x_1} = \frac{-2 - 7}{1 - (-4)} = \frac{-9}{5} = -\frac{9}{5}$$

Substitute carefully here.

Begin at $(-4, 7)$ and count grid squares in **FIGURE 22** to confirm your calculation.

What happens if we let $(1, -2) = (x_1, y_1)$ and $(-4, 7) = (x_2, y_2)$?

$$\text{slope } m = \frac{y_2 - y_1}{x_2 - x_1} = \frac{7 - (-2)}{-4 - 1} = \frac{9}{-5} = -\frac{9}{5}$$

The same slope is obtained.

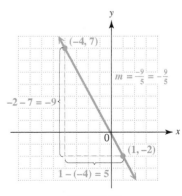

$y$

$(-4, 7)$

$m = \dfrac{-9}{5} = -\dfrac{9}{5}$

$-2 - 7 = -9$

0

$x$

$(1, -2)$

$1 - (-4) = 5$

**FIGURE 22**

NOW TRY
EXERCISE 2

Find the slope of the line
through $(4, -5)$ and
$(-2, -4)$.

**(b)** The line through $(-9, -2)$ and $(12, 5)$

y-value
↓
$$m = \frac{5 - (-2)}{12 - (-9)} = \frac{7}{21} = \frac{1}{3}$$
↑
Corresponding x-value

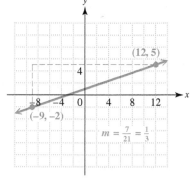

**FIGURE 23**

See **FIGURE 23**. Again, note that the same slope is
obtained by subtracting in reverse order.

y-value
↓
$$m = \frac{-2 - 5}{-9 - 12} = \frac{-7}{-21} = \frac{1}{3}$$
↑
Corresponding x-value

NOW TRY

---

⚠ **CAUTION** *It makes no difference which point is $(x_1, y_1)$ or $(x_2, y_2)$. Be
consistent, however.* Start with the $x$- and $y$-values of one point (either one), and
subtract the corresponding values of the other point.

---

The slopes we found for the lines in **FIGURES 22** and **23** suggest the following.

**Orientation of Lines with Positive and Negative Slopes**

A line with positive slope rises (slants up) from left to right.

A line with negative slope falls (slants down) from left to right.

NOW TRY
EXERCISE 3

Find the slope of the line
through $(1, -3)$ and $(4, -3)$.

**EXAMPLE 3** Finding the Slope of a Horizontal Line

Find the slope of the line through $(-5, 4)$ and $(2, 4)$.

$$m = \frac{4 - 4}{-5 - 2} = \frac{0}{-7} = 0 \quad \text{Slope 0}$$

As shown in **FIGURE 24**, the line through these two points is horizontal, with equation
$y = 4$. *All horizontal lines have slope 0,* since the difference in $y$-values is 0.

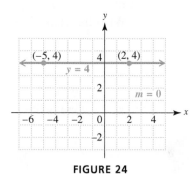

**FIGURE 24**

NOW TRY ANSWERS
2. $-\frac{1}{6}$
3. 0

NOW TRY

NOW TRY
EXERCISE 4
Find the slope of the line
through $(-2, 1)$ and
$(-2, -4)$.

EXAMPLE 4   Finding the Slope of a Vertical Line

Find the slope of the line through $(6, 2)$ and $(6, -4)$.

$$m = \frac{2 - (-4)}{6 - 6} = \frac{6}{0} \quad \text{Undefined slope}$$

Since division by 0 is undefined, the slope is undefined. The graph in **FIGURE 25** shows that the line through the given two points is vertical with equation $x = 6$. All points on a vertical line have the same $x$-value, so *the slope of any vertical line is undefined.*

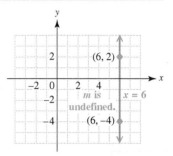

**FIGURE 25**

NOW TRY

**Slopes of Horizontal and Vertical Lines**

**Horizontal lines,** with equations of the form $y = k$, have **slope 0.**

**Vertical lines,** with equations of the form $x = k$, have **undefined slope.**

**FIGURE 26** summarizes the four cases for slopes of lines.

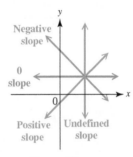

Slopes of lines
**FIGURE 26**

**OBJECTIVE 2   Find the slope from the equation of a line.** Consider this linear equation.

$$y = -3x + 5$$

We can find the slope of the line using any two points on the line. We get these two points by first choosing two different values of $x$ and then finding the corresponding values of $y$. We choose $x = -2$ and $x = 4$.

| | | | |
|---|---|---|---|
| $y = -3x + 5$ | | $y = -3x + 5$ | |
| $y = -3(-2) + 5$   Let $x = -2$. | | $y = -3(4) + 5$   Let $x = 4$. | |
| $y = 6 + 5$   Multiply. | | $y = -12 + 5$   Multiply. | |
| $y = 11$   Add. | | $y = -7$   Add. | |

The ordered pairs are $(-2, 11)$ and $(4, -7)$. Now we use the slope formula.

$$m = \frac{11 - (-7)}{-2 - 4} = \frac{18}{-6} = -3$$

**The slope, $-3$, is the same number as the coefficient of $x$ in the given equation $y = -3x + 5$.** It can be shown that this always happens, *as long as the equation is solved for y.* This fact is used to find the slope of a line from its equation.

NOW TRY ANSWER
4. undefined slope

> **Finding the Slope of a Line from Its Equation**
>
> ***Step 1*** Solve the equation for $y$.
>
> ***Step 2*** The slope is given by the coefficient of $x$.

**NOW TRY**
**EXERCISE 5**

Find the slope of the line.

$$3x + 5y = -1$$

**EXAMPLE 5** Finding Slopes from Equations

Find the slope of each line.

**(a)** $2x - 5y = 4$

    ***Step 1*** Solve the equation for $y$.

$$2x - 5y = 4$$

Isolate $y$ on one side.    $-5y = -2x + 4$     Subtract $2x$ from each side.

$$y = \frac{2}{5}x - \frac{4}{5}$$     Divide by $-5$.

Slope ⟶

    ***Step 2*** The slope is given by the coefficient of $x$, so the slope is $\frac{2}{5}$.

**(b)** $8x + 4y = 1$

Solve for $y$.    $4y = -8x + 1$     Subtract $8x$.

$$y = -2x + \frac{1}{4}$$     Divide by $4$.

The slope of this line is given by the coefficient of $x$, which is $-2$.     **NOW TRY**

---

**NOTE** We can solve the equation $Ax + By = C$ (with $B \neq 0$) for $y$ to show that, in general, the slope of the line is $m = -\frac{A}{B}$.

---

**OBJECTIVE 3** Use slopes to determine whether two lines are parallel, perpendicular, or neither. Two lines in a plane that never intersect are **parallel**. We use slopes to tell whether two lines are parallel.

    **FIGURE 27** on the next page shows the graphs of $x + 2y = 4$ and $x + 2y = -6$. These lines appear to be parallel. We solve each equation for $y$ to find the slope.

| | |
|---|---|
| $x + 2y = 4$ | $x + 2y = -6$ |
| $2y = -x + 4$   Subtract $x$. | $2y = -x - 6$   Subtract $x$. |
| $y = \dfrac{-x}{2} + 2$   Divide by $2$. | $y = \dfrac{-x}{2} - 3$   Divide by $2$. |
| $y = -\dfrac{1}{2}x + 2$    $\frac{-x}{2} = \frac{-1x}{2} = -\frac{1}{2}x$ | $y = -\dfrac{1}{2}x - 3$    $\frac{-x}{2} = \frac{-1x}{2} = -\frac{1}{2}x$ |

The slope is $-\frac{1}{2}$, not $-\frac{x}{2}$.

Slope                 Slope

**NOW TRY ANSWER**
**5.** $-\frac{3}{5}$

Both lines have slope $-\frac{1}{2}$. ***Nonvertical parallel lines always have equal slopes.***

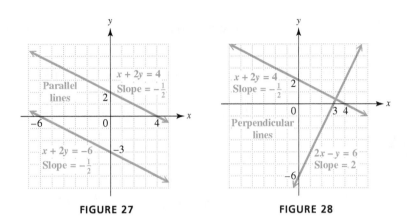

**FIGURE 27**          **FIGURE 28**

**FIGURE 28** shows the graphs of $x + 2y = 4$ and $2x - y = 6$. These lines appear to be **perpendicular** (that is, they intersect at a 90° angle). As shown earlier, solving $x + 2y = 4$ for $y$ gives $y = -\frac{1}{2}x + 2$, with slope $-\frac{1}{2}$. We must solve $2x - y = 6$ for $y$.

$$2x - y = 6$$
$$-y = -2x + 6 \qquad \text{Subtract } 2x.$$
$$y = 2x - 6 \qquad \text{Multiply by } -1.$$
$$\uparrow$$
$$\text{Slope}$$

| Number | Negative Reciprocal |
|--------|---------------------|
| $\frac{3}{4}$ | $-\frac{4}{3}$ |
| $\frac{1}{2}$ | $-\frac{2}{1}$, or $-2$ |
| $-6$, or $-\frac{6}{1}$ | $\frac{1}{6}$ |
| $-0.4$, or $-\frac{4}{10}$ | $\frac{10}{4}$, or $2.5$ |

*The product of each number and its negative reciprocal is* $-1$.

The product of the two slopes $-\frac{1}{2}$ and $2$ is

$$-\frac{1}{2}(2) = -1.$$

***The product of the slopes of two perpendicular lines, neither of which is vertical, is always*** $-1$. This means that the slopes of perpendicular lines are negative (or opposite) reciprocals—if one slope is the nonzero number $a$, the other is $-\frac{1}{a}$. The table in the margin shows several examples.

### Slopes of Parallel and Perpendicular Lines

Two lines with the same slope are parallel.

Two lines whose slopes have a product of $-1$ are perpendicular.

### EXAMPLE 6  Deciding Whether Two Lines Are Parallel or Perpendicular

Decide whether each pair of lines is *parallel, perpendicular,* or *neither.*

**(a)** $\quad x + 3y = 7$
$\quad -3x + \ y = 3$

Find the slope of each line by first solving each equation for $y$.

$$x + 3y = 7 \qquad\qquad\qquad\qquad -3x + y = 3$$
$$3y = -x + 7 \quad \text{Subtract } x. \qquad\qquad y = 3x + 3 \quad \text{Add } 3x.$$
$$y = -\frac{1}{3}x + \frac{7}{3} \quad \text{Divide by 3.}$$

Slope is $-\frac{1}{3}$.          Slope is $3$.

NOW TRY
EXERCISE 6

Decide whether the pair of lines is *parallel, perpendicular,* or *neither.*

$$2x - 3y = 1$$
$$4x + 6y = 5$$

Since the slopes $-\frac{1}{3}$ and 3 are not equal, the lines are not parallel. Check the product of the slopes.

$$-\frac{1}{3}(3) = -1 \qquad \text{The slopes are negative reciprocals.}$$

The two lines are perpendicular because the product of their slopes is $-1$.

**(b)** $4x - y = 4 \xrightarrow{\text{Solve for } y.} y = 4x - 4$

$8x - 2y = -12 \xrightarrow{\hspace{1cm}} y = 4x + 6$

Both lines have slope 4, so the lines are parallel.

**(c)** $4x + 3y = 6 \xrightarrow{\text{Solve for } y.} y = -\frac{4}{3}x + 2$

$2x - y = 5 \xrightarrow{\hspace{1cm}} y = 2x - 5$

Here the slopes are $-\frac{4}{3}$ and 2. These lines are neither parallel nor perpendicular, because $-\frac{4}{3} \neq 2$ and $-\frac{4}{3} \cdot 2 \neq -1$.

**(d)** $6x - y = 1 \xrightarrow{\text{Solve for } y.} y = 6x - 1$

$x - 6y = -12 \xrightarrow{\hspace{1cm}} y = \frac{1}{6}x + 2$

**NOW TRY ANSWER**
**6.** neither

The slopes are 6 and $\frac{1}{6}$. The lines are not parallel, nor are they perpendicular. $\left(\textbf{\textit{Be careful!}} \; 6\left(\frac{1}{6}\right) = 1, \textit{not} -1.\right)$

NOW TRY

## 3.3 EXERCISES

**MyMathLab**  Math XL PRACTICE   WATCH   DOWNLOAD   READ   REVIEW

🌐 *Complete solution available on the Video Resources on DVD*

*Use the indicated points to find the slope of each line.* ***See Example 1.***

🌐 **1.**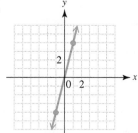

**2.**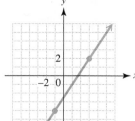

**3.**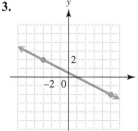

**4.**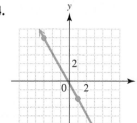

**5.**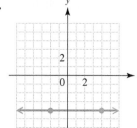

**6.**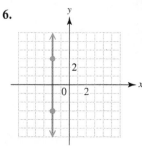

✏️ **7.** In the context of the graph of a straight line, what is meant by "rise"? What is meant by "run"?

✏️ **8.** Explain in your own words what is meant by *slope* of a line.

**9.** *Concept Check*   Match the graph of each line in (a)–(d) with its slope in A–D.

**(a)**

**(b)**

**(c)**

**(d)**

**A.** $\dfrac{2}{3}$   **B.** $\dfrac{3}{2}$   **C.** $-\dfrac{2}{3}$   **D.** $-\dfrac{3}{2}$

**10.** *Concept Check*   Decide whether the line with the given slope rises from left to right, falls from left to right, is horizontal, or is vertical.

**(a)** $m = -4$   **(b)** $m = 0$   **(c)** $m$ is undefined.   **(d)** $m = \dfrac{3}{7}$

*Concept Check*   *On a pair of axes similar to the one shown, sketch the graph of a straight line having the indicated slope.*

**11.** Negative

**12.** Positive

**13.** Undefined

**14.** Zero

*Concept Check*   *The figure at the right shows a line that has a positive slope (because it rises from left to right) and a positive y-value for the y-intercept (because it intersects the y-axis above the origin).*

*For each line in Exercises 15–20, decide whether **(a)** the slope is positive, negative, or zero and **(b)** the y-value of the y-intercept is positive, negative, or zero.*

**15.**

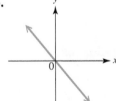

**16.**

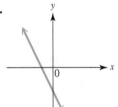

**17.**

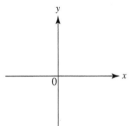

**18.**

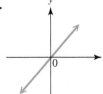

**19.**

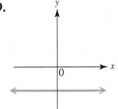

**20.**

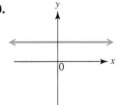

**21.** *Concept Check*   What is the slope (or grade) of this hill?

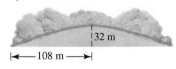

**22.** *Concept Check*   What is the slope (or pitch) of this roof?

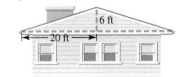

**23.** *Concept Check* What is the slope of the slide? (*Hint:* The slide *drops* 8 ft vertically as it extends 12 ft horizontally.)

**24.** *Concept Check* What is the slope (or grade) of this ski slope? (*Hint:* The ski slope drops 25 ft vertically for every 100 horizontal feet.)

**25.** *Concept Check* A student was asked to find the slope of the line through the points $(2, 5)$ and $(-1, 3)$. His answer, $-\frac{2}{3}$, was incorrect. He showed his work as

$$\frac{3-5}{2-(-1)} = \frac{-2}{3} = -\frac{2}{3}.$$

*WHAT WENT WRONG?* Give the correct slope.

**26.** *Concept Check* A student was asked to find the slope of the line through the points $(-2, 4)$ and $(6, -1)$. Her answer, $-\frac{8}{5}$, was incorrect. She showed her work as

$$\frac{6-(-2)}{-1-4} = \frac{8}{-5} = -\frac{8}{5}.$$

*WHAT WENT WRONG?* Give the correct slope.

*Find the slope of the line through each pair of points. See Examples 2–4.*

**27.** $(1, -2)$ and $(-3, -7)$     **28.** $(4, -1)$ and $(-2, -8)$     **29.** $(0, 3)$ and $(-2, 0)$

**30.** $(8, 0)$ and $(0, -5)$     **31.** $(4, 3)$ and $(-6, 3)$     **32.** $(6, 5)$ and $(-12, 5)$

**33.** $(-2, 4)$ and $(-3, 7)$     **34.** $(-4, 5)$ and $(-5, 8)$

**35.** $(-12, 3)$ and $(-12, -7)$     **36.** $(-8, 6)$ and $(-8, -1)$

**37.** $(4.8, 2.5)$ and $(3.6, 2.2)$     **38.** $(3.1, 2.6)$ and $(1.6, 2.1)$

**39.** $\left(-\frac{7}{5}, \frac{3}{10}\right)$ and $\left(\frac{1}{5}, -\frac{1}{2}\right)$     **40.** $\left(-\frac{4}{3}, \frac{1}{2}\right)$ and $\left(\frac{1}{3}, -\frac{5}{6}\right)$

*Find the slope of each line. See Example 5.*

**41.** $y = 5x + 12$     **42.** $y = 2x + 3$     **43.** $4y = x + 1$

**44.** $2y = x + 4$     **45.** $3x - 2y = 3$     **46.** $6x - 4y = 4$

**47.** $-3x + 2y = 5$     **48.** $-2x + 4y = 5$     **49.** $y = -5$

**50.** $y = 4$     **51.** $x = 6$     **52.** $x = -2$

**53.** *Concept Check* What is the slope of a line whose graph is parallel to the graph of $3x + y = 7$? Perpendicular to the graph of $3x + y = 7$?

**54.** *Concept Check* What is the slope of a line whose graph is parallel to the graph of $-5x + y = -3$? Perpendicular to the graph of $-5x + y = -3$?

**55.** *Concept Check* If two lines are both vertical or both horizontal, which of the following are they?

   **A.** Parallel     **B.** Perpendicular     **C.** Neither parallel nor perpendicular

**56.** *Concept Check* If a line is vertical, what is true of any line that is perpendicular to it?

*For each pair of equations, give the slopes of the lines and then determine whether the two lines are* parallel, perpendicular, *or neither.* ***See Example 6.***

**57.** $2x + 5y = 4$
$4x + 10y = 1$

**58.** $-4x + 3y = 4$
$-8x + 6y = 0$

**59.** $8x - 9y = 6$
$8x + 6y = -5$

**60.** $5x - 3y = -2$
$3x - 5y = -8$

**61.** $3x - 2y = 6$
$2x + 3y = 3$

**62.** $3x - 5y = -1$
$5x + 3y = 2$

**63.** $5x - y = 1$
$x - 5y = -10$

**64.** $3x - 4y = 12$
$4x + 3y = 12$

---

**RELATING CONCEPTS**   EXERCISES 65–70

**FOR INDIVIDUAL OR GROUP WORK**

**FIGURE A** *gives public school enrollment (in thousands) in grades 9–12 in the United States.* **FIGURE B** *gives the (average) number of public school students per computer.*

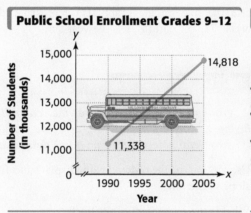

**Public School Enrollment Grades 9–12**

*Source:* U.S. Department of Education.

**FIGURE A**

**Students Per Computer**

*Source:* Quality Education Data, Inc.

**FIGURE B**

*Work Exercises 65–70 in order.*

**65.** Use the ordered pairs (1990, 11,338) and (2005, 14,818) to find the slope of the line in **FIGURE A**.

**66.** The slope of the line in **FIGURE A** is _____. This means that
(positive/negative)
during the period represented, enrollment _____.
(increased/decreased)

**67.** The slope of a line represents the *rate of change of the line.* On the basis of **FIGURE A**, what was the increase in students *per year* during the period shown?

**68.** Use the given information to find the slope, to the nearest hundredth, of the line in **FIGURE B**.

**69.** The slope of the line in **FIGURE B** is _____. This means that
(positive/negative)
the number of students per computer _____ during the period
represented.                              (increased/decreased)

**70.** On the basis of **FIGURE B**, what was the decrease in students per computer *per year* during the period shown?

*The graph shows album sales (which include CD, vinyl, cassette, and digital albums) and music purchases (which include digital tracks, albums, singles, and music videos) in millions of units from 2004 through 2008. Use the graph to work Exercises 71 and 72.*

**71.** Locate the line on the graph that represents music purchases.

   **(a)** Write two ordered pairs $(x, y)$, where $x$ is the year and $y$ is purchases in millions of units, to represent the data for the years 2004 and 2008.

   **(b)** Use the ordered pairs from part (a) to find the slope of the line.

   **(c)** Interpret the meaning of the slope in the context of this problem.

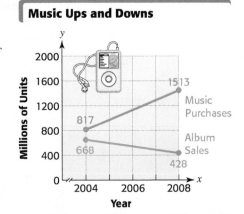

**Music Ups and Downs**

*Source:* Nielsen SoundScan.

**72.** Locate the line on the graph that represents album sales. Repeat parts (a)–(c) of **Exercise 71.** For part (a), $x$ is the year and $y$ is sales in millions of units.

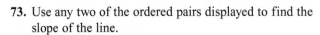

## TECHNOLOGY INSIGHTS    EXERCISES 73–76

*Some graphing calculators have the capability of displaying a table of points for a graph. The table shown here gives several points that lie on a line designated* $Y_1$.

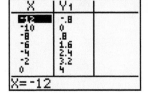

**73.** Use any two of the ordered pairs displayed to find the slope of the line.

**74.** What is the $x$-intercept of the line?

**75.** What is the $y$-intercept of the line?

**76.** Which one of the two lines shown is the graph of $Y_1$?

**A.**

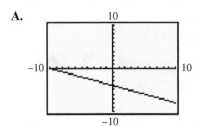

**B.**

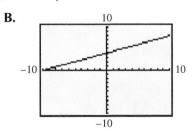

## PREVIEW EXERCISES

*Solve each equation for y. See Section 2.5.*

**77.** $2x + 5y = 15$       **78.** $-4x + 3y = 8$       **79.** $10x = 30 + 3y$

**80.** $8x = 8 - 2y$       **81.** $y - (-8) = 2(x - 4)$       **82.** $y - 3 = 4[x - (-6)]$

**3.4**

# Writing and Graphing Equations of Lines

**OBJECTIVES**

1. Use the slope-intercept form of the equation of a line.
2. Graph a line by using its slope and a point on the line.
3. Write an equation of a line by using its slope and any point on the line.
4. Write an equation of a line by using two points on the line.
5. Write an equation of a line that fits a data set.

**OBJECTIVE 1** Use the slope-intercept form of the equation of a line. In **Section 3.3**, we found the slope (steepness) of a line by solving the equation of the line for $y$. In that form, the slope is the coefficient of $x$. For example, the slope of the line with equation $y = 2x + 3$ is $2$. What does the number $3$ represent?

To find out, suppose a line has slope $m$ and $y$-intercept $(0, b)$. We can find an equation of this line by choosing another point $(x, y)$ on the line, as shown in **FIGURE 29**. Then we use the slope formula.

$$m = \frac{y - b}{x - 0} \quad \begin{array}{l}\leftarrow \text{Change in } y\text{-values} \\ \leftarrow \text{Change in } x\text{-values}\end{array}$$

$$m = \frac{y - b}{x} \quad \begin{array}{l}\text{Subtract in the} \\ \text{denominator.}\end{array}$$

$$mx = y - b \quad \text{Multiply by } x.$$

$$mx + b = y \quad \text{Add } b.$$

$$y = mx + b \quad \text{Rewrite.}$$

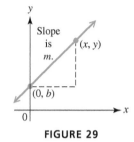

**FIGURE 29**

This result is the *slope-intercept form* of the equation of a line, because both the slope and the $y$-intercept of the line can be read directly from the equation. For the line with equation $y = 2x + 3$, the number $3$ gives the $y$-intercept $(0, 3)$.

**Slope-Intercept Form**

The **slope-intercept form** of the equation of a line with slope $m$ and $y$-intercept $(0, b)$ is

$$y = mx + b.$$

Slope ⤢    ⤡ $(0, b)$ is the $y$-intercept.

*Remember: The intercept given by slope-intercept form is the y-intercept.*

**NOW TRY EXERCISE 1**

Identify the slope and $y$-intercept of the line with each equation.

**(a)** $y = -\dfrac{3}{5}x - 9$

**(b)** $y = -\dfrac{x}{3} + \dfrac{7}{3}$

**EXAMPLE 1** Identifying Slopes and $y$-Intercepts

Identify the slope and $y$-intercept of the line with each equation.

**(a)** $y = -4x + 1$
Slope ⤢    ⤡ $y$-intercept $(0, 1)$

**(b)** $y = x - 8$ can be written as $y = 1x + (-8)$.
Slope ⤢    ⤡ $y$-intercept $(0, -8)$

**(c)** $y = 6x$ can be written as $y = 6x + 0$.
Slope ⤢    ⤡ $y$-intercept $(0, 0)$

**(d)** $y = \frac{x}{4} - \frac{3}{4}$ can be written as $y = \frac{1}{4}x + \left(-\frac{3}{4}\right)$.
Slope ⤢    ⤡ $y$-intercept $\left(0, -\frac{3}{4}\right)$

NOW TRY

**NOW TRY ANSWERS**

**1. (a)** slope: $-\frac{3}{5}$; $y$-intercept: $(0, -9)$

**(b)** slope: $-\frac{1}{3}$; $y$-intercept: $\left(0, \frac{7}{3}\right)$

Given the slope and $y$-intercept of a line, we can write an equation of the line.

*NOW TRY*
*EXERCISE 2*
Write an equation of the line with slope $-4$ and $y$-intercept $(0, 2)$.

**EXAMPLE 2** Writing an Equation of a Line

Write an equation of the line with slope $\frac{2}{3}$ and $y$-intercept $(0, -1)$.

Here, $m = \frac{2}{3}$ and $b = -1$, so the equation is

Slope $\longrightarrow$ $\qquad$ $y$-intercept is $(0, b)$.

$$y = mx + b \qquad \text{Slope-intercept form}$$

$$y = \frac{2}{3}x + (-1), \quad \text{or} \quad y = \frac{2}{3}x - 1. \qquad \text{NOW TRY}$$

**OBJECTIVE 2** **Graph a line by using its slope and a point on the line.** We can use the slope and $y$-intercept to graph a line.

**Graphing a Line by Using the Slope and $y$-Intercept**

**Step 1** Write the equation in slope-intercept form, if necessary, by solving for $y$.

**Step 2** Identify the $y$-intercept. Graph the point $(0, b)$.

**Step 3** Identify slope $m$ of the line. Use the geometric interpretation of slope ("rise over run") to find another point on the graph by counting from the $y$-intercept.

**Step 4** Join the two points with a line to obtain the graph. (If desired, obtain a third point, such as the $x$-intercept, as a check.)

**EXAMPLE 3** Graphing Lines by Using Slopes and $y$-intercepts

Graph the equation of each line by using the slope and $y$-intercept.

**(a)** $y = \frac{2}{3}x - 1$

**Step 1** The equation is in slope-intercept form.

$$y = \frac{2}{3}x - 1$$

$\qquad \uparrow \qquad \uparrow$

Slope $\quad$ Value of $b$ in $y$-intercept $(0, b)$

**Step 2** The $y$-intercept is $(0, -1)$. Graph this point. See **FIGURE 30**.

**Step 3** The slope is $\frac{2}{3}$. By the definition of slope,

$$m = \frac{\text{change in } y \text{ (rise)}}{\text{change in } x \text{ (run)}} = \frac{2}{3}.$$

From the $y$-intercept, count up 2 units and to the right 3 units to obtain the point $(3, 1)$.

**Step 4** Draw the line through the points $(0, -1)$ and $(3, 1)$ to obtain the graph in **FIGURE 30**.

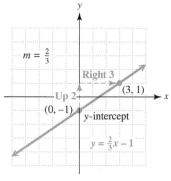

**FIGURE 30**

*NOW TRY ANSWER*
**2.** $y = -4x + 2$

*NOW TRY*
*EXERCISE 3*

Graph $3x + 2y = 8$ by using the slope and $y$-intercept.

**(b)** $3x + 4y = 8$

**Step 1**   Solve for $y$ to write the equation in slope-intercept form.

$$3x + 4y = 8$$

Isolate $y$ on one side.

$$4y = -3x + 8 \qquad \text{Subtract } 3x.$$

Slope-intercept form $\longrightarrow$ $y = -\dfrac{3}{4}x + 2 \qquad$ Divide by 4.

**Step 2**   The $y$-intercept is $(0, 2)$. Graph this point. See **FIGURE 31**.

**Step 3**   The slope is $-\dfrac{3}{4}$, which can be written as either $\dfrac{-3}{4}$ or $\dfrac{3}{-4}$. We use $\dfrac{-3}{4}$ here.

$$m = \frac{\text{change in } y \text{ (rise)}}{\text{change in } x \text{ (run)}} = \frac{-3}{4}$$

From the $y$-intercept, count *down* 3 units (because of the negative sign) and to the right 4 units, to obtain the point $(4, -1)$.

**Step 4**   Draw the line through the two points $(0, 2)$ and $(4, -1)$ to obtain the graph in **FIGURE 31**.

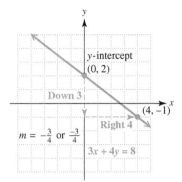

**FIGURE 31**

*NOW TRY*

---

**NOTE**   In Step 3 of **Example 3(b),** we could use $\dfrac{3}{-4}$ for the slope. From the $y$-intercept, count up 3 units and to the *left* 4 units (because of the negative sign) to obtain the point $(-4, 5)$. Confirm that this produces the same line.

---

 *NOW TRY*
*EXERCISE 4*

Graph the line through $(-3, -4)$ with slope $\dfrac{5}{2}$.

**EXAMPLE 4**   Graphing a Line by Using the Slope and a Point

Graph the line through $(-2, 3)$ with slope $-4$.

First, locate the point $(-2, 3)$. Write the slope as

$$m = \frac{\text{change in } y \text{ (rise)}}{\text{change in } x \text{ (run)}} = -4 = \frac{-4}{1}.$$

Locate another point on the line by counting *down* 4 units and then to the right 1 unit. Finally, draw the line through this new point $P$ and the given point $(-2, 3)$. See **FIGURE 32**.

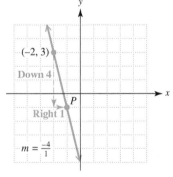

**FIGURE 32**

*NOW TRY*

NOW TRY ANSWERS

**3.**

**4.**

---

**NOTE**   In **Example 4,** we could have written the slope as $\dfrac{4}{-1}$ instead. Verify that this produces the same line.

---

**OBJECTIVE 3**   **Write an equation of a line by using its slope and any point on the line.**   We can use the slope-intercept form to write the equation of a line if we know the slope and any point on the line.

**NOW TRY**
**EXERCISE 5**

Write an equation, in slope-intercept form, of the line having slope 3 and passing through the point $(-2, 1)$.

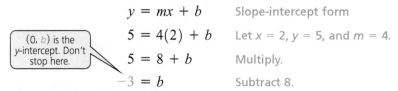

### EXAMPLE 5  Using the Slope-Intercept Form to Write an Equation

Write an equation, in slope-intercept form, of the line having slope 4 passing through the point $(2, 5)$.

Since the line passes through the point $(2, 5)$, we can substitute $x = 2$, $y = 5$, and the given slope $m = 4$ into $y = mx + b$ and solve for $b$.

$$y = mx + b \qquad \text{Slope-intercept form}$$

$$5 = 4(2) + b \qquad \text{Let } x = 2, y = 5, \text{ and } m = 4.$$

$(0, b)$ is the $y$-intercept. Don't stop here.

$$5 = 8 + b \qquad \text{Multiply.}$$

$$-3 = b \qquad \text{Subtract 8.}$$

Now substitute the values of $m$ and $b$ into slope-intercept form.

$$y = mx + b \qquad \text{Slope-intercept form}$$

$$y = 4x - 3 \qquad m = 4 \text{ and } b = -3 \qquad \text{NOW TRY}$$

There is another form that can be used to write the equation of a line. To develop this form, let $m$ represent the slope of a line and let $(x_1, y_1)$ represent a given point on the line. Let $(x, y)$ represent any other point on the line. See **FIGURE 33**. Then,

$$m = \frac{y - y_1}{x - x_1} \qquad \text{Definition of slope}$$

$$m(x - x_1) = y - y_1 \qquad \text{Multiply each side by } x - x_1.$$

$$y - y_1 = m(x - x_1). \qquad \text{Rewrite.}$$

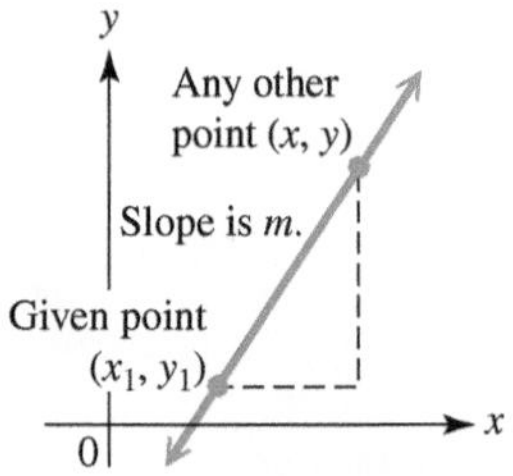

This result is the *point-slope form* of the equation of a line.

**FIGURE 33**

### Point-Slope Form

The **point-slope form** of the equation of a line with slope $m$ passing through the point $(x_1, y_1)$ is

$$y - y_1 = m(x - x_1).$$

Slope — Given point

### EXAMPLE 6  Using the Point-Slope Form to Write Equations

Write an equation of each line. Give the final answer in slope-intercept form.

**(a)** Through $(-2, 4)$, with slope $-3$

The given point is $(-2, 4)$ so $x_1 = -2$ and $y_1 = 4$. Also, $m = -3$.

$$y - y_1 = m(x - x_1) \qquad \text{Point-slope form}$$

Only $y_1$, $m$, and $x_1$ are replaced with numbers.

$$y - 4 = -3[x - (-2)] \qquad \text{Let } y_1 = 4, m = -3, x_1 = -2.$$

$$y - 4 = -3(x + 2) \qquad \text{Definition of subtraction}$$

$$y - 4 = -3x - 6 \qquad \text{Distributive property}$$

$$y = -3x - 2 \qquad \text{Add 4.}$$

*NOW TRY ANSWER*
**5.** $y = 3x + 7$

NOW TRY
EXERCISE 6

Write an equation of the line through $(3, -1)$, with slope $-\frac{2}{5}$. Give the final answer in slope-intercept form.

**(b)** Through $(4, 2)$, with slope $\frac{3}{5}$

$$y - y_1 = m(x - x_1) \qquad \text{Point-slope form}$$

$$y - 2 = \frac{3}{5}(x - 4) \qquad \text{Let } y_1 = 2, m = \frac{3}{5}, x_1 = 4.$$

$$y - 2 = \frac{3}{5}x - \frac{12}{5} \qquad \text{Distributive property}$$

$$y = \frac{3}{5}x - \frac{12}{5} + \frac{10}{5} \qquad \text{Add} \qquad \text{to each side.}$$

$$y = \frac{3}{5}x - \frac{2}{5} \qquad \text{Combine like terms.} \qquad \text{NOW TRY}$$

**OBJECTIVE 4**  **Write an equation of a line by using two points on the line.** Many of the linear equations in **Sections 3.1–3.3** were given in the form

$$Ax + By = C, \qquad \text{Standard form}$$

called **standard form**, where $A$, $B$, and $C$ are real numbers and $A$ and $B$ are not both 0. In most cases, $A$, $B$, and $C$ are rational numbers. For consistency in this book, we give answers so that $A$, $B$, and $C$ are integers with greatest common factor 1 and $A \geq 0$.

---

**NOTE**  The definition of standard form is not the same in all texts. A linear equation can be written in many different, equally correct, ways. For example,

$$3x + 4y = 12, \quad 6x + 8y = 24, \quad \text{and} \quad -9x - 12y = -36$$

all represent the same set of ordered pairs. When giving answers in standard form, let us agree that $3x + 4y = 12$ is preferable to the other forms because the greatest common factor of 3, 4, and 12 is 1 and $A \geq 0$.

---

NOW TRY
EXERCISE 7

Write an equation of the line through the points $(4, 1)$ and $(6, -2)$. Give the final answer in

**(a)** slope-intercept form and

**(b)** standard form.

**EXAMPLE 7**  **Writing the Equation of a Line by Using Two Points**

Write an equation of the line through the points $(-2, 5)$ and $(3, 4)$. Give the final answer in slope-intercept form and then in standard form.

First, find the slope of the line, using the slope formula.

$$\text{slope } m = \frac{y_2 - y_1}{x_2 - x_1} = \frac{5 - 4}{-2 - 3} = \frac{1}{-5} = -\frac{1}{5}$$

Now use either $(-2, 5)$ or $(3, 4)$ and either slope-intercept or point-slope form.

$$y - y_1 = m(x - x_1) \qquad \begin{array}{l}\text{We choose } (3, 4) \text{ and} \\ \text{point-slope form.}\end{array}$$

$$y - 4 = -\frac{1}{5}(x - 3) \qquad \text{Let } y_1 = 4, m = -\frac{1}{5}, x_1 = 3.$$

$$y - 4 = -\frac{1}{5}x + \frac{3}{5} \qquad \text{Distributive property}$$

$$y = -\frac{1}{5}x + \frac{3}{5} + \frac{20}{5} \qquad \text{Add } 4 = \frac{20}{5} \text{ to each side.}$$

Slope-intercept form $\longrightarrow$ $y = -\frac{1}{5}x + \frac{23}{5} \qquad \text{Combine like terms.}$

$$5y = -x + 23 \qquad \text{Multiply by 5 to clear fractions.}$$

Standard form $\longrightarrow$ $x + 5y = 23 \qquad \text{Add } x. \qquad \text{NOW TRY}$

NOW TRY ANSWERS
**6.** $y = -\frac{2}{5}x + \frac{1}{5}$
**7. (a)** $y = -\frac{3}{2}x + 7$
  **(b)** $3x + 2y = 14$

> **NOTE** In **Example 7,** the same result would be found by using $(-2, 5)$ for $(x_1, y_1)$. We could also substitute the slope and either given point in slope-intercept form $y = mx + b$ and then solve for $b$, as in **Example 5.**

A summary of the forms of linear equations follows.

| Forms of Linear Equations | | |
|---|---|---|
| *Equation* | *Description* | *Example* |
| $x = k$ | **Vertical line**<br>Slope is undefined.<br>$x$-intercept is $(k, 0)$. | $x = 3$ |
| $y = k$ | **Horizontal line**<br>Slope is 0.<br>$y$-intercept is $(0, k)$. | $y = 3$ |
| $y = mx + b$ | **Slope-intercept form**<br>Slope is $m$.<br>$y$-intercept is $(0, b)$. | $y = \frac{3}{2}x - 6$ |
| $y - y_1 = m(x - x_1)$ | **Point-slope form**<br>Slope is $m$.<br>Line passes through $(x_1, y_1)$. | $y + 3 = \frac{3}{2}(x - 2)$ |
| $Ax + By = C$ | **Standard form**<br>Slope is $-\frac{A}{B}$.<br>$x$-intercept is $\left(\frac{C}{A}, 0\right)$.<br>$y$-intercept is $\left(0, \frac{C}{B}\right)$. | $3x - 2y = 12$ |

> **NOTE** Slope-intercept form is an especially useful form for a linear equation because of the information we can determine from it. It is also the form used by graphing calculators and the one that describes *a linear function*.

**OBJECTIVE 5** **Write an equation of a line that fits a data set.** If a given set of data fits a linear pattern—that is, if its graph consists of points lying close to a straight line—we can write a linear equation that models the data.

**EXAMPLE 8** Writing an Equation of a Line That Describes Data

The table lists the average annual cost (in dollars) of tuition and fees for in-state students at public 4-year colleges and universities for selected years. Year 1 represents 2001, year 3 represents 2003, and so on. Plot the data and write an equation that approximates it.

Letting $y$ represent the cost in year $x$, we plot the data as shown in **FIGURE 34** on the next page.

| Year | Cost (in dollars) |
|---|---|
| 1 | 3766 |
| 3 | 4645 |
| 5 | 5491 |
| 7 | 6185 |

*Source:* The College Board.

*NOW TRY*
*EXERCISE 8*
Use the points $(3, 4645)$ and $(5, 5491)$ to write an equation in slope-intercept form that approximates the data of **Example 8.** How well does this equation approximate the cost in 2007?

**AVERAGE ANNUAL COSTS AT PUBLIC 4-YEAR COLLEGES**

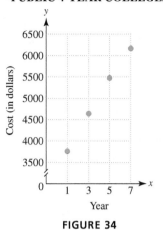

**FIGURE 34**

The points appear to lie approximately in a straight line. We choose the ordered pairs $(5, 5491)$ and $(7, 6185)$ from the table and find the slope of the line through these points.

$$m = \frac{y_2 - y_1}{x_2 - x_1} = \frac{6185 - 5491}{7 - 5} = 347 \qquad \begin{array}{l} \text{Let } (7, 6185) = (x_2, y_2) \\ \text{and } (5, 5491) = (x_1, y_1). \end{array}$$

The slope, 347, is positive, indicating that tuition and fees *increased* \$347 each year. Now use this slope and the point $(5, 5491)$ in the slope-intercept form to find an equation of the line.

$$y = mx + b \qquad \text{Slope-intercept form}$$
$$5491 = 347(5) + b \qquad \text{Substitute for } x, y, \text{ and } m.$$
$$5491 = 1735 + b \qquad \text{Multiply.}$$
$$3756 = b \qquad \text{Subtract 1735.}$$

Thus, $m = 347$ and $b = 3756$, so we can write an equation of the line.

$$y = 347x + 3756$$

To see how well this equation approximates the ordered pairs in the data table, let $x = 3$ (for 2003) and find $y$.

$$y = 347x + 3756 \qquad \text{Equation of the line}$$
$$y = 347(3) + 3756 \qquad \text{Substitute 3 for } x.$$
$$y = 4797 \qquad \text{Multiply and then add.}$$

The corresponding value in the table for $x = 3$ is 4645, so the equation approximates the data reasonably well. With caution, the equation could be used to predict values for years that are not included in the table. *NOW TRY*

---

**NOTE** In **Example 8,** if we had chosen two different data points, we would have found a slightly different equation.

---

*NOW TRY ANSWER*
**8.** $y = 423x + 3376$;
The equation gives $y = 6337$ when $x = 7$, which approximates the data reasonably well.

## 3.4 EXERCISES

🌐 *Complete solution available on the Video Resources on DVD*

*Concept Check*  *Match the description in Column I with the correct equation in Column II.*

| I | II |
|---|---|
| **1.** Slope $= -2$, passes through $(4, 1)$ | **A.** $y = 4x$ |
| **2.** Slope $= -2$, $y$-intercept $(0, 1)$ | **B.** $y = \frac{1}{4}x$ |
| **3.** Passes through $(0, 0)$ and $(4, 1)$ | **C.** $y = -4x$ |
| **4.** Passes through $(0, 0)$ and $(1, 4)$ | **D.** $y = -2x + 1$ |
| | **E.** $y - 1 = -2(x - 4)$ |

*Concept Check*  *Match each equation with the graph in A–D that would most closely resemble its graph.*

**5.** $y = x + 3$  **6.** $y = -x + 3$  **7.** $y = x - 3$  **8.** $y = -x - 3$

**A.**   **B.**   **C.**   **D.**

*Identify the slope and y-intercept of the line with each equation.* **See Example 1.**

**9.** $y = \frac{5}{2}x - 4$  **10.** $y = \frac{7}{3}x - 6$  **11.** $y = -x + 9$

**12.** $y = x + 1$  **13.** $y = \frac{x}{5} - \frac{3}{10}$  **14.** $y = \frac{x}{7} - \frac{5}{14}$

*Concept Check*  *Use the geometric interpretation of slope (rise divided by run, from* **Section 3.3***) to find the slope of each line. Then, by identifying the y-intercept from the graph, write the slope-intercept form of the equation of the line.*

**15.** 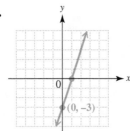  **16.** 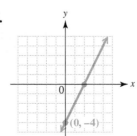  **17.**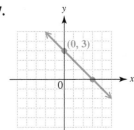

**18.** 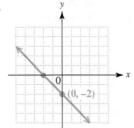  **19.** 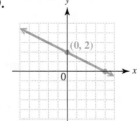  **20.**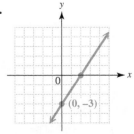

*Write the equation of each line with the given slope and y-intercept.* ***See Example 2.***

**21.** $m = 4, (0, -3)$    **22.** $m = -5, (0, 6)$    **23.** $m = -1, (0, -7)$

**24.** $m = 1, (0, -9)$    **25.** $m = 0, (0, 3)$    **26.** $m = 0, (0, -4)$

**27.** Undefined slope, $(0, -2)$        **28.** Undefined slope, $(0, 5)$

*Graph each equation by using the slope and y-intercept.* ***See Example 3.***

**29.** $y = 3x + 2$    **30.** $y = 4x - 4$    **31.** $y = -\dfrac{1}{3}x + 4$

**32.** $y = -\dfrac{1}{2}x + 2$    **33.** $2x + y = -5$    **34.** $3x + y = -2$

**35.** $4x - 5y = 20$        **36.** $6x - 5y = 30$

*Graph each line passing through the given point and having the given slope. (In Exercises 45–48, recall the types of lines having slope 0 and undefined slope.)* ***See Example 4.***

**37.** $(0, 1), m = 4$    **38.** $(0, -5), m = -2$    **39.** $(1, -5), m = -\dfrac{2}{5}$

**40.** $(2, -1), m = -\dfrac{1}{3}$    **41.** $(-1, 4), m = \dfrac{2}{5}$    **42.** $(-2, 2), m = \dfrac{3}{2}$

**43.** $(0, 0), m = -2$        **44.** $(0, 0), m = -3$

**45.** $(-2, 3), m = 0$        **46.** $(3, 2), m = 0$

**47.** $(2, 4)$, undefined slope        **48.** $(3, -2)$, undefined slope

**49.** *Concept Check*   What is the common name given to a vertical line whose $x$-intercept is the origin?

**50.** *Concept Check*   What is the common name given to a line with slope 0 whose $y$-intercept is the origin?

*Write an equation for each line passing through the given point and having the given slope. Give the final answer in slope-intercept form.* ***See Examples 5 and 6.***

**51.** $(4, 1), m = 2$    **52.** $(2, 7), m = 3$    **53.** $(-1, 3), m = -4$

**54.** $(-3, 1), m = -2$    **55.** $(9, 3), m = 1$    **56.** $(8, 4), m = 1$

**57.** $(-4, 1), m = \dfrac{3}{4}$    **58.** $(2, 1), m = \dfrac{5}{2}$    **59.** $(-2, 5), m = \dfrac{2}{3}$

**60.** $(4, 2), m = -\dfrac{1}{3}$    **61.** $(6, -3), m = -\dfrac{4}{5}$    **62.** $(7, -2), m = -\dfrac{7}{2}$

**63.** *Concept Check*   Which equations are equivalent to $2x - 3y = 6$?

**A.** $y = \dfrac{2}{3}x - 2$        **B.** $-2x + 3y = -6$

**C.** $y = -\dfrac{3}{2}x + 3$        **D.** $y - 2 = \dfrac{2}{3}(x - 6)$

**64.** *Concept Check*   In the summary box on **page 216,** we give the equations

$$y = \frac{3}{2}x - 6 \quad \text{and} \quad y + 3 = \frac{3}{2}(x - 2)$$

as examples of equations in slope-intercept form and point-slope form, respectively. Write each of these equations in standard form. What do you notice?

*Write an equation for each line passing through the given pair of points. Give the final answer in (a) slope-intercept form and (b) standard form. See Example 7.*

**65.** $(4, 10)$ and $(6, 12)$

**66.** $(8, 5)$ and $(9, 6)$

**67.** $(-4, 0)$ and $(0, 2)$

**68.** $(0, -2)$ and $(-3, 0)$

**69.** $(-2, -1)$ and $(3, -4)$

**70.** $(-1, -7)$ and $(-8, -2)$

**71.** $\left(-\dfrac{2}{3}, \dfrac{8}{3}\right)$ and $\left(\dfrac{1}{3}, \dfrac{7}{3}\right)$

**72.** $\left(\dfrac{1}{2}, \dfrac{3}{2}\right)$ and $\left(-\dfrac{1}{4}, \dfrac{5}{4}\right)$

*Write an equation of the line satisfying the given conditions. Give the final answer in slope-intercept form. (Hint: Recall the relationships among slopes of parallel and perpendicular lines in Section 3.3.)*

**73.** Perpendicular to $x - 2y = 7$;   $y$-intercept $(0, -3)$

**74.** Parallel to $5x - y = 10$;   $y$-intercept $(0, -2)$

**75.** Through $(2, 3)$;   parallel to $4x - y = -2$

**76.** Through $(4, 2)$;   perpendicular to $x - 3y = 7$

**77.** Through $(2, -3)$;   parallel to $3x = 4y + 5$

**78.** Through $(-1, 4)$;   perpendicular to $2x = -3y + 8$

*The cost y of producing x items is, in some cases, expressed as $y = mx + b$. The number b gives the **fixed cost** (the cost that is the same no matter how many items are produced), and the number m is the **variable cost** (the cost of producing an additional item). Use this information to work Exercises 79 and 80.*

**79.** It costs $400 to start up a business selling snow cones. Each snow cone costs $0.25 to produce.

   **(a)** What is the fixed cost?

   **(b)** What is the variable cost?

   **(c)** Write the cost equation.

   **(d)** What will be the cost of producing 100 snow cones, based on the cost equation?

   **(e)** How many snow cones will be produced if the total cost is $775?

**80.** It costs $2000 to purchase a copier, and each copy costs $0.02 to make.

   **(a)** What is the fixed cost?

   **(b)** What is the variable cost?

   **(c)** Write the cost equation.

   **(d)** What will be the cost of producing 10,000 copies, based on the cost equation?

   **(e)** How many copies will be produced if the total cost is $2600?

*Solve each problem. See Example 8.*

**81.** The table lists the average annual cost (in dollars) of tuition and fees at 2-year colleges for selected years, where year 1 represents 2004, year 2 represents 2005, and so on.

| Year | Cost (in dollars) |
|------|-------------------|
| 1 | 2079 |
| 2 | 2182 |
| 3 | 2272 |
| 4 | 2361 |
| 5 | 2402 |

*Source:* The College Board.

(a) Write five ordered pairs from the data.

(b) Plot the ordered pairs. Do the points lie approximately in a straight line?

(c) Use the ordered pairs $(1, 2079)$ and $(4, 2361)$ to write an equation of a line that approximates the data. Give the final equation in slope-intercept form.

(d) Use the equation from part (c) to estimate the average annual cost at 2-year colleges in 2009 to the nearest dollar. (*Hint:* What is the value of $x$ for 2009?)

82. The table gives heavy-metal nuclear waste (in thousands of metric tons) from spent reactor fuel stored temporarily at reactor sites, awaiting permanent storage. (*Source:* "Burial of Radioactive Nuclear Waste Under the Seabed," *Scientific American,* January 1998.)

| Year x | Waste y |
|--------|---------|
| 1995 | 32 |
| 2000 | 42 |
| 2010* | 61 |
| 2020* | 76 |

*Estimated by the U.S. Department of Energy.

Let $x = 0$ represent 1995, $x = 5$ represent 2000 (since $2000 - 1995 = 5$), and so on.

(a) For 1995, the ordered pair is $(0, 32)$. Write ordered pairs for the data for the other years given in the table.

(b) Plot the ordered pairs $(x, y)$. Do the points lie approximately in a straight line?

(c) Use the ordered pairs $(0, 32)$ and $(25, 76)$ to write the equation of a line that approximates the other ordered pairs. Give the equation in slope-intercept form.

(d) Use the equation from part (c) to estimate the amount of nuclear waste in 2015. (*Hint:* What is the value of $x$ for 2015?)

*The points on the graph show the number of colleges that teamed up with banks to issue student ID cards which doubled as debit cards from 2002 through 2007. The graph of a linear equation that models the data is also shown.*

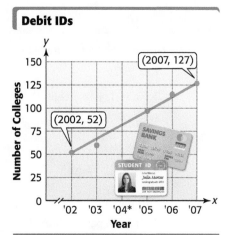

**Debit IDs**

Source: CR80News.
* Data for 2004 unavailable.

83. Use the ordered pairs shown on the graph to write an equation of the line that models the data. Give the equation in slope-intercept form.

84. Use the equation from **Exercise 83** to estimate the number of colleges that teamed up with banks to offer debit IDs in 2004, the year with unavailable data.

In Exercises 85 and 86, two graphing calculator views of the same line are shown. Use the displays at the bottom of the screen to write an equation of the form $y = mx + b$ for each line.

**85.**

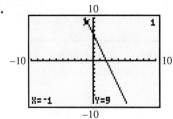 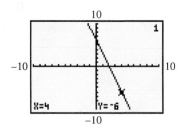

**86.**

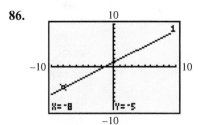 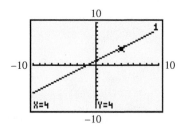

PREVIEW EXERCISES

Solve each inequality, and graph the solution set on a number line. **See Section 2.8.**

**87.** $3x + 8 > -1$

**88.** $\frac{1}{2}x - 3 < 2$

**89.** $5 - 3x \le -10$

**90.** $-x < 0$

SUMMARY EXERCISES on Linear Equations and Graphs

Graph each line, using the given information or equation.

**1.** $x - 2y = -4$

**2.** $2x + 3y = 12$

**3.** $m = 1$, $y$-intercept $(0, -2)$

**4.** $y = -2x + 6$

**5.** $m = -\frac{2}{3}$, passes through $(3, -4)$

**6.** Undefined slope, passes through $(-3.5, 0)$

**7.** $x - 4y = 0$

**8.** $y - 4 = -9$

**9.** $8x = 6y + 24$

**10.** $m = 1$, $y$-intercept $(0, -4)$

**11.** $5x + 2y = 10$

**12.** $m = -\frac{3}{4}$, passes through $(4, -4)$

**13.** $m = 0$, passes through $\left(0, \frac{3}{2}\right)$

**14.** $x + 5y = 0$

**15.** $y = -x + 6$

**16.** $4x = 3y - 24$

**17.** $x + 4 = 0$

**18.** $x - 3y = 6$

**19.** *Concept Check* Match the description in Column I with the correct equation in Column II.

|  I  |  II  |
|-----|------|
| **(a)** Slope $-0.5$, $b = -2$ | **A.** $y = -\frac{1}{2}x$ |
| **(b)** $x$-intercept $(4, 0)$, $y$-intercept $(0, 2)$ | **B.** $y = -\frac{1}{2}x - 2$ |
| **(c)** Passes through $(4, -2)$ and $(0, 0)$ | **C.** $x - 2y = 2$ |
| **(d)** $m = \frac{1}{2}$, passes through $(-2, -2)$ | **D.** $x + 2y = 4$ |
|  | **E.** $x = 2y$ |

**20.** *Concept Check* Which equations are equivalent to $2x + 5y = 20$?

**A.** $y = -\frac{2}{5}x + 4$    **B.** $y - 2 = -\frac{2}{5}(x - 5)$

**C.** $y = \frac{5}{2}x - 4$    **D.** $2x = 5y - 20$

*Write an equation for each line. Give the final answer in slope-intercept form if possible.*

**21.** $m = -3$, $b = -6$  
**22.** $m = \frac{3}{2}$, through $(-4, 6)$

**23.** Through $(1, -7)$ and $(-2, 5)$  
**24.** Through $(0, 0)$ and $(5, 3)$

**25.** Through $(0, 0)$, undefined slope  
**26.** Through $(3, 0)$ and $(0, -3)$

**27.** Through $(0, 0)$ and $(3, 2)$  
**28.** $m = -2$, $b = -4$

**29.** Through $(5, 0)$ and $(0, -5)$  
**30.** Through $(0, 0)$, $m = 0$

**31.** $m = \frac{5}{3}$, through $(-3, 0)$  
**32.** Through $(1, -13)$ and $(-2, 2)$

---

## 3.5 Graphing Linear Inequalities in Two Variables

**OBJECTIVES**

1 Graph linear inequalities in two variables.

2 Graph an inequality with a boundary line through the origin.

In **Section 3.2,** we graphed linear equations such as

$$2x + 3y = 6.$$

We now extend this work to *linear inequalities in two variables,* such as

$$2x + 3y \leq 6.$$

**Linear Inequality in Two Variables**

An inequality that can be written as

$$Ax + By < C, \quad Ax + By \leq C, \quad Ax + By > C, \quad \text{or} \quad Ax + By \geq C,$$

where $A$, $B$, and $C$ are real numbers and $A$ and $B$ are not both 0, is a **linear inequality in two variables.**

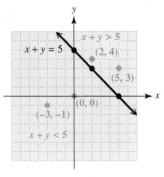

**FIGURE 35**

**OBJECTIVE 1** Graph linear inequalities in two variables. Consider the graph in **FIGURE 35**. The graph of the line $x + y = 5$ divides the points in the rectangular coordinate system into three sets:

1. Those points that lie on the line itself and satisfy the equation $x + y = 5$ [like $(0, 5)$, $(2, 3)$, and $(5, 0)$]

2. Those that lie in the region above the line and satisfy the inequality $x + y > 5$ [like $(5, 3)$ and $(2, 4)$]

3. Those that lie in the region below the line and satisfy the inequality $x + y < 5$ [like $(0, 0)$ and $(-3, -1)$].

The graph of the line $x + y = 5$ is called the **boundary line** for the inequalities

$$x + y > 5 \quad \text{and} \quad x + y < 5.$$

*Graphs of linear inequalities in two variables are regions in the real number plane that may or may not include boundary lines.*

**NOW TRY EXERCISE 1**

Graph $x + 3y \le 6$.

**EXAMPLE 1**   Graphing a Linear Inequality

Graph $2x + 3y \le 6$.

The inequality $2x + 3y \le 6$ means that

$$2x + 3y < 6 \quad \text{or} \quad 2x + 3y = 6.$$

We begin by graphing the equation $2x + 3y = 6$, a line with intercepts $(0, 2)$ and $(3, 0)$, as shown in **FIGURE 36**. This boundary line divides the plane into two regions, one of which satisfies the inequality. A *test point* gives a quick way to find the correct region. We choose any point *not* on the boundary line and substitute it into the given inequality to see whether the resulting statement is true or false. The point $(0, 0)$ is a convenient choice.

$$2x + 3y \le 6 \qquad \text{Original inequality}$$
$$2(0) + 3(0) \overset{?}{\le} 6 \qquad \text{Let } x = 0 \text{ and } y = 0.$$
$$0 + 0 \overset{?}{\le} 6$$

Use $(0, 0)$ as a test point.

$$0 \le 6 \qquad \text{True}$$

Since the last statement is true, we shade the region that includes the test point $(0, 0)$. See **FIGURE 36**. The shaded region, along with the boundary line, is the desired graph.

**NOW TRY ANSWER**

1.

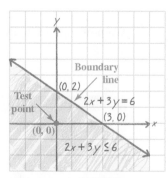

**FIGURE 36**

NOW TRY

**NOTE** Alternatively in **Example 1,** we can find the required region by solving the given inequality for $y$.

$$2x + 3y \leq 6 \qquad \text{Inequality from Example 1}$$

$$3y \leq -2x + 6 \qquad \text{Subtract } 2x.$$

$$y \leq -\frac{2}{3}x + 2 \qquad \text{Divide by 3.}$$

Ordered pairs in which $y$ is equal to $-\frac{2}{3}x + 2$ are on the boundary line, so pairs in which $y$ *is less than* $-\frac{2}{3}x + 2$ will be *below* that line. As we move *down* vertically, the $y$-values *decrease*.) This gives the same region that we shaded in **FIGURE 36**. (Ordered pairs in which $y$ is *greater than* $-\frac{2}{3}x + 2$ will be *above* the boundary line.)

**NOW TRY**
**EXERCISE 2**
Graph $2x - 4y > 8$.

**EXAMPLE 2** Graphing a Linear Inequality

Graph $x - y > 5$.

This inequality does *not* include the equals symbol. Therefore, the points on the line $x - y = 5$ do *not* belong to the graph. However, the line still serves as a boundary for two regions, one of which satisfies the inequality.

To graph the inequality, first graph the equation $x - y = 5$. Use a *dashed line* to show that the points on the line are *not* solutions of the inequality $x - y > 5$. See **FIGURE 37**.

Now choose a test point to see which side of the line satisfies the inequality.

$$x - y > 5 \qquad \text{Original inequality}$$

(0, 0) is a convenient test point. $\quad 0 - 0 \overset{?}{>} 5 \qquad \text{Let } x = 0 \text{ and } y = 0.$

$$0 > 5 \qquad \text{False}$$

Since $0 > 5$ is false, the graph of the inequality is the region that *does not* contain $(0, 0)$. Shade the *other* region, as shown in **FIGURE 37**, to obtain the required graph.

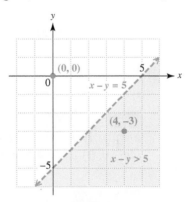

**FIGURE 37**

To check that the correct region is shaded, we test a point in the shaded region. For example, use $(4, -3)$ from the shaded region as follows.

CHECK $\qquad\qquad x - y > 5 \qquad \text{Original inequality}$

$$4 - (-3) \overset{?}{>} 5 \qquad \text{Let } x = 4 \text{ and } y = -3.$$

Use parentheses to avoid errors.

$$7 > 5 \;\checkmark \quad \text{True}$$

This true statement verifies that the correct region was shaded in **FIGURE 37**.

NOW TRY

NOW TRY ANSWER
**2.**

$2x - 4y > 8$

**Graphing a Linear Inequality**

*Step 1*   **Graph the boundary.** Graph the line that is the boundary of the region. Use the methods of **Section 3.2.** Draw a solid line if the inequality has $\leq$ or $\geq$ because of the equality portion of the symbol. Draw a dashed line if the inequality has $<$ or $>$.

*Step 2*   **Shade the appropriate region.** Use any point not on the line as a test point. Substitute for $x$ and $y$ in the *inequality*. If a true statement results, shade the region containing the test point. If a false statement results, shade the other region.

NOW TRY
EXERCISE 3

Graph $x > 2$.

**EXAMPLE 3**   Graphing a Linear Inequality with a Vertical Boundary Line

Graph $x < 3$.

First, we graph $x = 3$, a vertical line passing through the point $(3, 0)$. We use a dashed line (why?) and choose $(0, 0)$ as a test point.

$$x < 3 \qquad \text{Original inequality}$$
$$0 \overset{?}{<} 3 \qquad \text{Let } x = 0.$$
$$0 < 3 \qquad \text{True}$$

Since $0 < 3$ is true, we shade the region containing $(0, 0)$, as in **FIGURE 38.**

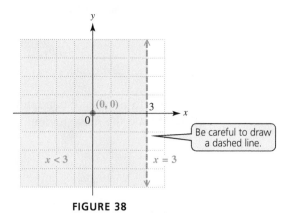

Be careful to draw a dashed line.

**FIGURE 38**

NOW TRY

**OBJECTIVE 2**   **Graph an inequality with a boundary line through the origin.** *If the graph of an inequality has a boundary line that goes through the origin, $(0, 0)$ cannot be used as a test point.*

**EXAMPLE 4**   Graphing a Linear Inequality with a Boundary Line through the Origin

Graph $x \leq 2y$.

Graph $x = 2y$, using a solid line. Some ordered pairs that can be used to graph this line are $(0, 0)$, $(6, 3)$, and $(4, 2)$. Since $(0, 0)$ is *on* the line $x = 2y$, it cannot be used as a test point. Instead, we choose a test point *off* the line, say $(1, 3)$.

$$x \leq 2y \qquad \text{Original inequality}$$
$$1 \overset{?}{\leq} 2(3) \qquad \text{Let } x = 1 \text{ and } y = 3.$$
$$1 \leq 6 \qquad \text{True}$$

NOW TRY ANSWER

3.

NOW TRY
EXERCISE 4

Graph $y \le -2x$.

Since $1 \le 6$ is true, shade the region containing the test point $(1, 3)$. See **FIGURE 39**.

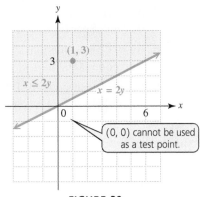

**FIGURE 39**

NOW TRY

---

CONNECTIONS

Graphing calculators have a feature that allows us to shade regions in the plane, so they can be used to graph a linear inequality in two variables. The calculator will not draw the graph as a dashed line, so it is still necessary to understand what is and what is not included in the solution set.

To solve the inequalities in one variable, $-2x + 4 > 0$ and $-2x + 4 < 0$, we use the graph of

$$y = -2x + 4$$

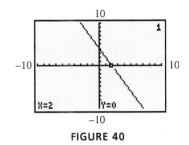

**FIGURE 40**

in **FIGURE 40**. For $y = -2x + 4 > 0$, we want the values of $x$ such that $y > 0$, so that the line is *above* the $x$-axis. From **FIGURE 40**, we see that this is the case for $x < 2$. Thus, the solution set is $(-\infty, 2)$. Similarly, the solution set of $y = -2x + 4 < 0$ is $(2, \infty)$, because the line is *below* the $x$-axis when $x > 2$.

**For Discussion or Writing**

Use a graphing calculator to solve the following inequalities in one variable from **Section 2.8.**

1. $3x + 2 - 5 > -x + 7 + 2x$ **(Example 4, page 156)**

2. $3x + 2 - 5 < -x + 7 + 2x$ (Use the result from part (a).)

3. $4 < 3x - 5 \le 10$ **(Example 8(a), page 158)**

NOW TRY ANSWER

4.

---

**3.5 EXERCISES**    *MyMathLab*    Math XL PRACTICE    WATCH    DOWNLOAD    READ    REVIEW

⊕ *Complete solution available on the Video Resources on DVD*

*Concept Check*   *The following statements each include one or more phrases that can be symbolized with one of the inequality symbols* $<, \le, >,$ *or* $\ge$. *In Exercises 1–6, give the inequality symbol for the boldface italic words.*

1. Since it was recognized in 1981, HIV/AIDS has killed **more than** 25 million people worldwide and infected **more than** 60 million, about two-thirds of whom live in Africa. (*Source:* The President's Emergency Plan for AIDS Relief, February, 2008.)

2. The average national automobile insurance premium of $1896 in 2007 was $20 **less than** the 2006 average premium. (*Source:* 2007 Mid-Year Auto Insurance Pricing Report.)

**3.** As of December 2007, airline passengers were allowed one carry-on bag, with dimensions totaling **at most** 45 in. (*Source: The Gazette.*)

**4.** As of February 2008, all major airlines except US Airways award **at least** 500 frequent flier miles per flight. (*Source: USA Today.*)

**5.** By 1937, a population of as many as a million Attwater's prairie chickens had been cut to **less than** 9000. (*Source: National Geographic,* March 2002.)

**6.** [Easter Island's] nearly 1000 statues, some **almost** 30 feet tall and weighing **as much as** 80 tons, are still an enigma. (*Source: Smithsonian,* March 2002.)

*Concept Check*    *Answer* true *or* false *to each of the following.*

**7.** The point $(4, 0)$ lies on the graph of $3x - 4y < 12$.

**8.** The point $(4, 0)$ lies on the graph of $3x - 4y \leq 12$.

**9.** The points $(4, 1)$ and $(0, 0)$ lie on the graph of $3x - 2y \geq 0$.

**10.** The graph of $y > x$ does not contain points in quadrant IV.

*In Exercises 11–16, the straight-line boundary has been drawn. Complete the graph by shading the correct region.* ***See Examples 1–4.***

**11.** $x + 2y \geq 7$

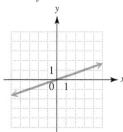

**12.** $2x + y \geq 5$

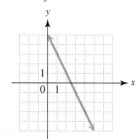

**13.** $-3x + 4y > 12$

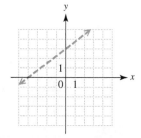

**14.** $x \leq 3y$

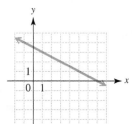

**15.** $y < -1$

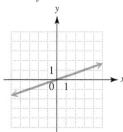

**16.** $x > 4$

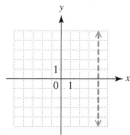

**17.** Explain how to determine whether to use a dashed line or a solid line when graphing a linear inequality in two variables.

**18.** Explain why the point $(0, 0)$ is not an appropriate choice for a test point when graphing an inequality whose boundary goes through the origin.

*Graph each linear inequality.* ***See Examples 1–4.***

**19.** $x + y \leq 5$      **20.** $x + y \geq 3$      **21.** $2x + 3y > -6$

**22.** $3x + 4y < 12$      **23.** $y \geq 2x + 1$      **24.** $y < -3x + 1$

**25.** $x < -2$      **26.** $x > 1$      **27.** $y \leq 5$

**28.** $y \leq -3$      **29.** $y \geq 4x$      **30.** $y \leq 2x$

**31.** Explain why the graph of $y > x$ cannot lie in quadrant IV.

**32.** Explain why the graph of $y < x$ cannot lie in quadrant II.

*For the given information, (a) graph the inequality (here, $x \geq 0$ and $y \geq 0$, so graph only the part of the inequality in quadrant I) and (b) give two ordered pairs that satisfy the inequality.*

**33.** A company will ship $x$ units of merchandise to outlet I and $y$ units of merchandise to outlet II. The company must ship a total of at least 500 units to these two outlets. The preceding information can be expressed by writing

$$x + y \geq 500.$$

**34.** A toy manufacturer makes stuffed bears and geese. It takes 20 min to sew a bear and 30 min to sew a goose. There is a total of 480 min of sewing time available to make $x$ bears and $y$ geese. These restrictions lead to the inequality

$$20x + 30y \leq 480.$$

**PREVIEW EXERCISES**

*Find the value of $3x^2 + 8x + 5$ for each given value of x. **See Section 1.3.***

**35.** 0                 **36.** $-1$                 **37.** 4

**38.** $-\dfrac{5}{3}$       **39.** 1                   **40.** $-4$

## 3.6  Introduction to Functions

**OBJECTIVES**

**1** Understand the definition of a relation.

**2** Understand the definition of a function.

**3** Decide whether an equation defines a function.

**4** Find domains and ranges.

**5** Use function notation.

**6** Apply the function concept in an application.

NOW TRY
EXERCISE 1

Identify the domain and range of the relation.

$$\{(-2, 3), (0, 7), (2, 8), (2, 10)\}$$

NOW TRY ANSWER
**1.** domain: $\{-2, 0, 2\}$;
   range: $\{3, 7, 8, 10\}$

If gasoline costs \$3.00 per gal and we buy 1 gal, then we must pay $\$3.00(1) = \$3.00$. If we buy 2 gal, then the cost is $\$3.00(2) = \$6.00$. If we buy 3 gal, then the cost is $\$3.00(3) = \$9.00$, and so on. Generalizing, if $x$ represents the number of gallons, then the cost is $\$3.00x$. If we let $y$ represent the cost, then the equation

$$y = 3.00x$$

*relates* the number of gallons, $x$, to the cost in dollars, $y$. The ordered pairs $(x, y)$ that satisfy this equation form a *relation*.

**OBJECTIVE 1**  **Understand the definition of a relation.** In an ordered pair $(x, y)$, $x$ and $y$ are called the **components** of the ordered pair. Any set of ordered pairs is called a **relation.** The set of all first components of the ordered pairs of a relation is the **domain** of the relation, and the set of all second components of the ordered pairs is the **range** of the relation.

**EXAMPLE 1**  **Identifying Domains and Ranges of Relations**

Identify the domain and range of each relation.

**(a)** $\{(0, 1), (2, 5), (3, 8), (4, 2)\}$

This relation has domain $\{0, 2, 3, 4\}$ and range $\{1, 2, 5, 8\}$. The correspondence between the elements of the domain and the elements of the range is shown in **FIGURE 41.**

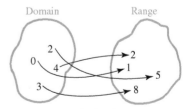

**FIGURE 41**

**(b)** $\{(3, 5), (3, 6), (3, 7), (3, 8)\}$

This relation has domain $\{3\}$ and range $\{5, 6, 7, 8\}$.

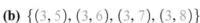
NOW TRY

**OBJECTIVE 2** Understand the definition of a function. We now investigate an important type of relation called a *function*.

> ### Function
>
> A **function** is a set of ordered pairs in which each first component corresponds to exactly one second component.

The relation in **Example 1(a)**, $\{(0, 1), (2, 5), (3, 8), (4, 2)\}$, is a function. The relation $\{(3, 5), (3, 6), (3, 7), (3, 8)\}$ in **Example 1(b)** is *not* a function, because the same first component, 3, corresponds to more than one second component. If the ordered pairs in **Example 1(b)** were interchanged, giving the relation

$$\{(5, 3), (6, 3), (7, 3), (8, 3)\},$$

the result *would* be a function. ***In that case, each domain element (first component) corresponds to exactly one range element (second component).***

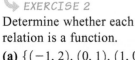
*NOW TRY*
*EXERCISE 2*
Determine whether each relation is a function.
(a) $\{(-1, 2), (0, 1), (1, 0), (4, 3), (4, 5)\}$
(b) $\{(-1, -3), (0, 2), (3, 1), (8, 1)\}$

**EXAMPLE 2** Determining Whether Relations Are Functions

Determine whether each relation is a function.

(a) $\{(-2, 4), (-1, 1), (0, 0), (1, 1), (2, 4)\}$

Each first component appears once and only once. The relation is a function.

(b) $\{(9, 3), (9, -3), (4, 2)\}$

The first component 9 appears in two ordered pairs and corresponds to two different second components. Therefore, this relation is not a function. *NOW TRY*

Most functions have an infinite number of ordered pairs and are usually defined with equations that tell how to get the second components (outputs), given the first components (inputs). Here are some everyday examples of functions.

1. The cost $y$ in dollars charged by an express mail company is a function of the weight $x$ in pounds determined by the equation $y = 1.5(x - 1) + 9$.

2. In Cedar Rapids, Iowa, the sales tax is 7% of the price of an item. The tax $y$ on a particular item is a function of the price $x$, because $y = 0.07x$.

3. The distance $d$ traveled by a car moving at a constant speed of 45 mph is a function of the time $t$. Thus, $d = 45t$.

The function concept can be illustrated by an input-output "machine," as seen in **FIGURE 42**. The express mail company equation $y = 1.5(x - 1) + 9$ provides an output (the cost $y$ in dollars) for a given input (the weight $x$ in pounds).

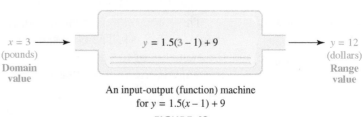

$x = 3$ (pounds) Domain value → $y = 1.5(3 - 1) + 9$ → $y = 12$ (dollars) Range value

An input-output (function) machine
for $y = 1.5(x - 1) + 9$

**FIGURE 42**

*NOW TRY ANSWERS*
**2. (a)** not a function **(b)** function

**OBJECTIVE 3** **Decide whether an equation defines a function.** Given the graph of an equation, the definition of a function can be used to decide whether or not the graph represents a function. By the definition of a function, each $x$-value must lead to exactly one $y$-value.

In **FIGURE 43(a)**, the indicated $x$-value leads to two $y$-values, so this graph is *not* the graph of a function. A vertical line can be drawn that intersects the graph in more than one point.

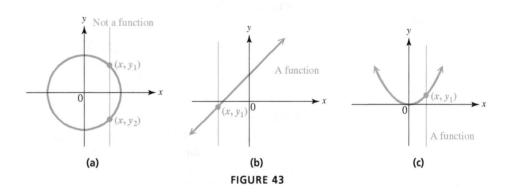

**FIGURE 43**

By contrast, in **FIGURE 43(b)** and **FIGURE 43(c)** any vertical line will intersect each graph in no more than one point, so these graphs are graphs of functions. This idea leads to the **vertical line test** for a function.

> ## Vertical Line Test
>
> If a vertical line intersects a graph in more than one point, then the graph is not the graph of a function.

As **FIGURE 43(b)** suggests, any nonvertical line is the graph of a function. ***Thus, any linear equation of the form $y = mx + b$ defines a function.*** (Recall that a vertical line has undefined slope.)

**EXAMPLE 3** **Determining Whether Relations Define Functions**

Determine whether each relation graphed or defined here is a function.

**(a)**

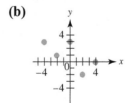

Because there are two ordered pairs with first component $-4$, as shown in red, this is not the graph of a function.

**(b)**

Every first component is matched with one and only one second component, and as a result, no vertical line intersects the graph in more than one point. Therefore, this is the graph of a function.

**(c)** $y = 2x - 9$

This linear equation is in the form $y = mx + b$. Since the graph of this equation is a line that is not vertical, the equation defines a function.

NOW TRY
EXERCISE 3
Determine whether each relation is a function.

(a) $y = x - 5$

(b)

(d)

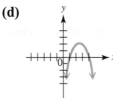

Use the vertical line test. Any vertical line will intersect the graph just once, so this is the graph of a function.

(f) $x = 4$

The graph of $x = 4$ is a vertical line, so the equation does *not* define a function.

NOW TRY

(e)

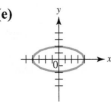

The vertical line test shows that this graph is not the graph of a function. A vertical line could intersect the graph twice.

---

NOTE  An equation in which $y$ is squared does not usually define a function, because most $x$-values will lead to two $y$-values. This is true for *any even* power of $y$, such as $y^2$, $y^4$, $y^6$, and so on. Similarly, an equation involving $|y|$ does not usually define a function, because some $x$-values lead to more than one $y$-value.

---

**OBJECTIVE 4** **Find domains and ranges.** The set of all numbers that can be used as replacements for $x$ in a function is the domain of the function, and the set of all possible values of $y$ is the range of the function.

NOW TRY
EXERCISE 4
Find the domain and range of the function.

$$y = x^2 - 2$$

**EXAMPLE 4** **Finding the Domain and Range of Functions**

Find the domain and range of each function.

(a) $y = 2x - 4$

Any number may be used for $x$, so the domain is the set of all real numbers. Also, any number may be used for $y$, so the range is also the set of all real numbers. As indicated in **FIGURE 44**, the graph of the equation is a straight line that extends infinitely in both directions, confirming that both the domain and range are $(-\infty, \infty)$.

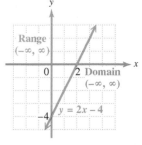

**FIGURE 44**

(b) $y = x^2$

Any number can be squared, so the domain is the set of all real numbers. However, since $y = x^2$, the values of $y$ cannot be negative, making the range the set of all nonnegative numbers, or $[0, \infty)$ in interval notation. The ordered pairs shown in the table are used to get the graph of the function in **FIGURE 45**.

| $x$ | $y$ |
|---|---|
| 0 | 0 |
| 1 | 1 |
| $-1$ | 1 |
| 2 | 4 |
| $-2$ | 4 |
| 3 | 9 |
| $-3$ | 9 |

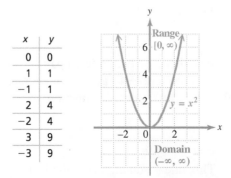

**FIGURE 45**

While $x$ can take any real number value, notice that $y$ is always greater than or equal to 0.

NOW TRY

NOW TRY ANSWERS
**3.** (a) yes (b) no
**4.** domain: $(-\infty, \infty)$; range: $[-2, \infty)$

**OBJECTIVE 5**  Use function notation. The letters $f$, $g$, and $h$ are commonly used to name functions. The function $f$ defined by $y = 3x + 5$ may be written

$$f(x) = 3x + 5,$$

where $f(x)$, which represents the value of $f$ at $x$, is read **"$f$ of $x$."** The notation $f(x)$ is another way of writing $y$ in the function $f$. For the function defined by $f(x) = 3x + 5$, if $x = 7$, then

$$f(7) = 3 \cdot 7 + 5 \qquad \text{Let } x = 7.$$
$$= 21 + 5 \qquad \text{Multiply.}$$
$$= 26. \qquad \text{Add.}$$

Read this result, $f(7) = 26$, as "$f$ of 7 equals 26." The notation $f(7)$ means the value of $y$ when $x$ is 7. The statement $f(7) = 26$ says that the value of $y$ is 26 when $x$ is 7. It also indicates that the point $(7, 26)$ lies on the graph of $f$.

Similarly, to find $f(-3)$, substitute $-3$ for $x$.

$$f(-3) = 3(-3) + 5 \qquad \text{Let } x = -3.$$

Use parentheses to avoid errors.

$$= -9 + 5 \qquad \text{Multiply.}$$
$$= -4 \qquad \text{Add.}$$

⚠ **CAUTION**   The notation $f(x)$ does *not* mean $f$ times $x$. ***It represents the y-value that corresponds to x in function f.***

### Function Notation

In the notation $f(x)$,

| | |
|---|---|
| $f$ | is the name of the function, |
| $x$ | is the domain value, |
| and    $f(x)$ | is the range value $y$ for the domain value $x$. |

**NOW TRY**
**EXERCISE 5**

Find $f(-2)$ for the function.

$$f(x) = x^3 - 7$$

**EXAMPLE 5**   Using Function Notation

For the function defined by $f(x) = x^2 - 3$, find the following.

**(a)** $f(4)$

$$f(x) = x^2 - 3$$
$$f(4) = 4^2 - 3 \qquad \text{Let } x = 4.$$

Think: $4^2 = 4 \cdot 4$

$$= 16 - 3 \qquad \text{Apply the exponent.}$$
$$= 13 \qquad \text{Subtract.}$$

**(b)** $f(0) = 0^2 - 3$

$$= 0 - 3$$
$$= -3$$

Think: $(-3)^2 = -3 \cdot (-3)$

**(c)** $f(-3) = (-3)^2 - 3$

$$= 9 - 3$$
$$= 6$$

**NOW TRY ANSWER**
**5.** $-15$

**NOW TRY**

*NOW TRY*
*EXERCISE 6*

Refer to **Example 6.**

**(a)** Find $f(2006)$ and interpret this result.

**(b)** For what $x$-value does $f(x)$ equal 9.7 million?

**OBJECTIVE 6** **Apply the function concept in an application.**

**EXAMPLE 6** Applying the Function Concept to Population

Asian-American populations (in millions) are shown in the table.

| Year | Population (in millions) |
|------|--------------------------|
| 1996 | 9.7 |
| 2000 | 11.2 |
| 2004 | 13.1 |
| 2006 | 14.9 |

*Source*: U.S. Census Bureau.

**(a)** Use the table to write a set of ordered pairs that defines a function $f$.

If we choose the years as the domain elements and the populations as the range elements, the information in the table can be written as a set of four ordered pairs. In set notation, the function $f$ is defined as follows.

$$f = \{(1996, 9.7), (2000, 11.2), (2004, 13.1), (2006, 14.9)\}$$    *y*-values are in millions.

**(b)** What is the domain of $f$?   What is the range?
The domain is the set of years, or $x$-values.

$$\{1996, 2000, 2004, 2006\}$$

The range is the set of populations, in millions, or $y$-values.

$$\{9.7, 11.2, 13.1, 14.9\}$$

**(c)** Find $f(1996)$ and $f(2004)$.
We refer to the table or the ordered pairs in part (a).

$$f(1996) = 9.7 \text{ million} \quad \text{and} \quad f(2004) = 13.1 \text{ million}$$

*NOW TRY ANSWERS*
**6. (a)** $f(2006) = 14.9$; The population of Asian-Americans was 14.9 million in 2006.
  **(b)** 1996

**(d)** For what $x$-value does $f(x)$ equal 14.9 million?   11.2 million?
We use the table or the ordered pairs found in part (a).

$$f(2006) = 14.9 \text{ million} \quad \text{and} \quad f(2000) = 11.2 \text{ million}$$    *NOW TRY*

---

## 3.6 EXERCISES

🌐 *Complete solution available on the Video Resources on DVD*

*Complete the table for the linear function defined by* $f(x) = x + 2$.

| x | x + 2 | f(x) | (x, y) |
|---|-------|------|--------|
| 0 | 2 | 2 | (0, 2) |
| **1.** 1 | | | |
| **2.** 2 | | | |
| **3.** 3 | | | |
| **4.** t | | | |

**5.** Describe the graph of function $f$ in **Exercises 1–3** if the domain is $\{0, 1, 2, 3\}$.

**6.** Describe the graph of function $f$ in **Exercises 1–3** if the domain is the set of real numbers $(-\infty, \infty)$.

*Determine whether each relation is or is not a function. In Exercises 7–12, give the domain and the range.* **See Examples 1–3.**

🌐 **7.** $\{(-4, 3), (-2, 1), (0, 5), (-2, -8)\}$

**8.** $\{(3, 7), (1, 4), (0, -2), (-1, -1), (-2, 5)\}$

**9.**

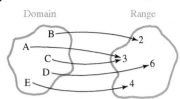

**10.**

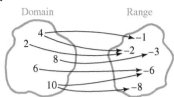

**11.**

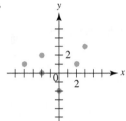

**12.**

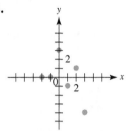

**13.**

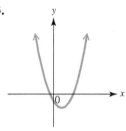

**14.**

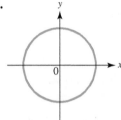

**15.**

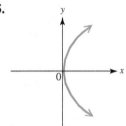

**16.**

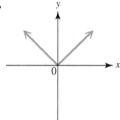

*Decide whether each equation defines y as a function of x. (Remember that, to be a function, every value of x must give one and only one value of y.)*

**17.** $y = 5x + 3$  **18.** $y = -7x + 12$  **19.** $y = x^2$

**20.** $y = -3x^2$  **21.** $x = y^2$  **22.** $x = |y|$

*Find the domain and the range for each function.* **See Example 4.**

**23.** $y = 3x - 2$  **24.** $y = x^2 - 3$  **25.** $y = x^2 + 2$

**26.** $y = -x + 3$  **27.** $f(x) = \sqrt{x}$  **28.** $f(x) = |x|$

---

*RELATING CONCEPTS*  EXERCISES 29–32

**FOR INDIVIDUAL OR GROUP WORK**

*A function defined by the equation of a line, such as*

$$f(x) = 3x - 4,$$

*is called a* **linear function.** *It can be graphed by replacing f(x) with y and then using the methods described earlier in this chapter. Let us assume that some function is written in the form f(x) = mx + b, for particular values of m and b.* **Work Exercises 29–32 in order.**

**29.** If $f(2) = 4$, name the coordinates of one point on the line.

**30.** If $f(-1) = -4$, name the coordinates of another point on the line.

**31.** Use the results of **Exercises 29 and 30** to find the slope of the line.

**32.** Use the slope-intercept form of the equation of a line to write the function in the form $f(x) = mx + b$.

*For each function f, find (a) f(2), (b) f(0), and (c) f(−3). See Example 5.*

**33.** $f(x) = 4x + 3$      **34.** $f(x) = -3x + 5$      🌐 **35.** $f(x) = x^2 - x + 2$

**36.** $f(x) = x^3 + x$      **37.** $f(x) = |x|$      **38.** $f(x) = |x + 7|$

*The graph shows the number of U.S. foreign-born residents (in millions) for selected years. Use the information in the graph to work Exercises 39–44. See Example 6.*

**39.** Write the information in the graph as a set of ordered pairs. Does this set define a function?

**40.** Name the function g in **Exercise 39.** Give the five years specified in the domain of g.

**41.** Find $g(1980)$ and $g(2000)$.

**42.** For what value of x does $g(x) = 19.8$?

**43.** For what value of x does $g(x) = 37.3$?

🖉 **44.** Suppose $g(2005) = 35.7$. What does this tell you in the context of the application?

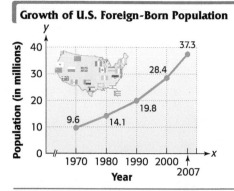

**Growth of U.S. Foreign-Born Population**

*Source:* U.S. Census Bureau.

*A calculator can be thought of as a function machine. We input a number value (from the domain), and then, by pressing the appropriate key, we obtain an output value (from the range). Use your calculator, follow the directions, and then answer each question.*

**45.** Suppose we enter the value 4 and then take the square root (that is, activate the square root *function*, using the key labeled $\sqrt{x}$).

   **(a)** What is the domain value here?      **(b)** What range value is obtained?

**46.** Enter the value $-8$ and then activate the squaring function, using the key labeled $x^2$.

   **(a)** What is the domain value here?      **(b)** What range value is obtained?

---

**TECHNOLOGY INSIGHTS**   EXERCISES 47–52

*The table was generated by a graphing calculator. The expression $Y_1$ represents $f(X)$.*

**47.** When $X = 3$, $Y_1 = $ _____.

**48.** What is $f(3)$?

**49.** When $Y_1 = 2$, $X = $ _____.

**50.** If $f(X) = 2$, what is the value of X?

**51.** The points represented in the table all lie in a straight line.

   **(a)** What is the slope of the line?

   **(b)** What is the *y*-intercept of the line?

**52.** Write the function in the form $y = mx + b$, for the appropriate values of m and b.

| X | Y1 | |
|---|---|---|
| -2 | -1 | |
| -1 | 0 | |
| 0 | 1 | |
| 1 | 2 | |
| 2 | 3 | |
| 3 | 4 | |
| 4 | 5 | |

X=-2

---

**PREVIEW EXERCISES**

*Graph each pair of equations on the same coordinate axes. See Section 3.2.*

**53.** $2x + 3y = 12$     **54.** $x + y = 4$     **55.** $-5x + 2y = 10$     **56.** $2y = -3x$

     $4x - 2y = 8$         $2x = 8 - 2y$         $2y = -4 + 5x$        $-2x + 3y = 0$

## Analyzing Your Test Results

*An exam is a learning opportunity—learn from your mistakes.* After a test is returned, do the following:

▶ **Note what you got wrong and why you had points deducted.**

▶ **Figure out how to solve the problems you missed.** Check your textbook or notes, or ask your instructor. Rework the problems correctly.

▶ **Keep all quizzes and tests that are returned to you.** Use them to study for future tests and the final exam.

### Typical Reasons for Errors on Math Tests

These are **test taking errors.** They are easy to correct if you read carefully, show all your work, proofread, and double-check units and labels.

1. You read the directions wrong.
2. You read the question wrong or skipped over something.
3. You made a computation error.
4. You made a careless error. (For example, you incorrectly copied a correct answer onto a separate answer sheet.)
5. Your answer is not complete.
6. You labeled your answer wrong. (For example, you labeled an answer "ft" instead of "ft$^2$.")
7. You didn't show your work.

These are **test preparation errors.** You must practice the kinds of problems that you will see on tests.

8. You didn't understand a concept.
9. You were unable to set up the problem (in an application).
10. You were unable to apply a procedure.

*Below are sample charts for tracking your test taking progress. Use them to find out if you tend to make certain kinds of errors on tests. Check the appropriate box when you've made an error in a particular category.*

**Test Taking Errors**

| Test | Read directions wrong | Read question wrong | Computation error | Not exact or accurate | Not complete | Labeled wrong | Didn't show work |
|---|---|---|---|---|---|---|---|
| 1 | | | | | | | |
| 2 | | | | | | | |
| 3 | | | | | | | |

**Test Preparation Errors**

| Test | Didn't understand concept | Didn't set up problem correctly | Couldn't apply concept to new situation |
|---|---|---|---|
| 1 | | | |
| 2 | | | |
| 3 | | | |

*What will you do to avoid these kinds of errors on your next test?*

CHAPTER **3** SUMMARY

## KEY TERMS

**3.1**
line graph
linear equation in two
    variables
ordered pair
table of values
*x*-axis
*y*-axis
origin
rectangular (Cartesian)
    coordinate system

quadrant
plane
coordinates
plot
scatter diagram

**3.2**
graph, graphing
*y*-intercept
*x*-intercept
horizontal line
vertical line

**3.3**
rise
run
slope
subscript notation
parallel lines
perpendicular lines

**3.5**
linear inequality in two
    variables
boundary line

**3.6**
components
relation
domain
range
function
function notation

## NEW SYMBOLS

$(a, b)$   an ordered pair

$m$   slope

$(x_1, y_1)$   *x*-sub-one,
         *y*-sub-one

$f(x)$   function $f$ of $x$

## TEST YOUR WORD POWER

*See how well you have learned the vocabulary in this chapter.*

1. An **ordered pair** is a pair of
   numbers written
   A. in numerical order between
      brackets
   B. between parentheses or brackets
   C. between parentheses in which
      order is important
   D. between parentheses in which
      order does not matter.

2. An **intercept** is
   A. the point where the *x*-axis and
      *y*-axis intersect
   B. a pair of numbers written in
      parentheses in which order
      matters
   C. one of the four regions
      determined by a rectangular
      coordinate system

   D. the point where a graph intersects
      the *x*-axis or the *y*-axis.

3. The **slope** of a line is
   A. the measure of the run over the
      rise of the line
   B. the distance between two points
      on the line
   C. the ratio of the change in *y* to the
      change in *x* along the line
   D. the horizontal change compared
      with the vertical change of two
      points on the line.

4. Two lines in a plane are **parallel** if
   A. they represent the same line
   B. they never intersect
   C. they intersect at a 90° angle
   D. one has a positive slope and one
      has a negative slope.

5. Two lines in a plane are
   **perpendicular** if
   A. they represent the same line
   B. they never intersect
   C. they intersect at a 90° angle
   D. one has a positive slope and one
      has a negative slope.

6. A **function** is
   A. any set of ordered pairs
   B. a set of ordered pairs in which
      each first component
      corresponds to exactly one
      second component
   C. two sets of ordered pairs that are
      related
   D. a graph of ordered pairs.

**ANSWERS**
1. C; *Examples:* $(0, 3)$, $(-3, 8)$, $(4, 0)$   2. D; *Example:* The graph of the equation $4x - 3y = 12$ has *x*-intercept $(3, 0)$ and *y*-intercept $(0, -4)$.
3. C; *Example:* The line through $(3, 6)$ and $(5, 4)$ has slope $\frac{4 - 6}{5 - 3} = \frac{-2}{2} = -1$.   4. B; *Example:* See **FIGURE 27** in **Section 3.3.**
5. C; *Example:* See **FIGURE 28** in **Section 3.3.**   6. B; *Example:* The set of ordered pairs $\{(0, 2), (2, 4), (3, 6)\}$ is a function, since
each *x*-value corresponds to exactly one *y*-value.

**CONCEPTS**

**EXAMPLES**

### 3.1 Linear Equations in Two Variables; The Rectangular Coordinate System

An ordered pair is a solution of an equation if it satisfies the equation.

Is $(2, -5)$ or $(0, -6)$ a solution of $4x - 3y = 18$?

$$4(2) - 3(-5) = 23 \neq 18 \qquad \bigg| \qquad 4(0) - 3(-6) = 18$$

$(2, -5)$ is not a solution. $\qquad \bigg| \qquad (0, -6)$ is a solution.

If a value of either variable in an equation is given, then the other variable can be found by substitution.

Complete the ordered pair $(0, \underline{\phantom{x}})$ for $3x = y + 4$.

$$3(0) = y + 4 \qquad \text{Let } x = 0.$$

$$0 = y + 4 \qquad \text{Multiply.}$$

$$-4 = y \qquad \text{Subtract 4.}$$

The ordered pair is $(0, -4)$.

Plot the ordered pair $(-3, 4)$ by starting at the origin, moving 3 units to the left, and then moving 4 units up.

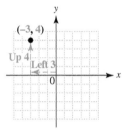

### 3.2 Graphing Linear Equations in Two Variables

To graph a linear equation, follow these steps.

**Step 1**  Find at least two ordered pairs that satisfy the equation.

**Step 2**  Plot the corresponding points.

**Step 3**  Draw a straight line through the points.

| x | y |
|---|---|
| 0 | -2 |
| 4 | 0 |

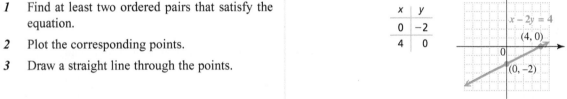

The graph of $Ax + By = 0$ passes through the origin. Find and plot another point that satisfies the equation. Then draw the line through the two points.

The graph of $y = k$ is a horizontal line through $(0, k)$.

The graph of $x = k$ is a vertical line through $(k, 0)$.

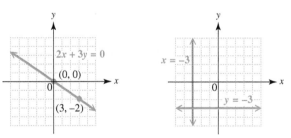

(continued)

| CONCEPTS | EXAMPLES |
|---|---|
| **3.3** The Slope of a Line | |
| The slope of the line through $(x_1, y_1)$ and $(x_2, y_2)$ is $$m = \frac{\text{change in } y}{\text{change in } x} = \frac{y_2 - y_1}{x_2 - x_1} \quad (\text{where } x_1 \neq x_2).$$ | The line through $(-2, 3)$ and $(4, -5)$ has slope as follows. $$m = \frac{-5 - 3}{4 - (-2)} = \frac{-8}{6} = -\frac{4}{3}$$ |
| **Horizontal lines have slope 0.** | The line $y = -2$ has slope $0$. |
| **Vertical lines have undefined slope.** | The line $x = 4$ has undefined slope. |
| To find the slope of a line from its equation, solve for $y$. The slope is the coefficient of $x$. | Find the slope of $3x - 4y = 12$. $$-4y = -3x + 12 \qquad \text{Add } -3x.$$ $$y = \frac{3}{4}x - 3 \qquad \text{Divide by } -4.$$ Slope ⤴ |
| Parallel lines have the same slope. | The lines $y = 3x - 1$ and $y = 3x + 4$ are parallel because both have slope $3$. |
| The slopes of perpendicular lines are negative reciprocals (that is, their product is $-1$). | The lines $y = -3x - 1$ and $y = \frac{1}{3}x + 4$ are perpendicular because their slopes are $-3$ and $\frac{1}{3}$, and $-3\left(\frac{1}{3}\right) = -1$. |
| **3.4** Writing and Graphing Equations of Lines | |
| **Slope-Intercept Form** $$y = mx + b$$ $m$ is the slope. $(0, b)$ is the $y$-intercept. | Write an equation of the line with slope $2$ and $y$-intercept $(0, -5)$. $$y = 2x - 5$$ |
| **Point-Slope Form** $$y - y_1 = m(x - x_1)$$ $m$ is the slope. $(x_1, y_1)$ is a point on the line. | Write an equation of the line with slope $-\frac{1}{2}$ through $(-4, 5)$. $$y - 5 = -\frac{1}{2}[x - (-4)] \qquad \text{Substitute.}$$ $$y - 5 = -\frac{1}{2}(x + 4) \qquad \text{Definition of subtraction}$$ $$y - 5 = -\frac{1}{2}x - 2 \qquad \text{Distributive property}$$ $$y = -\frac{1}{2}x + 3 \qquad \text{Add 5.}$$ |
| **Standard Form** $$Ax + By = C$$ $A$, $B$, and $C$ are real numbers and $A$ and $B$ are not both 0. | The equation $y = -\frac{1}{2}x + 3$ is written in standard form as $$x + 2y = 6,$$ with $A = 1$, $B = 2$, and $C = 6$. |

(continued)

| CONCEPTS | EXAMPLES |
|---|---|
| **3.5** Graphing Linear Inequalities in Two Variables | Graph $2x + y \leq 5$. |

**Step 1** Graph the line that is the boundary of the region. Make it solid if the inequality is $\leq$ or $\geq$ because of the equality portion of the symbol. Make it dashed if the inequality is $<$ or $>$.

Graph the line $2x + y = 5$. Make it solid because of the equality portion of the symbol $\leq$.

**Step 2** Use any point not on the line as a test point. Substitute for $x$ and $y$ in the inequality. If the result is true, shade the region of the line containing the test point. If the result is false, shade the other region.

Use $(0, 0)$ as a test point.

$$2(0) + 0 \overset{?}{\leq} 5$$

$$0 \leq 5 \quad \text{True}$$

Shade the side of the line containing $(0, 0)$.

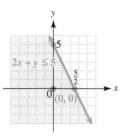

---

**3.6** Introduction to Functions

**Vertical Line Test**
If a vertical line intersects a graph in more than one point, the graph is not the graph of a function.

The **domain** of a function is the set of numbers that can replace $x$ in the expression for the function. The **range** is the set of $y$-values that result as $x$ is replaced by each number in the domain.

To find $f(x)$ for a specific value of $x$, replace $x$ by that value in the expression for the function.

The graph shown is not the graph of a function.

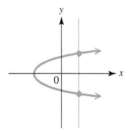

Let $f(x) = x - 1$. Find
**(a)** the domain of $f$, **(b)** the range of $f$,
**(c)** $f(-1)$.

**(a)** The domain is $(-\infty, \infty)$.

**(b)** The range is $(-\infty, \infty)$.

**(c)** $f(-1) = -1 - 1 = -2$

---

# CHAPTER 3

# REVIEW EXERCISES

## 3.1

1. The line graph shows the number, in millions, of real Christmas trees purchased for the years 2002 through 2007.

   **(a)** Between which years did the number of real trees purchased increase?

   **(b)** Between which years did the number of real trees purchased decrease?

   **(c)** Estimate the number of real trees purchased in 2005 and 2006.

   **(d)** By about how much did the number of real trees purchased between 2005 and 2006 decrease?

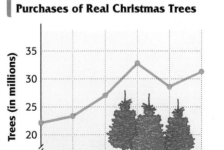

**Purchases of Real Christmas Trees**

*Source:* National Christmas Tree Association.

*Complete the given ordered pairs for each equation.*

**2.** $y = 3x + 2$; $(-1, \_\_)$, $(0, \_\_)$, $(\_\_, 5)$

**3.** $4x + 3y = 6$; $(0, \_\_)$, $(\_\_, 0)$, $(-2, \_\_)$

**4.** $x = 3y$; $(0, \_\_)$, $(8, \_\_)$, $(\_\_, -3)$

**5.** $x - 7 = 0$; $(\_\_, -3)$, $(\_\_, 0)$, $(\_\_, 5)$

*Determine whether the given ordered pair is a solution of the given equation.*

**6.** $x + y = 7$; $(2, 5)$     **7.** $2x + y = 5$; $(-1, 3)$     **8.** $3x - y = 4$; $\left(\frac{1}{3}, -3\right)$

*Name the quadrant in which each ordered pair lies. Then plot each pair in a rectangular coordinate system.*

**9.** $(2, 3)$       **10.** $(-4, 2)$       **11.** $(3, 0)$       **12.** $(0, -6)$

**13.** *Concept Check* If $xy > 0$, in what quadrant or quadrants must $(x, y)$ lie?

**3.2** *Find the x- and y-intercepts for the line that is the graph of each equation, and graph the line.*

**14.** $y = 2x + 5$       **15.** $3x + 2y = 8$       **16.** $x + 2y = -4$

**3.3** *Find the slope of each line.*

**17.** Through $(2, 3)$ and $(-4, 6)$       **18.** Through $(2, 5)$ and $(2, 8)$

**19.** $y = 3x - 4$                      **20.** $y = 5$

**21.**

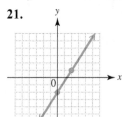

**22.**

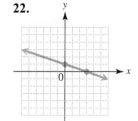

**23.** The line passing through these points

| x | y |
|---|---|
| 0 | 1 |
| 2 | 4 |
| 6 | 10 |

**24. (a)** A line parallel to the graph of $y = 2x + 3$

    **(b)** A line perpendicular to the graph of $y = -3x + 3$

*Decide whether each pair of lines is* parallel, perpendicular, *or* neither.

**25.** $3x + 2y = 6$       **26.** $x - 3y = 1$       **27.** $x - 2y = 8$

      $6x + 4y = 8$          $3x + y = 4$          $x + 2y = 8$

**3.4** *Write an equation for each line. Give the final answer in slope-intercept form if possible.*

**28.** $m = -1, b = \frac{2}{3}$                **29.** Through $(2, 3)$ and $(-4, 6)$

**30.** Through $(4, -3), m = 1$         **31.** Through $(-1, 4), m = \frac{2}{3}$

**32.** Through $(1, -1), m = -\frac{3}{4}$      **33.** $m = -\frac{1}{4}, b = \frac{3}{2}$

**34.** Slope 0, through $(-4, 1)$        **35.** Through $\left(\frac{1}{3}, -\frac{5}{4}\right)$, undefined slope

**3.5**  *Graph each linear inequality.*

**36.** $3x + 5y > 9$          **37.** $2x - 3y > -6$          **38.** $x - 2y \geq 0$

**3.6**  *Decide whether each relation* is *or* is not *a function. In Exercises 39 and 40, give the domain and the range.*

**39.** $\{(-2, 4), (0, 8), (2, 5), (2, 3)\}$          **40.** $\{(8, 3), (7, 4), (6, 5), (5, 6), (4, 7)\}$

**41.**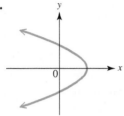

**42.**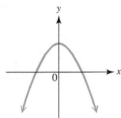

**43.** $2x + 3y = 12$          **44.** $y = x^2$

*Find (a) $f(2)$ and (b) $f(-1)$.*

**45.** $f(x) = 3x + 2$          **46.** $f(x) = 2x^2 - 1$          **47.** $f(x) = |x + 3|$

## MIXED REVIEW EXERCISES

*Concept Check  In Exercises 48–53, match each statement to the appropriate graph or graphs in A–D. Graphs may be used more than once.*

**A.** 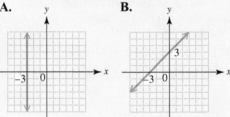  **B.**  **C.** 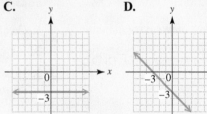  **D.**

**48.** The line shown in the graph has undefined slope.

**49.** The graph of the equation has $y$-intercept $(0, -3)$.

**50.** The graph of the equation has $x$-intercept $(-3, 0)$.

**51.** The line shown in the graph has negative slope.

**52.** The graph is that of the equation $y = -3$.

**53.** The line shown in the graph has slope 1.

*Find the intercepts and the slope of each line. Then graph the line.*

**54.** $y = -2x - 5$          **55.** $x + 3y = 0$          **56.** $y - 5 = 0$

*Write an equation for each line. Give the final answer in slope-intercept form.*

**57.** $m = -\frac{1}{4}, b = -\frac{5}{4}$          **58.** Through $(8, 6), m = -3$

**59.** Through $(3, -5)$ and $(-4, -1)$          **60.** Slope 0, through $(5, -5)$

*Graph each inequality.*

**61.** $x - 2y \leq 6$          **62.** $y < -4x$

*The percents of four-year college students in public schools who earned a degree within five years of entry between 2002 and 2007 are shown in the graph. Use the graph to work Exercises 63–66.*

63. Since the points of the graph lie approximately in a linear pattern, a straight line can be used to model the data. Will this line have positive or negative slope? Explain.

64. Write two ordered pairs for the data for 2002 and 2007.

65. Use the two ordered pairs from **Exercise 64** to write an equation of a line that models the data. Give the equation in slope-intercept form.

66. Use the equation from **Exercise 65** to approximate the percents for 2003 through 2006.

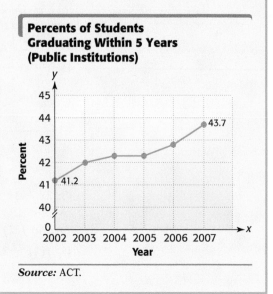

**Percents of Students Graduating Within 5 Years (Public Institutions)**

*Source:* ACT.

---

# CHAPTER 3

# TEST

CHAPTER Test Prep VIDEOS

Step-by-step test solutions are found on the Chapter Test Prep Videos available via the Video Resources on DVD, in *MyMathLab*, or on YouTube (search "LialBeginningAlgebra").

*View the complete solutions to all Chapter Test exercises on the Video Resources on DVD.*

1. Complete the ordered pairs $(0, \_\_)$, $(\_\_, 0)$, $(\_\_, -3)$ for the equation $3x + 5y = -30$.

2. Is $(4, -1)$ a solution of $4x - 7y = 9$?

3. How do you find the *x*-intercept of the graph of a linear equation in two variables? How do you find the *y*-intercept?

*Graph each linear equation. Give the x- and y-intercepts.*

4. $3x + y = 6$       5. $y - 2x = 0$       6. $x + 3 = 0$

7. $y = 1$       8. $x - y = 4$

*Find the slope of each line.*

9. Through $(-4, 6)$ and $(-1, -2)$       10. $2x + y = 10$

11. $x + 12 = 0$       12. A line parallel to the graph of $y - 4 = 6$

13.

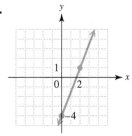

*Write an equation for each line. Give the final answer in slope-intercept form.*

**14.** Through $(-1, 4)$, $m = 2$  **15.** The line in **Exercise 13**

**16.** Through $(2, -6)$ and $(1, 3)$

*Graph each linear inequality.*

**17.** $x + y \leq 3$  **18.** $3x - y > 0$

*The graph shows worldwide snowmobile sales from 2000 through 2007, where 2000 corresponds to $x = 0$. Use the graph to work Exercises 19–22.*

**Worldwide Snowmobile Sales**

*Source:* www.snowmobile.org

**19.** Is the slope of the line in the graph positive or negative? Explain.

**20.** Write two ordered pairs for the data points shown in the graph. Use them to write an equation of a line that models the data. Give the equation in slope-intercept form.

**21.** Use the equation from **Exercise 20** to approximate worldwide snowmobile sales for 2005. How does your answer compare to the actual sales of 173.7 thousand?

**22.** What does the ordered pair $(7, 160)$ mean in the context of this problem?

**23.** Decide whether each relation represents a function. If it does, give the domain and the range.

  **(a)** $\{(2, 3), (2, 4), (2, 5)\}$  **(b)** $\{(0, 2), (1, 2), (2, 2)\}$

**24.** Use the vertical line test to determine whether the graph is that of a function.

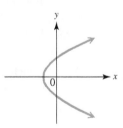

**25.** If $f(x) = 3x + 7$, find $f(-2)$.

# CHAPTERS 1–3 CUMULATIVE REVIEW EXERCISES

*Perform each indicated operation.*

**1.** $10\dfrac{5}{8} - 3\dfrac{1}{10}$

**2.** $\dfrac{3}{4} \div \dfrac{1}{8}$

**3.** $5 - (-4) + (-2)$

**4.** $\dfrac{(-3)^2 - (-4)(2^4)}{5(2) - (-2)^3}$

**5.** *True* or *false?* $\dfrac{4(3-9)}{2-6} \geq 6$

**6.** Find the value of $xz^3 - 5y^2$ when $x = -2$, $y = -3$, and $z = -1$.

**7.** What property does $3(-2 + x) = -6 + 3x$ illustrate?

**8.** Simplify $-4p - 6 + 3p + 8$ by combining like terms.

*Solve.*

**9.** $V = \dfrac{1}{3}\pi r^2 h$ for $h$

**10.** $6 - 3(1 + x) = 2(x + 5) - 2$

**11.** $-(m - 3) = 5 - 2m$

**12.** $\dfrac{x-2}{3} = \dfrac{2x+1}{5}$

*Solve each inequality, and graph the solution set.*

**13.** $-2.5x < 6.5$

**14.** $4(x + 3) - 5x < 12$

**15.** $\dfrac{2}{3}x - \dfrac{1}{6}x \leq -2$

*Solve each problem.*

**16.** The gap in average annual earnings by level of education has increased over time. In 2008, the average full-time worker age 25 or over with a bachelor's degree earned $20,124 more than a full-time worker with only a high school diploma. Together, these two individuals earned a total of $81,588. How much did the average worker at each level of education earn? (*Source:* U.S. Bureau of Labor Statistics.)

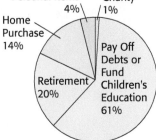

**17.** Baby boomers are expected to inherit $10.4 trillion from their parents over the next 45 yr, an average of $50,000 each. The circle graph shows how they plan to spend their inheritances.

(a) How much of the $50,000 is expected to go toward a home purchase?

(b) How much is expected to go toward retirement?

**18.** Use the answer from **Exercise 17(b)** to estimate the amount expected to go toward paying off debts or funding children's education.

**Spending Their Inheritances**

Personal Items 4%
Charity 1%
Home Purchase 14%
Pay Off Debts or Fund Children's Education 61%
Retirement 20%

*Source:* First Interstate Bank Trust and Private Banking Group.

*Consider the linear equation $-3x + 4y = 12$. Find the following.*

**19.** The $x$- and $y$-intercepts

**20.** The slope

**21.** The graph

**22.** Are the lines with equations $x + 5y = -6$ and $y = 5x - 8$ *parallel, perpendicular,* or *neither*?

*Write an equation for each line. Give the final answer in slope-intercept form if possible.*

**23.** Through $(2, -5)$, slope 3

**24.** Through $(0, 4)$ and $(2, 4)$

# Systems of Linear Equations and Inequalities

NO

Over the years, Americans have continued their fascination with Hollywood and the movies. In 2009, the number of tickets sold at domestic movie theaters topped 1.4 billion, with a total gross of almost $10.6 billion. The top box office draws of that year—*Avatar* and *Transformers 2: Revenge of the Fallen*—attracted millions of adults and children wishing to get away from it all for a few hours. (*Source:* www.boxofficemojo.com)

In **Exercises 13 and 14** of **Section 4.4,** we use *systems of equations* to find out how much money these and other top films earned in 2009.

247

4.1

# Solving Systems of Linear Equations by Graphing

**OBJECTIVES**

1. Decide whether a given ordered pair is a solution of a system.
2. Solve linear systems by graphing.
3. Solve special systems by graphing.
4. Identify special systems without graphing.

A **system of linear equations,** often called a **linear system,** consists of two or more linear equations with the same variables.

$$2x + 3y = 4 \qquad\qquad x + 3y = 1 \qquad\qquad x - y = 1$$
$$3x - y = -5 \qquad\qquad -y = 4 - 2x \qquad\qquad y = 3$$

Linear systems

**NOTE** In the system on the right, think of $y = 3$ as an equation in two variables by writing it as $0x + y = 3$.

**OBJECTIVE 1** Decide whether a given ordered pair is a solution of a system. A **solution of a system** of linear equations is an ordered pair that makes both equations true at the same time. A solution of an equation is said to *satisfy* the equation.

**NOW TRY EXERCISE 1**

Decide whether the ordered pair $(5, 2)$ is a solution of each system.

**(a)** $2x + 5y = 20$
$\qquad x - y = 7$

**(b)** $3x - y = 13$
$\qquad 2x + y = 12$

**EXAMPLE 1** Determining Whether an Ordered Pair Is a Solution

Decide whether the ordered pair $(4, -3)$ is a solution of each system.

**(a)** $\quad x + 4y = -8$
$\qquad 3x + 2y = 6$

To decide whether $(4, -3)$ is a solution of the system, substitute 4 for $x$ and $-3$ for $y$ in each equation.

| | | |
|---|---|---|
| $x + 4y = -8$ | | $3x + 2y = 6$ |
| $4 + 4(-3) \stackrel{?}{=} -8$ | Substitute. | $3(4) + 2(-3) \stackrel{?}{=} 6$ | Substitute. |
| $4 + (-12) \stackrel{?}{=} -8$ | Multiply. | $12 + (-6) \stackrel{?}{=} 6$ | Multiply. |
| $-8 = -8$ ✓ True | | $6 = 6$ ✓ True |

Because $(4, -3)$ satisfies both equations, it is a solution of the system.

**(b)** $2x + 5y = -7$
$\quad 3x + 4y = 2$

Again, substitute 4 for $x$ and $-3$ for $y$ in both equations.

| | | |
|---|---|---|
| $2x + 5y = -7$ | | $3x + 4y = 2$ |
| $2(4) + 5(-3) \stackrel{?}{=} -7$ | Substitute. | $3(4) + 4(-3) \stackrel{?}{=} 2$ | Substitute. |
| $8 + (-15) \stackrel{?}{=} -7$ | Multiply. | $12 + (-12) \stackrel{?}{=} 2$ | Multiply. |
| $-7 = -7$ ✓ True | | $0 = 2$ | False |

The ordered pair $(4, -3)$ is not a solution of this system because it does not satisfy the second equation.

NOW TRY

**OBJECTIVE 2** Solve linear systems by graphing. The set of all ordered pairs that are solutions of a system is its **solution set.** One way to find the solution set of a system of two linear equations is to graph both equations on the same axes.

Any intersection point would be on both lines and would therefore be a solution of *both* equations. ***Thus, the coordinates of any point at which the lines intersect give a solution of the system.***

The graph in **FIGURE 1** shows that the solution of the system in **Example 1(a)** is the intersection point $(4, -3)$. Because two *different* straight lines can intersect at no more than one point, there can never be more than one solution for such a system.

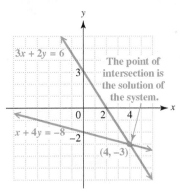

**FIGURE 1**

NOW TRY
EXERCISE 2

Solve the system by graphing.

$$x - 2y = 4$$
$$2x + y = 3$$

**EXAMPLE 2**  Solving a System by Graphing

Solve the system of equations by graphing both equations on the same axes.

$$2x + 3y = 4$$
$$3x - y = -5$$

We graph these two lines by plotting several points for each line. Recall from **Section 3.2** that the intercepts are often convenient choices.

$2x + 3y = 4$

| x | y |
|---|---|
| 0 | $\frac{4}{3}$ |
| 2 | 0 |
| -2 | $\frac{8}{3}$ |

Find a third ordered pair as a check.

$3x - y = -5$

| x | y |
|---|---|
| 0 | 5 |
| $-\frac{5}{3}$ | 0 |
| -2 | -1 |

The lines in **FIGURE 2** suggest that the graphs intersect at the point $(-1, 2)$. We check this by substituting $-1$ for $x$ and $2$ for $y$ in both equations.

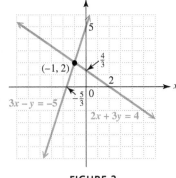

| CHECK | | |
|---|---|---|
| $2x + 3y = 4$ | | First equation |
| $2(-1) + 3(2) \stackrel{?}{=} 4$ | | Substitute. |
| $4 = 4$ ✓ | | True |
| $3x - y = -5$ | | Second equation |
| $3(-1) - 2 \stackrel{?}{=} -5$ | | Substitute. |
| $-5 = -5$ ✓ | | True |

**FIGURE 2**

NOW TRY ANSWER
**2.** $\{(2, -1)\}$

Because $(-1, 2)$ satisfies both equations, the solution set of this system is $\{(-1, 2)\}$.

NOW TRY

> ### Solving a Linear System by Graphing
>
> *Step 1* **Graph each equation** of the system on the same coordinate axes.
>
> *Step 2* **Find the coordinates of the point of intersection** of the graphs if possible. This is the solution of the system.
>
> *Step 3* **Check** the solution in *both* of the original equations. Then write the solution set.

⚠ **CAUTION** With the graphing method, it may not be possible to determine the exact coordinates of the point that represents the solution, particularly if those coordinates are not integers. The graphing method does, however, show geometrically how solutions are found and is useful when approximate answers will do.

---

**OBJECTIVE 3** **Solve special systems by graphing.** Sometimes the graphs of the two equations in a system either do not intersect at all or are the same line.

⤹ *NOW TRY*
*EXERCISE 3*

Solve each system by graphing.

(a) $5x - 3y = 2$
$10x - 6y = 4$

(b) $4x + y = 7$
$12x + 3y = 10$

**EXAMPLE 3** Solving Special Systems by Graphing

Solve each system by graphing.

(a) $2x + y = 2$
$2x + y = 8$

The graphs of these lines are shown in **FIGURE 3**. The two lines are parallel and have no points in common. For such a system, there is no solution. We write the solution set as $\emptyset$.

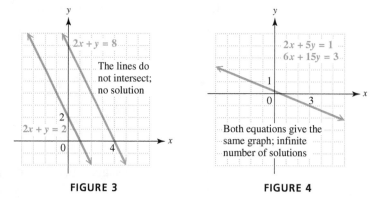

FIGURE 3    FIGURE 4

(b) $2x + 5y = 1$
$6x + 15y = 3$

The graphs of these two equations are the same line. See **FIGURE 4**. We can obtain the second equation by multiplying each side of the first equation by 3. In this case, every point on the line is a solution of the system, and the solution set contains an infinite number of ordered pairs, each of which satisfies both equations of the system. We write the solution set as

$$\{(x, y) \mid 2x + 5y = 1\},$$

> This is the first equation in the system. See the Note on the next page.

read "the set of ordered pairs $(x, y)$ such that $2x + 5y = 1$." Recall from **Section 1.4** that this notation is called **set-builder notation**.

*NOW TRY*

**NOW TRY ANSWERS**
3. (a) $\{(x, y) \mid 5x - 3y = 2\}$
   (b) $\emptyset$

---

NOTE When a system has an infinite number of solutions, as in **Example 3(b)**, either equation of the system could be used to write the solution set. *We prefer to use the equation in standard form with integer coefficients that have greatest common factor 1.* If neither of the given equations is in this form, we will use an *equivalent* equation that is in standard form with integer coefficients that have greatest common factor 1.

---

The system in **Example 2** has exactly one solution. A system with at least one solution is called a **consistent system.** A system with no solution, such as the one in **Example 3(a),** is called an **inconsistent system.**

The equations in **Example 2** are **independent equations** with different graphs. The equations of the system in **Example 3(b)** have the same graph and are equivalent. Because they are different forms of the same equation, these equations are called **dependent equations.**

**Examples 2 and 3** show the three cases that may occur when solving a system of equations with two variables.

### Three Cases for Solutions of Systems

1. The graphs intersect at exactly one point, which gives the (single) ordered-pair solution of the system. The **system is consistent** and the **equations are independent.** See FIGURE 5(a).

2. The graphs are parallel lines, so there is no solution and the solution set is $\emptyset$. The **system is inconsistent** and the **equations are independent.** See FIGURE 5(b).

3. The graphs are the same line. There is an infinite number of solutions, and the solution set is written in set-builder notation as

$$\{(x,y)\,|\,\underline{\qquad}\},$$

where one of the equations is written after the $|$ symbol. The **system is consistent** and the **equations are dependent.** See FIGURE 5(c).

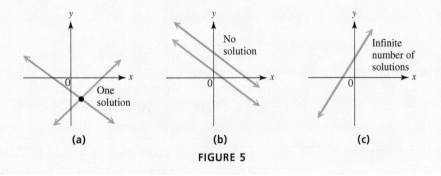

(a)                    (b)                    (c)

**FIGURE 5**

---

**OBJECTIVE 4** **Identify special systems without graphing. Example 3** showed that the graphs of an inconsistent system are parallel lines and the graphs of a system of dependent equations are the same line. We can recognize these special kinds of systems without graphing by using slopes.

NOW TRY
EXERCISE 4

Describe each system without graphing. State the number of solutions.

**(a)** $5x - 8y = 4$
$x - \frac{8}{5}y = \frac{4}{5}$

**(b)** $2x + y = 7$
$3y = -6x - 12$

**(c)** $y - 3x = 7$
$3y - x = 0$

---

**EXAMPLE 4** Identifying the Three Cases by Using Slopes

Describe each system without graphing. State the number of solutions.

**(a)** $3x + 2y = 6$
$-2y = 3x - 5$
Write each equation in slope-intercept form, $y = mx + b$, by solving for $y$.

| $3x + 2y = 6$ | $-2y = 3x - 5$ |
|---|---|
| $2y = -3x + 6$    Subtract 3x. | $y = -\frac{3}{2}x + \frac{5}{2}$    Divide by $-2$. |
| $y = -\frac{3}{2}x + 3$    Divide by 2. | |

Both equations have slope $-\frac{3}{2}$ but they have different $y$-intercepts, $3$ and $\frac{5}{2}$. In **Section 3.3,** we found that lines with the same slope are parallel, so these equations have graphs that are parallel lines. Thus, the system has no solution.

**(b)** $2x - y = 4$
$x = \frac{y}{2} + 2$

Again, write the equations in slope-intercept form.

| $2x - y = 4$ | $x = \frac{y}{2} + 2$ |
|---|---|
| $-y = -2x + 4$    Subtract 2x. | $\frac{y}{2} + 2 = x$    Interchange sides. |
| $y = 2x - 4$    Multiply by $-1$. | $\frac{y}{2} = x - 2$    Subtract 2. |
| | $y = 2x - 4$    Multiply by 2. |

The equations are exactly the same—their graphs are the same line. Thus, the system has an infinite number of solutions.

**(c)** $x - 3y = 5$
$2x + y = 8$

In slope-intercept form, the equations are as follows.

| $x - 3y = 5$ | $2x + y = 8$ |
|---|---|
| $-3y = -x + 5$    Subtract x. | $y = -2x + 8$    Subtract 2x. |
| $y = \frac{1}{3}x - \frac{5}{3}$    Divide by $-3$. | |

The graphs of these equations are neither parallel nor the same line, since the slopes are different. This system has exactly one solution.

NOW TRY

---

NOW TRY ANSWERS

**4. (a)** The equations represent the same line. The system has an infinite number of solutions.
**(b)** The equations represent parallel lines. The system has no solution.
**(c)** The equations represent lines that are neither parallel nor the same line. The system has exactly one solution.

**NOTE** The solution set of the system in **Example 4(a)** is $\emptyset$, since the graphs of the equations of the system are parallel lines. The solution set of the system in **Example 4(b),** written using set-builder notation and the first equation, is

$$\{(x, y) \mid 2x - y = 4\}.$$

If we try to solve the system in **Example 4(c)** by graphing, we will have difficulty identifying the point of intersection of the graphs. We introduce an algebraic method for solving systems like this in **Section 4.2.**

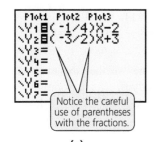

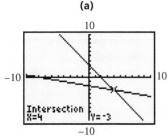

Notice the careful use of parentheses with the fractions.

**(a)**

The display at the bottom of the screen indicates that the solution set is $\{(4, -3)\}$.

**(b)**

**FIGURE 6**

 We can solve the system from **Example 1(a)** by graphing with a calculator.

$$x + 4y = -8$$
$$3x + 2y = 6$$

To enter the equations in a graphing calculator, first solve each equation for $y$.

| | |
|---|---|
| $x + 4y = -8$ | $3x + 2y = 6$ |
| $4y = -x - 8$      Subtract $x$. | $2y = -3x + 6$      Subtract $3x$. |
| $y = -\dfrac{1}{4}x - 2$      Divide by 4. | $y = -\dfrac{3}{2}x + 3$      Divide by 2. |

We designate the first equation $Y_1$ and the second equation $Y_2$. See **FIGURE 6(a)**. We graph the two equations using a standard window and then use the capability of the calculator to find the coordinates of the point of intersection of the graphs. See **FIGURE 6(b)**.

**For Discussion or Writing**

Use a graphing calculator to solve each system.

**1.** $3x + y = 2$
$\quad\;\; 2x - y = -7$

**2.** $8x + 4y = 0$
$\quad\;\; 4x - 2y = 2$

**3.** $3x + 3y = 0$
$\quad\;\; 4x + 2y = 3$

---

**4.1 EXERCISES**   **MyMathLab**   Math XL PRACTICE   WATCH   DOWNLOAD   READ   REVIEW

🌐 *Complete solution available on the Video Resources on DVD*

**1.** *Concept Check*  Which ordered pair could not be a solution of the system graphed? Why is it the only valid choice?

    **A.** $(-4, -4)$      **B.** $(-2, 2)$

    **C.** $(-4, 4)$      **D.** $(-3, 3)$

**2.** *Concept Check*  Which ordered pair could be a solution of the system graphed? Why is it the only valid choice?

    **A.** $(2, 0)$      **B.** $(0, 2)$

    **C.** $(-2, 0)$      **D.** $(0, -2)$

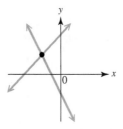

*Decide whether the given ordered pair is a solution of the given system. See Example 1.*

🌐 **3.** $(2, -3)$
$\quad\;\; x + \;\; y = -1$
$\quad\;\; 2x + 5y = 19$

**4.** $(4, 3)$
$\quad\;\; x + 2y = 10$
$\quad\;\; 3x + 5y = 3$

**5.** $(-1, -3)$
$\quad\;\; 3x + 5y = -18$
$\quad\;\; 4x + 2y = -10$

**6.** $(-9, -2)$
$\quad\;\; 2x - 5y = -8$
$\quad\;\; 3x + 6y = -39$

**7.** $(7, -2)$
$\quad\;\; 4x = 26 - \;\; y$
$\quad\;\; 3x = 29 + 4y$

**8.** $(9, 1)$
$\quad\;\; 2x = 23 - 5y$
$\quad\;\; 3x = 24 + 3y$

**9.** $(6, -8)$
$$-2y = x + 10$$
$$3y = 2x + 30$$

**10.** $(-5, 2)$
$$5y = 3x + 20$$
$$3y = -2x - 4$$

**11.** $(0, 0)$
$$4x + 2y = 0$$
$$x + y = 0$$

**12.** *Concept Check* When a student was asked to determine whether the ordered pair $(1, -2)$ is a solution of the following system, he answered "yes." His reasoning was that the ordered pair satisfies the equation $x + y = -1$, since $1 + (-2) = -1$. *WHAT WENT WRONG?*

$$x + y = -1$$
$$2x + y = 4$$

**13.** *Concept Check* Each ordered pair in (a)–(d) is a solution of one of the systems graphed in A–D. Because of the location of the point of intersection, you should be able to determine the correct system for each solution. Match each system from A–D with its solution from (a)–(d).

**(a)** $(3, 4)$     **A.**

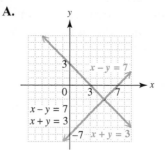

**(b)** $(-2, 3)$

**B.**

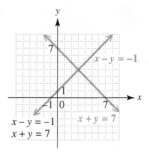

**(c)** $(-3, 2)$     **C.**

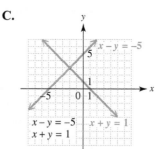

**(d)** $(5, -2)$

**D.**

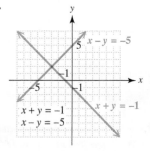

**14.** *Concept Check* The following system has infinitely many solutions. Write its solution set, using set-builder notation as described in **Example 3(b)**.

$$6x - 4y = 8$$
$$3x - 2y = 4$$

*Solve each system of equations by graphing. If the system is inconsistent or the equations are dependent, say so.* **See Examples 2 and 3.**

**15.** $x - y = 2$
$x + y = 6$

**16.** $x - y = 3$
$x + y = -1$

**17.** $x + y = 4$
$y - x = 4$

**18.** $x + y = -5$
$y - x = -5$

**19.** $x - 2y = 6$
$x + 2y = 2$

**20.** $2x - y = 4$
$4x + y = 2$

**21.** $3x - 2y = -3$
$-3x - y = -6$

**22.** $2x - y = 4$
$2x + 3y = 12$

**23.** $2x - 3y = -6$
$y = -3x + 2$

**24.** $-3x + y = -3$
$y = x - 3$

**25.** $2x - y = 6$
$4x - 2y = 8$

**26.** $x + 2y = 4$
$2x + 4y = 12$

**27.** $3x + y = 5$
$6x + 2y = 10$

**28.** $2x - y = 4$
$4x - 2y = 8$

**29.** $3x - 4y = 24$
$y = -\dfrac{3}{2}x + 3$

**30.** $4x + y = 5$

$\quad\quad y = \dfrac{3}{2}x - 6$

**31.** $2x = y - 4$

$\quad\quad 4x + 4 = 2y$

**32.** $3x = y + 5$

$\quad\quad 6x - 5 = 2y$

**33.** Solve the system by graphing. Can you check your solution? Why or why not?

$$2x + 3y = 6$$
$$x - 3y = 5$$

**34.** Explain one of the drawbacks of solving a system of equations graphically.

*Without graphing, answer the following questions for each linear system.* ***See Example 4.***

*(a) Is the system inconsistent, are the equations dependent, or neither?*

*(b) Is the graph a pair of intersecting lines, a pair of parallel lines, or one line?*

*(c) Does the system have one solution, no solution, or an infinite number of solutions?*

**35.** $y - x = -5$

$\quad\quad x + y = 1$

**36.** $y + 2x = 6$

$\quad\quad x - 3y = -4$

**37.** $x + 2y = 0$

$\quad\quad 4y = -2x$

**38.** $2x - y = 4$

$\quad\quad y + 4 = 2x$

**39.** $x - 3y = 5$

$\quad\quad 2x + y = 8$

**40.** $2x + 3y = 12$

$\quad\quad 2x - y = 4$

**41.** $5x + 4y = 7$

$\quad\quad 10x + 8y = 4$

**42.** $3x + 2y = 5$

$\quad\quad 6x + 4y = 3$

*Work each problem using the graph provided.*

**43.** The numbers of daily morning and evening newspapers in the United States in selected years over the period 1980–2008 are shown in the graph.

**(a)** For which years were there more evening dailies than morning dailies?

**(b)** Estimate the year in which the number of evening and morning dailies was closest to the same. About how many newspapers of each type were there in that year?

**Number of Daily Newspapers**

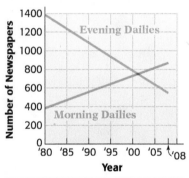

*Source:* Editor & Publisher International Year Book.

**44.** The graph shows how sales of music CDs and digital downloads of single songs (in millions) in the United States have changed over the years 2004 through 2007.

**(a)** In what year did Americans purchase about the same number of CDs as single digital downloads? How many units was this?

**(b)** Express the point of intersection of the two graphs as an ordered pair of the form (year, units in millions).

**(c)** Describe the trend in sales of music CDs over the years 2004 to 2007. If a straight line were used to approximate its graph, would the line have positive, negative, or zero slope? Explain.

**(d)** If a straight line were used to approximate the graph of sales of digital downloads over the years 2004 to 2007, would the line have positive, negative, or zero slope? Explain.

**Music Going Digital**

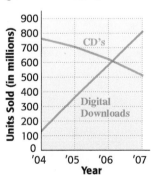

*Source:* Recording Industry Association of America.

**45.** The graph shows how college students managed their money during the years 1997 through 2004.

    **(a)** During what period did ATM use dominate both credit card *and* debit card use?

    **(b)** In what year did debit card use overtake credit card use?

    **(c)** In what year did debit card use overtake ATM use?

    **(d)** Write an ordered pair for the debit card use data in the year 1998.

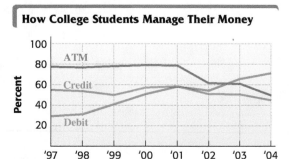

**How College Students Manage Their Money**

*Source:* Georgetown University Credit Research Center.

*An application of mathematics in economics deals with* **supply and demand.** *Typically, as the price of an item increases, the demand for the item decreases while the supply increases. If supply and demand can be described by straight-line equations, the point at which the lines intersect determines the* **equilibrium supply** *and* **equilibrium demand.**

*The price per unit, p, and the demand, x, for a particular aluminum siding are related by the linear equation $p = 60 - \frac{3}{4}x$, while the supply is given by the linear equation $p = \frac{3}{4}x$, as shown in the figure.*

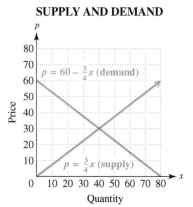

**SUPPLY AND DEMAND**

*Use the graph to answer the questions in Exercises 46–48.*

**46.** At what value of $x$ does supply equal demand?

**47.** At what value of $p$ does supply equal demand?

**48.** When $x > 40$, does demand exceed supply or does supply exceed demand?

---

**TECHNOLOGY INSIGHTS**    EXERCISES 49–52

*Match the graphing calculator screens in choices A–D with the appropriate system in Exercises 49–52.* **See the Connections box.**

**A.**
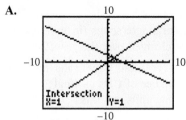

**B.**
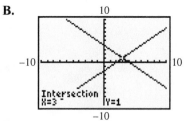

**C.**
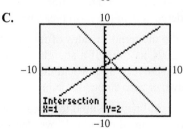

**D.**
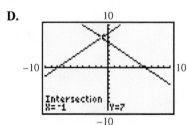

**49.** $x + y = 4$
     $x - y = 2$

**50.** $x + y = 6$
     $x - y = -8$

**51.** $2x + 3y = 5$
     $x - y = 0$

**52.** $3x + 2y = 7$
     $-x + y = 1$

*Solve each equation for y.* ***See Sections 2.5 and 3.3.***

**53.** $3x + y = 4$    **54.** $-2x + y = 9$    **55.** $9x - 2y = 4$    **56.** $5x - 3y = 12$

*Solve each equation. Check the solution.* ***See Section 2.3.***

**57.** $-2(x - 2) + 5x = 10$    **58.** $4(3 - 2k) + 3k = 12$

**59.** $4x - 2(1 - 3x) = 6$    **60.** $t + 3(2t - 4) = -13$

# 4.2 Solving Systems of Linear Equations by Substitution

**OBJECTIVES**

1. Solve linear systems by substitution.
2. Solve special systems by substitution.
3. Solve linear systems with fractions and decimals by substitution.

**OBJECTIVE 1** Solve linear systems by substitution. Graphing to solve a system of equations has a serious drawback. For example, consider the system graphed in **FIGURE 7**. It is difficult to determine an accurate solution of the system from the graph.

As a result, there are algebraic methods for solving systems of equations. The **substitution method,** which gets its name from the fact that an expression in one variable is *substituted* for the other variable, is one such method.

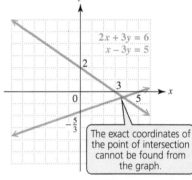

2x + 3y = 6
x - 3y = 5

The exact coordinates of the point of intersection cannot be found from the graph.

**FIGURE 7**

---

**EXAMPLE 1** Using the Substitution Method

Solve the system by the substitution method.

$$3x + 5y = 26 \quad (1)$$

We number the equations for reference in our discussion.

$$y = 2x \quad (2)$$

Equation (2), $y = 2x$, is already solved for $y$, so we substitute $2x$ for $y$ in equation (1).

$$3x + 5y = 26 \quad (1)$$
$$3x + 5(2x) = 26 \quad \text{Let } y = 2x.$$
$$3x + 10x = 26 \quad \text{Multiply.}$$
$$13x = 26 \quad \text{Combine like terms.}$$

Don't stop here. $\longrightarrow$ $x = 2$ Divide by 13.

Now we can find the value of $y$ by substituting 2 for $x$ in either equation. We choose equation (2).

$$y = 2x \quad (2)$$
$$y = 2(2) \quad \text{Let } x = 2.$$
$$y = 4 \quad \text{Multiply.}$$

**NOW TRY
EXERCISE 1**
Solve the system by the substitution method.

$$2x - 4y = 28$$
$$y = -3x$$

We check the solution $(2, 4)$ by substituting $2$ for $x$ and $4$ for $y$ in *both* equations.

| CHECK | $3x + 5y = 26$ | (1) | $y = 2x$ | (2) |
|---|---|---|---|---|
| | $3(2) + 5(4) \stackrel{?}{=} 26$ | Substitute. | $4 \stackrel{?}{=} 2(2)$ | Substitute. |
| | $6 + 20 \stackrel{?}{=} 26$ | Multiply. | $4 = 4$ ✓ | True |
| | $26 = 26$ ✓ | True | | |

Since $(2, 4)$ satisfies both equations, the solution set is $\{(2, 4)\}$.　　**NOW TRY**

---

⚠ **CAUTION** *A system is not completely solved until values for both x and y are found.* Write the solution set as a set containing an ordered pair.

---

**NOW TRY
EXERCISE 2**
Solve the system by the substitution method.

$$4x + 9y = 1$$
$$x = y - 3$$

**EXAMPLE 2** Using the Substitution Method

Solve the system by the substitution method.

$$2x + 5y = 7 \quad (1)$$
$$x = -1 - y \quad (2)$$

Equation (2) gives $x$ in terms of $y$. Substitute $-1 - y$ for $x$ in equation (1).

| $2x + 5y = 7$ | (1) |
|---|---|
| $2(-1 - y) + 5y = 7$ | Let $x = -1 - y$. |
| $-2 - 2y + 5y = 7$ | Distributive property |
| $-2 + 3y = 7$ | Combine like terms. |
| $3y = 9$ | Add 2. |
| $y = 3$ | Divide by 3. |

*Distribute 2 to both −1 and −y.*

To find $x$, substitute $3$ for $y$ in equation (2), $x = -1 - y$, to get

$$x = -1 - 3 = -4.$$

*Write the x-coordinate first.*

Check that the solution set of the given system is $\{(-4, 3)\}$.　　**NOW TRY**

---

⚠ **CAUTION** Even though we found $y$ first in **Example 2**, *the x-coordinate is always written first in the ordered-pair solution of a system.*

---

**Solving a Linear System by Substitution**

*Step 1* **Solve one equation for either variable.** If one of the variables has coefficient 1 or −1, choose it, since it usually makes the substitution method easier.

*Step 2* **Substitute** for that variable in the other equation. The result should be an equation with just one variable.

*Step 3* **Solve** the equation from Step 2.

*Step 4* **Substitute** the result from Step 3 into the equation from Step 1 to find the value of the other variable.

*Step 5* **Check** the solution in both of the original equations. Then write the solution set.

NOW TRY
EXERCISE 3

Use substitution to solve the system.

$$2y = x - 2$$
$$4x - 5y = -4$$

EXAMPLE 3  Using the Substitution Method

Use substitution to solve the system.

$$2x = 4 - y \qquad (1)$$
$$5x + 3y = 10 \qquad (2)$$

**Step 1**  We must solve one of the equations for either $x$ or $y$. Because the coefficient of $y$ in equation (1) is $-1$, we avoid fractions by solving this equation for $y$.

$$2x = 4 - y \qquad (1)$$
$$y + 2x = 4 \qquad \text{Add } y.$$
$$y = -2x + 4 \qquad \text{Subtract } 2x.$$

**Step 2**  Now substitute $-2x + 4$ for $y$ in equation (2).

$$5x + 3y = 10 \qquad (2)$$
$$5x + 3(-2x + 4) = 10 \qquad \text{Let } y = -2x + 4.$$

**Step 3**  Solve the equation from Step 2.

$$5x - 6x + 12 = 10 \qquad \text{Distributive property}$$

Distribute 3 to both $-2x$ and 4.

$$-x + 12 = 10 \qquad \text{Combine like terms.}$$
$$-x = -2 \qquad \text{Subtract 12.}$$
$$x = 2 \qquad \text{Multiply by } -1.$$

**Step 4**  Equation (1) solved for $y$ is $y = -2x + 4$. Since $x = 2$,

$$y = -2(2) + 4 = 0.$$

**Step 5**  Check that $(2, 0)$ is the solution.

CHECK

| | |
|---|---|
| $2x = 4 - y \qquad (1)$ | $5x + 3y = 10 \qquad (2)$ |
| $2(2) \stackrel{?}{=} 4 - 0 \qquad \text{Substitute.}$ | $5(2) + 3(0) \stackrel{?}{=} 10 \qquad \text{Substitute.}$ |
| $4 = 4 \ \checkmark \qquad \text{True}$ | $10 = 10 \ \checkmark \quad \text{True}$ |

Since both results are true, the solution set of the system is $\{(2, 0)\}$.  NOW TRY

OBJECTIVE 2  **Solve special systems by substitution.**  Recall from **Section 4.1** that systems of equations with graphs that are parallel lines have no solution. Systems of equations with graphs that are the same line have an infinite number of solutions.

EXAMPLE 4  Solving an Inconsistent System by Substitution

Use substitution to solve the system.

$$x = 5 - 2y \qquad (1)$$
$$2x + 4y = 6 \qquad (2)$$

Equation (1) is already solved for $x$, so substitute $5 - 2y$ for $x$ in equation (2).

$$2x + 4y = 6 \qquad (2)$$
$$2(5 - 2y) + 4y = 6 \qquad \text{Let } x = 5 - 2y \text{ from equation (1).}$$
$$10 - 4y + 4y = 6 \qquad \text{Distributive property}$$
$$10 = 6 \qquad \text{False}$$

NOW TRY ANSWER
**3.** $\{(-6, -4)\}$

NOW TRY
EXERCISE 4

Use substitution to solve the system.

$$8x - 2y = 1$$
$$y = 4x - 8$$

The false result $10 = 6$ means that the equations in the system have graphs that are parallel lines. The system is inconsistent and has no solution, so the solution set is $\emptyset$. See **FIGURE 8**.

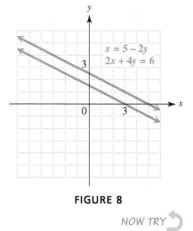

**FIGURE 8**

NOW TRY

---

⚠ **CAUTION** It is a common error to give "false" as the solution of an inconsistent system. The correct response is $\emptyset$.

---

NOW TRY
EXERCISE 5

Solve the system by the substitution method.

$$5x - y = 6$$
$$-10x + 2y = -12$$

**EXAMPLE 5** Solving a System with Dependent Equations by Substitution

Solve the system by the substitution method.

$$3x - y = 4 \qquad (1)$$
$$-9x + 3y = -12 \qquad (2)$$

Begin by solving equation (1) for $y$ to get $y = 3x - 4$. Substitute $3x - 4$ for $y$ in equation (2) and solve the resulting equation.

$$-9x + 3y = -12 \qquad (2)$$
$$-9x + 3(3x - 4) = -12 \qquad \text{Let } y = 3x - 4 \text{ from equation (1).}$$
$$-9x + 9x - 12 = -12 \qquad \text{Distributive property}$$
$$0 = 0 \qquad \text{Add 12. Combine like terms.}$$

This true result means that every solution of one equation is also a solution of the other, so the system has an infinite number of solutions. The solution set is

$$\{(x, y) \mid 3x - y = 4\}.$$

A graph of the equations of this system is shown in **FIGURE 9**.

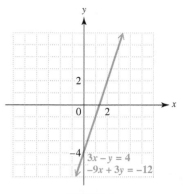

**FIGURE 9**

NOW TRY

---

⚠ **CAUTION** It is a common error to give "true" as the solution of a system of dependent equations. Write the solution set in set-builder notation using the equation in the system (or an equivalent equation) that is in standard form, with integer coefficients that have greatest common factor 1.

NOW TRY ANSWERS
**4.** $\emptyset$  **5.** $\{(x, y) \mid 5x - y = 6\}$

**OBJECTIVE 3** Solve linear systems with fractions and decimals by substitution.

NOW TRY
EXERCISE 6

Solve the system by the substitution method.

$$x + \frac{1}{2}y = \frac{1}{2}$$
$$\frac{1}{6}x - \frac{1}{3}y = \frac{4}{3}$$

**EXAMPLE 6** Using the Substitution Method with Fractions as Coefficients

Solve the system by the substitution method.

$$3x + \frac{1}{4}y = 2 \qquad (1)$$

$$\frac{1}{2}x + \frac{3}{4}y = -\frac{5}{2} \qquad (2)$$

Clear equation (1) of fractions by multiplying each side by 4.

$$4\left(3x + \frac{1}{4}y\right) = 4(2) \qquad \text{Multiply by 4.}$$

$$4(3x) + 4\left(\frac{1}{4}y\right) = 4(2) \qquad \text{Distributive property}$$

$$12x + y = 8 \qquad (3)$$

Now clear equation (2) of fractions by multiplying each side by 4.

$$4\left(\frac{1}{2}x + \frac{3}{4}y\right) = 4\left(-\frac{5}{2}\right) \qquad \begin{array}{l}\text{Multiply by 4, the common}\\\text{denominator.}\end{array}$$

$$4\left(\frac{1}{2}x\right) + 4\left(\frac{3}{4}y\right) = 4\left(-\frac{5}{2}\right) \qquad \text{Distributive property}$$

$$2x + 3y = -10 \qquad (4)$$

The given system of equations has been simplified to an equivalent system.

$$12x + y = 8 \qquad (3)$$
$$2x + 3y = -10 \qquad (4)$$

To solve this system by substitution, solve equation (3) for $y$.

$$12x + y = 8 \qquad (3)$$
$$y = -12x + 8 \qquad \text{Subtract } 12x.$$

Now substitute this result for $y$ in equation (4).

$$2x + 3y = -10 \qquad (4)$$
$$2x + 3(-12x + 8) = -10 \qquad \text{Let } y = -12x + 8.$$
$$2x - 36x + 24 = -10 \qquad \text{Distributive property}$$
$$-34x = -34 \qquad \text{Combine like terms. Subtract 24.}$$
$$x = 1 \qquad \text{Divide by } -34.$$

Distribute 3 to both $-12x$ and 8.

Since equation (3) solved for $y$ is $y = -12x + 8$, substitute 1 for $x$ to get

$$y = -12(1) + 8 = -4.$$

NOW TRY ANSWER
6. $\{(2, -3)\}$

Check by substituting 1 for $x$ and $-4$ for $y$ in both of the original equations. The solution set is $\{(1, -4)\}$.

NOW TRY

NOW TRY
EXERCISE 7

Solve the system by the substitution method.

$$0.2x + 0.3y = 0.5$$
$$0.3x - 0.1y = 1.3$$

**EXAMPLE 7** Using the Substitution Method with Decimals as Coefficients

Solve the system by the substitution method.

$$0.5x + 2.4y = 4.2 \quad (1)$$
$$-0.1x + 1.5y = 5.1 \quad (2)$$

Clear each equation of decimals by multiplying by 10.

$$10(0.5x + 2.4y) = 10(4.2) \qquad \text{Multiply equation (1) by 10.}$$
$$10(0.5x) + 10(2.4y) = 10(4.2) \qquad \text{Distributive property}$$
$$5x + 24y = 42 \quad (3)$$

$$10(-0.1x + 1.5y) = 10(5.1) \qquad \text{Multiply equation (2) by 10.}$$
$$10(-0.1x) + 10(1.5y) = 10(5.1) \qquad \text{Distributive property}$$
$$\boxed{10(-0.1x) = -1x = -x} \rightarrow -x + 15y = 51 \quad (4)$$

Now solve the equivalent system of equations by substitution.

$$5x + 24y = 42 \quad (3)$$
$$-x + 15y = 51 \quad (4)$$

Equation (4) can be solved for $x$.

$$x = 15y - 51 \qquad \text{Equation (4) solved for } x$$

Substitute this result for $x$ in equation (3).

$$5x + 24y = 42 \quad (3)$$
$$5(15y - 51) + 24y = 42 \qquad \text{Let } x = 15y - 51.$$
$$75y - 255 + 24y = 42 \qquad \text{Distributive property}$$
$$99y = 297 \qquad \text{Combine like terms. Add 255.}$$
$$y = 3 \qquad \text{Divide by 99.}$$

Since equation (4) solved for $x$ is $x = 15y - 51$, substitute 3 for $y$ to get

$$x = 15(3) - 51 = -6.$$

NOW TRY ANSWER
7. $\{(4, -1)\}$

Check $(-6, 3)$ in both of the original equations. The solution set is $\{(-6, 3)\}$.

NOW TRY

## 4.2 EXERCISES

MyMathLab    Math XL PRACTICE     WATCH     DOWNLOAD     READ     REVIEW

⊕ *Complete solution available on the Video Resources on DVD*

**1.** *Concept Check* A student solves the following system and finds that $x = 3$, which is correct. The student gives the solution set as $\{3\}$. *WHAT WENT WRONG?*

$$5x - y = 15$$
$$7x + y = 21$$

**2.** *Concept Check* A student solves the following system and obtains the equation $0 = 0$. The student gives the solution set as $\{(0, 0)\}$. *WHAT WENT WRONG?*

$$x + y = 4$$
$$2x + 2y = 8$$

*Solve each system by the substitution method. Check each solution.* ***See Examples 1–5.***

**3.** $x + y = 12$
$y = 3x$

**4.** $x + 3y = -28$
$y = -5x$

**5.** $3x + 2y = 27$
$x = y + 4$

**6.** $4x + 3y = -5$
$x = y - 3$

**7.** $3x + 4 = -y$
$2x + y = 0$

**8.** $2x - 5 = -y$
$x + 3y = 0$

**9.** $7x + 4y = 13$
$x + y = 1$

**10.** $3x - 2y = 19$
$x + y = 8$

**11.** $3x + 5y = 25$
$x - 2y = -10$

**12.** $5x + 2y = -15$
$2x - y = -6$

**13.** $3x - y = 5$
$y = 3x - 5$

**14.** $4x - y = -3$
$y = 4x + 3$

**15.** $2x + y = 0$
$4x - 2y = 2$

**16.** $x + y = 0$
$4x + 2y = 3$

**17.** $2x + 8y = 3$
$x = 8 - 4y$

**18.** $2x + 10y = 3$
$x = 1 - 5y$

**19.** $2y = 4x + 24$
$2x - y = -12$

**20.** $2y = 14 - 6x$
$3x + y = 7$

*Solve each system by the substitution method. Check each solution.* ***See Examples 6 and 7.***

**21.** $\dfrac{1}{2}x + \dfrac{1}{3}y = 3$
$y = 3x$

**22.** $\dfrac{1}{4}x - \dfrac{1}{5}y = 9$
$y = 5x$

**23.** $\dfrac{1}{2}x + \dfrac{1}{3}y = -\dfrac{1}{3}$
$\dfrac{1}{2}x + 2y = -7$

**24.** $\dfrac{1}{6}x + \dfrac{1}{6}y = 1$
$-\dfrac{1}{2}x - \dfrac{1}{3}y = -5$

**25.** $\dfrac{x}{5} + 2y = \dfrac{8}{5}$
$\dfrac{3x}{5} + \dfrac{y}{2} = -\dfrac{7}{10}$

**26.** $\dfrac{x}{2} + \dfrac{y}{3} = \dfrac{7}{6}$
$\dfrac{x}{4} - \dfrac{3y}{2} = \dfrac{9}{4}$

**27.** $\dfrac{1}{6}x + \dfrac{1}{3}y = 8$
$\dfrac{1}{4}x + \dfrac{1}{2}y = 12$

**28.** $\dfrac{1}{2}x - \dfrac{1}{8}y = -\dfrac{1}{4}$
$\dfrac{1}{3}x - \dfrac{1}{12}y = -\dfrac{1}{6}$

**29.** $0.2x - 1.3y = -3.2$
$-0.1x + 2.7y = 9.8$

**30.** $0.1x + 0.9y = -2$
$0.5x - 0.2y = 4.1$

**31.** $0.3x - 0.1y = 2.1$
$0.6x + 0.3y = -0.3$

**32.** $0.8x - 0.1y = 1.3$
$2.2x + 1.5y = 8.9$

---

*RELATING CONCEPTS*   EXERCISES 33–36

**FOR INDIVIDUAL OR GROUP WORK**

*A system of linear equations can be used to model the cost and the revenue of a business.*
***Work Exercises 33–36 in order.***

 **33.** Suppose that you start a business manufacturing and selling bicycles, and it costs you $5000 to get started. Each bicycle will cost $400 to manufacture. Explain why the linear equation

$$y_1 = 400x + 5000 \quad (y_1 \text{ in dollars})$$

gives your *total* cost of manufacturing $x$ bicycles.

**34.** You decide to sell each bike for $600. Write an equation using $y_2$ (in dollars) to express your revenue when you sell $x$ bikes.

**35.** Form a system from the two equations in **Exercises 33 and 34.** Solve the system.

**36.** The value of $x$ from **Exercise 35** is the number of bikes it takes to *break even*. Fill in the blanks:   When _____ bikes are sold, the break-even point is reached. At that point, you have spent _____ dollars and taken in _____ dollars.

*Solve each system by substitution. Then graph both lines in the standard viewing window of a graphing calculator, and use the intersection feature to support your answer. See the Connections box in **Section 4.1**. (In Exercises 41 and 42, solve each equation for y before graphing.)*

**37.** $y = 6 - x$
$y = 2x$

**38.** $y = 4x - 4$
$y = -3x - 11$

**39.** $y = -\dfrac{4}{3}x + \dfrac{19}{3}$
$y = \dfrac{15}{2}x - \dfrac{5}{2}$

**40.** $y = -\dfrac{15}{2}x + 10$
$y = \dfrac{25}{3}x - \dfrac{65}{3}$

**41.** $4x + 5y = 5$
$2x + 3y = 1$

**42.** $6x + 5y = 13$
$3x + 3y = 4$

## PREVIEW EXERCISES

*Simplify. **See Section 1.8.***

**43.** $(14x - 3y) + (2x + 3y)$

**44.** $(-6x + 8y) + (6x + 2y)$

**45.** $(-x + 7y) + (3y + x)$

**46.** $(3x - 4y) + (4y - 3x)$

**47.** What must be added to $-4x$ to get a sum of 0?

**48.** What must be added to $6y$ to get a sum of 0?

**49.** What must $4y$ be multiplied by so that when the product is added to $8y$, the sum is 0?

**50.** What must $-3x$ be multiplied by so that when the product is added to $-12x$, the result is 0?

# 4.3 Solving Systems of Linear Equations by Elimination

**OBJECTIVES**

1 Solve linear systems by elimination.
2 Multiply when using the elimination method.
3 Use an alternative method to find the second value in a solution.
4 Solve special systems by elimination.

**OBJECTIVE 1** **Solve linear systems by elimination.** Recall that adding the same quantity to each side of an equation results in equal sums.

$$\text{If } A = B, \text{ then } A + C = B + C.$$

We can take this addition a step further. Adding *equal* quantities, rather than the *same* quantity, to each side of an equation also results in equal sums.

$$\text{If } A = B \text{ and } C = D, \text{ then } A + C = B + D.$$

Using the addition property of equality to solve systems is called the **elimination method.**

**EXAMPLE 1** Using the Elimination Method

Use the elimination method to solve the system.

$$x + y = 5 \quad (1)$$
$$x - y = 3 \quad (2)$$

Each equation in this system is a statement of equality, so the sum of the right sides equals the sum of the left sides. Adding vertically in this way gives the following.

$$\begin{array}{ll} x + y = 5 & (1) \\ \underline{x - y = 3} & (2) \\ 2x \quad\quad = 8 & \text{Add left sides and add right sides.} \\ x = 4 & \text{Divide by 2.} \end{array}$$

NOW TRY
EXERCISE 1

Use the elimination method
to solve the system.

$$x - y = 4$$
$$3x + y = 8$$

Notice that $y$ has been eliminated. The result, $x = 4$, gives the $x$-value of the solution of the given system. To find the $y$-value of the solution, substitute 4 for $x$ in either of the two equations of the system. We choose equation (1).

$$x + y = 5 \quad \text{(1)}$$
$$4 + y = 5 \quad \text{Let } x = 4.$$
$$y = 1 \quad \text{Subtract 4.}$$

Check the solution, $(4, 1)$, in both equations of the given system.

CHECK   $x + y = 5$     (1)       $x - y = 3$     (2)

$4 + 1 \overset{?}{=} 5$     Substitute.     $4 - 1 \overset{?}{=} 3$     Substitute.

$5 = 5$ ✓   True       $3 = 3$ ✓   True

Since both results are true, the solution set of the system is $\{(4, 1)\}$.    NOW TRY

With the elimination method, the idea is to *eliminate* one of the variables. ***To do this, one pair of variable terms in the two equations must have coefficients that are opposites (additive inverses).***

### Solving a Linear System by Elimination

**Step 1**   **Write both equations in standard form,** $Ax + By = C$.

**Step 2**   **Transform the equations as needed so that the coefficients of one pair of variable terms are opposites.** Multiply one or both equations by appropriate numbers so that the sum of the coefficients of either the $x$- or $y$-terms is 0.

**Step 3**   **Add** the new equations to eliminate a variable. The sum should be an equation with just one variable.

**Step 4**   **Solve** the equation from Step 3 for the remaining variable.

**Step 5**   **Substitute** the result from Step 4 into either of the original equations, and solve for the other variable.

**Step 6**   **Check** the solution in both of the original equations. Then write the solution set.

*It does not matter which variable is eliminated first. Usually, we choose the one that is more convenient to work with.*

**EXAMPLE 2**   Using the Elimination Method

Solve the system.

$$y + 11 = 2x \quad \text{(1)}$$
$$5x = y + 26 \quad \text{(2)}$$

**Step 1**   Write both equations in standard form, $Ax + By = C$.

$$-2x + y = -11 \quad \text{Subtract } 2x \text{ and } 11 \text{ in equation (1).}$$
$$5x - y = 26 \quad \text{Subtract } y \text{ in equation (2).}$$

**Step 2**   Because the coefficients of $y$ are 1 and $-1$, adding will eliminate $y$. It is not necessary to multiply either equation by a number.

NOW TRY ANSWER
**1.** $\{(3, -1)\}$

NOW TRY
EXERCISE 2

Solve the system.
$$2x - 6 = -3y$$
$$5x - 3y = -27$$

**Step 3** Add the two equations.

$$-2x + y = -11$$
$$5x - y = 26$$
$$\overline{\qquad 3x \qquad = 15} \qquad \text{Add in columns.}$$

**Step 4** Solve. $\qquad x = 5 \qquad$ Divide by 3.

**Step 5** Find the value of $y$ by substituting 5 for $x$ in either of the original equations.

$$y + 11 = 2x \qquad (1)$$
$$y + 11 = 2(5) \qquad \text{Let } x = 5.$$
$$y + 11 = 10 \qquad \text{Multiply.}$$
$$y = -1 \qquad \text{Subtract 11.}$$

**Step 6** Check by substituting $x = 5$ and $y = -1$ into both of the original equations.

CHECK $\qquad y + 11 = 2x \qquad (1) \qquad\qquad 5x = y + 26 \qquad (2)$

$$(-1) + 11 \overset{?}{=} 2(5) \quad \text{Substitute.} \qquad 5(5) = -1 + 26 \quad \text{Substitute.}$$
$$10 = 10 \ \checkmark \quad \text{True} \qquad\qquad 25 = 25 \ \checkmark \qquad \text{True}$$

Since $(5, -1)$ is a solution of *both* equations, the solution set is $\{(5, -1)\}$.

NOW TRY

**OBJECTIVE 2** **Multiply when using the elimination method.** Sometimes we need to multiply each side of one or both equations in a system by some number before adding will eliminate a variable.

NOW TRY
EXERCISE 3

Solve the system.
$$3x - 5y = 25$$
$$2x + 8y = -6$$

**EXAMPLE 3** Using the Elimination Method

Solve the system.

$$2x + 3y = -15 \qquad (1)$$
$$5x + 2y = 1 \qquad (2)$$

Adding the two equations gives $7x + 5y = -14$, which does not eliminate either variable. However, we can multiply each equation by a suitable number so that the coefficients of one of the two variables are opposites. For example, to eliminate $x$, we multiply each side of $2x + 3y = -15$ (equation (1)) by 5 and each side of $5x + 2y = 1$ (equation (2)) by $-2$.

$$10x + 15y = -75 \qquad \text{Multiply equation (1) by 5.}$$
$$-10x - 4y = -2 \qquad \text{Multiply equation (2) by } -2.$$
$$\overline{\qquad 11y = -77} \qquad \text{Add.}$$

The coefficients of $x$ are opposites.

$$y = -7 \qquad \text{Divide by 11.}$$

Find the value of $x$ by substituting $-7$ for $y$ in either equation (1) or (2).

$$5x + 2y = 1 \qquad (2)$$
$$5x + 2(-7) = 1 \qquad \text{Let } y = -7.$$
$$5x - 14 = 1 \qquad \text{Multiply.}$$
$$5x = 15 \qquad \text{Add 14.}$$
$$x = 3 \qquad \text{Divide by 5.}$$

NOW TRY ANSWERS
2. $\{(-3, 4)\}$  3. $\{(5, -2)\}$

Check that the solution set of the system is $\{(3, -7)\}$. NOW TRY

**NOTE** In **Example 3,** we eliminated the variable $x$. Alternatively, we could multiply each equation of the system by a suitable number so that the variable $y$ is eliminated.

$$2x + 3y = -15 \quad \text{(1)} \quad \xrightarrow{\text{Multiply by 2.}} \quad 4x + 6y = -30$$

$$5x + 2y = 1 \quad \text{(2)} \quad \xrightarrow{\text{Multiply by } -3.} \quad -15x - 6y = -3$$

Complete this approach and confirm that the same solution results.

⚠ **CAUTION** When using the elimination method, remember to *multiply both sides* of an equation by the same nonzero number.

**OBJECTIVE 3** Use an alternative method to find the second value in a solution. Sometimes it is easier to find the value of the second variable in a solution by using the elimination method twice.

⌒ *NOW TRY*
↳ *EXERCISE 4*

Solve the system.

$$4x + 9y = 3$$
$$5y = 6 - 3x$$

**EXAMPLE 4** Finding the Second Value by Using an Alternative Method

Solve the system.

$$4x = 9 - 3y \quad \text{(1)}$$
$$5x - 2y = 8 \quad \text{(2)}$$

Write equation (1) in standard form by adding $3y$ to each side.

$$4x + 3y = 9 \quad \text{(3)}$$
$$5x - 2y = 8 \quad \text{(2)}$$

One way to proceed is to eliminate $y$ by multiplying each side of equation (3) by 2 and each side of equation (2) by 3 and then adding.

$$
\begin{array}{ll}
8x + 6y = 18 & \text{Multiply equation (3) by 2.} \\
\underline{15x - 6y = 24} & \text{Multiply equation (2) by 3.} \\
23x \quad\quad = 42 & \text{Add.} \\
\end{array}
$$

The coefficients of $y$ are opposites.

$$x = \frac{42}{23} \quad \text{Divide by 23.}$$

Substituting $\frac{42}{23}$ for $x$ in one of the given equations would give $y$, but the arithmetic would be messy. Instead, solve for $y$ by starting again with the original equations written in standard form (equations (3) and (2)) and eliminating $x$.

$$
\begin{array}{ll}
20x + 15y = \quad 45 & \text{Multiply equation (3) by 5.} \\
\underline{-20x + \quad 8y = -32} & \text{Multiply equation (2) by } -4. \\
23y = \quad 13 & \text{Add.} \\
\end{array}
$$

The coefficients of $x$ are opposites.

$$y = \frac{13}{23} \quad \text{Divide by 23.}$$

Check that the solution set is $\left\{ \left( \frac{42}{23}, \frac{13}{23} \right) \right\}$.

*NOW TRY* ↻

NOW TRY ANSWER
**4.** $\left\{ \left( \frac{39}{7}, -\frac{15}{7} \right) \right\}$

**NOTE** When the value of the first variable is a fraction, the method used in **Example 4** helps avoid arithmetic errors. This method could be used to solve any system.

NOW TRY
EXERCISE 5

Solve each system by the elimination method.

(a)   $x - y = 2$
      $5x - 5y = 10$

(b)   $4x + 3y = 0$
      $-4x - 3y = -1$

**OBJECTIVE 4** Solve special systems by elimination.

**EXAMPLE 5** Solving Special Systems Using the Elimination Method

Solve each system by the elimination method.

(a)           $2x + 4y = 5$    (1)

              $4x + 8y = -9$    (2)

Multiply each side of equation (1) by $-2$. Then add the two equations.

$$-4x - 8y = -10 \quad \text{Multiply equation (1) by } -2.$$
$$\underline{\phantom{-}4x + 8y = \phantom{-}-9} \quad \text{(2)}$$
$$0 = -19 \quad \text{False}$$

The false statement $0 = -19$ indicates that the given system has solution set $\emptyset$.

(b)           $3x - y = 4$      (1)

              $-9x + 3y = -12$   (2)

Multiply each side of equation (1) by 3. Then add the two equations.

$$9x - 3y = \phantom{-}12 \quad \text{Multiply equation (1) by 3.}$$
$$\underline{-9x + 3y = -12} \quad \text{(2)}$$
$$0 = \phantom{-}0 \quad \text{True}$$

A true statement occurs when the equations are equivalent. This indicates that every solution of one equation is also a solution of the other. The solution set is

$$\{(x, y) \mid 3x - y = 4\}. \qquad \textit{NOW TRY}$$

NOW TRY ANSWERS
5. (a) $\{(x, y) \mid x - y = 2\}$
   (b) $\emptyset$

---

## 4.3 EXERCISES

MyMathLab   Math XL PRACTICE   WATCH   DOWNLOAD   READ   REVIEW

⊕ *Complete solution available on the Video Resources on DVD*

*Concept Check*   Answer true *or* false *for each statement. If false, tell why.*

1. If the elimination method leads to $0 = -1$, the solution set of the system is $\{(0, -1)\}$.

2. A system that includes the equation $5x - 4y = 0$ cannot have $(4, -5)$ as a solution.

*Solve each system by the elimination method. Check each solution.* **See Examples 1 and 2.**

⊕ **3.** $x - y = -2$ 　　**4.** $x + y = 10$ 　　**5.** $2x + y = -5$
　　 $x + y = 10$ 　　　　　 $x - y = -6$ 　　　　　 $x - y = 2$

**6.** $2x + y = -15$ 　⊕ **7.** $2y = -3x$ 　　**8.** $5x = y + 5$
　　 $-x - y = 10$ 　　　　 $-3x - y = 3$ 　　　　 $-5x + 2y = 0$

**9.** $6x - y = -1$ 　　　　　　　　**10.** $y = 9 - 6x$
　　 $5y = 17 + 6x$ 　　　　　　　　　 $-6x + 3y = 15$

*Solve each system by the elimination method. (Hint: In Exercises 29–34, first clear all fractions or decimals.) Check each solution.* **See Examples 3–5.***

**11.** $2x - y = 12$ 　　**12.** 　$x + y = 3$ 　　**13.** 　$x + 4y = 16$
　　 $3x + 2y = -3$ 　　　　 $-3x + 2y = -19$ 　　　 $3x + 5y = 20$

---

*The authors thank Mitchel Levy of Broward College for his suggestions for this group of exercises.

**14.** $2x + y = 8$
$5x - 2y = -16$

**15.** $2x - 8y = 0$
$4x + 5y = 0$

**16.** $3x - 15y = 0$
$6x + 10y = 0$

**17.** $3x + 3y = 33$
$5x - 2y = 27$

**18.** $4x - 3y = -19$
$3x + 2y = 24$

**19.** $5x + 4y = 12$
$3x + 5y = 15$

**20.** $2x + 3y = 21$
$5x - 2y = -14$

**21.** $5x - 4y = 15$
$-3x + 6y = -9$

**22.** $4x + 5y = -16$
$5x - 6y = -20$

**23.** $-x + 3y = 4$
$-2x + 6y = 8$

**24.** $6x - 2y = 24$
$-3x + y = -12$

**25.** $5x - 2y = 3$
$10x - 4y = 5$

**26.** $3x - 5y = 1$
$6x - 10y = 4$

**27.** $6x - 2y = -22$
$-3x + 4y = 17$

**28.** $5x - 4y = -1$
$x + 8y = -9$

**29.** $3x = 3 + 2y$
$-\dfrac{4}{3}x + y = \dfrac{1}{3}$

**30.** $3x = 27 + 2y$
$x - \dfrac{7}{2}y = -25$

**31.** $\dfrac{1}{5}x + y = \dfrac{6}{5}$
$\dfrac{1}{10}x + \dfrac{1}{3}y = \dfrac{5}{6}$

**32.** $\dfrac{1}{3}x + \dfrac{1}{2}y = \dfrac{13}{6}$
$\dfrac{1}{2}x - \dfrac{1}{4}y = -\dfrac{3}{4}$

**33.** $2.4x + 1.7y = 7.6$
$1.2x - 0.5y = 9.2$

**34.** $0.5x + 3.4y = 13$
$1.5x - 2.6y = -25$

**35.** $x + 3y = 6$
$-2x + 12 = 6y$

**36.** $7x + 2y = 0$
$4y = -14x$

**37.** $4x - 3y = 1$
$8x = 3 + 6y$

**38.** $5x + 8y = 10$
$24y = -15x - 10$

**39.** $4x = 3y - 2$
$5x + 3 = 2y$

**40.** $2x + 3y = 0$
$4x + 12 = 9y$

**41.** $24x + 12y = -7$
$16x - 18y = 17$

**42.** $9x + 4y = -3$
$6x + 6y = -7$

---

## *RELATING CONCEPTS*  EXERCISES 43–48

**FOR INDIVIDUAL OR GROUP WORK**

*The graph shows average U.S. movie theater ticket prices from 2000 through 2008. In 2000, the average price was $5.39, as represented by the point P(2000, 5.39). In 2008, the average price was $7.18, as represented by the point Q(2008, 7.18).* **Work Exercises 43–48 in order.**

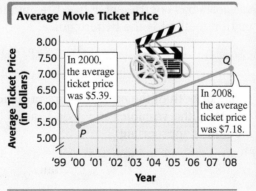

Average Movie Ticket Price

In 2000, the average ticket price was $5.39.

In 2008, the average ticket price was $7.18.

***Source:*** Motion Picture Association of America.

**43.** Line segment $PQ$ has an equation that can be written in the form $y = ax + b$. Using the coordinates of point $P$ with $x = 2000$ and $y = 5.39$, write an equation in the variables $a$ and $b$.

**44.** Using the coordinates of point $Q$ with $x = 2008$ and $y = 7.18$, write a second equation in the variables $a$ and $b$.

**45.** Write the system of equations formed from the two equations in **Exercises 43 and 44,** and solve the system by using the elimination method.

**46. (a)** What is the equation of the line on which segment $PQ$ lies?

**(b)** Let $x = 2007$ in the equation from part (a), and solve for $y$ (to two decimal places). How does the result compare with the actual figure of $6.88$?

**PREVIEW EXERCISES**

*Solve each applied problem. See Sections 2.4–2.7.*

**47.** As of 2009, the all-time top scorer in the National Hockey League was Wayne Gretzky. During his NHL career, Gretsky had a total of 2857 points (goals plus assists) in regular season play. He had 1069 more assists than goals. How many goals and how many assists did he have? (*Source: World Almanac and Book of Facts.*)

**48.** The perimeter of a rectangle is 46 ft. The width is 7 ft less than the length. Find the width.

**49.** Antonnette Gibbs, a cashier, has $10-bills and $20-bills. There are 6 more tens than twenties. If there are 32 bills altogether, how many of them are twenties?

**50.** Teresa Hodge traveled for 2 hr at a constant speed. Because of roadwork, she reduced her speed by 7 mph for the next 2 hr. If she traveled 206 mi, what was her speed on the first part of the trip?

## SUMMARY EXERCISES on Solving Systems of Linear Equations

### Guidelines for Choosing a Method to Solve a System of Linear Equations

**1.** If one of the equations of the system is already solved for one of the variables, as in the following systems, the substitution method is the better choice.

$$3x + 4y = 9 \qquad\qquad -5x + 3y = 9$$
$$\text{and}$$
$$y = 2x - 6 \qquad\qquad x = 3y - 7$$

**2.** If both equations are in standard $Ax + By = C$ form and none of the variables has coefficient $-1$ or $1$, as in the following system, the elimination method is the better choice.

$$4x - 11y = 3$$
$$-2x + 3y = 4$$

**3.** If one or both of the equations are in standard form and the coefficient of one of the variables is $-1$ or $1$, as in the following systems, either method is appropriate.

$$3x + y = -2 \qquad\qquad -x + 3y = -4$$
$$\text{and}$$
$$-5x + 2y = 4 \qquad\qquad 3x - 2y = 8$$

*Concept Check   Use the preceding guidelines to solve each problem.*

**1.** To minimize the amount of work required, tell whether you would use the substitution or elimination method to solve each system, and why. *Do not actually solve.*

**(a)** $3x + 5y = 69$
$\quad y = 4x$

**(b)** $3x + y = -7$
$\quad x - y = -5$

**(c)** $3x - 2y = 0$
$\quad 9x + 8y = 7$

**2.** Which system would be easier to solve with the substitution method? Why?

System A:   $5x - 3y = 7$
$\qquad\qquad 2x + 8y = 3$

System B:   $7x + 2y = 4$
$\qquad\qquad y = -3x + 1$

*In Exercises 3 and 4, **(a)** solve the system by the elimination method, **(b)** solve the system by the substitution method, and **(c)** tell which method you prefer for that particular system and why.*

**3.** $4x - 3y = -8$
$\quad\ x + 3y = 13$

**4.** $2x + 5y = 0$
$\quad\ x = -3y + 1$

*Solve each system by the method of your choice. (For Exercises 5–7, see your answers to* **Exercise 1.***)*

**5.** $3x + 5y = 69$
$\quad y = 4x$

**6.** $3x + y = -7$
$\quad x - y = -5$

**7.** $3x - 2y = 0$
$\quad 9x + 8y = 7$

**8.** $x + y = 7$
$\quad x = -3 - y$

**9.** $6x + 7y = 4$
$\quad 5x + 8y = -1$

**10.** $6x - y = 5$
$\qquad y = 11x$

**11.** $\quad 4x - 6y = 10$
$\quad -10x + 15y = -25$

**12.** $3x - 5y = 7$
$\quad 2x + 3y = 30$

**13.** $5x = 7 + 2y$
$\quad 5y = 5 - 3x$

**14.** $4x + 3y = 1$
$\quad 3x + 2y = 2$

**15.** $\quad 2x - 3y = 7$
$\quad -4x + 6y = 14$

**16.** $\quad 2x + 3y = 10$
$\quad -3x + \ y = 18$

**17.** $2x + 5y = 4$
$\quad\ x + \ y = -1$

**18.** $\quad x - 3y = 7$
$\quad 4x + \ y = 5$

**19.** $7x - 4y = 0$
$\quad 3x = 2y$

*Solve each system by any method. First clear all fractions or decimals.*

**20.** $\dfrac{1}{5}x + \dfrac{2}{3}y = -\dfrac{8}{5}$
$\quad 3x - \ \ y = 9$

**21.** $\quad \dfrac{1}{6}x + \dfrac{1}{6}y = 2$
$\quad -\dfrac{1}{2}x - \dfrac{1}{3}y = -8$

**22.** $\dfrac{x}{3} - \dfrac{3y}{4} = -\dfrac{1}{2}$
$\quad \dfrac{x}{6} + \dfrac{y}{8} = \dfrac{3}{4}$

**23.** $\dfrac{x}{2} - \dfrac{y}{3} = 9$
$\quad \dfrac{x}{5} - \dfrac{y}{4} = 5$

**24.** $0.1x + \ \ y = 1.6$
$\quad 0.6x + 0.5y = -1.4$

**25.** $0.2x - 0.3y = 0.1$
$\quad 0.3x - 0.2y = 0.9$

**4.4**

## Applications of Linear Systems

OBJECTIVES

**1** Solve problems about unknown numbers.

**2** Solve problems about quantities and their costs.

**3** Solve problems about mixtures.

**4** Solve problems about distance, rate (or speed), and time.

Recall from **Section 2.4** the six-step method for solving applied problems. We modify those steps slightly to allow for two variables and two equations.

---

**Solving an Applied Problem with Two Variables**

*Step 1* **Read** the problem carefully. What information is given? What are you asked to find?

*Step 2* **Assign variables** to represent the unknown values. Use a sketch, diagram, or table, as needed. Write down what each variable represents.

*Step 3* **Write two equations** using both variables.

*Step 4* **Solve** the system of two equations.

*Step 5* **State the answer.** Label it appropriately. Does it seem reasonable?

*Step 6* **Check** the answer in the words of the *original* problem.

---

**OBJECTIVE 1** **Solve problems about unknown numbers.**

**EXAMPLE 1** Solving a Problem about Two Unknown Numbers

In 2008, sales of sports footwear were $6627 million more than sales of sports clothing. Together, the total sales for these items amounted to $27,753 million. What were the sales for each? (*Source:* National Sporting Goods Association.)

*Step 1* **Read** the problem. We must find 2008 sales (in millions of dollars) for sports footwear and sports clothing. We know how much more sports footwear sales were than sports clothing sales. Also, we know the total sales.

*Step 2* **Assign variables.**

Let $x$ = sales of sports footwear in millions of dollars,

and $y$ = sales of sports clothing in millions of dollars.

*Step 3* **Write two equations.**

$x = 6627 + y$    Sales of sports footwear were $6627 million more than sales of sports clothing.

$x + y = 27{,}753$    Total sales were $27,753 million.

*Step 4* **Solve** the system from Step 3. We use the substitution method, since the first equation is already solved for $x$.

$$x + y = 27{,}753 \quad \text{Second equation}$$

$$(6627 + y) + y = 27{,}753 \quad \text{Let } x = 6627 + y.$$

$$6627 + 2y = 27{,}753 \quad \text{Combine like terms.}$$

$$2y = 21{,}126 \quad \text{Subtract 6627.}$$

$$\boxed{\text{Don't stop here!}} \longrightarrow y = 10{,}563 \quad \text{Divide by 2.}$$

We substitute 10,563 for $y$ in either equation to find that $x = 17{,}190$.

NOW TRY
EXERCISE 1

Marina Polyakova pays a total of $1150 per month for rent and electricity. It costs $650 more for rent per month than for electricity. What are the costs for each?

***Step 5***   **State the answer.** Footwear sales were $17,190 million and clothing sales were $10,563 million.

***Step 6***   **Check** the answer in the original problem. Since

$$17{,}190 - 10{,}563 = 6627 \quad \text{and} \quad 17{,}190 + 10{,}563 = 27{,}753,$$

the answer satisfies the information in the problem.   NOW TRY

---

⚠ **CAUTION**   If an applied problem asks for *two* values, as in **Example 1,** be sure to give both of them in your answer.

---

**OBJECTIVE 2**   **Solve problems about quantities and their costs.**

**EXAMPLE 2**   Solving a Problem about Quantities and Costs

For a production of the musical *Wicked* at the Ford Center in Chicago, main floor tickets cost $148, while the best balcony tickets cost $65. Suppose that the members of a club spent a total of $2614 for 30 tickets to *Wicked*. How many tickets of each kind did they buy? (*Source:* www.ticketmaster.com)

***Step 1***   **Read** the problem several times.

***Step 2***   **Assign variables.**

Let $x$ = the number of main floor tickets,

and $y$ = the number of balcony tickets.

Summarize the information given in the problem in a table.

| | Number of Tickets | Price per Ticket (in dollars) | Total Value |
|---|---|---|---|
| Main Floor | $x$ | 148 | 148$x$ |
| Balcony | $y$ | 65 | 65$y$ |
| Total | 30 | | 2614 |

The entries in the first two rows of the Total Value column were found by multiplying the number of tickets sold by the price per ticket.

***Step 3***   **Write two equations.**

$$x + y = 30 \qquad \text{Total number of tickets was 30.} \quad (1)$$
$$148x + 65y = 2614 \qquad \text{Total value of tickets was \$2614.} \quad (2)$$

***Step 4***   **Solve** the system from Step 3 using the elimination method.

$$
\begin{array}{ll}
-65x - 65y = -1950 & \text{Multiply equation (1) by } -65.\\
\underline{148x + 65y = \phantom{-}2614} & (2)\\
83x \phantom{-65y} = \phantom{-}664 & \text{Add.}\\
x = 8 & \text{Divide by 83.}
\end{array}
$$

Substitute 8 for $x$ in equation (1).

$$
\begin{array}{ll}
x + y = 30 & (1)\\
8 + y = 30 & \text{Let } x = 8.\\
y = 22 & \text{Subtract 8.}
\end{array}
$$

NOW TRY ANSWER
**1.** rent: $900; electricity: $250

NOW TRY
EXERCISE 2
General admission rates at a local water park are $19 for adults and $16 for children. If a group of 27 people paid $462 for admission, how many adults and how many children were there?

*Step 5* **State the answer.** The club members bought 8 main floor tickets and 22 balcony tickets.

*Step 6* **Check.** The sum of 8 and 22 is 30, so the total number of tickets is correct. Since 8 tickets were purchased at $148 each and 22 at $65 each, the total of all the ticket prices is

$$\$148(8) + \$65(22) = \$2614,$$

which agrees with the total amount stated in the problem. NOW TRY

---

**OBJECTIVE 3** **Solve problems about mixtures.** In **Section 2.7,** we solved mixture problems by using one variable. Many mixture problems can also be solved by using a system of two equations in two variables.

---

**EXAMPLE 3** Solving a Mixture Problem Involving Percent

Joe Castillo, a pharmacist, needs 100 L of a 50% alcohol solution. He has on hand a 30% alcohol solution and an 80% alcohol solution, which he can mix. How many liters of each will be required to make the 100 L of a 50% alcohol solution?

*Step 1* **Read** the problem. Note the percentage of each solution and of the mixture.

*Step 2* **Assign variables.**

Let $x$ = the number of liters of 30% alcohol needed,

and $y$ = the number of liters of 80% alcohol needed.

| Liters of Solution | Percent (as a decimal) | Liters of Pure Alcohol |
|---|---|---|
| $x$ | 0.30 | 0.30$x$ |
| $y$ | 0.80 | 0.80$y$ |
| 100 | 0.50 | 0.50(100) |

Summarize the information in a table. Percents are written as decimals.

**FIGURE 10** gives an idea of what is happening in this problem.

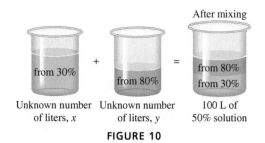

**FIGURE 10**

*Step 3* **Write two equations.** The total number of liters in the final mixture will be 100, which gives the first equation.

$$x + y = 100$$

To find the amount of pure alcohol in each mixture, multiply the number of liters by the concentration. The amount of pure alcohol in the 30% solution added to the amount of pure alcohol in the 80% solution will equal the amount of pure alcohol in the final 50% solution. This gives the second equation.

$$0.30x + 0.80y = 0.50(100)$$

NOW TRY ANSWER
**2.** 10 adults, 17 children

NOW TRY
EXERCISE 3

A biologist needs 80 L of a 30% saline solution. He has a 10% saline solution and a 35% saline solution with which to work. How many liters of each will be required to make the 80 L of a 30% solution?

These two equations form this system.

Be sure to write *two equations.*

$$x + y = 100 \quad \text{(1)}$$
$$0.30x + 0.80y = 50 \quad \text{(2)} \quad 0.50(100) = 50$$

**Step 4**  **Solve** the system by the substitution method. Solving equation (1) for $x$ gives $x = 100 - y$. Substitute $100 - y$ for $x$ in equation (2).

$$0.30x + 0.80y = 50 \quad \text{(2)}$$
$$0.30(100 - y) + 0.80y = 50 \qquad \text{Let } x = 100 - y.$$

Distribute 0.30 to *both* 100 and $-y$.

$$30 - 0.30y + 0.80y = 50 \qquad \text{Distributive property}$$
$$30 + 0.50y = 50 \qquad \text{Combine like terms.}$$
$$0.50y = 20 \qquad \text{Subtract 30.}$$
$$y = 40 \qquad \text{Divide by 0.50.}$$

Then $x = 100 - y = 100 - 40 = 60.$

**Step 5**  **State the answer.** The pharmacist should use 60 L of the 30% solution and 40 L of the 80% solution.

**Step 6**  **Check.** Since $60 + 40 = 100$ and $0.30(60) + 0.80(40) = 50,$ this mixture will give 100 L of the 50% solution, as required.   NOW TRY

---

**NOTE**  In **Example 3,** we could have used the elimination method. Also, we could have cleared decimals by multiplying each side of equation (2) by 10.

---

**OBJECTIVE 4**  **Solve problems about distance, rate (or speed), and time.** Problems that use the distance formula $d = rt$ were solved in **Section 2.7.**

**EXAMPLE 4**  Solving a Problem about Distance, Rate, and Time

Two executives in cities 400 mi apart drive to a business meeting at a location on the line between their cities. They meet after 4 hr. Find the rate (speed) of each car if one travels 20 mph faster than the other.

**Step 1**  **Read** the problem carefully.

**Step 2**  **Assign variables.**

Let $x$ = the rate of the faster car,

and $y$ = the rate of the slower car.

Make a table and draw a sketch. See **FIGURE 11.**

| | $r$ | $t$ | $d$ |
|---|---|---|---|
| Faster Car | $x$ | 4 | $4x$ |
| Slower Car | $y$ | 4 | $4y$ |

Since each car travels for 4 hr, the time $t$ for each car is 4. Find $d$, using $d = rt$.

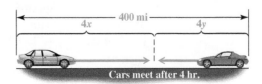

**FIGURE 11**

NOW TRY ANSWER
**3.** 16 L of 10%; 64 L of 35%

NOW TRY
EXERCISE 4

From a truck stop, two trucks travel in opposite directions on a straight highway. In 3 hr they are 405 mi apart. Find the rate of each truck if one travels 5 mph faster than the other.

**Step 3** **Write two equations.** The total distance traveled by both cars is 400 mi, which gives the first equation.

$$4x + 4y = 400$$

The faster car goes 20 mph faster than the slower car, which gives the second equation.

$$x = 20 + y$$

**Step 4** **Solve** the system of equations.

$$4x + 4y = 400 \quad (1)$$
$$x = 20 + y \quad (2)$$

Use substitution. Replace $x$ with $20 + y$ in equation (1) and solve for $y$.

| | |
|---|---|
| $4x + 4y = 400$ | (1) |
| $4(20 + y) + 4y = 400$ | Let $x = 20 + y$. |
| $80 + 4y + 4y = 400$ | Distributive property |
| $80 + 8y = 400$ | Combine like terms. |
| $8y = 320$ | Subtract 80. |
| $y = 40$ | Divide by 8. |

Distribute 4 to both 20 and $y$.

Then $x = 20 + y = 20 + 40 = 60$.

**Step 5** **State the answer.** The rates of the two cars are 40 mph and 60 mph.

**Step 6** **Check.** Since each car travels for 4 hr, the total distance traveled is

$$4(60) + 4(40) = 240 + 160 = 400 \text{ mi}, \quad \text{as required.}$$

NOW TRY

NOW TRY ANSWER
4. faster truck: 70 mph; slower truck: 65 mph

---

## 4.4 EXERCISES

MyMathLab    MathXL PRACTICE    WATCH    DOWNLOAD    READ    REVIEW

🌐 *Complete solution available on the Video Resources on DVD*

*Concept Check* Choose the correct response in Exercises 1–7.

**1.** Which expression represents the monetary value of $x$ 5-dollar bills?

    **A.** $\dfrac{x}{5}$ dollars      **B.** $\dfrac{5}{x}$ dollars      **C.** $(5 + x)$ dollars      **D.** $5x$ dollars

**2.** Which expression represents the cost of $t$ pounds of candy that sells for $4.95 per lb?

    **A.** $4.95t$      **B.** $\dfrac{\$4.95}{t}$      **C.** $\dfrac{t}{\$4.95}$      **D.** $\$4.95 + t$

**3.** Which expression represents the amount of interest earned on $d$ dollars at an interest rate of 3%?

    **A.** $3d$ dollars      **B.** $0.03d$ dollars      **C.** $0.3d$ dollars      **D.** $300d$ dollars

**4.** Suppose that Ira Spector wants to mix $x$ liters of a 40% acid solution with $y$ liters of a 35% solution to obtain 100 L of a 38% solution. One equation in a system for solving this problem is $x + y = 100$. Which one of the following is the other equation?

    **A.** $0.35x + 0.40y = 0.38(100)$      **B.** $0.40x + 0.35y = 0.38(100)$

    **C.** $35x + 40y = 38$      **D.** $40x + 35y = 0.38(100)$

**5.** According to *Natural History* magazine, the speed of a cheetah is 70 mph. If a cheetah runs for *x* hours, how many miles does the cheetah cover?

**A.** $(70 + x)$ miles
**B.** $(70 - x)$ miles
**C.** $\dfrac{70}{x}$ miles
**D.** $70x$ miles

**6.** How far does a car travel in 2.5 hr if it travels at an average rate of *x* miles per hour?

**A.** $(x + 2.5)$ miles
**B.** $\dfrac{2.5}{x}$ miles
**C.** $\dfrac{x}{2.5}$ miles
**D.** $2.5x$ miles

**7.** What is the speed of a plane that travels at a rate of 650 mph *with* a wind of *r* mph?

**A.** $\dfrac{r}{650}$ mph
**B.** $(650 - r)$ mph
**C.** $(650 + r)$ mph
**D.** $(r - 650)$ mph

**8.** What is the speed of a plane that travels at a rate of 650 mph *against* a wind of *r* mph?

**A.** $(650 + r)$ mph
**B.** $\dfrac{650}{r}$ mph
**C.** $(650 - r)$ mph
**D.** $(r - 650)$ mph

*Exercises 9 and 10 are good warm-up problems. Refer to the six-step problem-solving method, fill in the blanks for Steps 2 and 3, and complete the solution by applying Steps 4–6.*

**9.** The sum of two numbers is 98. The difference between them is 48. Find the two numbers.

*Step 1*  **Read** the problem carefully.

*Step 2*  **Assign variables.**

Let *x* = the first number and let *y* = _____.

*Step 3*  **Write two equations.**

First equation: $x + y = 98$;   Second equation: _____

**10.** The sum of two numbers is 201. The difference between them is 11. Find the two numbers.

*Step 1*  **Read** the problem carefully.

*Step 2*  **Assign variables.**

Let *x* = the first number and let *y* = _____.

*Step 3*  **Write two equations.**

First equation: $x + y = 201$;   Second equation: _____

*Write a system of equations for each problem, and then solve the system.* ***See Example 1.***

**11.** The two longest-running shows in Broadway history were *The Phantom of the Opera* and *Cats*. As of October 7, 2008, there had been a total of 16,088 performances of the two shows, with 1118 more performances of *The Phantom of the Opera* than *Cats*. How many performances were there of each show? (*Source:* The Broadway League.)

**12.** Two other musicals that had long Broadway runs were *A Chorus Line* and *Beauty and the Beast*. There were 676 fewer performances of *Beauty and the Beast* than of *A Chorus Line,* and a total of 11,598 performances of the two shows. How many performances were there of each show? (*Source:* The Broadway League.)

**13.** The two domestic top-grossing movies of 2009 were *Avatar* and *Transformers 2: Revenge of the Fallen*. The movie *Transformers 2* grossed $26.9 million less than *Avatar*, and together the two films took in $831.1 million. How much did each of these movies earn? (*Source:* www.boxofficemojo.com)

**14.** Two other domestic top-grossing movies of 2009 were *Up* and *Harry Potter and the Half-Blood Prince*. *Up* grossed $8.9 million more than *Harry Potter and the Half-Blood Prince*, and together the two films took in $594.9 million. How much did each of these movies earn? (*Source:* www.boxofficemojo.com)

*If x units of a product cost C dollars to manufacture and earn revenue of R dollars, the value of x at which the expressions for C and R are equal is called the **break-even quantity**—the number of units that produce 0 profit.*

*In Exercises 15 and 16, **(a)** find the break-even quantity, and **(b)** decide whether the product should be produced on the basis of whether it will earn a profit. (Profit = Revenue − Cost.)*

**15.** $C = 85x + 900$; $R = 105x$
No more than 38 units can be sold.

**16.** $C = 105x + 6000$; $R = 255x$
No more than 400 units can be sold.

*Write a system of equations for each problem, and then solve the system. **See Example 2.***

**17.** Jonathan, a second grader, counted the money in his piggy bank. He had only quarters and dimes. When he added up his money, he had 39 coins worth a total of $7.50. How many coins of each kind did he have?

**18.** Marilyn Mcintosh went to the post office to stock up on stamps. She spent $19.44 on 56 stamps, made up of a combination of 39-cent and 24-cent stamps. How many stamps of each denomination did she buy?

| Number of Coins | Value per Coin | Total Value |
|---|---|---|
| x | $0.25 | |
| y | $0.10 | |
| 39 | | $7.50 |

| Number of Stamps | Denomination | Total Value |
|---|---|---|
| x | $0.39 | |
| y | $0.24 | |
| | | $19.44 |

**19.** Joyce Nemeth bought each of her seven nephews a gift, either a DVD of the movie *The Blind Side* or the latest Beyoncé CD. The DVD cost $14.95 and the CD cost $16.88, and she spent a total of $114.30. How many of each DVD and CD did she buy?

**20.** Jason Williams bought each of his five nieces a gift, either a DVD of *The Twilight Saga: New Moon* or the CD soundtrack to *High School Musical 3: Senior Year*. The DVD cost $14.99 and the soundtrack cost $13.88, and he spent a total of $70.51. How many of each DVD and CD did he buy?

**21.** Karen Walsh has twice as much money invested at 5% simple annual interest as she does at 4%. If her yearly income from these two investments is $350, how much does she have invested at each rate?

**22.** Glenmore Wiggan invested some money in two accounts, one paying 3% annual simple interest and the other paying 2% interest. He earned a total of $11 interest. If he invested three times as much in the 3% account as he did in the 2% account, how much did he invest at each rate?

**23.** Two of the top-grossing North American concert tours in 2008 were The Police and Madonna. Based on average ticket prices, it cost a total of $1297 to buy six tickets for The Police and five tickets to a Madonna concert. Three tickets for The Police and four tickets for Madonna cost a total of $854. How much did an average ticket cost for each tour? (*Source:* www.CNBC.com)

**24.** Two other top-grossing North American concert tours in 2008 were Celine Dion and Kenny Chesney. Based on average ticket prices, it cost a total of $1203 to buy eight tickets for Celine Dion and three tickets for a Kenny Chesney concert. Four tickets for Celine Dion and five tickets for Kenny Chesney cost $857. How much did an average ticket cost for each tour? (*Source:* www.CNBC.com)

*Write a system of equations for each problem, and then solve the system.* ***See Example 3.***

**25.** A 40% dye solution is to be mixed with a 70% dye solution to get 120 L of a 50% solution. How many liters of the 40% and 70% solutions will be needed?

| Liters of Solution | Percent (as a decimal) | Liters of Pure Dye |
|---|---|---|
| x | 0.40 | |
| y | 0.70 | |
| 120 | 0.50 | |

**26.** A 90% antifreeze solution is to be mixed with a 75% solution to make 120 L of a 78% solution. How many liters of the 90% and 75% solutions will be used?

| Liters of Solution | Percent (as a decimal) | Liters of Pure Antifreeze |
|---|---|---|
| x | 0.90 | |
| y | 0.75 | |
| 120 | 0.78 | |

**27.** Deoraj Bharath wishes to mix coffee worth $6 per lb with coffee worth $3 per lb to get 90 lb of a mixture worth $4 per lb. How many pounds of the $6 and the $3 coffees will be needed?

| Pounds | Dollars per Pound | Cost |
|---|---|---|
| x | 6 | |
| y | . | |
| 90 | | |

**28.** Andrea Mendelsohn wishes to blend candy selling for $1.20 per lb with candy selling for $1.80 per lb to get a mixture that will be sold for $1.40 per lb. How many pounds of the $1.20 and the $1.80 candies should be used to get 45 lb of the mixture?

| Pounds | Dollars per Pound | Cost |
|---|---|---|
| x | | |
| y | 1.80 | |
| 45 | | |

**29.** How many pounds of nuts selling for $6 per lb and raisins selling for $3 per lb should Theresa Rebello combine to obtain 60 lb of a trail mix selling for $5 per lb?

30. Jasmine Vazquez, who works at a delicatessen, is preparing a cheese tray using some cheeses that sell for $8 per lb and others that sell for $12 per lb. How many pounds of cheese at each price should she use in order for the cheeses on the tray to weigh a total of 56 lb and sell for $10.50 per lb?

*Write a system of equations for each problem, and then solve the system.* **See Example 4.**

31. Two trains start from towns 495 mi apart and travel toward each other on parallel tracks. They pass each other 4.5 hr later. If one train travels 10 mph faster than the other, find the rate of each train.

32. Two trains that are 495 mi apart travel toward each other. They pass each other 5 hr later. If one train travels half as fast as the other, what are their rates?

33. Kansas City and Denver are 600 mi apart. Two cars start from these cities, traveling toward each other. They pass each other after 6 hr. Find the rate of each car if one travels 30 mph slower than the other.

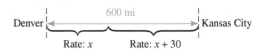

34. Toledo and Cincinnati are 200 mi apart. A car leaves Toledo traveling toward Cincinnati, and another car leaves Cincinnati at the same time, traveling toward Toledo. The car leaving Toledo averages 15 mph faster than the other car, and they pass each other after 1 hr and 36 min. What are the rates of the cars?

35. **RAGBRAI**®, the *Des Moines Register's* **A**nnual **G**reat **B**icycle **R**ide **A**cross **I**owa, is the longest and oldest touring bicycle ride in the world. Suppose a cyclist began the 471 mi ride on July 20, 2008, in western Iowa at the same time that a car traveling toward it left eastern Iowa. If the bicycle and the car met after 7.5 hr and the car traveled 35.8 mph faster than the bicycle, find the average rate of each. (*Source:* www.ragbrai.com)

36. In 2008, Atlanta's Hartsfield Airport was the world's busiest. Suppose two planes leave Hartsfield at the same time, one traveling east and the other traveling west. If the planes are 2100 mi apart after 2 hr and one plane travels 50 mph faster than the other, find the rate of each plane. (*Source:* Airports Council International.)

37. A boat takes 3 hr to go 24 mi upstream. It can go 36 mi downstream in the same time. Find the rate of the current and the rate of the boat in still water if $x$ = the rate of the boat in still water and $y$ = the rate of the current.

|  | $r$ | $t$ | $d$ |
|---|---|---|---|
| Downstream | $x + y$ | 3 | $3(x + y)$ |
| Upstream | $x - y$ | 3 | |

(*Hint:* Because the current pushes the boat when it is going downstream, the rate of the boat downstream is the *sum* of the rate of the boat and the rate of the current. The current slows down the boat when it is going upstream, so the rate of the boat upstream is the *difference* of the rate of the boat and the rate of the current.)

38. It takes a boat $1\frac{1}{2}$ hr to go 12 mi downstream, and 6 hr to return. Find the rate of the boat in still water and the rate of the current. Let $x$ = the rate of the boat in still water and $y$ = the rate of the current.

|  | $r$ | $t$ | $d$ |
|---|---|---|---|
| Downstream | $x + y$ | $\frac{3}{2}$ | |
| Upstream | $x - y$ | 6 | |

**39.** If a plane can travel 440 mph into the wind and 500 mph with the wind, find the speed of the wind and the speed of the plane in still air.

**40.** A small plane travels 200 mph with the wind and 120 mph against it. Find the speed of the wind and the speed of the plane in still air.

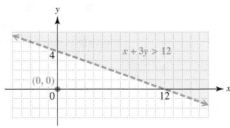

440 mph
into wind

500 mph
with wind

*Brain Busters*  *Solve each problem.*

**41.** At the beginning of a bicycle ride for charity, Yady Saldarriaga and Dane McGuckian are 30 mi apart. If they leave at the same time and ride in the same direction, Yady overtakes Dane in 6 hr. If they ride toward each other, they pass each other in 1 hr. What are their rates?

**42.** Humera Shams left Farmersville in a plane at noon to travel to Exeter. Walter Wooden left Exeter in his automobile at 2 P.M. to travel to Farmersville. It is 400 mi from Exeter to Farmersville. If the sum of their rates was 120 mph, and if they crossed paths at 4 P.M., find the rate of each.

### PREVIEW EXERCISES

*Graph each linear inequality.* ***See Section 3.5.***

**43.** $x + y \leq 4$         **44.** $y \geq -3x + 2$         **45.** $3x + 2y < 0$

## 4.5  Solving Systems of Linear Inequalities

**OBJECTIVE**

**1** Solve systems of linear inequalities by graphing.

We graphed the solutions of a linear inequality in **Section 3.5.** For example, recall that to graph the solutions of

$$x + 3y > 12,$$

we first graph $x + 3y = 12$ by finding and plotting a few ordered pairs that satisfy the equation. Because the points on the line do *not* satisfy the inequality, we use a dashed line. To decide which region includes the points that are solutions, we choose a test point not on the line.

$$x + 3y > 12 \quad \text{Original inequality}$$

We choose (0, 0) as a test point. $\quad 0 + 3(0) \stackrel{?}{>} 12 \quad \text{Let } x = 0 \text{ and } y = 0.$

$$0 > 12 \quad \text{False}$$

This false result indicates that the solutions are those points on the side of the line that does *not* include $(0, 0)$, as shown in **FIGURE 12.**

**FIGURE 12**

Now we use the same techniques to solve *systems* of linear inequalities.

**OBJECTIVE 1** Solve systems of linear inequalities by graphing. A **system of linear inequalities** consists of two or more linear inequalities. The **solution set of a system of linear inequalities** includes all ordered pairs that make all inequalities of the system true at the same time.

### Solving a System of Linear Inequalities

***Step 1*** **Graph the inequalities.** Graph each linear inequality, using the method described in **Section 3.5.**

***Step 2*** **Choose the intersection.** Indicate the solution set of the system by shading the intersection of the graphs (the region where the graphs overlap).

NOW TRY
EXERCISE 1
Graph the solution set of the system.

$$4x - 2y \leq 8$$
$$x + 3y \geq 3$$

**EXAMPLE 1** Solving a System of Linear Inequalities

Graph the solution set of the system.

$$3x + 2y \leq 6$$
$$2x - 5y \geq 10$$

***Step 1*** To graph $3x + 2y \leq 6$, graph the solid boundary line $3x + 2y = 6$ and shade the region containing the test point $(0, 0)$, as shown in **FIGURE 13(a)**.

Then graph $2x - 5y \geq 10$ with solid boundary line $2x - 5y = 10$. The test point $(0, 0)$ makes this inequality false, so shade the region on the other side of the boundary line. See **FIGURE 13(b)**.

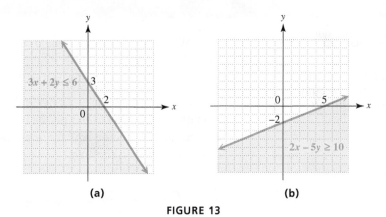

(a)                    (b)

**FIGURE 13**

***Step 2*** The solution set of this system includes all points in the intersection (overlap) of the graphs of the two inequalities. As shown in **FIGURE 14**, this intersection is the gray shaded region and portions of the two boundary lines that surround it.

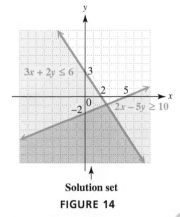

Solution set

**FIGURE 14**

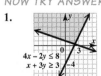
NOW TRY

NOW TRY
EXERCISE 2

Graph the solution set of the system.

$$2x + 5y > 10$$
$$x - 2y < 0$$

**NOTE** We usually do all the work on one set of axes. In the remaining examples, only one graph is shown. Be sure that the region of the final solution is clearly indicated.

**EXAMPLE 2** Solving a System of Linear Inequalities

Graph the solution set of the system.

$$x - y > 5$$
$$2x + y < 2$$

**FIGURE 15** shows the graphs of both $x - y > 5$ and $2x + y < 2$. Dashed lines show that the graphs of the inequalities do not include their boundary lines. Use $(0, 0)$ as a test point to determine the region to shade for each inequality.

The solution set of the system is the region with the gray shading. The solution set does not include either boundary line.

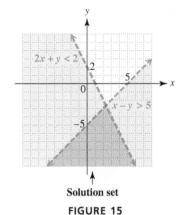

**FIGURE 15**

NOW TRY

NOW TRY
EXERCISE 3

Graph the solution set of the system.

$$x - y < 2$$
$$x \geq -2$$
$$y \leq 4$$

**EXAMPLE 3** Solving a System of Three Linear Inequalities

Graph the solution set of the system.

$$4x - 3y \leq 8$$
$$x \geq 2$$
$$y \leq 4$$

Recall that $x = 2$ is a vertical line through the point $(2, 0)$, and $y = 4$ is a horizontal line through the point $(0, 4)$. The graph of the solution set is the shaded region in **FIGURE 16**, including all boundary lines. (Here, use $(3, 2)$ as a test point to confirm that the correct region is shaded.)

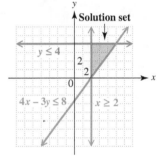

**FIGURE 16**

NOW TRY

**CONNECTIONS**

We can graph the solution set of the following system with a calculator.

$$y < 3x + 2$$
$$y > -2x - 5$$

To graph the first inequality, we direct the calculator to shade *below* the line

$$Y_1 = 3X + 2 \quad \text{(because of the } < \text{ symbol).}$$

To graph the second inequality, we direct the calculator to shade *above* the line

$$Y_2 = -2X - 5 \quad \text{(because of the } > \text{ symbol).}$$

**FIGURE 17(a)** on the next page shows these directions on a TI-83/84 Plus calculator. Graphing in the standard viewing window gives the screen in **FIGURE 17(b)**.

NOW TRY ANSWERS

**2.**

**3.**

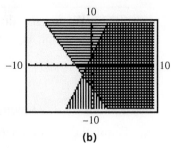

The crosshatched region is the intersection of the solution sets of the two individual inequalities and represents the solution set of the system.

(a)                    (b)

**FIGURE 17**

If the inequalities of a system are not solved for $y$ as in this example, we must do so in order to enter them into the calculator. Notice that we cannot determine from the screen in **FIGURE 17(b)** whether the boundary lines are included or excluded in the solution set. For this system, neither boundary line is included.

### For Discussion or Writing

Use a graphing calculator to graph the solution sets of the systems of linear inequalities from **Examples 1 and 2.** Compare your calculator graphs to the graphs in **FIGURES 14 AND 15** on **pages 282 and 283.**

---

## 4.5 EXERCISES

**MyMathLab** · Math XL PRACTICE · WATCH · DOWNLOAD · READ · REVIEW

🌐 *Complete solution available on the Video Resources on DVD*

*Concept Check* *Match each system of inequalities with the correct graph from choices A–D.*

**1.** $x \geq 5$
$y \leq -3$

**A.**

**B.**

**2.** $x \leq 5$
$y \geq -3$

**3.** $x > 5$
$y < -3$

**C.**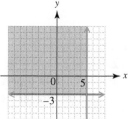

**D.**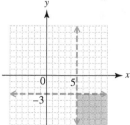

**4.** $x < 5$
$y > -3$

*Graph the solution set of each system of linear inequalities.* **See Examples 1 and 2.**

🌐 **5.** $x + y \leq 6$
$x - y \geq 1$

**6.** $x + y \leq 2$
$x - y \geq 3$

**7.** $4x + 5y \geq 20$
$x - 2y \leq 5$

**8.** $x + 4y \leq 8$
$2x - y \geq 4$

🌐 **9.** $2x + 3y < 6$
$x - y < 5$

**10.** $x + 2y < 4$
$x - y < -1$

**11.** $y \le 2x - 5$
$x < 3y + 2$

**12.** $x \ge 2y + 6$
$y > -2x + 4$

**13.** $4x + 3y < 6$
$x - 2y > 4$

**14.** $3x + y > 4$
$x + 2y < 2$

**15.** $x \le 2y + 3$
$x + y < 0$

**16.** $x \le 4y + 3$
$x + y > 0$

**17.** $-3x + y \ge 1$
$6x - 2y \ge -10$

**18.** $2x + 3y < 6$
$4x + 6y > 18$

**19.** $x - 3y \le 6$
$x \ge -4$

**20.** $x - 2y \ge 4$
$x \le -2$

*Graph the solution set of each system.* ***See Example 3.***

**21.** $4x + 5y < 8$
$y > -2$
$x > -4$

**22.** $x + y \ge -3$
$x - y \le 3$
$y \le 3$

**23.** $3x - 2y \ge 6$
$x + y \le 4$
$x \ge 0$
$y \ge -4$

**24.** $2x - 3y < 6$
$x + y > 3$
$x < 4$
$y < 4$

## TECHNOLOGY INSIGHTS  EXERCISES 25–28

*Match each system of inequalities with its solution set.* ***See the Connections box.***

**A.**
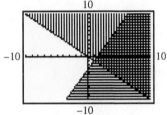

**B.**
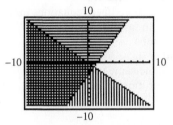

**C.**
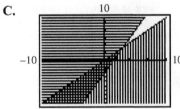

**D.**
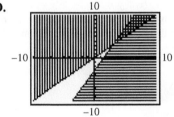

**25.** $y \ge x$
$y \le 2x - 3$

**26.** $y \le x$
$y \ge 2x - 3$

**27.** $y \ge -x$
$y \le 2x - 3$

**28.** $y \le -x$
$y \ge 2x - 3$

## PREVIEW EXERCISES

*Evaluate each expression.* ***See Section 1.2.***

**29.** $2 \cdot 2 \cdot 2 \cdot 2 \cdot 2 \cdot 2$

**30.** $3 \cdot 3 \cdot 3$

**31.** $5 \cdot 5 \cdot 5 \cdot 5$

**32.** $4 \cdot 4 \cdot 4 \cdot 4 \cdot 4$

**33.** $\dfrac{2}{3} \cdot \dfrac{2}{3} \cdot \dfrac{2}{3}$

**34.** $\dfrac{5}{8} \cdot \dfrac{5}{8}$

# CHAPTER 4 SUMMARY

## KEY TERMS

**4.1**

system of linear equations (linear system)

solution of a system
solution set of a system
set-builder notation
consistent system

inconsistent system
independent equations
dependent equations

**4.5**

system of linear inequalities
solution set of a system of linear inequalities

## TEST YOUR WORD POWER

*See how well you have learned the vocabulary in this chapter.*

1. A **system of linear equations** consists of
   A. at least two linear equations with different variables
   B. two or more linear equations that have an infinite number of solutions
   C. two or more linear equations with the same variables
   D. two or more linear inequalities.

2. A **consistent system** is a system of equations
   A. with one solution
   B. with no solution
   C. with an infinite number of solutions
   D. that have the same graph.

3. An **inconsistent system** is a system of equations
   A. with one solution
   B. with no solution

   C. with an infinite number of solutions
   D. that have the same graph.

4. **Dependent equations**
   A. have different graphs
   B. have no solution
   C. have one solution
   D. are different forms of the same equation.

**ANSWERS**

**1.** C; *Example:* $2x + y = 7$, $3x - y = 3$ **2.** A; *Example:* The system in **Answer 1** is consistent. The graphs of the equations intersect at exactly one point—in this case, the solution $(2, 3)$. **3.** B; *Example:* The equations of two parallel lines make up an inconsistent system. Their graphs never intersect, so there is no solution to the system. **4.** D; *Example:* The equations $4x - y = 8$ and $8x - 2y = 16$ are dependent because their graphs are the same line.

## QUICK REVIEW

**CONCEPTS**

**EXAMPLES**

### 4.1 Solving Systems of Linear Equations by Graphing

An ordered pair is a solution of a system if it makes all equations of the system true at the same time.

Is $(4, -1)$ a solution of the following system?
$$x + y = 3$$
$$2x - y = 9$$

Yes, because $4 + (-1) = 3$ and $2(4) - (-1) = 9$ are both true, $(4, -1)$ is a solution.

To solve a linear system by graphing, follow these steps.

*Step 1* Graph each equation of the system on the same axes.

*Step 2* Find the coordinates of the point of intersection.

*Step 3* Check. Write the solution set.

Solve the system by graphing.
$$x + y = 5$$
$$2x - y = 4$$

The solution $(3, 2)$ checks, so $\{(3, 2)\}$ is the solution set.

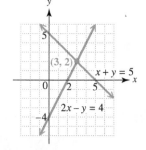

(continued)

| CONCEPTS | EXAMPLES |
|---|---|

### 4.2 Solving Systems of Linear Equations by Substitution

**Step 1** Solve one equation for either variable.

Solve by substitution.

$$x + 2y = -5 \quad (1)$$
$$y = -2x - 1 \quad (2)$$

Equation (2) is already solved for $y$.

**Step 2** Substitute for that variable in the other equation to get an equation in one variable.

Substitute $-2x - 1$ for $y$ in equation (1).

$$x + 2(-2x - 1) = -5 \quad \text{Let } y = -2x - 1 \text{ in (1)}.$$

**Step 3** Solve the equation from Step 2.

$$x - 4x - 2 = -5 \quad \text{Distributive property}$$
$$-3x - 2 = -5 \quad \text{Combine like terms.}$$
$$-3x = -3 \quad \text{Add 2.}$$
$$x = 1 \quad \text{Divide by } -3.$$

**Step 4** Substitute the result into the equation from Step 1 to get the value of the other variable.

To find $y$, let $x = 1$ in equation (2).

$$y = -2(1) - 1 = -3$$

**Step 5** Check. Write the solution set.

The solution, $(1, -3)$, checks, so $\{(1, -3)\}$ is the solution set.

### 4.3 Solving Systems of Linear Equations by Elimination

**Step 1** Write both equations in standard form, $Ax + By = C$.

Solve by elimination.

$$x + 3y = 7 \quad (1)$$
$$3x - y = 1 \quad (2)$$

**Step 2** Multiply to transform the equations so that the coefficients of one pair of variable terms are opposites.

Multiply equation (1) by $-3$ to eliminate the $x$-terms.

$$
\begin{array}{ll}
-3x - 9y = -21 & \text{Multiply equation (1) by } -3. \\
\underline{3x - y = \phantom{-}1} & (2) \\
-10y = -20 & \text{Add.} \\
y = 2 & \text{Divide by } -10.
\end{array}
$$

**Step 3** Add the equations to get an equation with only one variable.

**Step 4** Solve the equation from Step 3.

**Step 5** Substitute the solution from Step 4 into either of the original equations to find the value of the remaining variable.

Substitute to get the value of $x$.

$$x + 3y = 7 \quad (1)$$
$$x + 3(2) = 7 \quad \text{Let } y = 2.$$
$$x + 6 = 7 \quad \text{Multiply.}$$
$$x = 1 \quad \text{Subtract 6.}$$

**Step 6** Check. Write the solution set.

Since $1 + 3(2) = 7$ and $3(1) - 2 = 1$, the solution set is $\{(1, 2)\}$.

If the result of the addition step (Step 3) is a false statement, such as $0 = 4$, the graphs are parallel lines and *there is no solution. The solution set is $\emptyset$.*

$$
\begin{array}{ll}
x - 2y = \phantom{-}6 & \\
\underline{-x + 2y = -2} & \\
0 = \phantom{-}4 & \text{Solution set: } \emptyset
\end{array}
$$

If the result is a true statement, such as $0 = 0$, the graphs are the same line, and an *infinite number of ordered pairs are solutions. The solution set is written in set-builder notation as $\{(x, y) \mid \underline{\hspace{2cm}}\}$, where a form of the equation is written in the blank.*

$$
\begin{array}{ll}
x - 2y = \phantom{-}6 & \\
\underline{-x + 2y = -6} & \\
0 = \phantom{-}0 & \text{Solution set: } \{(x, y) \mid x - 2y = 6\}
\end{array}
$$

(continued)

| CONCEPTS | EXAMPLES |
|---|---|

**4.4** **Applications of Linear Systems**

Use the modified six-step method.

*Step 1*    Read.

*Step 2*    Assign variables.

*Step 3*    Write two equations using both variables.

*Step 4*    Solve the system.

*Step 5*    State the answer.

*Step 6*    Check.

The sum of two numbers is 30. Their difference is 6. Find the numbers.

Let $x =$ one number, and let $y =$ the other number.

$$
\begin{aligned}
x + y &= 30 \quad (1)\\
\underline{x - y} &= \underline{\phantom{0}6} \quad (2)\\
2x \phantom{- y} &= 36 \quad \text{Add.}\\
x &= 18 \quad \text{Divide by 2.}
\end{aligned}
$$

Let $x = 18$ in equation (1): $18 + y = 30$. Solve to get $y = 12$.

The two numbers are 18 and 12.

$18 + 12 = 30$ and $18 - 12 = 6$, so the solution checks.

**4.5** **Solving Systems of Linear Inequalities**

To solve a system of linear inequalities, follow these steps.

*Step 1*    Graph each inequality on the same axes. (This was explained in **Section 3.5**.)

*Step 2*    Choose the intersection. The solution set of the system is formed by the overlap of the regions of the two graphs.

The shaded region shows the solution set of the system.

$$2x + 4y \geq 5$$
$$x \geq 1$$

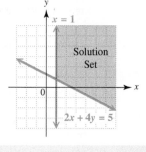

---

CHAPTER ( 4 )

# REVIEW EXERCISES

**4.1**    *Decide whether the given ordered pair is a solution of the given system.*

**1.** $(3, 4)$
$$4x - 2y = 4$$
$$5x + \phantom{0}y = 19$$

**2.** $(-5, 2)$
$$x - 4y = -13$$
$$2x + 3y = 4$$

*Solve each system by graphing.*

**3.** $x + y = 4$
$\phantom{}2x - y = 5$

**4.** $x - 2y = 4$
$\phantom{}2x + \phantom{}y = -2$

**5.** $2x + 4 = 2y$
$\phantom{}y - x = -3$

**6.** $x - 2 \phantom{0}= 2y$
$\phantom{}2x - 4y = 4$

**4.2**

**7.** *Concept Check*    Suppose that you were asked to solve the following system by substitution. Which variable in which equation would be easiest to solve for in your first step?

$$5x - 3y = 7$$
$$-x + 2y = 4$$

**8.** *Concept Check* After solving a system of linear equations by the substitution method, a student obtained the equation "0 = 0." He gave the solution set of the system as $\{(0, 0)\}$. *WHAT WENT WRONG?*

*Solve each system by the substitution method.*

**9.** $3x + y = 7$
$x = 2y$

**10.** $2x - 5y = -19$
$y = x + 2$

**11.** $4x + 5y = 44$
$x + 2 = 2y$

**12.** $5x + 15y = 30$
$x + 3y = 6$

**4.3**

**13.** *Concept Check* Which system does not require that we multiply one or both equations by a constant to solve the system by the elimination method?

**A.** $-4x + 3y = 7$
$3x - 4y = 4$

**B.** $5x + 8y = 13$
$12x + 24y = 36$

**C.** $2x + 3y = 5$
$x - 3y = 12$

**D.** $x + 2y = 9$
$3x - y = 6$

**14.** *Concept Check* For the system

$$2x + 12y = 7 \quad \text{(1)}$$
$$3x + 4y = 1, \quad \text{(2)}$$

if we were to multiply equation (1) by $-3$, by what number would we have to multiply equation (2) in order to

**(a)** eliminate the $x$-terms when solving by the elimination method?

**(b)** eliminate the $y$-terms when solving by the elimination method?

*Solve each system by the elimination method.*

**15.** $2x - y = 13$
$x + y = 8$

**16.** $-4x + 3y = 25$
$6x - 5y = -39$

**17.** $3x - 4y = 9$
$6x - 8y = 18$

**18.** $2x + y = 3$
$-4x - 2y = 6$

**4.1–4.3** *Solve each system by any method.*

**19.** $2x + 3y = -5$
$3x + 4y = -8$

**20.** $6x - 9y = 0$
$2x - 3y = 0$

**21.** $x - 2y = 5$
$y = x - 7$

**22.** $\dfrac{x}{2} + \dfrac{y}{3} = 7$
$\dfrac{x}{4} + \dfrac{2y}{3} = 8$

**23.** $\dfrac{3}{4}x - \dfrac{1}{3}y = \dfrac{7}{6}$
$\dfrac{1}{2}x + \dfrac{2}{3}y = \dfrac{5}{3}$

**24.** $0.4x - 0.5y = -2.2$
$0.3x + 0.2y = -0.5$

**4.4** *Solve each problem by using a system of equations.*

**25.** The two leading pizza chains in the United States are Pizza Hut and Domino's Pizza. In July 2009, Pizza Hut had 6118 more locations than Domino's, and together the two chains had 23,400 locations. How many locations did each chain have? (*Source: PMQ Pizza Magazine.*)

**26.** Two popular magazines in the United States are *Reader's Digest* and *People*. Together, the average paid circulation for these two magazines in 2007 was 12.9 million. The circulation for *People* was 5.7 million less than that of *Reader's Digest*. What were the circulation figures for each magazine? (*Source:* Audit Bureau of Circulations.)

**27.** The perimeter of a rectangle is 90 m. Its length is $1\frac{1}{2}$ times its width. Find the length and width of the rectangle.

**28.** Laura Mancini has 20 bills, all of which are $10 or $20 bills. The total value of the money is $330. How many of each denomination does she have?

**29.** Sharon Klein has candy that sells for $1.30 per lb, to be mixed with candy selling for $0.90 per lb to get 100 lb of a mix that will sell for $1 per lb. How much of each type should she use?

**30.** A 40% antifreeze solution is to be mixed with a 70% solution to get 90 L of a 50% solution. How many liters of the 40% and 70% solutions will be needed?

| Number of Liters | Percent (as a decimal) | Amount of Pure Antifreeze |
|---|---|---|
| x | 0.40 | |
| y | 0.70 | |
| 90 | 0.50 | |

**31.** Nancy Johnson invested $18,000. Part of it was invested at 3% annual simple interest, and the rest was invested at 4%. Her interest income for the first year was $650. How much did she invest at each rate?

| Amount of Principal | Rate | Interest |
|---|---|---|
| x | 0.03 | |
| y | 0.04 | |
| $18,000 | | |

**32.** A certain plane flying with the wind travels 540 mi in 2 hr. Later, flying against the same wind, the plane travels 690 mi in 3 hr. Find the speed of the plane in still air and the speed of the wind.

**4.5**   *Graph the solution set of each system of linear inequalities.*

**33.** $x + y \geq 2$
   $x - y \leq 4$

**34.** $y \geq 2x$
   $2x + 3y \leq 6$

**35.** $x + y < 3$
   $2x > y$

**36.** $3x - y \leq 3$
   $x \geq -1$
   $y \leq 2$

## MIXED REVIEW EXERCISES

*Solve each problem.*

**37.** Patricia Pinkston compared the monthly payments she would incur for two types of mortgages: fixed rate and variable rate. Her observations led to the graph shown.

   **(a)** For which years would the monthly payment be more for the fixed rate mortgage than for the variable rate mortgage?

   **(b)** In what year would the payments be the same, and what would those payments be?

**Mortgage Shopping**

**38.** *Concept Check*   Why would it be easier to solve System B by the substitution method than System A?

   *System A:* $-5x + 6y = -7$
   $2x + 5y = -5$

   *System B:* $2x + 9y = 13$
   $y = 3x - 2$

**39.** *Concept Check*   Which system of linear inequalities is graphed in the figure?

   **A.** $x \leq 3$
   $y \leq 1$

   **B.** $x \leq 3$
   $y \geq 1$

   **C.** $x \geq 3$
   $y \leq 1$

   **D.** $x \geq 3$
   $y \geq 1$

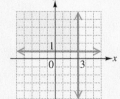

**40.** $\dfrac{2x}{3} + \dfrac{y}{4} = \dfrac{14}{3}$

$\dfrac{x}{2} + \dfrac{y}{12} = \dfrac{8}{3}$

**41.** $x = y + 6$

$2y - 2x = -12$

**42.** $3x + 4y = 6$

$4x - 5y = 8$

**43.** $0.4x - 0.9y = 0.7$

$0.3x + 0.2y = 1.4$

**44.** $x + y < 5$

$x - y \geq 2$

**45.** $y \leq 2x$

$x + 2y > 4$

**46.** The perimeter of an isosceles triangle measures 29 in. One side of the triangle is 5 in. longer than each of the two equal sides. Find the lengths of the sides of the triangle.

**47.** In 2007, a total of 7.5 million people visited the Statue of Liberty and the National World War II Memorial, two popular tourist attractions. The Statue of Liberty had 0.7 million fewer visitors than the National World War II Memorial. How many visitors did each of these attractions have? (*Source:* National Park Service.)

**48.** Two cars leave from the same place and travel in opposite directions. One car travels 30 mph faster than the other. After $2\frac{1}{2}$ hr, they are 265 mi apart. What are the rates of the cars?

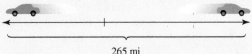

265 mi

---

# CHAPTER ( 4 )

## TEST

CHAPTER **Test Prep** VIDEOS   Step-by-step test solutions are found on the Chapter Test Prep Videos available via the Video Resources on DVD, in *MyMathLab* , or on **You Tube** (search "LialBeginningAlgebra").

*View the complete solutions to all Chapter Test exercises on the Video Resources on DVD.*

**1.** Decide whether each ordered pair is a solution of the system.

$$2x + y = -3$$
$$x - y = -9$$

**(a)** $(1, -5)$    **(b)** $(1, 10)$    **(c)** $(-4, 5)$

**2.** Solve the system

$x + 2y = 6$

$-2x + y = -7$    by graphing.

*Solve each system by substitution.*

**3.** $2x + y = -4$

$x = y + 7$

**4.** $4x + 3y = -35$

$x + y = 0$

*Solve each system by elimination.*

**5.** $2x - y = 4$

$3x + y = 21$

**6.** $4x + 2y = 2$

$5x + 4y = 7$

**7.** $3x + 4y = 9$

$2x + 5y = 13$

**8.** $4x + 5y = 2$

$-8x - 10y = 6$

**9.** $6x - 5y = 0$

$-2x + 3y = 0$

*Solve each system by any method.*

**10.** $4y = -3x + 5$

$6x = -8y + 10$

**11.** $\dfrac{6}{5}x - \dfrac{1}{3}y = -20$

$-\dfrac{2}{3}x + \dfrac{1}{6}y = 11$

*Solve each problem by using a system of equations.*

**12.** The distance between Memphis and Atlanta is 782 mi less than the distance between Minneapolis and Houston. Together, the two distances total 1570 mi. How far is it between Memphis and Atlanta? How far is it between Minneapolis and Houston?

**13.** In 2008, the two most popular amusement parks in the United States were Disneyland and the Magic Kingdom at Walt Disney World. Disneyland had 2.4 million fewer visitors than the Magic Kingdom, and together they had 31.8 million visitors. How many visitors did each park have? (*Source:* 2008 TEA/ERA Attraction Attendance Report.)

**14.** Sohail Chughtai has a 25% solution of alcohol to mix with a 40% solution to get 50 L of a final mixture that is 30% alcohol. How much of each of the original solutions should be used?

**15.** Two cars leave from Perham, Minnesota, at the same time and travel in the same direction. One car travels one and one-third times as fast as the other. After 3 hr, they are 45 mi apart. What are the rates of the cars?

*Graph the solution set of each system of inequalities.*

**16.** $2x + 7y \leq 14$
     $x - y \geq 1$

**17.** $2x - y > 6$
     $4y + 12 \geq -3x$

**18.** *Concept Check*   Without actually graphing, determine which one of the following systems of inequalities has no solution.

**A.** $x \geq 4$
     $y \leq 3$

**B.** $x + y > 4$
     $x + y < 3$

**C.** $x > 2$
     $y < 1$

**D.** $x + y > 4$
     $x - y < 3$

---

CHAPTERS (1–4)

# CUMULATIVE REVIEW EXERCISES

**1.** List all integer factors of 40.

**2.** Evaluate $-2 + 6\left[3 - (4 - 9)\right]$.

**3.** Find the value of the expression $\dfrac{3x^2 + 2y^2}{10y + 3}$ for $x = 1$ and $y = 5$.

**4.** Name the property that justifies the statement: $r(s - k) = rs - rk$.

*Solve each linear equation.*

**5.** $2 - 3(6x + 2) = 4(x + 1) + 18$

**6.** $\dfrac{3}{2}\left(\dfrac{1}{3}x + 4\right) = 6\left(\dfrac{1}{4} + x\right)$

**7.** Solve the formula $P = \dfrac{kT}{V}$ for $T$.

*Solve each linear inequality.*

**8.** $-\dfrac{5}{6}x < 15$

**9.** $-8 < 2x + 3$

**10.** A survey measured public recognition of some classic advertising slogans. Complete the results shown in the table if 2500 people were surveyed.

| Slogan (product or company) | Percent Recognition (nearest tenth of a percent) | Actual Number That Recognized Slogan (nearest whole number) |
|---|---|---|
| Please Don't Squeeze the . . . (Charmin®) | 80.4% | |
| The Breakfast of Champions (Wheaties) | 72.5% | |
| The King of Beers (Budweiser®) | | 1570 |
| Like a Good Neighbor (State Farm) | | 1430 |

(Other slogans included "You're in Good Hands" (Allstate), "Snap, Crackle, Pop" (Rice Krispies®), and "The Un-Cola" (7-Up).)
*Source:* Department of Integrated Marketing Communications, Northwestern University.

*Solve each problem.*

**11.** On August 6, 2009, the U.S. Senate confirmed Sonia Sotomayor, as the 111th Justice of the United States Supreme Court. With 99 senators voting, 37 more voted in favor of her confirmation than voted against it. How many senators voted each way? (*Source: The New York Times.*)

**12.** Two angles of a triangle have the same measure. The measure of the third angle is 4° less than twice the measure of each of the equal angles. Find the measures of the three angles.

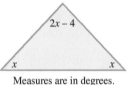

Measures are in degrees.

*Graph each linear equation.*

**13.** $x - y = 4$

**14.** $3x + y = 6$

*Find the slope of each line.*

**15.** Through $(-5, 6)$ and $(1, -2)$

**16.** Perpendicular to the line $y = 4x - 3$

*Find an equation for each line. Write it in slope-intercept form.*

**17.** Through $(-4, 1)$ with slope $\frac{1}{2}$

**18.** Through the points $(1, 3)$ and $(-2, -3)$

**19.** **(a)** Write an equation of the vertical line through $(9, -2)$.

   **(b)** Write an equation of the horizontal line through $(4, -1)$.

*Solve each system by any method.*

**20.** $2x - y = -8$
$x + 2y = 11$

**21.** $4x + 5y = -8$
$3x + 4y = -7$

**22.** $3x + 4y = 2$
$6x + 8y = 1$

*Use a system of equations to solve each problem.*

**23.** Admission prices at a high school football game were $6 for adults and $2 for children. The total value of the tickets sold was $2528, and 454 tickets were sold. How many adult and how many child tickets were sold?

| Kind of Ticket | Number Sold | Cost of Each (in dollars) | Total Value (in dollars) |
|---|---|---|---|
| Adult | x | 6 | 6x |
| Child | y | | |
| Total | 454 | | |

**24.** A chemist needs 12 L of a 40% alcohol solution. She must mix a 20% solution and a 50% solution. How many liters of each will be required to obtain what she needs?

**25.** Graph the solution set of the system $\begin{array}{l} x + 2y \le 12 \\ 2x - y \le 8 \end{array}$.

# Exponents and Polynomials

Just how much is a *trillion*? A trillion, written 1,000,000,000,000, is a million million, or a thousand billion. A trillion seconds would last more than 31,000 years—that is, 310 centuries. The U.S. government projects that by 2017, consumers and taxpayers will spend more than $4 trillion on health care, accounting for $1 of every $5 spent. (*Source:* Centers for Medicare and Medicaid Services.)

In **Section 5.3,** we use *exponents* and *scientific notation* to write and calculate with large numbers, such as the national debt, tax revenue, and the distances from Earth to celestial objects.

# 5.1 The Product Rule and Power Rules for Exponents

**OBJECTIVE 1** **Use exponents.** Recall from **Section 1.2** that in the expression $5^2$, the number 5 is the **base** and 2 is the **exponent,** or **power.** The expression $5^2$ is called an **exponential expression.** Although we do not usually write the exponent when it is 1, in general, for any quantity $a$,

$$a^1 = a.$$

**EXAMPLE 1** Using Exponents

Write $3 \cdot 3 \cdot 3 \cdot 3$ in exponential form and evaluate.

Since 3 occurs as a factor four times, the base is 3 and the exponent is 4. The exponential expression is $3^4$, read "3 to the fourth power" or simply "3 to the fourth."

$$\underbrace{3 \cdot 3 \cdot 3 \cdot 3}_{\text{4 factors of 3}} = 3^4 = 81$$

NOW TRY

**NOW TRY EXERCISE 1**

Write $4 \cdot 4 \cdot 4$ in exponential form and evaluate.

**EXAMPLE 2** Evaluating Exponential Expressions

Evaluate. Name the base and the exponent.

**(a)** $5^4 = 5 \cdot 5 \cdot 5 \cdot 5 = 625$

| Expression | Base | Exponent |
|------------|------|----------|
| $5^4$ | 5 | 4 |
| $-5^4$ | 5 | 4 |
| $(-5)^4$ | $-5$ | 4 |

The base is 5.

**(b)** $-5^4 = -1 \cdot 5^4 = -1 \cdot (5 \cdot 5 \cdot 5 \cdot 5) = -625$

**(c)** $(-5)^4 = (-5)(-5)(-5)(-5) = 625$

NOW TRY

**NOW TRY EXERCISE 2**

Evaluate. Name the base and the exponent.

**(a)** $(-3)^4$  **(b)** $-3^4$

⚠ **CAUTION** Note the differences between **Example 2(b) and 2(c).** In $-5^4$, the absence of parentheses shows that the exponent 4 applies only to the base 5, not $-5$. In $(-5)^4$, the parentheses show that the exponent 4 applies to the base $-5$. In summary, $-a^n$ and $(-a)^n$ are not necessarily the same.

| Expression | Base | Exponent | Example |
|------------|------|----------|---------|
| $-a^n$ | $a$ | $n$ | $-3^2 = -(3 \cdot 3) = -9$ |
| $(-a)^n$ | $-a$ | $n$ | $(-3)^2 = (-3)(-3) = 9$ |

**OBJECTIVE 2** **Use the product rule for exponents.** To develop the product rule, we use the definition of exponents.

$$2^4 \cdot 2^3 = (\overbrace{2 \cdot 2 \cdot 2 \cdot 2}^{\text{4 factors}})(\overbrace{2 \cdot 2 \cdot 2}^{\text{3 factors}})$$

$$= \underbrace{2 \cdot 2 \cdot 2 \cdot 2 \cdot 2 \cdot 2 \cdot 2}_{4 + 3 = 7 \text{ factors}}$$

$$= 2^7$$

*NOW TRY ANSWERS*
**1.** $4^3 = 64$
**2.** **(a)** $81; -3; 4$  **(b)** $-81; 3; 4$

Also,

$$6^2 \cdot 6^3 = (6 \cdot 6)(6 \cdot 6 \cdot 6)$$
$$= 6 \cdot 6 \cdot 6 \cdot 6 \cdot 6$$
$$= 6^5.$$

Generalizing from these examples, we have

$$2^4 \cdot 2^3 = 2^{4+3} = 2^7 \quad \text{and} \quad 6^2 \cdot 6^3 = 6^{2+3} = 6^5.$$

This suggests the **product rule for exponents.**

---

### Product Rule for Exponents

For any positive integers $m$ and $n$,   $a^m \cdot a^n = a^{m+n}$.
(Keep the same base and add the exponents.)

*Example:*   $6^2 \cdot 6^5 = 6^{2+5} = 6^7$

---

⚠ **CAUTION**  Do not multiply the bases when using the product rule. ***Keep the same base and add the exponents.*** For example,

$$6^2 \cdot 6^5 = 6^7, \quad \textbf{\textit{not}} \quad 36^7.$$

---

◝ *NOW TRY*
↳ *EXERCISE 3*

Use the product rule for exponents to find each product if possible.

(a) $(-5)^2(-5)^4$

(b) $y^2 \cdot y \cdot y^5$

(c) $(2x^3)(4x^7)$

(d) $2^4 \cdot 5^3$

(e) $3^2 + 3^3$

### EXAMPLE 3   Using the Product Rule

Use the product rule for exponents to find each product if possible.

(a) $6^3 \cdot 6^5 = 6^{3+5} = 6^8$
　　$\boxed{\text{Keep the same base.}}$

(b) $(-4)^7(-4)^2 = (-4)^{7+2} = (-4)^9$

(c) $x^2 \cdot x = x^2 \cdot x^1 = x^{2+1} = x^3$

(d) $m^4 m^3 m^5 = m^{4+3+5} = m^{12}$

(e) $2^3 \cdot 3^2$

The product rule does not apply, since the bases are different.

$$2^3 \cdot 3^2 = 8 \cdot 9 = 72 \quad \text{Evaluate } 2^3 \text{ and } 3^2. \text{ Then multiply.}$$

$\boxed{\text{Think: } 2^3 = 2 \cdot 2 \cdot 2}$   $\boxed{\text{Think: } 3^2 = 3 \cdot 3}$

(f) $2^3 + 2^4$

The product rule does not apply, since this is a *sum,* not a *product.*

$$2^3 + 2^4 = 8 + 16 = 24 \quad \text{Evaluate } 2^3 \text{ and } 2^4. \text{ Then add.}$$

(g) $(2x^3)(3x^7)$  ⟵ $\boxed{2x^3 \text{ means } 2 \cdot x^3 \text{ and } 3x^7 \text{ means } 3 \cdot x^7.}$

$$= (2 \cdot 3) \cdot (x^3 \cdot x^7) \quad \text{Commutative and associative properties}$$
$$= 6x^{3+7} \quad \text{Multiply; product rule}$$
$$= 6x^{10} \quad \text{Add.} \qquad\qquad \textit{NOW TRY} ↻$$

---

NOW TRY ANSWERS
**3.** (a) $(-5)^6$  (b) $y^8$  (c) $8x^{10}$
  (d) The product rule does not
  apply; 2000  (e) The product
  rule does not apply; 36

⚠ **CAUTION**  Be sure that you understand the difference between *adding* and *multiplying* exponential expressions. For example, consider the following.

$$8x^3 + 5x^3 = (8 + 5)x^3 = 13x^3$$
$$(8x^3)(5x^3) = (8 \cdot 5)x^{3+3} = 40x^6$$

**OBJECTIVE 3** Use the rule $(a^m)^n = a^{mn}$. Consider the following.

$$(8^3)^2 = (8^3)(8^3) = 8^{3+3} = 8^6 \qquad \text{Product rule for exponents}$$

The product of the exponents in $(8^3)^2$, $3 \cdot 2$, gives the exponent in $8^6$. Also

$$(5^2)^4 = 5^2 \cdot 5^2 \cdot 5^2 \cdot 5^2 \qquad \text{Definition of exponent}$$
$$= 5^{2+2+2+2} \qquad \text{Product rule}$$
$$= 5^8, \qquad \text{Add the exponents.}$$

and $2 \cdot 4 = 8$. These examples suggest **power rule (a) for exponents.**

### Power Rule (a) for Exponents

For any positive integers $m$ and $n$, $\quad (a^m)^n = a^{mn}$.
(Raise a power to a power by multiplying exponents.)

*Example:* $\quad (3^2)^4 = 3^{2 \cdot 4} = 3^8$

⌐ NOW TRY
⌐ EXERCISE 4

Simplify.

**(a)** $(4^7)^5$  **(b)** $(y^4)^7$

**EXAMPLE 4** Using Power Rule (a)

Use power rule (a) for exponents to simplify.

**(a)** $(2^5)^3 = 2^{5 \cdot 3} = 2^{15}$  **(b)** $(5^7)^2 = 5^{7(2)} = 5^{14}$  **(c)** $(x^2)^5 = x^{2(5)} = x^{10}$

NOW TRY ⟳

**OBJECTIVE 4** Use the rule $(ab)^m = a^m b^m$. Consider the following.

$$(4x)^3 = (4x)(4x)(4x) \qquad \text{Definition of exponent}$$
$$= (4 \cdot 4 \cdot 4)(x \cdot x \cdot x) \qquad \text{Commutative and associative properties}$$
$$= 4^3 \cdot x^3 \qquad \text{Definition of exponent}$$

This example suggests **power rule (b) for exponents.**

### Power Rule (b) for Exponents

For any positive integer $m$, $\quad (ab)^m = a^m b^m$.
(Raise a product to a power by raising each factor to the power.)

*Example:* $\quad (2p)^5 = 2^5 p^5$

**EXAMPLE 5** Using Power Rule (b)

Use power rule (b) for exponents to simplify.

**(a)** $(3xy)^2$

$= 3^2 x^2 y^2 \qquad$ Power rule (b)

$= 9x^2 y^2 \qquad 3^2 = 3 \cdot 3 = 9$

**(b)** $5(pq)^2$

$= 5(p^2 q^2) \qquad$ Power rule (b)

$= 5p^2 q^2 \qquad$ Multiply.

**(c)** $3(2m^2 p^3)^4$

$= 3[2^4 (m^2)^4 (p^3)^4] \qquad$ Power rule (b)

$= 3 \cdot 2^4 m^8 p^{12} \qquad$ Power rule (a)

$= 48 m^8 p^{12} \qquad 3 \cdot 2^4 = 3 \cdot 16 = 48$

NOW TRY ANSWERS

**4. (a)** $4^{35}$ **(b)** $y^{28}$

*NOW TRY*
*EXERCISE 5*
Simplify.
**(a)** $(-5ab)^3$    **(b)** $3(4t^3p^5)^2$

**(d)** $(-5^6)^3$

$\quad = (-1 \cdot 5^6)^3 \qquad\quad -a = -1 \cdot a$

$\quad = (-1)^3 \cdot (5^6)^3 \qquad$ Power rule (b)

$\quad = -1 \cdot 5^{18} \qquad\qquad$ Power rule (a)

$\quad = -5^{18}$

Raise $-1$ to the designated power.

*NOW TRY*

---

⚠ **CAUTION**  *Power rule (b) does not apply to a sum.* For example,

$$(4x)^2 = 4^2x^2, \qquad \text{but} \qquad (4 + x)^2 \neq 4^2 + x^2.$$

---

**OBJECTIVE 5**  **Use the rule** $\left(\dfrac{a}{b}\right)^m = \dfrac{a^m}{b^m}$. Since the quotient $\dfrac{a}{b}$ can be written as $a\left(\dfrac{1}{b}\right)$, we use this fact and power rule (b) to get **power rule (c) for exponents.**

### Power Rule (c) for Exponents

For any positive integer $m$,    $\left(\dfrac{a}{b}\right)^m = \dfrac{a^m}{b^m}$   $(b \neq 0)$.

(Raise a quotient to a power by raising both numerator and denominator to the power.)

*Example:*  $\left(\dfrac{5}{3}\right)^2 = \dfrac{5^2}{3^2}$

*NOW TRY*
*EXERCISE 6*
Simplify.

**(a)** $\left(\dfrac{p}{q}\right)^5$    **(b)** $\left(\dfrac{1}{4}\right)^3$
$\quad (q \neq 0)$

### EXAMPLE 6  Using Power Rule (c)

Use power rule (c) for exponents to simplify.

**(a)** $\left(\dfrac{2}{3}\right)^5 = \dfrac{2^5}{3^5} = \dfrac{32}{243}$    **(b)** $\left(\dfrac{m}{n}\right)^3 = \dfrac{m^3}{n^3}$   $(n \neq 0)$

**(c)** $\left(\dfrac{1}{5}\right)^4 = \dfrac{1^4}{5^4} = \dfrac{1}{5^4} = \dfrac{1}{625}$    $1^4 = 1 \cdot 1 \cdot 1 \cdot 1 = 1$

*NOW TRY*

---

**NOTE**  In **Example 6(c)**, we used the fact that $1^4 = 1$.

*In general, $1^n = 1$, for any integer $n$.*

---

### Rules for Exponents

For positive integers $m$ and $n$, the following are true.

| | | **Examples** |
|---|---|---|
| **Product rule** | $a^m \cdot a^n = a^{m+n}$ | $6^2 \cdot 6^5 = 6^{2+5} = 6^7$ |
| **Power rules (a)** | $(a^m)^n = a^{mn}$ | $(3^2)^4 = 3^{2 \cdot 4} = 3^8$ |
| **(b)** | $(ab)^m = a^m b^m$ | $(2p)^5 = 2^5 p^5$ |
| **(c)** | $\left(\dfrac{a}{b}\right)^m = \dfrac{a^m}{b^m}$  $(b \neq 0)$ | $\left(\dfrac{5}{3}\right)^2 = \dfrac{5^2}{3^2}$ |

NOW TRY ANSWERS
**5. (a)** $-125a^3b^3$  **(b)** $48t^6p^{10}$
**6. (a)** $\dfrac{p^5}{q^5}$  **(b)** $\dfrac{1}{64}$

OBJECTIVE 6 Use combinations of rules.

NOW TRY
EXERCISE 7

Simplify.

**(a)** $\left(\dfrac{3}{5}\right)^3 \cdot 3^2$   **(b)** $(8k)^5(8k)^4$

**(c)** $(x^4y)^5(-2x^2y^5)^3$

EXAMPLE 7 Using Combinations of Rules

Simplify.

**(a)** $\left(\dfrac{2}{3}\right)^2 \cdot 2^3$

$= \dfrac{2^2}{3^2} \cdot \dfrac{2^3}{1}$   Power rule (c)

$= \dfrac{2^2 \cdot 2^3}{3^2 \cdot 1}$   Multiply fractions.

$= \dfrac{2^{2+3}}{3^2}$   Product rule

$= \dfrac{2^5}{3^2}$,   or   $\dfrac{32}{9}$

**(b)** $(5x)^3(5x)^4$

$= (5x)^7$   Product rule

$= 5^7x^7$   Power rule (b)

**(c)** $(2x^2y^3)^4(3xy^2)^3$

$= 2^4(x^2)^4(y^3)^4 \cdot 3^3x^3(y^2)^3$   Power rule (b)

$= 2^4x^8y^{12} \cdot 3^3x^3y^6$   Power rule (a)

$= 2^4 \cdot 3^3x^8x^3y^{12}y^6$   Commutative and associative properties

$= 16 \cdot 27x^{11}y^{18}$,   or   $432x^{11}y^{18}$   Product rule; multiply.

Notice that $(2x^2y^3)^4$ means $2^4x^{2 \cdot 4}y^{3 \cdot 4}$, **not** $(2 \cdot 4)x^{2 \cdot 4}y^{3 \cdot 4}$.

**(d)** $(-x^3y)^2(-x^5y^4)^3$   [Don't forget each factor of $-1$.]

$= (-1 \cdot x^3y)^2(-1 \cdot x^5y^4)^3$   $-a = -1 \cdot a$

$= (-1)^2(x^3)^2y^2 \cdot (-1)^3(x^5)^3(y^4)^3$   Power rule (b)

$= (-1)^2(x^6)(y^2)(-1)^3(x^{15})(y^{12})$   Power rule (a)

$= (-1)^5(x^{21})(y^{14})$   Product rule

$= -x^{21}y^{14}$   Simplify.   NOW TRY

⚠ CAUTION Be aware of the distinction between $(2y)^3$ and $2y^3$.

$(2y)^3 = 2y \cdot 2y \cdot 2y = 8y^3$,   while   $2y^3 = 2 \cdot y \cdot y \cdot y$.

OBJECTIVE 7 Use the rules for exponents in a geometry application.

EXAMPLE 8 Using Area Formulas

Find an expression that represents the area in **(a)** FIGURE 1 and **(b)** FIGURE 2.

NOW TRY ANSWERS

7. **(a)** $\frac{243}{125}$  **(b)** $8^9k^9$
   **(c)** $-8x^{26}y^{20}$

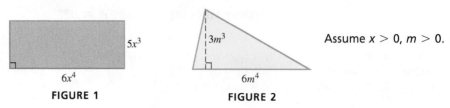

Assume $x > 0$, $m > 0$.

$5x^3$   $3m^3$   $6m^4$

$6x^4$

FIGURE 1     FIGURE 2

*NOW TRY EXERCISE 8*

Write an expression that represents the area of the figure. Assume $x > 0$.

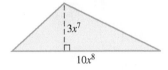

**(a)** For **FIGURE 1**, use the formula for the area of a rectangle, $A = LW$.

$A = (6x^4)(5x^3)$    Area formula

$A = 6 \cdot 5 \cdot x^{4+3}$    Commutative property; product rule

$A = 30x^7$    Multiply. Add the exponents.

**(b)** **FIGURE 2** is a triangle with base $6m^4$ and height $3m^3$.

$A = \dfrac{1}{2}bh$    Area formula

$A = \dfrac{1}{2}(6m^4)(3m^3)$    Substitute.

$A = \dfrac{1}{2}(18m^7)$, or $9m^7$    Product rule; multiply.    *NOW TRY*

**NOW TRY ANSWER**
**8.** $15x^{15}$

---

# 5.1 EXERCISES

**MyMathLab**   Math XL PRACTICE   WATCH   DOWNLOAD   READ   REVIEW

⊕ *Complete solution available on the Video Resources on DVD*

*Concept Check*   *Decide whether each statement is* true *or* false. *If false, tell why.*

**1.** $3^3 = 9$     **2.** $(-3)^4 = 3^4$     **3.** $(x^2)^3 = x^5$     **4.** $\left(\dfrac{1}{5}\right)^2 = \dfrac{1}{5^2}$

*Write each expression by using exponents. **See Example 1.***

**5.** $w \cdot w \cdot w \cdot w \cdot w \cdot w$        **6.** $t \cdot t \cdot t \cdot t \cdot t \cdot t \cdot t$

⊕ **7.** $\left(\dfrac{1}{2}\right)\left(\dfrac{1}{2}\right)\left(\dfrac{1}{2}\right)\left(\dfrac{1}{2}\right)\left(\dfrac{1}{2}\right)\left(\dfrac{1}{2}\right)$     **8.** $\left(\dfrac{1}{4}\right)\left(\dfrac{1}{4}\right)\left(\dfrac{1}{4}\right)\left(\dfrac{1}{4}\right)\left(\dfrac{1}{4}\right)$

**9.** $(-4)(-4)(-4)(-4)$        **10.** $(-3)(-3)(-3)(-3)(-3)(-3)$

**11.** $(-7y)(-7y)(-7y)(-7y)$     **12.** $(-8p)(-8p)(-8p)(-8p)(-8p)$

✐ **13.** Explain how the expressions $(-3)^4$ and $-3^4$ are different.

✐ **14.** Explain how the expressions $(5x)^3$ and $5x^3$ are different.

*Identify the base and the exponent for each exponential expression. In Exercises 15–18, also evaluate each expression. **See Example 2.***

⊕ **15.** $3^5$     **16.** $2^7$     ⊕ **17.** $(-3)^5$     **18.** $(-2)^7$

**19.** $(-6x)^4$     **20.** $(-8x)^4$     **21.** $-6x^4$     **22.** $-8x^4$

✐ **23.** Explain why the product rule does not apply to the expression $5^2 + 5^3$. Then evaluate the expression by finding the individual powers and adding the results.

✐ **24.** Repeat **Exercise 23** for the expression $(-4)^3 + (-4)^4$.

*Use the product rule, if possible, to simplify each expression. Write each answer in exponential form. **See Example 3.***

⊕ **25.** $5^2 \cdot 5^6$      **26.** $3^6 \cdot 3^7$      **27.** $4^2 \cdot 4^7 \cdot 4^3$

**28.** $5^3 \cdot 5^8 \cdot 5^2$      **29.** $(-7)^3(-7)^6$      **30.** $(-9)^8(-9)^5$

⊕ **31.** $t^3 \cdot t^8 \cdot t^{13}$      **32.** $n^5 \cdot n^6 \cdot n^9$      **33.** $(-8r^4)(7r^3)$

**34.** $(10a^7)(-4a^3)$      ⊕ **35.** $(-6p^5)(-7p^5)$      **36.** $(-5w^8)(-9w^8)$

**37.** $(5x^2)(-2x^3)(3x^4)$      **38.** $(12y^3)(4y)(-3y^5)$      ⊕ **39.** $3^8 + 3^9$

**40.** $4^{12} + 4^5$      **41.** $5^8 \cdot 3^9$      **42.** $6^3 \cdot 8^9$

*Use the power rules for exponents to simplify each expression. Write each answer in exponential form.* ***See Examples 4–6.***

⊕ **43.** $(4^3)^2$  **44.** $(8^3)^6$  ⊕ **45.** $(t^4)^5$  **46.** $(y^6)^5$

**47.** $(7r)^3$  **48.** $(11x)^4$  ⊕ **49.** $(5xy)^5$  **50.** $(9pq)^6$

**51.** $(-5^2)^6$  **52.** $(-9^4)^8$  **53.** $(-8^3)^5$  **54.** $(-7^5)^7$

**55.** $8(qr)^3$  **56.** $4(vw)^5$  **57.** $\left(\dfrac{9}{5}\right)^8$

**58.** $\left(\dfrac{12}{7}\right)^3$  ⊕ **59.** $\left(\dfrac{1}{2}\right)^3$  **60.** $\left(\dfrac{1}{3}\right)^5$

**61.** $\left(\dfrac{a}{b}\right)^3$  $(b \neq 0)$  **62.** $\left(\dfrac{r}{t}\right)^4$  $(t \neq 0)$  **63.** $\left(\dfrac{x}{2}\right)^3$

**64.** *Concept Check*  Will $(-a)^n$ ever equal $a^n$? If so, when?

*Simplify each expression.* ***See Example 7.***

**65.** $\left(\dfrac{5}{2}\right)^3 \cdot \left(\dfrac{5}{2}\right)^2$  **66.** $\left(\dfrac{3}{4}\right)^5 \cdot \left(\dfrac{3}{4}\right)^6$  ⊕ **67.** $\left(\dfrac{9}{8}\right)^3 \cdot 9^2$

**68.** $\left(\dfrac{8}{5}\right)^4 \cdot 8^3$  **69.** $(2x)^9(2x)^3$  **70.** $(6y)^5(6y)^8$

**71.** $(-6p)^4(-6p)$  **72.** $(-13q)^3(-13q)$  **73.** $(6x^2y^3)^5$

**74.** $(5r^5t^6)^7$  **75.** $(x^2)^3(x^3)^5$  **76.** $(y^4)^5(y^3)^5$

**77.** $(2w^2x^3y)^2(x^4y)^5$  **78.** $(3x^4y^2z)^3(yz^4)^5$  ⊕ **79.** $(-r^4s)^2(-r^2s^3)^5$

**80.** $(-ts^6)^4(-t^3s^5)^3$  **81.** $\left(\dfrac{5a^2b^5}{c^6}\right)^3$  $(c \neq 0)$  **82.** $\left(\dfrac{6x^3y^9}{z^5}\right)^4$  $(z \neq 0)$

**83.** *Concept Check*  A student simplified $(10^2)^3$ as $1000^6$. *WHAT WENT WRONG?*

✎ **84.** Explain why $(3x^2y^3)^4$ is *not* equivalent to $(3 \cdot 4)x^8y^{12}$.

*Find an expression that represents the area of each figure.* ***See Example 8.*** *(If necessary, refer to the formulas on the inside covers. The ⌐ in the figures indicate 90° right angles.)*

⊕ **85.**

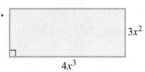

$3x^2$

$4x^3$

**86.**

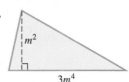

$m^2$

$3m^4$

**87.**

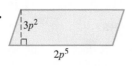

$3p^2$

$2p^5$

**88.**

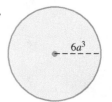

$6a^3$

*Find an expression that represents the volume of each figure. (If necessary, refer to the formulas on the inside covers.)*

**89.**

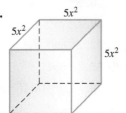

$5x^2$

$5x^2$

$5x^2$

**90.**

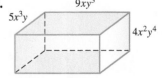

$9xy^3$

$5x^3y$

$4x^2y^4$

✐  **91.** Assume that $a$ is a number greater than 1. Arrange the following terms in order from least to greatest:  $-(-a)^3, -a^3, (-a)^4, -a^4$. Explain how you decided on the order.

✐  **92.** Devise a rule that tells whether an exponential expression with a negative base is positive or negative.

**Compound interest** is interest paid on the principal and the interest earned earlier. The formula for compound interest, which involves an exponential expression, is

$$A = P(1 + r)^n,$$

where $A$ is the amount accumulated from a principal of $P$ dollars left untouched for $n$ years with an annual interest rate $r$ (expressed as a decimal).

*In Exercises 93–96, use the preceding formula and a calculator to find A to the nearest cent.*

**93.** $P = \$250, r = 0.04, n = 5$         **94.** $P = \$400, r = 0.04, n = 3$

**95.** $P = \$1500, r = 0.035, n = 6$       **96.** $P = \$2000, r = 0.025, n = 4$

### PREVIEW EXERCISES

*Give the reciprocal of each number. **See Section 1.1.***

**97.** 9          **98.** $-3$          **99.** $-\dfrac{1}{8}$          **100.** 0.5

*Perform each subtraction. **See Section 1.5.***

**101.** $8 - (-4)$          **102.** $-4 - 8$

**103.** Subtract $-6$ from $-3$.          **104.** Subtract $-3$ from $-6$.

## 5.2  Integer Exponents and the Quotient Rule

**OBJECTIVES**

**1** Use 0 as an exponent.

**2** Use negative numbers as exponents.

**3** Use the quotient rule for exponents.

**4** Use combinations of rules.

Consider the following list.

$$2^4 = 16$$
$$2^3 = 8$$
$$2^2 = 4$$

Each time we reduce the exponent by 1, the value is divided by 2 (the base). Using this pattern, we can continue the list to lesser and lesser integer exponents.

$$2^1 = 2$$
$$2^0 = 1$$
$$2^{-1} = \tfrac{1}{2}$$
$$2^{-2} = \tfrac{1}{4}$$
$$2^{-3} = \tfrac{1}{8}$$

From the preceding list, it appears that we should define $2^0$ as 1 and bases raised to negative exponents as reciprocals of those bases.

**OBJECTIVE 1** Use 0 as an exponent. The definitions of 0 and negative exponents must satisfy the rules for exponents from **Section 5.1.** For example, if $6^0 = 1$, then

$$6^0 \cdot 6^2 = 1 \cdot 6^2 = 6^2 \quad \text{and} \quad 6^0 \cdot 6^2 = 6^{0+2} = 6^2,$$

so that the product rule is satisfied. Check that the power rules are also valid for a 0 exponent. Thus, we define a 0 exponent as follows.

### Zero Exponent

For any nonzero real number $a$, $\quad a^0 = 1.$

*Example:* $\quad 17^0 = 1$

**NOW TRY**
**EXERCISE 1**
Evaluate.
(a) $6^0$
(b) $-12^0$
(c) $(-12x)^0 \quad (x \neq 0)$
(d) $14^0 - 12^0$

**EXAMPLE 1** Using Zero Exponents

Evaluate.

(a) $60^0 = 1$

(b) $(-60)^0 = 1$

(c) $-60^0 = -(1) = -1$

(d) $y^0 = 1 \quad (y \neq 0)$

(e) $6y^0 = 6(1) = 6 \quad (y \neq 0)$

(f) $(6y)^0 = 1 \quad (y \neq 0)$

(g) $8^0 + 11^0 = 1 + 1 = 2$

(h) $-8^0 - 11^0 = -1 - 1 = -2$ NOW TRY

> ⚠ **CAUTION** Look again at **Examples 1(b) and 1(c).** In $(-60)^0$, the base is $-60$, and since any nonzero base raised to the 0 exponent is 1, $(-60)^0 = 1$. In $-60^0$, which can be written $-(60)^0$, the base is 60, so $-60^0 = -1$.

**OBJECTIVE 2** Use negative numbers as exponents. From the lists at the beginning of this section, since $2^{-2} = \frac{1}{4}$ and $2^{-3} = \frac{1}{8}$, we can deduce that $2^{-n}$ should equal $\frac{1}{2^n}$. Is the product rule valid in such cases? For example,

$$6^{-2} \cdot 6^2 = 6^{-2+2} = 6^0 = 1.$$

The expression $6^{-2}$ behaves as if it were the reciprocal of $6^2$, since their product is 1. The reciprocal of $6^2$ is also $\frac{1}{6^2}$, leading us to define $6^{-2}$ as $\frac{1}{6^2}$.

### Negative Exponents

For any nonzero real number $a$ and any integer $n$, $\quad a^{-n} = \dfrac{1}{a^n}.$

*Example:* $\quad 3^{-2} = \dfrac{1}{3^2}$

By definition, $a^{-n}$ and $a^n$ are reciprocals, since

$$a^n \cdot a^{-n} = a^n \cdot \frac{1}{a^n} = 1.$$

Because $1^n = 1$, the definition of $a^{-n}$ can also be written

$$a^{-n} = \frac{1}{a^n} = \frac{1^n}{a^n} = \left(\frac{1}{a}\right)^n.$$

**NOW TRY ANSWERS**
**1. (a)** 1  **(b)** $-1$  **(c)** 1  **(d)** 0

For example, $\qquad 6^{-3} = \left(\dfrac{1}{6}\right)^3 \quad \text{and} \quad \left(\dfrac{1}{3}\right)^{-2} = 3^2.$

*NOW TRY*
*EXERCISE 2*
Simplify.

**(a)** $2^{-3}$     **(b)** $\left(\dfrac{1}{7}\right)^{-2}$

**(c)** $\left(\dfrac{3}{2}\right)^{-4}$     **(d)** $3^{-2} + 4^{-2}$

**(e)** $p^{-4}$   $(p \neq 0)$

### EXAMPLE 2   Using Negative Exponents

Simplify by writing with positive exponents. Assume that all variables represent nonzero real numbers.

**(a)** $3^{-2} = \dfrac{1}{3^2} = \dfrac{1}{9}$

**(b)** $5^{-3} = \dfrac{1}{5^3} = \dfrac{1}{125}$

**(c)** $\left(\dfrac{1}{2}\right)^{-3} = 2^3 = 8$    $\frac{1}{2}$ and 2 are reciprocals.

*Notice that we can change the base to its reciprocal if we also change the sign of the exponent.*

**(d)** $\left(\dfrac{2}{5}\right)^{-4} = \left(\dfrac{5}{2}\right)^{4} = \dfrac{625}{16}$

   $\frac{2}{5}$ and $\frac{5}{2}$ are reciprocals.

**(e)** $\left(\dfrac{4}{3}\right)^{-5} = \left(\dfrac{3}{4}\right)^{5} = \dfrac{243}{1024}$

**(f)** $4^{-1} - 2^{-1} = \dfrac{1}{4} - \dfrac{1}{2} = \dfrac{1}{4} - \dfrac{2}{4} = -\dfrac{1}{4}$    Apply the exponents first, and then subtract.

> Remember to find a common denominator.

**(g)** $p^{-2} = \dfrac{1}{p^2}$

**(h)** $\dfrac{1}{x^{-4}} = \dfrac{1^{-4}}{x^{-4}}$    It is convenient to write 1 as $1^{-4}$ here, because $-4$ is the exponent in the denominator.

$= \left(\dfrac{1}{x}\right)^{-4}$    Power rule (c)

$= x^4$    $\frac{1}{x}$ and $x$ are reciprocals.

**(i)** $x^3 y^{-4} = \dfrac{x^3}{y^4}$      *NOW TRY*

Consider the following.

$$\dfrac{2^{-3}}{3^{-4}} = \dfrac{\dfrac{1}{2^3}}{\dfrac{1}{3^4}} = \dfrac{1}{2^3} \div \dfrac{1}{3^4} = \dfrac{1}{2^3} \cdot \dfrac{3^4}{1} = \dfrac{3^4}{2^3}$$    To divide by a fraction, multiply by its reciprocal.

Therefore,     $\dfrac{2^{-3}}{3^{-4}} = \dfrac{3^4}{2^3}$.

### Changing from Negative to Positive Exponents

For any nonzero numbers $a$ and $b$ and any integers $m$ and $n$, the following are true.

$$\dfrac{a^{-m}}{b^{-n}} = \dfrac{b^n}{a^m} \quad \text{and} \quad \left(\dfrac{a}{b}\right)^{-m} = \left(\dfrac{b}{a}\right)^{m}$$

*Examples:*   $\dfrac{3^{-5}}{2^{-4}} = \dfrac{2^4}{3^5}$   and   $\left(\dfrac{4}{5}\right)^{-3} = \left(\dfrac{5}{4}\right)^{3}$

*NOW TRY ANSWERS*
**2. (a)** $\dfrac{1}{8}$   **(b)** $49$   **(c)** $\dfrac{16}{81}$
   **(d)** $\dfrac{25}{144}$   **(e)** $\dfrac{1}{p^4}$

NOW TRY
EXERCISE 3

Simplify by writing with positive exponents. Assume that all variables represent nonzero real numbers.

**(a)** $\dfrac{5^{-3}}{6^{-2}}$  **(b)** $m^2 n^{-4}$

**(c)** $\dfrac{x^2 y^{-3}}{5z^{-4}}$

---

**EXAMPLE 3**  Changing from Negative to Positive Exponents

Simplify by writing with positive exponents. Assume that all variables represent nonzero real numbers.

**(a)** $\dfrac{4^{-2}}{5^{-3}} = \dfrac{5^3}{4^2} = \dfrac{125}{16}$

**(b)** $\dfrac{m^{-5}}{p^{-1}} = \dfrac{p^1}{m^5} = \dfrac{p}{m^5}$

**(c)** $\dfrac{a^{-2}b}{3d^{-3}} = \dfrac{bd^3}{3a^2}$    Notice that $b$ in the numerator and 3 in the denominator are not affected.

**(d)** $\left(\dfrac{x}{2y}\right)^{-4} = \left(\dfrac{2y}{x}\right)^4 = \dfrac{2^4 y^4}{x^4} = \dfrac{16y^4}{x^4}$

NOW TRY

---

⚠ CAUTION  Be careful. We cannot use this rule to change negative exponents to positive exponents if the exponents occur in a *sum or difference* of terms. For example,

$$\dfrac{5^{-2} + 3^{-1}}{7 - 2^{-3}} \quad \text{would be written with positive exponents as} \quad \dfrac{\dfrac{1}{5^2} + \dfrac{1}{3}}{7 - \dfrac{1}{2^3}}.$$

---

**OBJECTIVE 3**  Use the quotient rule for exponents.  Consider the following.

$$\dfrac{6^5}{6^3} = \dfrac{6 \cdot 6 \cdot 6 \cdot 6 \cdot 6}{6 \cdot 6 \cdot 6} = 6^2$$

The difference between the exponents, $5 - 3 = 2$, is the exponent in the quotient.

Also,

$$\dfrac{6^2}{6^4} = \dfrac{6 \cdot 6}{6 \cdot 6 \cdot 6 \cdot 6} = \dfrac{1}{6^2} = 6^{-2}.$$

Here, $2 - 4 = -2$. These examples suggest the **quotient rule for exponents.**

> **Quotient Rule for Exponents**
>
> For any nonzero real number $a$ and any integers $m$ and $n$,
>
> $$\dfrac{a^m}{a^n} = a^{m-n}.$$
>
> (Keep the same base and subtract the exponents.)
>
> *Example:*  $\dfrac{5^8}{5^4} = 5^{8-4} = 5^4$

---

⚠ CAUTION  A common **error** is to write $\dfrac{5^8}{5^4} = 1^{8-4} = 1^4$. By the quotient rule, the quotient must have the *same base*, 5, just as in the product rule.

$$\dfrac{5^8}{5^4} = 5^{8-4} = 5^4$$

If you are not sure, use the definition of an exponent to write out the factors.

$$\dfrac{5^8}{5^4} = \dfrac{5 \cdot 5 \cdot 5 \cdot 5 \cdot 5 \cdot 5 \cdot 5 \cdot 5}{5 \cdot 5 \cdot 5 \cdot 5} = 5^4$$

---

NOW TRY ANSWERS

**3. (a)** $\dfrac{6^2}{5^3}$, or $\dfrac{36}{125}$  **(b)** $\dfrac{m^2}{n^4}$

**(c)** $\dfrac{x^2 z^4}{5y^3}$

*NOW TRY*
*EXERCISE 4*

Simplify by writing with positive exponents. Assume that all variables represent nonzero real numbers.

**(a)** $\dfrac{6^3}{6^4}$    **(b)** $\dfrac{t^4}{t^{-5}}$

**(c)** $\dfrac{(p+q)^{-3}}{(p+q)^{-7}}$   $(p \neq -q)$

**(d)** $\dfrac{5^2 x y^{-3}}{3^{-1} x^{-2} y^2}$

---

**EXAMPLE 4** Using the Quotient Rule

Simplify by writing with positive exponents. Assume that all variables represent nonzero real numbers.

**(a)** $\dfrac{5^8}{5^6} = 5^{8-6} = 5^2 = 25$   ⎣Keep the same base.⎦

**(b)** $\dfrac{4^2}{4^9} = 4^{2-9} = 4^{-7} = \dfrac{1}{4^7}$

**(c)** $\dfrac{5^{-3}}{5^{-7}} = 5^{-3-(-7)} = 5^4 = 625$   ⎣Be careful with signs.⎦

**(d)** $\dfrac{q^5}{q^{-3}} = q^{5-(-3)} = q^8$

**(e)** $\dfrac{3^2 x^5}{3^4 x^3}$

$= \dfrac{3^2}{3^4} \cdot \dfrac{x^5}{x^3}$

$= 3^{2-4} \cdot x^{5-3}$    Quotient rule

$= 3^{-2} x^2$    Subtract.

$= \dfrac{x^2}{3^2},$   or   $\dfrac{x^2}{9}$

**(f)** $\dfrac{(m+n)^{-2}}{(m+n)^{-4}}$

$= (m+n)^{-2-(-4)}$

$= (m+n)^{-2+4}$

$= (m+n)^2,$   $m \neq -n$

**(g)** $\dfrac{7x^{-3} y^2}{2^{-1} x^2 y^{-5}}$

$= \dfrac{7 \cdot 2^1 y^2 y^5}{x^2 x^3}$    Negative-to-positive rule

$= \dfrac{14 y^7}{x^5}$    Product rule

*NOW TRY*

The definitions and rules for exponents are summarized here.

| **Definitions and Rules for Exponents** | | |
|---|---|---|
| For any integers $m$ and $n$, the following are true. | | **Examples** |
| **Product rule** | $a^m \cdot a^n = a^{m+n}$ | $7^4 \cdot 7^5 = 7^{4+5} = 7^9$ |
| **Zero exponent** | $a^0 = 1 \quad (a \neq 0)$ | $(-3)^0 = 1$ |
| **Negative exponent** | $a^{-n} = \dfrac{1}{a^n} \quad (a \neq 0)$ | $5^{-3} = \dfrac{1}{5^3}$ |
| **Quotient rule** | $\dfrac{a^m}{a^n} = a^{m-n} \quad (a \neq 0)$ | $\dfrac{2^2}{2^5} = 2^{2-5} = 2^{-3} = \dfrac{1}{2^3}$ |
| **Power rule (a)** | $(a^m)^n = a^{mn}$ | $(4^2)^3 = 4^{2 \cdot 3} = 4^6$ |
| **Power rule (b)** | $(ab)^m = a^m b^m$ | $(3k)^4 = 3^4 k^4$ |
| **Power rule (c)** | $\left(\dfrac{a}{b}\right)^m = \dfrac{a^m}{b^m} \quad (b \neq 0)$ | $\left(\dfrac{2}{3}\right)^2 = \dfrac{2^2}{3^2}$ |
| **Negative-to-positive rules** | $\dfrac{a^{-m}}{b^{-n}} = \dfrac{b^n}{a^m} \quad (a \neq 0, b \neq 0)$ | $\dfrac{2^{-4}}{5^{-3}} = \dfrac{5^3}{2^4}$ |
| | $\left(\dfrac{a}{b}\right)^{-m} = \left(\dfrac{b}{a}\right)^m$ | $\left(\dfrac{4}{7}\right)^{-2} = \left(\dfrac{7}{4}\right)^2$ |

*NOW TRY ANSWERS*

**4. (a)** $\dfrac{1}{6}$   **(b)** $t^9$

   **(c)** $(p+q)^4$   **(d)** $\dfrac{75x^3}{y^5}$

*NOW TRY*
*EXERCISE 5*

Simplify. Assume that all variables represent nonzero real numbers.

**(a)** $\dfrac{3^{15}}{(3^3)^4}$  **(b)** $(4t)^5(4t)^{-3}$

**(c)** $\left(\dfrac{7y^4}{10}\right)^{-3}$  **(d)** $\dfrac{(a^2b^{-2}c)^{-3}}{(2ab^3c^{-4})^5}$

**OBJECTIVE 4** Use combinations of rules.

**EXAMPLE 5** Using Combinations of Rules

Simplify. Assume that all variables represent nonzero real numbers.

**(a)** $\dfrac{(4^2)^3}{4^5}$

$= \dfrac{4^6}{4^5}$  Power rule (a)

$= 4^{6-5}$  Quotient rule

$= 4^1$

$= 4$

**(b)** $(2x)^3(2x)^2$

$= (2x)^5$  Product rule

$= 2^5x^5$  Power rule (b)

$= 32x^5$

**(c)** $\left(\dfrac{2x^3}{5}\right)^{-4}$

$= \left(\dfrac{5}{2x^3}\right)^4$  Negative-to-positive rule

$= \dfrac{5^4}{2^4x^{12}}$  Power rules (a)–(c)

$= \dfrac{625}{16x^{12}}$

**(d)** $\left(\dfrac{3x^{-2}}{4^{-1}y^3}\right)^{-3}$

$= \dfrac{3^{-3}x^6}{4^3y^{-9}}$  Power rules (a)–(c)

$= \dfrac{x^6y^9}{4^3 \cdot 3^3}$  Negative-to-positive rule

$= \dfrac{x^6y^9}{1728}$

**(e)** $\dfrac{(4m)^{-3}}{(3m)^{-4}}$

$= \dfrac{4^{-3}m^{-3}}{3^{-4}m^{-4}}$  Power rule (b)

$= \dfrac{3^4m^4}{4^3m^3}$  Negative-to-positive rule

$= \dfrac{3^4m^{4-3}}{4^3}$  Quotient rule

$= \dfrac{3^4m}{4^3}$,  or  $\dfrac{81m}{64}$

 NOW TRY

*NOW TRY ANSWERS*
**5. (a)** $3^3$, or 27  **(b)** $16t^2$
**(c)** $\dfrac{1000}{343y^{12}}$  **(d)** $\dfrac{c^{17}}{32a^{11}b^9}$

---

## 5.2 EXERCISES

*MyMathLab*  Math XL PRACTICE  WATCH  DOWNLOAD  READ  REVIEW

● *Complete solution available on the Video Resources on DVD*

Decide whether each expression is equal to 0, 1, or $-1$. *See Example 1.*

● **1.** $9^0$  **2.** $3^0$  **3.** $(-2)^0$  **4.** $(-12)^0$

**5.** $-8^0$  **6.** $-6^0$  **7.** $-(-6)^0$  **8.** $-(-13)^0$

**9.** $(-4)^0 - 4^0$  **10.** $(-11)^0 - 11^0$  **11.** $\dfrac{0^{10}}{12^0}$  **12.** $\dfrac{0^5}{2^0}$

**13.** $8^0 - 12^0$  **14.** $6^0 - 13^0$  **15.** $\dfrac{0^2}{2^0 + 0^2}$  **16.** $\dfrac{2^0}{0^2 + 2^0}$

*Concept Check*   In Exercises 17 and 18, match each expression in Column I with the equivalent expression in Column II. Choices in Column II may be used once, more than once, or not at all. (In Exercise 17, $x \neq 0$.)

| I | II | | I | II |
|---|---|---|---|---|
| **17. (a)** $x^0$ | **A.** 0 | | **18. (a)** $-2^{-4}$ | **A.** 8 |
| **(b)** $-x^0$ | **B.** 1 | | **(b)** $(-2)^{-4}$ | **B.** 16 |
| **(c)** $7x^0$ | **C.** $-1$ | | **(c)** $2^{-4}$ | **C.** $-\dfrac{1}{16}$ |
| **(d)** $(7x)^0$ | **D.** 7 | | **(d)** $\dfrac{1}{2^{-4}}$ | **D.** $-8$ |
| **(e)** $-7x^0$ | **E.** $-7$ | | **(e)** $\dfrac{1}{-2^{-4}}$ | **E.** $-16$ |
| **(f)** $(-7x)^0$ | **F.** $\dfrac{1}{7}$ | | **(f)** $\dfrac{1}{(-2)^{-4}}$ | **F.** $\dfrac{1}{16}$ |

*Evaluate each expression.* ***See Examples 1 and 2.***

**19.** $6^0 + 8^0$  **20.** $4^0 + 2^0$  🌐 **21.** $4^{-3}$

**22.** $5^{-4}$  **23.** $\left(\dfrac{1}{2}\right)^{-4}$  **24.** $\left(\dfrac{1}{3}\right)^{-3}$

**25.** $\left(\dfrac{6}{7}\right)^{-2}$  **26.** $\left(\dfrac{2}{3}\right)^{-3}$  **27.** $(-3)^{-4}$

**28.** $(-4)^{-3}$  **29.** $5^{-1} + 3^{-1}$  **30.** $6^{-1} + 2^{-1}$

**31.** $3^{-2} - 2^{-1}$  **32.** $6^{-2} - 3^{-1}$

**33.** $\left(\dfrac{1}{2}\right)^{-1} + \left(\dfrac{2}{3}\right)^{-1}$  **34.** $\left(\dfrac{1}{3}\right)^{-1} + \left(\dfrac{4}{3}\right)^{-1}$

*Simplify by writing each expression with positive exponents. Assume that all variables represent nonzero real numbers.* ***See Examples 2–4.***

🌐 **35.** $\dfrac{5^8}{5^5}$  **36.** $\dfrac{11^6}{11^3}$  🌐 **37.** $\dfrac{3^{-2}}{5^{-3}}$  **38.** $\dfrac{4^{-3}}{3^{-2}}$

**39.** $\dfrac{5}{5^{-1}}$  **40.** $\dfrac{6}{6^{-2}}$  **41.** $\dfrac{x^{12}}{x^{-3}}$  **42.** $\dfrac{y^4}{y^{-6}}$

**43.** $\dfrac{1}{6^{-3}}$  **44.** $\dfrac{1}{5^{-2}}$  **45.** $\dfrac{2}{r^{-4}}$  **46.** $\dfrac{3}{s^{-8}}$

**47.** $\dfrac{4^{-3}}{5^{-2}}$  **48.** $\dfrac{6^{-2}}{5^{-4}}$  **49.** $p^5 q^{-8}$  **50.** $x^{-8} y^4$

**51.** $\dfrac{r^5}{r^{-4}}$  **52.** $\dfrac{a^6}{a^{-4}}$  **53.** $\dfrac{x^{-3}y}{4z^{-2}}$  **54.** $\dfrac{p^{-5}q^{-4}}{9r^{-3}}$

**55.** $\dfrac{(a+b)^{-3}}{(a+b)^{-4}}$  **56.** $\dfrac{(x+y)^{-8}}{(x+y)^{-9}}$  **57.** $\dfrac{(x+2y)^{-3}}{(x+2y)^{-5}}$  **58.** $\dfrac{(p-3q)^{-2}}{(p-3q)^{-4}}$

**FOR INDIVIDUAL OR GROUP WORK**

*In **Objective 1**, we showed how $6^0$ acts as 1 when it is applied to the product rule, thus motivating the definition of 0 as an exponent. We can also use the quotient rule to motivate this definition. **Work Exercises 59–62 in order.***

**59.** Consider the expression $\frac{25}{25}$. What is its simplest form?

**60.** Because $25 = 5^2$, the expression $\frac{25}{25}$ can be written as the quotient of powers of 5. Write the expression in this way.

**61.** Apply the quotient rule for exponents to the expression you wrote in **Exercise 60**. Give the answer as a power of 5.

**62.** Your answers in **Exercises 59 and 61** must be equal because they both represent $\frac{25}{25}$. Write this equality. What definition does this result support?

*Simplify by writing each expression with positive exponents. Assume that all variables represent nonzero real numbers. **See Example 5.***

**63.** $\dfrac{(7^4)^3}{7^9}$     **64.** $\dfrac{(5^3)^2}{5^2}$     **65.** $x^{-3} \cdot x^5 \cdot x^{-4}$     **66.** $y^{-8} \cdot y^5 \cdot y^{-2}$

**67.** $\dfrac{(3x)^{-2}}{(4x)^{-3}}$     **68.** $\dfrac{(2y)^{-3}}{(5y)^{-4}}$     ◐ **69.** $\left(\dfrac{x^{-1}y}{z^2}\right)^{-2}$     **70.** $\left(\dfrac{p^{-4}q}{r^{-3}}\right)^{-3}$

**71.** $(6x)^4(6x)^{-3}$     **72.** $(10y)^9(10y)^{-8}$     **73.** $\dfrac{(m^7n)^{-2}}{m^{-4}n^3}$     **74.** $\dfrac{(m^8n^{-4})^2}{m^{-2}n^5}$

**75.** $\dfrac{(x^{-1}y^2z)^{-2}}{(x^{-3}y^3z)^{-1}}$     **76.** $\dfrac{(a^{-2}b^{-3}c^{-4})^{-5}}{(a^2b^3c^4)^{-4}}$     **77.** $\left(\dfrac{xy^{-2}}{x^2y}\right)^{-3}$     **78.** $\left(\dfrac{wz^{-5}}{w^{-3}z}\right)^{-2}$

*Brain Busters*   *Simplify by writing each expression wth positive exponents. Assume that all variables represent nonzero real numbers.*

**79.** $\dfrac{(4a^2b^3)^{-2}(2ab^{-1})^3}{(a^3b)^{-4}}$       **80.** $\dfrac{(m^6n)^{-2}(m^2n^{-2})^3}{m^{-1}n^{-2}}$

**81.** $\dfrac{(2y^{-1}z^2)^2(3y^{-2}z^{-3})^3}{(y^3z^2)^{-1}}$       **82.** $\dfrac{(3p^{-2}q^3)^2(5p^{-1}q^{-4})^{-1}}{(p^2q^{-2})^{-3}}$

**83.** $\dfrac{(9^{-1}z^{-2}x)^{-1}(4z^2x^4)^{-2}}{(5z^{-2}x^{-3})^2}$       **84.** $\dfrac{(4^{-1}a^{-1}b^{-2})^{-2}(5a^{-3}b^4)^{-2}}{(3a^{-3}b^{-5})^2}$

**85.** *Concept Check*   A student simplified $\frac{16^3}{2^2}$ as shown.

$$\frac{16^3}{2^2} = \left(\frac{16}{2}\right)^{3-2} = 8^1 = 8$$

**WHAT WENT WRONG?** Give the correct answer.

**86.** *Concept Check*   A student simplified $-5^4$ as shown.

$$-5^4 = (-5)^4 = 625$$

**WHAT WENT WRONG?** Give the correct answer.

**PREVIEW EXERCISES**

*Evaluate.*

**87.** $10(6428)$     **88.** $100(72.79)$     **89.** $1000(1.53)$     **90.** $10{,}000(36.94)$

**91.** $38 \div 10$     **92.** $6504 \div 100$     **93.** $277 \div 1000$     **94.** $49 \div 10{,}000$

## SUMMARY EXERCISES on the Rules for Exponents

*Simplify each expression. Use only positive exponents in your answers. Assume that all variables represent nonzero real numbers.*

**1.** $(10x^2y^4)^2(10xy^2)^3$

**2.** $(-2ab^3c)^4(-2a^2b)^3$

**3.** $\left(\dfrac{9wx^3}{y^4}\right)^3$

**4.** $(4x^{-2}y^{-3})^{-2}$

**5.** $\dfrac{c^{11}(c^2)^4}{(c^3)^3(c^2)^{-6}}$

**6.** $\left(\dfrac{k^4t^2}{k^2t^{-4}}\right)^{-2}$

**7.** $5^{-1} + 6^{-1}$

**8.** $\dfrac{(3y^{-1}z^3)^{-1}(3y^2)}{(y^3z^2)^{-3}}$

**9.** $\dfrac{(2xy^{-1})^3}{2^3x^{-3}y^2}$

**10.** $-4^0 + (-4)^0$

**11.** $(z^4)^{-3}(z^{-2})^{-5}$

**12.** $\left(\dfrac{r^2st^5}{3r}\right)^{-2}$

**13.** $\dfrac{(3^{-1}x^{-3}y)^{-1}(2x^2y^{-3})^2}{(5x^{-2}y^2)^{-2}}$

**14.** $\left(\dfrac{5x^2}{3x^{-4}}\right)^{-1}$

**15.** $\left(\dfrac{-9x^{-2}}{9x^2}\right)^{-2}$

**16.** $\dfrac{(x^{-4}y^2)^3(x^2y)^{-1}}{(xy^2)^{-3}}$

**17.** $\dfrac{(a^{-2}b^3)^{-4}}{(a^{-3}b^2)^{-2}(ab)^{-4}}$

**18.** $(2a^{-30}b^{-29})(3a^{31}b^{30})$

**19.** $5^{-2} + 6^{-2}$

**20.** $\left[\dfrac{(x^{43}y^{23})^2}{x^{-26}y^{-42}}\right]^0$

**21.** $\left(\dfrac{7a^2b^3}{2}\right)^3$

**22.** $-(-19^0)$

**23.** $-(-13)^0$

**24.** $\dfrac{0^{13}}{13^0}$

**25.** $\dfrac{(2xy^{-3})^{-2}}{(3x^{-2}y^4)^{-3}}$

**26.** $\left(\dfrac{a^2b^3c^4}{a^{-2}b^{-3}c^{-4}}\right)^{-2}$

**27.** $(6x^{-5}z^3)^{-3}$

**28.** $(2p^{-2}qr^{-3})(2p)^{-4}$

**29.** $\dfrac{(xy)^{-3}(xy)^5}{(xy)^{-4}}$

**30.** $52^0 - (-8)^0$

**31.** $\dfrac{(7^{-1}x^{-3})^{-2}(x^4)^{-6}}{7^{-1}x^{-3}}$

**32.** $\left(\dfrac{3^{-4}x^{-3}}{3^{-3}x^{-6}}\right)^{-2}$

**33.** $(5p^{-2}q)^{-3}(5pq^3)^4$

**34.** $8^{-1} + 6^{-1}$

**35.** $\left[\dfrac{4r^{-6}s^{-2}t}{2r^8s^{-4}t^2}\right]^{-1}$

**36.** $(13x^{-6}y)(13x^{-6}y)^{-1}$

**37.** $\dfrac{(8pq^{-2})^4}{(8p^{-2}q^{-3})^3}$

**38.** $\left(\dfrac{mn^{-2}p}{m^2np^4}\right)^{-2}\left(\dfrac{mn^{-2}p}{m^2np^4}\right)^3$

**39.** $-(-8^0)^0$

**40.** *Concept Check*  Match each expression (a)–(j) in Column I with the equivalent expression A–J in Column II. Choices in Column II may be used once, more than once, or not at all.

|  | I |  |  | II |  |
|---|---|---|---|---|---|
| **(a)** $2^0 + 2^0$ | **(b)** $2^1 \cdot 2^0$ | | **A.** 0 | **B.** 1 | |
| **(c)** $2^0 - 2^{-1}$ | **(d)** $2^1 - 2^0$ | | **C.** $-1$ | **D.** 2 | |
| **(e)** $2^0 \cdot 2^{-2}$ | **(f)** $2^1 \cdot 2^1$ | | **E.** $\dfrac{1}{2}$ | **F.** 4 | |
| **(g)** $2^{-2} - 2^{-1}$ | **(h)** $2^0 \cdot 2^0$ | | **G.** $-2$ | **H.** $-4$ | |
| **(i)** $2^{-2} \div 2^{-1}$ | **(j)** $2^0 \div 2^{-2}$ | | **I.** $-\dfrac{1}{4}$ | **J.** $\dfrac{1}{4}$ | |

## An Application of Exponents: Scientific Notation

**OBJECTIVES**

1 Express numbers in scientific notation.
2 Convert numbers in scientific notation to numbers without exponents.
3 Use scientific notation in calculations.

**OBJECTIVE 1** Express numbers in scientific notation. Numbers occurring in science are often extremely large (such as the distance from Earth to the sun, 93,000,000 mi) or extremely small (the wavelength of yellow-green light, approximately 0.0000006 m). Because of the difficulty of working with many zeros, scientists often express such numbers with exponents, using a form called *scientific notation*.

### Scientific Notation

A number is written in **scientific notation** when it is expressed in the form

$$a \times 10^n, \quad \text{where } 1 \le |a| < 10 \text{ and } n \text{ is an integer.}$$

In scientific notation, there is always one nonzero digit before the decimal point.

| | |
|---|---|
| $3.19 \times 10^1 = 3.19 \times 10 = 31.9$ | Decimal point moves 1 place to the right. |
| $3.19 \times 10^2 = 3.19 \times 100 = 319.$ | Decimal point moves 2 places to the right. |
| $3.19 \times 10^3 = 3.19 \times 1000 = 3190.$ | Decimal point moves 3 places to the right. |
| $3.19 \times 10^{-1} = 3.19 \times 0.1 = 0.319$ | Decimal point moves 1 place to the left. |
| $3.19 \times 10^{-2} = 3.19 \times 0.01 = 0.0319$ | Decimal point moves 2 places to the left. |
| $3.19 \times 10^{-3} = 3.19 \times 0.001 = 0.00319$ | Decimal point moves 3 places to the left. |

---

**NOTE** In work with scientific notation, the times symbol, $\times$, is commonly used.

---

*A number in scientific notation is always written with the decimal point after the first nonzero digit and then multiplied by the appropriate power of 10.* For example, 56,200 is written $5.62 \times 10^4$, since

$$56{,}200 = 5.62 \times 10{,}000 = 5.62 \times 10^4.$$

Other examples include

| | | | |
|---|---|---|---|
| | 42,000,000 | written | $4.2 \times 10^7$, |
| | 0.000586 | written | $5.86 \times 10^{-4}$, |
| and | 2,000,000,000 | written | $2 \times 10^9$. |

> It is not necessary to write 2.0.

To write a number in scientific notation, follow these steps. (For a negative number, follow these steps using the *absolute value* of the number. Then make the result negative.)

### Writing a Number in Scientific Notation

**Step 1** Move the decimal point to the right of the first nonzero digit.

**Step 2** Count the number of places you moved the decimal point.

**Step 3** The number of places in Step 2 is the absolute value of the exponent on 10.

**Step 4** The exponent on 10 is positive if the original number is greater than the number in Step 1. The exponent is negative if the original number is less than the number in Step 1. If the decimal point is not moved, the exponent is 0.

*NOW TRY*
*EXERCISE 1*
Write each number in scientific notation.

**(a)** 12,600,000

**(b)** 0.00027

**(c)** −0.0000341

---

**EXAMPLE 1** Using Scientific Notation

Write each number in scientific notation.

**(a)** 93,000,000
Move the decimal point to follow the first nonzero digit (the 9). Count the number of places the decimal point was moved.

$$93{,}000{,}000. \longleftarrow \text{Decimal point}$$
7 places

The number will be written in scientific notation as $9.3 \times 10^n$. To find the value of *n*, first compare the original number, 93,000,000, with 9.3. Since 93,000,000 is *greater* than 9.3, we must multiply by a *positive* power of 10 so that the product $9.3 \times 10^n$ will equal the larger number.

Since the decimal point was moved seven places, and since *n* is positive,

$$93{,}000{,}000 = 9.3 \times 10^7.$$

**(b)** $63{,}200{,}000{,}000 = 6.3200000000 = 6.32 \times 10^{10}$
10 places

**(c)** 0.00462
Move the decimal point to the right of the first nonzero digit, and count the number of places the decimal point was moved.

$$0.00462 \qquad \text{3 places}$$

Since 0.00462 is *less* than 4.62, the exponent must be *negative*.

$$0.00462 = 4.62 \times 10^{-3}$$

**(d)** $-0.0000762 = -7.62 \times 10^{-5}$
5 places
Remember the negative sign.

NOW TRY

---

**NOTE** To choose the exponent when you write a positive number in scientific notation, think as follows.

**1.** If the original number is "large," like 93,000,000, use a *positive* exponent on 10, since positive is greater than negative.

**2.** If the original number is "small," like 0.00462, use a *negative* exponent on 10, since negative is less than positive.

---

**OBJECTIVE 2** Convert numbers in scientific notation to numbers without exponents. To do this, we work in reverse. *Multiplying a number by a positive power of 10 will make the number greater. Multiplying by a negative power of 10 will make the number less.*

**EXAMPLE 2** Writing Numbers without Exponents

Write each number without exponents.

**(a)** $6.2 \times 10^3$
Since the exponent is positive, we make 6.2 greater by moving the decimal point three places to the right. We attach two zeros.

$$6.2 \times 10^3 = 6.200 = 6200$$

*NOW TRY ANSWERS*
**1. (a)** $1.26 \times 10^7$
   **(b)** $2.7 \times 10^{-4}$
   **(c)** $-3.41 \times 10^{-5}$

NOW TRY
EXERCISE 2

Write each number without exponents.

(a) $5.71 \times 10^4$

(b) $2.72 \times 10^{-5}$

(b) $4.283 \times 10^6 = 4.283000 = 4{,}283{,}000$    Move 6 places to the right. Attach zeros as necessary.

(c) $7.04 \times 10^{-3} = 0.00704$    Move 3 places to the left.

*The exponent tells the number of places and the direction that the decimal point is moved.*

NOW TRY

---

**OBJECTIVE 3** Use scientific notation in calculations.

NOW TRY
EXERCISE 3

Perform each calculation. Write answers in scientific notation and also without exponents.

(a) $(6 \times 10^7)(7 \times 10^{-4})$

(b) $\dfrac{18 \times 10^{-3}}{6 \times 10^4}$

**EXAMPLE 3** Multiplying and Dividing with Scientific Notation

Perform each calculation.

(a)　$(7 \times 10^3)(5 \times 10^4)$

$= (7 \times 5)(10^3 \times 10^4)$　Commutative and associative properties

$= 35 \times 10^7$　Multiply; product rule

$= (3.5 \times 10^1) \times 10^7$　Write 35 in scientific notation.

$= 3.5 \times (10^1 \times 10^7)$　Associative property

$= 3.5 \times 10^8$　Product rule

$= 350{,}000{,}000$　Write without exponents.

> Don't stop! This number is *not* in scientific notation, since 35 is not between 1 and 10.

(b) $\dfrac{4 \times 10^{-5}}{2 \times 10^3} = \dfrac{4}{2} \times \dfrac{10^{-5}}{10^3} = 2 \times 10^{-8} = 0.00000002$　NOW TRY

---

**NOTE** Multiplying or dividing numbers written in scientific notation may produce an answer in the form $a \times 10^0$. Since $10^0 = 1$, $a \times 10^0 = a$. For example,

$$(8 \times 10^{-4})(5 \times 10^4) = 40 \times 10^0 = 40.$$    $10^0 = 1$

Also, if $a = 1$, then $a \times 10^n = 10^n$. For example, we could write $1{,}000{,}000$ as $10^6$ instead of $1 \times 10^6$.

---

NOW TRY
EXERCISE 4

See **Example 4.** About how much would 8,000,000 nanometers measure in inches?

**EXAMPLE 4** Using Scientific Notation to Solve an Application

A *nanometer* is a very small unit of measure that is equivalent to about 0.00000003937 in. About how much would 700,000 nanometers measure in inches? (*Source: World Almanac and Book of Facts.*)

Write each number in scientific notation, and then multiply.

$700{,}000(0.00000003937)$

$= (7 \times 10^5)(3.937 \times 10^{-8})$　Write in scientific notation.

$= (7 \times 3.937)(10^5 \times 10^{-8})$　Properties of real numbers

$= 27.559 \times 10^{-3}$　Multiply; product rule

$= (2.7559 \times 10^1) \times 10^{-3}$　Write 27.559 in scientific notation.

$= 2.7559 \times 10^{-2}$　Product rule

$= 0.027559$　Write without exponents.

> Don't stop here.

Thus, 700,000 nanometers would measure

$$2.7559 \times 10^{-2} \text{ in., \quad or \quad } 0.027559 \text{ in.}$$    NOW TRY

NOW TRY ANSWERS
2. (a) 57,100  (b) 0.0000272
3. (a) $4.2 \times 10^4$, or 42,000
   (b) $3 \times 10^{-7}$, or 0.0000003
4. $3.1496 \times 10^{-1}$ in., or 0.31496 in.

NOW TRY
EXERCISE 5
The land area of California is approximately $1.6 \times 10^5$ mi², and the 2008 estimated population of California was approximately $4 \times 10^7$ people. Use this information to estimate the number of square miles per California resident in 2008. (*Source:* U.S. Census Bureau.)

**EXAMPLE 5** Using Scientific Notation to Solve an Application

In 2008, the national debt was $\$1.0025 \times 10^{13}$ (which is more than \$10 trillion). The population of the United States was approximately 304 million that year. About how much would each person have had to contribute in order to pay off the national debt? (*Source:* Bureau of Public Land; U.S. Census Bureau.)

   Write the population in scientific notation. Then divide to obtain the per person contribution.

$$\frac{1.0025 \times 10^{13}}{304,000,000} = \frac{1.0025 \times 10^{13}}{3.04 \times 10^8} \qquad \text{Write 304 million in scientific notation.}$$

$$= \frac{1.0025}{3.04} \times 10^5 \qquad \text{Quotient rule}$$

$$= 0.32977 \times 10^5 \qquad \text{Divide. Round to 5 decimal places.}$$

$$= 32,977 \qquad \text{Write without exponents.}$$

Each person would have to pay about \$32,977.   NOW TRY

---

### CONNECTIONS

In 1935, Charles F. Richter devised a scale to compare the intensities of earthquakes. The *intensity* of an earthquake is measured relative to the intensity of a standard *zero-level* earthquake of intensity $I_0$. The relationship is equivalent to $I = I_0 \times 10^R$, where $R$ is the **Richter scale** measure.

   For example, if an earthquake has magnitude 5.0 on the Richter scale, then its intensity is calculated as

$$I = I_0 \times 10^{5.0} = I_0 \times 100,000,$$

which is 100,000 times as intense as a zero-level earthquake.

| Intensity | $I_0 \times 10^0$ | $I_0 \times 10^1$ | $I_0 \times 10^2$ | $I_0 \times 10^3$ | $I_0 \times 10^4$ | $I_0 \times 10^5$ | $I_0 \times 10^6$ | $I_0 \times 10^7$ | $I_0 \times 10^8$ |
|---|---|---|---|---|---|---|---|---|---|
| Richter Scale | 0 | 1 | 2 | 3 | 4 | 5 | 6 | 7 | 8 |

   To compare two earthquakes, a ratio of the intensities is calculated. For example, to compare an earthquake that measures 8.0 on the Richter scale with one that measures 5.0, find the ratio of the intensities.

$$\frac{\text{intensity } 8.0}{\text{intensity } 5.0} = \frac{I_0 \times 10^{8.0}}{I_0 \times 10^{5.0}} = \frac{10^8}{10^5} = 10^{8-5} = 10^3 = 1000$$

Therefore, an earthquake that measures 8.0 on the Richter scale is 1000 times as intense as one that measures 5.0.

**For Discussion or Writing**

| Year | Earthquake Location | Richter Scale Measurement |
|---|---|---|
| 1964 | Prince William Sound, Alaska | 9.2 |
| 2004 | Sumatra, Indonesia | 9.0 |
| 2007 | Central Peru | 8.0 |
| 2008 | E. Sichuan Province, China | 7.9 |
| 2002 | Hindu Kush, Afghanistan | 5.9 |

*Source:* U.S. Geological Survey.

NOW TRY ANSWER
**5.** $4 \times 10^{-3}$ mi², or 0.004 mi²

1. Compare the intensity of the 2004 Indonesia earthquake with the 2007 Peru earthquake.

2. Compare the intensity of the 2002 Afghanistan earthquake with the 2008 China earthquake.

3. Compare the intensity of the 1964 Alaska earthquake with the 2008 China earthquake. (*Hint*: Use a calculator.)

4. Suppose an earthquake measures 7.2 on the Richter scale. How would the intensity of a second earthquake compare if its Richter scale measure differed by +3.0?   By −1.0?

## 5.3 EXERCISES

MyMathLab   Math XL PRACTICE    WATCH    DOWNLOAD    READ    REVIEW

🌐 *Complete solution available on the Video Resources on DVD*

*Concept Check*   *Match each number written in scientific notation in Column I with the correct choice from Column II. Not all choices in Column II will be used.*

| | I | II | | I | II |
|---|---|---|---|---|---|
| **1.** | **(a)** $4.6 \times 10^{-4}$ | **A.** 46,000 | **2.** | **(a)** $1 \times 10^{9}$ | **A.** 1 billion |
| | **(b)** $4.6 \times 10^{4}$ | **B.** 460,000 | | **(b)** $1 \times 10^{6}$ | **B.** 100 million |
| | **(c)** $4.6 \times 10^{5}$ | **C.** 0.00046 | | **(c)** $1 \times 10^{8}$ | **C.** 1 million |
| | **(d)** $4.6 \times 10^{-5}$ | **D.** 0.000046 | | **(d)** $1 \times 10^{10}$ | **D.** 10 billion |
| | | **E.** 4600 | | | **E.** 100 billion |

*Concept Check*   *Determine whether or not each number is written in scientific notation as defined in* **Objective 1.** *If it is not, write it as such.*

**3.** $4.56 \times 10^{4}$     **4.** $7.34 \times 10^{6}$     **5.** 5,600,000     **6.** 34,000

**7.** $0.8 \times 10^{2}$     **8.** $0.9 \times 10^{3}$     **9.** 0.004     **10.** 0.0007

📝 **11.** Explain what it means for a number to be written in scientific notation. Give examples.

📝 **12.** Explain how to multiply a number by a positive power of 10. Then explain how to multiply a number by a negative power of 10.

*Write each number in scientific notation.* **See Example 1.**

🌐 **13.** 5,876,000,000     **14.** 9,994,000,000     **15.** 82,350     **16.** 78,330

**17.** 0.000007     **18.** 0.0000004     **19.** 0.00203     **20.** 0.0000578

**21.** −13,000,000     **22.** −25,000,000,000     **23.** −0.006     **24.** −0.01234

*Write each number without exponents.* **See Example 2.**

🌐 **25.** $7.5 \times 10^{5}$     **26.** $8.8 \times 10^{6}$     **27.** $5.677 \times 10^{12}$     **28.** $8.766 \times 10^{9}$

**29.** $1 \times 10^{12}$     **30.** $1 \times 10^{7}$     **31.** $6.21 \times 10^{0}$     **32.** $8.56 \times 10^{0}$

**33.** $7.8 \times 10^{-4}$     **34.** $8.9 \times 10^{-5}$     **35.** $5.134 \times 10^{-9}$     **36.** $7.123 \times 10^{-10}$

**37.** $-4 \times 10^{-3}$     **38.** $-6 \times 10^{-4}$     **39.** $-8.1 \times 10^{5}$     **40.** $-9.6 \times 10^{6}$

*Perform the indicated operations. Write each answer* **(a)** *in scientific notation and* **(b)** *without exponents.* **See Example 3.**

**41.** $(2 \times 10^{8})(3 \times 10^{3})$     **42.** $(4 \times 10^{7})(3 \times 10^{3})$

🌐 **43.** $(5 \times 10^{4})(3 \times 10^{2})$     **44.** $(8 \times 10^{5})(2 \times 10^{3})$

**45.** $(3 \times 10^{-4})(-2 \times 10^8)$        **46.** $(4 \times 10^{-3})(-2 \times 10^7)$

**47.** $(6 \times 10^3)(4 \times 10^{-2})$        **48.** $(7 \times 10^5)(3 \times 10^{-4})$

**49.** $(9 \times 10^4)(7 \times 10^{-7})$        **50.** $(6 \times 10^4)(8 \times 10^{-8})$

**51.** $\dfrac{9 \times 10^{-5}}{3 \times 10^{-1}}$      **52.** $\dfrac{12 \times 10^{-4}}{4 \times 10^{-3}}$      **53.** $\dfrac{8 \times 10^3}{-2 \times 10^2}$

**54.** $\dfrac{15 \times 10^4}{-3 \times 10^3}$      **55.** $\dfrac{2.6 \times 10^{-3}}{2 \times 10^2}$      **56.** $\dfrac{9.5 \times 10^{-1}}{5 \times 10^3}$

**57.** $\dfrac{4 \times 10^5}{8 \times 10^2}$      **58.** $\dfrac{3 \times 10^9}{6 \times 10^5}$      **59.** $\dfrac{-4.5 \times 10^4}{1.5 \times 10^{-2}}$

**60.** $\dfrac{-7.2 \times 10^3}{6.0 \times 10^{-1}}$      **61.** $\dfrac{-8 \times 10^{-4}}{-4 \times 10^3}$      **62.** $\dfrac{-5 \times 10^{-6}}{-2 \times 10^2}$

---

## *TECHNOLOGY INSIGHTS*    EXERCISES 63–68

*Graphing calculators such as the TI-83/84 Plus can display numbers in scientific notation (when in scientific mode), using the format shown in the screen on the left. For 5400, the calculator displays 5.4E3 to represent $5.4 \times 10^3$. The display 5.4E-4 means $5.4 \times 10^{-4}$. The calculator will also perform operations with numbers entered in scientific notation, as shown in the screen on the right. Notice how the rules for exponents are applied.*

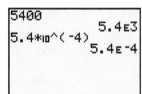  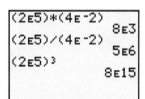

*Predict the display the calculator would give for the expression shown in each screen.*

**63.** `.00000047`        **64.** `.000021`

**65.** `(8E5)/(4E-2)`        **66.** `(9E-4)/(3E3)`

**67.** `(2E6)*(2E-3)/(4E 2)`        **68.** `(5E-3)*(1E9)/(5E 3)`

---

*Brain Busters*   *Use scientific notation to calculate the answer to each problem. Write answers in scientific notation.*

**69.** $\dfrac{650{,}000{,}000(0.0000032)}{0.00002}$      **70.** $\dfrac{3{,}400{,}000{,}000(0.000075)}{0.00025}$

**71.** $\dfrac{0.00000072(0.00023)}{0.000000018}$      **72.** $\dfrac{0.000000081(0.000036)}{0.00000048}$

**73.** $\dfrac{0.0000016(240{,}000{,}000)}{0.00002(0.0032)}$      **74.** $\dfrac{0.000015(42{,}000{,}000)}{0.000009(0.000005)}$

*Each statement comes from* Astronomy! A Brief Edition *by James B. Kaler (Addison-Wesley). If the number in boldface italics is in scientific notation, write it without exponents. If the number is written without exponents, write it in scientific notation.*

75. Multiplying this view over the whole sky yields a galaxy count of more than *10 billion.* (page 496)

76. The circumference of the solar orbit is . . . about *4.7 million* km . . . . (in reference to the orbit of Jupiter, page 395)

77. The solar luminosity requires that $2 \times 10^9$ kg of mass be converted into energy every second. (page 327)

78. At maximum, a cosmic ray particle—a mere atomic nucleus of only $10^{-13}$ cm across—can carry the energy of a professionally pitched baseball. (page 445)

Spiral Galaxy M81    Spitzer Space Telescope • IRAC

*Each statement contains a number in boldface italics. Write the number in scientific notation.*

79. At the end of 2007, the total number of cellular telephone subscriptions in the world reached about *3,305,000,000.* (*Source:* International Telecommunications Union.)

80. In 2007, the leading U.S. advertiser was the Procter and Gamble Company, which spent approximately *$5,230,000,000.* (*Source:* Crain Communications, Inc.)

81. During 2008, worldwide motion picture box office receipts (in U.S. dollars) totaled *$28,100,000,000.* (*Source:* Motion Picture Association of America.)

82. In 2007, assets of the insured commercial banks in the United States totaled about *$13,039,000,000,000.* (*Source:* U.S. Federal Deposit Insurance Corporation.)

*Use scientific notation to calculate the answer to each problem.* ***See Examples 3–5.***

83. The body of a 150-lb person contains about $2.3 \times 10^{-4}$ lb of copper. How much copper is contained in the bodies of 1200 such people?

84. In 2007, the state of Minnesota had about $7.9 \times 10^4$ farms with an average of $3.5 \times 10^2$ acres per farm. What was the total number of acres devoted to farmland in Minnesota that year? (*Source:* U.S. Department of Agriculture.)

85. Venus is $6.68 \times 10^7$ mi from the sun. If light travels at a speed of $1.86 \times 10^5$ mi per sec, how long does it take light to travel from the sun to Venus? (*Source: World Almanac and Book of Facts.*)

86. (a) The distance to Earth from Pluto is $4.58 \times 10^9$ km. In April 1983, *Pioneer 10* transmitted radio signals from Pluto to Earth at the speed of light, $3.00 \times 10^5$ km per sec. How long (in seconds) did it take for the signals to reach Earth?

    (b) How many hours did it take for the signals to reach Earth?

87. During the 2007–2008 season, Broadway shows grossed a total of $9.38 \times 10^8$ dollars. Total attendance for the season was $1.23 \times 10^7$. What was the average ticket price for a Broadway show? (*Source:* The Broadway League.)

88. In 2007, $9.63 \times 10^9$ dollars were spent to attend motion pictures in the United States. Domestic admissions (the total number of tickets sold) for that year totaled 1.4 billion. What was the average ticket price? (*Source:* Motion Picture Association of America.)

**89.** On February 17, 2009, Congress raised the U.S. government's debt limit to $1.2 \times 10^{13}$. When this national debt limit is reached, about how much will it be for every man, women, and child in the country? Use 300 million as the population of the United States. (*Source:* The Concord Coalition.)

**90.** In theory there are $1 \times 10^9$ possible Social Security numbers. The population of the United States is about $3 \times 10^8$. How many Social Security numbers are available for each person? (*Source:* U.S. Census Bureau.)

**91.** Astronomers using the Spitzer Space Telescope discovered a twisted double-helix nebula, a conglomeration of dust and gas stretching across the center of the Milky Way galaxy. This nebula is 25,000 light-years from Earth. If one light-year is about 6,000,000,000,000 (that is, 6 trillion) miles, about how many miles is the twisted double-helix nebula from Earth? (*Source:* http://articles.news.aol.com)

**92.** A computer can perform 466,000,000 calculations per second. How many calculations can it perform per minute?   Per hour?

**93.** In 2008, the U.S. government collected about $4013 per person in personal income taxes. If the population was 304,000,000, how much did the government collect in taxes for 2008? (*Source:* U.S. Office of Management and Budget.)

**94.** Pollux, one of the brightest stars in the night sky, is 33.7 light-years from Earth. If one light-year is about 6,000,000,000,000 mi, about how many miles is Pollux from Earth? (*Source: World Almanac and Book of Facts.*)

**95.** In September of 2009, the population of the United States was about 307.5 million. To the nearest dollar, calculate how much each person in the United States would have had to contribute in order to make one lucky person a trillionaire (that is, to give that person $1,000,000,000,000). (*Source:* U.S. Census Bureau.)

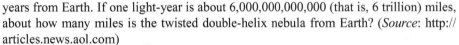

**96.** In 2006, national expenditures for health care reached $2,106,000,000,000. Using 300 million as the population of the United States, about how much, to the nearest dollar, was spent on health care per person in 2006? (*Source:* U.S. Centers for Medicare and Medicaid Services.)

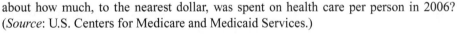

**PREVIEW EXERCISES**

*Simplify. See Section 1.8.*

**97.** $-3(2x + 4) + 4(2x - 6)$

**98.** $-8(-3x + 7) - 4(2x + 3)$

*Evaluate each expression for $x = 3$. See Sections 1.3 and 1.6.*

**99.** $2x^2 - 3x + 10$

**100.** $3x^2 - 3x + 4$

**101.** $4x^3 - 5x^2 + 2x - 5$

**102.** $-4x^3 + 2x^2 - 9x - 2$

## 5.4 Adding and Subtracting Polynomials; Graphing Simple Polynomials

**OBJECTIVE 1** **Identify terms and coefficients.** In an expression such as

$$4x^3 + 6x^2 + 5x + 8,$$

the quantities $4x^3$, $6x^2$, $5x$, and 8 are called **terms.** (See **Section 1.8.**) In the first (or *leading*) term $4x^3$, the number 4 is called the **numerical coefficient,** or simply the **coefficient,** of $x^3$. In the same way, 6 is the coefficient of $x^2$ in the term $6x^2$, and 5 is the coefficient of $x$ in the term $5x$. The constant term 8 can be thought of as $8 \cdot 1 = 8x^0$, since $x^0 = 1$, so 8 is the coefficient in the term 8.

**EXAMPLE 1** Identifying Coefficients

Name the coefficient of each term in these expressions.

**(a)** $x - 6x^4$ can be written as $1x + (-6x^4)$.

The coefficients are 1 and −6.

**(b)** $5 - v^3$ can be written as $5v^0 + (-1v^3)$.

The coefficients are 5 and −1.

NOW TRY

**OBJECTIVE 2** **Add like terms.** Recall from **Section 1.8** that **like terms** have exactly the same combination of variables, with the same exponents on the variables. *Only the coefficients may differ.*

| $19m^5$ and $14m^5$ | |
|---|---|
| $6y^9$, $-37y^9$, and $y^9$ | Examples of like terms |
| $3pq$ and $-2pq$ | |
| $2xy^2$ and $-xy^2$ | |

| $7x$ and $7y$ | |
|---|---|
| $z^4$ and $z$ | Examples of unlike terms |
| $2pq$ and $2p$ | |
| $-4xy^2$ and $5x^2y$ | |

Using the distributive property, we combine, or add, like terms by adding their coefficients.

**EXAMPLE 2** Adding Like Terms

Simplify by adding like terms.

**(a)** $-4x^3 + 6x^3$

$= (-4 + 6)x^3$     Distributive property

$= 2x^3$     Add.

**(b)** $9x^6 - 14x^6 + x^6$

$= (9 - 14 + 1)x^6$     $x^6 = 1x^6$

$= -4x^6$

**(c)** $12m^2 + 5m + 4m^2$

$= (12 + 4)m^2 + 5m$

$= 16m^2 + 5m$

**(d)** $3x^2y + 4x^2y - x^2y$

$= (3 + 4 - 1)x^2y$

$= 6x^2y$

NOW TRY

NOW TRY
EXERCISE 1

Name the coefficient of each term in the expression.

$$t - 10t^2$$

NOW TRY
EXERCISE 2

Simplify by adding like terms.

$$3x^2 - x^2 + 2x$$

NOW TRY ANSWERS

**1.** 1; −10
**2.** $2x^2 + 2x$

⚠ **CAUTION**  In **Example 2(c)**, we cannot combine $16m^2$ and $5m$, because the exponents on the variables are different. *Unlike terms have different variables or different exponents on the same variables.*

---

**OBJECTIVE 3**  **Know the vocabulary for polynomials.**    A **polynomial in $x$** is a term or the sum of a finite number of terms of the form $ax^n$, for any real number $a$ and any whole number $n$. For example,

$$16x^8 - 7x^6 + 5x^4 - 3x^2 + 4 \qquad \text{Polynomial in } x \\ \text{(The 4 can be written as } 4x^0\text{.)}$$

is a polynomial in $x$. This polynomial is written in **descending powers** of the variable, since the exponents on $x$ decrease from left to right. By contrast,

$$2x^3 - x^2 + \frac{4}{x}, \quad \text{or} \quad 2x^3 - x^2 + 4x^{-1}, \qquad \text{Not a polynomial}$$

is not a polynomial in $x$. A variable appears in a denominator or to a negative power.

---

**NOTE**  We can define *polynomial* using any variable and not just $x$, as in **Example 2(c)**. Polynomials may have terms with more than one variable, as in **Example 2(d)**.

---

The **degree of a term** is the sum of the exponents on the variables. The **degree of a polynomial** is the greatest degree of any nonzero term of the polynomial. The table gives several examples.

| Term | Degree | Polynomial | Degree |
|------|--------|------------|--------|
| $3x^4$ | 4 | $3x^4 - 5x^2 + 6$ | 4 |
| $5x$, or $5x^1$ | 1 | $5x + 7$ | 1 |
| $-7$, or $-7x^0$ | 0 | $x^2y + xy - 5y^2$ | 3 |
| $2x^2y$, or $2x^2y^1$ | $2 + 1 = 3$ | $x^5 + 3x^6$ | 6 |

Three types of polynomials are common and are given special names. A polynomial with only one term is called a **monomial.** (*Mono* means "one," as in *mono*rail.)

$$9m, \quad -6y^5, \quad a^2, \quad \text{and} \quad 6 \qquad \text{Monomials}$$

A polynomial with exactly two terms is called a **binomial.** (*Bi*- means "two," as in *bi*cycle.)

$$-9x^4 + 9x^3, \quad 8m^2 + 6m, \quad \text{and} \quad 3m^5 - 9m^2 \qquad \text{Binomials}$$

A polynomial with exactly three terms is called a **trinomial.** (*Tri*- means "three," as in *tri*angle.)

$$9m^3 - 4m^2 + 6, \quad \frac{19}{3}y^2 + \frac{8}{3}y + 5, \quad \text{and} \quad -3m^5 - 9m^2 + 2 \qquad \text{Trinomials}$$

**EXAMPLE 3**  Classifying Polynomials

For each polynomial, first simplify, if possible. Then give the degree and tell whether the polynomial is a *monomial*, a *binomial*, a *trinomial*, or *none of these*.

**(a)** $2x^3 + 5$    The polynomial cannot be simplified. It is a binomial of degree 3.

**(b)** $4xy - 5xy + 2xy$

Add like terms:  $4xy - 5xy + 2xy = xy$, which is a monomial of degree 2.

NOW TRY

---

⌇ *NOW TRY*
↳ *EXERCISE 3*

Simplify, give the degree, and tell whether the simplified polynomial is a *monomial*, a *binomial*, a *trinomial*, or *none of these*.

$$x^2 + 4x - 2x - 8$$

*NOW TRY ANSWER*
**3.** $x^2 + 2x - 8$; degree 2; trinomial

**OBJECTIVE 4** **Evaluate polynomials.** A polynomial usually represents different numbers for different values of the variable.

NOW TRY
EXERCISE 4
Find the value for $t = -3$.
$$4t^3 - t^2 - t$$

**EXAMPLE 4** Evaluating a Polynomial

Find the value of $3x^4 + 5x^3 - 4x - 4$ for **(a)** $x = -2$ and **(b)** $x = 3$.

**(a)** First, substitute $-2$ for $x$.

$$3x^4 + 5x^3 - 4x - 4$$

$$= 3(-2)^4 + 5(-2)^3 - 4(-2) - 4 \qquad \text{Let } x = -2.$$

> Use parentheses to avoid errors.

$$= 3(16) + 5(-8) - 4(-2) - 4 \qquad \text{Apply the exponents.}$$

$$= 48 - 40 + 8 - 4 \qquad \text{Multiply.}$$

$$= 12 \qquad \text{Add and subtract.}$$

**(b)** $\qquad 3x^4 + 5x^3 - 4x - 4$

> Replace $x$ with 3.

$$= 3(3)^4 + 5(3)^3 - 4(3) - 4 \qquad \text{Let } x = 3.$$

$$= 3(81) + 5(27) - 12 - 4 \qquad \text{Apply the exponents.}$$

$$= 243 + 135 - 12 - 4 \qquad \text{Multiply.}$$

$$= 362 \qquad \text{Add and subtract.} \quad \text{NOW TRY}$$

---

⚠ **CAUTION** Use parentheses around the numbers that are substituted for the variable, as in **Example 4**. *Be particularly careful when substituting a negative number for a variable that is raised to a power, or a sign error may result.*

---

**OBJECTIVE 5** **Add and subtract polynomials.**

**Adding Polynomials**

To add two polynomials, add like terms.

NOW TRY
EXERCISE 5
Add $4y^3 - 2y^2 + y - 1$ and $y^3 - y - 7$ vertically.

**EXAMPLE 5** Adding Polynomials Vertically

**(a)** Add $6x^3 - 4x^2 + 3$ and $-2x^3 + 7x^2 - 5$.

$$\begin{array}{r} 6x^3 - 4x^2 + 3 \\ -2x^3 + 7x^2 - 5 \end{array} \qquad \text{Write like terms in columns.}$$

Now add, column by column.

> Combine the coefficients only. Do *not* add the exponents.

$$\begin{array}{ccc} 6x^3 & -4x^2 & 3 \\ -2x^3 & 7x^2 & -5 \\ \hline 4x^3 & 3x^2 & -2 \end{array}$$

Add the three sums together.

$$4x^3 + 3x^2 + (-2) = 4x^3 + 3x^2 - 2 \leftarrow \text{Final sum}$$

**(b)** Add $2x^2 - 4x + 3$ and $x^3 + 5x$.

Write like terms in columns and add column by column.

$$\begin{array}{r} 2x^2 - 4x + 3 \\ x^3 \qquad + 5x \\ \hline x^3 + 2x^2 + \quad x + 3 \end{array}$$

> Leave spaces for missing terms.

NOW TRY

NOW TRY ANSWERS
4. $-114$
5. $5y^3 - 2y^2 - 8$

The polynomials in **Example 5** also can be added horizontally.

NOW TRY
EXERCISE 6
Add $10x^4 - 3x^2 - x$ and $x^4 - 3x^2 + 5x$ horizontally.

**EXAMPLE 6** Adding Polynomials Horizontally

**(a)** Add $6x^3 - 4x^2 + 3$ and $-2x^3 + 7x^2 - 5$.
Combine like terms.

$$(6x^3 - 4x^2 + 3) + (-2x^3 + 7x^2 - 5) = 4x^3 + 3x^2 - 2$$
Same answer as found in **Example 5(a)**

**(b)** Add $2x^2 - 4x + 3$ and $x^3 + 5x$.

$$(2x^2 - 4x + 3) + (x^3 + 5x)$$
$$= x^3 + 2x^2 - 4x + 5x + 3 \quad \text{Commutative property}$$
$$= x^3 + 2x^2 + x + 3 \quad \text{Combine like terms.}$$

NOW TRY

In **Section 1.5**, we defined the difference $x - y$ as $x + (-y)$. (We find the difference $x - y$ by adding $x$ and the opposite of $y$.) For example,

$$7 - 2 = 7 + (-2) = 5 \quad \text{and} \quad -8 - (-2) = -8 + 2 = -6.$$

A similar method is used to subtract polynomials.

## Subtracting Polynomials

To subtract two polynomials, change all the signs in the second polynomial and add the result to the first polynomial.

NOW TRY
EXERCISE 7
Subtract $5t^4 - 3t^2 + 1$ from $4t^4 - t^2 + 7$.

**EXAMPLE 7** Subtracting Polynomials Horizontally

**(a)** Perform the subtraction $(5x - 2) - (3x - 8)$.

$$(5x - 2) - (3x - 8)$$
$$= (5x - 2) + [-(3x - 8)] \quad \text{Definition of subtraction}$$
$$= (5x - 2) + [-1(3x - 8)] \quad -a = -1a$$
$$= (5x - 2) + (-3x + 8) \quad \text{Distributive property}$$
$$= 2x + 6 \quad \text{Combine like terms.}$$

**(b)** Subtract $6x^3 - 4x^2 + 2$ from $11x^3 + 2x^2 - 8$.

$$(11x^3 + 2x^2 - 8) - (6x^3 - 4x^2 + 2)$$
Be careful to write the problem in the correct order.
$$= (11x^3 + 2x^2 - 8) + (-6x^3 + 4x^2 - 2)$$
$$= 5x^3 + 6x^2 - 10 \quad \text{Answer}$$

CHECK To check a subtraction problem, use the fact that

$$\text{if} \quad a - b = c, \quad \text{then} \quad a = b + c.$$

Here, add $6x^3 - 4x^2 + 2$ and $5x^3 + 6x^2 - 10$.

$$(6x^3 - 4x^2 + 2) + (5x^3 + 6x^2 - 10)$$
$$= 11x^3 + 2x^2 - 8 \quad \checkmark$$

NOW TRY

NOW TRY ANSWERS
**6.** $11x^4 - 6x^2 + 4x$
**7.** $-t^4 + 2t^2 + 6$

We use vertical subtraction in **Section 5.7** when we divide polynomials.

NOW TRY
EXERCISE 8
Subtract by columns.
$$(12x^2 - 9x + 4)$$
$$- (-10x^2 - 3x + 7)$$

**EXAMPLE 8** Subtracting Polynomials Vertically

Subtract by columns to find

$$(14y^3 - 6y^2 + 2y - 5) - (2y^3 - 7y^2 - 4y + 6).$$

$$\begin{array}{l} 14y^3 - 6y^2 + 2y - 5 \\ \underline{2y^3 - 7y^2 - 4y + 6} \end{array}$$    Arrange like terms in columns.

Change all signs in the second row, and then add.

$$\begin{array}{l} 14y^3 - 6y^2 + 2y - \phantom{0}5 \\ \underline{-2y^3 + 7y^2 + 4y - \phantom{0}6} \\ 12y^3 + \phantom{0}y^2 + 6y - 11 \end{array}$$    Change all signs.

Add.    NOW TRY

NOW TRY
EXERCISE 9
Subtract.
$$(4x^2 - 2xy + y^2)$$
$$- (6x^2 - 7xy + 2y^2)$$

**EXAMPLE 9** Adding and Subtracting Polynomials with More Than One Variable

Add or subtract as indicated.

**(a)** $(4a + 2ab - b) + (3a - ab + b)$

$= 4a + 2ab - b + 3a - ab + b$

$= 7a + ab$    Combine like terms.

**(b)** $(2x^2y + 3xy + y^2) - (3x^2y - xy - 2y^2)$

$= 2x^2y + 3xy + y^2 - 3x^2y + xy + 2y^2$

$= -x^2y + 4xy + 3y^2$

Be careful with signs.
The coefficient of $xy$ is 1.    NOW TRY

**OBJECTIVE 6** Graph equations defined by polynomials of degree 2. In **Chapter 3,** we introduced graphs of linear equations (which are actually polynomial equations of degree 1). By plotting points selectively, we can graph polynomial equations of degree 2.

**EXAMPLE 10** Graphing Equations Defined by Polynomials of Degree 2

Graph each equation.

**(a)** $y = x^2$

Select values for $x$. Then find the corresponding $y$-values. Selecting $x = 2$ gives

$$y = x^2 = 2^2 = 4,$$

so the point $(2, 4)$ is on the graph of $y = x^2$. (Recall that in an ordered pair such as $(2, 4)$, *the x-value comes first and the y-value second.*) We show some ordered pairs that satisfy $y = x^2$ in the table with **FIGURE 3** on the next page. If we plot the ordered pairs from the table on a coordinate system and draw a smooth curve through them, we obtain the graph shown in **FIGURE 3**.

NOW TRY ANSWERS
8. $22x^2 - 6x - 3$
9. $-2x^2 + 5xy - y^2$

NOW TRY
EXERCISE 10

Graph $y = -x^2 - 1$.

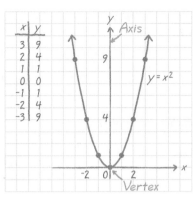

FIGURE 3

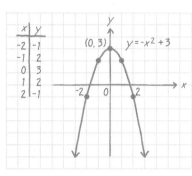

FIGURE 4

The graph of $y = x^2$ is the graph of a function, since each input $x$ is related to just one output $y$. The curve in **FIGURE 3** is called a **parabola.** The point $(0, 0)$, the *lowest* point on this graph, is called the **vertex** of the parabola. The vertical line through the vertex (the $y$-axis here) is called the **axis** of the parabola. The axis of a parabola is a **line of symmetry** for the graph. If the graph is folded on this line, the two halves will match.

**(b)** $y = -x^2 + 3$

Once again, plot points to obtain the graph. For example, if $x = -2$, then

$$y = -(-2)^2 + 3 = -4 + 3 = -1.$$

The point $(-2, -1)$ and several others are shown in the table that accompanies the graph in **FIGURE 4**. The vertex of this parabola is $(0, 3)$. Now the vertex is the *highest* point on the graph. The graph opens downward because $x^2$ has a negative coefficient.

NOW TRY

NOW TRY ANSWER

**10.**

NOTE *All polynomials of degree 2 have parabolas as their graphs.* When graphing, find points until the vertex and points on either side of it are located. (In this section, all parabolas have their vertices on the $x$-axis or the $y$-axis.)

---

## 5.4 EXERCISES

MyMathLab   Math XL PRACTICE   WATCH   DOWNLOAD   READ   REVIEW

🌐 *Complete solution available on the Video Resources on DVD*

*Concept Check* *Fill in each blank with the correct response.*

**1.** In the term $4x^6$, the coefficient is _____ and the exponent is _____.

**2.** The expression $4x^3 - 5x^2$ has _____ term(s).
(how many?)

**3.** The degree of the term $-3x^9$ is _____.

**4.** The polynomial $4x^2 + y^2$ _____ an example of a trinomial.
(is/is not)

**5.** When $x^2 + 10$ is evaluated for $x = 3$, the result is _____.

**6.** $5x^{\underline{\hspace{0.5cm}}} + 3x^3 - 7x$ is a trinomial of degree 6.

**7.** $-3xy - 2xy + 5xy = $ _____

**8.** _____ is an example of a monomial with coefficient 8, in the variable $x$, having degree 5.

*For each polynomial, determine the number of terms and name the coefficients of the terms. See Example 1.*

**9.** $6x^4$      **10.** $-9y^5$      **11.** $t^4$      **12.** $s^7$

**13.** $-19r^2 - r$      **14.** $2y^3 - y$      **15.** $x + 8x^2 + 5x^3$      **16.** $v - 2v^3 - v^7$

*In each polynomial, add like terms whenever possible. Write the result in descending powers of the variable. See Example 2.*

**17.** $-3m^5 + 5m^5$      **18.** $-4y^3 + 3y^3$      **19.** $2r^5 + (-3r^5)$

**20.** $9y^2 + (-19y^2)$      **21.** $0.2m^5 - 0.5m^2$      **22.** $-0.9y + 0.9y^2$

**23.** $-3x^5 + 3x^5 - 5x^5$      **24.** $6x^3 - 9x^3 + 10x^3$

**25.** $-4p^7 + 8p^7 + 5p^9$      **26.** $-3a^8 + 4a^8 - 3a^2$

**27.** $-4xy^2 + 3xy^2 - 2xy^2 + xy^2$      **28.** $3pr^5 - 8pr^5 + pr^5 + 2pr^5$

*For each polynomial, first simplify, if possible, and write it in descending powers of the variable. Then give the degree of the resulting polynomial and tell whether it is a* monomial, *a* binomial, *a* trinomial, *or* none of these. *See Example 3.*

**29.** $6x^4 - 9x$      **30.** $7t^3 - 3t$

**31.** $5m^4 - 3m^2 + 6m^4 - 7m^3$      **32.** $6p^5 + 4p^3 - 8p^5 + 10p^2$

**33.** $\dfrac{5}{3}x^4 - \dfrac{2}{3}x^4$      **34.** $\dfrac{4}{5}r^6 + \dfrac{1}{5}r^6$

**35.** $0.8x^4 - 0.3x^4 - 0.5x^4 + 7$      **36.** $1.2t^3 - 0.9t^3 - 0.3t^3 + 9$

*Find the value of each polynomial for (a)* $x = 2$ *and (b)* $x = -1$. *See Example 4.*

**37.** $2x^2 - 3x - 5$      **38.** $x^2 + 5x - 10$

**39.** $-3x^2 + 14x - 2$      **40.** $-2x^2 + 5x - 1$

**41.** $2x^5 - 4x^4 + 5x^3 - x^2$      **42.** $x^4 - 6x^3 + x^2 - x$

*Add. See Example 5.*

**43.** $\begin{array}{r} 2x^2 - 4x \\ 3x^2 + 2x \\ \hline \end{array}$      **44.** $\begin{array}{r} -5y^3 + 3y \\ 8y^3 - 4y \\ \hline \end{array}$      **45.** $\begin{array}{r} 3m^2 + 5m + 6 \\ 2m^2 - 2m - 4 \\ \hline \end{array}$

**46.** $\begin{array}{r} 4a^3 - 4a^2 - 4 \\ 6a^3 + 5a^2 - 8 \\ \hline \end{array}$      **47.** $\begin{array}{r} \frac{2}{3}x^2 + \frac{1}{5}x + \frac{1}{6} \\ \frac{1}{2}x^2 - \frac{1}{3}x + \frac{2}{3} \\ \hline \end{array}$      **48.** $\begin{array}{r} \frac{4}{7}y^2 - \frac{1}{5}y + \frac{7}{9} \\ \frac{1}{3}y^2 - \frac{1}{3}y + \frac{2}{5} \\ \hline \end{array}$

**49.** $9m^3 - 5m^2 + 4m - 8$ and $-3m^3 + 6m^2 - 6$

**50.** $12r^5 + 11r^4 - 7r^3 - 2r^2$ and $-8r^5 + 3r^3 + 2r^2$

*Subtract. See Example 8.*

**51.** $\begin{array}{r} 5y^3 - 3y^2 \\ 2y^3 + 8y^2 \\ \hline \end{array}$      **52.** $\begin{array}{r} -6t^3 + 4t^2 \\ 8t^3 - 6t^2 \\ \hline \end{array}$

**53.** $\begin{array}{r} 12x^4 - x^2 + x \\ 8x^4 + 3x^2 - 3x \\ \hline \end{array}$      **54.** $\begin{array}{r} 13y^5 - y^3 - 8y^2 \\ 7y^5 + 5y^3 + y^2 \\ \hline \end{array}$

**55.** $\begin{array}{r} 12m^3 - 8m^2 + 6m + 7 \\ -3m^3 + 5m^2 - 2m - 4 \\ \hline \end{array}$      **56.** $\begin{array}{r} 5a^4 - 3a^3 + 2a^2 - a + 6 \\ -6a^4 + a^3 - a^2 + a - 1 \\ \hline \end{array}$

**57.** After reading **Examples 5–8,** do you have a preference regarding horizontal or vertical addition and subtraction of polynomials? Explain your answer.

**58.** Write a paragraph explaining how to add and subtract polynomials. Give an example using addition.

*Perform each indicated operation.* ***See Examples 6 and 7.***

🌐 **59.** $(8m^2 - 7m) - (3m^2 + 7m - 6)$　　**60.** $(x^2 + x) - (3x^2 + 2x - 1)$

🌐 **61.** $(16x^3 - x^2 + 3x) + (-12x^3 + 3x^2 + 2x)$

**62.** $(-2b^6 + 3b^4 - b^2) + (b^6 + 2b^4 + 2b^2)$

**63.** Subtract $18y^4 - 5y^2 + y$ from $7y^4 + 3y^2 + 2y$.

**64.** Subtract $19t^5 - 6t^3 + t$ from $8t^5 + 3t^3 + 5t$.

**65.** $(9a^4 - 3a^2 + 2) + (4a^4 - 4a^2 + 2) + (-12a^4 + 6a^2 - 3)$

**66.** $(4m^2 - 3m + 2) + (5m^2 + 13m - 4) + (-16m^2 - 4m + 3)$

**67.** $[(8m^2 + 4m - 7) - (2m^2 - 5m + 2)] - (m^2 + m + 1)$

**68.** $[(9b^3 - 4b^2 + 3b + 2) - (-2b^3 - 3b^2 + b)] - (8b^3 + 6b + 4)$

**69.** $[(3x^2 - 2x + 7) - (4x^2 + 2x - 3)] - [(9x^2 + 4x - 6) + (-4x^2 + 4x + 4)]$

**70.** $[(6t^2 - 3t + 1) - (12t^2 + 2t - 6)] - [(4t^2 - 3t - 8) + (-6t^2 + 10t - 12)]$

**71.** *Concept Check*　Without actually performing the operations, determine mentally the coefficient of the $x^2$-term in the simplified form of

$$(-4x^2 + 2x - 3) - (-2x^2 + x - 1) + (-8x^2 + 3x - 4).$$

**72.** *Concept Check*　Without actually performing the operations, determine mentally the coefficient of the $x$-term in the simplified form of

$$(-8x^2 - 3x + 2) - (4x^2 - 3x + 8) - (-2x^2 - x + 7).$$

*Add or subtract as indicated.* ***See Example 9.***

🌐 **73.** $(6b + 3c) + (-2b - 8c)$　　**74.** $(-5t + 13s) + (8t - 3s)$

**75.** $(4x + 2xy - 3) - (-2x + 3xy + 4)$　　**76.** $(8ab + 2a - 3b) - (6ab - 2a + 3b)$

**77.** $(5x^2y - 2xy + 9xy^2) - (8x^2y + 13xy + 12xy^2)$

**78.** $(16t^3s^2 + 8t^2s^3 + 9ts^4) - (-24t^3s^2 + 3t^2s^3 - 18ts^4)$

*Find a polynomial that represents the perimeter of each rectangle, square, or triangle.*

**79.** 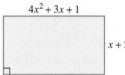 $4x^2 + 3x + 1$ ; $x + 2$

**80.** 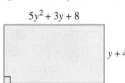 $5y^2 + 3y + 8$ ; $y + 4$

**81.** 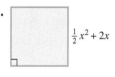 $\frac{1}{2}x^2 + 2x$

**82.** 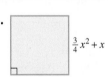 $\frac{3}{4}x^2 + x$

**83.** 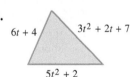 $6t + 4$ ; $3t^2 + 2t + 7$ ; $5t^2 + 2$

**84.** 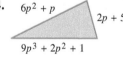 $6p^2 + p$ ; $2p + 5$ ; $9p^3 + 2p^2 + 1$

*Find **(a)** a polynomial that represents the perimeter of each triangle and **(b)** the degree measures of the angles of the triangle.*

**85.**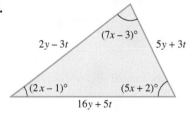

$2y - 3t$ ; $(7x - 3)°$ ; $5y + 3t$ ; $(2x - 1)°$ ; $(5x + 2)°$ ; $16y + 5t$

**86.**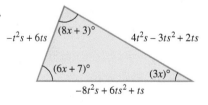

$-t^2s + 6ts$ ; $(8x + 3)°$ ; $4t^2s - 3ts^2 + 2ts$ ; $(6x + 7)°$ ; $(3x)°$ ; $-8t^2s + 6ts^2 + ts$

*Perform each indicated operation.*

**87.** Find the difference between the sum of $5x^2 + 2x - 3$ and $x^2 - 8x + 2$ and the sum of $7x^2 - 3x + 6$ and $-x^2 + 4x - 6$.

**88.** Subtract the sum of $9t^3 - 3t + 8$ and $t^2 - 8t + 4$ from the sum of $12t + 8$ and $t^2 - 10t + 3$.

*Graph each equation by completing the table of values.* ***See Example 10.***

**89.** $y = x^2 - 4$

| x | y |
|---|---|
| -2 | |
| -1 | |
| 0 | |
| 1 | |
| 2 | |

**90.** $y = x^2 - 6$

| x | y |
|---|---|
| -2 | |
| -1 | |
| 0 | |
| 1 | |
| 2 | |

**91.** $y = 2x^2 - 1$

| x | y |
|---|---|
| -2 | |
| -1 | |
| 0 | |
| 1 | |
| 2 | |

**92.** $y = 2x^2 + 2$

| x | y |
|---|---|
| -2 | |
| -1 | |
| 0 | |
| 1 | |
| 2 | |

**93.** $y = -x^2 + 4$

| x | y |
|---|---|
| -2 | |
| -1 | |
| 0 | |
| 1 | |
| 2 | |

**94.** $y = -x^2 + 2$

| x | y |
|---|---|
| -2 | |
| -1 | |
| 0 | |
| 1 | |
| 2 | |

**95.** $y = (x + 3)^2$

| x | -5 | -4 | -3 | -2 | -1 |
|---|---|---|---|---|---|
| y | | | | | |

**96.** $y = (x - 4)^2$

| x | 2 | 3 | 4 | 5 | 6 |
|---|---|---|---|---|---|
| y | | | | | |

## RELATING CONCEPTS    EXERCISES 97–100

**FOR INDIVIDUAL OR GROUP WORK**

*The polynomial equation*

$$y = -0.0545x^2 + 5.047x + 11.78$$

*gives a good approximation of the age of a dog in human years y, where x represents age in dog years. Each time we evaluate this polynomial for a value of x, we get one and only one output value y. For example, if a dog is 4 in dog years, let x = 4 to find that y ≈ 31.1. (Verify this.) This means that the dog is about 31 yr old in human years. This illustrates the concept of a function, one of the most important topics in mathematics.*

   ***Exercises 97–100*** *further illustrate the function concept with polynomials.* ***Work these exercises in order.***

**97.** It used to be thought that each dog year was about 7 human years, so that $y = 7x$ gave the number of human years for $x$ dog years. Evaluate $y$ for $x = 9$, and interpret the result.

**98.** Use the polynomial equation given in the directions above to find the number of human years equivalent to 3 dog years.

**99.** If an object is projected upward under certain conditions, its height in feet is given by the trinomial

$$-16x^2 + 60x + 80,$$

where $x$ is in seconds. Evaluate this polynomial for $x = 2.5$. Use the result to fill in the blanks: If _____ seconds have elapsed, the height of the object is _____ feet.

**100.** If it costs $15 to rent a chain saw, plus $2 per day, the binomial $2x + 15$ gives the cost to rent the chain saw for $x$ days. Evaluate this polynomial for $x = 6$. Use the result to fill in the blanks: If the saw is rented for _____ days, the cost is _____.

*Multiply. See **Section 1.8.***

**101.** $5(x + 4)$          **102.** $-3(x^2 + 7)$          **103.** $4(2a + 6b)$          **104.** $\frac{1}{2}(4m - 8n)$

*Multiply. See **Section 5.1.***

**105.** $(2a)(-5ab)$          **106.** $(3xz)(4x)$          **107.** $(-m^2)(m^5)$          **108.** $(2c)(3c^2)$

## 5.5  Multiplying Polynomials

**OBJECTIVES**

1 Multiply a monomial and a polynomial.
2 Multiply two polynomials.
3 Multiply binomials by the FOIL method.

**OBJECTIVE 1** Multiply a monomial and a polynomial. As shown in **Section 5.1,** we find the product of two monomials by using the rules for exponents and the commutative and associative properties. Consider this example.

$$-8m^6(-9n^6)$$
$$= -8(-9)(m^6)(n^6)$$
$$= 72m^6n^6$$

⚠ **CAUTION**  *Do not confuse addition of terms with multiplication of terms.* For instance,

$$7q^5 + 2q^5 = 9q^5, \quad \text{but} \quad (7q^5)(2q^5) = 7 \cdot 2q^{5+5} = 14q^{10}.$$

**NOW TRY**
**EXERCISE 1**
Find the product.
$$-3x^5(2x^3 - 5x^2 + 10)$$

**EXAMPLE 1**  Multiplying Monomials and Polynomials

Find each product.

**(a)** $4x^2(3x + 5)$

$$4x^2(3x + 5) = 4x^2(3x) + 4x^2(5) \qquad \text{Distributive property}$$
$$= 12x^3 + 20x^2 \qquad \text{Multiply monomials.}$$

**(b)** $-8m^3(4m^3 + 3m^2 + 2m - 1)$

$$= -8m^3(4m^3) + (-8m^3)(3m^2)$$
$$+ (-8m^3)(2m) + (-8m^3)(-1) \qquad \text{Distributive property}$$
$$= -32m^6 - 24m^5 - 16m^4 + 8m^3 \qquad \text{Multiply monomials.} \qquad \text{NOW TRY}$$

**OBJECTIVE 2** Multiply two polynomials. To find the product of the polynomials $x^2 + 3x + 5$ and $x - 4$, we can think of $x - 4$ as a single quantity and use the distributive property as follows.

$$(x^2 + 3x + 5)(x - 4)$$
$$= x^2(x - 4) + 3x(x - 4) + 5(x - 4) \qquad \text{Distributive property}$$
$$= x^2(x) + x^2(-4) + 3x(x) + 3x(-4) + 5(x) + 5(-4)$$
$$\qquad \qquad \qquad \qquad \qquad \text{Distributive property again}$$
$$= x^3 - 4x^2 + 3x^2 - 12x + 5x - 20 \qquad \text{Multiply monomials.}$$
$$= x^3 - x^2 - 7x - 20 \qquad \text{Combine like terms.}$$

**NOW TRY ANSWER**
**1.** $-6x^8 + 15x^7 - 30x^5$

## Multiplying Polynomials

To multiply two polynomials, multiply each term of the second polynomial by each term of the first polynomial and add the products.

*NOW TRY*
*EXERCISE 2*
Multiply.

$(x^2 - 4)(2x^2 - 5x + 3)$

**EXAMPLE 2** Multiplying Two Polynomials

Multiply $(m^2 + 5)(4m^3 - 2m^2 + 4m)$.

$(m^2 + 5)(4m^3 - 2m^2 + 4m)$  Multiply each term of the second polynomial by each term of the first.

$= m^2(4m^3) + m^2(-2m^2) + m^2(4m) + 5(4m^3) + 5(-2m^2) + 5(4m)$

$= 4m^5 - 2m^4 + 4m^3 + 20m^3 - 10m^2 + 20m$

$= 4m^5 - 2m^4 + 24m^3 - 10m^2 + 20m$  Combine like terms.  *NOW TRY*

*NOW TRY*
*EXERCISE 3*
Multiply.

$$5t^2 - 7t + 4$$
$$\underline{\quad\quad 2t - 6}$$

**EXAMPLE 3** Multiplying Polynomials Vertically

Multiply $(x^3 + 2x^2 + 4x + 1)(3x + 5)$ vertically.

$$x^3 + 2x^2 + 4x + 1$$
$$\underline{\quad\quad\quad\quad 3x + 5}$$  Write the polynomials vertically

Begin by multiplying each of the terms in the top row by 5.

$$x^3 + 2x^2 + 4x + 1$$
$$\underline{\quad\quad\quad\quad 3x + 5}$$
$$5x^3 + 10x^2 + 20x + 5$$  $5(x^3 + 2x^2 + 4x + 1)$

Now multiply each term in the top row by $3x$. Then add like terms.

$$x^3 + 2x^2 + 4x + 1$$
$$\underline{\quad\quad\quad\quad 3x + 5}$$
$$5x^3 + 10x^2 + 20x + 5$$
$$\underline{3x^4 + 6x^3 + 12x^2 + 3x}$$
$$3x^4 + 11x^3 + 22x^2 + 23x + 5 \leftarrow \text{Product}$$

Place like terms in columns so they can be added.

This process is similar to multiplication of whole numbers.

$3x(x^3 + 2x^2 + 4x + 1)$

*NOW TRY*

*NOW TRY*
*EXERCISE 4*
Find the product of

$9x^3 - 12x^2 + 3$ and $\frac{1}{3}x^2 - \frac{2}{3}$.

**EXAMPLE 4** Multiplying Polynomials with Fractional Coefficients Vertically

Find the product of $4m^3 - 2m^2 + 4m$ and $\frac{1}{2}m^2 + \frac{5}{2}$.

$$4m^3 - 2m^2 + 4m$$
$$\underline{\quad\quad\quad \frac{1}{2}m^2 + \frac{5}{2}}$$
$$10m^3 - 5m^2 + 10m$$  Terms of top row are multiplied by $\frac{5}{2}$.
$$\underline{2m^5 - m^4 + 2m^3}$$  Terms of top row are multiplied by $\frac{1}{2}m^2$.
$$2m^5 - m^4 + 12m^3 - 5m^2 + 10m$$  Add.  *NOW TRY*

We can use a rectangle to model polynomial multiplication. For example, to find

$$(2x + 1)(3x + 2),$$

label a rectangle with each term as shown next on the left. Then put the product of each pair of monomials in the appropriate box, as shown on the right.

*NOW TRY ANSWERS*
2. $2x^4 - 5x^3 - 5x^2 + 20x - 12$
3. $10t^3 - 44t^2 + 50t - 24$
4. $3x^5 - 4x^4 - 6x^3 + 9x^2 - 2$

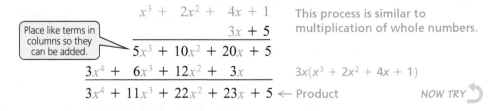

The product of the binomials is the sum of the four monomial products.

$$(2x + 1)(3x + 2)$$
$$= 6x^2 + 4x + 3x + 2$$
$$= 6x^2 + 7x + 2$$

This approach can be extended to polynomials with any number of terms.

**OBJECTIVE 3** **Multiply binomials by the FOIL method.** When multiplying binomials, the **FOIL method** reduces the rectangle method to a systematic approach without the rectangle. Consider this example.

$$(x + 3)(x + 5)$$

| | |
|---|---|
| $= (x + 3)x + (x + 3)5$ | Distributive property |
| $= x(x) + 3(x) + x(5) + 3(5)$ | Distributive property again |
| $= x^2 + 3x + 5x + 15$ | Multiply. |
| $= x^2 + 8x + 15$ | Combine like terms. |

The letters of the word FOIL originate as shown.

$(x + 3)(x + 5)$    Multiply the **F**irst terms: $x(x)$.    F

$(x + 3)(x + 5)$    Multiply the **O**uter terms: $x(5)$.    O
This is the **outer product**.

$(x + 3)(x + 5)$    Multiply the **I**nner terms: $3(x)$.    I
This is the **inner product**.

$(x + 3)(x + 5)$    Multiply the **L**ast terms: $3(5)$.    L

The outer product, $5x$, and the inner product, $3x$, should be added mentally to get $8x$ so that the three terms of the answer can be written without extra steps.

$$(x + 3)(x + 5)$$
$$= x^2 + 8x + 15$$

---

**Multiplying Binomials by the FOIL Method**

*Step 1*  Multiply the two **F**irst terms of the binomials to get the first term of the answer.

*Step 2*  Find the **O**uter product and the **I**nner product and add them (when possible) to get the middle term of the answer.

*Step 3*  Multiply the two **L**ast terms of the binomials to get the last term of the answer.

$$\mathbf{F} = x^2 \qquad \mathbf{L} = 15$$

$$(x + 3)(x + 5)$$

$$\mathbf{I} \qquad 3x$$
$$\mathbf{O} \qquad 5x$$
$$\overline{\qquad 8x} \qquad \text{Add.}$$

NOW TRY
EXERCISE 5

Use the FOIL method to find
the product.

$$(t - 6)(t + 5)$$

### EXAMPLE 5   Using the FOIL Method

Use the FOIL method to find the product $(x + 8)(x - 6)$.

**Step 1**   F   Multiply the First terms:   $x(x) = x^2$.

**Step 2**   O   Find the Outer product:   $x(-6) = -6x$.

  I   Find the Inner product:   $8(x) = 8x$.

  Add the outer and inner products mentally:   $-6x + 8x = 2x$.

**Step 3**   L   Multiply the Last terms:   $8(-6) = -48$.

$$(x + 8)(x - 6) = x^2 + 2x - 48$$

Add the terms found in Steps 1–3.

Shortcut:

First   Last

$$(x + 8)(x - 6)$$

Inner

Outer

$$x^2 \quad -48$$

$$(x + 8)(x - 6)$$

$8x$

$-6x$

$2x$   Add.

NOW TRY

NOW TRY
EXERCISE 6

Multiply.

$$(7y - 3)(2x + 5)$$

### EXAMPLE 6   Using the FOIL Method

Multiply $(9x - 2)(3y + 1)$.

First   $(9x - 2)(3y + 1)$   $27xy$

Outer   $(9x - 2)(3y + 1)$   $9x$

Inner   $(9x - 2)(3y + 1)$   $-6y$

Last   $(9x - 2)(3y + 1)$   $-2$

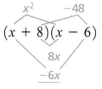
These unlike terms cannot be combined.

F   O   I   L

The product $(9x - 2)(3y + 1)$   is   $27xy + 9x - 6y - 2$.

NOW TRY

NOW TRY
EXERCISE 7

Find each product.

**(a)** $(3p - 5q)(4p - q)$

**(b)** $5x^2(3x + 1)(x - 5)$

### EXAMPLE 7   Using the FOIL Method

Find each product.

**(a)** $(2k + 5y)(k + 3y)$

  F   O   I   L

$$= 2k(k) + 2k(3y) + 5y(k) + 5y(3y)$$

$$= 2k^2 + 6ky + 5ky + 15y^2 \qquad \text{Multiply.}$$

$$= 2k^2 + 11ky + 15y^2 \qquad \text{Combine like terms.}$$

**(b)** $(7p + 2q)(3p - q)$

$$= 21p^2 - pq - 2q^2 \qquad \text{FOIL}$$

**(c)** $2x^2(x - 3)(3x + 4)$

$$= 2x^2(3x^2 - 5x - 12) \qquad \text{FOIL}$$

$$= 6x^4 - 10x^3 - 24x^2 \qquad \begin{array}{l}\text{Distributive} \\ \text{property}\end{array}$$

NOW TRY

---

**NOTE** Alternatively, **Example 7(c)** can be solved as follows.

$$2x^2(x - 3)(3x + 4) \qquad \text{Multiply } 2x^2 \text{ and } x - 3 \text{ first.}$$

$$= (2x^3 - 6x^2)(3x + 4) \qquad \text{Multiply that product and } 3x + 4.$$

$$= 6x^4 - 10x^3 - 24x^2 \qquad \text{Same answer}$$

NOW TRY ANSWERS
**5.** $t^2 - t - 30$
**6.** $14yx + 35y - 6x - 15$
**7.** **(a)** $12p^2 - 23pq + 5q^2$
  **(b)** $15x^4 - 70x^3 - 25x^2$

## 5.5 EXERCISES

**MyMathLab**

🌐 *Complete solution available on the Video Resources on DVD*

*Concept Check* In Exercises 1 and 2, match each product in Column I with the correct polynomial in Column II.

| | I | II | | I | II |
|---|---|---|---|---|---|
| **1.** | **(a)** $5x^3(6x^7)$ | **A.** $125x^{21}$ | **2.** | **(a)** $(x-5)(x+4)$ | **A.** $x^2 + 9x + 20$ |
| | **(b)** $-5x^7(6x^3)$ | **B.** $30x^{10}$ | | **(b)** $(x+5)(x+4)$ | **B.** $x^2 - 9x + 20$ |
| | **(c)** $(5x^7)^3$ | **C.** $-216x^9$ | | **(c)** $(x-5)(x-4)$ | **C.** $x^2 - x - 20$ |
| | **(d)** $(-6x^3)^3$ | **D.** $-30x^{10}$ | | **(d)** $(x+5)(x-4)$ | **D.** $x^2 + x - 20$ |

*Find each product.* **See Objective 1.**

**3.** $5y^4(3y^7)$      **4.** $10p^2(5p^3)$      **5.** $-15a^4(-2a^5)$

**6.** $-3m^6(-5m^4)$      **7.** $5p(3q^2)$      **8.** $4a^3(3b^2)$

**9.** $-6m^3(3n^2)$      **10.** $9r^3(-2s^2)$      **11.** $y^5 \cdot 9y \cdot y^4$

**12.** $x^2 \cdot 3x^3 \cdot 2x$      **13.** $(4x^3)(2x^2)(-x^5)$      **14.** $(7t^5)(3t^4)(-t^8)$

*Find each product.* **See Example 1.**

🌐 **15.** $2m(3m + 2)$      **16.** $4x(5x + 3)$

**17.** $3p(-2p^3 + 4p^2)$      **18.** $4x(3 + 2x + 5x^3)$

**19.** $-8z(2z + 3z^2 + 3z^3)$      **20.** $-7y(3 + 5y^2 - 2y^3)$

**21.** $2y^3(3 + 2y + 5y^4)$      **22.** $2m^4(6 + 5m + 3m^2)$

**23.** $-4r^3(-7r^2 + 8r - 9)$      **24.** $-9a^5(-3a^6 - 2a^4 + 8a^2)$

**25.** $3a^2(2a^2 - 4ab + 5b^2)$      **26.** $4z^3(8z^2 + 5zy - 3y^2)$

**27.** $7m^3n^2(3m^2 + 2mn - n^3)$      **28.** $2p^2q(3p^2q^2 - 5p + 2q^2)$

*Find each product.* **See Examples 2–4.**

🌐 **29.** $(6x + 1)(2x^2 + 4x + 1)$      **30.** $(9a + 2)(9a^2 + a + 1)$

**31.** $(9y - 2)(8y^2 - 6y + 1)$      **32.** $(2r - 1)(3r^2 + 4r - 4)$

🌐 **33.** $(4m + 3)(5m^3 - 4m^2 + m - 5)$      **34.** $(2y + 8)(3y^4 - 2y^2 + 1)$

**35.** $(2x - 1)(3x^5 - 2x^3 + x^2 - 2x + 3)$      **36.** $(2a + 3)(a^4 - a^3 + a^2 - a + 1)$

**37.** $(5x^2 + 2x + 1)(x^2 - 3x + 5)$      **38.** $(2m^2 + m - 3)(m^2 - 4m + 5)$

🌐 **39.** $(6x^4 - 4x^2 + 8x)\left(\dfrac{1}{2}x + 3\right)$      **40.** $(8y^6 + 4y^4 - 12y^2)\left(\dfrac{3}{4}y^2 + 2\right)$

*Find each product. Use the FOIL method.* **See Examples 5–7.**

🌐 **41.** $(m + 7)(m + 5)$      **42.** $(n + 9)(n + 3)$      **43.** $(n - 1)(n + 4)$

**44.** $(t - 3)(t + 8)$      **45.** $(x + 5)(x - 5)$      **46.** $(y + 8)(y - 8)$

**47.** $(2x + 3)(6x - 4)$      **48.** $(3y + 5)(8y - 6)$      **49.** $(9 + t)(9 - t)$

**50.** $(10 + r)(10 - r)$      **51.** $(3x - 2)(3x - 2)$      **52.** $(4m + 3)(4m + 3)$

**53.** $(5a + 1)(2a + 7)$      **54.** $(b + 8)(6b - 2)$      **55.** $(6 - 5m)(2 + 3m)$

**56.** $(8 - 3a)(2 + a)$      **57.** $(5 - 3x)(4 + x)$      **58.** $(6 - 5x)(2 + x)$

**59.** $(3t - 4s)(t + 3s)$      **60.** $(2m - 3n)(m + 5n)$      🌐 **61.** $(4x + 3)(2y - 1)$

**62.** $(5x + 7)(3y - 8)$      🌐 **63.** $(3x + 2y)(5x - 3y)$      **64.** $(5a + 3b)(5a - 4b)$

**65.** $3y^3(2y + 3)(y - 5)$

**66.** $2x^2(2x - 5)(x + 3)$

**67.** $-8r^3(5r^2 + 2)(5r^2 - 2)$

**68.** $-5t^4(2t^4 + 1)(2t^4 - 1)$

*Find polynomials that represent **(a)** the area and **(b)** the perimeter of each square or rectangle. (If necessary, refer to the formulas on the inside covers.)*

**69.**

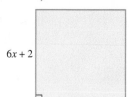

$3y + 7$

$y + 1$

**70.**

$6x + 2$

*Find each product. In Exercises 81–84, 89, and 90, apply the meaning of exponents.*

**71.** $\left(3p + \dfrac{5}{4}q\right)\left(2p - \dfrac{5}{3}q\right)$

**72.** $\left(2x + \dfrac{2}{3}y\right)\left(3x - \dfrac{3}{4}y\right)$

**73.** $(x + 7)^2$

**74.** $(m + 6)^2$

**75.** $(a - 4)(a + 4)$

**76.** $(b - 10)(b + 10)$

**77.** $(2p - 5)^2$

**78.** $(3m - 1)^2$

**79.** $(5k + 3q)^2$

**80.** $(8m + 3n)^2$

**81.** $(m - 5)^3$

**82.** $(p - 3)^3$

**83.** $(2a + 1)^3$

**84.** $(3m + 1)^3$

**85.** $-3a(3a + 1)(a - 4)$

**86.** $-4r(3r + 2)(2r - 5)$

**87.** $7(4m - 3)(2m + 1)$

**88.** $5(3k - 7)(5k + 2)$

**89.** $(3r - 2s)^4$

**90.** $(2z - 5y)^4$

**91.** $3p^3(2p^2 + 5p)(p^3 + 2p + 1)$

**92.** $5k^2(k^3 - 3)(k^2 - k + 4)$

**93.** $-2x^5(3x^2 + 2x - 5)(4x + 2)$

**94.** $-4x^3(3x^4 + 2x^2 - x)(-2x + 1)$

*The figures in Exercises 95–98 are composed of triangles, squares, rectangles, and circles. Find a polynomial that represents the area of each shaded region. In Exercises 97 and 98, leave $\pi$ in your answers. (If necessary, refer to the formulas on the inside covers.)*

**95.**

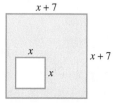

$x + 7$

$x$

$x$

$x + 7$

**96.**

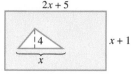

$2x + 5$

$4$

$x$

$x + 1$

**97.**

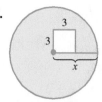

$3$

$3$

$x$

**98.**

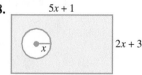

$5x + 1$

$x$

$2x + 3$

**PREVIEW EXERCISES**

*Apply a power rule for exponents. **See Section 5.1.***

**99.** $(3m)^2$

**100.** $(5p)^2$

**101.** $(-2r)^2$

**102.** $(-5a)^2$

**103.** $(4x^2)^2$

**104.** $(8y^3)^2$

## 5.6  Special Products

**OBJECTIVES**

**1** Square binomials.

**2** Find the product of the sum and difference of two terms.

**3** Find greater powers of binomials.

**OBJECTIVE 1  Square binomials.** The square of a binomial can be found quickly by using the method suggested by **Example 1.**

**EXAMPLE 1  Squaring a Binomial**

Find $(m + 3)^2$.

$$(m + 3)(m + 3) \quad \boxed{\begin{array}{c}(m + 3)^2 \text{ means} \\ (m + 3)(m + 3).\end{array}}$$

$$= m^2 + 3m + 3m + 9 \quad \text{FOIL}$$

$$= m^2 + 6m + 9 \quad \boxed{\begin{array}{c}\text{Combine like terms.} \\ \text{This is the answer.}\end{array}}$$

This result has the squares of the first and the last terms of the binomial.

$$m^2 = m^2 \quad \text{and} \quad 3^2 = 9$$

*The middle term, 6m, is twice the product of the two terms of the binomial,* since the outer and inner products are $m(3)$ and $3(m)$. Then we find their sum.

$$m(3) + 3(m) = 2(m)(3) = 6m \qquad \text{NOW TRY} \, \circlearrowleft$$

**NOW TRY**
*EXERCISE 1*
Find $(x + 5)^2$.

---

**Square of a Binomial**

The square of a binomial is a trinomial consisting of

$$\begin{array}{c} \text{the square of} \\ \text{the first term} \end{array} + \begin{array}{c} \text{twice the product} \\ \text{of the two terms} \end{array} + \begin{array}{c} \text{the square of} \\ \text{the last term.} \end{array}$$

For $x$ and $y$, the following are true.

$$(x + y)^2 = x^2 + 2xy + y^2$$

$$(x - y)^2 = x^2 - 2xy + y^2$$

---

**EXAMPLE 2  Squaring Binomials**

Find each binomial square and simplify.

$$(x - y)^2 \; = \; x^2 - \; 2 \cdot x \cdot y \; + \; y^2$$

**(a)** $(5z - 1)^2 = (5z)^2 - 2(5z)(1) + (1)^2$

$$= 25z^2 - 10z + 1 \qquad (5z)^2 = 5^2 z^2 = 25z^2$$

**(b)** $(3b + 5r)^2$

$$= (3b)^2 + 2(3b)(5r) + (5r)^2$$

$$= 9b^2 + 30br + 25r^2$$

**(c)** $(2a - 9x)^2$

$$= (2a)^2 - 2(2a)(9x) + (9x)^2$$

$$= 4a^2 - 36ax + 81x^2$$

**(d)** $\left(4m + \dfrac{1}{2}\right)^2$

$$= (4m)^2 + 2(4m)\left(\frac{1}{2}\right) + \left(\frac{1}{2}\right)^2$$

$$= 16m^2 + 4m + \frac{1}{4}$$

*NOW TRY ANSWER*
**1.** $x^2 + 10x + 25$

NOW TRY
EXERCISE 2

Find each binomial square and simplify.

**(a)** $(3x - 1)^2$

**(b)** $(4p - 5q)^2$

**(c)** $\left(6t - \frac{1}{3}\right)^2$

**(d)** $m(2m + 3)^2$

**(e)** $x(4x - 3)^2$    [Remember the middle term.]

$= x(16x^2 - 24x + 9)$    Square the binomial.

$= 16x^3 - 24x^2 + 9x$    Distributive property     *NOW TRY*

*In the square of a sum, all of the terms are positive,* as in **Examples 2(b) and (d).** *In the square of a difference, the middle term is negative,* as in **Examples 2(a), (c), and (e).**

---

⚠ **CAUTION** A common error when squaring a binomial is to forget the middle term of the product. In general,

$$(x + y)^2 = x^2 + 2xy + y^2, \quad not \quad x^2 + y^2,$$

and

$$(x - y)^2 = x^2 - 2xy + y^2, \quad not \quad x^2 - y^2.$$

---

**OBJECTIVE 2** Find the product of the sum and difference of two terms.
In binomial products of the form $(x + y)(x - y)$, one binomial is the sum of two terms and the other is the difference of the *same* two terms. Consider $(x + 2)(x - 2)$.

$$(x + 2)(x - 2)$$

$$= x^2 - 2x + 2x - 4 \quad \text{FOIL}$$

$$= x^2 - 4 \quad \text{Combine like terms.}$$

Thus, the product of $x + y$ and $x - y$ is the difference of two squares.

---

**Product of the Sum and Difference of Two Terms**

$$(x + y)(x - y) = x^2 - y^2$$

---

NOW TRY
EXERCISE 3

Find the product.

$$(t + 10)(t - 10)$$

**EXAMPLE 3** Finding the Product of the Sum and Difference of Two Terms

Find each product.

**(a)** $(x + 4)(x - 4)$

Use the rule for the product of the sum and difference of two terms.

$$(x + 4)(x - 4)$$

$$= x^2 - 4^2$$

$$= x^2 - 16$$

**(b)** $\left(\frac{2}{3} - w\right)\left(\frac{2}{3} + w\right)$

$$= \left(\frac{2}{3} + w\right)\left(\frac{2}{3} - w\right) \quad \text{Commutative property}$$

$$= \left(\frac{2}{3}\right)^2 - w^2 \quad (x + y)(x - y) = x^2 - y^2$$

$$= \frac{4}{9} - w^2 \quad \text{Square } \frac{2}{3}. \quad \text{*NOW TRY*}$$

NOW TRY ANSWERS

**2. (a)** $9x^2 - 6x + 1$
   **(b)** $16p^2 - 40pq + 25q^2$
   **(c)** $36t^2 - 4t + \frac{1}{9}$
   **(d)** $4m^3 + 12m^2 + 9m$
**3.** $t^2 - 100$

NOW TRY
EXERCISE 4

Find each product.

**(a)** $(4x - 6)(4x + 6)$

**(b)** $\left(5r - \frac{4}{5}\right)\left(5r + \frac{4}{5}\right)$

**(c)** $y(3y + 1)(3y - 1)$

*EXAMPLE 4* Finding the Product of the Sum and Difference of Two Terms

Find each product.

$$(x \; + \; y) \;\; (x \; - \; y)$$
$$\downarrow \quad \downarrow \quad \downarrow \quad \downarrow$$

**(a)** $(5m + 3)(5m - 3)$

Use the rule for the product of the sum and difference of two terms.

$$(5m + 3)(5m - 3)$$
$$= (5m)^2 - 3^2 \qquad (x + y)(x - y) = x^2 - y^2$$
$$= 25m^2 - 9 \qquad \text{Apply the exponents.}$$

**(b)** $(4x + y)(4x - y)$

$$= (4x)^2 - y^2$$
$$= 16x^2 - y^2$$

**(c)** $\left(z - \frac{1}{4}\right)\left(z + \frac{1}{4}\right)$

$$= z^2 - \frac{1}{16}$$

**(d)** $p(2p + 1)(2p - 1)$

$$= p(4p^2 - 1)$$
$$= 4p^3 - p \qquad \text{Distributive property} \qquad \text{NOW TRY}$$

**OBJECTIVE 3** **Find greater powers of binomials.** The methods used in the previous section and this section can be combined to find greater powers of binomials.

NOW TRY
EXERCISE 5

Find the product.

$$(2m - 1)^3$$

*EXAMPLE 5* Finding Greater Powers of Binomials

Find each product.

**(a)** $(x + 5)^3$

$$= (x + 5)^2(x + 5) \qquad a^3 = a^2 \cdot a$$
$$= (x^2 + 10x + 25)(x + 5) \qquad \text{Square the binomial.}$$
$$= x^3 + 10x^2 + 25x + 5x^2 + 50x + 125 \qquad \text{Multiply polynomials.}$$
$$= x^3 + 15x^2 + 75x + 125 \qquad \text{Combine like terms.}$$

**(b)** $(2y - 3)^4$

$$= (2y - 3)^2(2y - 3)^2 \qquad a^4 = a^2 \cdot a^2$$
$$= (4y^2 - 12y + 9)(4y^2 - 12y + 9) \qquad \text{Square each binomial.}$$
$$= 16y^4 - 48y^3 + 36y^2 - 48y^3 + 144y^2 \qquad \text{Multiply polynomials.}$$
$$\quad - 108y + 36y^2 - 108y + 81$$
$$= 16y^4 - 96y^3 + 216y^2 - 216y + 81 \qquad \text{Combine like terms.}$$

**(c)** $-2r(r + 2)^3$

$$= -2r(r + 2)(r + 2)^2 \qquad a^3 = a \cdot a^2$$
$$= -2r(r + 2)(r^2 + 4r + 4) \qquad \text{Square the binomial.}$$
$$= -2r(r^3 + 4r^2 + 4r + 2r^2 + 8r + 8) \qquad \text{Multiply polynomials.}$$
$$= -2r(r^3 + 6r^2 + 12r + 8) \qquad \text{Combine like terms.}$$
$$= -2r^4 - 12r^3 - 24r^2 - 16r \qquad \text{Multiply.} \qquad \text{NOW TRY}$$

NOW TRY ANSWERS
**4. (a)** $16x^2 - 36$
 **(b)** $25r^2 - \frac{16}{25}$
 **(c)** $9y^3 - y$
**5.** $8m^3 - 12m^2 + 6m - 1$

**5.6 EXERCISES**

🌐 *Complete solution available on the Video Resources on DVD*

**1.** *Concept Check* Consider the square $(4x + 3)^2$.

    **(a)** What is the simplest form of the square of the first term, $(4x)^2$?

    **(b)** What is the simplest form of twice the product of the two terms, $2(4x)(3)$?

    **(c)** What is the simplest form of the square of the last term, $3^2$?

    **(d)** Write the final product, which is a trinomial, using your results in parts (a)–(c).

📝 **2.** Explain in your own words how to square a binomial. Give an example.

*Find each product. See Examples 1 and 2.*

**3.** $(m + 2)^2$      **4.** $(x + 8)^2$      **5.** $(r - 3)^2$

**6.** $(z - 5)^2$      🌐 **7.** $(x + 2y)^2$      **8.** $(p - 3m)^2$

**9.** $(5p + 2q)^2$      **10.** $(8a + 3b)^2$      **11.** $(4a + 5b)^2$

**12.** $(9y + 4z)^2$      🌐 **13.** $\left(6m - \dfrac{4}{5}n\right)^2$      **14.** $\left(5x + \dfrac{2}{5}y\right)^2$

**15.** $t(3t - 1)^2$      **16.** $x(2x + 5)^2$      **17.** $3t(4t + 1)^2$

**18.** $2x(7x - 2)^2$      **19.** $-(4r - 2)^2$      **20.** $-(3y - 8)^2$

**21.** *Concept Check* Consider the product $(7x + 3y)(7x - 3y)$.

    **(a)** What is the simplest form of the product of the first terms, $7x(7x)$?

    **(b)** Multiply the outer terms, $7x(-3y)$. Then multiply the inner terms, $3y(7x)$. Add the results. What is this sum?

    **(c)** What is the simplest form of the product of the last terms, $3y(-3y)$?

    **(d)** Write the final product, using your results in parts (a) and (c). Why is the sum found in part (b) omitted here?

📝 **22.** Explain in your own words how to find the product of the sum and the difference of two terms. Give an example.

*Find each product. See Examples 3 and 4.*

🌐 **23.** $(k + 5)(k - 5)$      **24.** $(a + 8)(a - 8)$      **25.** $(4 - 3t)(4 + 3t)$

**26.** $(7 - 2x)(7 + 2x)$      **27.** $(5x + 2)(5x - 2)$      **28.** $(2m + 5)(2m - 5)$

**29.** $(5y + 3x)(5y - 3x)$      **30.** $(3x + 4y)(3x - 4y)$      🌐 **31.** $(10x + 3y)(10x - 3y)$

**32.** $(13r + 2z)(13r - 2z)$      **33.** $(2x^2 - 5)(2x^2 + 5)$      **34.** $(9y^2 - 2)(9y^2 + 2)$

🌐 **35.** $\left(\dfrac{3}{4} - x\right)\left(\dfrac{3}{4} + x\right)$      **36.** $\left(\dfrac{2}{3} + r\right)\left(\dfrac{2}{3} - r\right)$      **37.** $\left(9y + \dfrac{2}{3}\right)\left(9y - \dfrac{2}{3}\right)$

**38.** $\left(7x + \dfrac{3}{7}\right)\left(7x - \dfrac{3}{7}\right)$      🌐 **39.** $q(5q - 1)(5q + 1)$      **40.** $p(3p + 7)(3p - 7)$

📝 **41.** Does $(a + b)^2$ equal $a^2 + b^2$ in general? Explain.

📝 **42.** Does $(a + b)^3$ equal $a^3 + b^3$ in general? Explain.

*Find each product. See Example 5.*

🌐 **43.** $(x + 1)^3$      **44.** $(y + 2)^3$      **45.** $(t - 3)^3$      **46.** $(m - 5)^3$

**47.** $(r + 5)^3$      **48.** $(p + 3)^3$      **49.** $(2a + 1)^3$      **50.** $(3m + 1)^3$

🌐 **51.** $(4x - 1)^4$      **52.** $(2x - 1)^4$      **53.** $(3r - 2t)^4$      **54.** $(2z + 5y)^4$

**55.** $2x(x + 1)^3$      **56.** $3y(y + 2)^3$      **57.** $-4t(t + 3)^3$

**58.** $-5r(r + 1)^3$      **59.** $(x + y)^2(x - y)^2$      **60.** $(s + 2)^2(s - 2)^2$

**FOR INDIVIDUAL OR GROUP WORK**

*Special products can be illustrated by using areas of rectangles. Use the figure, and* **work Exercises 61–66 in order** *to justify the special product*

$$(a + b)^2 = a^2 + 2ab + b^2.$$

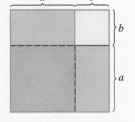

**61.** Express the area of the large square as the square of a binomial.

**62.** Give the monomial that represents the area of the red square.

**63.** Give the monomial that represents the sum of the areas of the blue rectangles.

**64.** Give the monomial that represents the area of the yellow square.

**65.** What is the sum of the monomials you obtained in **Exercises 62–64?**

**66.** Explain why the binomial square you found in **Exercise 61** must equal the polynomial you found in **Exercise 65.**

*To understand how the special product* $(a + b)^2 = a^2 + 2ab + b^2$ *can be applied to a purely numerical problem,* **work Exercises 67–70 in order.**

**67.** Evaluate $35^2$, using either traditional paper-and-pencil methods or a calculator.

**68.** The number 35 can be written as $30 + 5$. Therefore, $35^2 = (30 + 5)^2$. Use the special product for squaring a binomial with $a = 30$ and $b = 5$ to write an expression for $(30 + 5)^2$. Do not simplify at this time.

**69.** Use the order of operations to simplify the expression you found in **Exercise 68.**

**70.** How do the answers in **Exercises 67 and 69** compare?

*The special product*

$$(x + y)(x - y) = x^2 - y^2$$

*can be used to perform some multiplication problems. Here are two examples.*

$$51 \times 49 = (50 + 1)(50 - 1) \qquad 102 \times 98 = (100 + 2)(100 - 2)$$
$$= 50^2 - 1^2 \qquad\qquad\qquad = 100^2 - 2^2$$
$$= 2500 - 1 \qquad\qquad\qquad = 10{,}000 - 4$$
$$= 2499 \qquad\qquad\qquad\quad = 9996$$

*Once these patterns are recognized, multiplications of this type can be done mentally. Use this method to calculate each product mentally.*

**71.** $101 \times 99$

**72.** $103 \times 97$

**73.** $201 \times 199$

**74.** $301 \times 299$

**75.** $20\frac{1}{2} \times 19\frac{1}{2}$

**76.** $30\frac{1}{3} \times 29\frac{2}{3}$

*Determine a polynomial that represents the area of each figure. (If necessary, refer to the formulas on the inside covers.)*

**77.**

$m - 2n$

$m + 2n$

**78.**

$6p + q$

$6p + q$

**79.**

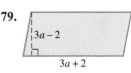

$3a - 2$

$3a + 2$

**80.**

**81.**

**82.**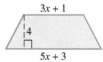

*In Exercises 83 and 84, refer to the figure shown here.*

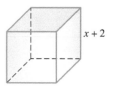

**83.** Find a polynomial that represents the volume of the cube (in cubic units).

**84.** If the value of $x$ is 6, what is the volume of the cube (in cubic units)?

**PREVIEW EXERCISES**

*Write each product as a sum of terms. Write answers with positive exponents only. Simplify each term. **See Section 1.8.***

**85.** $\dfrac{1}{2p}(4p^2 + 2p + 8)$

**86.** $\dfrac{1}{5x}(5x^2 - 10x + 45)$

**87.** $\dfrac{1}{3m}(m^3 + 9m^2 - 6m)$

**88.** $\dfrac{1}{4y}(y^4 + 6y^2 + 8)$

*Find each product. **See Section 5.5.***

**89.** $-3k(8k^2 - 12k + 2)$

**90.** $(3r + 5)(2r + 1)$

**91.** $(-2k + 1)(8k^2 + 9k + 3)$

**92.** $(x^2 - 2)(3x^2 + x + 4)$

*Subtract. **See Section 5.4.***

**93.** $\begin{aligned} &5t^2 + 2t - 6 \\ &\underline{5t^2 - 3t - 9} \end{aligned}$

**94.** $\begin{aligned} &x^5 + x^3 - 2x^2 + 3 \\ &\underline{-4x^5 \qquad\quad + 3x^2 - 8} \end{aligned}$

---

## 5.7 Dividing Polynomials

**OBJECTIVES**

1. Divide a polynomial by a monomial.
2. Divide a polynomial by a polynomial.

**OBJECTIVE 1** **Divide a polynomial by a monomial.** We add two fractions with a common denominator as follows.

$$\frac{a}{c} + \frac{b}{c} = \frac{a + b}{c}$$

In reverse, this statement gives a rule for dividing a polynomial by a monomial.

---

**Dividing a Polynomial by a Monomial**

To divide a polynomial by a monomial, divide each term of the polynomial by the monomial.

$$\frac{a + b}{c} = \frac{a}{c} + \frac{b}{c} \quad (c \neq 0)$$

*Examples:* $\quad \dfrac{2 + 5}{3} = \dfrac{2}{3} + \dfrac{5}{3} \quad$ and $\quad \dfrac{x + 3z}{2y} = \dfrac{x}{2y} + \dfrac{3z}{2y}$

The parts of a division problem are named here.

$$\text{Dividend} \rightarrow \frac{12x^2 + 6x}{6x} \leftarrow \text{Divisor} = 2x + 1 \leftarrow \text{Quotient}$$

NOW TRY
EXERCISE 1
Divide $16a^6 - 12a^4$ by $4a^2$.

**EXAMPLE 1** Dividing a Polynomial by a Monomial

Divide $5m^5 - 10m^3$ by $5m^2$.

$$\frac{5m^5 - 10m^3}{5m^2}$$

$$= \frac{5m^5}{5m^2} - \frac{10m^3}{5m^2} \qquad \text{Use the preceding rule, with } + \text{ replaced by } -.$$

$$= m^3 - 2m \qquad \text{Quotient rule}$$

CHECK    Multiply:   $5m^2 \cdot (m^3 - 2m) = 5m^5 - 10m^3.$

                                        Original polynomial
            Divisor    Quotient         (Dividend)

Because division by 0 is undefined, the quotient $\frac{5m^5 - 10m^3}{5m^2}$ is undefined if $5m^2 = 0$, or $m = 0$. From now on, we assume that no denominators are 0.     NOW TRY

NOW TRY
EXERCISE 2
Divide.

$$\frac{36x^5 + 24x^4 - 12x^3}{6x^4}$$

**EXAMPLE 2** Dividing a Polynomial by a Monomial

Divide.

$$\frac{16a^5 - 12a^4 + 8a^2}{4a^3}$$

> This becomes $\frac{2}{a}$, **not** $2a$.

$$= \frac{16a^5}{4a^3} - \frac{12a^4}{4a^3} + \frac{8a^2}{4a^3} \qquad \text{Divide each term by } 4a^3.$$

$$= 4a^2 - 3a + \frac{2}{a} \qquad \text{Quotient rule}$$

The quotient $4a^2 - 3a + \frac{2}{a}$ is *not* a polynomial because of the presence of the expression $\frac{2}{a}$, which has a variable in the denominator. While the sum, difference, and product of two polynomials are always polynomials, the quotient of two polynomials may not be a polynomial.

CHECK    $4a^3\left(4a^2 - 3a + \frac{2}{a}\right)$        Divisor × Quotient should equal Dividend.

$$= 4a^3(4a^2) + 4a^3(-3a) + 4a^3\left(\frac{2}{a}\right) \qquad \text{Distributive property}$$

$$= 16a^5 - 12a^4 + 8a^2 \checkmark \qquad \text{Dividend} \qquad \text{NOW TRY}$$

⚠ **CAUTION**   The most frequent error in a problem like that in **Example 2** is with the last term of the quotient.

$$\frac{8a^2}{4a^3} = \frac{8}{4}a^{2-3} = 2a^{-1} = 2\left(\frac{1}{a}\right) = \frac{2}{a}$$

NOW TRY ANSWERS
1. $4a^4 - 3a^2$
2. $6x + 4 - \frac{2}{x}$

NOW TRY
EXERCISE 3
Divide $7y^4 - 40y^5 + 100y^2$
by $-5y^2$.

**EXAMPLE 3** Dividing a Polynomial by a Monomial with a Negative Coefficient

Divide $-7x^3 + 12x^4 - 4x$ by $-4x$.

Write the polynomial in descending powers as $12x^4 - 7x^3 - 4x$ before dividing.

Write in descending powers.

$$\frac{12x^4 - 7x^3 - 4x}{-4x}$$

$$= \frac{12x^4}{-4x} - \frac{7x^3}{-4x} - \frac{4x}{-4x} \qquad \text{Divide each term by } -4x.$$

$$= -3x^3 - \frac{7x^2}{-4} - (-1) \qquad \text{Quotient rule}$$

$$= -3x^3 + \frac{7x^2}{4} + 1 \qquad \boxed{\text{Be sure to include 1 in the answer.}}$$

*Check* by multiplying.

NOW TRY

NOW TRY
EXERCISE 4
Divide $35m^5n^4 - 49m^2n^3 + 12mn$ by $7m^2n$.

**EXAMPLE 4** Dividing a Polynomial by a Monomial

Divide $180x^4y^{10} - 150x^3y^8 + 120x^2y^6 - 90xy^4 + 100y$ by $30xy^2$.

$$\frac{180x^4y^{10} - 150x^3y^8 + 120x^2y^6 - 90xy^4 + 100y}{30xy^2}$$

$$= \frac{180x^4y^{10}}{30xy^2} - \frac{150x^3y^8}{30xy^2} + \frac{120x^2y^6}{30xy^2} - \frac{90xy^4}{30xy^2} + \frac{100y}{30xy^2}$$

$$= 6x^3y^8 - 5x^2y^6 + 4xy^4 - 3y^2 + \frac{10}{3xy}$$

NOW TRY

**OBJECTIVE 2** **Divide a polynomial by a polynomial.** As shown in the box, we use a method of "long division" to divide a polynomial by a polynomial (other than a monomial). *Both polynomials must first be written in descending powers.*

NOW TRY ANSWERS

3. $8y^3 - \dfrac{7y^2}{5} - 20$

4. $5m^3n^3 - 7n^2 + \dfrac{12}{7m}$

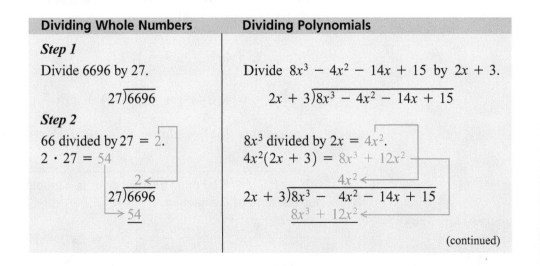

| Dividing Whole Numbers | Dividing Polynomials |
|---|---|
| *Step 1* | |
| Divide 6696 by 27. | Divide $8x^3 - 4x^2 - 14x + 15$ by $2x + 3$. |
| $27\overline{)6696}$ | $2x + 3\overline{)8x^3 - 4x^2 - 14x + 15}$ |
| *Step 2* | |
| 66 divided by $27 = 2$. | $8x^3$ divided by $2x = 4x^2$. |
| $2 \cdot 27 = 54$ | $4x^2(2x + 3) = 8x^3 + 12x^2$ |
| $\begin{array}{r} 2 \\ 27\overline{)6696} \\ 54 \end{array}$ | $\begin{array}{r} 4x^2 \\ 2x + 3\overline{)8x^3 - 4x^2 - 14x + 15} \\ 8x^3 + 12x^2 \end{array}$ |

(continued)

**Step 3**

Subtract. Then bring down the next digit.

$$
\begin{array}{r}
2\phantom{000} \\
27\overline{)6696} \\
54\phantom{0}\downarrow \\
\hline
129
\end{array}
$$

Subtract. Then bring down the next term.

$$
\begin{array}{r}
4x^2 \phantom{00000000000} \\
2x + 3\overline{)8x^3 - 4x^2 - 14x + 15} \\
\underline{8x^3 + 12x^2}\phantom{000}\downarrow\phantom{0000000} \\
-16x^2 - 14x
\end{array}
$$

***(To subtract two polynomials, change the signs of the second and then add.)***

$-16x^2$ divided by $2x = -8x$.
$-8x(2x + 3) = -16x^2 - 24x$

$$
\begin{array}{r}
4x^2 - \phantom{0}8x \phantom{000000} \\
2x + 3\overline{)8x^3 - 4x^2 - 14x + 15} \\
\underline{8x^3 + 12x^2}\phantom{0000000000} \\
-16x^2 - 14x \phantom{0000} \\
-16x^2 - 24x \phantom{0000}
\end{array}
$$

**Step 4**

129 divided by 27 = 4.
4 · 27 = 108

$$
\begin{array}{r}
24\phantom{0} \\
27\overline{)6696} \\
54\phantom{0} \\
\hline
129 \\
108
\end{array}
$$

**Step 5**

Subtract. Then bring down the next digit.

$$
\begin{array}{r}
24\phantom{0} \\
27\overline{)6696} \\
54\phantom{0} \\
\hline
129\phantom{0} \\
108\downarrow \\
\hline
216
\end{array}
$$

Subtract. Then bring down the next term.

$$
\begin{array}{r}
4x^2 - \phantom{0}8x \phantom{000000000} \\
2x + 3\overline{)8x^3 - 4x^2 - 14x + 15} \\
\underline{8x^3 + 12x^2}\phantom{00000000000} \\
-16x^2 - 14x \phantom{00000} \\
\underline{-16x^2 - 24x}\phantom{00}\downarrow\phantom{00} \\
10x + 15
\end{array}
$$

**Step 6**

216 divided by 27 = 8.
8 · 27 = 216

$$
\begin{array}{r}
248 \\
27\overline{)6696} \\
54\phantom{0} \\
\hline
129 \\
108 \\
\hline
216 \\
216
\end{array}
$$

Remainder $\longrightarrow$ 0

6696 divided by 27 is 248. The remainder is 0.

$10x$ divided by $2x = 5$.
$5(2x + 3) = 10x + 15$

$$
\begin{array}{r}
4x^2 - \phantom{0}8x + \phantom{0}5 \\
2x + 3\overline{)8x^3 - 4x^2 - 14x + 15} \\
\underline{8x^3 + 12x^2}\phantom{0000000000} \\
-16x^2 - 14x \phantom{00000} \\
\underline{-16x^2 - 24x}\phantom{00000} \\
10x + 15 \\
10x + 15
\end{array}
$$

Remainder $\longrightarrow$ 0

$8x^3 - 4x^2 - 14x + 15$ divided by $2x + 3$ is $4x^2 - 8x + 5$. The remainder is 0.

**Step 7**

CHECK Multiply.

$$27 \cdot 248 = 6696 \checkmark$$

CHECK Multiply.

$$(2x + 3)(4x^2 - 8x + 5)$$
$$= 8x^3 - 4x^2 - 14x + 15 \checkmark$$

NOW TRY
EXERCISE 5

Divide.

$$\frac{4x^2 + x - 18}{x - 2}$$

**EXAMPLE 5** Dividing a Polynomial by a Polynomial

Divide. $\dfrac{3x^2 - 5x - 28}{x - 4}$

*Step 1*  $3x^2$ divided by $x$ is $3x$.
$3x(x - 4) = 3x^2 - 12x$

*Step 2*  Subtract $3x^2 - 12x$ from $3x^2 - 5x$. Bring down $-28$.

*Step 3*  $7x$ divided by $x$ is $7$.
$7(x - 4) = 7x - 28$

*Step 4*  Subtract $7x - 28$ from $7x - 28$. The remainder is 0.

$$\begin{array}{r} 3x + 7 \leftarrow \text{Quotient} \\ x - 4\overline{)3x^2 - 5x - 28} \leftarrow \text{Dividend} \\ \underline{3x^2 - 12x} \\ 7x - 28 \\ \underline{7x - 28} \\ 0 \end{array}$$

Divisor $\longrightarrow$

CHECK   Multiply the divisor, $x - 4$, by the quotient, $3x + 7$. The product must be the original dividend, $3x^2 - 5x - 28$.

$$(x - 4)(3x + 7) = 3x^2 + 7x - 12x - 28$$
$$= 3x^2 - 5x - 28 \checkmark$$

Divisor   Quotient

Dividend

NOW TRY

**EXAMPLE 6** Dividing a Polynomial by a Polynomial

Divide. $\dfrac{5x + 4x^3 - 8 - 4x^2}{2x - 1}$

The first polynomial must be written in descending powers as $4x^3 - 4x^2 + 5x - 8$. Then divide by $2x - 1$.

$$\begin{array}{r} 2x^2 - x + 2 \\ 2x - 1\overline{)4x^3 - 4x^2 + 5x - 8} \\ \underline{4x^3 - 2x^2} \\ -2x^2 + 5x \\ \underline{-2x^2 + x} \\ 4x - 8 \\ \underline{4x - 2} \\ -6 \leftarrow \text{Remainder} \end{array}$$

Write in descending powers.

Each time you subtract, add the opposite.

*Step 1*  $4x^3$ divided by $2x$ is $2x^2$.   $2x^2(2x - 1) = 4x^3 - 2x^2$

*Step 2*  Subtract. Bring down the next term.

*Step 3*  $-2x^2$ divided by $2x$ is $-x$.   $-x(2x - 1) = -2x^2 + x$

*Step 4*  Subtract. Bring down the next term.

*Step 5*  $4x$ divided by $2x$ is $2$.   $2(2x - 1) = 4x - 2$

*Step 6*  Subtract. The remainder is $-6$. Write the remainder as the numerator of a fraction that has $2x - 1$ as its denominator. Because of the nonzero remainder, the answer is not a polynomial.

Remember to add $\frac{\text{remainder}}{\text{divisor}}$. Don't forget the + sign.

$$\text{Dividend} \rightarrow \frac{4x^3 - 4x^2 + 5x - 8}{2x - 1} = \underbrace{2x^2 - x + 2}_{\substack{\text{Quotient} \\ \text{polynomial}}} + \underbrace{\frac{-6}{2x - 1}}_{\substack{\text{Fractional part} \\ \text{of quotient}}}$$

Divisor $\rightarrow$

$\leftarrow$ Remainder
$\leftarrow$ Divisor

NOW TRY ANSWER
**5.** $4x + 9$

NOW TRY
EXERCISE 6
Divide.

$$\frac{6k^3 - 20k - k^2 + 1}{2k - 3}$$

**Step 7**  CHECK

$$(2x - 1)\left(2x^2 - x + 2 + \frac{-6}{2x - 1}\right) \quad \text{Multiply Divisor} \times \text{(Quotient including the Remainder)}.$$

$$= (2x - 1)(2x^2) + (2x - 1)(-x) + (2x - 1)(2) + (2x - 1)\left(\frac{-6}{2x - 1}\right)$$

$$= 4x^3 - 2x^2 - 2x^2 + x + 4x - 2 - 6$$

$$= 4x^3 - 4x^2 + 5x - 8 \ \checkmark$$

NOW TRY

---

⚠ **CAUTION**  Remember to include "$+ \frac{\text{remainder}}{\text{divisor}}$" as part of the answer.

---

NOW TRY
EXERCISE 7
Divide $m^3 - 1000$ by $m - 10$.

**EXAMPLE 7**  Dividing into a Polynomial with Missing Terms

Divide $x^3 - 1$ by $x - 1$.

Here, the dividend, $x^3 - 1$, is missing the $x^2$-term and the $x$-term. We use $0$ as the coefficient for each missing term. Thus, $x^3 - 1 = x^3 + 0x^2 + 0x - 1$.

$$
\begin{array}{r}
x^2 + x + 1 \\
x - 1 \overline{)x^3 + 0x^2 + 0x - 1} \\
\underline{x^3 - x^2} \\
x^2 + 0x \\
\underline{x^2 - x} \\
x - 1 \\
\underline{x - 1} \\
0
\end{array}
$$

Insert placeholders for the missing terms.

The remainder is 0. The quotient is $x^2 + x + 1$.

CHECK  $(x - 1)(x^2 + x + 1) = x^3 - 1$  ✓  Divisor × Quotient = Dividend

NOW TRY

NOW TRY
EXERCISE 8
Divide.

$y^4 - 5y^3 + 6y^2 + y - 4$ by $y^2 + 2$.

**EXAMPLE 8**  Dividing by a Polynomial with Missing Terms

Divide $x^4 + 2x^3 + 2x^2 - x - 1$ by $x^2 + 1$.

Since the divisor, $x^2 + 1$, has a missing $x$-term, write it as $x^2 + 0x + 1$.

$$
\begin{array}{r}
x^2 + 2x + 1 \\
x^2 + 0x + 1 \overline{)x^4 + 2x^3 + 2x^2 - x - 1} \\
\underline{x^4 + 0x^3 + x^2} \\
2x^3 + x^2 - x \\
\underline{2x^3 + 0x^2 + 2x} \\
x^2 - 3x - 1 \\
\underline{x^2 + 0x + 1} \\
-3x - 2 \leftarrow \text{Remainder}
\end{array}
$$

Insert a placeholder for the missing term.

When the result of subtracting ($-3x - 2$ here) is a constant or a polynomial of degree less than the divisor ($x^2 + 0x + 1$), that constant or polynomial is the remainder. The answer is

$$x^2 + 2x + 1 + \frac{-3x - 2}{x^2 + 1}.$$

Remember to write "$+ \frac{\text{remainder}}{\text{divisor}}$."

*Multiply* to check that this is correct.

NOW TRY

**NOW TRY ANSWERS**

6. $3k^2 + 4k - 4 + \dfrac{-11}{2k - 3}$

7. $m^2 + 10m + 100$

8. $y^2 - 5y + 4 + \dfrac{11y - 12}{y^2 + 2}$

NOW TRY
EXERCISE 9

Divide $10x^3 + 21x^2 + 5x - 8$ by $2x + 4$.

---

EXAMPLE 9 Dividing a Polynomial When the Quotient Has Fractional Coefficients

Divide $4x^3 + 2x^2 + 3x + 2$ by $4x - 4$.

$$
\begin{array}{r}
\frac{6x^2}{4x} = \frac{3}{2}x \\
x^2 + \frac{3}{2}x + \frac{9}{4} \leftarrow \frac{9x}{4x} = \frac{9}{4} \\
4x - 4 \overline{)4x^3 + 2x^2 + 3x + 2} \\
\underline{4x^3 - 4x^2} \\
6x^2 + 3x \\
\underline{6x^2 - 6x} \\
9x + 2 \\
\underline{9x - 9} \\
11
\end{array}
$$

NOW TRY ANSWER

9. $5x^2 + \frac{1}{2}x + \frac{3}{2} + \frac{-14}{2x + 4}$

The answer is $x^2 + \frac{3}{2}x + \frac{9}{4} + \frac{11}{4x - 4}$.

NOW TRY

---

# 5.7 EXERCISES

MyMathLab | Math XL PRACTICE | WATCH | DOWNLOAD | READ | REVIEW

🌐 *Complete solution available on the Video Resources on DVD*

*Concept Check* Fill in each blank with the correct response.

1. In the statement $\frac{10x^2 + 8}{2} = 5x^2 + 4$, _____ is the dividend, _____ is the divisor, and _____ is the quotient.

2. The expression $\frac{3x + 13}{x}$ is undefined if $x =$ _____.

3. To check the division shown in **Exercise 1,** multiply _____ by _____ and show that the product is _____.

4. The expression $5x^2 - 4x + 6 + \frac{2}{x}$ _____ a polynomial.
$\underset{\text{(is/is not)}}{}$

📝 5. Explain why the division problem $\frac{16m^3 - 12m^2}{4m}$ can be performed by using the methods of this section, while the division problem $\frac{4m}{16m^3 - 12m^2}$ cannot.

6. *Concept Check* A polynomial in the variable $x$ has degree 6 and is divided by a monomial in the variable $x$ having degree 4. What is the degree of the quotient?

*Perform each division.* **See Examples 1–3.**

7. $\dfrac{60x^4 - 20x^2 + 10x}{2x}$

8. $\dfrac{120x^6 - 60x^3 + 80x^2}{2x}$

9. $\dfrac{20m^5 - 10m^4 + 5m^2}{5m^2}$

10. $\dfrac{12t^5 - 6t^3 + 6t^2}{6t^2}$

11. $\dfrac{8t^5 - 4t^3 + 4t^2}{2t}$

12. $\dfrac{8r^4 - 4r^3 + 6r^2}{2r}$

🌐 13. $\dfrac{4a^5 - 4a^2 + 8}{4a}$

14. $\dfrac{5t^8 + 5t^7 + 15}{5t}$

15. $\dfrac{18p^5 + 12p^3 - 6p^2}{-6p^3}$

16. $\dfrac{32x^8 + 24x^5 - 8x^2}{-8x^2}$

17. $\dfrac{-7r^7 + 6r^5 - r^4}{-r^5}$

18. $\dfrac{-13t^9 + 8t^6 - t^5}{-t^6}$

*Divide each polynomial by $3x^2$.* **See Examples 1–3.**

🌐 19. $12x^5 - 9x^4 + 6x^3$

20. $24x^6 - 12x^5 + 30x^4$

21. $3x^2 + 15x^3 - 27x^4$

22. $3x^2 - 18x^4 + 30x^5$

23. $36x + 24x^2 + 6x^3$

24. $9x - 12x^2 + 9x^3$

25. $4x^4 + 3x^3 + 2x$

26. $5x^4 - 6x^3 + 8x$

27. $-81x^5 + 30x^4 + 12x^2$

**28.** *Concept Check*  If $-60x^5 - 30x^4 + 20x^3$ is divided by $3x^2$, what is the sum of the coefficients of the third- and second-degree terms in the quotient?

*Perform each division.* ***See Examples 1–4.***

**29.** $\dfrac{-27r^4 + 36r^3 - 6r^2 - 26r + 2}{-3r}$  **30.** $\dfrac{-8k^4 + 12k^3 + 2k^2 - 7k + 3}{-2k}$

**31.** $\dfrac{2m^5 - 6m^4 + 8m^2}{-2m^3}$  **32.** $\dfrac{6r^5 - 8r^4 + 10r^2}{-2r^4}$

**33.** $(20a^4 - 15a^5 + 25a^3) \div (5a^4)$  **34.** $(36y^2 - 12y^3 + 20y) \div (4y^2)$

**35.** $(120x^{11} - 60x^{10} + 140x^9 - 100x^8) \div (10x^{12})$

**36.** $(120x^{12} - 84x^9 + 60x^8 - 36x^7) \div (12x^9)$

**37.** $(120x^5y^4 - 80x^2y^3 + 40x^2y^4 - 20x^5y^3) \div (20xy^2)$

**38.** $(200a^5b^6 - 160a^4b^7 - 120a^3b^9 + 40a^2b^2) \div (40a^2b)$

---

*RELATING CONCEPTS* **EXERCISES 39–42**

**FOR INDIVIDUAL OR GROUP WORK**

*Our system of numeration is called a decimal system. In a whole number such as 2846, each digit is understood to represent the number of powers of 10 for its place value. The 2 represents two thousands* $(2 \times 10^3)$, *the 8 represents eight hundreds* $(8 \times 10^2)$, *the 4 represents four tens* $(4 \times 10^1)$, *and the 6 represents six ones (or units)* $(6 \times 10^0)$.

$$2846 = (2 \times 10^3) + (8 \times 10^2) + (4 \times 10^1) + (6 \times 10^0) \quad \text{Expanded form}$$

*Keeping this information in mind,* **work Exercises 39–42 in order.**

**39.** Divide 2846 by 2, using paper-and-pencil methods: $2\overline{)2846}$.

**40.** Write your answer from **Exercise 39** in expanded form.

**41.** Divide the polynomial $2x^3 + 8x^2 + 4x + 6$ by 2.

**42.** How are your answers in **Exercises 40 and 41** similar? Different? For what value of $x$ does the answer in **Exercise 41** equal the answer in **Exercise 40**?

---

*Perform each division using the "long division" process.* ***See Examples 5 and 6.***

**43.** $\dfrac{x^2 - x - 6}{x - 3}$  **44.** $\dfrac{m^2 - 2m - 24}{m - 6}$  **45.** $\dfrac{2y^2 + 9y - 35}{y + 7}$

**46.** $\dfrac{2y^2 + 9y + 7}{y + 1}$  **47.** $\dfrac{p^2 + 2p + 20}{p + 6}$  **48.** $\dfrac{x^2 + 11x + 16}{x + 8}$

**49.** $\dfrac{12m^2 - 20m + 3}{2m - 3}$  **50.** $\dfrac{12y^2 + 20y + 7}{2y + 1}$  **51.** $\dfrac{4a^2 - 22a + 32}{2a + 3}$

**52.** $\dfrac{9w^2 + 6w + 10}{3w - 2}$  **53.** $\dfrac{8x^3 - 10x^2 - x + 3}{2x + 1}$  **54.** $\dfrac{12t^3 - 11t^2 + 9t + 18}{4t + 3}$

**55.** $\dfrac{8k^4 - 12k^3 - 2k^2 + 7k - 6}{2k - 3}$  **56.** $\dfrac{27r^4 - 36r^3 - 6r^2 + 26r - 24}{3r - 4}$

**57.** $\dfrac{5y^4 + 5y^3 + 2y^2 - y - 8}{y + 1}$  **58.** $\dfrac{2r^3 - 5r^2 - 6r + 15}{r - 3}$

**59.** $\dfrac{3k^3 - 4k^2 - 6k + 10}{k - 2}$  **60.** $\dfrac{5z^3 - z^2 + 10z + 2}{z + 2}$

**61.** $\dfrac{6p^4 - 16p^3 + 15p^2 - 5p + 10}{3p + 1}$  **62.** $\dfrac{6r^4 - 11r^3 - r^2 + 16r - 8}{2r - 3}$

*Perform each division.* ***See Examples 6–9.***

**63.** $(x^3 + 2x^2 - 3) \div (x - 1)$

**64.** $(x^3 - 2x^2 - 9) \div (x - 3)$

**65.** $(2x^3 + x + 2) \div (x + 1)$

**66.** $(3x^3 + x + 5) \div (x + 1)$

**67.** $\dfrac{5 - 2r^2 + r^4}{r^2 - 1}$

**68.** $\dfrac{4t^2 + t^4 + 7}{t^2 + 1}$

**69.** $\dfrac{-4x + 3x^3 + 2}{x - 1}$

**70.** $\dfrac{2x^3 - 8x^2 - 11x^4 - 4}{x + 1}$

**71.** $\dfrac{y^3 + 1}{y + 1}$

**72.** $\dfrac{y^3 - 1}{y - 1}$

**73.** $\dfrac{a^4 - 1}{a^2 - 1}$

**74.** $\dfrac{a^4 - 1}{a^2 + 1}$

**75.** $\dfrac{x^4 - 4x^3 + 5x^2 - 3x + 2}{x^2 + 3}$

**76.** $\dfrac{3t^4 + 5t^3 - 8t^2 - 13t + 2}{t^2 - 5}$

**77.** $\dfrac{2x^5 + 9x^4 + 8x^3 + 10x^2 + 14x + 5}{2x^2 + 3x + 1}$

**78.** $\dfrac{4t^5 - 11t^4 - 6t^3 + 5t^2 - t + 3}{4t^2 + t - 3}$

**79.** $(3a^2 - 11a + 17) \div (2a + 6)$

**80.** $(4x^2 + 11x - 8) \div (3x + 6)$

**81.** $\dfrac{3x^3 + 5x^2 - 9x + 5}{3x - 3}$

**82.** $\dfrac{5x^3 + 4x^2 + 10x + 20}{5x + 5}$

*In Exercises 83–88, if necessary, refer to the formulas on the inside covers.*

**83.** The area of the rectangle is given by the polynomial

$$5x^3 + 7x^2 - 13x - 6.$$

What polynomial expresses the length (in appropriate units)?

$5x + 2$

**84.** The area of the rectangle is given by the polynomial

$$15x^3 + 12x^2 - 9x + 3.$$

What polynomial expresses the length (in appropriate units)?

$3$

**85.** The area of the triangle is given by the polynomial

$$24m^3 + 48m^2 + 12m.$$

What polynomial expresses the length of the base (in appropriate units)?

$m$

**86.** The area of the parallelogram is given by the polynomial

$$2x^3 + 2x^2 - 3x - 1.$$

What polynomial expresses the length of the base (in appropriate units)?

$x - 1$

**87.** If the distance traveled is $(5x^3 - 6x^2 + 3x + 14)$ miles and the rate is $(x + 1)$ mph, write an expression, in hours, for the time traveled.

**88.** If it costs $(4x^5 + 3x^4 + 2x^3 + 9x^2 - 29x + 2)$ dollars to fertilize a garden, and fertilizer costs $(x + 2)$ dollars per square yard, write an expression, in square yards, for the area of the garden.

**PREVIEW EXERCISES**

*List all positive integer factors of each number.* ***See Section 1.1.***

**89.** 18

**90.** 36

**91.** 48

**92.** 23

CHAPTER ( 5 )   SUMMARY

## NEW SYMBOLS

$x^{-n}$   $x$ to the negative $n$ power

## TEST YOUR WORD POWER

*See how well you have learned the vocabulary in this chapter.*

1. A **polynomial** is an algebraic expression made up of
   A. a term or a finite product of terms with positive coefficients and exponents
   B. a term or a finite sum of terms with real coefficients and whole number exponents
   C. the product of two or more terms with positive exponents
   D. the sum of two or more terms with whole number coefficients and exponents.

2. The **degree of a term** is
   A. the number of variables in the term

   B. the product of the exponents on the variables
   C. the least exponent on the variables
   D. the sum of the exponents on the variables.

3. **FOIL** is a method for
   A. adding two binomials
   B. adding two trinomials
   C. multiplying two binomials
   D. multiplying two trinomials.

4. A **binomial** is a polynomial with
   A. only one term
   B. exactly two terms
   C. exactly three terms
   D. more than three terms.

5. A **monomial** is a polynomial with
   A. only one term
   B. exactly two terms
   C. exactly three terms
   D. more than three terms.

6. A **trinomial** is a polynomial with
   A. only one term
   B. exactly two terms
   C. exactly three terms
   D. more than three terms.

### ANSWERS

**1.** B; *Example:* $5x^3 + 2x^2 - 7$   **2.** D; *Examples:* The term 6 has degree 0, $3x$ has degree 1, $-2x^8$ has degree 8, and $5x^2y^4$ has degree 6.

    F    O    I    L

**3.** C; *Example:* $(m + 4)(m - 3) = m(m) - 3m + 4m + 4(-3) = m^2 + m - 12$   **4.** B; *Example:* $3t^3 + 5t$   **5.** A; *Examples:* $-5$ and $4xy^5$
**6.** C; *Example:* $2a^2 - 3ab + b^2$

## QUICK REVIEW

| CONCEPTS | EXAMPLES |
|---|---|

**5.1 The Product Rule and Power Rules for Exponents**

For any integers $m$ and $n$, the following are true.

**Product Rule**     $a^m \cdot a^n = a^{m+n}$

**Power Rules**   **(a)**   $(a^m)^n = a^{mn}$

**(b)**   $(ab)^m = a^m b^m$

**(c)**   $\left(\dfrac{a}{b}\right)^m = \dfrac{a^m}{b^m}$   $(b \neq 0)$

Perform the operations by using rules for exponents.

$$2^4 \cdot 2^5 = 2^{4+5} = 2^9$$

$$(3^4)^2 = 3^{4 \cdot 2} = 3^8$$

$$(6a)^5 = 6^5 a^5$$

$$\left(\frac{2}{3}\right)^4 = \frac{2^4}{3^4}$$

**5.2 Integer Exponents and the Quotient Rule**

If $a \neq 0$, then for integers $m$ and $n$, the following are true.

**Zero Exponent**          $a^0 = 1$

**Negative Exponent**      $a^{-n} = \dfrac{1}{a^n}$

**Quotient Rule**          $\dfrac{a^m}{a^n} = a^{m-n}$

**Negative-to-Positive Rules**

$$\frac{a^{-m}}{b^{-n}} = \frac{b^n}{a^m} \quad (b \neq 0)$$

$$\left(\frac{a}{b}\right)^{-m} = \left(\frac{b}{a}\right)^m \quad (b \neq 0)$$

Simplify by using the rules for exponents.

$$15^0 = 1$$

$$5^{-2} = \frac{1}{5^2} = \frac{1}{25}$$

$$\frac{4^8}{4^3} = 4^{8-3} = 4^5$$

$$\frac{4^{-2}}{3^{-5}} = \frac{3^5}{4^2}$$

$$\left(\frac{6}{5}\right)^{-3} = \left(\frac{5}{6}\right)^3$$

**5.3 An Application of Exponents: Scientific Notation**

To write a number in scientific notation

$$a \times 10^n, \quad \text{where} \quad 1 \le |a| < 10,$$

move the decimal point to follow the first nonzero digit.

**1.** If moving the decimal point makes the number less, $n$ is positive.

**2.** If it makes the number greater, $n$ is negative.

**3.** If the decimal point is not moved, $n$ is 0.

Write in scientific notation.

$$247 = 2.47 \times 10^2$$

$$0.0051 = 5.1 \times 10^{-3}$$

$$4.8 = 4.8 \times 10^0$$

Write without exponents.

$$3.25 \times 10^5 = 325,000$$

$$8.44 \times 10^{-6} = 0.00000844$$

**5.4 Adding and Subtracting Polynomials; Graphing Simple Polynomials**

**Adding Polynomials**

Add like terms.

**Subtracting Polynomials**

Change the signs of the terms in the second polynomial and add the second polynomial to the first.

Add.

$$\begin{array}{r} 2x^2 + 5x - 3 \\ 5x^2 - 2x + 7 \\ \hline 7x^2 + 3x + 4 \end{array}$$

Subtract.

$$(2x^2 + 5x - 3) - (5x^2 - 2x + 7)$$

$$= (2x^2 + 5x - 3) + (-5x^2 + 2x - 7)$$

$$= -3x^2 + 7x - 10$$

*(continued)*

| *CONCEPTS* | *EXAMPLES* |
|---|---|

**Graphing Simple Polynomials**

To graph a simple polynomial equation such as $y = x^2 - 2$, plot points near the vertex. (In this chapter, all parabolas have a vertex on the $x$-axis or the $y$-axis.)

Graph $y = x^2 - 2$.

| $x$ | $y$ |
|---|---|
| $-2$ | $2$ |
| $-1$ | $-1$ |
| $0$ | $-2$ |
| $1$ | $-1$ |
| $2$ | $2$ |

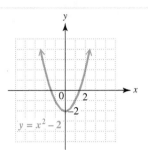

$y = x^2 - 2$

---

**5.5   Multiplying Polynomials**

**General Method for Multiplying Polynomials**

Multiply each term of the first polynomial by each term of the second polynomial. Then add like terms.

Multiply.

$$\begin{array}{r} 3x^3 - 4x^2 + 2x - 7 \\ 4x + 3 \\ \hline 9x^3 - 12x^2 + 6x - 21 \\ 12x^4 - 16x^3 + 8x^2 - 28x \\ \hline 12x^4 - 7x^3 - 4x^2 - 22x - 21 \end{array}$$

**FOIL Method for Multiplying Binomials**

*Step 1*   Multiply the two **F**irst terms to get the first term of the product.

*Step 2*   Find the **O**uter product and the **I**nner product, and mentally add them, when possible, to get the middle term of the product.

*Step 3*   Multiply the two **L**ast terms to get the last term of the product.

Add the terms found in Steps 1–3.

Multiply.   $(2x + 3)(5x - 4)$

$$2x(5x) = 10x^2 \qquad \textbf{F}$$

$$2x(-4) + 3(5x) = 7x \qquad \textbf{O, I}$$

$$3(-4) = -12 \qquad \textbf{L}$$

The product is $10x^2 + 7x - 12$.

---

**5.6   Special Products**

**Square of a Binomial**

$$(x + y)^2 = x^2 + 2xy + y^2$$
$$(x - y)^2 = x^2 - 2xy + y^2$$

**Product of the Sum and Difference of Two Terms**

$$(x + y)(x - y) = x^2 - y^2$$

Multiply.

$$(3x + 1)^2 = 9x^2 + 6x + 1$$
$$(2m - 5n)^2 = 4m^2 - 20mn + 25n^2$$

$$(4a + 3)(4a - 3) = 16a^2 - 9$$

---

**5.7   Dividing Polynomials**

**Dividing a Polynomial by a Monomial**

Divide each term of the polynomial by the monomial.

$$\frac{a + b}{c} = \frac{a}{c} + \frac{b}{c}$$

**Dividing a Polynomial by a Polynomial**

Use "long division."

Divide.

$$\frac{4x^3 - 2x^2 + 6x - 9}{2x} = 2x^2 - x + 3 - \frac{9}{2x}$$

Divide each term in the numerator by $2x$.

$$\begin{array}{r} 2x - 5 \\ 3x + 4 \overline{)6x^2 - 7x - 21} \\ 6x^2 + 8x \\ \hline -15x - 21 \\ -15x - 20 \\ \hline -1 \leftarrow \text{Remainder} \end{array}$$

The final answer is $2x - 5 + \frac{-1}{3x + 4}$.

# CHAPTER 5 REVIEW EXERCISES

**5.1** *Use the product rule, power rules, or both to simplify each expression. Write the answers in exponential form.*

**1.** $4^3 \cdot 4^8$

**2.** $(-5)^6(-5)^5$

**3.** $(-8x^4)(9x^3)$

**4.** $(2x^2)(5x^3)(x^9)$

**5.** $(19x)^5$

**6.** $(-4y)^7$

**7.** $5(pt)^4$

**8.** $\left(\dfrac{7}{5}\right)^6$

**9.** $(3x^2y^3)^3$

**10.** $(t^4)^8(t^2)^5$

**11.** $(6x^2z^4)^2(x^3yz^2)^4$

**12.** $\left(\dfrac{2m^3n}{p^2}\right)^3$

**13.** Why does the product rule for exponents not apply to the expression $7^2 + 7^4$?

**5.2** *Evaluate each expression.*

**14.** $6^0 + (-6)^0$

**15.** $-(-23)^0$

**16.** $-10^0$

*Simplify. Write each answer with only positive exponents. Assume that all variables represent nonzero real numbers.*

**17.** $-7^{-2}$

**18.** $\left(\dfrac{5}{8}\right)^{-2}$

**19.** $(5^{-2})^{-4}$

**20.** $9^3 \cdot 9^{-5}$

**21.** $2^{-1} + 4^{-1}$

**22.** $\dfrac{6^{-5}}{6^{-3}}$

**23.** $\dfrac{x^{-7}}{x^{-9}}$

**24.** $\dfrac{y^4 \cdot y^{-2}}{y^{-5}}$

**25.** $(3r^{-2})^{-4}$

**26.** $(3p)^4(3p^{-7})$

**27.** $\dfrac{ab^{-3}}{a^4b^2}$

**28.** $\dfrac{(6r^{-1})^2(2r^{-4})}{r^{-5}(r^2)^{-3}}$

**5.3** *Write each number in scientific notation.*

**29.** 48,000,000

**30.** 28,988,000,000

**31.** 0.0000000824

*Write each number without exponents.*

**32.** $2.4 \times 10^4$

**33.** $7.83 \times 10^7$

**34.** $8.97 \times 10^{-7}$

*Perform each indicated operation and write the answer without exponents.*

**35.** $(2 \times 10^{-3}) \times (4 \times 10^5)$

**36.** $\dfrac{8 \times 10^4}{2 \times 10^{-2}}$

**37.** $\dfrac{12 \times 10^{-5} \times 5 \times 10^4}{4 \times 10^3 \times 6 \times 10^{-2}}$

*Write each boldface italic number in the quote without exponents.*

**38.** The muon, a close relative of the electron produced by the bombardment of cosmic rays against the upper atmosphere, has a half-life of 2 millionths of a second (***2 × 10⁻⁶*** s). (Excerpt from *Conceptual Physics,* 6th edition, by Paul G. Hewitt. Copyright © by Paul G. Hewitt. Published by HarperCollins College Publishers.)

**39.** There are 13 red balls and 39 black balls in a box. Mix them up and draw 13 out one at a time without returning any ball . . . the probability that the 13 drawings each will produce a red ball is . . . ***1.6 × 10⁻¹²***. (Weaver, Warren, *Lady Luck.*)

*Write each boldface italic number in scientific notation.*

**40.** An electron and a positron attract each other in two ways: the electromagnetic attraction of their opposite electric charges, and the gravitational attraction of their two masses. The electromagnetic attraction is

*4,200,000,000,000,000,000,000,000,000,000,000,000,000,000*

times as strong as the gravitational. (Asimov, Isaac, *Isaac Asimov's Book of Facts.*)

**41.** The aircraft carrier USS John Stennis is a *97,000*-ton nuclear powered floating city with a crew of *5000.* (*Source:* Seelye, Katharine Q., "Staunch Allies Hard to Beat: Defense Dept., Hollywood," *New York Times,* in *Plain Dealer.*)

**42.** A googol is

*10,000,000,000,000,000,000,000,000,000,000,000,000,000,000,000,*
*000,000,000,000,000,000,000,000,000,000,000,000,000,000,000,000.*

The Web search engine Google is named after a googol. Sergey Brin, president and cofounder of Google, Inc., was a mathematics major. He chose the name Google to describe the vast reach of this search engine. (*Source: The Gazette.*)

**43.** According to Campbell, Mitchell, and Reece in *Biology Concepts and Connections* (Benjamin Cummings, 1994, p. 230), "The amount of DNA in a human cell is about *1000* times greater than the DNA in *E. coli.* Does this mean humans have 1000 times as many genes as the *2000* in *E. coli*? The answer is probably no; the human genome is thought to carry between *50,000* and *100,000* genes, which code for various proteins (as well as for tRNA and rRNA)."

> **5.4** *In Exercises 44–48, combine like terms where possible in each polynomial. Write the answer in descending powers of the variable. Give the degree of the answer. Identify the polynomial as a* monomial, *a* binomial, *a* trinomial, *or* none of these.

**44.** $9m^2 + 11m^2 + 2m^2$

**45.** $-4p + p^3 - p^2 + 8p + 2$

**46.** $12a^5 - 9a^4 + 8a^3 + 2a^2 - a + 3$

**47.** $-7y^5 - 8y^4 - y^5 + y^4 + 9y$

**48.** $(12r^4 - 7r^3 + 2r^2) - (5r^4 - 3r^3 + 2r^2 - 1)$

**49.** Simplify.   $(5x^3y^2 - 3xy^5 + 12x^2) - (-9x^2 - 8x^3y^2 + 2xy^5)$

*Add or subtract as indicated.*

**50.** Add.

$$-2a^3 + 5a^2$$
$$\underline{\phantom{-}3a^3 - \phantom{0}a^2}$$

**51.** Subtract.

$$6y^2 - 8y + 2$$
$$\underline{5y^2 + 2y - 7}$$

**52.** Subtract.

$$-12k^4 - 8k^2 + \phantom{0}7k$$
$$\underline{\phantom{-1}k^4 + 7k^2 - 11k}$$

*Graph each equation by completing the table of values.*

**53.** $y = -x^2 + 5$

| x | -2 | -1 | 0 | 1 | 2 |
|---|---|---|---|---|---|
| y |  |  |  |  |  |

**54.** $y = 3x^2 - 2$

| x | -2 | -1 | 0 | 1 | 2 |
|---|---|---|---|---|---|
| y |  |  |  |  |  |

> **5.5** *Find each product.*

**55.** $(a + 2)(a^2 - 4a + 1)$

**56.** $(3r - 2)(2r^2 + 4r - 3)$

**57.** $(5p^2 + 3p)(p^3 - p^2 + 5)$

**58.** $(m - 9)(m + 2)$

**59.** $(3k - 6)(2k + 1)$

**60.** $(a + 3b)(2a - b)$

**61.** $(6k + 5q)(2k - 7q)$

**62.** $(s - 1)^3$

**5.6**   *Find each product.*

**63.** $(a + 4)^2$

**64.** $(2r + 5t)^2$

**65.** $(6m - 5)(6m + 5)$

**66.** $(5a + 6b)(5a - 6b)$

**67.** $(r + 2)^3$

**68.** $t(5t - 3)^2$

**69.** Choose values for $x$ and $y$ to show that, in general, the following hold true.

   **(a)** $(x + y)^2 \neq x^2 + y^2$

   **(b)** $(x + y)^3 \neq x^3 + y^3$

**70.** Write an explanation on how to raise a binomial to the third power. Give an example.

**71.** Refer to **Exercise 69.** Suppose that you happened to let $x = 0$ and $y = 1$. Would your results be sufficient to illustrate the truth, in general, of the inequalities shown? If not, what would you need to do as your next step in working the exercise?

*In Exercises 72 and 73, if necessary, refer to the formulas on the inside covers.*

**72.** Find a polynomial that represents, in cubic centimeters, the volume of a cube with one side having length $(x^2 + 2)$ centimeters.

**73.** Find a polynomial that represents, in cubic inches, the volume of a sphere with radius $(x + 1)$ inches.

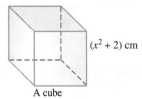

A cube

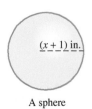

$(x + 1)$ in.

A sphere

**5.7**   *Perform each division.*

**74.** $\dfrac{-15y^4}{9y^2}$

**75.** $\dfrac{6y^4 - 12y^2 + 18y}{6y}$

**76.** $(-10m^4n^2 + 5m^3n^2 + 6m^2n^4) \div (5m^2n)$

**77.** *Concept Check*   What polynomial, when multiplied by $6m^2n$, gives the product

$$12m^3n^2 + 18m^6n^3 - 24m^2n^2?$$

**78.** *Concept Check*   One of your friends in class simplified

$$\frac{6x^2 - 12x}{6} \quad \text{as} \quad x^2 - 12x.$$

*WHAT WENT WRONG?*   Give the correct answer.

*Perform each division.*

**79.** $\dfrac{2r^2 + 3r - 14}{r - 2}$

**80.** $\dfrac{10a^3 + 9a^2 - 14a + 9}{5a - 3}$

**81.** $\dfrac{x^4 - 5x^2 + 3x^3 - 3x + 4}{x^2 - 1}$

**82.** $\dfrac{m^4 + 4m^3 - 12m - 5m^2 + 6}{m^2 - 3}$

**83.** $\dfrac{16x^2 - 25}{4x + 5}$

**84.** $\dfrac{25y^2 - 100}{5y + 10}$

**85.** $\dfrac{y^3 - 8}{y - 2}$

**86.** $\dfrac{1000x^6 + 1}{10x^2 + 1}$

**87.** $\dfrac{6y^4 - 15y^3 + 14y^2 - 5y - 1}{3y^2 + 1}$

**88.** $\dfrac{4x^5 - 8x^4 - 3x^3 + 22x^2 - 15}{4x^2 - 3}$

### MIXED REVIEW EXERCISES

*Perform each indicated operation. Write answers with only positive exponents. Assume that all variables represent nonzero real numbers.*

**89.** $5^0 + 7^0$

**90.** $\left(\dfrac{6r^2p}{5}\right)^3$

**91.** $(12a + 1)(12a - 1)$

**92.** $2^{-4}$

**93.** $(8^{-3})^4$

**94.** $\dfrac{2p^3 - 6p^2 + 5p}{2p^2}$

**95.** $\dfrac{(2m^{-5})(3m^2)^{-1}}{m^{-2}(m^{-1})^2}$

**96.** $(3k - 6)(2k^2 + 4k + 1)$

**97.** $\dfrac{r^9 \cdot r^{-5}}{r^{-2} \cdot r^{-7}}$

**98.** $(2r + 5s)^2$

**99.** $(-5y^2 + 3y - 11) + (4y^2 - 7y + 15)$

**100.** $(2r + 5)(5r - 2)$

**101.** $\dfrac{2y^3 + 17y^2 + 37y + 7}{2y + 7}$

**102.** $(25x^2y^3 - 8xy^2 + 15x^3y) \div (10x^2y^3)$

**103.** $(6p^2 - p - 8) - (-4p^2 + 2p - 3)$

**104.** $\dfrac{3x^3 - 2x + 5}{x - 3}$

**105.** $(-7 + 2k)^2$

**106.** $\left(\dfrac{x}{y^{-3}}\right)^{-4}$

**107.** Find polynomials that represent, in appropriate units, the **(a)** perimeter and **(b)** area of the rectangle shown.

2x − 3

x + 2

**108.** If the side of a square has a measure represented by $5x^4 + 2x^2$, what polynomials, in appropriate units, represent its **(a)** perimeter and **(b)** area?

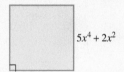

$5x^4 + 2x^2$

---

## CHAPTER ( 5 )

## TEST

*View the complete solutions to all Chapter Test exercises on the Video Resources on DVD.*

*Evaluate each expression.*

**1.** $5^{-4}$

**2.** $(-3)^0 + 4^0$

**3.** $4^{-1} + 3^{-1}$

**4.** Simplify $\dfrac{(3x^2y)^2(xy^3)^2}{(xy)^3}$. Assume that $x$ and $y$ represent nonzero numbers.

*Simplify, and write the answer using only positive exponents. Assume that all variables represent nonzero numbers.*

**5.** $\dfrac{8^{-1} \cdot 8^4}{8^{-2}}$

**6.** $\dfrac{(x^{-3})^{-2}(x^{-1}y)^2}{(xy^{-2})^2}$

**7.** Determine whether each expression represents a number that is *positive, negative,* or *zero.*

(a) $3^{-4}$    (b) $(-3)^4$    (c) $-3^4$    (d) $3^0$    (e) $(-3)^0 - 3^0$    (f) $(-3)^{-3}$

**8. (a)** Write 45,000,000,000 using scientific notation.

**(b)** Write $3.6 \times 10^{-6}$ without using exponents.

**(c)** Write the quotient without using exponents: $\dfrac{9.5 \times 10^{-1}}{5 \times 10^3}$.

**9.** A satellite galaxy of the Milky Way, known as the Large Magellanic Cloud, is ***1000*** light-years across. A *light-year* is equal to ***5,890,000,000,000*** mi. (*Source:* "Images of Brightest Nebula Unveiled," *USA Today.*)

**(a)** Write the two boldface italic numbers in scientific notation.

**(b)** How many miles across is the Large Magellanic Cloud?

*For each polynomial, combine like terms when possible and write the polynomial in descending powers of the variable. Give the degree of the simplified polynomial. Decide whether the simplified polynomial is a* monomial, *a* binomial, *a* trinomial, *or* none of these.

**10.** $5x^2 + 8x - 12x^2$

**11.** $13n^3 - n^2 + n^4 + 3n^4 - 9n^2$

**12.** Use the table to complete a set of ordered pairs that lie on the graph of $y = 2x^2 - 4$. Then graph the equation.

| $x$ | $-2$ | $-1$ | 0 | 1 | 2 |
|---|---|---|---|---|---|
| $y$ | | | | | |

*Perform each indicated operation.*

**13.** $(2y^2 - 8y + 8) + (-3y^2 + 2y + 3) - (y^2 + 3y - 6)$

**14.** $(-9a^3b^2 + 13ab^5 + 5a^2b^2) - (6ab^5 + 12a^3b^2 + 10a^2b^2)$

**15.** Subtract.

$$9t^3 - 4t^2 + 2t + 2$$
$$\underline{9t^3 + 8t^2 - 3t - 6}$$

**16.** $3x^2(-9x^3 + 6x^2 - 2x + 1)$

**17.** $(t - 8)(t + 3)$

**18.** $(4x + 3y)(2x - y)$

**19.** $(5x - 2y)^2$

**20.** $(10v + 3w)(10v - 3w)$

**21.** $(2r - 3)(r^2 + 2r - 5)$

**22.** What polynomial expression represents, in appropriate units, the perimeter of this square? The area?

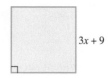

$3x + 9$

*Perform each division.*

**23.** $\dfrac{8y^3 - 6y^2 + 4y + 10}{2y}$

**24.** $(-9x^2y^3 + 6x^4y^3 + 12xy^3) \div (3xy)$

**25.** $\dfrac{5x^2 - x - 18}{5x + 9}$

**26.** $(3x^3 - x + 4) \div (x - 2)$

# CHAPTERS (1–5)

## CUMULATIVE REVIEW EXERCISES

*Write each fraction in lowest terms.*

**1.** $\dfrac{28}{16}$

**2.** $\dfrac{55}{11}$

**3.** A contractor installs sheds. Each requires $1\frac{1}{4}$ yd$^3$ of concrete. How much concrete would be needed for 25 sheds?

**4.** A retailer has \$34,000 invested in her business. She finds that last year she earned 5.4% on this investment. How much did she earn?

**5.** List all positive integer factors of 45.

**6.** If $x = -2$ and $y = 4$, find the value of $\dfrac{4x - 2y}{x + y}$.

*Perform each indicated operation.*

**7.** $\dfrac{(-13 + 15) - (3 + 2)}{6 - 12}$

**8.** $-7 - 3[2 + (5 - 8)]$

*Decide which property justifies each statement.*

**9.** $(9 + 2) + 3 = 9 + (2 + 3)$

**10.** $6(4 + 2) = 6(4) + 6(2)$

**11.** Simplify the expression $-3(2x^2 - 8x + 9) - (4x^2 + 3x + 2)$.

*Solve each equation.*

**12.** $2 - 3(t - 5) = 4 + t$

**13.** $2(5x + 1) = 10x + 4$

**14.** $d = rt$ for $r$

**15.** $\dfrac{x}{5} = \dfrac{x - 2}{7}$

**16.** $\dfrac{1}{3}p - \dfrac{1}{6}p = -2$

**17.** $0.05x + 0.15(50 - x) = 5.50$

**18.** $4 - (3x + 12) = (2x - 9) - (5x - 1)$

*Solve each problem.*

**19.** A husky running the Iditarod burns $5\frac{3}{8}$ calories in exertion for every 1 calorie burned in thermoregulation in extreme cold. According to one scientific study, a husky in top condition burns an amazing total of 11,200 calories per day. How many calories are burned for exertion, and how many are burned for regulation of body temperature? Round answers to the nearest whole number.

**2008 XXXVI Iditarod**

**20.** One side of a triangle is twice as long as a second side. The third side of the triangle is 17 ft long. The perimeter of the triangle cannot be more than 50 ft. Find the longest possible values for the other two sides of the triangle.

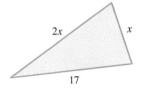

*Solve each inequality.*

**21.** $-2(x + 4) > 3x + 6$                **22.** $-3 \leq 2x + 5 < 9$

**23.** Graph $y = -3x + 6$.

**24.** Consider the two points $(-1, 5)$ and $(2, 8)$.

   **(a)** Find the slope of the line joining them.

   **(b)** Find the equation of the line joining them.

**25.** Does the point $(-1, 3)$ lie within the shaded region of the graph of $y \geq x + 5$?

**26.** If $f(x) = x + 7$, find $f(-8)$.

*Solve the system by using the method indicated.*

**27.** $y = 2x + 5$

   $x + y = -4$   (Substitution)

**28.** $3x + 2y = 2$

   $2x + 3y = -7$   (Elimination)

*Evaluate each expression.*

**29.** $4^{-1} + 3^0$                **30.** $\dfrac{8^{-5} \cdot 8^7}{8^2}$

**31.** Write with positive exponents only.   $\dfrac{(a^{-3}b^2)^2}{(2a^{-4}b^{-3})^{-1}}$

**32.** It takes about $3.6 \times 10^1$ sec at a speed of $3.0 \times 10^5$ km per sec for light from the sun to reach Venus. How far is Venus from the sun? (*Source: World Almanac and Book of Facts.*)

**33.** Graph $y = (x + 4)^2$, using the $x$-values $-6, -5, -4, -3$, and $-2$ to obtain a set of points.

*Perform each indicated operation.*

**34.** $(7x^3 - 12x^2 - 3x + 8) + (6x^2 + 4) - (-4x^3 + 8x^2 - 2x - 2)$

**35.** $(7x + 4)(9x + 3)$                **36.** $\dfrac{y^3 - 3y^2 + 8y - 6}{y - 1}$

# Factoring and Applications

Wireless communication uses radio waves to carry signals and messages across distances. Cellular phones, one of the most popular forms of wireless communication, have become an invaluable tool for people to stay connected to family, friends, and work while on the go. In 2007, there were about 243 million cell phone subscribers in the United States, with 81% of the population having cell phone service. Total revenue from this service was about $133 billion. (*Source:* CITA—The Wireless Association.)

In **Exercise 37** of **Section 6.6**, we use a *quadratic equation* to model the number of cell phone subscribers in the United States.

## The Greatest Common Factor; Factoring by Grouping

**OBJECTIVES**

1. Find the greatest common factor of a list of terms.
2. Factor out the greatest common factor.
3. Factor by grouping.

Recall from **Section 1.1** that to **factor** means "to write a quantity as a product." That is, factoring is the opposite of multiplying.

$$\text{Multiplying} \qquad\qquad \text{Factoring}$$

$$6 \cdot 2 = 12 \qquad\qquad 12 = 6 \cdot 2$$

Factors  Product          Product  Factors

Other **factored forms** of 12 are

$$-6(-2), \quad 3 \cdot 4, \quad -3(-4), \quad 12 \cdot 1, \quad \text{and} \quad -12(-1).$$

More than two factors may be used, so another factored form of 12 is $2 \cdot 2 \cdot 3$.

**OBJECTIVE 1  Find the greatest common factor of a list of terms.**  An integer that is a factor of two or more integers is a **common factor** of those integers. For example, 6 is a common factor of 18 and 24, since 6 is a factor of both 18 and 24. Other common factors of 18 and 24 are 1, 2, and 3.

The **greatest common factor (GCF)** of a list of integers is the largest common factor of those integers. Thus, 6 is the greatest common factor of 18 and 24, since it is the largest of their common factors.

**NOTE**  *Factors* of a number are also *divisors* of the number. The *greatest common factor* is actually the same as the *greatest common divisor.* Here are some useful divisibility rules for deciding what numbers divide into a given number.

| A Whole Number Divisible by | Must Have the Following Property: |
|---|---|
| 2 | Ends in 0, 2, 4, 6, or 8 |
| 3 | Sum of digits divisible by 3 |
| 4 | Last two digits form a number divisible by 4 |
| 5 | Ends in 0 or 5 |
| 6 | Divisible by both 2 and 3 |
| 8 | Last three digits form a number divisible by 8 |
| 9 | Sum of digits divisible by 9 |
| 10 | Ends in 0 |

**Finding the Greatest Common Factor (GCF)**

*Step 1*  **Factor.** Write each number in prime factored form.

*Step 2*  **List common factors.** List each prime number or each variable that is a factor of every term in the list. (If a prime does not appear in one of the prime factored forms, it cannot appear in the greatest common factor.)

*Step 3*  **Choose least exponents.** Use as exponents on the common prime factors the *least* exponents from the prime factored forms.

*Step 4*  **Multiply** the primes from Step 3. If there are no primes left after Step 3, the greatest common factor is 1.

NOW TRY
EXERCISE 1

Find the greatest common factor for each list of numbers.

**(a)** 24, 36

**(b)** 54, 90, 108

**(c)** 15, 19, 25

**EXAMPLE 1**  Finding the Greatest Common Factor for Numbers

Find the greatest common factor for each list of numbers.

**(a)** 30, 45

$$30 = 2 \cdot 3 \cdot 5$$
$$45 = 3 \cdot 3 \cdot 5$$

Write the prime factored form of each number.

*Use each prime the least number of times it appears in all the factored forms.* There is no 2 in the prime factored form of 45, so there will be no 2 in the greatest common factor. The least number of times 3 appears in all the factored forms is 1, and the least number of times 5 appears is also 1.

$$GCF = 3^1 \cdot 5^1 = 15$$

**(b)** 72, 120, 432

$$72 = 2 \cdot 2 \cdot 2 \cdot 3 \cdot 3$$
$$120 = 2 \cdot 2 \cdot 2 \cdot 3 \cdot 5$$
$$432 = 2 \cdot 2 \cdot 2 \cdot 2 \cdot 3 \cdot 3 \cdot 3$$

Write the prime factored form of each number.

The least number of times 2 appears in all the factored forms is 3, and the least number of times 3 appears is 1. There is no 5 in the prime factored form of either 72 or 432.

$$GCF = 2^3 \cdot 3^1 = 24$$

**(c)** 10, 11, 14

$$10 = 2 \cdot 5$$
$$11 = 11$$
$$14 = 2 \cdot 7$$

Write the prime factored form of each number.

There are no primes common to all three numbers, so the GCF is 1.  NOW TRY

The greatest common factor can also be found for a list of variable terms. For example, the terms $x^4$, $x^5$, $x^6$, and $x^7$ have $x^4$ as the greatest common factor because each of these terms can be written with $x^4$ as a factor.

$$x^4 = 1 \cdot x^4, \quad x^5 = x \cdot x^4, \quad x^6 = x^2 \cdot x^4, \quad x^7 = x^3 \cdot x^4$$

---

NOTE  *The exponent on a variable in the GCF is the least exponent that appears in all the common factors.*

---

**EXAMPLE 2**  Finding the Greatest Common Factor for Variable Terms

Find the greatest common factor for each list of terms.

**(a)** $21m^7$, $18m^6$, $45m^8$, $24m^5$

$$21m^7 = 3 \cdot 7 \cdot m^7$$
$$18m^6 = 2 \cdot 3 \cdot 3 \cdot m^6$$
$$45m^8 = 3 \cdot 3 \cdot 5 \cdot m^8$$
$$24m^5 = 2 \cdot 2 \cdot 2 \cdot 3 \cdot m^5$$

Here, 3 is the greatest common factor of the coefficients 21, 18, 45, and 24. The least exponent on $m$ is 5.

$$GCF = 3m^5$$

NOW TRY ANSWERS
**1. (a)** 12  **(b)** 18  **(c)** 1

NOW TRY
EXERCISE 2
Find the greatest common factor for each list of terms.

(a) $25k^3, 15k^2, 35k^5$

(b) $m^3n^5, m^4n^4, m^5n^2$

(b) $x^4y^2, \quad x^7y^5, \quad x^3y^7, \quad y^{15}$

$x^4y^2 = x^4 \cdot y^2$

$x^7y^5 = x^7 \cdot y^5$

$x^3y^7 = x^3 \cdot y^7$

$y^{15} = y^{15}$

There is no $x$ in the last term, $y^{15}$, so $x$ will not appear in the greatest common factor. There is a $y$ in each term, however, and 2 is the least exponent on $y$.

$$\text{GCF} = y^2$$

NOW TRY

**OBJECTIVE 2** **Factor out the greatest common factor.** Writing a polynomial (a sum) in factored form as a product is called **factoring.** For example, the polynomial

$$3m + 12$$

has two terms: $3m$ and 12. The greatest common factor of these two terms is 3. We can write $3m + 12$ so that each term is a product with 3 as one factor.

$$3m + 12$$

$$= 3 \cdot m + 3 \cdot 4 \qquad \text{GCF} = 3$$

$$= 3(m + 4) \qquad \text{Distributive property}$$

The factored form of $3m + 12$ is $3(m + 4)$. This process is called **factoring out the greatest common factor.**

⚠ CAUTION The polynomial $3m + 12$ is *not* in factored form when written as

$$3 \cdot m + 3 \cdot 4. \qquad \text{Not in factored form}$$

The *terms* are factored, but the polynomial is not. The factored form of $3m + 12$ is the *product*

$$3(m + 4). \qquad \text{In factored form}$$

**EXAMPLE 3** **Factoring Out the Greatest Common Factor**

Write in factored form by factoring out the greatest common factor.

(a) $5y^2 + 10y$

$$= 5y(y) + 5y(2) \qquad \text{GCF} = 5y$$

$$= 5y(y + 2) \qquad \text{Distributive property}$$

CHECK   Multiply the factored form.

$$5y(y + 2)$$

$$= 5y(y) + 5y(2) \qquad \text{Distributive property}$$

$$= 5y^2 + 10y \checkmark \qquad \text{Original polynomial}$$

(b) $20m^5 + 10m^4 + 15m^3$

$$= 5m^3(4m^2) + 5m^3(2m) + 5m^3(3) \qquad \text{GCF} = 5m^3$$

$$= 5m^3(4m^2 + 2m + 3) \qquad \text{Factor out } 5m^3.$$

CHECK   $5m^3(4m^2 + 2m + 3)$

$$= 20m^5 + 10m^4 + 15m^3 \checkmark \qquad \text{Original polynomial}$$

NOW TRY ANSWERS
**2. (a)** $5k^2$ **(b)** $m^3n^2$

NOW TRY
EXERCISE 3
Write in factored form by factoring out the greatest common factor.

**(a)** $7t^4 - 14t^3$

**(b)** $8x^6 - 20x^5 + 28x^4$

**(c)** $30m^4n^3 - 42m^2n^2$

**(c)** $x^5 + x^3$

$= x^3(x^2) + x^3(1)$   GCF $= x^3$

$= x^3(x^2 + 1)$ ◁─── Don't forget the 1.

*Check* mentally by distributing $x^3$ over each term inside the parentheses.

**(d)** $20m^7p^2 - 36m^3p^4$

$= 4m^3p^2(5m^4) - 4m^3p^2(9p^2)$   GCF $= 4m^3p^2$

$= 4m^3p^2(5m^4 - 9p^2)$   Factor out $4m^3p^2$.   NOW TRY

⚠ **CAUTION**   Be sure to include the 1 in a problem like **Example 3(c)**. *Check that the factored form can be multiplied out to give the original polynomial.*

NOW TRY
EXERCISE 4
Write in factored form by factoring out the greatest common factor.

**(a)** $x(x + 2) + 5(x + 2)$

**(b)** $a(t + 10) - b(t + 10)$

**EXAMPLE 4**   Factoring Out the Greatest Common Factor

Write in factored form by factoring out the greatest common factor.

Same

**(a)** $a(a + 3) + 4(a + 3)$   The binomial $a + 3$ is the greatest common factor.

$= (a + 3)(a + 4)$   Factor out $a + 3$.

**(b)** $x^2(x + 1) - 5(x + 1)$

$= (x + 1)(x^2 - 5)$   Factor out $x + 1$.   NOW TRY

**NOTE**   In factored forms like those in **Example 4,** the order of the factors does not matter because of the commutative property of multiplication.

$(a + 3)(a + 4)$   can also be written   $(a + 4)(a + 3)$.

**OBJECTIVE 3**   Factor by grouping.   *When a polynomial has four terms, common factors can sometimes be used to factor by grouping.*

**EXAMPLE 5**   Factoring by Grouping

Factor by grouping.

**(a)** $2x + 6 + ax + 3a$

Group the first two terms and the last two terms, since the first two terms have a common factor of 2 and the last two terms have a common factor of $a$.

$2x + 6 + ax + 3a$

$= (2x + 6) + (ax + 3a)$   Group the terms.

$= 2(x + 3) + a(x + 3)$   Factor each group.

The expression is still not in factored form because it is the *sum* of two terms. Now, however, $x + 3$ is a common factor and can be factored out.

NOW TRY ANSWERS
**3. (a)** $7t^3(t - 2)$
 **(b)** $4x^4(2x^2 - 5x + 7)$
 **(c)** $6m^2n^2(5m^2n - 7)$
**4. (a)** $(x + 2)(x + 5)$
 **(b)** $(t + 10)(a - b)$

$= 2(x + 3) + a(x + 3)$   $x + 3$ is a common factor.

$(2 + a)(x + 3)$
is also correct. ┐
$= (x + 3)(2 + a)$   Factor out $x + 3$.

NOW TRY
EXERCISE 5

Factor by grouping.

**(a)** $ab + 3a + 5b + 15$

**(b)** $12xy + 3x + 4y + 1$

**(c)** $x^3 + 5x^2 - 8x - 40$

The final result $(x + 3)(2 + a)$ is in factored form because it is a ***product.***

CHECK   $(x + 3)(2 + a)$

$= 2x + ax + 6 + 3a$     FOIL (Section 5.5)

$= 2x + 6 + ax + 3a$  ✓   Rearrange terms to obtain
the original polynomial.

**(b)** $6ax + 24x + a + 4$

$= (6ax + 24x) + (a + 4)$     Group the terms.

$= 6x(a + 4) + 1(a + 4)$     Factor each group.

Remember the 1.

$= (a + 4)(6x + 1)$     Factor out $a + 4$.

CHECK   $(a + 4)(6x + 1)$

$= 6ax + a + 24x + 4$     FOIL

$= 6ax + 24x + a + 4$  ✓   Rearrange terms to obtain the
original polynomial.

**(c)** $2x^2 - 10x + 3xy - 15y$

$= (2x^2 - 10x) + (3xy - 15y)$     Group the terms.

$= 2x(x - 5) + 3y(x - 5)$     Factor each group.

$= (x - 5)(2x + 3y)$     Factor out $x - 5$.

CHECK   $(x - 5)(2x + 3y)$

$= 2x^2 + 3xy - 10x - 15y$     FOIL

$= 2x^2 - 10x + 3xy - 15y$  ✓   Original polynomial

**(d)** $t^3 + 2t^2 - 3t - 6$

Write a + sign
between the groups.

$= (t^3 + 2t^2) + (-3t - 6)$     Group the terms.

$= t^2(t + 2) - 3(t + 2)$     Factor out $-3$ so there is a common factor,
$t + 2$; $-3(t + 2) = -3t - 6$.

Be careful
with signs.

$= (t + 2)(t^2 - 3)$     Factor out $t + 2$.

*Check* by multiplying.

NOW TRY

---

⚠ CAUTION   *Be careful with signs when grouping* in a problem like **Example 5(d).**
It is wise to check the factoring in the second step, as shown in the side comment in
that example, before continuing.

---

### Factoring a Polynomial with Four Terms by Grouping

*Step 1*   **Group terms.** Collect the terms into two groups so that each group
has a common factor.

*Step 2*   **Factor within groups.** Factor out the greatest common factor from
each group.

*Step 3*   **Factor the entire polynomial.** Factor out a common binomial
factor from the results of Step 2.

*Step 4*   **If necessary, rearrange terms.** If Step 2 does not result in a
common binomial factor, try a different grouping.

*NOW TRY ANSWERS*

**5. (a)** $(b + 3)(a + 5)$
   **(b)** $(4y + 1)(3x + 1)$
   **(c)** $(x + 5)(x^2 - 8)$

**NOW TRY**
**EXERCISE 6**

Factor by grouping.

(a) $12p^2 - 28q - 16pq + 21p$

(b) $5xy - 6 - 15x + 2y$

**EXAMPLE 6** Rearranging Terms before Factoring by Grouping

Factor by grouping.

(a) $10x^2 - 12y + 15x - 8xy$

Factoring out the common factor of 2 from the first two terms and the common factor of $x$ from the last two terms gives the following.

$$10x^2 - 12y + 15x - 8xy$$
$$= 2(5x^2 - 6y) + x(15 - 8y)$$

***This does not lead to a common factor, so we try rearranging the terms.***

$$10x^2 - 12y + 15x - 8xy$$

$$= 10x^2 - 8xy - 12y + 15x \qquad \text{Commutative property}$$
$$= (10x^2 - 8xy) + (-12y + 15x) \qquad \text{Group the terms.}$$
$$= 2x(5x - 4y) + 3(-4y + 5x) \qquad \text{Factor each group.}$$
$$= 2x(5x - 4y) + 3(5x - 4y) \qquad \text{Rewrite } -4y + 5x.$$
$$= (5x - 4y)(2x + 3) \qquad \text{Factor out } 5x - 4y.$$

CHECK $(5x - 4y)(2x + 3)$

$$= 10x^2 + 15x - 8xy - 12y \qquad \text{FOIL}$$
$$= 10x^2 - 12y + 15x - 8xy \ \checkmark \qquad \text{Original polynomial}$$

(b) $2xy + 12 - 3y - 8x$

We need to rearrange these terms to get two groups that each have a common factor. Trial and error suggests the following grouping.

$$2xy + 12 - 3y - 8x \qquad \boxed{\text{Write a + sign between the groups.}}$$

$$= (2xy - 3y) + (-8x + 12) \qquad \text{Group the terms.}$$
$$= y(2x - 3) - 4(2x - 3) \qquad \begin{array}{l}\text{Factor each group;} \\ -4(2x - 3) = -8x + 12.\end{array}$$
$$\boxed{\text{Be careful with signs.}}$$
$$= (2x - 3)(y - 4) \qquad \text{Factor out } 2x - 3.$$

Since the quantities in parentheses in the second step must be the same, we factored out $-4$ rather than 4. *Check* by multiplying.

**NOW TRY**

NOW TRY ANSWERS

6. (a) $(3p - 4q)(4p + 7)$
   (b) $(5x + 2)(y - 3)$

---

## 6.1 EXERCISES

🌐 *Complete solution available on the Video Resources on DVD*

*Find the greatest common factor for each list of numbers. **See Example 1.***

🌐 **1.** 40, 20, 4      **2.** 50, 30, 5      **3.** 18, 24, 36, 48

**4.** 15, 30, 45, 75      **5.** 6, 8, 9      **6.** 20, 22, 23

*Find the greatest common factor for each list of terms. **See Examples 1 and 2.***

**7.** $16y, 24$      **8.** $18w, 27$

**9.** $30x^3, 40x^6, 50x^7$      **10.** $60z^4, 70z^8, 90z^9$

**11.** $x^4y^3, xy^2$      **12.** $a^4b^5, a^3b$

**13.** $12m^3n^2, 18m^5n^4, 36m^8n^3$      **14.** $25p^5r^7, 30p^7r^8, 50p^5r^3$

*Concept Check* *An expression is factored when it is written as a product, not a sum. Which of the following are not factored?*

**15.** $2k^2(5k)$

**16.** $2k^2(5k + 1)$

**17.** $2k^2 + (5k + 1)$

**18.** $(2k^2 + 5k) + 1$

*Complete each factoring by writing each polynomial as the product of two factors.*

**19.** $9m^4$
$= 3m^2(\underline{\hspace{1cm}})$

**20.** $12p^5$
$= 6p^3(\underline{\hspace{1cm}})$

**21.** $-8z^9$
$= -4z^5(\underline{\hspace{1cm}})$

**22.** $-15k^{11}$
$= -5k^8(\underline{\hspace{1cm}})$

**23.** $6m^4n^5$
$= 3m^3n(\underline{\hspace{1cm}})$

**24.** $27a^3b^2$
$= 9a^2b(\underline{\hspace{1cm}})$

**25.** $12y + 24$
$= 12(\underline{\hspace{1cm}})$

**26.** $18p + 36$
$= 18(\underline{\hspace{1cm}})$

**27.** $10a^2 - 20a$
$= 10a(\underline{\hspace{1cm}})$

**28.** $15x^2 - 30x$
$= 15x(\underline{\hspace{1cm}})$

**29.** $8x^2y + 12x^3y^2$
$= 4x^2y(\underline{\hspace{1cm}})$

**30.** $18s^3t^2 + 10st$
$= 2st(\underline{\hspace{1cm}})$

**31.** How can you check your answer when you factor a polynomial?

**32.** *Concept Check* A student factored $18x^3y^2 + 9xy$ as $9xy(2x^2y)$. *WHAT WENT WRONG?* Factor correctly.

*Write in factored form by factoring out the greatest common factor.* ***See Examples 3 and 4.***

**33.** $x^2 - 4x$

**34.** $m^2 - 7m$

**35.** $6t^2 + 15t$

**36.** $8x^2 + 6x$

**37.** $27m^3 - 9m$

**38.** $36p^3 - 24p$

**39.** $16z^4 + 24z^2$

**40.** $25k^4 + 15k^2$

**41.** $12x^3 + 6x^2$

**42.** $21b^3 + 7b^2$

**43.** $65y^{10} + 35y^6$

**44.** $100a^5 + 16a^3$

**45.** $11w^3 - 100$

**46.** $13z^5 - 80$

**47.** $8mn^3 + 24m^2n^3$

**48.** $19p^2y + 38p^2y^3$

**49.** $13y^8 + 26y^4 - 39y^2$

**50.** $5x^5 + 25x^4 - 20x^3$

**51.** $36p^6q + 45p^5q^4 + 81p^3q^2$

**52.** $125a^3z^5 + 60a^4z^4 + 85a^5z^2$

**53.** $a^5 + 2a^3b^2 - 3a^5b^2 + 4a^4b^3$

**54.** $x^6 + 5x^4y^3 - 6xy^4 + 10xy$

**55.** $c(x + 2) - d(x + 2)$

**56.** $r(x + 5) - t(x + 5)$

**57.** $m(m + 2n) + n(m + 2n)$

**58.** $q(q + 4p) + p(q + 4p)$

**59.** $q^2(p - 4) + 1(p - 4)$

**60.** $y^2(x - 9) + 1(x - 9)$

Students often have difficulty when factoring by grouping because they are not able to tell when the polynomial is completely factored. For example,

$$5y(2x - 3) + 8t(2x - 3) \qquad \text{Not in factored form}$$

is not in factored form, because it is the *sum* of two terms:  $5y(2x - 3)$ and $8t(2x - 3)$. However, because $2x - 3$ is a common factor of these two terms, the expression can now be factored.

$$(2x - 3)(5y + 8t) \qquad \text{In factored form}$$

The factored form is a *product* of two factors:  $2x - 3$ and $5y + 8t$.

*Concept Check* *Determine whether each expression is in factored form or is not in factored form. If it is not in factored form, factor it if possible.*

**61.** $8(7t + 4) + x(7t + 4)$

**62.** $3r(5x - 1) + 7(5x - 1)$

**63.** $(8 + x)(7t + 4)$

**64.** $(3r + 7)(5x - 1)$

**65.** $18x^2(y + 4) + 7(y - 4)$

**66.** $12k^3(s - 3) + 7(s + 3)$

**67.** *Concept Check* Why is it not possible to factor the expression in **Exercise 65**?

**68.** *Concept Check*   A student factored $x^3 + 4x^2 - 2x - 8$ as follows.

$$x^3 + 4x^2 - 2x - 8$$
$$= (x^3 + 4x^2) + (-2x - 8)$$
$$= x^2(x + 4) + 2(-x - 4)$$

The student could not find a common factor of the two terms. *WHAT WENT WRONG?* Complete the factoring.

*Factor by grouping. **See Examples 5 and 6.***

**69.** $p^2 + 4p + pq + 4q$

**70.** $m^2 + 2m + mn + 2n$

**71.** $a^2 - 2a + ab - 2b$

**72.** $y^2 - 6y + yw - 6w$

**73.** $7z^2 + 14z - az - 2a$

**74.** $5m^2 + 15mp - 2mr - 6pr$

**75.** $18r^2 + 12ry - 3xr - 2xy$

**76.** $8s^2 - 4st + 6sy - 3yt$

**77.** $3a^3 + 3ab^2 + 2a^2b + 2b^3$

**78.** $4x^3 + 3x^2y + 4xy^2 + 3y^3$

**79.** $12 - 4a - 3b + ab$

**80.** $6 - 3x - 2y + xy$

**81.** $16m^3 - 4m^2p^2 - 4mp + p^3$

**82.** $10t^3 - 2t^2s^2 - 5ts + s^3$

**83.** $y^2 + 3x + 3y + xy$

**84.** $m^2 + 14p + 7m + 2mp$

**85.** $5m - 6p - 2mp + 15$

**86.** $7y - 9x - 3xy + 21$

**87.** $18r^2 - 2ty + 12ry - 3rt$

**88.** $12a^2 - 4bc + 16ac - 3ab$

**89.** $a^5 - 3 + 2a^5b - 6b$

**90.** $b^3 - 2 + 5ab^3 - 10a$

---

**RELATING CONCEPTS**   EXERCISES 91–94

**FOR INDIVIDUAL OR GROUP WORK**

*In many cases, the choice of which pairs of terms to group when factoring by grouping can be made in different ways. To see this for **Example 6 (b)**, work Exercises 91–94 in order.*

**91.** Start with the polynomial from **Example 6(b)**, $2xy + 12 - 3y - 8x$, and rearrange the terms as follows:

$$2xy - 8x - 3y + 12.$$

What property from **Section 1.7** allows this?

**92.** Group the first two terms and the last two terms of the rearranged polynomial in **Exercise 91.** Then factor each group.

**93.** Is your result from **Exercise 92** in factored form? Explain your answer.

**94.** If your answer to **Exercise 93** is *no,* factor the polynomial. Is the result the same as that shown for **Example 6(b)**?

---

**PREVIEW EXERCISES**

*Find each product. **See Section 5.5.***

**95.** $(x + 6)(x - 9)$

**96.** $(x - 3)(x - 6)$

**97.** $(x + 2)(x + 7)$

**98.** $2x(x + 5)(x - 1)$

**99.** $2x^2(x^2 + 3x + 5)$

**100.** $-5x^2(2x^2 - 4x - 9)$

## 6.2 Factoring Trinomials

Using the FOIL method, we can find the product of the binomials $k - 3$ and $k + 1$.

$$(k - 3)(k + 1) = k^2 - 2k - 3 \quad \text{Multiplying}$$

Suppose instead that we are given the polynomial $k^2 - 2k - 3$ and want to rewrite it as the product $(k - 3)(k + 1)$.

$$k^2 - 2k - 3 = (k - 3)(k + 1) \quad \text{Factoring}$$

Recall from **Section 6.1** that this process is called factoring the polynomial. Factoring reverses or "undoes" multiplying.

**OBJECTIVE 1** **Factor trinomials with a coefficient of 1 for the second-degree term.** When factoring polynomials with integer coefficients, we use only integers in the factors. For example, we can factor $x^2 + 5x + 6$ by finding integers $m$ and $n$ such that

$$x^2 + 5x + 6 \quad \text{is written as} \quad (x + m)(x + n).$$

To find these integers $m$ and $n$, we multiply the two binomials on the right.

$$(x + m)(x + n)$$
$$= x^2 + nx + mx + mn \quad \text{FOIL}$$
$$= x^2 + (n + m)x + mn \quad \text{Distributive property}$$

Comparing this result with $x^2 + 5x + 6$ shows that we must find integers $m$ and $n$ having a sum of 5 and a product of 6.

Product of $m$ and $n$ is 6.
$$\downarrow$$
$$x^2 + 5x + 6 = x^2 + (n + m)x + mn$$
$$\uparrow$$
Sum of $m$ and $n$ is 5.

Since many pairs of integers have a sum of 5, it is best to begin by listing those pairs of integers whose product is 6. Both 5 and 6 are positive, so we consider only pairs in which both integers are positive.

| Factors of 6 | Sums of Factors |
|:---:|:---:|
| 6, 1 | $6 + 1 = 7$ |
| 3, 2 | $3 + 2 = 5$ |

Sum is 5.

Both pairs have a product of 6, but only the pair 3 and 2 has a sum of 5. So 3 and 2 are the required integers.

$$x^2 + 5x + 6 \quad \text{factors as} \quad (x + 3)(x + 2).$$

Check by using the FOIL method to multiply the binomials. *Make sure that the sum of the outer and inner products produces the correct middle term.*

CHECK $(x + 3)(x + 2) = x^2 + 5x + 6$ ✓ Correct

$$3x$$
$$2x$$
$$5x \quad \text{Add.}$$

*NOW TRY*
*EXERCISE 1*
Factor $p^2 + 7p + 10$.

**EXAMPLE 1** Factoring a Trinomial with All Positive Terms

Factor $m^2 + 9m + 14$.

Look for two integers whose product is 14 and whose sum is 9. List pairs of integers whose product is 14, and examine the sums. Again, only positive integers are needed because all signs in $m^2 + 9m + 14$ are positive.

| Factors of 14 | Sums of Factors |
|---|---|
| 14, 1 | 14 + 1 = 15 |
| 7, 2 | 7 + 2 = 9 |

Sum is 9.

From the list, 7 and 2 are the required integers, since $7 \cdot 2 = 14$ and $7 + 2 = 9$.

$$m^2 + 9m + 14 \quad \text{factors as} \quad (m + 7)(m + 2).$$

$(m + 2)(m + 7)$ is also correct.

CHECK $(m + 7)(m + 2)$

$$= m^2 + 2m + 7m + 14 \quad \text{FOIL}$$
$$= m^2 + 9m + 14 \checkmark \quad \text{Original polynomial}$$

NOW TRY

*NOW TRY*
*EXERCISE 2*
Factor $t^2 - 9t + 18$.

**EXAMPLE 2** Factoring a Trinomial with a Negative Middle Term

Factor $x^2 - 9x + 20$.

We must find two integers whose product is 20 and whose sum is $-9$. Since the numbers we are looking for have a *positive product* and a *negative sum,* we consider only pairs of negative integers.

| Factors of 20 | Sums of Factors |
|---|---|
| -20, -1 | -20 + (-1) = -21 |
| -10, -2 | -10 + (-2) = -12 |
| -5, -4 | -5 + (-4) = -9 |

Sum is $-9$.

The required integers are $-5$ and $-4$.

$$x^2 - 9x + 20 \quad \text{factors as} \quad (x - 5)(x - 4).$$

The order of the factors does not matter.

CHECK $(x - 5)(x - 4)$

$$= x^2 - 4x - 5x + 20 \quad \text{FOIL}$$
$$= x^2 - 9x + 20 \checkmark \quad \text{Original polynomial}$$

NOW TRY

*NOW TRY*
*EXERCISE 3*
Factor $x^2 + x - 42$.

**EXAMPLE 3** Factoring a Trinomial with a Negative Last (Constant) Term

Factor $x^2 + x - 6$.

We must find two integers whose product is $-6$ and whose sum is 1 (since the coefficient of $x$, or $1x$, is 1). To get a *negative product,* the pairs of integers must have different signs.

Once we find the required pair, we can stop listing factors.

| Factors of -6 | Sums of Factors |
|---|---|
| 6, -1 | 6 + (-1) = 5 |
| -6, 1 | -6 + 1 = -5 |
| 3, -2 | 3 + (-2) = 1 |

Sum is 1.

NOW TRY ANSWERS
1. $(p + 2)(p + 5)$
2. $(t - 3)(t - 6)$
3. $(x + 7)(x - 6)$

The required integers are 3 and $-2$.

To check, multiply the factored form.

$$x^2 + x - 6 \quad \text{factors as} \quad (x + 3)(x - 2).$$

NOW TRY

NOW TRY
EXERCISE 4

Factor $x^2 - 4x - 21$.

**EXAMPLE 4** Factoring a Trinomial with Two Negative Terms

Factor $p^2 - 2p - 15$.

Find two integers whose product is $-15$ and whose sum is $-2$. Because the constant term, $-15$, is negative, list pairs of integers with different signs.

| Factors of $-15$ | Sums of Factors |
|---|---|
| 15, −1 | $15 + (-1) = 14$ |
| −15, 1 | $-15 + 1 = -14$ |
| 5, −3 | $5 + (-3) = 2$ |
| −5, 3 | $-5 + 3 = -2$ ← Sum is $-2$. |

The required integers are $-5$ and $3$.

To check, multiply the factored form.

$$p^2 - 2p - 15 \quad \text{factors as} \quad (p - 5)(p + 3).$$

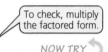 NOW TRY

**NOTE** In **Examples 1–4,** notice that we listed factors in descending order (disregarding their signs) when we were looking for the required pair of integers. This helps avoid skipping the correct combination.

Some trinomials cannot be factored by using only integers. We call such trinomials **prime polynomials.**

NOW TRY
EXERCISE 5

Factor each trinomial if possible.

**(a)** $m^2 + 5m + 8$

**(b)** $t^2 + 11t - 24$

**EXAMPLE 5** Deciding Whether Polynomials Are Prime

Factor each trinomial if possible.

**(a)** $x^2 - 5x + 12$

As in **Example 2,** both factors must be negative to give a positive product and a negative sum. List pairs of negative integers whose product is 12, and examine the sums.

| Factors of 12 | Sums of Factors |
|---|---|
| −12, −1 | $-12 + (-1) = -13$ |
| −6, −2 | $-6 + (-2) = -8$ |
| −4, −3 | $-4 + (-3) = -7$ ← No sum is $-5$. |

None of the pairs of integers has a sum of $-5$. Therefore, the trinomial $x^2 - 5x + 12$ *cannot be factored by using only integers.* It is a *prime polynomial.*

**(b)** $k^2 - 8k + 11$

There is no pair of integers whose product is 11 and whose sum is $-8$, so $k^2 - 8k + 11$ is a prime polynomial.

NOW TRY

---

**Guidelines for Factoring $x^2 + bx + c$**

Find two integers whose product is $c$ and whose sum is $b$.

**1.** Both integers must be positive if $b$ and $c$ are positive. (See **Example 1.**)

**2.** Both integers must be negative if $c$ is positive and $b$ is negative. (See **Example 2.**)

**3.** One integer must be positive and one must be negative if $c$ is negative. (See **Examples 3 and 4.**)

NOW TRY ANSWERS
**4.** $(x + 3)(x - 7)$
**5. (a)** prime **(b)** prime

NOW TRY
EXERCISE 6

Factor $a^2 + 2ab - 15b^2$.

**EXAMPLE 6** Factoring a Trinomial with Two Variables

Factor $z^2 - 2bz - 3b^2$.

Here, the coefficient of $z$ in the middle term is $-2b$, so we need to find two expressions whose product is $-3b^2$ and whose sum is $-2b$.

| Factors of $-3b^2$ | Sums of Factors |
|---|---|
| $3b, -b$ | $3b + (-b) = 2b$ |
| $-3b, b$ | $-3b + b = -2b$ |

Sum is $-2b$.

$z^2 - 2bz - 3b^2$ factors as $(z - 3b)(z + b)$.

CHECK $(z - 3b)(z + b)$

$\quad = z^2 + zb - 3bz - 3b^2$    FOIL

$\quad = z^2 + 1bz - 3bz - 3b^2$    Identity and commutative properties

$\quad = z^2 - 2bz - 3b^2$ ✓    Combine like terms.    NOW TRY

**OBJECTIVE 2** **Factor such trinomials after factoring out the greatest common factor.** If a trinomial has a common factor, first factor it out.

NOW TRY
EXERCISE 7

Factor $3y^4 - 27y^3 + 60y^2$.

**EXAMPLE 7** Factoring a Trinomial with a Common Factor

Factor $4x^5 - 28x^4 + 40x^3$.

$\qquad 4x^5 - 28x^4 + 40x^3$

$\qquad = 4x^3(x^2 - 7x + 10)$    Factor out the greatest common factor, $4x^3$.

Factor $x^2 - 7x + 10$. The integers $-5$ and $-2$ have a product of 10 and a sum of $-7$.

Include $4x^3$. $\qquad = 4x^3(x - 5)(x - 2)$    Completely factored form

CHECK $\quad 4x^3(x - 5)(x - 2)$

$\qquad = 4x^3(x^2 - 7x + 10)$    FOIL; Combine like terms.

$\qquad = 4x^5 - 28x^4 + 40x^3$ ✓    Distributive property    NOW TRY

NOW TRY ANSWERS
6. $(a + 5b)(a - 3b)$
7. $3y^2(y - 5)(y - 4)$

⚠ **CAUTION** *When factoring, always look for a common factor first.* Remember to include the common factor as part of the answer. Always check by multiplying.

## 6.2 EXERCISES

**MyMathLab**    Math XL PRACTICE     WATCH     DOWNLOAD     READ     REVIEW

🌐 *Complete solution available on the Video Resources on DVD*

*In Exercises 1–4, list all pairs of integers with the given product. Then find the pair whose sum is given.* **See the tables in Examples 1–4.**

**1.** Product: 48;   Sum: $-19$      **2.** Product: 18;   Sum: 9

**3.** Product: $-24$;   Sum: $-5$      **4.** Product: $-36$;   Sum: $-16$

**5.** *Concept Check*   If a trinomial in $x$ is factored as $(x + a)(x + b)$, what must be true of $a$ and $b$ if the coefficient of the constant term of the trinomial is negative?

**6.** *Concept Check* In **Exercise 5,** what must be true of *a* and *b* if the coefficient of the constant term is positive?

✍ **7.** What is meant by a *prime polynomial*?

✍ **8.** How can you check your work when factoring a trinomial? Does the check ensure that the trinomial is completely factored?

**9.** *Concept Check* Which is the correct factored form of $x^2 - 12x + 32$?

    **A.** $(x - 8)(x + 4)$     **B.** $(x + 8)(x - 4)$

    **C.** $(x - 8)(x - 4)$     **D.** $(x + 8)(x + 4)$

**10.** *Concept Check* What is the suggested first step in factoring $2x^3 + 8x^2 - 10x$? (See **Example 7.**)

**11.** *Concept Check* What polynomial can be factored as $(a + 9)(a + 4)$?

**12.** *Concept Check* What polynomial can be factored as $(y - 7)(y + 3)$?

*Complete each factoring.* ***See Examples 1–4.***

**13.** $p^2 + 11p + 30$
    $= (p + 5)(\underline{\hphantom{xxx}})$

**14.** $x^2 + 10x + 21$
    $= (x + 7)(\underline{\hphantom{xxx}})$

**15.** $x^2 + 15x + 44$
    $= (x + 4)(\underline{\hphantom{xxx}})$

**16.** $r^2 + 15r + 56$
    $= (r + 7)(\underline{\hphantom{xxx}})$

**17.** $x^2 - 9x + 8$
    $= (x - 1)(\underline{\hphantom{xxx}})$

**18.** $t^2 - 14t + 24$
    $= (t - 2)(\underline{\hphantom{xxx}})$

**19.** $y^2 - 2y - 15$
    $= (y + 3)(\underline{\hphantom{xxx}})$

**20.** $t^2 - t - 42$
    $= (t + 6)(\underline{\hphantom{xxx}})$

**21.** $x^2 + 9x - 22$
    $= (x - 2)(\underline{\hphantom{xxx}})$

**22.** $x^2 + 6x - 27$
    $= (x - 3)(\underline{\hphantom{xxx}})$

**23.** $y^2 - 7y - 18$
    $= (y + 2)(\underline{\hphantom{xxx}})$

**24.** $y^2 - 2y - 24$
    $= (y + 4)(\underline{\hphantom{xxx}})$

*Factor completely. If the polynomial cannot be factored, write* prime. ***See Examples 1–5.*** (Hint: *In Exercises 43 and 44, first write the trinomial in descending powers and then factor.*)

**25.** $y^2 + 9y + 8$      **26.** $a^2 + 9a + 20$      🌐 **27.** $b^2 + 8b + 15$

**28.** $x^2 + 6x + 8$      **29.** $m^2 + m - 20$      **30.** $p^2 + 4p - 5$

🌐 **31.** $y^2 - 8y + 15$      **32.** $y^2 - 6y + 8$      🌐 **33.** $x^2 + 4x + 5$

**34.** $t^2 + 11t + 12$      **35.** $z^2 - 15z + 56$      **36.** $x^2 - 13x + 36$

🌐 **37.** $r^2 - r - 30$      **38.** $q^2 - q - 42$      **39.** $a^2 - 8a - 48$

**40.** $d^2 - 4d - 45$      **41.** $x^2 + 3x - 39$      **42.** $m^2 + 10m - 30$

**43.** $-32 + 14x + x^2$          **44.** $-39 + 10x + x^2$

*Factor completely.* ***See Example 6.***

**45.** $r^2 + 3ra + 2a^2$      **46.** $x^2 + 5xa + 4a^2$      🌐 **47.** $t^2 - tz - 6z^2$

**48.** $a^2 - ab - 12b^2$      **49.** $x^2 + 4xy + 3y^2$      **50.** $p^2 + 9pq + 8q^2$

**51.** $v^2 - 11vw + 30w^2$          **52.** $v^2 - 11vx + 24x^2$

*Factor completely.* ***See Example 7.***

**53.** $4x^2 + 12x - 40$      **54.** $5y^2 - 5y - 30$      🌐 **55.** $2t^3 + 8t^2 + 6t$

**56.** $3t^3 + 27t^2 + 24t$          **57.** $2x^6 + 8x^5 - 42x^4$          **58.** $4y^5 + 12y^4 - 40y^3$

**59.** $5m^5 + 25m^4 - 40m^2$                    **60.** $12k^5 - 6k^3 + 10k^2$

**61.** $m^3n - 10m^2n^2 + 24mn^3$                    **62.** $y^3z + 3y^2z^2 - 54yz^3$

*Brain Busters*    *Factor each polynomial.*

**63.** $a^5 + 3a^4b - 4a^3b^2$          **64.** $m^3n - 2m^2n^2 - 3mn^3$          **65.** $y^3z + y^2z^2 - 6yz^3$

**66.** $k^7 - 2k^6m - 15k^5m^2$          **67.** $z^{10} - 4z^9y - 21z^8y^2$          **68.** $x^9 + 5x^8w - 24x^7w^2$

**69.** $(a + b)x^2 + (a + b)x - 12(a + b)$

**70.** $(x + y)n^2 + (x + y)n - 20(x + y)$

**71.** $(2p + q)r^2 - 12(2p + q)r + 27(2p + q)$

**72.** $(3m - n)k^2 - 13(3m - n)k + 40(3m - n)$

### PREVIEW EXERCISES

*Find each product.* ***See Section 5.5.***

**73.** $(2y - 7)(y + 4)$          **74.** $(3a + 2)(2a + 1)$          **75.** $(5z + 2)(3z - 2)$

## 6.3   More on Factoring Trinomials

**OBJECTIVES**

**1** Factor trinomials by grouping when the coefficient of the second-degree term is not 1.

**2** Factor trinomials by using the FOIL method.

Trinomials such as $2x^2 + 7x + 6$, in which the coefficient of the second-degree term is *not* 1, are factored with extensions of the methods from the previous sections.

**OBJECTIVE 1**  **Factor trinomials by grouping when the coefficient of the second-degree term is not 1.** A trinomial such as $m^2 + 3m + 2$ is factored by finding two numbers whose product is 2 and whose sum is 3. To factor $2x^2 + 7x + 6$, we look for two integers whose product is $2 \cdot 6 = 12$ and whose sum is 7.

$$\text{Sum is 7.}$$
$$\downarrow$$
$$2x^2 + 7x + 6$$
$$\uparrow \qquad\qquad \uparrow$$
$$\text{Product is } 2 \cdot 6 = 12.$$

By considering pairs of positive integers whose product is 12, we find the required integers, 3 and 4. We use these integers to write the middle term, $7x$, as $7x = 3x + 4x$.

$$2x^2 + 7x + 6$$
$$= 2x^2 + \underbrace{3x + 4x}_{7x} + 6$$
$$= (2x^2 + 3x) + (4x + 6) \qquad \text{Group the terms.}$$
$$= x(2x + 3) + 2(2x + 3) \qquad \text{Factor each group.}$$

Must be the same factor

$$= (2x + 3)(x + 2) \qquad \text{Factor out } 2x + 3.$$

*CHECK*   Multiply $(2x + 3)(x + 2)$  to obtain  $2x^2 + 7x + 6$.  ✓

**NOTE** In the preceding example, we could have written $7x$ as $4x + 3x$, rather than as $3x + 4x$. Factoring by grouping would give the same answer. Try this.

⟲ NOW TRY
⟶ EXERCISE 1

Factor.

**(a)** $2z^2 + 5z + 3$

**(b)** $15m^2 + m - 2$

**(c)** $8x^2 - 2xy - 3y^2$

**EXAMPLE 1** Factoring Trinomials by Grouping

Factor each trinomial.

**(a)** $6r^2 + r - 1$

We must find two integers with a product of $6(-1) = -6$ and a sum of 1.

Sum is 1.
$$6r^2 + 1r - 1$$
Product is $6(-1) = -6$.

The integers are $-2$ and 3. We write the middle term, $r$, as $-2r + 3r$.

$$6r^2 + r - 1$$
$$= 6r^2 - 2r + 3r - 1 \qquad r = -2r + 3r$$
$$= (6r^2 - 2r) + (3r - 1) \qquad \text{Group the terms.}$$
$$= 2r(3r - 1) + 1(3r - 1) \qquad \text{The binomials must be the same.}$$
⟨Remember the 1.⟩
$$= (3r - 1)(2r + 1) \qquad \text{Factor out } 3r - 1.$$

**CHECK** Multiply $(3r - 1)(2r + 1)$ to obtain $6r^2 + r - 1$. ✓

**(b)** $12z^2 - 5z - 2$

Look for two integers whose product is $12(-2) = -24$ and whose sum is $-5$. The required integers are 3 and $-8$.

$$12z^2 - 5z - 2$$
$$= 12z^2 + 3z - 8z - 2 \qquad -5z = 3z - 8z$$
$$= (12z^2 + 3z) + (-8z - 2) \qquad \text{Group the terms.}$$
$$= 3z(4z + 1) - 2(4z + 1) \qquad \text{Factor each group.}$$
⟨Be careful with signs.⟩
$$= (4z + 1)(3z - 2) \qquad \text{Factor out } 4z + 1.$$

**CHECK** Multiply $(4z + 1)(3z - 2)$ to obtain $12z^2 - 5z - 2$. ✓

**(c)** $10m^2 + mn - 3n^2$

Two integers whose product is $10(-3) = -30$ and whose sum is 1 are $-5$ and 6.

$$10m^2 + mn - 3n^2$$
$$= 10m^2 - 5mn + 6mn - 3n^2 \qquad mn = -5mn + 6mn$$
$$= (10m^2 - 5mn) + (6mn - 3n^2) \qquad \text{Group the terms.}$$
$$= 5m(2m - n) + 3n(2m - n) \qquad \text{Factor each group.}$$
$$= (2m - n)(5m + 3n) \qquad \text{Factor out } 2m - n.$$

**CHECK** Multiply $(2m - n)(5m + 3n)$ to obtain $10m^2 + mn - 3n^2$. ✓

NOW TRY ⟲

NOW TRY ANSWERS
**1.** **(a)** $(2z + 3)(z + 1)$
**(b)** $(3m - 1)(5m + 2)$
**(c)** $(4x - 3y)(2x + y)$

*NOW TRY*
*EXERCISE 2*
Factor $15z^6 + 18z^5 - 24z^4$.

**EXAMPLE 2**  Factoring a Trinomial with a Common Factor by Grouping

Factor $28x^5 - 58x^4 - 30x^3$.

$$28x^5 - 58x^4 - 30x^3$$
$$= 2x^3(14x^2 - 29x - 15) \quad \text{Factor out the greatest common factor, } 2x^3.$$

To factor $14x^2 - 29x - 15$, find two integers whose product is $14(-15) = -210$ and whose sum is $-29$. Factoring 210 into prime factors helps find these integers.

$$210 = 2 \cdot 3 \cdot 5 \cdot 7$$

Combine the prime factors of $210 = 2 \cdot 3 \cdot 5 \cdot 7$ into pairs in different ways, using one positive and one negative (to get $-210$). The factors 6 and $-35$ have the correct sum, $-29$.

$$28x^5 - 58x^4 - 30x^3$$
$$= 2x^3(14x^2 - 29x - 15)$$
$$= 2x^3(14x^2 + 6x - 35x - 15) \qquad -29x = 6x - 35x$$
$$= 2x^3[(14x^2 + 6x) + (-35x - 15)] \qquad \text{Group the terms.}$$
$$= 2x^3[2x(7x + 3) - 5(7x + 3)] \qquad \text{Factor each group.}$$
$$= 2x^3[(7x + 3)(2x - 5)] \qquad \text{Factor out } 7x + 3.$$
$$= 2x^3(7x + 3)(2x - 5) \qquad \text{Check by multiplying.} \qquad \textit{NOW TRY}$$

*Remember the common factor.*

**OBJECTIVE 2**  **Factor trinomials by using the FOIL method.** There is an alternative method of factoring trinomials that uses trial and error.

To factor $2x^2 + 7x + 6$ (the trinomial factored at the beginning of this section) by trial and error, we use the FOIL method in reverse. We want to write $2x^2 + 7x + 6$ as the product of two binomials.

$$2x^2 + 7x + 6$$
$$= (\underline{\quad\quad})(\underline{\quad\quad})$$

The product of the two first terms of the binomials is $2x^2$. The possible factors of $2x^2$ are $2x$ and $x$ or $-2x$ and $-x$. Since all terms of the trinomial are positive, we consider only positive factors. Thus, we have the following.

$$2x^2 + 7x + 6$$
$$= (2x\underline{\quad})(x\underline{\quad})$$

The product of the two last terms, 6, can be factored as $1 \cdot 6$, $6 \cdot 1$, $2 \cdot 3$, or $3 \cdot 2$. Try each pair to find the pair that gives the correct middle term, $7x$.

$$(2x + 1)(x + 6) \qquad \text{Incorrect}$$
$$x$$
$$12x$$
$$13x \qquad \text{Add.}$$

$$(2x + 6)(x + 1) \qquad \text{Incorrect}$$
$$6x$$
$$2x$$
$$8x \qquad \text{Add.}$$

Since $2x + 6 = 2(x + 3)$, the binomial $2x + 6$ has a common factor of 2, while $2x^2 + 7x + 6$ has no common factor other than 1. The product $(2x + 6)(x + 1)$ cannot be correct.

**NOTE**  If the terms of the original polynomial have greatest common factor 1, then each factor of that polynomial will also have terms with GCF 1.

*NOW TRY ANSWER*
**2.** $3z^4(5z - 4)(z + 2)$

Now try the numbers 2 and 3 as factors of 6. Because of the common factor 2 in $2x + 2$, the product $(2x + 2)(x + 3)$ will not work, so we try $(2x + 3)(x + 2)$.

$$(2x + 3)(x + 2) = 2x^2 + 7x + 6 \quad \text{Correct}$$

$$3x$$
$$\underline{4x}$$
$$7x \quad \text{Add.}$$

Thus, $2x^2 + 7x + 6$ factors as $(2x + 3)(x + 2)$.

*NOW TRY*
*EXERCISE 3*
Factor $8y^2 + 22y + 5$.

### EXAMPLE 3 Factoring a Trinomial with All Positive Terms by Using FOIL

Factor $8p^2 + 14p + 5$.

The number 8 has several possible pairs of factors, but 5 has only 1 and 5 or $-1$ and $-5$, so begin by considering the factors of 5. Ignore the negative factors, since all coefficients in the trinomial are positive. The factors will have this form.

$$(\underline{\quad} + 5)(\underline{\quad} + 1)$$

The possible pairs of factors of $8p^2$ are $8p$ and $p$, or $4p$ and $2p$. Try various combinations, checking in each case to see if the middle term is $14p$.

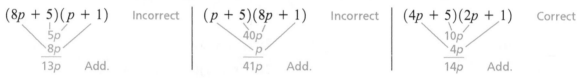

Since the combination on the right produces $14p$, the correct middle term,

$$8p^2 + 14p + 5 \quad \text{factors as} \quad (4p + 5)(2p + 1).$$

*CHECK* Multiply $(4p + 5)(2p + 1)$ to obtain $8p^2 + 14p + 5$ ✓ *NOW TRY*

*NOW TRY*
*EXERCISE 4*
Factor $10x^2 - 9x + 2$.

### EXAMPLE 4 Factoring a Trinomial with a Negative Middle Term by Using FOIL

Factor $6x^2 - 11x + 3$.

Since 3 has only 1 and 3 or $-1$ and $-3$ as factors, it is better here to begin by factoring 3. The last (constant) term of the trinomial $6x^2 - 11x + 3$ is positive and the middle term has a negative coefficient, so we consider only negative factors. We need two negative factors, because the *product* of two negative factors is positive and their *sum* is negative, as required. Try $-3$ and $-1$ as factors of 3.

$$(\underline{\quad} - 3)(\underline{\quad} - 1)$$

The factors of $6x^2$ may be either $6x$ and $x$ or $2x$ and $3x$.

$$(6x - 3)(x - 1) \quad \text{Incorrect} \quad | \quad (2x - 3)(3x - 1) \quad \text{Correct}$$

$$-3x \qquad\qquad\qquad\qquad -9x$$
$$\underline{-6x} \qquad\qquad\qquad\qquad \underline{-2x}$$
$$-9x \quad \text{Add.} \qquad\qquad -11x \quad \text{Add.}$$

The factors $2x$ and $3x$ produce $-11x$, the correct middle term. *Check by multiplying.*

$$6x^2 - 11x + 3 \quad \text{factors as} \quad (2x - 3)(3x - 1). \qquad \text{NOW TRY}$$

---

**NOTE** In **Example 4,** we might also realize that our initial attempt to factor $6x^2 - 11x + 3$ as $(6x - 3)(x - 1)$ *cannot* be correct, since the terms of $6x - 3$ have a common factor of 3, while those of the original polynomial do not.

*NOW TRY ANSWERS*
**3.** $(4y + 1)(2y + 5)$
**4.** $(5x - 2)(2x - 1)$

⌐ *NOW TRY*
↳ *EXERCISE 5*
Factor $10a^2 + 31a - 14$.

⌐ *NOW TRY*
↳ *EXERCISE 6*
Factor $8z^2 + 2wz - 15w^2$.

*EXAMPLE 5*  Factoring a Trinomial with a Negative Constant Term
by Using FOIL

Factor $8x^2 + 6x - 9$.

The integer 8 has several possible pairs of factors, as does $-9$. Since the constant term is negative, one positive factor and one negative factor of $-9$ are needed. Since the coefficient of the middle term is relatively small, it is wise to avoid large factors such as 8 or 9. We try $4x$ and $2x$ as factors of $8x^2$, and 3 and $-3$ as factors of $-9$.

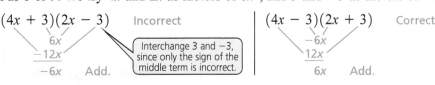

$(4x + 3)(2x - 3)$    Incorrect       $(4x - 3)(2x + 3)$    Correct
        6x                                        −6x
     − 12x                                       12x
     −6x      Add.    Interchange 3 and −3,        6x      Add.
                      since only the sign of the
                      middle term is incorrect.

The combination on the right produces the correct middle term.

$$8x^2 + 6x - 9 \quad \text{factors as} \quad (4x - 3)(2x + 3).$$    NOW TRY ↻

*EXAMPLE 6*  Factoring a Trinomial with Two Variables

Factor $12a^2 - ab - 20b^2$.

There are several pairs of factors of $12a^2$, including

$$12a \text{ and } a, \quad 6a \text{ and } 2a, \quad \text{and} \quad 3a \text{ and } 4a.$$

There are also many pairs of factors of $-20b^2$, including

$$20b \text{ and } -b, \quad -20b \text{ and } b, \quad 10b \text{ and } -2b, \quad -10b \text{ and } 2b,$$

$$4b \text{ and } -5b, \quad \text{and} \quad -4b \text{ and } 5b.$$

Once again, since the coefficient of the desired middle term is relatively small, avoid the larger factors. Try the factors $6a$ and $2a$, and $4b$ and $-5b$.

$$(6a + 4b)(2a - 5b)$$

This cannot be correct, since there is a factor of 2 in $6a + 4b$, while 2 is not a factor of the given trinomial. Try $3a$ and $4a$ with $4b$ and $-5b$.

$$(3a + 4b)(4a - 5b)$$
$$= 12a^2 + ab - 20b^2 \quad \text{Incorrect}$$

Here the middle term is $ab$ rather than $-ab$, so we interchange the signs of the last two terms in the factors.

$$12a^2 - ab - 20b^2 \quad \text{factors as} \quad (3a - 4b)(4a + 5b).$$    Check by multiplying.

NOW TRY ↻

*EXAMPLE 7*  Factoring Trinomials with Common Factors

Factor each trinomial.

**(a)** $15y^3 + 55y^2 + 30y$

$$= 5y(3y^2 + 11y + 6) \quad \text{Factor out the greatest common factor, } 5y.$$

To factor $3y^2 + 11y + 6$, try $3y$ and $y$ as factors of $3y^2$, and 2 and 3 as factors of 6.

$$(3y + 2)(y + 3)$$

$$= 3y^2 + 11y + 6 \quad \text{Correct}$$

*NOW TRY ANSWERS*
**5.** $(5a - 2)(2a + 7)$
**6.** $(4z - 5w)(2z + 3w)$

**NOW TRY
EXERCISE 7**
Factor $-10x^3 - 45x^2 + 90x$.

This leads to the completely factored form.

$$15y^3 + 55y^2 + 30y$$

Remember the common factor. $\longrightarrow = 5y(3y + 2)(y + 3)$

*CHECK*   $5y(3y + 2)(y + 3)$

$\qquad = 5y(3y^2 + 11y + 6)$     FOIL; Combine like terms.

$\qquad = 15y^3 + 55y^2 + 30y$   ✓   Distributive property

**(b)** $-24a^3 - 42a^2 + 45a$

The common factor could be $3a$ or $-3a$. If we factor out $-3a$, the first term of the trinomial will be positive, which makes it easier to factor the remaining trinomial.

$$-24a^3 - 42a^2 + 45a$$

$$= -3a(8a^2 + 14a - 15) \qquad \text{Factor out } -3a.$$

$$= -3a(4a - 3)(2a + 5) \qquad \text{Factor the trinomial.}$$

*Check* by multiplying.

NOW TRY

**NOW TRY ANSWER**
7. $-5x(2x - 3)(x + 6)$

⚠ **CAUTION**   *Include the common factor in the final factored form.*

---

## 6.3 EXERCISES

**MyMathLab**

PRACTICE    WATCH    DOWNLOAD    READ    REVIEW

🌐 *Complete solution available on the Video Resources on DVD*

*Concept Check*   The middle term of each trinomial has been rewritten. Now factor by grouping.

**1.** $10t^2 + 9t + 2$
$\quad = 10t^2 + 5t + 4t + 2$

**2.** $6x^2 + 13x + 6$
$\quad = 6x^2 + 9x + 4x + 6$

**3.** $15z^2 - 19z + 6$
$\quad = 15z^2 - 10z - 9z + 6$

**4.** $12p^2 - 17p + 6$
$\quad = 12p^2 - 9p - 8p + 6$

**5.** $8s^2 + 2st - 3t^2$
$\quad = 8s^2 - 4st + 6st - 3t^2$

**6.** $3x^2 - xy - 14y^2$
$\quad = 3x^2 - 7xy + 6xy - 14y^2$

*Concept Check*   Complete the steps to factor each trinomial by grouping.

**7.** $2m^2 + 11m + 12$

   **(a)** Find two integers whose product is

   _____ · _____ = _____

   and whose sum is _____.

   **(b)** The required integers are _____ and _____.

   **(c)** Write the middle term, $11m$, as _____ + _____.

   **(d)** Rewrite the given trinomial as _____.

   **(e)** Factor the polynomial in part (d) by grouping.

   **(f)** Check by multiplying.

**8.** $6y^2 - 19y + 10$

   **(a)** Find two integers whose product is

   _____ · _____ = _____

   and whose sum is _____.

   **(b)** The required integers are _____ and _____.

   **(c)** Write the middle term, $-19y$, as _____ + _____.

   **(d)** Rewrite the given trinomial as _____.

   **(e)** Factor the polynomial in part (d) by grouping.

   **(f)** Check by multiplying.

**9.** *Concept Check*   Which pair of integers would be used to rewrite the middle term when one is factoring $12y^2 + 5y - 2$ by grouping?

**A.** $-8, 3$     **B.** $8, -3$

**C.** $-6, 4$     **D.** $6, -4$

**10.** *Concept Check*   Which pair of integers would be used to rewrite the middle term when one is factoring $20b^2 - 13b + 2$ by grouping?

**A.** $10, 3$     **B.** $-10, -3$

**C.** $8, 5$      **D.** $-8, -5$

*Concept Check*   Which is the correct factored form of the given polynomial?

**11.** $2x^2 - x - 1$

   **A.** $(2x - 1)(x + 1)$

   **B.** $(2x + 1)(x - 1)$

**12.** $3a^2 - 5a - 2$

   **A.** $(3a + 1)(a - 2)$

   **B.** $(3a - 1)(a + 2)$

**13.** $4y^2 + 17y - 15$

   **A.** $(y + 5)(4y - 3)$

   **B.** $(2y - 5)(2y + 3)$

**14.** $12c^2 - 7c - 12$

   **A.** $(6c - 2)(2c + 6)$

   **B.** $(4c + 3)(3c - 4)$

*Complete each factoring.* ***See Examples 1–7.***

**15.** $6a^2 + 7ab - 20b^2$
   $= (3a - 4b)(\underline{\hspace{1.5cm}})$

**16.** $9m^2 + 6mn - 8n^2$
   $= (3m - 2n)(\underline{\hspace{1.5cm}})$

**17.** $2x^2 + 6x - 8$
   $= 2(\underline{\hspace{2cm}})$
   $= 2(\underline{\hspace{1cm}})(\underline{\hspace{1cm}})$

**18.** $3x^2 + 9x - 30$
   $= 3(\underline{\hspace{2cm}})$
   $= 3(\underline{\hspace{1cm}})(\underline{\hspace{1cm}})$

**19.** $4z^3 - 10z^2 - 6z$
   $= 2z(\underline{\hspace{2cm}})$
   $= 2z(\underline{\hspace{1cm}})(\underline{\hspace{1cm}})$

**20.** $15r^3 - 39r^2 - 18r$
   $= 3r(\underline{\hspace{2cm}})$
   $= 3r(\underline{\hspace{1cm}})(\underline{\hspace{1cm}})$

**21.** The polynomial $12x^2 + 7x - 12$ does not have 2 as a factor. Explain why the binomial $2x - 6$, then, cannot be a factor of the polynomial.

**22.** *Concept Check*   On a quiz, a student factored $3k^3 - 12k^2 - 15k$ by first factoring out the common factor $3k$ to get $3k(k^2 - 4k - 5)$. Then the student wrote the following.

$$k^2 - 4k - 5$$
$$= k^2 - 5k + k - 5$$
$$= k(k - 5) + 1(k - 5)$$
$$= (k - 5)(k + 1) \qquad \text{Her answer}$$

**WHAT WENT WRONG?**   What is the correct factored form?

*Factor each trinomial completely.* ***See Examples 1–7.*** *(Hint: In Exercises 55–58, first write the trinomial in descending powers and then factor.)*

**23.** $3a^2 + 10a + 7$

**24.** $7r^2 + 8r + 1$

**25.** $2y^2 + 7y + 6$

**26.** $5z^2 + 12z + 4$

**27.** $15m^2 + m - 2$

**28.** $6x^2 + x - 1$

**29.** $12s^2 + 11s - 5$

**30.** $20x^2 + 11x - 3$

**31.** $10m^2 - 23m + 12$

**32.** $6x^2 - 17x + 12$

**33.** $8w^2 - 14w + 3$

**34.** $9p^2 - 18p + 8$

**35.** $20y^2 - 39y - 11$

**36.** $10x^2 - 11x - 6$

**37.** $3x^2 - 15x + 16$

**38.** $2t^2 - 14t + 15$

**39.** $20x^2 + 22x + 6$

**40.** $36y^2 + 81y + 45$

**41.** $24x^2 - 42x + 9$

**42.** $48b^2 - 74b - 10$

**43.** $40m^2q + mq - 6q$

**44.** $15a^2b + 22ab + 8b$

**45.** $15n^4 - 39n^3 + 18n^2$

**46.** $24a^4 + 10a^3 - 4a^2$

**47.** $15x^2y^2 - 7xy^2 - 4y^2$

**48.** $14a^2b^3 + 15ab^3 - 9b^3$

**49.** $5a^2 - 7ab - 6b^2$

**50.** $6x^2 - 5xy - y^2$

**51.** $12s^2 + 11st - 5t^2$

**52.** $25a^2 + 25ab + 6b^2$

**53.** $6m^6n + 7m^5n^2 + 2m^4n^3$

**54.** $12k^3q^4 - 4k^2q^5 - kq^6$

**55.** $5 - 6x + x^2$

**56.** $7 - 8x + x^2$

**57.** $16 + 16x + 3x^2$

**58.** $18 + 65x + 7x^2$

**59.** $-10x^3 + 5x^2 + 140x$

**60.** $-18k^3 - 48k^2 + 66k$

**61.** $12x^2 - 47x - 4$

**62.** $12x^2 - 19x - 10$

**63.** $24y^2 - 41xy - 14x^2$

**64.** $24x^2 + 19xy - 5y^2$

**65.** $36x^4 - 64x^2y + 15y^2$

**66.** $36x^4 + 59x^2y + 24y^2$

**67.** $48a^2 - 94ab - 4b^2$

**68.** $48t^2 - 147ts + 9s^2$

**69.** $10x^4y^5 + 39x^3y^5 - 4x^2y^5$

**70.** $14x^7y^4 - 31x^6y^4 + 6x^5y^4$

**71.** $36a^3b^2 - 104a^2b^2 - 12ab^2$

**72.** $36p^4q + 129p^3q - 60p^2q$

**73.** $24x^2 - 46x + 15$

**74.** $24x^2 - 94x + 35$

**75.** $24x^4 + 55x^2 - 24$

**76.** $24x^4 + 17x^2 - 20$

**77.** $24x^2 + 38xy + 15y^2$

**78.** $24x^2 + 62xy + 33y^2$

If a trinomial has a negative coefficient for the squared term, as in $-2x^2 + 11x - 12$, it is usually easier to factor by first factoring out the common factor $-1$.

$$-2x^2 + 11x - 12$$
$$= -1(2x^2 - 11x + 12)$$
$$= -1(2x - 3)(x - 4)$$

*Use this method to factor each trinomial.* **See Example 7(b).**

**79.** $-x^2 - 4x + 21$

**80.** $-x^2 + x + 72$

**81.** $-3x^2 - x + 4$

**82.** $-5x^2 + 2x + 16$

**83.** $-2a^2 - 5ab - 2b^2$

**84.** $-3p^2 + 13pq - 4q^2$

*Brain Busters* Factor each polynomial. (Hint: *As the first step, factor out the greatest common factor.*)

**85.** $25q^2(m + 1)^3 - 5q(m + 1)^3 - 2(m + 1)^3$

**86.** $18x^2(y - 3)^2 - 21x(y - 3)^2 - 4(y - 3)^2$

**87.** $9x^2(r + 3)^3 + 12xy(r + 3)^3 + 4y^2(r + 3)^3$

**88.** $4t^2(k + 9)^7 + 20ts(k + 9)^7 + 25s^2(k + 9)^7$

*Brain Busters* Find all integers $k$ so that the trinomial can be factored by the methods of this section.

**89.** $5x^2 + kx - 1$

**90.** $2x^2 + kx - 3$

**91.** $2m^2 + km + 5$

**92.** $3y^2 + ky + 4$

### PREVIEW EXERCISES

*Find each product.* **See Section 5.6.**

**93.** $(7p + 3)(7p - 3)$

**94.** $(3h + 5k)(3h - 5k)$

**95.** $(x + 6)^2$

**96.** $(3t + 4)^2$

## 6.4 Special Factoring Techniques

By reversing the rules for multiplication of binomials from **Section 5.6,** we get rules for factoring polynomials in certain forms.

**OBJECTIVE 1** **Factor a difference of squares.** The formula for the product of the sum and difference of the same two terms is

$$(x + y)(x - y) = x^2 - y^2.$$

Reversing this rule leads to the following special factoring rule.

**Factoring a Difference of Squares**

$$x^2 - y^2 = (x + y)(x - y)$$

For example,
$$m^2 - 16$$
$$= m^2 - 4^2$$
$$= (m + 4)(m - 4).$$

The following conditions must be true for a binomial to be a difference of squares.

1. Both terms of the binomial must be squares, such as

$$x^2, \quad 9y^2 = (3y)^2, \quad 25 = 5^2, \quad 1 = 1^2, \quad m^4 = (m^2)^2.$$

2. The terms of the binomial must have different signs (one positive and one negative).

**NOW TRY
EXERCISE 1**

Factor each binomial if possible.
**(a)** $x^2 - 100$ **(b)** $x^2 + 49$

**EXAMPLE 1** Factoring Differences of Squares

Factor each binomial if possible.

$$x^2 - y^2 = (x + y)(x - y)$$

**(a)** $a^2 - 49 = a^2 - 7^2 = (a + 7)(a - 7)$ **(b)** $y^2 - m^2 = (y + m)(y - m)$

**(c)** $x^2 - 8$
Because 8 is not the square of an integer, this binomial does not satisfy the conditions above. It is a prime polynomial.

**(d)** $p^2 + 16$
Since $p^2 + 16$ is a *sum* of squares, it is not equal to $(p + 4)(p - 4)$. Also, we use FOIL and try the following.

$$(p - 4)(p - 4)$$
$$= p^2 - 8p + 16, \quad \text{not} \quad p^2 + 16.$$
$$(p + 4)(p + 4)$$
$$= p^2 + 8p + 16, \quad \text{not} \quad p^2 + 16.$$

Thus, $p^2 + 16$ is a prime polynomial.

NOW TRY

**NOW TRY ANSWERS**
**1. (a)** $(x + 10)(x - 10)$
 **(b)** prime

⚠ **CAUTION** *As **Example 1(d)** suggests, after any common factor is removed, a sum of squares cannot be factored.*

NOW TRY
EXERCISE 2

Factor each difference of squares.

**(a)** $9t^2 - 100$

**(b)** $36a^2 - 49b^2$

**EXAMPLE 2** Factoring Differences of Squares

Factor each difference of squares.

$$x^2 \quad - \quad y^2 = (x \quad + \quad y)(x \quad - \quad y)$$

**(a)** $25m^2 - 16 = (5m)^2 - 4^2 = (5m + 4)(5m - 4)$

**(b)** $49z^2 - 64t^2$

$\quad = (7z)^2 - (8t)^2$     Write each term as a square.

$\quad = (7z + 8t)(7z - 8t)$     Factor the difference of squares.     NOW TRY

---

**NOTE** *Always check a factored form by multiplying.*

---

NOW TRY
EXERCISE 3

Factor completely.

**(a)** $16k^2 - 64$

**(b)** $m^4 - 144$

**(c)** $v^4 - 625$

**EXAMPLE 3** Factoring More Complex Differences of Squares

Factor completely.

**(a)** $81y^2 - 36$

$\quad = 9(9y^2 - 4)$     Factor out the GCF, 9.

$\quad = 9[(3y)^2 - 2^2]$     Write each term as a square.

$\quad = 9(3y + 2)(3y - 2)$     Factor the difference of squares.

**(b)**         $p^4 - 36$

$\quad = (p^2)^2 - 6^2$     Write each term as a square.

$\boxed{\text{Neither binomial can be factored further.}} = (p^2 + 6)(p^2 - 6)$     Factor the difference of squares.

**(c)**        $m^4 - 16$

$\quad = (m^2)^2 - 4^2$

$\quad = (m^2 + 4)(m^2 - 4)$     Factor the difference of squares.

$\boxed{\text{Don't stop here.}} = (m^2 + 4)(m + 2)(m - 2)$     Factor the difference of squares again.

    NOW TRY

---

⚠ **CAUTION** *Factor again when any of the factors is a difference of squares,* as in **Example 3(c).** Check by multiplying.

---

**OBJECTIVE 2** Factor a perfect square trinomial. The expressions 144, $4x^2$, and $81m^6$ are called **perfect squares** because

$$144 = 12^2, \quad 4x^2 = (2x)^2, \quad \text{and} \quad 81m^6 = (9m^3)^2.$$

A **perfect square trinomial** is a trinomial that is the square of a binomial. For example, $x^2 + 8x + 16$ is a perfect square trinomial because it is the square of the binomial $x + 4$.

$$x^2 + 8x + 16$$

$$= (x + 4)(x + 4)$$

$$= (x + 4)^2$$

NOW TRY ANSWERS

**2. (a)** $(3t + 10)(3t - 10)$
   **(b)** $(6a + 7b)(6a - 7b)$

**3. (a)** $16(k + 2)(k - 2)$
   **(b)** $(m^2 + 12)(m^2 - 12)$
   **(c)** $(v^2 + 25)(v + 5)(v - 5)$

On the one hand, a necessary condition for a trinomial to be a perfect square is that *two of its terms be perfect squares.* For this reason, $16x^2 + 4x + 15$ is not a perfect square trinomial, because only the term $16x^2$ is a perfect square.

On the other hand, even if two of the terms are perfect squares, the trinomial may not be a perfect square trinomial. For example, $x^2 + 6x + 36$ has two perfect square terms, $x^2$ and 36, but it is not a perfect square trinomial.

### Factoring Perfect Square Trinomials

$$x^2 + 2xy + y^2 = (x + y)^2$$
$$x^2 - 2xy + y^2 = (x - y)^2$$

*The middle term of a perfect square trinomial is always twice the product of the two terms in the squared binomial (as shown in Section 5.6). Use this rule to check any attempt to factor a trinomial that appears to be a perfect square.*

*NOW TRY*
*EXERCISE 4*
Factor $y^2 + 14y + 49$.

### EXAMPLE 4  Factoring a Perfect Square Trinomial

Factor $x^2 + 10x + 25$.

The $x^2$-term is a perfect square, and so is 25.

$$\text{Try to factor} \quad x^2 + 10x + 25 \quad \text{as} \quad (x + 5)^2.$$

To check, take twice the product of the two terms in the squared binomial.

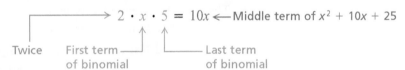

Since $10x$ is the middle term of the trinomial, the trinomial is a perfect square.

$$x^2 + 10x + 25 \quad \text{factors as} \quad (x + 5)^2. \qquad \text{NOW TRY}$$

### EXAMPLE 5  Factoring Perfect Square Trinomials

Factor each trinomial.

**(a)** $x^2 - 22x + 121$

The first and last terms are perfect squares ($121 = 11^2$ or $(-11)^2$). Check to see whether the middle term of $x^2 - 22x + 121$ is twice the product of the first and last terms of the binomial $x - 11$.

$$2 \cdot x \cdot (-11) = -22x \leftarrow \text{Middle term of } x^2 - 22x + 121$$

Twice— First    —Last
term    term

Thus, $x^2 - 22x + 121$ is a perfect square trinomial.

$$x^2 - 22x + 121 \quad \text{factors as} \quad (x - 11)^2.$$

Same sign

*NOW TRY ANSWER*
**4.** $(y + 7)^2$

*Notice that the sign of the second term in the squared binomial is the same as the sign of the middle term in the trinomial.*

*NOW TRY*
*EXERCISE 5*

Factor each trinomial.

**(a)** $t^2 - 18t + 81$

**(b)** $4p^2 - 28p + 49$

**(c)** $9x^2 + 6x + 4$

**(d)** $80x^3 + 120x^2 + 45x$

**(b)** $9m^2 - 24m + 16 = (3m)^2 + 2(3m)(-4) + (-4)^2 = (3m - 4)^2$

Twice ⎯ First term ⎯ Last term

**(c)** $25y^2 + 20y + 16$

The first and last terms are perfect squares.

$$25y^2 = (5y)^2 \quad \text{and} \quad 16 = 4^2$$

Twice the product of the first and last terms of the binomial $5y + 4$ is

$$2 \cdot 5y \cdot 4 = 40y,$$

which is *not* the middle term of

$$25y^2 + 20y + 16.$$

This trinomial is not a perfect square. In fact, the trinomial cannot be factored even with the methods of the previous sections. It is a prime polynomial.

**(d)** $12z^3 + 60z^2 + 75z$

$\quad = 3z(4z^2 + 20z + 25)$      Factor out the common factor, $3z$.

$\quad = 3z[(2z)^2 + 2(2z)(5) + 5^2]$    $4z^2 + 20z + 25$ is a perfect square trinomial.

$\quad = 3z(2z + 5)^2$      Factor.      *NOW TRY*

---

**NOTE**

1. The sign of the second term in the squared binomial is always the same as the sign of the middle term in the trinomial.

2. The first and last terms of a perfect square trinomial must be *positive,* because they are squares. For example, the polynomial $x^2 - 2x - 1$ cannot be a perfect square, because the last term is negative.

3. Perfect square trinomials can also be factored by using grouping or the FOIL method, although using the method of this section is often easier.

---

**OBJECTIVE 3** **Factor a difference of cubes.** We can factor a **difference of cubes** by using the following pattern.

**Factoring a Difference of Cubes**

$$x^3 - y^3 = (x - y)(x^2 + xy + y^2)$$

***This pattern for factoring a difference of cubes should be memorized.*** To see that the pattern is correct, multiply $(x - y)(x^2 + xy + y^2)$.

$$\begin{array}{r} x^2 + xy\ + y^2 \\ x\ - y \\ \hline -x^2y - xy^2 - y^3 \\ x^3 + x^2y + xy^2 \\ \hline x^3 \qquad\qquad - y^3 \end{array}$$

Multiply vertically. (Section 5.5)

$-y(x^2 + xy + y^2)$

$x(x^2 + xy + y^2)$

Add.

NOW TRY ANSWERS
**5.** **(a)** $(t - 9)^2$
   **(b)** $(2p - 7)^2$
   **(c)** prime
   **(d)** $5x(4x + 3)^2$

Notice the pattern of the terms in the factored form of $x^3 - y^3$.

- $x^3 - y^3 =$ (a binomial factor)(a trinomial factor)
- The binomial factor has the difference of the cube roots of the given terms.
- The terms in the trinomial factor are all positive.
- The terms in the binomial factor help to determine the trinomial factor.

$$x^3 - y^3 = (x - y)(\underset{\text{First term squared}}{x^2} + \underset{\substack{\text{positive} \\ \text{product of} \\ \text{the terms}}}{xy} + \underset{\substack{\text{second term} \\ \text{squared}}}{y^2})$$

---

⚠ **CAUTION**  The polynomial $x^3 - y^3$ is not equivalent to $(x - y)^3$.

$$x^3 - y^3 \qquad\qquad (x - y)^3$$
$$= (x - y)(x^2 + xy + y^2) \qquad = (x - y)(x - y)(x - y)$$
$$= (x - y)(x^2 - 2xy + y^2)$$

---

NOW TRY
EXERCISE 6
Factor each polynomial.

(a) $a^3 - 27$

(b) $8t^3 - 125$

(c) $3k^3 - 192$

(d) $125x^3 - 343y^6$

**EXAMPLE 6**  Factoring Differences of Cubes

Factor each polynomial.

(a) $m^3 - 125$

Let $x = m$ and $y = 5$ in the pattern for the difference of cubes.

$$x^3 - y^3 = (x - y)(x^2 + xy + y^2)$$
$$m^3 - 125 = m^3 - 5^3 = (m - 5)(m^2 + 5m + 5^2) \qquad \text{Let } x = m, y = 5.$$
$$= (m - 5)(m^2 + 5m + 25) \qquad\qquad 5^2 = 25$$

(b) $8p^3 - 27$

$$= (2p)^3 - 3^3 \qquad\qquad 8p^3 = (2p)^3 \text{ and } 27 = 3^3.$$
$$= (2p - 3)[(2p)^2 + (2p)3 + 3^2] \qquad \text{Let } x = 2p, y = 3.$$
$$= (2p - 3)(4p^2 + 6p + 9) \qquad \text{Apply the exponents. Multiply.}$$

$(2p)^2 = 2^2 p^2 = 4p^2,$ NOT $2p^2$.

(c) $4m^3 - 32$

$$= 4(m^3 - 8) \qquad\qquad \text{Factor out the common factor, 4.}$$
$$= 4(m^3 - 2^3) \qquad\qquad 8 = 2^3$$
$$= 4(m - 2)(m^2 + 2m + 4) \qquad \text{Factor the difference of cubes.}$$

(d) $125t^3 - 216s^6$

$$= (5t)^3 - (6s^2)^3 \qquad\qquad \text{Write each term as a cube.}$$
$$= (5t - 6s^2)[(5t)^2 + 5t(6s^2) + (6s^2)^2] \qquad \text{Factor the difference of cubes.}$$
$$= (5t - 6s^2)(25t^2 + 30ts^2 + 36s^4) \qquad \text{Apply the exponents. Multiply.}$$

NOW TRY ↻

NOW TRY ANSWERS
6. (a) $(a - 3)(a^2 + 3a + 9)$
   (b) $(2t - 5)(4t^2 + 10t + 25)$
   (c) $3(k - 4)(k^2 + 4k + 16)$
   (d) $(5x - 7y^2) \cdot$
   $(25x^2 + 35xy^2 + 49y^4)$

⚠ **CAUTION** A common error in factoring a difference of cubes, such as $x^3 - y^3 = (x - y)(x^2 + xy + y^2)$, is to try to factor $x^2 + xy + y^2$. This is usually not possible.

---

**OBJECTIVE 4** Factor a sum of cubes. A sum of squares, such as $m^2 + 25$, cannot be factored by using real numbers, but a **sum of cubes** can.

**Factoring a Sum of Cubes**

$$x^3 + y^3 = (x + y)(x^2 - xy + y^2)$$

Compare the pattern for the *sum* of cubes with that for the *difference* of cubes.

┌─ Positive ─┐

$$x^3 - y^3 = (x - y)(x^2 + xy + y^2)$$    Difference of cubes

└─ Same sign ─┘   └─ Opposite sign ─┘

The only difference between the patterns is the positive and negative signs.

┌─ Positive ─┐

$$x^3 + y^3 = (x + y)(x^2 - xy + y^2)$$    Sum of cubes

└─ Same sign ─┘   └─ Opposite sign ─┘

⌐ NOW TRY
  EXERCISE 7

Factor each polynomial.

**(a)** $x^3 + 125$

**(b)** $27a^3 + 8b^3$

*EXAMPLE 7* **Factoring Sums of Cubes**

Factor each polynomial.

**(a)** $k^3 + 27$

$\quad = k^3 + 3^3$ $\qquad\qquad$ $27 = 3^3$

$\quad = (k + 3)(k^2 - 3k + 3^2)$ $\quad$ Factor the sum of cubes.

$\quad = (k + 3)(k^2 - 3k + 9)$ $\quad$ Apply the exponent.

**(b)** $8m^3 + 125n^3$

$\quad = (2m)^3 + (5n)^3$ $\qquad\qquad\qquad$ $8m^3 = (2m)^3$ and $125n^3 = (5n)^3$.

$\quad = (2m + 5n)[(2m)^2 - 2m(5n) + (5n)^2]$ $\quad$ Factor the sum of cubes.

$\quad = (2m + 5n)(4m^2 - 10mn + 25n^2)$ ⟵ Be careful: $(2m)^2 = 2^2m^2$ and $(5n)^2 = 5^2n^2$.

**(c)** $1000a^6 + 27b^3$

$\quad = (10a^2)^3 + (3b)^3$

$\quad = (10a^2 + 3b)[(10a^2)^2 - (10a^2)(3b) + (3b)^2]$ $\quad$ Factor the sum of cubes.

$\quad = (10a^2 + 3b)(100a^4 - 30a^2b + 9b^2)$ $\qquad$ $(10a^2)^2 = 10^2(a^2)^2 = 100a^4$

NOW TRY ↻

*NOW TRY ANSWERS*

**7. (a)** $(x + 5)(x^2 - 5x + 25)$

$\quad$ **(b)** $(3a + 2b)(9a^2 - 6ab + 4b^2)$

The methods of factoring discussed in this section are summarized here.

> **Special Factorizations**
>
> **Difference of squares**       $x^2 - y^2 = (x + y)(x - y)$
>
> **Perfect square trinomials**   $x^2 + 2xy + y^2 = (x + y)^2$
>
> $x^2 - 2xy + y^2 = (x - y)^2$
>
> **Difference of cubes**         $x^3 - y^3 = (x - y)(x^2 + xy + y^2)$
>
> **Sum of cubes**                $x^3 + y^3 = (x + y)(x^2 - xy + y^2)$
>
> *The sum of squares can be factored only if the terms have a common factor.*

## 6.4 EXERCISES

**MyMathLab**  Math XL PRACTICE  WATCH  DOWNLOAD  READ  REVIEW

🌐 *Complete solution available on the Video Resources on DVD*

**1.** *Concept Check*  To help you factor the difference of squares, complete the following list of squares.

$1^2 =$ _____     $2^2 =$ _____     $3^2 =$ _____     $4^2 =$ _____     $5^2 =$ _____

$6^2 =$ _____     $7^2 =$ _____     $8^2 =$ _____     $9^2 =$ _____     $10^2 =$ _____

$11^2 =$ _____    $12^2 =$ _____    $13^2 =$ _____    $14^2 =$ _____    $15^2 =$ _____

$16^2 =$ _____    $17^2 =$ _____    $18^2 =$ _____    $19^2 =$ _____    $20^2 =$ _____

**2.** *Concept Check*  The following powers of $x$ are all perfect squares: $x^2, x^4, x^6, x^8, x^{10}$. On the basis of this observation, we may make a conjecture (an educated guess) that if the power of a variable is divisible by _____ (with 0 remainder), then we have a perfect square.

**3.** *Concept Check*  To help you factor the sum or difference of cubes, complete the following list of cubes.

$1^3 =$ _____     $2^3 =$ _____     $3^3 =$ _____     $4^3 =$ _____     $5^3 =$ _____

$6^3 =$ _____     $7^3 =$ _____     $8^3 =$ _____     $9^3 =$ _____     $10^3 =$ _____

**4.** *Concept Check*  The following powers of $x$ are all perfect cubes: $x^3, x^6, x^9, x^{12}, x^{15}$. On the basis of this observation, we may make a conjecture that if the power of a variable is divisible by _____ (with 0 remainder), then we have a perfect cube.

**5.** *Concept Check*  Identify each monomial as a *perfect square*, a *perfect cube*, *both of these*, or *neither of these*.

(a) $64x^6y^{12}$     (b) $125t^6$     (c) $49x^{12}$     (d) $81r^{10}$

**6.** *Concept Check*  What must be true for $x^n$ to be both a perfect square and a perfect cube?

*Factor each binomial completely. If the binomial is prime, say so. Use your answers from Exercises 1 and 2 as necessary. See Examples 1–3.*

🌐 **7.** $y^2 - 25$           **8.** $t^2 - 16$           **9.** $x^2 - 144$

**10.** $x^2 - 400$          **11.** $m^2 + 64$          **12.** $k^2 + 49$

**13.** $4m^2 + 16$          **14.** $9x^2 + 81$          🌐 **15.** $9r^2 - 4$

**16.** $4x^2 - 9$          🌐 **17.** $36x^2 - 16$          **18.** $32a^2 - 8$

**19.** $196p^2 - 225$      **20.** $361q^2 - 400$      **21.** $16r^2 - 25a^2$

**22.** $49m^2 - 100p^2$      **23.** $100x^2 + 49$      **24.** $81w^2 + 16$

**25.** $p^4 - 49$      **26.** $r^4 - 25$      **27.** $x^4 - 1$

**28.** $y^4 - 10,000$      **29.** $p^4 - 256$      **30.** $k^4 - 81$

**31.** *Concept Check*   When a student was directed to factor $k^4 - 81$ from **Exercise 30** completely, his teacher did not give him full credit for the answer

$$(k^2 + 9)(k^2 - 9).$$

The student argued that since his answer does indeed give $k^4 - 81$ when multiplied out, he should be given full credit. *WHAT WENT WRONG?* Give the correct factored form.

**32.** *Concept Check*   The binomial $4x^2 + 36$ is a sum of squares that *can* be factored. How is this binomial factored? When can the sum of squares be factored?

*Concept Check*   *Find the value of the indicated variable.*

**33.** Find $b$ so that $x^2 + bx + 25$ factors as $(x + 5)^2$.

**34.** Find $c$ so that $4m^2 - 12m + c$ factors as $(2m - 3)^2$.

**35.** Find $a$ so that $ay^2 - 12y + 4$ factors as $(3y - 2)^2$.

**36.** Find $b$ so that $100a^2 + ba + 9$ factors as $(10a + 3)^2$.

*Factor each trinomial completely.* **See Examples 4 and 5.**

**37.** $w^2 + 2w + 1$      **38.** $p^2 + 4p + 4$

**39.** $x^2 - 8x + 16$      **40.** $x^2 - 10x + 25$

**41.** $2x^2 + 24x + 72$      **42.** $3y^2 + 48y + 192$

**43.** $16x^2 - 40x + 25$      **44.** $36y^2 - 60y + 25$

**45.** $49x^2 - 28xy + 4y^2$      **46.** $4z^2 - 12zw + 9w^2$

**47.** $64x^2 + 48xy + 9y^2$      **48.** $9t^2 + 24tr + 16r^2$

**49.** $50h^2 - 40hy + 8y^2$      **50.** $18x^2 - 48xy + 32y^2$

**51.** $4k^3 - 4k^2 + 9k$      **52.** $9r^3 - 6r^2 + 16r$

**53.** $25z^4 + 5z^3 + z^2$      **54.** $4x^4 + 2x^3 + x^2$

*Factor each binomial completely. Use your answers from **Exercises 3 and 4** as necessary. See* **Examples 6 and 7.**

**55.** $a^3 - 1$      **56.** $m^3 - 8$      **57.** $m^3 + 8$

**58.** $b^3 + 1$      **59.** $k^3 + 1000$      **60.** $p^3 + 512$

**61.** $27x^3 - 64$      **62.** $64y^3 - 27$      **63.** $6p^3 + 6$

**64.** $81x^3 + 3$      **65.** $5x^3 + 40$      **66.** $128y^3 + 54$

**67.** $y^3 - 8x^3$      **68.** $w^3 - 216z^3$

**69.** $2x^3 - 16y^3$      **70.** $27w^3 - 216z^3$

**71.** $8p^3 + 729q^3$      **72.** $64x^3 + 125y^3$

**73.** $27a^3 + 64b^3$      **74.** $125m^3 + 8p^3$

**75.** $125t^3 + 8s^3$      **76.** $27r^3 + 1000s^3$

**77.** $8x^3 - 125y^6$      **78.** $27t^3 - 64s^6$

**79.** $27m^6 + 8n^3$      **80.** $1000r^6 + 27s^3$

**81.** $x^9 + y^9$      **82.** $x^9 - y^9$

*Although we usually factor polynomials using integers, we can apply the same concepts to factoring using fractions and decimals.*

$$z^2 - \frac{9}{16}$$

$$= z^2 - \left(\frac{3}{4}\right)^2 \qquad \frac{9}{16} = \left(\frac{3}{4}\right)^2$$

$$= \left(z + \frac{3}{4}\right)\left(z - \frac{3}{4}\right) \qquad \text{Factor the difference of squares.}$$

*Apply the special factoring rules of this section to factor each binomial or trinomial.*

**83.** $p^2 - \dfrac{1}{9}$

**84.** $q^2 - \dfrac{1}{4}$

**85.** $36m^2 - \dfrac{16}{25}$

**86.** $100b^2 - \dfrac{4}{49}$

**87.** $x^2 - 0.64$

**88.** $y^2 - 0.36$

**89.** $t^2 + t + \dfrac{1}{4}$

**90.** $m^2 + \dfrac{2}{3}m + \dfrac{1}{9}$

**91.** $x^2 - 1.0x + 0.25$

**92.** $y^2 - 1.4y + 0.49$

**93.** $x^3 + \dfrac{1}{8}$

**94.** $x^3 + \dfrac{1}{64}$

*Brain Busters*    *Factor each polynomial completely.*

**95.** $(m + n)^2 - (m - n)^2$

**96.** $(a - b)^3 - (a + b)^3$

**97.** $m^2 - p^2 + 2m + 2p$

**98.** $3r - 3k + 3r^2 - 3k^2$

## PREVIEW EXERCISES

*Solve each equation.* ***See Sections 2.1 and 2.2.***

**99.** $m - 4 = 0$      **100.** $3t + 2 = 0$      **101.** $2t + 10 = 0$      **102.** $7x = 0$

## SUMMARY EXERCISES on Factoring

As you factor a polynomial, ask yourself these questions to decide on a suitable factoring technique.

### Factoring a Polynomial

**1. Is there a common factor?** If so, factor it out.

**2. How many terms are in the polynomial?**

*Two terms:* Check to see whether it is a difference of squares or a sum or difference of cubes. If so, factor as in **Section 6.4.**

*Three terms:* Is it a perfect square trinomial? If the trinomial is not a perfect square, check to see whether the coefficient of the second-degree term is 1. If so, use the method of **Section 6.2.** If the coefficient of the second-degree term of the trinomial is not 1, use the general factoring methods of **Section 6.3.**

*Four terms:* Try to factor the polynomial by grouping, as in **Section 6.1.**

**3. Can any factors be factored further?** If so, factor them.

(continued)

*Match each polynomial in Column I with the best choice for factoring it in Column II. The choices in Column II may be used once, more than once, or not at all.*

**I**

1. $12x^2 + 20x + 8$
2. $x^2 - 17x + 72$
3. $16m^2n + 24mn - 40mn^2$
4. $64a^2 - 121b^2$
5. $36p^2 - 60pq + 25q^2$
6. $z^2 - 4z + 6$
7. $8r^3 - 125$
8. $x^6 + 4x^4 - 3x^2 - 12$
9. $4w^2 + 49$
10. $z^2 - 24z + 144$

**II**

**A.** Factor out the GCF. No further factoring is possible.

**B.** Factor a difference of squares.

**C.** Factor a difference of cubes.

**D.** Factor a sum of cubes.

**E.** Factor a perfect square trinomial.

**F.** Factor by grouping.

**G.** Factor out the GCF. Then factor a trinomial by grouping or trial and error.

**H.** Factor into two binomials by finding two integers whose product is the constant in the trinomial and whose sum is the coefficient of the middle term.

**I.** The polynomial is prime.

*Factor each polynomial completely.*

11. $a^2 - 4a - 12$
12. $a^2 + 17a + 72$
13. $6y^2 - 6y - 12$
14. $7y^6 + 14y^5 - 168y^4$
15. $6a + 12b + 18c$
16. $m^2 - 3mn - 4n^2$
17. $p^2 - 17p + 66$
18. $z^2 - 6z + 7z - 42$
19. $10z^2 - 7z - 6$
20. $2m^2 - 10m - 48$
21. $17x^3y^2 + 51xy$
22. $15y + 5$
23. $8a^5 - 8a^4 - 48a^3$
24. $8k^2 - 10k - 3$
25. $z^2 - 3za - 10a^2$
26. $50z^2 - 100$
27. $x^2 - 4x - 5x + 20$
28. $100n^2r^2 + 30nr^3 - 50n^2r$
29. $6n^2 - 19n + 10$
30. $9y^2 + 12y - 5$
31. $16x + 20$
32. $m^2 + 2m - 15$
33. $6y^2 - 5y - 4$
34. $m^2 - 81$
35. $6z^2 + 31z + 5$
36. $12x^2 + 47x - 4$
37. $4k^2 - 12k + 9$
38. $8p^2 + 23p - 3$
39. $54m^2 - 24z^2$
40. $8m^2 - 2m - 3$
41. $3k^2 + 4k - 4$
42. $45a^3b^5 - 60a^4b^2 + 75a^6b^4$
43. $14k^3 + 7k^2 - 70k$
44. $5 + r - 5s - rs$
45. $y^4 - 16$
46. $20y^5 - 30y^4$
47. $8m - 16m^2$
48. $k^2 - 16$
49. $z^3 - 8$
50. $y^2 - y - 56$
51. $k^2 + 9$
52. $27p^{10} - 45p^9 - 252p^8$
53. $32m^9 + 16m^5 + 24m^3$
54. $8m^3 + 125$
55. $16r^2 + 24rm + 9m^2$
56. $z^2 - 12z + 36$
57. $15h^2 + 11hg - 14g^2$
58. $5z^3 - 45z^2 + 70z$
59. $k^2 - 11k + 30$
60. $64p^2 - 100m^2$

**61.** $3k^3 - 12k^2 - 15k$

**62.** $y^2 - 4yk - 12k^2$

**63.** $1000p^3 + 27$

**64.** $64r^3 - 343$

**65.** $6 + 3m + 2p + mp$

**66.** $2m^2 + 7mn - 15n^2$

**67.** $16z^2 - 8z + 1$

**68.** $125m^4 - 400m^3n + 195m^2n^2$

**69.** $108m^2 - 36m + 3$

**70.** $100a^2 - 81y^2$

**71.** $x^2 - xy + y^2$

**72.** $4y^2 - 25$

**73.** $32z^3 + 56z^2 - 16z$

**74.** $10m^2 + 25m - 60$

**75.** $20 + 5m + 12n + 3mn$

**76.** $4 - 2q - 6p + 3pq$

**77.** $6a^2 + 10a - 4$

**78.** $36y^6 - 42y^5 - 120y^4$

**79.** $a^3 - b^3 + 2a - 2b$

**80.** $16k^2 - 48k + 36$

**81.** $64m^2 - 80mn + 25n^2$

**82.** $72y^3z^2 + 12y^2 - 24y^4z^2$

**83.** $8k^2 - 2kh - 3h^2$

**84.** $2a^2 - 7a - 30$

**85.** $2x^3 + 128$

**86.** $8a^3 - 27$

**87.** $10y^2 - 7yz - 6z^2$

**88.** $m^2 - 4m + 4$

**89.** $8a^2 + 23ab - 3b^2$

**90.** $a^4 - 625$

---

*RELATING CONCEPTS*   EXERCISES 91–98

**FOR INDIVIDUAL OR GROUP WORK**

*A binomial may be both a difference of squares and a difference of cubes. One example of such a binomial is $x^6 - 1$. With the techniques of **Section 6.4,** one factoring method will give the completely factored form, while the other will not. **Work Exercises 91–98 in order** to determine the method to use if you have to make such a decision.*

**91.** Factor $x^6 - 1$ as the difference of squares.

**92.** The factored form obtained in **Exercise 91** consists of a difference of cubes multiplied by a sum of cubes. Factor each binomial further.

**93.** Now start over and factor $x^6 - 1$ as the difference of cubes.

**94.** The factored form obtained in **Exercise 93** consists of a binomial that is a difference of squares and a trinomial. Factor the binomial further.

**95.** Compare your results in **Exercises 92 and 94.** Which one of these is factored completely?

**96.** Verify that the trinomial in the factored form in **Exercise 94** is the product of the two trinomials in the factored form in **Exercise 92.**

**97.** Use the results of **Exercises 91–96** to complete the following statement: In general, if I must choose between factoring first with the method for the difference of squares or the method for the difference of cubes, I should choose the _____ method to eventually obtain the completely factored form.

**98.** Find the *completely* factored form of $x^6 - 729$ by using the knowledge you gained in **Exercises 91–97.**

## 6.5 Solving Quadratic Equations by Factoring

**Galileo Galilei (1564–1642)**

Galileo Galilei developed theories to explain physical phenomena and set up experiments to test his ideas. According to legend, Galileo dropped objects of different weights from the Leaning Tower of Pisa to disprove the belief that heavier objects fall faster than lighter objects. He developed the formula

$$d = 16t^2$$

describing the motion of freely falling objects. In this formula, $d$ is the distance in feet that an object falls (disregarding air resistance) in $t$ seconds, regardless of weight.

The equation $d = 16t^2$ is a *quadratic equation*. A quadratic equation contains a second-degree term and no terms of greater degree.

### Quadratic Equation

A **quadratic equation** is an equation that can be written in the form

$$ax^2 + bx + c = 0,$$

where $a$, $b$, and $c$ are real numbers, with $a \neq 0$.

The form $ax^2 + bx + c = 0$ is the **standard form** of a quadratic equation.

$$x^2 + 5x + 6 = 0, \quad 2x^2 - 5x = 3, \quad x^2 = 4 \qquad \text{Quadratic equations}$$

Of these quadratic equations, only $x^2 + 5x + 6 = 0$ is in standard form.

We have factored many quadratic *expressions* of the form $ax^2 + bx + c$. In this section, we use factored quadratic expressions to solve quadratic *equations*.

**OBJECTIVE 1** Solve quadratic equations by factoring. We use the **zero-factor property** to solve a quadratic equation by factoring.

### Zero-Factor Property

**If $a$ and $b$ are real numbers and if $ab = 0$, then $a = 0$ or $b = 0$.**

That is, if the product of two numbers is 0, then at least one of the numbers must be 0. One number *must* be 0, but both *may* be 0.

### EXAMPLE 1 Using the Zero-Factor Property

Solve each equation.

**(a)** $(x + 3)(2x - 1) = 0$

The product $(x + 3)(2x - 1)$ is equal to 0. By the zero-factor property, the only way that the product of these two factors can be 0 is if at least one of the factors equals 0. Therefore, either $x + 3 = 0$ or $2x - 1 = 0$.

$$x + 3 = 0 \quad \text{or} \quad 2x - 1 = 0 \qquad \text{Zero-factor property}$$
$$x = -3 \qquad\qquad 2x = 1 \qquad \text{Solve each equation.}$$
$$x = \frac{1}{2} \qquad \text{Divide each side by 2.}$$

NOW TRY
EXERCISE 1
Solve each equation.

**(a)** $(x - 4)(3x + 1) = 0$

**(b)** $y(4y - 5) = 0$

The original equation, $(x + 3)(2x - 1) = 0$, has two solutions, $-3$ and $\frac{1}{2}$. Check these solutions by substituting $-3$ for $x$ in this equation. ***Then start over*** and substitute $\frac{1}{2}$ for $x$.

*CHECK*   Let $x = -3$.
$$(x + 3)(2x - 1) = 0$$
$$(-3 + 3)[2(-3) - 1] \stackrel{?}{=} 0$$
$$0(-7) = 0 \; \checkmark \; \text{True}$$

Let $x = \frac{1}{2}$.
$$(x + 3)(2x - 1) = 0$$
$$\left(\frac{1}{2} + 3\right)\left(2 \cdot \frac{1}{2} - 1\right) \stackrel{?}{=} 0$$
$$\frac{7}{2}(1 - 1) \stackrel{?}{=} 0$$
$$\frac{7}{2} \cdot 0 = 0 \; \checkmark \; \text{True}$$

Both $-3$ and $\frac{1}{2}$ result in true equations, so the solution set is $\left\{-3, \frac{1}{2}\right\}$.

**(b)**
$$y(3y - 4) = 0$$
$$y = 0 \quad \text{or} \quad 3y - 4 = 0 \qquad \text{Zero-factor property}$$

Don't forget that 0 is a solution.

$$3y = 4$$
$$y = \frac{4}{3}$$

*Check* these solutions by substituting each one into the original equation. The solution set is $\left\{0, \frac{4}{3}\right\}$.

NOW TRY

---

**NOTE**  The word *or* as used in **Example 1** means "one or the other or both."

---

If the polynomial in an equation is not already factored, first make sure that the equation is in standard form. Then factor.

**EXAMPLE 2**  Solving Quadratic Equations

Solve each equation.

**(a)** $x^2 - 5x = -6$

First, rewrite the equation in standard form by adding 6 to each side.

Don't factor $x$ out at this step.
$$x^2 - 5x = -6$$
$$x^2 - 5x + 6 = 0 \qquad \text{Add 6.}$$

Now factor $x^2 - 5x + 6$. Find two numbers whose product is 6 and whose sum is $-5$. These two numbers are $-2$ and $-3$, so we factor as follows.

$$(x - 2)(x - 3) = 0 \qquad \text{Factor.}$$
$$x - 2 = 0 \quad \text{or} \quad x - 3 = 0 \qquad \text{Zero-factor property}$$
$$x = 2 \quad \text{or} \qquad x = 3 \qquad \text{Solve each equation.}$$

NOW TRY ANSWERS
**1. (a)** $\left\{-\frac{1}{3}, 4\right\}$  **(b)** $\left\{0, \frac{5}{4}\right\}$

**NOW TRY
EXERCISE 2**
Solve $t^2 = -3t + 18$.

*CHECK* Let $x = 2$.

$$x^2 - 5x = -6$$
$$2^2 - 5(2) \stackrel{?}{=} -6$$
$$4 - 10 \stackrel{?}{=} -6$$
$$-6 = -6 \checkmark \text{ True}$$

Let $x = 3$.

$$x^2 - 5x = -6$$
$$3^2 - 5(3) \stackrel{?}{=} -6$$
$$9 - 15 \stackrel{?}{=} -6$$
$$-6 = -6 \checkmark \text{ True}$$

Both solutions check, so the solution set is $\{2, 3\}$.

**(b)**

$$y^2 = y + 20 \quad \boxed{\text{Write this equation in standard form.}}$$

Standard form $\longrightarrow y^2 - y - 20 = 0 \qquad$ Subtract $y$ and 20.

$$(y - 5)(y + 4) = 0 \qquad \text{Factor.}$$

$$y - 5 = 0 \quad \text{or} \quad y + 4 = 0 \qquad \text{Zero-factor property}$$

$$y = 5 \quad \text{or} \qquad y = -4 \qquad \text{Solve each equation.}$$

*Check* each solution to verify that the solution set is $\{-4, 5\}$.          NOW TRY

---

**Solving a Quadratic Equation by Factoring**

*Step 1* **Write the equation in standard form**—that is, with all terms on one side of the equals symbol in descending powers of the variable and 0 on the other side.

*Step 2* **Factor** completely.

*Step 3* **Use the zero-factor property** to set each factor with a variable equal to 0.

*Step 4* **Solve** the resulting equations.

*Step 5* **Check** each solution in the original equation.

---

**NOTE** Not all quadratic equations can be solved by factoring. A more general method for solving such equations is given in **Chapter 9.**

---

**NOW TRY
EXERCISE 3**
Solve $10p^2 + 65p = 35$.

**EXAMPLE 3** Solving a Quadratic Equation with a Common Factor

Solve $4p^2 + 40 = 26p$.

$$4p^2 + 40 = 26p$$
$$4p^2 - 26p + 40 = 0 \qquad \text{Standard form}$$
$$\boxed{\text{This 2 is } not \text{ a solution of the equation.}} \, 2(2p^2 - 13p + 20) = 0 \qquad \text{Factor out 2.}$$
$$2p^2 - 13p + 20 = 0 \qquad \text{Divide each side by 2.}$$
$$(2p - 5)(p - 4) = 0 \qquad \text{Factor.}$$
$$2p - 5 = 0 \quad \text{or} \quad p - 4 = 0 \qquad \text{Zero-factor property}$$
$$2p = 5 \qquad\qquad p = 4 \qquad \text{Solve each equation.}$$
$$p = \frac{5}{2}$$

**NOW TRY ANSWERS**
2. $\{-6, 3\}$   3. $\{-7, \frac{1}{2}\}$

*Check* each solution to verify that the solution set is $\{\frac{5}{2}, 4\}$.          NOW TRY

⚠ **CAUTION** A common error is to include the common factor $2$ as a solution in **Example 3.** *Only factors containing variables lead to solutions,* such as the factor $y$ in the equation $y(3y - 4) = 0$ in **Example 1(b).**

⌐ NOW TRY
  EXERCISE 4

Solve each equation.

**(a)** $9x^2 - 64 = 0$

**(b)** $m^2 = 5m$

**(c)** $p(6p - 1) = 2$

**EXAMPLE 4** Solving Quadratic Equations

Solve each equation.

**(a)**
$$16m^2 - 25 = 0$$
$$(4m + 5)(4m - 5) = 0 \qquad \text{Factor the difference of squares. (Section 6.4)}$$
$$4m + 5 = 0 \quad \text{or} \quad 4m - 5 = 0 \qquad \text{Zero-factor property}$$
$$4m = -5 \quad \text{or} \qquad 4m = 5 \qquad \text{Solve each equation.}$$
$$m = -\frac{5}{4} \quad \text{or} \qquad m = \frac{5}{4}$$

*Check* the solutions, $-\frac{5}{4}$ and $\frac{5}{4}$, in the original equation. The solution set is $\left\{-\frac{5}{4}, \frac{5}{4}\right\}$.

**(b)**
$$y^2 = 2y$$
$$y^2 - 2y = 0 \qquad \text{Standard form}$$
$$y(y - 2) = 0 \qquad \text{Factor.}$$
$$y = 0 \quad \text{or} \quad y - 2 = 0 \qquad \text{Zero-factor property}$$
$$y = 2 \qquad \text{Solve.}$$

> Don't forget to set the variable factor $y$ equal to 0.

The solution set is $\{0, 2\}$.

**(c)**
$$k(2k + 1) = 3$$

> To be in standard form, 0 must be on the right side.

$$2k^2 + k = 3 \qquad \text{Distributive property}$$
$$\text{Standard form} \longrightarrow 2k^2 + k - 3 = 0 \qquad \text{Subtract 3.}$$
$$(2k + 3)(k - 1) = 0 \qquad \text{Factor.}$$
$$2k + 3 = 0 \quad \text{or} \quad k - 1 = 0 \qquad \text{Zero-factor property}$$
$$2k = -3 \qquad\qquad k = 1 \qquad \text{Solve each equation.}$$
$$k = -\frac{3}{2}$$

The solution set is $\left\{-\frac{3}{2}, 1\right\}$.

NOW TRY ↻

⚠ **CAUTION** In **Example 4(b),** it is tempting to begin by dividing both sides of
$$y^2 = 2y$$
by $y$ to get $y = 2$. Note, however, that we do not get the other solution, 0, if we divide by a variable. (We *may* divide each side of an equation by a *nonzero* real number, however. For instance, in **Example 3** we divided each side by 2.)

In **Example 4(c),** we could not use the zero-factor property to solve the equation
$$k(2k + 1) = 3$$
in its given form because of the 3 on the right. *The zero-factor property applies only to a product that equals 0.*

NOW TRY ANSWERS

**4. (a)** $\left\{-\frac{8}{3}, \frac{8}{3}\right\}$ **(b)** $\{0, 5\}$

**(c)** $\left\{-\frac{1}{2}, \frac{2}{3}\right\}$

↶ NOW TRY
→ EXERCISE 5
Solve.

$$4x^2 - 4x + 1 = 0$$

**EXAMPLE 5** Solving Quadratic Equations with Double Solutions

Solve each equation.

**(a)**
$$z^2 - 22z + 121 = 0$$

$$(z - 11)^2 = 0 \qquad \text{Factor the perfect square trinomial.}$$

$$(z - 11)(z - 11) = 0 \qquad a^2 = a \cdot a$$

$$z - 11 = 0 \quad \text{or} \quad z - 11 = 0 \qquad \text{Zero-factor property}$$

Because the two factors are identical, they both lead to the same solution. (This is called a **double solution.**)

$$z = 11 \qquad \text{Add 11.}$$

CHECK
$$z^2 - 22z + 121 = 0$$

$$11^2 - 22(11) + 121 \overset{?}{=} 0 \qquad \text{Let } z = 11.$$

$$121 - 242 + 121 \overset{?}{=} 0$$

$$0 = 0 \ \checkmark \quad \text{True}$$

The solution set is $\{11\}$.

**(b)**
$$9t^2 - 30t = -25$$

$$9t^2 - 30t + 25 = 0 \qquad \text{Standard form}$$

$$(3t - 5)^2 = 0 \qquad \text{Factor the perfect square trinomial.}$$

$$3t - 5 = 0 \quad \text{or} \quad 3t - 5 = 0 \qquad \text{Zero-factor property}$$

$$3t = 5 \qquad \text{Solve the equation.}$$

$$t = \frac{5}{3} \qquad \tfrac{5}{3} \text{ is a double solution.}$$

*Check* by substituting $\frac{5}{3}$ in the original equation. The solution set is $\left\{\frac{5}{3}\right\}$.

NOW TRY ↻

⚠ **CAUTION** Each of the equations in **Example 5** has only *one* distinct solution. *There is no need to write the same number more than once in a solution set.*

**OBJECTIVE 2** **Solve other equations by factoring.** We can also use the zero-factor property to solve equations that involve more than two factors with variables. (These equations are *not* quadratic equations. Why not?)

**EXAMPLE 6** Solving Equations with More Than Two Variable Factors

Solve each equation.

**(a)**
$$6z^3 - 6z = 0$$

$$6z(z^2 - 1) = 0 \qquad \text{Factor out } 6z.$$

$$6z(z + 1)(z - 1) = 0 \qquad \text{Factor } z^2 - 1.$$

By an extension of the zero-factor property, this product can equal 0 only if at least one of the factors is 0. Write and solve three equations, one for each factor with a variable.

NOW TRY ANSWER
**5.** $\left\{\frac{1}{2}\right\}$

NOW TRY
EXERCISE 6

Solve each equation.

(a) $3x^3 - 27x = 0$

(b) $(3a - 1) \cdot$
$(2a^2 - 5a - 12) = 0$

$$6z = 0 \quad \text{or} \quad z + 1 = 0 \quad \text{or} \quad z - 1 = 0$$

$$z = 0 \quad \text{or} \qquad z = -1 \quad \text{or} \qquad z = 1$$

*Check* by substituting, in turn, $0$, $-1$, and $1$ into the original equation. The solution set is $\{-1, 0, 1\}$.

(b)
$$(3x - 1)(x^2 - 9x + 20) = 0$$

$$(3x - 1)(x - 5)(x - 4) = 0 \qquad \text{Factor } x^2 - 9x + 20.$$

$$3x - 1 = 0 \quad \text{or} \quad x - 5 = 0 \quad \text{or} \quad x - 4 = 0 \qquad \text{Zero-factor property}$$

$$x = \frac{1}{3} \quad \text{or} \qquad x = 5 \quad \text{or} \qquad x = 4 \qquad \text{Solve each equation.}$$

*Check* each solution to verify that the solution set is $\left\{\frac{1}{3}, 4, 5\right\}$.     NOW TRY

---

⚠ CAUTION   In **Example 6(b),** it would be unproductive to begin by multiplying the two factors together. The zero-factor property requires the *product* of two or more factors to equal $0$. ***Always consider first whether an equation is given in an appropriate form for the zero-factor property to apply.***

---

NOW TRY
EXERCISE 7

Solve.

$x(4x - 9) = (x - 2)^2 + 24$

**EXAMPLE 7**  Solving an Equation Requiring Multiplication before Factoring

Solve $(3x + 1)x = (x + 1)^2 + 5$.

The zero-factor property requires the *product* of two or more factors to equal $0$.

$$(3x + 1)x = (x + 1)^2 + 5 \qquad \boxed{(x + 1)^2 = (x + 1)(x + 1)}$$

$$3x^2 + x = x^2 + 2x + 1 + 5 \qquad \text{Multiply.}$$

$$3x^2 + x = x^2 + 2x + 6 \qquad \text{Combine like terms.}$$

$$2x^2 - x - 6 = 0 \qquad \text{Standard form}$$

$$(2x + 3)(x - 2) = 0 \qquad \text{Factor.}$$

$$2x + 3 = 0 \quad \text{or} \quad x - 2 = 0 \qquad \text{Zero-factor property}$$

$$x = -\frac{3}{2} \quad \text{or} \qquad x = 2 \qquad \text{Solve each equation.}$$

*Check* that the solution set is $\left\{-\frac{3}{2}, 2\right\}$.     NOW TRY

NOW TRY ANSWERS
6. (a) $\{-3, 0, 3\}$   (b) $\left\{-\frac{3}{2}, \frac{1}{3}, 4\right\}$
7. $\left\{-\frac{7}{3}, 4\right\}$

---

## 6.5 EXERCISES

*MyMathLab*    Math XL
PRACTICE

 WATCH

 DOWNLOAD

 READ

 REVIEW

⊙ *Complete solution available on the Video Resources on DVD*

*Concept Check*   In Exercises 1–5, fill in the blank with the correct response.

1. A quadratic equation in $x$ is an equation that can be put into the form _____ $= 0$.

2. The form $ax^2 + bx + c = 0$ is called _____ form.

3. If a quadratic equation is in standard form, to solve the equation we should begin by attempting to _____ the polynomial.

4. The equation $x^3 + x^2 + x = 0$ is not a quadratic equation, because _____.

5. If a quadratic equation $ax^2 + bx + c = 0$ has $c = 0$, then _____ *must* be a solution because _____ is a factor of the polynomial.

**6.** *Concept Check* Identify each equation as *linear* or *quadratic*.

(a) $2x - 5 = 6$          (b) $x^2 - 5 = -4$

(c) $x^2 + 2x - 3 = 2x^2 - 2$          (d) $5^2x + 2 = 0$

**7.** Students often become confused as to how to handle a constant, such as 2 in the equation $2x(3x - 4) = 0$. How would you explain to someone how to solve this equation and how to handle the constant 2?

**8.** *Concept Check* The number 9 is a *double solution* of the equation $(x - 9)^2 = 0$. Why is this so?

**9.** *Concept Check* Look at this "solution." **WHAT WENT WRONG?**

$$x(7x - 1) = 0$$
$$7x - 1 = 0 \quad \text{Zero-factor property}$$
$$x = \frac{1}{7}$$

The solution set is $\left\{\frac{1}{7}\right\}$.

**10.** *Concept Check* Look at this "solution." **WHAT WENT WRONG?**

$$3x(5x - 4) = 0$$
$$x = 3 \quad \text{or} \quad x = 0 \quad \text{or} \quad 5x - 4 = 0$$
$$x = \frac{4}{5}$$

The solution set is $\left\{3, 0, \frac{4}{5}\right\}$.

*Solve each equation, and check your solutions.* ***See Example 1.***

**11.** $(x + 5)(x - 2) = 0$      **12.** $(x - 1)(x + 8) = 0$

**13.** $(2m - 7)(m - 3) = 0$      **14.** $(6x + 5)(x + 4) = 0$

**15.** $(2x + 1)(6x - 1) = 0$      **16.** $(3x + 2)(10x - 1) = 0$

**17.** $t(6t + 5) = 0$      **18.** $w(4w + 1) = 0$

**19.** $2x(3x - 4) = 0$      **20.** $6y(4y + 9) = 0$

**21.** $(x - 6)(x - 6) = 0$      **22.** $(y + 1)(y + 1) = 0$

*Solve each equation, and check your solutions.* ***See Examples 2–7.***

**23.** $y^2 + 3y + 2 = 0$    **24.** $p^2 + 8p + 7 = 0$    **25.** $y^2 - 3y + 2 = 0$

**26.** $r^2 - 4r + 3 = 0$    **27.** $x^2 = 24 - 5x$    **28.** $t^2 = 2t + 15$

**29.** $x^2 = 3 + 2x$    **30.** $x^2 = 4 + 3x$    **31.** $z^2 + 3z = -2$

**32.** $p^2 - 2p = 3$    **33.** $m^2 + 8m + 16 = 0$    **34.** $x^2 - 6x + 9 = 0$

**35.** $3x^2 + 5x - 2 = 0$    **36.** $6r^2 - r - 2 = 0$    **37.** $12p^2 = 8 - 10p$

**38.** $18x^2 = 12 + 15x$    **39.** $9s^2 + 12s = -4$    **40.** $36x^2 + 60x = -25$

**41.** $y^2 - 9 = 0$    **42.** $m^2 - 100 = 0$    **43.** $16x^2 - 49 = 0$

**44.** $4w^2 - 9 = 0$    **45.** $n^2 = 121$    **46.** $x^2 = 400$

**47.** $x^2 = 7x$    **48.** $t^2 = 9t$    **49.** $6r^2 = 3r$

**50.** $10y^2 = -5y$    **51.** $x(x - 7) = -10$    **52.** $r(r - 5) = -6$

**53.** $3z(2z + 7) = 12$      **54.** $4x(2x + 3) = 36$

**55.** $2y(y + 13) = 136$      **56.** $t(3t - 20) = -12$

**57.** $(2r + 5)(3r^2 - 16r + 5) = 0$      **58.** $(3m + 4)(6m^2 + m - 2) = 0$

**59.** $(2x + 7)(x^2 + 2x - 3) = 0$      **60.** $(x + 1)(6x^2 + x - 12) = 0$

**61.** $9y^3 - 49y = 0$      **62.** $16r^3 - 9r = 0$

**63.** $r^3 - 2r^2 - 8r = 0$      **64.** $x^3 - x^2 - 6x = 0$

**65.** $x^3 + x^2 - 20x = 0$      **66.** $y^3 - 6y^2 + 8y = 0$

**67.** $r^4 = 2r^3 + 15r^2$      **68.** $x^3 = 3x + 2x^2$

**69.** $3x(x + 1) = (2x + 3)(x + 1)$      **70.** $2x(x + 3) = (3x + 1)(x + 3)$

🌐 **71.** $x^2 + (x + 1)^2 = (x + 2)^2$      **72.** $(x - 7)^2 + x^2 = (x + 1)^2$

*Brain Busters*    *Solve each equation, and check your solutions.*

**73.** $(2x)^2 = (2x + 4)^2 - (x + 5)^2$      **74.** $5 - (x - 1)^2 = (x - 2)^2$

**75.** $(x + 3)^2 - (2x - 1)^2 = 0$      **76.** $(4y - 3)^3 - 9(4y - 3) = 0$

**77.** $6p^2(p + 1) = 4(p + 1) - 5p(p + 1)$

**78.** $6x^2(2x + 3) = 4(2x + 3) + 5x(2x + 3)$

*Galileo's formula describing the motion of freely falling objects is*

$$d = 16t^2.$$

*The distance d in feet an object falls depends on the time t elapsed, in seconds. (This is an example of an important mathematical concept, the **function**.)*

**79. (a)** Use Galileo's formula and complete the following table. (*Hint:* Substitute each given value into the formula and solve for the unknown value.)

| t in seconds | 0 | 1 | 2 | 3 | | |
|---|---|---|---|---|---|---|
| d in feet | 0 | 16 | | | 256 | 576 |

✏️ **(b)** When $t = 0$, $d = 0$. Explain this in the context of the problem.

✏️ **80.** When you substituted 256 for *d* and solved the formula for *t* in **Exercise 79,** you should have found two solutions:   4 and $-4$. Why doesn't $-4$ make sense as an answer?

**TECHNOLOGY INSIGHTS**    EXERCISES 81–82

*In **Section 3.2,** we showed how an equation in one variable can be solved with a graphing calculator by getting 0 on one side and then replacing 0 with y to get a corresponding equation in two variables. The x-values of the x-intercepts of the graph of the two-variable equation then give the solutions of the original equation.*

     *Use the calculator screens to determine the solution set of each quadratic equation. Verify your answers by substitution.*

**81.** $x^2 + 0.4x - 0.05 = 0$

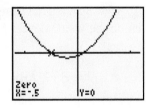 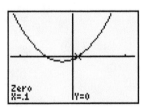

**82.** $2x^2 - 7.2x + 6.3 = 0$

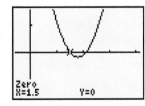 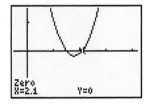

*Solve each problem. **See Sections 2.4 and 2.5.***

**83.** If a number is doubled and 6 is subtracted from this result, the answer is 3684. The unknown number is the year that Texas was admitted to the Union. What year was Texas admitted?

**84.** The length of the rectangle is 3 m more than its width. The perimeter of the rectangle is 34 m. Find the width of the rectangle.

**85.** Twice the sum of two consecutive integers is 28 more than the greater integer. Find the integers.

**86.** The area of a triangle with base 12 in. is 48 in.$^2$. Find the height of the triangle.

## 6.6 Applications of Quadratic Equations

### OBJECTIVES

**1** Solve problems involving geometric figures.

**2** Solve problems involving consecutive integers.

**3** Solve problems by applying the Pythagorean theorem.

**4** Solve problems by using given quadratic models.

We use factoring to solve quadratic equations that arise in application problems. We follow the same six problem-solving steps given in **Section 2.4.**

**Solving an Applied Problem**

*Step 1* **Read** the problem carefully. What information is given? What are you asked to find?

*Step 2* **Assign a variable** to represent the unknown value. Use a sketch, diagram, or table, as needed. If necessary, express any other unknown values in terms of the variable.

*Step 3* **Write an equation,** using the variable expression(s).

*Step 4* **Solve** the equation.

*Step 5* **State the answer.** Label it appropriately. Does it seem reasonable?

*Step 6* **Check** the answer in the words of the original problem.

**OBJECTIVE 1** **Solve problems involving geometric figures.** Refer to the formulas given on the inside covers of the text, if necessary.

**EXAMPLE 1** Solving an Area Problem

Abe Biggs wants to plant a triangular flower bed in a corner of his garden. One leg of the right-triangular flower bed will be 2 m shorter than the other leg. He wants the bed to have an area of 24 m$^2$. See **FIGURE 1**. Find the lengths of the legs.

*Step 1* **Read** the problem. We need to find the lengths of the legs of a right triangle with area 24 m$^2$.

*Step 2* **Assign a variable.**

Let $x$ = the length of one leg.

Then $x - 2$ = the length of the other leg.

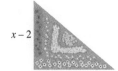

**FIGURE 1**

*NOW TRY*
*EXERCISE 1*
A right triangle has one leg that is 4 ft shorter than the other leg. The area of the triangle is 6 ft². Determine the lengths of the legs.

**Step 3**  **Write an equation.** The area of a right triangle is given by the formula

$$\text{area} = \frac{1}{2} \times \text{base} \times \text{height}.$$

In a right triangle, the legs are the base and height, so we substitute 24 for the area, $x$ for the base, and $x - 2$ for the height in the formula.

$$\mathcal{A} = \frac{1}{2}bh \qquad \text{Formula for the area of a triangle}$$

$$24 = \frac{1}{2}x(x - 2) \qquad \text{Let } \mathcal{A} = 24, b = x, h = x - 2.$$

**Step 4**  **Solve.**  $\quad 48 = x(x - 2) \qquad$ Multiply by 2.

$$48 = x^2 - 2x \qquad \text{Distributive property}$$

$$x^2 - 2x - 48 = 0 \qquad \text{Standard form}$$

$$(x + 6)(x - 8) = 0 \qquad \text{Factor.}$$

$$x + 6 = 0 \quad \text{or} \quad x - 8 = 0 \qquad \text{Zero-factor property}$$

$$x = -6 \quad \text{or} \qquad x = 8 \qquad \text{Solve each equation.}$$

**Step 5**  **State the answer.** The solutions are $-6$ and 8. Because a triangle cannot have a side of negative length, we discard the solution $-6$. Then the lengths of the legs will be 8 m and $8 - 2 = 6$ m.

**Step 6**  **Check.** The length of one leg is 2 m less than the length of the other leg, and the area is

$$\frac{1}{2}(8)(6) = 24 \text{ m}^2, \quad \text{as required.} \qquad \textit{NOW TRY}$$

⚠ **CAUTION**  *In solving applied problems, always check solutions against physical facts and discard any answers that are not appropriate.*

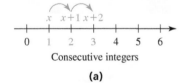

Consecutive integers

**(a)**

Consecutive even integers

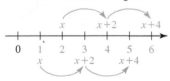

Consecutive odd integers

**(b)**

**FIGURE 2**

**OBJECTIVE 2**  **Solve problems involving consecutive integers.** Recall from our work in **Section 2.4** that **consecutive integers** are integers that are next to each other on a number line, such as 3 and 4, or $-11$ and $-10$. See **FIGURE 2(a)**.

**Consecutive odd integers** are *odd* integers that are next to each other, such as 3 and 5, or $-13$ and $-11$. **Consecutive even integers** are defined similarly—for example, 4 and 6 are consecutive even integers, as are $-10$ and $-8$. See **FIGURE 2(b)**.

**PROBLEM-SOLVING HINT**

If $x$ represents the lesser integer, then, for any

two consecutive integers, use $\qquad x, \quad x + 1;$

three consecutive integers, use $\qquad x, \quad x + 1, \quad x + 2;$

two consecutive even or odd integers, use $\qquad x, \quad x + 2;$

three consecutive even or odd integers, use $\qquad x, \quad x + 2, \quad x + 4.$

NOW TRY ANSWER
**1.** 2 ft, 6 ft

As a general rule in this book, we list consecutive integers in increasing order when solving applications.

NOW TRY
EXERCISE 2

The product of the first and second of three consecutive integers is 2 more than 8 times the third integer. Find the integers.

**EXAMPLE 2** Solving a Consecutive Integer Problem

The product of the second and third of three consecutive integers is 2 more than 7 times the first integer. Find the integers.

*Step 1* **Read** the problem. Note that the integers are consecutive.

*Step 2* **Assign a variable.**

Let $x =$ the first integer.

Then $x + 1 =$ the second integer,

and $x + 2 =$ the third integer.

*Step 3* **Write an equation.**

The product of the second and third   is   2 more than 7 times the first.

$$(x + 1)(x + 2) \qquad = \qquad 7x + 2$$

*Step 4* **Solve.**

$$x^2 + 3x + 2 = 7x + 2 \qquad \text{Multiply.}$$

$$x^2 - 4x = 0 \qquad \text{Standard form}$$

$$x(x - 4) = 0 \qquad \text{Factor.}$$

$$x = 0 \quad \text{or} \quad x = 4 \qquad \text{Zero-factor property}$$

*Step 5* **State the answer.** The solutions 0 and 4 each lead to a correct answer.

$$0, 1, 2 \qquad \text{or} \qquad 4, 5, 6$$

*Step 6* **Check.** The product of the second and third integers must equal 2 more than 7 times the first. Since $1 \cdot 2 = 7 \cdot 0 + 2$ and $5 \cdot 6 = 7 \cdot 4 + 2$, both sets of consecutive integers satisfy the statement of the problem.

NOW TRY

**OBJECTIVE 3** Solve problems by applying the Pythagorean theorem.

**Pythagorean Theorem**

If a right triangle has longest side of length $c$ and two other sides of lengths $a$ and $b$, then

$$a^2 + b^2 = c^2.$$

The longest side, the **hypotenuse**, is opposite the right angle. The two shorter sides are the **legs** of the triangle.

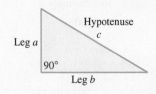

**EXAMPLE 3** Applying the Pythagorean Theorem

Patricia Walker and Ali Ulku leave their office, Patricia traveling north and Ali traveling east. When Ali is 1 mi farther than Patricia from the office, the distance between them is 2 mi more than Patricia's distance from the office. Find their distances from the office and the distance between them.

*Step 1* **Read** the problem again. There will be three answers to this problem.

NOW TRY ANSWER
**2.** 9, 10, 11 or $-2, -1, 0$

NOW TRY
EXERCISE 3
The longer leg of a right triangle is 7 ft longer than the shorter leg and the hypotenuse is 8 ft longer than the shorter leg. Find the lengths of the sides of the triangle.

*Step 2* **Assign a variable.**

Let $x$ = Patricia's distance from the office.

Then $x + 1$ = Ali's distance from the office,

and $x + 2$ = the distance between them.

Place these expressions on a right triangle, as in **FIGURE 3**.

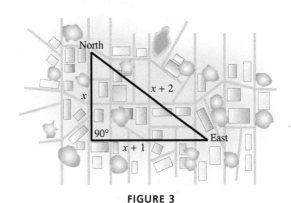

**FIGURE 3**

*Step 3* **Write an equation.** Use the Pythagorean theorem.

$$a^2 + b^2 = c^2$$
$$x^2 + (x + 1)^2 = (x + 2)^2$$

Be careful to substitute properly.

*Step 4* **Solve.**

$$x^2 + x^2 + 2x + 1 = x^2 + 4x + 4 \quad \text{Square each binomial.}$$
$$x^2 - 2x - 3 = 0 \quad \text{Standard form}$$
$$(x - 3)(x + 1) = 0 \quad \text{Factor.}$$
$$x - 3 = 0 \quad \text{or} \quad x + 1 = 0 \quad \text{Zero-factor property}$$
$$x = 3 \quad \text{or} \quad x = -1 \quad \text{Solve each equation.}$$

*Step 5* **State the answer.** Since $-1$ cannot represent a distance, 3 is the only possible answer. Patricia's distance is 3 mi, Ali's distance is $3 + 1 = 4$ mi, and the distance between them is $3 + 2 = 5$ mi.

*Step 6* **Check.** Since $3^2 + 4^2 = 5^2$, the answers are correct. NOW TRY

**PROBLEM-SOLVING HINT**

In solving a problem involving the Pythagorean theorem, be sure that the expressions for the sides are properly placed.

$$(\text{one leg})^2 + (\text{other leg})^2 = \text{hypotenuse}^2$$

**OBJECTIVE 4** Solve problems by using given quadratic models. In **Examples 1–3**, we wrote quadratic equations to model, or mathematically describe, various situations and then solved the equations. In the last two examples of this section, we are given the quadratic models and must use them to determine data.

*NOW TRY ANSWER*
**3.** 5 ft, 12 ft, 13 ft

NOW TRY
EXERCISE 4
Refer to **Example 4.** How long will it take for the ball to reach a height of 50 ft?

EXAMPLE 4    Finding the Height of a Ball

A tennis player's serve travels 180 ft per sec (123 mph). If she hits the ball directly upward, the height $h$ of the ball in feet at time $t$ in seconds is modeled by the quadratic equation

$$h = -16t^2 + 180t + 6.$$

How long will it take for the ball to reach a height of 206 ft?

A height of 206 ft means that $h = 206$, so we substitute 206 for $h$ in the equation.

$$h = -16t^2 + 180t + 6$$

$$206 = -16t^2 + 180t + 6 \qquad \text{Let } h = 206.$$

$$-16t^2 + 180t + 6 = 206 \qquad \text{Interchange sides.}$$

$$-16t^2 + 180t - 200 = 0 \qquad \text{Standard form}$$

$$4t^2 - 45t + 50 = 0 \qquad \text{Divide by } -4.$$

$$(4t - 5)(t - 10) = 0 \qquad \text{Factor.}$$

$$4t - 5 = 0 \quad \text{or} \quad t - 10 = 0 \qquad \text{Zero-factor property}$$

$$4t = 5 \quad \text{or} \qquad t = 10 \qquad \text{Solve each equation.}$$

$$t = \frac{5}{4}$$

Since we found two acceptable answers, the ball will be 206 ft above the ground twice, once on its way up and once on its way down, at $\frac{5}{4}$ sec and at 10 sec. See **FIGURE 4.**

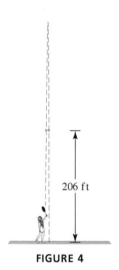

206 ft

**FIGURE 4**

NOW TRY

EXAMPLE 5    Modeling the Foreign-Born Population of the United States

The foreign-born population of the United States over the years 1930–2007 can be modeled by the quadratic equation

$$y = 0.01048x^2 - 0.5400x + 15.43,$$

where $x = 0$ represents 1930, $x = 10$ represents 1940, and so on, and $y$ is the number of people in millions. (*Source:* U.S. Census Bureau.)

**(a)** Use the model to find the foreign-born population in 1980 to the nearest tenth of a million.

Since $x = 0$ represents 1930, $x = 50$ represents 1980. Substitute 50 for $x$ in the equation.

$$y = 0.01048(50)^2 - 0.5400(50) + 15.43 \qquad \text{Let } x = 50.$$

$$y = 14.6 \qquad \qquad \text{Round to the nearest tenth.}$$

In 1980, the foreign-born population of the United States was about 14.6 million.

**(b)** Repeat part (a) for 2007.

$$y = 0.01048(77)^2 - 0.5400(77) + 15.43 \qquad \text{For 2007, let } x = 77.$$

$$y = 36.0 \qquad \qquad \text{Round to the nearest tenth.}$$

In 2007, the foreign-born population of the United States was about 36.0 million.

NOW TRY ANSWER
4. $\frac{1}{4}$ sec and 11 sec

NOW TRY
EXERCISE 5

Use the model in **Example 5** to find the foreign-born population of the United States in the year 2000. Give your answer to the nearest tenth of a million. How does it compare to the actual value from the table?

**(c)** The model used in parts (a) and (b) was developed using the data in the table below. How do the results in parts (a) and (b) compare to the actual data from the table?

| Year | Foreign-Born Population (millions) |
|------|------------------------------------|
| 1930 | 14.2 |
| 1940 | 11.6 |
| 1950 | 10.3 |
| 1960 | 9.7 |
| 1970 | 9.6 |
| 1980 | 14.1 |
| 1990 | 19.8 |
| 2000 | 28.4 |
| 2007 | 37.3 |

NOW TRY ANSWER
**5.** 29.0 million; The actual value is 28.4 million, so the answer using the model is slightly high.

From the table, the actual value for 1980 is 14.1 million. Our answer in part (a), 14.6 million, is slightly high. For 2007, the actual value is 37.3 million, so our answer of 36.0 million in part (b) is somewhat low.     NOW TRY

# 6.6 EXERCISES

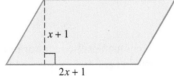    

🌐 *Complete solution available on the Video Resources on DVD*

**1.** *Concept Check*   To review the six problem-solving steps first introduced in **Section 2.4,** complete each statement.

   ***Step 1:*** _____ the problem carefully.

   ***Step 2:*** Assign a _____ to represent the unknown value.

   ***Step 3:*** Write a(n) _____ using the variable expression(s).

   ***Step 4:*** _____ the equation.

   ***Step 5:*** State the _____.

   ***Step 6:*** _____ the answer in the words of the _____ problem.

📝 **2.** A student solves an applied problem and gets 6 or −3 for the length of the side of a square. Which of these answers is reasonable? Explain.

*In Exercises 3–6, a figure and a corresponding geometric formula are given. Using x as the variable, complete Steps 3–6 for each problem. (Refer to the steps in Exercise 1 as needed.)*

**3.**

$x + 1$

$2x + 1$

Area of a parallelogram: $\mathcal{A} = bh$

The area of this parallelogram is 45 sq. units. Find its base and height.

**4.**

$x + 5$

$3x + 6$

Area of a triangle: $\mathcal{A} = \dfrac{1}{2}bh$

The area of this triangle is 60 sq. units. Find its base and height.

**5.**

$x - 8$

$x + 8$

**6.**

$x + 2$   $x$   $4$

Area of a rectangular rug: $A = LW$

The area of this rug is 80 sq. units. Find its length and width.

Volume of a rectangular Chinese box: $V = LWH$

The volume of this box is 192 cu. units. Find its length and width.

*Solve each problem. Check your answers to be sure that they are reasonable. Refer to the formulas on the inside covers.* **See Example 1.**

**7.** The length of a standard jewel case is 2 cm more than its width. The area of the rectangular top of the case is 168 cm². Find the length and width of the jewel case.

**8.** A standard DVD case is 6 cm longer than it is wide. The area of the rectangular top of the case is 247 cm². Find the length and width of the case.

**9.** The area of a triangle is 30 in.². The base of the triangle measures 2 in. more than twice the height of the triangle. Find the measures of the base and the height.

**10.** A certain triangle has its base equal in measure to its height. The area of the triangle is 72 m². Find the equal base and height measure.

**11.** A 10-gal aquarium is 3 in. higher than it is wide. Its length is 21 in., and its volume is 2730 in.³. What are the height and width of the aquarium?

**12.** A toolbox is 2 ft high, and its width is 3 ft less than its length. If its volume is 80 ft³, find the length and width of the box.

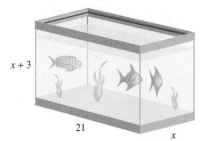

$x + 3$

$21$   $x$

$2$

$x$   $x - 3$

**13.** The dimensions of an HPf1905 flat-panel monitor are such that its length is 3 in. more than its width. If the length were doubled and if the width were decreased by 1 in., the area would be increased by 150 in.². What are the length and width of the flat panel?

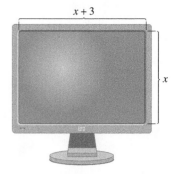

$x + 3$

$x$

**14.** The keyboard that accompanies the monitor in **Exercise 13** is 11 in. longer than it is wide. If the length were doubled and if 2 in. were added to the width, the area would be increased by 198 in.². What are the length and width of the keyboard? (*Source:* Author's computer.)

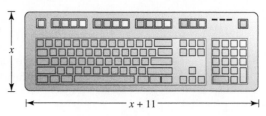

$x$

$x + 11$

**15.** A square mirror has sides measuring 2 ft less than the sides of a square painting. If the difference between their areas is 32 ft$^2$, find the lengths of the sides of the mirror and the painting.

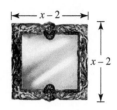

**16.** The sides of one square have length 3 m more than the sides of a second square. If the area of the larger square is subtracted from 4 times the area of the smaller square, the result is 36 m$^2$. What are the lengths of the sides of each square?

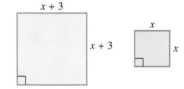

*Solve each problem. **See Example 2.***

**17.** The product of the numbers on two consecutive volumes of research data is 420. Find the volume numbers. See the figure.

**18.** The product of the page numbers on two facing pages of a book is 600. Find the page numbers.

**19.** The product of the second and third of three consecutive integers is 2 more than 10 times the first integer. Find the integers.

**20.** The product of the first and third of three consecutive integers is 3 more than 3 times the second integer. Find the integers.

**21.** Find three consecutive odd integers such that 3 times the sum of all three is 18 more than the product of the first and second integers.

**22.** Find three consecutive odd integers such that the sum of all three is 42 less than the product of the second and third integers.

**23.** Find three consecutive even integers such that the sum of the squares of the first and second integers is equal to the square of the third integer.

**24.** Find three consecutive even integers such that the square of the sum of the first and second integers is equal to twice the third integer.

*Solve each problem. **See Example 3.***

**25.** The hypotenuse of a right triangle is 1 cm longer than the longer leg. The shorter leg is 7 cm shorter than the longer leg. Find the length of the longer leg of the triangle.

**26.** The longer leg of a right triangle is 1 m longer than the shorter leg. The hypotenuse is 1 m shorter than twice the shorter leg. Find the length of the shorter leg of the triangle.

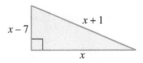

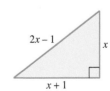

**27.** Tram works due north of home. Her husband Alan works due east. They leave for work at the same time. By the time Tram is 5 mi from home, the distance between them is 1 mi more than Alan's distance from home. How far from home is Alan?

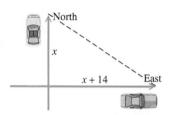

**28.** Two cars left an intersection at the same time. One traveled north. The other traveled 14 mi farther, but to the east. How far apart were they at that time if the distance between them was 4 mi more than the distance traveled east?

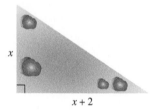

**29.** A ladder is leaning against a building. The distance from the bottom of the ladder to the building is 4 ft less than the length of the ladder. How high up the side of the building is the top of the ladder if that distance is 2 ft less than the length of the ladder?

**30.** A lot has the shape of a right triangle with one leg 2 m longer than the other. The hypotenuse is 2 m less than twice the length of the shorter leg. Find the length of the shorter leg.

*If an object is projected upward with an initial velocity of 128 ft per sec, its height h after t seconds is*

$$h = -16t^2 + 128t.$$

*Find the height of the object after each time listed.* ***See Example 4.***

**31.** 1 sec           **32.** 2 sec           **33.** 4 sec

**34.** How long does it take the object just described to return to the ground? (*Hint:* When the object hits the ground, $h = 0$.)

*Solve each problem.* ***See Examples 4 and 5.***

**35.** An object projected from a height of 48 ft with an initial velocity of 32 ft per sec after $t$ seconds has height

$$h = -16t^2 + 32t + 48.$$

**(a)** After how many seconds is the height 64 ft? (*Hint:* Let $h = 64$ and solve.)

**(b)** After how many seconds is the height 60 ft?

**(c)** After how many seconds does the object hit the ground?

**(d)** The quadratic equation from part (c) has two solutions, yet only one of them is appropriate for answering the question. Why is this so?

**36.** If an object is projected upward from ground level with an initial velocity of 64 ft per sec, its height $h$ in feet $t$ seconds later is

$$h = -16t^2 + 64t.$$

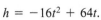

**(a)** After how many seconds is the height 48 ft?

**(b)** The object reaches its maximum height 2 sec after it is projected. What is this maximum height?

**(c)** After how many seconds does the object hit the ground?

**(d)** Find the number of seconds after which the height is 60 ft.

**(e)** What is the physical interpretation of why part (d) has two answers?

**(f)** The quadratic equation from part (c) has two solutions, yet only one of them is appropriate for answering the question. Why is this so?

**37.** The table shows the number of cellular phone subscribers (in millions) in the United States.

| Year | Subscribers (in millions) |
|------|---------------------------|
| 1990 | 5 |
| 1992 | 11 |
| 1994 | 24 |
| 1996 | 44 |
| 1998 | 69 |
| 2000 | 109 |
| 2002 | 141 |
| 2004 | 182 |
| 2006 | 233 |
| 2008 | 263 |

*Source:* CTIA—The Wireless Association.

We used the preceding data to develop the quadratic equation

$$y = 0.590x^2 + 4.523x + 0.136,$$

which models the number $y$ of cellular phone subscribers (in millions) in the year $x$, where $x = 0$ represents 1990, $x = 2$ represents 1992, and so on.

**(a)** Use the model to find the number of subscribers in 2000, to the nearest tenth. How does the result compare with the actual data in the table?

**(b)** What value of $x$ corresponds to 2008?

**(c)** Use the model to find the number of cellular phone subscribers in 2008, to the nearest tenth. How does the result compare with the actual data in the table?

**(d)** Assuming that the trend in the data continues, use the quadratic equation to estimate the number of cellular phone subscribers in 2010, to the nearest tenth.

**38.** Annual revenue in billions of dollars for eBay is shown in the table.

| Year | Annual Revenue (in billions of dollars) |
|------|----------------------------------------|
| 2002 | 1.21 |
| 2003 | 2.17 |
| 2004 | 3.27 |
| 2005 | 4.55 |
| 2006 | 5.97 |
| 2007 | 7.67 |

*Source*: eBay.

Using the data, we developed the quadratic equation

$$y = 0.089x^2 + 0.841x + 1.224$$

to model eBay revenues $y$ in year $x$, where $x = 0$ represents 2002, $x = 1$ represents 2003, and so on.

**(a)** Use the model to find annual revenue for eBay in 2005 and 2007, to the nearest hundredth. How do the results compare with the actual data in the table?

**(b)** Use the model to estimate annual revenue for eBay in 2009, to the nearest hundredth.

**(c)** Actual revenue for eBay in 2009 was $8.73 billion. How does the result from part (b) compare with the actual revenue in 2009?

**(d)** Should the quadratic equation be used to estimate eBay revenue for years after 2007? Explain.

## PREVIEW EXERCISES

*Write each fraction in lowest terms.* ***See Section 1.1.***

**39.** $\dfrac{50}{72}$      **40.** $\dfrac{-26}{156}$      **41.** $\dfrac{48}{-27}$      **42.** $\dfrac{-35}{-21}$

# CHAPTER 6 SUMMARY

## KEY TERMS

**6.1**
factor
factored form
common factor
greatest common
  factor (GCF)

**6.2**
prime polynomial

**6.4**
perfect square
perfect square trinomial

**6.5**
quadratic equation
standard form
double solution

**6.6**
hypotenuse
legs

## TEST YOUR WORD POWER

*See how well you have learned the vocabulary in this chapter.*

**1. Factoring** is
  **A.** a method of multiplying polynomials
  **B.** the process of writing a polynomial as a product
  **C.** the answer in a multiplication problem
  **D.** a way to add the terms of a polynomial.

**2.** A polynomial is in **factored form** when
  **A.** it is prime
  **B.** it is written as a sum
  **C.** the squared term has a coefficient of 1
  **D.** it is written as a product.

**3.** A **perfect square trinomial** is a trinomial
  **A.** that can be factored as the square of a binomial
  **B.** that cannot be factored
  **C.** that is multiplied by a binomial
  **D.** all of whose terms are perfect squares.

**4.** A **quadratic equation** is an equation that can be written in the form
  **A.** $y = mx + b$
  **B.** $ax^2 + bx + c = 0$  $(a \neq 0)$

  **C.** $Ax + By = C$
  **D.** $x = k$.

**5.** A **hypotenuse** is
  **A.** either of the two shorter sides of a triangle
  **B.** the shortest side of a triangle
  **C.** the side opposite the right angle in a triangle
  **D.** the longest side in any triangle.

**ANSWERS**

**1.** B; *Example:* $x^2 - 5x - 14$ factors as $(x - 7)(x + 2)$.    **2.** D; *Example:* The factored form of $x^2 - 5x - 14$ is $(x - 7)(x + 2)$.    **3.** A; *Example:* $a^2 + 2a + 1$ is a perfect square trinomial. Its factored form is $(a + 1)^2$.    **4.** B; *Examples:* $y^2 - 3y + 2 = 0, x^2 - 9 = 0, 2m^2 = 6m + 8$
**5.** C; *Example:* In **FIGURE 3** of **Section 6.6**, the hypotenuse is the side labeled $x + 2$.

| CONCEPTS | EXAMPLES |
|---|---|

### 6.1 The Greatest Common Factor; Factoring by Grouping

**Finding the Greatest Common Factor (GCF)**

*Step 1*   Write each number in prime factored form.

*Step 2*   List each prime number or each variable that is a factor of every term in the list.

*Step 3*   Use as exponents on the common prime factors the *least* exponents from the prime factored forms.

*Step 4*   Multiply the primes from Step 3.

Find the greatest common factor of $4x^2y$, $6x^2y^3$, and $2xy^2$.

$$4x^2y = 2 \cdot 2 \cdot x^2 \cdot y$$
$$6x^2y^3 = 2 \cdot 3 \cdot x^2 \cdot y^3$$
$$2xy^2 = 2 \cdot x \cdot y^2$$

The greatest common factor is $2xy$.

**Factoring by Grouping**

*Step 1*   Group the terms.

*Step 2*   Factor out the greatest common factor in each group.

*Step 3*   Factor out a common binomial factor from the results of Step 2.

*Step 4*   If necessary, try a different grouping.

Factor by grouping.

$3x^2 + 5x - 24xy - 40y$

$= (3x^2 + 5x) + (-24xy - 40y)$     Group the terms.

$= x(3x + 5) - 8y(3x + 5)$     Factor each group.

$= (3x + 5)(x - 8y)$     Factor out $3x + 5$.

### 6.2 Factoring Trinomials

To factor $x^2 + bx + c$, find $m$ and $n$ such that $mn = c$ and $m + n = b$.

$$
\overset{\displaystyle mn = c}{\underset{\displaystyle m + n = b}{x^2 + bx + c}}
$$

Then   $x^2 + bx + c$   factors as   $(x + m)(x + n)$.

Check by multiplying.

Factor $x^2 + 6x + 8$.

$$
\overset{\displaystyle mn = 8}{\underset{\displaystyle m + n = 6}{x^2 + 6x + 8}} \quad m = 2 \text{ and } n = 4
$$

$x^2 + 6x + 8$   factors as   $(x + 2)(x + 4)$.

$CHECK$   $(x + 2)(x + 4)$

$= x^2 + 4x + 2x + 8$

$= x^2 + 6x + 8$ ✓

### 6.3 More on Factoring Trinomials

To factor $ax^2 + bx + c$, use one of the following methods.

**Grouping**

Find $m$ and $n$.

$$
\overset{\displaystyle mn = ac}{\underset{\displaystyle m + n = b}{ax^2 + bx + c}}
$$

**Trial and Error**

Use FOIL in reverse.

Factor $3x^2 + 14x - 5$.

$$\overset{\qquad\qquad -15 \qquad\qquad}{3x^2 + 14x - 5}$$

$mn = -15$, $m + n = 14$

The required integers are $m = -1$ and $n = 15$.

By trial and error or by grouping,

$$3x^2 + 14x - 5 \quad \text{factors as} \quad (3x - 1)(x + 5).$$

(continued)

| CONCEPTS | EXAMPLES |
|---|---|

**6.4   Special Factoring Techniques**

**Difference of Squares**

$$x^2 - y^2 = (x + y)(x - y)$$

**Perfect Square Trinomials**

$$x^2 + 2xy + y^2 = (x + y)^2$$

$$x^2 - 2xy + y^2 = (x - y)^2$$

**Difference of Cubes**

$$x^3 - y^3 = (x - y)(x^2 + xy + y^2)$$

**Sum of Cubes**

$$x^3 + y^3 = (x + y)(x^2 - xy + y^2)$$

Factor.

$$4x^2 - 9$$
$$= (2x + 3)(2x - 3)$$

$$9x^2 + 6x + 1 \qquad 4x^2 - 20x + 25$$
$$= (3x + 1)^2 \qquad = (2x - 5)^2$$

$$m^3 - 8 \qquad\qquad z^3 + 27$$
$$= m^3 - 2^3 \qquad\qquad = z^3 + 3^3$$
$$= (m - 2)(m^2 + 2m + 4) \qquad = (z + 3)(z^2 - 3z + 9)$$

---

**6.5   Solving Quadratic Equations by Factoring**

**Zero-Factor Property**

If $a$ and $b$ are real numbers and if $ab = 0$, then $a = 0$ or $b = 0$.

**Solving a Quadratic Equation by Factoring**

*Step 1*   Write the equation in standard form.

*Step 2*   Factor.

*Step 3*   Use the zero-factor property.

*Step 4*   Solve the resulting equations.

*Step 5*   Check.

If $(x - 2)(x + 3) = 0$, then $x - 2 = 0$ or $x + 3 = 0$.

Solve $2x^2 = 7x + 15$.

$$2x^2 - 7x - 15 = 0$$
$$(2x + 3)(x - 5) = 0$$
$$2x + 3 = 0 \quad \text{or} \quad x - 5 = 0$$
$$2x = -3 \qquad\qquad x = 5$$
$$x = -\frac{3}{2}$$

Both solutions satisfy the original equation. The solution set is $\left\{-\frac{3}{2}, 5\right\}$.

---

**6.6   Applications of Quadratic Equations**

**Pythagorean Theorem**

In a right triangle, the square of the hypotenuse equals the sum of the squares of the legs.

$$a^2 + b^2 = c^2$$

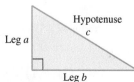

In a right triangle, one leg measures 2 ft longer than the other. The hypotenuse measures 4 ft longer than the shorter leg. Find the lengths of the three sides of the triangle.

Let $x =$ the length of the shorter leg. Then

$$x^2 + (x + 2)^2 = (x + 4)^2.$$

Verify that the solutions of this equation are $-2$ and 6. Discard $-2$ as a solution. Check that the sides have lengths

$$6 \text{ ft}, \quad 6 + 2 = 8 \text{ ft}, \quad \text{and} \quad 6 + 4 = 10 \text{ ft.}$$

CHAPTER **6**

## REVIEW EXERCISES

**6.1** *Factor out the greatest common factor, or factor by grouping.*

**1.** $7t + 14$

**2.** $60z^3 + 30z$

**3.** $2xy - 8y + 3x - 12$

**4.** $6y^2 + 9y + 4xy + 6x$

**6.2** *Factor completely.*

**5.** $x^2 + 5x + 6$

**6.** $y^2 - 13y + 40$

**7.** $q^2 + 6q - 27$

**8.** $r^2 - r - 56$

**9.** $r^2 - 4rs - 96s^2$

**10.** $p^2 + 2pq - 120q^2$

**11.** $8p^3 - 24p^2 - 80p$

**12.** $3x^4 + 30x^3 + 48x^2$

**13.** $p^7 - p^6q - 2p^5q^2$

**14.** $3r^5 - 6r^4s - 45r^3s^2$

**15.** $9x^4y - 9x^3y - 54x^2y$

**16.** $2x^7 + 2x^6y - 12x^5y^2$

**6.3**

**17.** *Concept Check* To begin factoring $6r^2 - 5r - 6$, what are the possible first terms of the two binomial factors if we consider only positive integer coefficients?

**18.** *Concept Check* What is the first step you would use to factor $2z^3 + 9z^2 - 5z$?

*Factor completely.*

**19.** $2k^2 - 5k + 2$

**20.** $3r^2 + 11r - 4$

**21.** $6r^2 - 5r - 6$

**22.** $10z^2 - 3z - 1$

**23.** $8v^2 + 17v - 21$

**24.** $24x^5 - 20x^4 + 4x^3$

**25.** $-6x^2 + 3x + 30$

**26.** $10r^3s + 17r^2s^2 + 6rs^3$

**27.** $48x^4y + 4x^3y^2 - 4x^2y^3$

**28.** *Concept Check* On a quiz, a student factored $16x^2 - 24x + 5$ by grouping as follows.

$$16x^2 - 24x + 5$$
$$= 16x^2 - 4x - 20x + 5$$
$$= 4x(4x - 1) - 5(4x - 1) \quad \text{His answer}$$

He thought his answer was correct, since it checked by multiplication. *WHAT WENT WRONG?* Give the correct factored form.

**6.4**

**29.** *Concept Check* Which one of the following is the difference of squares?

**A.** $32x^2 - 1$ **B.** $4x^2y^2 - 25z^2$ **C.** $x^2 + 36$ **D.** $25y^3 - 1$

**30.** *Concept Check* Which one of the following is a perfect square trinomial?

**A.** $x^2 + x + 1$ **B.** $y^2 - 4y + 9$ **C.** $4x^2 + 10x + 25$ **D.** $x^2 - 20x + 100$

*Factor completely.*

**31.** $n^2 - 49$

**32.** $25b^2 - 121$

**33.** $49y^2 - 25w^2$

**34.** $144p^2 - 36q^2$

**35.** $x^2 + 100$

**36.** $r^2 - 12r + 36$

**37.** $9t^2 - 42t + 49$

**38.** $m^3 + 1000$

**39.** $125k^3 + 64x^3$

**40.** $343x^3 - 64$

**41.** $1000 - 27x^6$

**42.** $x^6 - y^6$

**6.5** *Solve each equation, and check your solutions.*

**43.** $(4t + 3)(t - 1) = 0$

**44.** $(x + 7)(x - 4)(x + 3) = 0$

**45.** $x(2x - 5) = 0$

**46.** $z^2 + 4z + 3 = 0$

**47.** $m^2 - 5m + 4 = 0$

**48.** $x^2 = -15 + 8x$

**49.** $3z^2 - 11z - 20 = 0$

**50.** $81t^2 - 64 = 0$

**51.** $y^2 = 8y$

**52.** $n(n - 5) = 6$

**53.** $t^2 - 14t + 49 = 0$

**54.** $t^2 = 12(t - 3)$

**55.** $(5z + 2)(z^2 + 3z + 2) = 0$

**56.** $x^2 = 9$

---

**6.6**   *Solve each problem.*

**57.** The length of a rug is 6 ft more than the width. The area is 40 ft². Find the length and width of the rug.

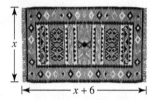

**58.** The surface area $S$ of a box is given by

$$S = 2WH + 2WL + 2LH.$$

A treasure chest from a sunken galleon has the dimensions shown in the figure. Its surface area is 650 ft². Find its width.

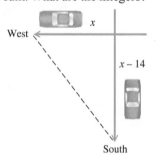

**59.** The product of two consecutive integers is 29 more than their sum. What are the integers?

**60.** Two cars left an intersection at the same time. One traveled west, and the other traveled 14 mi less, but to the south. How far apart were they at that time, if the distance between them was 16 mi more than the distance traveled south?

**61.** If an object is dropped, the distance $d$ in feet it falls in $t$ seconds (disregarding air resistance) is given by the quadratic equation

$$d = 16t^2.$$

Find the distance an object would fall in **(a)** 4 sec and **(b)** 8 sec.

**62.** The numbers of alternative-fueled vehicles in use in the United States, in thousands, for the years 2001–2006 are given in the table.

| Year | Number (in thousands) |
|------|-----------------------|
| 2001 | 425 |
| 2002 | 471 |
| 2003 | 534 |
| 2004 | 565 |
| 2005 | 592 |
| 2006 | 635 |

*Source:* Energy Information Administration.

Using statistical methods, we developed the quadratic equation

$$y = -2.84x^2 + 61.1x + 366$$

to model the number of vehicles $y$ in year $x$. Here, we used $x = 1$ for 2001, $x = 2$ for 2002, and so on.

(a) Use the model to find the number of alternative-fueled vehicles in 2005, to the nearest thousand. How does the result compare with the actual data in the table?

(b) Use the model to estimate the number of alternative-fueled vehicles in 2007, to the nearest thousand.

(c) Why might the estimate for 2007 be unreliable?

## MIXED REVIEW EXERCISES

**63.** *Concept Check* Which of the following is *not* factored completely?

    **A.** $3(7t)$    **B.** $3x(7t + 4)$    **C.** $(3 + x)(7t + 4)$    **D.** $3(7t + 4) + x(7t + 4)$

**64.** A student factored $6x^2 + 16x - 32$ as $(2x + 8)(3x - 4)$. Explain why the polynomial is not factored completely, and give the completely factored form.

*Factor completely.*

**65.** $3k^2 + 11k + 10$               **66.** $z^2 - 11zx + 10x^2$

**67.** $y^4 - 625$                    **68.** $15m^2 + 20m - 12mp - 16p$

**69.** $24ab^3c^2 - 56a^2bc^3 + 72a^2b^2c$     **70.** $6m^3 - 21m^2 - 45m$

**71.** $12x^2yz^3 + 12xy^2z - 30x^3y^2z^4$     **72.** $25a^2 + 15ab + 9b^2$

**73.** $12r^2 + 18rq - 10r - 15q$      **74.** $2a^5 - 8a^4 - 24a^3$

**75.** $49t^2 + 56t + 16$            **76.** $1000a^3 + 27$

*Solve.*

**77.** $t(t - 7) = 0$       **78.** $x^2 + 3x = 10$       **79.** $25x^2 + 20x + 4 = 0$

**80.** The product of the first and second of three consecutive integers is equal to 23 plus the third. Find the integers.

**81.** A pyramid has a rectangular base with a length that is 2 m more than its width. The height of the pyramid is 6 m, and its volume is 48 m³. Find the length and width of the base.

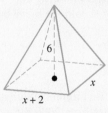

**82.** A lot is in the shape of a right triangle. The hypotenuse is 3 m longer than the longer leg. The longer leg is 6 m longer than twice the length of the shorter leg. Find the lengths of the sides of the lot.

**83.** The triangular sail of a schooner has an area of 30 m². The height of the sail is 4 m more than the base. Find the base of the sail.

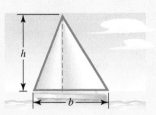

**84.** The floor plan for a house is a rectangle with length 7 m more than its width. The area is 170 m². Find the width and length of the house.

CHAPTER 6 TEST

CHAPTER
Test Prep
VIDEOS

Step-by-step test solutions are found on the Chapter Test Prep Videos available via the Video Resources on DVD, in *MyMathLab* , or on You Tube (search "LialBeginningAlgebra").

*View the complete solutions to all Chapter Test exercises on the Video Resources on DVD.*

1. *Concept Check* Which one of the following is the correct completely factored form of $2x^2 - 2x - 24$?

   **A.** $(2x + 6)(x - 4)$   **B.** $(x + 3)(2x - 8)$

   **C.** $2(x + 4)(x - 3)$   **D.** $2(x + 3)(x - 4)$

*Factor each polynomial completely. If the polynomial is prime, say so.*

2. $12x^2 - 30x$

3. $2m^3n^2 + 3m^3n - 5m^2n^2$

4. $2ax - 2bx + ay - by$

5. $x^2 - 5x - 24$

6. $2x^2 + x - 3$

7. $10z^2 - 17z + 3$

8. $t^2 + 2t + 3$

9. $x^2 + 36$

10. $12 - 6a + 2b - ab$

11. $9y^2 - 64$

12. $4x^2 - 28xy + 49y^2$

13. $-2x^2 - 4x - 2$

14. $6t^4 + 3t^3 - 108t^2$

15. $r^3 - 125$

16. $8k^3 + 64$

17. $x^4 - 81$

18. $81x^4 - 16y^4$

19. $9x^6y^4 + 12x^3y^2 + 4$

*Solve each equation.*

20. $2r^2 - 13r + 6 = 0$

21. $25x^2 - 4 = 0$

22. $t^2 = 9t$

23. $x(x - 20) = -100$

24. $(s + 8)(6s^2 + 13s - 5) = 0$

*Solve each problem.*

25. The length of a rectangular flower bed is 3 ft less than twice its width. The area of the bed is 54 ft². Find the dimensions of the flower bed.

26. Find two consecutive integers such that the square of the sum of the two integers is 11 more than the first integer.

27. A carpenter needs to cut a brace to support a wall stud, as shown in the figure. The brace should be 7 ft less than three times the length of the stud. If the brace will be anchored on the floor 15 ft away from the stud, how long should the brace be?

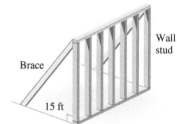

28. The public debt $y$ (in billions of dollars) of the United States from 2000 through 2008 can be approximated by the quadratic equation

    $$y = 29.92x^2 + 305.8x + 5581,$$

    where $x = 0$ represents 2000, $x = 1$ represents 2001, and so on. (*Source:* Bureau of Public Debt.) Use the model to estimate the public debt, to the nearest billion dollars, in the year 2006.

# CHAPTERS (1–6) CUMULATIVE REVIEW EXERCISES

*Solve each equation.*

**1.** $3x + 2(x - 4) = 4(x - 2)$

**2.** $0.3x + 0.9x = 0.06$

**3.** $\dfrac{2}{3}m - \dfrac{1}{2}(m - 4) = 3$

**4.** Solve for $P$:   $A = P + Prt$.

**5.** Find the measures of the marked angles.

$(2x + 16)°$   $(x + 23)°$

*Solve each problem.*

**6.** At the 2006 Winter Olympics in Torino, Italy, the top medal winner was Germany, which won a total of 29 medals. Germany won 1 more silver medal than gold and 5 more gold medals than bronze. Find the number of each type of medal won. (*Source:* www.infoplease.com.)

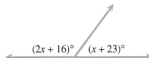

**7.** From a list of "technology-related items," adults were recently surveyed as to those items they couldn't live without. Complete the results shown in the table if 500 adults were surveyed.

| Item | Percent That Couldn't Live Without | Number That Couldn't Live Without |
|---|---|---|
| Personal computer | 46% | |
| Cell phone | 41% | |
| High-speed Internet | | 190 |
| MP3 player | | 60 |

(Other items included digital cable, HDTV, and electronic gaming console.)
*Source:* Ipsos for AP.

**8.** Fill in each blank with *positive* or *negative*. The point with coordinates $(a, b)$ is in

  **(a)** quadrant II if $a$ is _____ and $b$ is _____.

  **(b)** quadrant III if $a$ is _____ and $b$ is _____.

**9.** Consider the equation $y = 12x + 3$. Find the following.

  **(a)** The $x$- and $y$-intercepts   **(b)** The slope   **(c)** The graph

**10.** The points on the graph show the total retail sales of prescription drugs in the United States in the years 2001–2007, along with a graph of a linear equation that models the data.

  **(a)** Use the ordered pairs shown on the graph to find the slope of the line to the nearest whole number. Interpret the slope.

  **(b)** Use the graph to estimate sales in the year 2005. Write your answer as an ordered pair of the form (year, sales in billions of dollars).

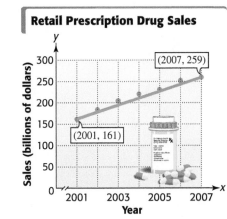

**Retail Prescription Drug Sales**

(2007, 259)

(2001, 161)

*Source:* National Association of Chain Drug Stores.

*Solve each system of equations.*

**11.** $4x - y = -6$
$2x + 3y = 4$

**12.** $5x + 3y = 10$
$2x + \dfrac{6}{5}y = 5$

*Evaluate each expression.*

**13.** $\left(\dfrac{3}{4}\right)^{-2}$

**14.** $\left(\dfrac{4^{-3} \cdot 4^4}{4^5}\right)^{-1}$

*Simplify each expression, and write the answer with only positive exponents. Assume that no denominators are 0.*

**15.** $\dfrac{(p^2)^3 p^{-4}}{(p^{-3})^{-1} p}$

**16.** $\dfrac{(m^{-2})^3 m}{m^5 m^{-4}}$

*Perform each indicated operation.*

**17.** $(2k^2 + 4k) - (5k^2 - 2) - (k^2 + 8k - 6)$ **18.** $(9x + 6)(5x - 3)$

**19.** $(3p + 2)^2$

**20.** $\dfrac{8x^4 + 12x^3 - 6x^2 + 20x}{2x}$

**21.** To make a pound of honey, bees may travel 55,000 mi and visit more than 2,000,000 flowers. (*Source: Home & Garden.*) Write the two given numbers in scientific notation.

*Factor completely.*

**22.** $2a^2 + 7a - 4$

**23.** $10m^2 + 19m + 6$

**24.** $8t^2 + 10tv + 3v^2$

**25.** $4p^2 - 12p + 9$

**26.** $25r^2 - 81t^2$

**27.** $2pq + 6p^3q + 8p^2q$

*Solve each equation.*

**28.** $6m^2 + m - 2 = 0$

**29.** $8x^2 = 64x$

**30.** The length of the hypotenuse of a right triangle is twice the length of the shorter leg, plus 3 m. The longer leg is 7 m longer than the shorter leg. Find the lengths of the sides.

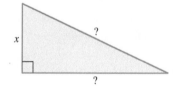

# Rational Expressions and Applications

In 2006, Earth's temperature was within 1.8°F of its highest level in 12,000 years. This temperature increase is causing ocean levels to rise as ice fields in Greenland and elsewhere melt. To demonstrate the effects that such global warming is having, British adventurer and endurance swimmer Lewis Gordon Pugh swam at the North Pole in July 2007 in waters that were completely frozen 10 years ago. The swim, in a water hole where polar ice had melted, was in 28.8°F waters, the coldest ever endured by a human. Pugh, who has also swum in the waters of Antarctica, hopes his efforts will inspire world leaders to take climate change seriously. (*Source:* www.breitbart.com, IPCC.)

In **Exercise 11** of **Section 7.7,** we use a *rational expression* to determine the time Pugh swam at the North Pole.

# The Fundamental Property of Rational Expressions

**OBJECTIVES**

**1** Find the numerical value of a rational expression.

**2** Find the values of the variable for which a rational expression is undefined.

**3** Write rational expressions in lowest terms.

**4** Recognize equivalent forms of rational expressions.

The quotient of two integers (with denominator not 0), such as $\frac{2}{3}$ or $-\frac{3}{4}$, is called a *rational number.* In the same way, the quotient of two polynomials with denominator not equal to 0 is called a *rational expression.*

**Rational Expression**

A **rational expression** is an expression of the form $\frac{P}{Q}$, where $P$ and $Q$ are polynomials and $Q \neq 0$.

$$\frac{-6x}{x^3 + 8}, \quad \frac{9x}{y + 3}, \quad \text{and} \quad \frac{2m^3}{8} \qquad \text{Rational expressions}$$

Our work with rational expressions requires much of what we learned in **Chapters 5 and 6** on polynomials and factoring, as well as the rules for fractions from **Section 1.1.**

**OBJECTIVE 1** Find the numerical value of a rational expression. We use substitution to evaluate a rational expression for a given value of the variable.

*NOW TRY EXERCISE 1*

Find the value of the following rational expression for $x = -3$.

$$\frac{2x - 1}{x + 4}$$

**EXAMPLE 1** Evaluating Rational Expressions

Find the numerical value of $\frac{3x + 6}{2x - 4}$ for the given value of $x$.

**(a)** $x = 1$

$$\frac{3x + 6}{2x - 4}$$

$$= \frac{3(1) + 6}{2(1) - 4} \qquad \text{Let } x = 1.$$

$$= \frac{9}{-2} \qquad \text{Simplify.}$$

$$= -\frac{9}{2} \qquad \frac{a}{-b} = -\frac{a}{b}$$

**(b)** $x = -2$

> Use parentheses around negative numbers to avoid errors.

$$\frac{3x + 6}{2x - 4}$$

$$= \frac{3(-2) + 6}{2(-2) - 4} \qquad \text{Let } x = -2.$$

$$= \frac{0}{-8} \qquad \text{Simplify.}$$

$$= 0 \qquad \frac{0}{b} = 0$$

*NOW TRY*

**OBJECTIVE 2** Find the values of the variable for which a rational expression is undefined. In the definition of a rational expression $\frac{P}{Q}$, $Q$ cannot equal 0. *The denominator of a rational expression cannot equal 0 because division by 0 is undefined.*

For instance, in the rational expression

$$\frac{3x + 6}{2x - 4} \leftarrow \text{Denominator cannot equal 0.}$$

from **Example 1,** the variable $x$ can take on any real number value except 2. If $x$ is 2, then the denominator becomes $2(2) - 4 = 0$, making the expression undefined. Thus, $x$ cannot equal 2. We indicate this restriction by writing $x \neq 2$.

*NOW TRY ANSWER*
**1.** $-7$

NOTE *The numerator of a rational expression may be any real number.* If the numerator equals 0 and the denominator does not equal 0, then the rational expression equals 0. See **Example 1(b).**

---

### Determining When a Rational Expression Is Undefined

*Step 1*  Set the denominator of the rational expression equal to 0.

*Step 2*  Solve this equation.

*Step 3*  The solutions of the equation are the values that make the rational expression undefined. The variable *cannot* equal these values.

NOW TRY
EXERCISE 2

Find any values of the variable for which each rational expression is undefined.

(a) $\dfrac{k - 4}{2k - 1}$

(b) $\dfrac{2x}{x^2 + 5x - 14}$

(c) $\dfrac{y + 10}{y^2 + 10}$

**EXAMPLE 2**  Finding Values That Make Rational Expressions Undefined

Find any values of the variable for which each rational expression is undefined.

(a) $\dfrac{x + 5}{3x + 2}$   We must find any value of $x$ that makes the *denominator* equal to 0, since division by 0 is undefined.

*Step 1*  Set the denominator equal to 0.
$$3x + 2 = 0$$

*Step 2*  Solve.     $3x = -2$   Subtract 2.

$$x = -\frac{2}{3}$$   Divide by 3.

*Step 3*  The given expression is undefined for $-\frac{2}{3}$, so $x \neq -\frac{2}{3}$.

(b) $\dfrac{8x^2 + 1}{x - 3}$   The denominator $x - 3 = 0$ when $x$ is 3. The given expression is undefined for 3, so $x \neq 3$.

(c) $\dfrac{9m^2}{m^2 - 5m + 6}$

$$m^2 - 5m + 6 = 0 \quad \text{Set the denominator equal to 0.}$$
$$(m - 2)(m - 3) = 0 \quad \text{Factor.}$$
$$m - 2 = 0 \quad \text{or} \quad m - 3 = 0 \quad \text{Zero-factor property}$$
$$m = 2 \quad \text{or} \qquad m = 3 \quad \text{Solve for } m.$$

The given expression is undefined for 2 and 3, so $m \neq 2$, $m \neq 3$.

(d) $\dfrac{2r}{r^2 + 1}$   This denominator will not equal 0 for any value of $r$, because $r^2$ is always greater than or equal to 0, and adding 1 makes the sum greater than or equal to 1. There are no values for which this expression is undefined.

NOW TRY

---

**OBJECTIVE 3**  Write rational expressions in lowest terms. A fraction such as $\frac{2}{3}$ is said to be in *lowest terms.*

### Lowest Terms

A rational expression $\frac{P}{Q}$ ($Q \neq 0$) is in **lowest terms** if the greatest common factor of its numerator and denominator is 1.

NOW TRY ANSWERS
**2.** (a) $k \neq \frac{1}{2}$  (b) $x \neq -7, x \neq 2$
  (c) never undefined

We use the **fundamental property of rational expressions** to write a rational expression in lowest terms.

---

**Fundamental Property of Rational Expressions**

If $\frac{P}{Q}$ ($Q \neq 0$) is a rational expression and if $K$ represents any polynomial, where $K \neq 0$, then the following is true.

$$\frac{PK}{QK} = \frac{P}{Q}$$

---

This property is based on the identity property of multiplication.

$$\frac{PK}{QK} = \frac{P}{Q} \cdot \frac{K}{K} = \frac{P}{Q} \cdot 1 = \frac{P}{Q}$$

**NOW TRY
EXERCISE 3**

Write the rational expression in lowest terms.

$$\frac{21y^5}{7y^2}$$

**EXAMPLE 3**   Writing in Lowest Terms

Write each rational expression in lowest terms.

**(a)** $\dfrac{30}{72}$

Begin by factoring.

$$\frac{30}{72} = \frac{2 \cdot 3 \cdot 5}{2 \cdot 2 \cdot 2 \cdot 3 \cdot 3}$$

**(b)** $\dfrac{14k^2}{2k^3}$

Write $k^2$ as $k \cdot k$ and $k^3$ as $k \cdot k \cdot k$.

$$\frac{14k^2}{2k^3} = \frac{2 \cdot 7 \cdot k \cdot k}{2 \cdot k \cdot k \cdot k}$$

Group any factors common to the numerator and denominator.

$$\frac{30}{72} = \frac{5 \cdot (2 \cdot 3)}{2 \cdot 2 \cdot 3 \cdot (2 \cdot 3)}$$

$$\frac{14k^2}{2k^3} = \frac{7(2 \cdot k \cdot k)}{k(2 \cdot k \cdot k)}$$

Use the fundamental property.

$$\frac{30}{72} = \frac{5}{2 \cdot 2 \cdot 3} = \frac{5}{12}$$

$$\frac{14k^2}{2k^3} = \frac{7}{k}$$

NOW TRY

---

**Writing a Rational Expression in Lowest Terms**

*Step 1*   **Factor** the numerator and denominator completely.

*Step 2*   **Use the fundamental property** to divide out any common factors.

---

**EXAMPLE 4**   Writing in Lowest Terms

Write each rational expression in lowest terms.

**(a)** $\dfrac{3x - 12}{5x - 20}$    $x \neq 4$, since the denominator is 0 for this value.

$$= \frac{3(x - 4)}{5(x - 4)}$$    Factor. (Step 1)

$$= \frac{3}{5}$$    Fundamental property (Step 2)

The given expression is equal to $\frac{3}{5}$ for all values of $x$, where $x \neq 4$ (since the denominator of the original rational expression is 0 when $x$ is 4).

**NOW TRY ANSWER**
**3.** $3y^3$

**NOW TRY**
**EXERCISE 4**
Write each rational expression in lowest terms.

(a) $\dfrac{3x + 15}{5x + 25}$

(b) $\dfrac{k^2 - 36}{k^2 + 8k + 12}$

(b) $\dfrac{2y^2 - 8}{2y + 4}$ $\quad$ [$y \neq -2$, since the denominator is 0 for this value.]

$= \dfrac{2(y^2 - 4)}{2(y + 2)}$ $\qquad$ Factor. (Step 1)

$= \dfrac{2(y + 2)(y - 2)}{2(y + 2)}$ $\qquad$ Factor the numerator completely.

$= y - 2$ $\qquad$ Fundamental property (Step 2)

(c) $\dfrac{m^2 + 2m - 8}{2m^2 - m - 6}$

$= \dfrac{(m + 4)(m - 2)}{(2m + 3)(m - 2)}$ $\quad$ [$m \neq -\frac{3}{2}$, $m \neq 2$]

$\qquad$ Factor. (Step 1)

$= \dfrac{m + 4}{2m + 3}$ $\qquad$ Fundamental property (Step 2) $\qquad$ *NOW TRY*

*We write statements of equality of rational expressions with the understanding that they apply only to real numbers that make neither denominator equal to 0.*

⚠ CAUTION *Rational expressions cannot be written in lowest terms until after the numerator and denominator have been factored.*

$$\dfrac{6x + 9}{4x + 6} = \dfrac{3(2x + 3)}{2(2x + 3)} = \dfrac{3}{2} \qquad \dfrac{6 + x}{4x} \leftarrow \text{Numerator cannot be factored.}$$

↑
Divide out the common factor. $\qquad$ Already in lowest terms

**NOW TRY**
**EXERCISE 5**
Write in lowest terms.

$$\dfrac{10 - a^2}{a^2 - 10}$$

**EXAMPLE 5** Writing in Lowest Terms (Factors Are Opposites)

Write $\dfrac{x - y}{y - x}$ in lowest terms.

To get a common factor, the denominator $y - x$ can be factored as follows.

$y - x$ $\quad$ [We are factoring out $-1$, **NOT** multiplying by it.]

$= -1(-y + x)$ $\qquad$ Factor out $-1$.

$= -1(x - y)$ $\qquad$ Commutative property

With this result in mind, we simplify.

$\dfrac{x - y}{y - x}$

$= \dfrac{1(x - y)}{-1(x - y)}$ $\qquad$ $y - x = -1(x - y)$ from above.

$= \dfrac{1}{-1}$, or $-1$ $\qquad$ Fundamental property $\qquad$ *NOW TRY*

**NOTE** The numerator *or* the denominator could have been factored in the first step in **Example 5.** Factor $-1$ from the numerator, and confirm that the result is the same.

**NOW TRY ANSWERS**
**4. (a)** $\frac{3}{5}$ **(b)** $\frac{k - 6}{k + 2}$
**5.** $-1$

In **Example 5,** notice that $y - x$ is the **opposite** (or **additive inverse**) of $x - y$.

---

### Quotient of Opposites

If the numerator and the denominator of a rational expression are opposites, as in $\dfrac{x - y}{y - x}$, then the rational expression is equal to $-1$.

---

Based on this result, the following are true.

Numerator and denominator are opposites. → $\dfrac{q - 7}{7 - q} = -1$   and   $\dfrac{-5a + 2b}{5a - 2b} = -1$

However, the following expression cannot be simplified further.

$$\dfrac{x - 2}{x + 2}$$   Numerator and denominator are *not* opposites.

**NOW TRY**
**EXERCISE 6**

Write each rational expression in lowest terms.

(a) $\dfrac{p - 4}{4 - p}$   (b) $\dfrac{4m^2 - n^2}{2n - 4m}$

(c) $\dfrac{x + y}{x - y}$

**EXAMPLE 6**   Writing in Lowest Terms (Factors Are Opposites)

Write each rational expression in lowest terms.

(a) $\dfrac{2 - m}{m - 2}$   Since $2 - m$ and $m - 2$ are opposites, this expression equals $-1$.

(b) $\dfrac{4x^2 - 9}{6 - 4x}$

$= \dfrac{(2x + 3)(2x - 3)}{2(3 - 2x)}$   Factor the numerator and denominator.

$= \dfrac{(2x + 3)(2x - 3)}{2(-1)(2x - 3)}$   Write $3 - 2x$ in the denominator as $-1(2x - 3)$.

$= \dfrac{2x + 3}{2(-1)}$   Fundamental property

$= \dfrac{2x + 3}{-2}$,   or   $-\dfrac{2x + 3}{2}$   $\frac{a}{-b} = -\frac{a}{b}$

(c) $\dfrac{3 + r}{3 - r}$   $3 - r$ is *not* the opposite of $3 + r$.

This rational expression is already in lowest terms.   **NOW TRY**

---

**OBJECTIVE 4**   **Recognize equivalent forms of rational expressions.** The common fraction $-\dfrac{5}{6}$ can also be written $\dfrac{-5}{6}$ and $\dfrac{5}{-6}$.

Consider the final rational expression from **Example 6(b).**

$$-\dfrac{2x + 3}{2}$$

The $-$ sign representing the factor $-1$ is in front of the expression, even with the fraction bar. The factor $-1$ may instead be placed in the numerator or denominator.

Use parentheses.

$$\dfrac{-(2x + 3)}{2}$$   and   $$\dfrac{2x + 3}{-2}$$

**NOW TRY ANSWERS**
6. (a) $-1$
(b) $\frac{2m + n}{-2}$,   or   $-\frac{2m + n}{2}$
(c) already in lowest terms

The distributive property can also be applied.

$$\frac{-(2x + 3)}{2} \text{ can also be written } \frac{-2x - 3}{2}.$$

> Multiply *each* term in the numerator by $-1$.

---

⚠ **CAUTION**   $\frac{-2x + 3}{2}$ is *not* an equivalent form of $\frac{-(2x + 3)}{2}$. The sign preceding 3 in the numerator of $\frac{-2x + 3}{2}$ should be $-$ rather than $+$. **Be careful to apply the distributive property correctly.**

---

NOW TRY
EXERCISE 7

Write four equivalent forms of the rational expression.

$$-\frac{4k - 9}{k + 3}$$

**EXAMPLE 7**   Writing Equivalent Forms of a Rational Expression

Write four equivalent forms of the rational expression.

$$-\frac{3x + 2}{x - 6}$$

If we apply the negative sign to the numerator, we obtain these equivalent forms.

$$① \rightarrow \frac{-(3x + 2)}{x - 6} \text{ and, by the distributive property, } \frac{-3x - 2}{x - 6} \leftarrow ②$$

If we apply the negative sign to the denominator, we obtain two more forms.

$$③ \rightarrow \frac{3x + 2}{-(x - 6)} \text{ or, distributing once again, } \frac{3x + 2}{-x + 6} \leftarrow ④$$

NOW TRY

---

⚠ **CAUTION**   Recall that $-\frac{5}{6} \neq \frac{-5}{-6}$. Thus, in **Example 7,** it would be incorrect to distribute the negative sign in $-\frac{3x + 2}{x - 6}$ to *both* the numerator *and* the denominator. (Doing this would actually lead to the *opposite* of the original expression.)

---

### CONNECTIONS

In **Section 5.7,** we used long division to find the quotient of two polynomials such as $(2x^2 + 5x - 12) \div (2x - 3)$, as shown on the left. The quotient is $x + 4$. We get the same quotient by expressing the division problem as a rational expression (fraction) and writing this rational expression in lowest terms, as shown on the right.

$$
\begin{array}{r}
x + 4 \\
2x - 3 \overline{)2x^2 + 5x - 12} \\
\underline{2x^2 - 3x} \\
8x - 12 \\
\underline{8x - 12} \\
0
\end{array}
$$

$$\frac{2x^2 + 5x - 12}{2x - 3}$$

$$= \frac{(2x - 3)(x + 4)}{2x - 3} \quad \text{Factor.}$$

$$= x + 4 \quad \text{Fundamental property}$$

**For Discussion or Writing**

What kind of division problem has a quotient that cannot be found by writing a fraction in lowest terms? Try using rational expressions to solve each division problem. Then use long division and compare.

**1.** $(3x^2 + 11x + 8) \div (x + 2)$       **2.** $(x^3 - 8) \div (x^2 + 2x + 4)$

NOW TRY ANSWER
**7.** $\frac{-(4k - 9)}{k + 3}$,  $\frac{-4k + 9}{k + 3}$,  $\frac{4k - 9}{-(k + 3)}$,
$\frac{4k - 9}{-k - 3}$

## 7.1 EXERCISES

MyMathLab  Math XL PRACTICE  WATCH  DOWNLOAD READ  REVIEW

🌐 *Complete solution available on the Video Resources on DVD*

*Find the numerical value of each rational expression for* **(a)** $x = 2$ *and* **(b)** $x = -3$. ***See Example 1.***

🌐 **1.** $\dfrac{3x + 1}{5x}$

**2.** $\dfrac{5x - 2}{4x}$

**3.** $\dfrac{x^2 - 4}{2x + 1}$

**4.** $\dfrac{2x^2 - 4x}{3x - 1}$

**5.** $\dfrac{(-2x)^3}{3x + 9}$

**6.** $\dfrac{(-3x)^2}{4x + 12}$

**7.** $\dfrac{7 - 3x}{3x^2 - 7x + 2}$

**8.** $\dfrac{5x + 2}{4x^2 - 5x - 6}$

**9.** $\dfrac{(x + 3)(x - 2)}{500x}$

**10.** $\dfrac{(x - 2)(x + 3)}{1000x}$

**11.** $\dfrac{x^2 - 4}{x^2 - 9}$

**12.** $\dfrac{x^2 - 9}{x^2 - 4}$

**13.** Define *rational expression* in your own words, and give an example.

**14.** *Concept Check* Fill in each blank with the correct response: The rational expression $\frac{x + 5}{x - 3}$ is undefined when $x$ is _____, so $x \neq$ _____. This rational expression is equal to 0 when $x =$ _____.

**15.** Why can't the denominator of a rational expression equal 0?

**16.** If 2 is substituted for $x$ in the rational expression $\frac{x - 2}{x^2 - 4}$, the result is $\frac{0}{0}$. An often-heard statement is "Any number divided by itself is 1." Does this mean that this expression is equal to 1 for $x = 2$? If not, explain.

*Find any values of the variable for which each rational expression is undefined. Write answers with the symbol $\neq$. **See Example 2.***

**17.** $\dfrac{12}{5y}$

**18.** $\dfrac{-7}{3z}$

**19.** $\dfrac{x + 1}{x - 6}$

**20.** $\dfrac{m - 2}{m - 5}$

🌐 **21.** $\dfrac{4x^2}{3x + 5}$

**22.** $\dfrac{2x^3}{3x + 4}$

**23.** $\dfrac{5m + 2}{m^2 + m - 6}$

**24.** $\dfrac{2r - 5}{r^2 - 5r + 4}$

**25.** $\dfrac{x^2 + 3x}{4}$

**26.** $\dfrac{x^2 - 4x}{6}$

**27.** $\dfrac{3x - 1}{x^2 + 2}$

**28.** $\dfrac{4q + 2}{q^2 + 9}$

**29.** **(a)** Identify the two *terms* in the numerator and the two *terms* in the denominator of the rational expression $\frac{x^2 + 4x}{x + 4}$.

**(b)** Describe the steps you would use to write the rational expression in part (a) in lowest terms. (*Hint:* It simplifies to $x$.)

**30.** *Concept Check* Which one of these rational expressions can be simplified?

**A.** $\dfrac{x^2 + 2}{x^2}$

**B.** $\dfrac{x^2 + 2}{2}$

**C.** $\dfrac{x^2 + y^2}{y^2}$

**D.** $\dfrac{x^2 - 5x}{x}$

*Write each rational expression in lowest terms. **See Examples 3 and 4.***

🌐 **31.** $\dfrac{18r^3}{6r}$

**32.** $\dfrac{27p^4}{3p}$

**33.** $\dfrac{4(y - 2)}{10(y - 2)}$

**34.** $\dfrac{15(m - 1)}{9(m - 1)}$

**35.** $\dfrac{(x + 1)(x - 1)}{(x + 1)^2}$

**36.** $\dfrac{(t + 5)(t - 3)}{(t + 5)^2}$

🌐 **37.** $\dfrac{7m + 14}{5m + 10}$

**38.** $\dfrac{16x + 8}{14x + 7}$

**39.** $\dfrac{6m - 18}{7m - 21}$

**40.** $\dfrac{5r + 20}{3r + 12}$

**41.** $\dfrac{m^2 - n^2}{m + n}$

**42.** $\dfrac{a^2 - b^2}{a - b}$

**43.** $\dfrac{2t + 6}{t^2 - 9}$

**44.** $\dfrac{5s - 25}{s^2 - 25}$

**45.** $\dfrac{12m^2 - 3}{8m - 4}$

**46.** $\dfrac{20p^2 - 45}{6p - 9}$

**47.** $\dfrac{3m^2 - 3m}{5m - 5}$

**48.** $\dfrac{6t^2 - 6t}{5t - 5}$

**49.** $\dfrac{9r^2 - 4s^2}{9r + 6s}$

**50.** $\dfrac{16x^2 - 9y^2}{12x - 9y}$

**51.** $\dfrac{5k^2 - 13k - 6}{5k + 2}$

**52.** $\dfrac{7t^2 - 31t - 20}{7t + 4}$

**53.** $\dfrac{x^2 + 2x - 15}{x^2 + 6x + 5}$

**54.** $\dfrac{y^2 - 5y - 14}{y^2 + y - 2}$

**55.** $\dfrac{2x^2 - 3x - 5}{2x^2 - 7x + 5}$

**56.** $\dfrac{3x^2 + 8x + 4}{3x^2 - 4x - 4}$

**57.** $\dfrac{3x^3 + 13x^2 + 14x}{3x^3 - 5x^2 - 28x}$

**58.** $\dfrac{2x^3 + 7x^2 - 30x}{2x^3 - 11x^2 + 15x}$

**59.** $\dfrac{-3t + 6t^2 - 3t^3}{7t^2 - 14t^3 + 7t^4}$

**60.** $\dfrac{-20r - 20r^2 - 5r^3}{24r^2 + 24r^3 + 6r^4}$

*Exercises 61–82 involve factoring by grouping **(Section 6.1)** and factoring sums and differences of cubes **(Section 6.4)**. Write each rational expression in lowest terms.*

**61.** $\dfrac{zw + 4z - 3w - 12}{zw + 4z + 5w + 20}$

**62.** $\dfrac{km + 4k - 4m - 16}{km + 4k + 5m + 20}$

**63.** $\dfrac{pr + qr + ps + qs}{pr + qr - ps - qs}$

**64.** $\dfrac{wt + ws + xt + xs}{wt - xs - xt + ws}$

**65.** $\dfrac{ac - ad + bc - bd}{ac - ad - bc + bd}$

**66.** $\dfrac{ac - bc - ad + bd}{ac - ad - bd + bc}$

**67.** $\dfrac{m^2 - n^2 - 4m - 4n}{2m - 2n - 8}$

**68.** $\dfrac{x^2 - y^2 - 7y - 7x}{3x - 3y - 21}$

**69.** $\dfrac{x^2y + y + x^2z + z}{xy + xz}$

**70.** $\dfrac{y^2k + pk - y^2z - pz}{yk - yz}$

**71.** $\dfrac{1 + p^3}{1 + p}$

**72.** $\dfrac{8 + x^3}{2 + x}$

**73.** $\dfrac{x^3 - 27}{x - 3}$

**74.** $\dfrac{r^3 - 1000}{r - 10}$

**75.** $\dfrac{b^3 - a^3}{a^2 - b^2}$

**76.** $\dfrac{8y^3 - 27z^3}{9z^2 - 4y^2}$

**77.** $\dfrac{k^3 + 8}{k^2 - 4}$

**78.** $\dfrac{r^3 + 27}{r^2 - 9}$

**79.** $\dfrac{z^3 + 27}{z^3 - 3z^2 + 9z}$

**80.** $\dfrac{t^3 + 64}{t^3 - 4t^2 + 16t}$

**81.** $\dfrac{1 - 8r^3}{8r^2 + 4r + 2}$

**82.** $\dfrac{8 - 27x^3}{27x^2 + 18x + 12}$

**83.** *Concept Check*  Which two of the following rational expressions equal $-1$?

**A.** $\dfrac{2x + 3}{2x - 3}$    **B.** $\dfrac{2x - 3}{3 - 2x}$    **C.** $\dfrac{2x + 3}{3 + 2x}$    **D.** $\dfrac{2x + 3}{-2x - 3}$

**84.** *Concept Check*  Make the correct choice for the blank: $\dfrac{4 - r^2}{4 + r^2}$ _____ equal to $-1$.
$\underset{\text{(is/is not)}}{}$

*Write each rational expression in lowest terms. **See Examples 5 and 6.***

**85.** $\dfrac{6 - t}{t - 6}$

**86.** $\dfrac{2 - k}{k - 2}$

**87.** $\dfrac{m^2 - 1}{1 - m}$

**88.** $\dfrac{a^2 - b^2}{b - a}$

**89.** $\dfrac{q^2 - 4q}{4q - q^2}$

**90.** $\dfrac{z^2 - 5z}{5z - z^2}$

**91.** $\dfrac{p + 6}{p - 6}$

**92.** $\dfrac{5 - x}{5 + x}$

**93.** *Concept Check* Which one of these rational expressions is *not* equivalent to $\frac{x-3}{4-x}$?

**A.** $\dfrac{3-x}{x-4}$    **B.** $\dfrac{x+3}{4+x}$    **C.** $-\dfrac{3-x}{4-x}$    **D.** $-\dfrac{x-3}{x-4}$

**94.** *Concept Check* Make the correct choice for the blank: $\frac{5+2x}{3-x}$ and $\frac{-5-2x}{x-3}$ _____ equivalent rational expressions.   (are/are not)

*Write four equivalent forms for each rational expression.* ***See Example 7.***

**🌐 95.** $-\dfrac{x+4}{x-3}$        **96.** $-\dfrac{x+6}{x-1}$        **97.** $-\dfrac{2x-3}{x+3}$

**98.** $-\dfrac{5x-6}{x+4}$        **99.** $-\dfrac{3x-1}{5x-6}$        **100.** $-\dfrac{2x-9}{7x-1}$

**101.** The area of the rectangle is represented by
$$x^4 + 10x^2 + 21.$$
What is the width? ($Hint:$ Use $W = \frac{\mathscr{A}}{L}$.)

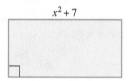

$x^2 + 7$

**102.** The volume of the box is represented by
$$(x^2 + 8x + 15)(x + 4).$$
Find the polynomial that represents the area of the bottom of the box.

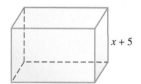

$x + 5$

*Solve each problem.*

**103.** The average number of vehicles waiting in line to enter a sports arena parking area is approximated by the rational expression
$$\frac{x^2}{2(1-x)},$$
where $x$ is a quantity between 0 and 1 known as the **traffic intensity.** (*Source:* Mannering, F., and W. Kilareski, *Principles of Highway Engineering and Traffic Control,* John Wiley and Sons.) To the nearest tenth, find the average number of vehicles waiting if the traffic intensity is the given number.

**(a)** 0.1     **(b)** 0.8     **(c)** 0.9

**(d)** What happens to waiting time as traffic intensity increases?

**104.** The percent of deaths caused by smoking is modeled by the rational expression
$$\frac{x-1}{x},$$
where $x$ is the number of times a smoker is more likely than a nonsmoker to die of lung cancer. This is called the **incidence rate.** (*Source:* Walker, A., *Observation and Inference: An Introduction to the Methods of Epidemiology,* Epidemiology Resources Inc.) For example, $x = 10$ means that a smoker is 10 times more likely than a nonsmoker to die of lung cancer. Find the percent of deaths if the incidence rate is the given number.

**(a)** 5     **(b)** 10     **(c)** 20

**✎ (d)** Can the incidence rate equal 0? Explain.

**PREVIEW EXERCISES**

*Multiply or divide as indicated. Write each answer in lowest terms.* ***See Section 1.1.***

**105.** $\dfrac{2}{3} \cdot \dfrac{5}{6}$        **106.** $\dfrac{3}{7} \cdot \dfrac{4}{5}$        **107.** $\dfrac{10}{3} \div \dfrac{5}{6}$        **108.** $\dfrac{7}{12} \div \dfrac{15}{4}$

## 7.2 Multiplying and Dividing Rational Expressions

**OBJECTIVES**

1. Multiply rational expressions.
2. Divide rational expressions.

**OBJECTIVE 1** **Multiply rational expressions.** The product of two fractions is found by multiplying the numerators and multiplying the denominators. Rational expressions are multiplied in the same way.

**Multiplying Rational Expressions**

The product of the rational expressions $\frac{P}{Q}$ and $\frac{R}{S}$ is defined as follows.

$$\frac{P}{Q} \cdot \frac{R}{S} = \frac{PR}{QS}$$

That is, to multiply rational expressions, multiply the numerators and multiply the denominators.

**NOW TRY**
**EXERCISE 1**
Multiply. Write the answer in lowest terms.

$$\frac{4k^2}{7} \cdot \frac{14}{11k}$$

**EXAMPLE 1** **Multiplying Rational Expressions**

Multiply. Write each answer in lowest terms.

**(a)** $\dfrac{3}{10} \cdot \dfrac{5}{9}$      **(b)** $\dfrac{6}{x} \cdot \dfrac{x^2}{12}$

Indicate the product of the numerators and the product of the denominators.

$$= \frac{3 \cdot 5}{10 \cdot 9} \qquad\qquad = \frac{6 \cdot x^2}{x \cdot 12}$$

Leave the products in factored form because common factors are needed to write the product in lowest terms. Factor the numerator and denominator to further identify any common factors. Then use the fundamental property to write each product in lowest terms.

$$= \frac{3 \cdot 5}{2 \cdot 5 \cdot 3 \cdot 3} \qquad\qquad = \frac{6 \cdot x \cdot x}{2 \cdot 6 \cdot x}$$

$$= \frac{1}{6} \qquad\qquad\qquad = \frac{x}{2}$$

Remember to write 1 in the numerator.

NOW TRY

**NOTE** It is also possible to divide out common factors in the numerator and denominator *before* multiplying the rational expressions. Consider this example.

$$\frac{6}{5} \cdot \frac{35}{22}$$

$$= \frac{2 \cdot 3}{5} \cdot \frac{5 \cdot 7}{2 \cdot 11} \qquad \text{Identify the common factors.}$$

$$= \frac{3}{1} \cdot \frac{7}{11} \qquad\qquad \text{Divide out the common factors.}$$

$$= \frac{21}{11} \qquad\qquad\quad \text{Multiply.}$$

**NOW TRY ANSWER**
1. $\frac{8k}{11}$

*NOW TRY*
*EXERCISE 2*

Multiply. Write the answer in lowest terms.

$$\frac{m-3}{3m} \cdot \frac{9m^2}{8(m-3)^2}$$

**EXAMPLE 2** Multiplying Rational Expressions

Multiply. Write the answer in lowest terms.

$$\frac{x+y}{2x} \cdot \frac{x^2}{(x+y)^2}$$

> Use parentheses here around $x+y$.

$$= \frac{(x+y)x^2}{2x(x+y)^2}$$  Multiply numerators.
Multiply denominators.

$$= \frac{(x+y)x \cdot x}{2x(x+y)(x+y)}$$  Factor. Identify the common factors.

$$= \frac{x}{2(x+y)}$$  $\frac{(x+y)x}{x(x+y)} = 1$; Write in lowest terms.

*NOW TRY*

*NOW TRY*
*EXERCISE 3*

Multiply. Write the answer in lowest terms.

$$\frac{y^2-3y-28}{y^2-9y+14} \cdot \frac{y^2-7y+10}{y^2+4y}$$

**EXAMPLE 3** Multiplying Rational Expressions

Multiply. Write the answer in lowest terms.

$$\frac{x^2+3x}{x^2-3x-4} \cdot \frac{x^2-5x+4}{x^2+2x-3}$$

$$= \frac{(x^2+3x)(x^2-5x+4)}{(x^2-3x-4)(x^2+2x-3)}$$  Definition of multiplication

$$= \frac{x(x+3)(x-4)(x-1)}{(x-4)(x+1)(x+3)(x-1)}$$  Factor.

$$= \frac{x}{x+1}$$  Divide out the common factors.

The quotients $\frac{x+3}{x+3}, \frac{x-4}{x-4}$, and $\frac{x-1}{x-1}$ all equal 1, justifying the final product $\frac{x}{x+1}$.

*NOW TRY*

**OBJECTIVE 2** **Divide rational expressions.** Suppose we have $\frac{7}{8}$ gal of milk and want to find how many quarts we have. Since 1 qt is $\frac{1}{4}$ gal, we ask, "How many $\frac{1}{4}$s are there in $\frac{7}{8}$?" This would be interpreted as follows.

$$\frac{7}{8} \div \frac{1}{4}, \quad \text{or} \quad \frac{\frac{7}{8}}{\frac{1}{4}} \leftarrow \text{The fraction bar means division.}$$

The fundamental property of rational expressions discussed earlier can be applied to rational number values of $P$, $Q$, and $K$.

$$\frac{P}{Q} = \frac{P \cdot K}{Q \cdot K} = \frac{\frac{7}{8} \cdot 4}{\frac{1}{4} \cdot 4} = \frac{\frac{7}{8} \cdot 4}{1} = \frac{7}{8} \cdot \frac{4}{1}$$  Let $P = \frac{7}{8}$, $Q = \frac{1}{4}$, and $K = 4$.
($K$ is the reciprocal of $Q = \frac{1}{4}$.)

NOW TRY ANSWERS
2. $\frac{3m}{8(m-3)}$
3. $\frac{y-5}{y}$

So, to divide $\frac{7}{8}$ by $\frac{1}{4}$, we multiply $\frac{7}{8}$ by the reciprocal of $\frac{1}{4}$, namely, 4. Since $\frac{7}{8}(4) = \frac{7}{2}$, there are $\frac{7}{2}$, or $3\frac{1}{2}$, qt in $\frac{7}{8}$ gal.

The preceding discussion illustrates dividing common fractions. Division of rational expressions is defined in the same way.

---

**Dividing Rational Expressions**

If $\dfrac{P}{Q}$ and $\dfrac{R}{S}$ are any two rational expressions with $\dfrac{R}{S} \neq 0$, then their quotient is defined as follows.

$$\frac{P}{Q} \div \frac{R}{S} = \frac{P}{Q} \cdot \frac{S}{R} = \frac{PS}{QR}$$

That is, to divide one rational expression by another rational expression, multiply the first rational expression (dividend) by the reciprocal of the second rational expression (divisor).

---

**NOW TRY**
**EXERCISE 4**

Divide. Write the answer in lowest terms.

$$\frac{2x - 5}{3x^2} \div \frac{2x - 5}{12x}$$

**EXAMPLE 4**   Dividing Rational Expressions

Divide. Write each answer in lowest terms.

**(a)** $\dfrac{5}{8} \div \dfrac{7}{16}$

**(b)** $\dfrac{y}{y + 3} \div \dfrac{4y}{y + 5}$

Multiply the dividend by the reciprocal of the divisor.

$= \dfrac{5}{8} \cdot \dfrac{16}{7}$   ← Reciprocal of $\frac{7}{16}$

$= \dfrac{5 \cdot 16}{8 \cdot 7}$

$= \dfrac{5 \cdot 8 \cdot 2}{8 \cdot 7}$

$= \dfrac{10}{7}$

$= \dfrac{y}{y + 3} \cdot \dfrac{y + 5}{4y}$   ← Reciprocal of $\frac{4y}{y + 5}$

$= \dfrac{y(y + 5)}{(y + 3)(4y)}$

$= \dfrac{y + 5}{4(y + 3)}$

NOW TRY

---

**NOW TRY**
**EXERCISE 5**

Divide. Write the answer in lowest terms.

$$\frac{(3k)^3}{2j^4} \div \frac{9k^2}{6j}$$

**EXAMPLE 5**   Dividing Rational Expressions

Divide. Write the answer in lowest terms.

$$\frac{(3m)^2}{(2p)^3} \div \frac{6m^3}{16p^2}$$

$= \dfrac{(3m)^2}{(2p)^3} \cdot \dfrac{16p^2}{6m^3}$   Multiply by the reciprocal.

$(3m)^2 = 3^2 m^2;$
$(2p)^3 = 2^3 p^3$   $= \dfrac{9m^2}{8p^3} \cdot \dfrac{16p^2}{6m^3}$   Power rule for exponents

$= \dfrac{9 \cdot 16m^2 p^2}{8 \cdot 6p^3 m^3}$   Multiply numerators.
Multiply denominators.

$= \dfrac{3}{mp}$   Lowest terms

**NOW TRY ANSWERS**
**4.** $\dfrac{4}{x}$   **5.** $\dfrac{9k}{j^3}$

NOW TRY

NOW TRY
EXERCISE 6
Divide. Write the answer in lowest terms.

$$\frac{(t + 2)(t - 5)}{-4t} \div \frac{t^2 - 25}{(t + 5)(t + 2)}$$

**EXAMPLE 6** Dividing Rational Expressions

Divide. Write the answer in lowest terms.

$$\frac{x^2 - 4}{(x + 3)(x - 2)} \div \frac{(x + 2)(x + 3)}{-2x}$$

$$= \frac{x^2 - 4}{(x + 3)(x - 2)} \cdot \frac{-2x}{(x + 2)(x + 3)} \qquad \text{Multiply by the reciprocal.}$$

$$= \frac{-2x(x^2 - 4)}{(x + 3)(x - 2)(x + 2)(x + 3)} \qquad \begin{array}{l}\text{Multiply numerators.}\\ \text{Multiply denominators.}\end{array}$$

$$= \frac{-2x(x + 2)(x - 2)}{(x + 3)(x - 2)(x + 2)(x + 3)} \qquad \text{Factor the numerator.}$$

$$= \frac{-2x}{(x + 3)^2}, \quad \text{or} \quad -\frac{2x}{(x + 3)^2} \qquad \text{Lowest terms; } \frac{-a}{b} = -\frac{a}{b}$$

NOW TRY

NOW TRY
EXERCISE 7
Divide. Write the answer in lowest terms.

$$\frac{7 - x}{2x + 6} \div \frac{x^2 - 49}{x^2 + 6x + 9}$$

**EXAMPLE 7** Dividing Rational Expressions (Factors Are Opposites)

Divide. Write the answer in lowest terms.

$$\frac{m^2 - 4}{m^2 - 1} \div \frac{2m^2 + 4m}{1 - m}$$

$$= \frac{m^2 - 4}{m^2 - 1} \cdot \frac{1 - m}{2m^2 + 4m} \qquad \text{Multiply by the reciprocal.}$$

$$= \frac{(m^2 - 4)(1 - m)}{(m^2 - 1)(2m^2 + 4m)} \qquad \begin{array}{l}\text{Multiply numerators.}\\ \text{Multiply denominators.}\end{array}$$

$$= \frac{(m + 2)(m - 2)(1 - m)}{(m + 1)(m - 1)(2m)(m + 2)} \qquad \text{Factor; } 1 - m \text{ and } m - 1 \text{ are opposites.}$$

$$= \frac{-1(m - 2)}{2m(m + 1)} \qquad \text{From Section 7.1, } \frac{1 - m}{m - 1} = -1.$$

$$= \frac{-m + 2}{2m(m + 1)}, \quad \text{or} \quad \frac{2 - m}{2m(m + 1)} \qquad \begin{array}{l}\text{Distribute } -1 \text{ in the numerator.}\\ \text{Rewrite } -m + 2 \text{ as } 2 - m.\end{array}$$

NOW TRY

In summary, use the following steps to multiply or divide rational expressions.

---

**Multiplying or Dividing Rational Expressions**

*Step 1*  **Note the operation.** If the operation is division, use the definition of division to rewrite it as multiplication.

*Step 2*  **Multiply** numerators and multiply denominators.

*Step 3*  **Factor** all numerators and denominators completely.

*Step 4*  **Write in lowest terms** using the fundamental property.

***Note: Steps 2 and 3 may be interchanged based on personal preference.***

---

NOW TRY ANSWERS

6. $\frac{(t + 2)^2}{-4t}$, or $-\frac{(t + 2)^2}{4t}$

7. $\frac{-x - 3}{2(x + 7)}$, or $-\frac{x + 3}{2(x + 7)}$

## 7.2 EXERCISES

*MyMathLab*

🌐 *Complete solution available on the Video Resources on DVD*

**1.** *Concept Check* Match each multiplication problem in Column I with the correct product in Column II.

| I | II |
|---|---|
| **(a)** $\dfrac{5x^3}{10x^4} \cdot \dfrac{10x^7}{4x}$ | **A.** $\dfrac{4}{5x^5}$ |
| **(b)** $\dfrac{10x^4}{5x^3} \cdot \dfrac{10x^7}{4x}$ | **B.** $\dfrac{5x^5}{4}$ |
| **(c)** $\dfrac{5x^3}{10x^4} \cdot \dfrac{4x}{10x^7}$ | **C.** $\dfrac{1}{5x^7}$ |
| **(d)** $\dfrac{10x^4}{5x^3} \cdot \dfrac{4x}{10x^7}$ | **D.** $5x^7$ |

**2.** *Concept Check* Match each division problem in Column I with the correct quotient in Column II.

| I | II |
|---|---|
| **(a)** $\dfrac{5x^3}{10x^4} \div \dfrac{10x^7}{4x}$ | **A.** $\dfrac{5x^5}{4}$ |
| **(b)** $\dfrac{10x^4}{5x^3} \div \dfrac{10x^7}{4x}$ | **B.** $5x^7$ |
| **(c)** $\dfrac{5x^3}{10x^4} \div \dfrac{4x}{10x^7}$ | **C.** $\dfrac{4}{5x^5}$ |
| **(d)** $\dfrac{10x^4}{5x^3} \div \dfrac{4x}{10x^7}$ | **D.** $\dfrac{1}{5x^7}$ |

*Multiply. Write each answer in lowest terms.* ***See Examples 1 and 2.***

🌐 **3.** $\dfrac{15a^2}{14} \cdot \dfrac{7}{5a}$

**4.** $\dfrac{21b^6}{18} \cdot \dfrac{9}{7b^4}$

**5.** $\dfrac{12x^4}{18x^3} \cdot \dfrac{-8x^5}{4x^2}$

**6.** $\dfrac{12m^5}{-2m^2} \cdot \dfrac{6m^6}{28m^3}$

**7.** $\dfrac{2(c+d)}{3} \cdot \dfrac{18}{6(c+d)^2}$

**8.** $\dfrac{4(y-2)}{x} \cdot \dfrac{3x}{6(y-2)^2}$

🌐 **9.** $\dfrac{(x-y)^2}{2} \cdot \dfrac{24}{3(x-y)}$

**10.** $\dfrac{(a+b)^2}{5} \cdot \dfrac{30}{2(a+b)}$

**11.** $\dfrac{t-4}{8} \cdot \dfrac{4t^2}{t-4}$

**12.** $\dfrac{z+9}{12} \cdot \dfrac{3z^2}{z+9}$

**13.** $\dfrac{3x}{x+3} \cdot \dfrac{(x+3)^2}{6x^2}$

**14.** $\dfrac{(t-2)^2}{4t^2} \cdot \dfrac{2t}{t-2}$

*Divide. Write each answer in lowest terms.* ***See Examples 4 and 5.***

**15.** $\dfrac{9z^4}{3z^5} \div \dfrac{3z^2}{5z^3}$

**16.** $\dfrac{35x^8}{7x^9} \div \dfrac{5x^5}{9x^6}$

🌐 **17.** $\dfrac{4t^4}{2t^5} \div \dfrac{(2t)^3}{-6}$

**18.** $\dfrac{-12a^6}{3a^2} \div \dfrac{(2a)^3}{27a}$

🌐 **19.** $\dfrac{3}{2y-6} \div \dfrac{6}{y-3}$

**20.** $\dfrac{4m+16}{10} \div \dfrac{3m+12}{18}$

**21.** $\dfrac{7t+7}{-6} \div \dfrac{4t+4}{15}$

**22.** $\dfrac{8z-16}{-20} \div \dfrac{3z-6}{40}$

**23.** $\dfrac{2x}{x-1} \div \dfrac{x^2}{x+2}$

**24.** $\dfrac{y^2}{y+1} \div \dfrac{3y}{y-3}$

**25.** $\dfrac{(x-3)^2}{6x} \div \dfrac{x-3}{x^2}$

**26.** $\dfrac{2a}{a+4} \div \dfrac{a^2}{(a+4)^2}$

*Multiply or divide. Write each answer in lowest terms.* ***See Examples 3, 6, and 7.***

**27.** $\dfrac{5x-15}{3x+9} \cdot \dfrac{4x+12}{6x-18}$

**28.** $\dfrac{8r+16}{24r-24} \cdot \dfrac{6r-6}{3r+6}$

**29.** $\dfrac{2-t}{8} \div \dfrac{t-2}{6}$

**30.** $\dfrac{m-2}{4} \div \dfrac{2-m}{6}$

**31.** $\dfrac{27-3z}{4} \cdot \dfrac{12}{2z-18}$

**32.** $\dfrac{35-5x}{6} \cdot \dfrac{12}{3x-21}$

🌐 **33.** $\dfrac{p^2+4p-5}{p^2+7p+10} \div \dfrac{p-1}{p+4}$

**34.** $\dfrac{z^2-3z+2}{z^2+4z+3} \div \dfrac{z-1}{z+1}$

🌐 **35.** $\dfrac{m^2-4}{16-8m} \div \dfrac{m+2}{8}$

**36.** $\dfrac{r^2-36}{54-9r} \div \dfrac{r+6}{9}$

**37.** $\dfrac{2x^2-7x+3}{x-3} \cdot \dfrac{x+2}{x-1}$

**38.** $\dfrac{3x^2-5x-2}{x-2} \cdot \dfrac{x-3}{x+1}$

**39.** $\dfrac{2k^2-k-1}{2k^2+5k+3} \div \dfrac{4k^2-1}{2k^2+k-3}$

**40.** $\dfrac{3t^2-4t-4}{3t^2+10t+8} \div \dfrac{9t^2+21t+10}{3t^2+14t+15}$

**41.** $\dfrac{2k^2 + 3k - 2}{6k^2 - 7k + 2} \cdot \dfrac{4k^2 - 5k + 1}{k^2 + k - 2}$

**42.** $\dfrac{2m^2 - 5m - 12}{m^2 - 10m + 24} \cdot \dfrac{m^2 - 9m + 18}{4m^2 - 9}$

**43.** $\dfrac{m^2 + 2mp - 3p^2}{m^2 - 3mp + 2p^2} \div \dfrac{m^2 + 4mp + 3p^2}{m^2 + 2mp - 8p^2}$

**44.** $\dfrac{r^2 + rs - 12s^2}{r^2 - rs - 20s^2} \div \dfrac{r^2 - 2rs - 3s^2}{r^2 + rs - 30s^2}$

**45.** $\dfrac{m^2 + 3m + 2}{m^2 + 5m + 4} \cdot \dfrac{m^2 + 10m + 24}{m^2 + 5m + 6}$

**46.** $\dfrac{z^2 - z - 6}{z^2 - 2z - 8} \cdot \dfrac{z^2 + 7z + 12}{z^2 - 9}$

**47.** $\dfrac{y^2 + y - 2}{y^2 + 3y - 4} \div \dfrac{y + 2}{y + 3}$

**48.** $\dfrac{r^2 + r - 6}{r^2 + 4r - 12} \div \dfrac{r + 3}{r - 1}$

**49.** $\dfrac{2m^2 + 7m + 3}{m^2 - 9} \cdot \dfrac{m^2 - 3m}{2m^2 + 11m + 5}$

**50.** $\dfrac{6s^2 + 17s + 10}{s^2 - 4} \cdot \dfrac{s^2 - 2s}{6s^2 + 29s + 20}$

**51.** $\dfrac{r^2 + rs - 12s^2}{r^2 - rs - 20s^2} \div \dfrac{r^2 - 2rs - 3s^2}{r^2 + rs - 30s^2}$

**52.** $\dfrac{m^2 + 8mn + 7n^2}{m^2 + mn - 42n^2} \div \dfrac{m^2 - 3mn - 4n^2}{m^2 - mn - 30n^2}$

**53.** $\dfrac{(q - 3)^4(q + 2)}{q^2 + 3q + 2} \div \dfrac{q^2 - 6q + 9}{q^2 + 4q + 4}$

**54.** $\dfrac{(x + 4)^3(x - 3)}{x^2 - 9} \div \dfrac{x^2 + 8x + 16}{x^2 + 6x + 9}$

*Brain Busters* *Exercises 55–60 involve grouping symbols* **(Section 1.2)**, *factoring by grouping* **(Section 6.1)**, *and factoring sums and differences of cubes* **(Section 6.4)**. *Multiply or divide as indicated. Write each answer in lowest terms.*

**55.** $\dfrac{x + 5}{x + 10} \div \left( \dfrac{x^2 + 10x + 25}{x^2 + 10x} \cdot \dfrac{10x}{x^2 + 15x + 50} \right)$

**56.** $\dfrac{m - 8}{m - 4} \div \left( \dfrac{m^2 - 12m + 32}{8m} \cdot \dfrac{m^2 - 8m}{m^2 - 8m + 16} \right)$

**57.** $\dfrac{3a - 3b - a^2 + b^2}{4a^2 - 4ab + b^2} \cdot \dfrac{4a^2 - b^2}{2a^2 - ab - b^2}$

**58.** $\dfrac{4r^2 - t^2 + 10r - 5t}{2r^2 + rt + 5r} \cdot \dfrac{4r^3 + 4r^2t + rt^2}{2r + t}$

**59.** $\dfrac{-x^3 - y^3}{x^2 - 2xy + y^2} \div \dfrac{3y^2 - 3xy}{x^2 - y^2}$

**60.** $\dfrac{b^3 - 8a^3}{4a^3 + 4a^2b + ab^2} \div \dfrac{4a^2 + 2ab + b^2}{-a^3 - ab^3}$

**61.** If the rational expression $\dfrac{5x^2y^3}{2pq}$ represents the area of a rectangle and $\dfrac{2xy}{p}$ represents the length, what rational expression represents the width?

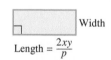

Width

Length $= \dfrac{2xy}{p}$

The area is $\dfrac{5x^2y^3}{2pq}$.

**62.** *Concept Check* If you are given the following problem, what must be the polynomial that is represented by the question mark?

$$\dfrac{4y + 12}{2y - 10} \div \dfrac{?}{y^2 - y - 20} = \dfrac{2(y + 4)}{y - 3}$$

---

**PREVIEW EXERCISES**

*Write the prime factored form of each number. **See Section 1.1.***

**63.** 18      **64.** 48      **65.** 108      **66.** 60

*Find the greatest common factor of each group of terms. **See Section 6.1.***

**67.** $24m, 18m^2, 6$      **68.** $14t^2, 28t, 7$      **69.** $84q^3, 90q^6$      **70.** $54k^3, 36k^4$

## 7.3 Least Common Denominators

**OBJECTIVES**

1 Find the least common denominator for a group of fractions.

2 Write equivalent rational expressions.

**OBJECTIVE 1** Find the least common denominator for a group of fractions. Adding or subtracting rational expressions often requires a **least common denominator (LCD).** The LCD is the simplest expression that is divisible by all of the denominators in all of the expressions. For example, the fractions

$$\frac{2}{9} \quad \text{and} \quad \frac{5}{12} \quad \text{have LCD 36,}$$

because 36 is the least positive number divisible by both 9 and 12.

We can often find least common denominators by inspection. In other cases, we find the LCD by a procedure similar to that used in **Section 6.1** for finding the greatest common factor.

---

**Finding the Least Common Denominator (LCD)**

*Step 1* **Factor** each denominator into prime factors.

*Step 2* **List each different denominator factor** the *greatest* number of times it appears in any of the denominators.

*Step 3* **Multiply** the denominator factors from Step 2 to get the LCD.

---

When each denominator is factored into prime factors, every prime factor must be a factor of the least common denominator.

*NOW TRY*
*EXERCISE 1*

Find the LCD for each pair of fractions.

(a) $\dfrac{5}{48}, \dfrac{1}{30}$  (b) $\dfrac{3}{10y}, \dfrac{1}{6y}$

**EXAMPLE 1** Finding the LCD

Find the LCD for each pair of fractions.

(a) $\dfrac{1}{24}, \dfrac{7}{15}$  (b) $\dfrac{1}{8x}, \dfrac{3}{10x}$

*Step 1* Write each denominator in factored form with numerical coefficients in prime factored form.

$$24 = 2 \cdot 2 \cdot 2 \cdot 3 = 2^3 \cdot 3 \qquad 8x = 2 \cdot 2 \cdot 2 \cdot x = 2^3 \cdot x$$
$$15 = 3 \cdot 5 \qquad\qquad\qquad 10x = 2 \cdot 5 \cdot x$$

*Step 2* Find the LCD by taking each different factor the *greatest* number of times it appears as a factor in any of the denominators.

The factor 2 appears three times in one product and not at all in the other, so the greatest number of times 2 appears is three. The greatest number of times both 3 and 5 appear is one.

Here, 2 appears three times in one product and once in the other, so the greatest number of times 2 appears is three. The greatest number of times 5 appears is one, and the greatest number of times $x$ appears in either product is one.

*Step 3* LCD $= 2 \cdot 2 \cdot 2 \cdot 3 \cdot 5$
$= 2^3 \cdot 3 \cdot 5$
$= 120$

LCD $= 2 \cdot 2 \cdot 2 \cdot 5 \cdot x$
$= 2^3 \cdot 5 \cdot x$
$= 40x$     *NOW TRY*

*NOW TRY ANSWERS*
**1. (a)** 240 **(b)** $30y$

NOW TRY
EXERCISE 2

Find the LCD for the pair of fractions.

$$\frac{5}{6x^4} \quad \text{and} \quad \frac{7}{8x^3}$$

**EXAMPLE 2** Finding the LCD

Find the LCD for $\dfrac{5}{6r^2}$ and $\dfrac{3}{4r^3}$.

**Step 1** Factor each denominator.

$$6r^2 = 2 \cdot 3 \cdot r^2$$
$$4r^3 = 2 \cdot 2 \cdot r^3 = 2^2 \cdot r^3$$

**Step 2** The greatest number of times 2 appears is two, the greatest number of times 3 appears is one, and the greatest number of times $r$ appears is three.

**Step 3** $\qquad \text{LCD} = 2^2 \cdot 3 \cdot r^3 = 12r^3$ NOW TRY

---

⚠ **CAUTION** When finding the LCD, use each factor the *greatest* number of times it appears in any *single* denominator, not the *total* number of times it appears. For instance, the greatest number of times $r$ appears as a factor in one denominator in **Example 2** is 3, *not* 5.

---

NOW TRY
EXERCISE 3

Find the LCD for the fractions in each list.

**(a)** $\dfrac{3t}{2t^2 - 10t}, \dfrac{t+4}{t^2 - 25}$

**(b)** $\dfrac{1}{x^2 + 7x + 12}$,

$\dfrac{2}{x^2 + 6x + 9}, \dfrac{5}{x^2 + 2x - 8}$

**(c)** $\dfrac{2}{a-4}, \dfrac{1}{4-a}$

**EXAMPLE 3** Finding LCDs

Find the LCD for the fractions in each list.

**(a)** $\dfrac{6}{5m}, \dfrac{4}{m^2 - 3m}$

$$\left.\begin{array}{l} 5m = 5 \cdot m \\ m^2 - 3m = m(m-3) \end{array}\right\} \text{ Factor each denominator.}$$

Use each different factor the greatest number of times it appears.
Be sure to include $m$ as a factor in the LCD.

$$\text{LCD} = 5 \cdot m \cdot (m-3) = 5m(m-3)$$

Because $m$ is not a *factor* of $m - 3$, both $m$ and $m - 3$ must appear in the LCD.

**(b)** $\dfrac{1}{r^2 - 4r - 5}, \dfrac{3}{r^2 - r - 20}, \dfrac{1}{r^2 - 10r + 25}$

$$\left.\begin{array}{l} r^2 - 4r - 5 = (r-5)(r+1) \\ r^2 - r - 20 = (r-5)(r+4) \\ r^2 - 10r + 25 = (r-5)^2 \end{array}\right\} \text{ Factor each denominator.}$$

Use each different factor the greatest number of times it appears as a factor.

$$\text{LCD} = (r-5)^2(r+1)(r+4)$$

Be sure to include the exponent 2.

**(c)** $\dfrac{1}{q-5}, \dfrac{3}{5-q}$

The expressions $q - 5$ and $5 - q$ are opposites of each other. This means that if we multiply $q - 5$ by $-1$, we will get $5 - q$.

$$-(q-5) = -q + 5 = 5 - q$$

Therefore, either $q - 5$ or $5 - q$ can be used as the LCD. NOW TRY

NOW TRY ANSWERS
**2.** $24x^4$
**3. (a)** $2t(t-5)(t+5)$
  **(b)** $(x+3)^2(x+4)(x-2)$
  **(c)** either $a - 4$ or $4 - a$

**OBJECTIVE 2** Write equivalent rational expressions. Once the LCD has been found, the next step in preparing to add or subtract two rational expressions is to use the fundamental property to write equivalent rational expressions.

---

**Writing a Rational Expression with a Specified Denominator**

*Step 1*  **Factor** both denominators.

*Step 2*  **Decide what factor(s) the denominator must be multiplied by** in order to equal the specified denominator.

*Step 3*  **Multiply** the rational expression by that factor divided by itself. (That is, multiply by 1.)

---

NOW TRY
EXERCISE 4

Rewrite each rational expression with the indicated denominator.

**(a)** $\dfrac{2}{9} = \dfrac{?}{27}$  **(b)** $\dfrac{4t}{11} = \dfrac{?}{33t}$

**EXAMPLE 4**  Writing Equivalent Rational Expressions

Rewrite each rational expression with the indicated denominator.

**(a)** $\dfrac{3}{8} = \dfrac{?}{40}$  |  **(b)** $\dfrac{9k}{25} = \dfrac{?}{50k}$

*Step 1*  For each example, first factor the denominator on the right. Then compare the denominator on the left with the one on the right to decide what factors are missing. (It may sometimes be necessary to factor both denominators.)

$$\dfrac{3}{8} = \dfrac{?}{5 \cdot 8} \qquad\qquad \dfrac{9k}{25} = \dfrac{?}{25 \cdot 2k}$$

*Step 2*  A factor of 5 is missing.  Factors of 2 and $k$ are missing.

*Step 3*  Multiply $\frac{3}{8}$ by $\frac{5}{5}$.  Multiply $\frac{9k}{25}$ by $\frac{2k}{2k}$.

$$\dfrac{3}{8} = \dfrac{3}{8} \cdot \dfrac{5}{5} = \dfrac{15}{40} \qquad \dfrac{9k}{25} = \dfrac{9k}{25} \cdot \dfrac{2k}{2k} = \dfrac{18k^2}{50k}$$

$\dfrac{5}{5} = 1$  $\dfrac{2k}{2k} = 1$

NOW TRY

**EXAMPLE 5**  Writing Equivalent Rational Expressions

Rewrite each rational expression with the indicated denominator.

**(a)**  $\dfrac{8}{3x + 1} = \dfrac{?}{12x + 4}$

$\dfrac{8}{3x + 1} = \dfrac{?}{4(3x + 1)}$   Factor the denominator on the right.

The missing factor is 4, so multiply the fraction on the left by $\frac{4}{4}$.

$$\dfrac{8}{3x + 1} \cdot \dfrac{4}{4} = \dfrac{32}{12x + 4} \qquad \text{Fundamental property}$$

NOW TRY ANSWERS

**4. (a)** $\dfrac{6}{27}$  **(b)** $\dfrac{12t^2}{33t}$

Rewrite each rational expression with the indicated denominator.

**(a)** $\dfrac{8k}{5k - 2} = \dfrac{?}{25k - 10}$

**(b)** $\dfrac{2t - 1}{t^2 + 4t} = \dfrac{?}{t^3 + 12t^2 + 32t}$

**(b)** $\dfrac{12p}{p^2 + 8p} = \dfrac{?}{p^3 + 4p^2 - 32p}$

Factor the denominator in each rational expression.

$$\frac{12p}{p(p + 8)} = \frac{?}{p(p + 8)(p - 4)}$$

$$\boxed{\begin{aligned} p^3 + 4p^2 - 32p \\ = p(p^2 + 4p - 32) \\ = p(p + 8)(p - 4) \end{aligned}}$$

The factor $p - 4$ is missing, so multiply $\dfrac{12p}{p(p + 8)}$ by $\dfrac{p - 4}{p - 4}$.

$$\frac{12p}{p^2 + 8p} = \frac{12p}{p(p + 8)} \cdot \frac{p - 4}{p - 4} \qquad \text{Fundamental property}$$

$$= \frac{12p(p - 4)}{p(p + 8)(p - 4)} \qquad \begin{aligned}&\text{Multiply numerators.}\\&\text{Multiply denominators.}\end{aligned}$$

$$= \frac{12p^2 - 48p}{p^3 + 4p^2 - 32p} \qquad \text{Multiply the factors.} \qquad \textit{NOW TRY}$$

**NOW TRY ANSWERS**

**5. (a)** $\dfrac{40k}{25k - 10}$

**(b)** $\dfrac{2t^2 + 15t - 8}{t^3 + 12t^2 + 32t}$

**NOTE** While it is beneficial to leave the denominator in factored form, we multiplied the factors in the denominator in **Example 5** to give the answer in the same form as the original problem.

---

## 7.3 EXERCISES

*MyMathLab* | Math XL PRACTICE | WATCH | DOWNLOAD | READ | REVIEW

⊕ *Complete solution available on the Video Resources on DVD*

*Concept Check* *Choose the correct response in Exercises 1–4.*

**1.** Suppose that the greatest common factor of $x$ and $y$ is 1. What is the least common denominator for $\frac{1}{x}$ and $\frac{1}{y}$?

 **A.** $x$    **B.** $y$    **C.** $xy$    **D.** 1

**2.** If $x$ is a factor of $y$, what is the least common denominator for $\frac{1}{x}$ and $\frac{1}{y}$?

 **A.** $x$    **B.** $y$    **C.** $xy$    **D.** 1

**3.** What is the least common denominator for $\frac{9}{20}$ and $\frac{1}{2}$?

 **A.** 40    **B.** 2    **C.** 20    **D.** none of these

**4.** Suppose that we wish to write the fraction $\frac{1}{(x - 4)^2(y - 3)}$ with denominator $(x - 4)^3(y - 3)^2$. By what must we multiply both the numerator and the denominator?

 **A.** $(x - 4)(y - 3)$    **B.** $(x - 4)^2$    **C.** $x - 4$    **D.** $(x - 4)^2(y - 3)$

*Find the LCD for the fractions in each list. **See Examples 1–3.***

⊕ **5.** $\dfrac{7}{15}, \dfrac{21}{20}$

**6.** $\dfrac{9}{10}, \dfrac{13}{25}$

**7.** $\dfrac{17}{100}, \dfrac{23}{120}, \dfrac{43}{180}$

**8.** $\dfrac{17}{250}, \dfrac{21}{300}, \dfrac{1}{360}$

**9.** $\dfrac{9}{x^2}, \dfrac{8}{x^5}$

**10.** $\dfrac{12}{m^7}, \dfrac{14}{m^8}$

**11.** $\dfrac{-2}{5p}, \dfrac{13}{6p}$

**12.** $\dfrac{-14}{15k}, \dfrac{11}{4k}$

⊕ **13.** $\dfrac{17}{15y^2}, \dfrac{55}{36y^4}$

**14.** $\dfrac{4}{25m^3}, \dfrac{7}{10m^4}$

**15.** $\dfrac{5}{21r^3}, \dfrac{7}{12r^5}$

**16.** $\dfrac{6}{35t^2}, \dfrac{5}{49t^6}$

**17.** $\dfrac{13}{5a^2b^3}, \dfrac{29}{15a^5b}$     **18.** $\dfrac{7}{3r^4s^5}, \dfrac{23}{9r^6s^8}$     🌐 **19.** $\dfrac{7}{6p}, \dfrac{15}{4p - 8}$

**20.** $\dfrac{7}{8k}, \dfrac{28}{12k - 24}$     **21.** $\dfrac{9}{28m^2}, \dfrac{3}{12m - 20}$     **22.** $\dfrac{14}{27a^3}, \dfrac{7}{9a - 45}$

**23.** $\dfrac{7}{5b - 10}, \dfrac{11}{6b - 12}$     **24.** $\dfrac{3}{7x^2 + 21x}, \dfrac{2}{5x^2 + 15x}$

**25.** $\dfrac{37}{6r - 12}, \dfrac{25}{9r - 18}$     **26.** $\dfrac{14}{5p - 30}, \dfrac{11}{6p - 36}$

**27.** $\dfrac{5}{12p + 60}, \dfrac{-17}{p^2 + 5p}, \dfrac{-16}{p^2 + 10p + 25}$     **28.** $\dfrac{13}{r^2 + 7r}, \dfrac{-3}{5r + 35}, \dfrac{-4}{r^2 + 14r + 49}$

**29.** $\dfrac{-3}{8y + 16}, \dfrac{-22}{y^2 + 3y + 2}$     **30.** $\dfrac{-2}{9m - 18}, \dfrac{-6}{m^2 - 7m + 10}$

**31.** $\dfrac{5}{c - d}, \dfrac{8}{d - c}$     **32.** $\dfrac{4}{y - x}, \dfrac{8}{x - y}$     **33.** $\dfrac{12}{m - 3}, \dfrac{-4}{3 - m}$

**34.** $\dfrac{3}{a - 8}, \dfrac{-17}{8 - a}$     **35.** $\dfrac{29}{p - q}, \dfrac{18}{q - p}$     **36.** $\dfrac{16}{z - x}, \dfrac{9}{x - z}$

**37.** $\dfrac{3}{k^2 + 5k}, \dfrac{2}{k^2 + 3k - 10}$     **38.** $\dfrac{1}{z^2 - 4z}, \dfrac{9}{z^2 - 3z - 4}$

**39.** $\dfrac{6}{a^2 + 6a}, \dfrac{-5}{a^2 + 3a - 18}$     **40.** $\dfrac{8}{y^2 - 5y}, \dfrac{-5}{y^2 - 2y - 15}$

**41.** $\dfrac{5}{p^2 + 8p + 15}, \dfrac{3}{p^2 - 3p - 18}, \dfrac{12}{p^2 - p - 30}$

**42.** $\dfrac{10}{y^2 - 10y + 21}, \dfrac{2}{y^2 - 2y - 3}, \dfrac{15}{y^2 - 6y - 7}$

**43.** $\dfrac{-5}{k^2 + 2k - 35}, \dfrac{-8}{k^2 + 3k - 40}, \dfrac{19}{k^2 - 2k - 15}$

**44.** $\dfrac{-19}{z^2 + 4z - 12}, \dfrac{-16}{z^2 + z - 30}, \dfrac{16}{z^2 + 2z - 24}$

*RELATING CONCEPTS*   **EXERCISES 45–50**

**FOR INDIVIDUAL OR GROUP WORK**

*Work Exercises 45–50 in order.*

**45.** Suppose that you want to write $\frac{3}{4}$ as an equivalent fraction with denominator 28. By what number must you multiply both the numerator and the denominator?

**46.** If you write $\frac{3}{4}$ as an equivalent fraction with denominator 28, by what number are you actually multiplying the fraction?

**47.** What property of multiplication is being used when we write a common fraction as an equivalent one with a larger denominator? (See **Section 1.7.**)

**48.** Suppose that you want to write $\frac{2x + 5}{x - 4}$ as an equivalent fraction with denominator $7x - 28$. By what number must you multiply both the numerator and the denominator?

**49.** If you write $\frac{2x + 5}{x - 4}$ as an equivalent fraction with denominator $7x - 28$, by what number are you actually multiplying the fraction?

**50.** Repeat **Exercise 47,** changing "a common" to "an algebraic."

*Rewrite each rational expression with the indicated denominator. **See Examples 4 and 5.***

**51.** $\dfrac{4}{11} = \dfrac{?}{55}$

**52.** $\dfrac{8}{7} = \dfrac{?}{42}$

**53.** $\dfrac{-5}{k} = \dfrac{?}{9k}$

**54.** $\dfrac{-4}{q} = \dfrac{?}{6q}$

**55.** $\dfrac{15m^2}{8k} = \dfrac{?}{32k^4}$

**56.** $\dfrac{7t^2}{3y} = \dfrac{?}{9y^2}$

**57.** $\dfrac{19z}{2z - 6} = \dfrac{?}{6z - 18}$

**58.** $\dfrac{3r}{5r - 5} = \dfrac{?}{15r - 15}$

**59.** $\dfrac{-2a}{9a - 18} = \dfrac{?}{18a - 36}$

**60.** $\dfrac{-7y}{6y + 18} = \dfrac{?}{24y + 72}$

**61.** $\dfrac{6}{k^2 - 4k} = \dfrac{?}{k(k - 4)(k + 1)}$

**62.** $\dfrac{25}{m^2 - 9m} = \dfrac{?}{m(m - 9)(m + 8)}$

**63.** $\dfrac{36r}{r^2 - r - 6} = \dfrac{?}{(r - 3)(r + 2)(r + 1)}$

**64.** $\dfrac{4m}{m^2 + m - 2} = \dfrac{?}{(m - 1)(m - 3)(m + 2)}$

**65.** $\dfrac{a + 2b}{2a^2 + ab - b^2} = \dfrac{?}{2a^3b + a^2b^2 - ab^3}$

**66.** $\dfrac{m - 4}{6m^2 + 7m - 3} = \dfrac{?}{12m^3 + 14m^2 - 6m}$

**67.** $\dfrac{4r - t}{r^2 + rt + t^2} = \dfrac{?}{t^3 - r^3}$

**68.** $\dfrac{3x - 1}{x^2 + 2x + 4} = \dfrac{?}{x^3 - 8}$

**69.** $\dfrac{2(z - y)}{y^2 + yz + z^2} = \dfrac{?}{y^4 - z^3y}$

**70.** $\dfrac{2p + 3q}{p^2 + 2pq + q^2} = \dfrac{?}{(p + q)(p^3 + q^3)}$

**PREVIEW EXERCISES**

*Add or subtract as indicated. Write each answer in lowest terms. **See Section 1.1.***

**71.** $\dfrac{1}{2} + \dfrac{7}{8}$

**72.** $\dfrac{2}{3} + \dfrac{8}{27}$

**73.** $\dfrac{7}{5} - \dfrac{3}{4}$

**74.** $\dfrac{11}{6} - \dfrac{2}{5}$

---

## 7.4 Adding and Subtracting Rational Expressions

**OBJECTIVES**

1. Add rational expressions having the same denominator.
2. Add rational expressions having different denominators.
3. Subtract rational expressions.

**OBJECTIVE 1** Add rational expressions having the same denominator.
We find the sum of two rational expressions with the same denominator using the same procedure that we used in **Section 1.1** for adding two common fractions.

**Adding Rational Expressions (Same Denominator)**

The rational expressions $\dfrac{P}{Q}$ and $\dfrac{R}{Q}$ ($Q \neq 0$) are added as follows.

$$\dfrac{P}{Q} + \dfrac{R}{Q} = \dfrac{P + R}{Q}$$

That is, to add rational expressions with the same denominator, add the numerators and keep the same denominator.

NOW TRY
EXERCISE 1

Add. Write each answer in lowest terms.

**(a)** $\dfrac{2}{7k} + \dfrac{4}{7k}$

**(b)** $\dfrac{4y}{y+3} + \dfrac{12}{y+3}$

**EXAMPLE 1**  Adding Rational Expressions (Same Denominator)

Add. Write each answer in lowest terms.

**(a)** $\dfrac{4}{9} + \dfrac{2}{9}$  |  **(b)** $\dfrac{3x}{x+1} + \dfrac{3}{x+1}$

The denominators are the same, so the sum is found by adding the two numerators and keeping the same (common) denominator.

$= \dfrac{4+2}{9}$   Add.

$= \dfrac{6}{9}$

$= \dfrac{2 \cdot 3}{3 \cdot 3}$   Factor.

$= \dfrac{2}{3}$   Lowest terms

$= \dfrac{3x+3}{x+1}$   Add.

$= \dfrac{3(x+1)}{x+1}$   Factor.

$= 3$   Lowest terms

NOW TRY

**OBJECTIVE 2**  Add rational expressions having different denominators.
As in **Section 1.1,** we use the following steps to add fractions having different denominators.

**Adding Rational Expressions (Different Denominators)**

*Step 1*  **Find the least common denominator (LCD).**

*Step 2*  **Rewrite each rational expression** as an equivalent rational expression with the LCD as the denominator.

*Step 3*  **Add** the numerators to get the numerator of the sum. The LCD is the denominator of the sum.

*Step 4*  **Write in lowest terms** using the fundamental property.

**EXAMPLE 2**  Adding Rational Expressions (Different Denominators)

Add. Write each answer in lowest terms.

**(a)** $\dfrac{1}{12} + \dfrac{7}{15}$  |  **(b)** $\dfrac{2}{3y} + \dfrac{1}{4y}$

*Step 1*  First find the LCD, using the methods of the previous section.

$12 = 2 \cdot 2 \cdot 3 = 2^2 \cdot 3$  |  $3y = 3 \cdot y$

$15 = 3 \cdot 5$  |  $4y = 2 \cdot 2 \cdot y = 2^2 \cdot y$

LCD $= 2^2 \cdot 3 \cdot 5 = 60$  |  LCD $= 2^2 \cdot 3 \cdot y = 12y$

*Step 2*  Now rewrite each rational expression as a fraction with the LCD (60 and 12y, respectively) as the denominator.

$\dfrac{1}{12} + \dfrac{7}{15} = \dfrac{1(5)}{12(5)} + \dfrac{7(4)}{15(4)}$  |  $\dfrac{2}{3y} + \dfrac{1}{4y} = \dfrac{2(4)}{3y(4)} + \dfrac{1(3)}{4y(3)}$

$= \dfrac{5}{60} + \dfrac{28}{60}$  |  $= \dfrac{8}{12y} + \dfrac{3}{12y}$

NOW TRY ANSWERS
**1. (a)** $\frac{6}{7k}$  **(b)** 4

NOW TRY
EXERCISE 2

Add. Write each answer in lowest terms.

(a) $\dfrac{5}{12} + \dfrac{3}{20}$   (b) $\dfrac{3}{5x} + \dfrac{2}{7x}$

**Step 3**   Add the numerators. The LCD is the denominator.

**Step 4**   Write in lowest terms if necessary.

$$= \frac{5 + 28}{60}$$

$$= \frac{33}{60}, \text{ or } \frac{11}{20}$$

$$= \frac{8 + 3}{12y}$$

$$= \frac{11}{12y}$$   NOW TRY

NOW TRY
EXERCISE 3

Add. Write the answer in lowest terms.

$$\frac{6t}{t^2 - 9} + \frac{-3}{t + 3}$$

---

### EXAMPLE 3   Adding Rational Expressions

Add. Write the answer in lowest terms.

$$\frac{2x}{x^2 - 1} + \frac{-1}{x + 1}$$

**Step 1**   Since the denominators are different, find the LCD.

$$\left. \begin{array}{l} x^2 - 1 = (x + 1)(x - 1) \\ x + 1 \text{ is prime.} \end{array} \right\} \quad \text{The LCD is } (x + 1)(x - 1).$$

**Step 2**   Rewrite each rational expression with the LCD as the denominator.

$$\frac{2x}{x^2 - 1} + \frac{-1}{x + 1} \qquad \text{LCD} = (x + 1)(x - 1)$$

$$= \frac{2x}{(x + 1)(x - 1)} + \frac{-1(x - 1)}{(x + 1)(x - 1)} \qquad \text{Multiply the second fraction by } \tfrac{x - 1}{x - 1}.$$

$$= \frac{2x}{(x + 1)(x - 1)} + \frac{-x + 1}{(x + 1)(x - 1)} \qquad \text{Distributive property}$$

**Step 3**   $$= \frac{2x - x + 1}{(x + 1)(x - 1)} \qquad \begin{array}{l}\text{Add numerators.} \\ \text{Keep the same denominator.}\end{array}$$

$$= \frac{x + 1}{(x + 1)(x - 1)} \qquad \text{Combine like terms.}$$

**Step 4**   $$= \frac{1(x + 1)}{(x + 1)(x - 1)} \qquad \begin{array}{l}\text{Identity property of} \\ \text{multiplication}\end{array}$$

Remember to write 1 in the numerator. $$= \frac{1}{x - 1} \qquad \begin{array}{l}\text{Divide out the common} \\ \text{factors.}\end{array}$$

NOW TRY

---

### EXAMPLE 4   Adding Rational Expressions

Add. Write the answer in lowest terms.

$$\frac{2x}{x^2 + 5x + 6} + \frac{x + 1}{x^2 + 2x - 3}$$

$$= \frac{2x}{(x + 2)(x + 3)} + \frac{x + 1}{(x + 3)(x - 1)} \qquad \begin{array}{l}\text{Factor the} \\ \text{denominators.}\end{array}$$

$$= \frac{2x(x - 1)}{(x + 2)(x + 3)(x - 1)} + \frac{(x + 1)(x + 2)}{(x + 2)(x + 3)(x - 1)} \qquad \begin{array}{l}\text{The LCD is} \\ (x + 2)(x + 3)(x - 1).\end{array}$$

NOW TRY ANSWERS

**2.** (a) $\dfrac{17}{30}$   (b) $\dfrac{31}{35x}$

**3.** $\dfrac{3}{t - 3}$

NOW TRY
EXERCISE 4

Add. Write the answer in lowest terms.

$$\frac{x-1}{x^2+6x+8}+\frac{4x}{x^2+x-12}$$

$$=\frac{2x(x-1)+(x+1)(x+2)}{(x+2)(x+3)(x-1)}$$  Add numerators.
Keep the same denominator.

$$=\frac{2x^2-2x+x^2+3x+2}{(x+2)(x+3)(x-1)}$$  Multiply.

$$=\frac{3x^2+x+2}{(x+2)(x+3)(x-1)}$$  Combine like terms.

The numerator cannot be factored here, so the expression is in lowest terms.

NOW TRY

---

**NOTE** If the final expression in **Example 4** could be written in lower terms, the numerator would have a factor of $x+2$, $x+3$, or $x-1$. Therefore, it is only necessary to check for possible factored forms of the numerator that would contain one of these binomials.

---

NOW TRY
EXERCISE 5

Add. Write the answer in lowest terms.

$$\frac{2k}{k-7}+\frac{5}{7-k}$$

**EXAMPLE 5**  Adding Rational Expressions (Denominators Are Opposites)

Add. Write the answer in lowest terms.

$$\frac{y}{y-2}+\frac{8}{2-y}$$

The denominators are opposites. Use the process of multiplying one of the fractions by 1 in the form $\frac{-1}{-1}$ to get the same denominator for both fractions.

$$=\frac{y}{y-2}+\frac{8(-1)}{(2-y)(-1)}$$  Multiply $\frac{8}{2-y}$ by $\frac{-1}{-1}$.

$$=\frac{y}{y-2}+\frac{-8}{-2+y}$$  Distributive property

$$=\frac{y}{y-2}+\frac{-8}{y-2}$$  Rewrite $-2+y$ as $y-2$.

$$=\frac{y-8}{y-2}$$  Add numerators.
Keep the same denominator.

If we had chosen $2-y$ as the common denominator, the final answer would be $\frac{8-y}{2-y}$, which is equivalent to $\frac{y-8}{y-2}$.

NOW TRY

**OBJECTIVE 3**  Subtract rational expressions.

**Subtracting Rational Expressions (Same Denominator)**

The rational expressions $\frac{P}{Q}$ and $\frac{R}{Q}$ ($Q \neq 0$) are subtracted as follows.

$$\frac{P}{Q}-\frac{R}{Q}=\frac{P-R}{Q}$$

That is, to subtract rational expressions with the same denominator, subtract the numerators and keep the same denominator.

NOW TRY ANSWERS
4. $\dfrac{5x^2+4x+3}{(x+4)(x+2)(x-3)}$

5. $\dfrac{2k-5}{k-7}$, or $\dfrac{5-2k}{7-k}$

*NOW TRY*
*EXERCISE 6*
Subtract. Write the answer in lowest terms.

$$\frac{2x}{x+5} - \frac{x+1}{x+5}$$

**EXAMPLE 6** Subtracting Rational Expressions (Same Denominator)

Subtract. Write the answer in lowest terms.

$$\frac{2m}{m-1} - \frac{m+3}{m-1}$$

> Use parentheses around the numerator of the subtrahend.

$$= \frac{2m-(m+3)}{m-1}$$    Subtract numerators. Keep the same denominator.

> Be careful with signs.

$$= \frac{2m-m-3}{m-1}$$    Distributive property

$$= \frac{m-3}{m-1}$$    Combine like terms.    *NOW TRY*

---

⚠ **CAUTION** Sign errors often occur in subtraction problems like the one in **Example 6.** The numerator of the fraction being subtracted must be treated as a single quantity. ***Be sure to use parentheses after the subtraction symbol.***

---

*NOW TRY*
*EXERCISE 7*
Subtract. Write the answer in lowest terms.

$$\frac{6}{y-6} - \frac{2}{y}$$

**EXAMPLE 7** Subtracting Rational Expressions (Different Denominators)

Subtract. Write the answer in lowest terms.

$$\frac{9}{x-2} - \frac{3}{x}$$    The LCD is $x(x-2)$.

$$= \frac{9x}{x(x-2)} - \frac{3(x-2)}{x(x-2)}$$    Write each expression with the LCD.

$$= \frac{9x-3(x-2)}{x(x-2)}$$    Subtract numerators. Keep the same denominator.

> Be careful with signs.

$$= \frac{9x-3x+6}{x(x-2)}$$    Distributive property

$$= \frac{6x+6}{x(x-2)}, \quad \text{or} \quad \frac{6(x+1)}{x(x-2)}$$    Combine like terms. Factor the numerator.    *NOW TRY*

---

**NOTE** We factored the final numerator in **Example 7** to get $\frac{6(x+1)}{x(x-2)}$. The fundamental property does not apply, however since there are no common factors to divide out. The answer is in lowest terms.

---

**EXAMPLE 8** Subtracting Rational Expressions (Denominators Are Opposites)

Subtract. Write the answer in lowest terms.

$$\frac{3x}{x-5} - \frac{2x-25}{5-x}$$    The denominators are opposites. We choose $x-5$ as the common denominator.

$$= \frac{3x}{x-5} - \frac{(2x-25)(-1)}{(5-x)(-1)}$$    Multiply $\frac{2x-25}{5-x}$ by $\frac{-1}{-1}$ to get a common denominator.

$$= \frac{3x}{x-5} - \frac{-2x+25}{x-5}$$    $(5-x)(-1) = -5+x = x-5$

NOW TRY ANSWERS
6. $\frac{x-1}{x+5}$
7. $\frac{4(y+3)}{y(y-6)}$

NOW TRY
EXERCISE 8

Subtract. Write the answer in lowest terms.

$$\frac{2m}{m-4} - \frac{m-12}{4-m}$$

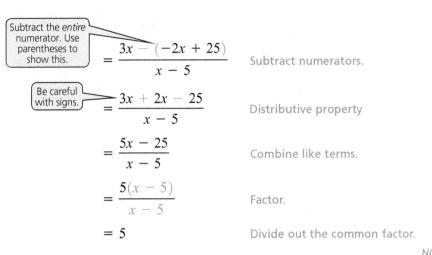

Subtract the *entire* numerator. Use parentheses to show this.
$$= \frac{3x - (-2x + 25)}{x - 5}$$   Subtract numerators.

Be careful with signs.
$$= \frac{3x + 2x - 25}{x - 5}$$   Distributive property

$$= \frac{5x - 25}{x - 5}$$   Combine like terms.

$$= \frac{5(x - 5)}{x - 5}$$   Factor.

$$= 5$$   Divide out the common factor.

NOW TRY

NOW TRY
EXERCISE 9

Subtract. Write the answer in lowest terms.

$$\frac{5}{t^2 - 6t + 9} - \frac{2t}{t^2 - 9}$$

**EXAMPLE 9**   Subtracting Rational Expressions

Subtract. Write the answer in lowest terms.

$$\frac{6x}{x^2 - 2x + 1} - \frac{1}{x^2 - 1}$$

$$= \frac{6x}{(x - 1)^2} - \frac{1}{(x - 1)(x + 1)}$$   Factor the denominators. LCD $= (x - 1)(x - 1)(x + 1)$, or $(x - 1)^2(x + 1)$

$$= \frac{6x(x + 1)}{(x - 1)^2(x + 1)} - \frac{1(x - 1)}{(x - 1)(x - 1)(x + 1)}$$   Fundamental property

$$= \frac{6x(x + 1) - 1(x - 1)}{(x - 1)^2(x + 1)}$$   Subtract numerators.

$$= \frac{6x^2 + 6x - x + 1}{(x - 1)^2(x + 1)}$$   Distributive property

$$= \frac{6x^2 + 5x + 1}{(x - 1)^2(x + 1)}, \quad \text{or} \quad \frac{(2x + 1)(3x + 1)}{(x - 1)^2(x + 1)}$$   Combine like terms. Factor the numerator.

NOW TRY

NOW TRY ANSWERS
**8.** 3
**9.** $\dfrac{-2t^2 + 11t + 15}{(t - 3)^2(t + 3)}$

## 7.4 EXERCISES

*MyMathLab*   Math XL PRACTICE   WATCH   DOWNLOAD   READ   REVIEW

🌐 *Complete solution available on the Video Resources on DVD*

*Concept Check*   Match each expression in Column I with the correct sum or difference in Column II.

**I**

1. $\dfrac{x}{x + 8} + \dfrac{8}{x + 8}$     2. $\dfrac{2x}{x - 8} - \dfrac{16}{x - 8}$

3. $\dfrac{8}{x - 8} - \dfrac{x}{x - 8}$     4. $\dfrac{8}{x + 8} - \dfrac{x}{x + 8}$

5. $\dfrac{x}{x + 8} - \dfrac{8}{x + 8}$     6. $\dfrac{1}{x} + \dfrac{1}{8}$

7. $\dfrac{1}{8} - \dfrac{1}{x}$     8. $\dfrac{1}{8x} - \dfrac{1}{8x}$

**II**

**A.** 2     **B.** $\dfrac{x - 8}{x + 8}$

**C.** $-1$     **D.** $\dfrac{8 + x}{8x}$

**E.** 1     **F.** 0

**G.** $\dfrac{x - 8}{8x}$     **H.** $\dfrac{8 - x}{x + 8}$

*Note: When adding and subtracting rational expressions, several different equivalent forms of the answer often exist. If your answer does not look exactly like the one given in the back of the book, check to see whether you have written an equivalent form.*

*Add or subtract. Write each answer in lowest terms.* **See Examples 1 and 6.**

9. $\dfrac{4}{m} + \dfrac{7}{m}$

10. $\dfrac{5}{p} + \dfrac{12}{p}$

11. $\dfrac{5}{y+4} - \dfrac{1}{y+4}$

12. $\dfrac{6}{t+3} - \dfrac{3}{t+3}$

13. $\dfrac{x}{x+y} + \dfrac{y}{x+y}$

14. $\dfrac{a}{a+b} + \dfrac{b}{a+b}$

15. $\dfrac{5m}{m+1} - \dfrac{1+4m}{m+1}$

16. $\dfrac{4x}{x+2} - \dfrac{2+3x}{x+2}$

17. $\dfrac{a+b}{2} - \dfrac{a-b}{2}$

18. $\dfrac{x-y}{2} - \dfrac{x+y}{2}$

19. $\dfrac{x^2}{x+5} + \dfrac{5x}{x+5}$

20. $\dfrac{t^2}{t-3} + \dfrac{-3t}{t-3}$

21. $\dfrac{y^2 - 3y}{y+3} + \dfrac{-18}{y+3}$

22. $\dfrac{r^2 - 8r}{r-5} + \dfrac{15}{r-5}$

23. $\dfrac{x}{x^2 - 9} - \dfrac{-3}{x^2 - 9}$

24. $\dfrac{-4}{y^2 - 16} - \dfrac{-y}{y^2 - 16}$

*Add or subtract. Write each answer in lowest terms.* **See Examples 2, 3, 4, and 7.**

25. $\dfrac{z}{5} + \dfrac{1}{3}$

26. $\dfrac{p}{8} + \dfrac{4}{5}$

27. $\dfrac{5}{7} - \dfrac{r}{2}$

28. $\dfrac{20}{9} - \dfrac{z}{3}$

29. $-\dfrac{3}{4} - \dfrac{1}{2x}$

30. $-\dfrac{7}{8} - \dfrac{3}{2a}$

31. $\dfrac{6}{5x} + \dfrac{9}{2x}$

32. $\dfrac{3}{2x} + \dfrac{3}{7x}$

33. $\dfrac{x+1}{6} + \dfrac{3x+3}{9}$

34. $\dfrac{2x-6}{4} + \dfrac{x+5}{6}$

35. $\dfrac{x+3}{3x} + \dfrac{2x+2}{4x}$

36. $\dfrac{x+2}{5x} + \dfrac{6x+3}{3x}$

37. $\dfrac{7}{3p^2} - \dfrac{2}{p}$

38. $\dfrac{12}{5m^2} - \dfrac{5}{m}$

39. $\dfrac{1}{k+4} - \dfrac{2}{k}$

40. $\dfrac{3}{m+1} - \dfrac{4}{m}$

41. $\dfrac{x}{x-2} + \dfrac{-8}{x^2 - 4}$

42. $\dfrac{2x}{x-1} + \dfrac{-4}{x^2 - 1}$

43. $\dfrac{4m}{m^2 + 3m + 2} + \dfrac{2m-1}{m^2 + 6m + 5}$

44. $\dfrac{a}{a^2 + 3a - 4} + \dfrac{4a}{a^2 + 7a + 12}$

45. $\dfrac{4y}{y^2 - 1} - \dfrac{5}{y^2 + 2y + 1}$

46. $\dfrac{2x}{x^2 - 16} - \dfrac{3}{x^2 + 8x + 16}$

47. $\dfrac{t}{t+2} + \dfrac{5-t}{t} - \dfrac{4}{t^2 + 2t}$

48. $\dfrac{2p}{p-3} + \dfrac{2+p}{p} - \dfrac{-6}{p^2 - 3p}$

49. *Concept Check* What are the two possible LCDs that could be used for the sum $\dfrac{10}{m-2} + \dfrac{5}{2-m}$?

50. *Concept Check* If one form of the correct answer to a sum or difference of rational expressions is $\dfrac{4}{k-3}$, what would an alternative form of the answer be if the denominator is $3-k$?

*Add or subtract. Write each answer in lowest terms.* **See Examples 5 and 8.**

51. $\dfrac{4}{x-5} + \dfrac{6}{5-x}$

52. $\dfrac{10}{m-2} + \dfrac{5}{2-m}$

53. $\dfrac{-1}{1-y} - \dfrac{4y-3}{y-1}$

**54.** $\dfrac{-4}{p-3} - \dfrac{p+1}{3-p}$

**55.** $\dfrac{2}{x-y^2} + \dfrac{7}{y^2-x}$

**56.** $\dfrac{-8}{p-q^2} + \dfrac{3}{q^2-p}$

**57.** $\dfrac{x}{5x-3y} - \dfrac{y}{3y-5x}$

**58.** $\dfrac{t}{8t-9s} - \dfrac{s}{9s-8t}$

**59.** $\dfrac{3}{4p-5} + \dfrac{9}{5-4p}$

**60.** $\dfrac{8}{3-7y} - \dfrac{2}{7y-3}$

*In these subtraction problems, the rational expression that follows the subtraction sign has a numerator with more than one term.* **Be careful with signs** *and find each difference.* **See Example 9.**

**61.** $\dfrac{2m}{m-n} - \dfrac{5m+n}{2m-2n}$

**62.** $\dfrac{5p}{p-q} - \dfrac{3p+1}{4p-4q}$

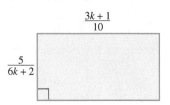 **63.** $\dfrac{5}{x^2-9} - \dfrac{x+2}{x^2+4x+3}$

**64.** $\dfrac{1}{a^2-1} - \dfrac{a-1}{a^2+3a-4}$

**65.** $\dfrac{2q+1}{3q^2+10q-8} - \dfrac{3q+5}{2q^2+5q-12}$

**66.** $\dfrac{4y-1}{2y^2+5y-3} - \dfrac{y+3}{6y^2+y-2}$

*Perform each indicated operation.* **See Examples 1–9.**

**67.** $\dfrac{4}{r^2-r} + \dfrac{6}{r^2+2r} - \dfrac{1}{r^2+r-2}$

**68.** $\dfrac{6}{k^2+3k} - \dfrac{1}{k^2-k} + \dfrac{2}{k^2+2k-3}$

**69.** $\dfrac{x+3y}{x^2+2xy+y^2} + \dfrac{x-y}{x^2+4xy+3y^2}$

**70.** $\dfrac{m}{m^2-1} + \dfrac{m-1}{m^2+2m+1}$

**71.** $\dfrac{r+y}{18r^2+9ry-2y^2} + \dfrac{3r-y}{36r^2-y^2}$

**72.** $\dfrac{2x-z}{2x^2+xz-10z^2} - \dfrac{x+z}{x^2-4z^2}$

**73.** Refer to the rectangle in the figure.

   **(a)** Find an expression that represents its perimeter. Give the simplified form.

   **(b)** Find an expression that represents its area. Give the simplified form.

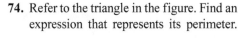

**74.** Refer to the triangle in the figure. Find an expression that represents its perimeter.

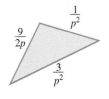

*A* **concours d'elegance** *is a competition in which a maximum of* 100 *points is awarded to a car based on its general attractiveness. The rational expression*

$$\dfrac{1010}{49(101-x)} - \dfrac{10}{49}$$

*approximates the cost, in thousands of dollars, of restoring a car so that it will win x points.*

   *Use this information to work* **Exercises 75 and 76.**

**75.** Simplify the given expression by performing the indicated subtraction.

**76.** Use the simplified expression from **Exercise 75** to determine how much it would cost to win 95 points.

**PREVIEW EXERCISES**

*Perform the indicated operations, using the order of operations as necessary.* **See Section 1.1.**

**77.** $\dfrac{\frac{5}{6}}{\frac{2}{3}}$  **78.** $\dfrac{\frac{3}{8}}{\frac{1}{4}}$  **79.** $\dfrac{\frac{3}{2}}{\frac{7}{4}}$  **80.** $\dfrac{\frac{5}{7}}{\frac{5}{3}}$

# 7.5 Complex Fractions

## OBJECTIVES

**1** Simplify a complex fraction by writing it as a division problem (Method 1).

**2** Simplify a complex fraction by multiplying numerator and denominator by the least common denominator (Method 2).

The quotient of two mixed numbers in arithmetic, such as $2\frac{1}{2} \div 3\frac{1}{4}$, can be written as a fraction.

$$2\frac{1}{2} \div 3\frac{1}{4} = \frac{2\frac{1}{2}}{3\frac{1}{4}} = \frac{2 + \frac{1}{2}}{3 + \frac{1}{4}}$$

We do this to illustrate a *complex fraction.*

In algebra, some rational expressions have fractions in the numerator, or denominator, or both.

### Complex Fraction

A quotient with one or more fractions in the numerator, or denominator, or both, is called a **complex fraction.**

$$\frac{2 + \frac{1}{2}}{3 + \frac{1}{4}}, \quad \frac{\frac{3x^2 - 5x}{6x^2}}{2x - \frac{1}{x}}, \quad \text{and} \quad \frac{3 + x}{5 - \frac{2}{x}} \qquad \text{Complex fractions}$$

The parts of a complex fraction are named as follows.

$$\left.\begin{array}{c}\frac{2}{p} - \frac{1}{q} \\ \hline \frac{3}{p} + \frac{5}{q}\end{array}\right.$$

← Numerator of complex fraction
← Main fraction bar
← Denominator of complex fraction

**OBJECTIVE 1** **Simplify a complex fraction by writing it as a division problem (Method 1).** Since the main fraction bar represents division in a complex fraction, one method of simplifying a complex fraction involves division.

### Method 1 for Simplifying a Complex Fraction

*Step 1* Write both the numerator and denominator as single fractions.

*Step 2* Change the complex fraction to a division problem.

*Step 3* Perform the indicated division.

NOW TRY
EXERCISE 1
Simplify each complex fraction.

(a) $\dfrac{\dfrac{2}{5} + \dfrac{1}{4}}{\dfrac{1}{6} + \dfrac{3}{8}}$  (b) $\dfrac{2 + \dfrac{4}{x}}{\dfrac{5}{6} + \dfrac{5x}{12}}$

**EXAMPLE 1**  Simplifying Complex Fractions (Method 1)

Simplify each complex fraction.

(a) $\dfrac{\dfrac{2}{3} + \dfrac{5}{9}}{\dfrac{1}{4} + \dfrac{1}{12}}$  (b) $\dfrac{6 + \dfrac{3}{x}}{\dfrac{x}{4} + \dfrac{1}{8}}$

**Step 1**  First, write each numerator as a single fraction.

$$\frac{2}{3} + \frac{5}{9} = \frac{2(3)}{3(3)} + \frac{5}{9}$$

$$= \frac{6}{9} + \frac{5}{9} = \frac{11}{9}$$

$$6 + \frac{3}{x} = \frac{6}{1} + \frac{3}{x}$$

$$= \frac{6x}{x} + \frac{3}{x} = \frac{6x + 3}{x}$$

Now, write each denominator as a single fraction.

$$\frac{1}{4} + \frac{1}{12} = \frac{1(3)}{4(3)} + \frac{1}{12}$$

$$= \frac{3}{12} + \frac{1}{12} = \frac{4}{12}$$

$$\frac{x}{4} + \frac{1}{8} = \frac{x(2)}{4(2)} + \frac{1}{8}$$

$$= \frac{2x}{8} + \frac{1}{8} = \frac{2x + 1}{8}$$

**Step 2**  Write the equivalent complex fraction as a division problem.

$$\frac{\dfrac{11}{9}}{\dfrac{4}{12}} = \frac{11}{9} \div \frac{4}{12}$$

$$\frac{\dfrac{6x + 3}{x}}{\dfrac{2x + 1}{8}} = \frac{6x + 3}{x} \div \frac{2x + 1}{8}$$

**Step 3**  Use the rule for division and the fundamental property.

Multiply by the reciprocal.

$$\frac{11}{9} \div \frac{4}{12} = \frac{11}{9} \cdot \frac{12}{4}$$

$$= \frac{11 \cdot 3 \cdot 4}{3 \cdot 3 \cdot 4}$$

$$= \frac{11}{3}$$

Multiply by the reciprocal.

$$\frac{6x + 3}{x} \div \frac{2x + 1}{8} = \frac{6x + 3}{x} \cdot \frac{8}{2x + 1}$$

$$= \frac{3(2x + 1)}{x} \cdot \frac{8}{2x + 1}$$

$$= \frac{24}{x}$$

NOW TRY

NOW TRY
EXERCISE 2
Simplify the complex fraction.

$$\frac{\dfrac{a^2 b}{c}}{\dfrac{ab^2}{c^3}}$$

NOW TRY ANSWERS

1. (a) $\dfrac{6}{5}$  (b) $\dfrac{24}{5x}$

2. $\dfrac{ac^2}{b}$

**EXAMPLE 2**  Simplifying a Complex Fraction (Method 1)

Simplify the complex fraction.

$$\frac{\dfrac{xp}{q^3}}{\dfrac{p^2}{qx^2}}$$

The numerator and denominator are single fractions, so use the definition of division and then the fundamental property.

$$\frac{xp}{q^3} \div \frac{p^2}{qx^2}$$

$$= \frac{xp}{q^3} \cdot \frac{qx^2}{p^2}$$

$$= \frac{x^3}{q^2 p}$$

NOW TRY

NOW TRY
EXERCISE 3

Simplify the complex fraction.

$$\dfrac{5 + \dfrac{2}{a-3}}{\dfrac{1}{a-3} - 2}$$

**EXAMPLE 3**   Simplifying a Complex Fraction (Method 1)

Simplify the complex fraction.

$$\dfrac{\dfrac{3}{x+2} - 4}{\dfrac{2}{x+2} + 1}$$

$$= \dfrac{\dfrac{3}{x+2} - \dfrac{4(x+2)}{x+2}}{\dfrac{2}{x+2} + \dfrac{1(x+2)}{x+2}}$$     Write both second terms with a denominator of $x + 2$.

$$= \dfrac{\dfrac{3 - 4(x+2)}{x+2}}{\dfrac{2 + 1(x+2)}{x+2}}$$     Subtract in the numerator.

                Add in the denominator.

*Be careful with signs.*

$$= \dfrac{\dfrac{3 - 4x - 8}{x+2}}{\dfrac{2 + x + 2}{x+2}}$$     Distributive property

$$= \dfrac{\dfrac{-5 - 4x}{x+2}}{\dfrac{4 + x}{x+2}}$$     Combine like terms.

$$= \dfrac{-5 - 4x}{x+2} \cdot \dfrac{x+2}{4+x}$$     Multiply by the reciprocal of the denominator (divisor).

$$= \dfrac{-5 - 4x}{4 + x}$$     Divide out the common factor.

NOW TRY

---

**OBJECTIVE 2**   **Simplify a complex fraction by multiplying numerator and denominator by the least common denominator (Method 2).** Any expression can be multiplied by a form of 1 to get an equivalent expression. Thus we can multiply both the numerator and the denominator of a complex fraction by the same nonzero expression to get an equivalent rational expression. If we choose the expression to be the LCD of all the fractions within the complex fraction, the complex fraction can then be simplified. This is Method 2.

---

**Method 2 for Simplifying a Complex Fraction**

*Step 1*   Find the LCD of all fractions within the complex fraction.

*Step 2*   Multiply both the numerator and the denominator of the complex fraction by this LCD using the distributive property as necessary. Write in lowest terms.

---

NOW TRY ANSWER

**3.** $\frac{5a - 13}{7 - 2a}$

NOW TRY
EXERCISE 4

Simplify each complex fraction.

**(a)** $\dfrac{\dfrac{3}{5} - \dfrac{1}{4}}{\dfrac{1}{8} + \dfrac{3}{20}}$  **(b)** $\dfrac{\dfrac{2}{x} - 3}{7 + \dfrac{x}{5}}$

**EXAMPLE 4**  Simplifying Complex Fractions (Method 2)

Simplify each complex fraction.

**(a)** $\dfrac{\dfrac{2}{3} + \dfrac{5}{9}}{\dfrac{1}{4} + \dfrac{1}{12}}$    **(b)** $\dfrac{6 + \dfrac{3}{x}}{\dfrac{x}{4} + \dfrac{1}{8}}$   (In **Example 1**, we simplified these same fractions using Method 1.)

***Step 1***  Find the LCD for all denominators in the complex fraction.

The LCD for 3, 9, 4, and 12 is 36.    |    The LCD for $x$, 4, and 8 is $8x$.

***Step 2***  $\dfrac{\dfrac{2}{3} + \dfrac{5}{9}}{\dfrac{1}{4} + \dfrac{1}{12}}$     $\dfrac{6 + \dfrac{3}{x}}{\dfrac{x}{4} + \dfrac{1}{8}}$   Multiply numerator and denominator of the complex fraction by the LCD.

$= \dfrac{36\left(\dfrac{2}{3} + \dfrac{5}{9}\right)}{36\left(\dfrac{1}{4} + \dfrac{1}{12}\right)}$     $= \dfrac{8x\left(6 + \dfrac{3}{x}\right)}{8x\left(\dfrac{x}{4} + \dfrac{1}{8}\right)}$

Multiply each term by 36.
$= \dfrac{36\left(\dfrac{2}{3}\right) + 36\left(\dfrac{5}{9}\right)}{36\left(\dfrac{1}{4}\right) + 36\left(\dfrac{1}{12}\right)}$   Multiply each term by 8x.   $= \dfrac{8x(6) + 8x\left(\dfrac{3}{x}\right)}{8x\left(\dfrac{x}{4}\right) + 8x\left(\dfrac{1}{8}\right)}$   Distributive property

$= \dfrac{24 + 20}{9 + 3}$     $= \dfrac{48x + 24}{2x^2 + x}$   Multiply.

$= \dfrac{44}{12} = \dfrac{4 \cdot 11}{4 \cdot 3}$, or $\dfrac{11}{3}$    $= \dfrac{24(2x + 1)}{x(2x + 1)}$, or $\dfrac{24}{x}$   NOW TRY

NOW TRY
EXERCISE 5

Simplify the complex fraction.

$\dfrac{\dfrac{1}{y} + \dfrac{2}{3y^2}}{\dfrac{5}{4y^2} - \dfrac{3}{2y^3}}$

**EXAMPLE 5**  Simplifying a Complex Fraction (Method 2)

Simplify the complex fraction.

$\dfrac{\dfrac{3}{5m} - \dfrac{2}{m^2}}{\dfrac{9}{2m} + \dfrac{3}{4m^2}}$   The LCD for $5m$, $m^2$, $2m$, and $4m^2$ is $20m^2$.

$= \dfrac{20m^2\left(\dfrac{3}{5m} - \dfrac{2}{m^2}\right)}{20m^2\left(\dfrac{9}{2m} + \dfrac{3}{4m^2}\right)}$   Multiply numerator and denominator by $20m^2$.

$= \dfrac{20m^2\left(\dfrac{3}{5m}\right) - 20m^2\left(\dfrac{2}{m^2}\right)}{20m^2\left(\dfrac{9}{2m}\right) + 20m^2\left(\dfrac{3}{4m^2}\right)}$   Distributive property.

$= \dfrac{12m - 40}{90m + 15}$   Multiply and simplify.   NOW TRY

NOW TRY ANSWERS

**4.** **(a)** $\dfrac{14}{11}$  **(b)** $\dfrac{10 - 15x}{x^2 + 35x}$

**5.** $\dfrac{12y^2 + 8y}{15y - 18}$

Some students prefer Method 1 for problems like **Example 2,** which is the quotient of two fractions. They will use Method 2 for problems like **Examples 1, 3, 4, and 5,** which have sums or differences in the numerators, or denominators, or both.

**EXAMPLE 6** Deciding on a Method and Simplifying Complex Fractions

Simplify each complex fraction.

**(a)** $\dfrac{\dfrac{1}{y} + \dfrac{2}{y+2}}{\dfrac{4}{y} - \dfrac{3}{y+2}}$    There are sums and differences in the numerator and denominator. Use Method 2.

$$= \dfrac{\left(\dfrac{1}{y} + \dfrac{2}{y+2}\right) \cdot y(y+2)}{\left(\dfrac{4}{y} - \dfrac{3}{y+2}\right) \cdot y(y+2)}$$    Multiply numerator and denominator by the LCD, $y(y+2)$.

$$= \dfrac{\left(\dfrac{1}{y}\right) y(y+2) + \left(\dfrac{2}{y+2}\right) y(y+2)}{\left(\dfrac{4}{y}\right) y(y+2) - \left(\dfrac{3}{y+2}\right) y(y+2)}$$    Distributive property

$$= \dfrac{1(y+2) + 2y}{4(y+2) - 3y}$$    Fundamental property

$$= \dfrac{y + 2 + 2y}{4y + 8 - 3y}$$    Distributive property

$$= \dfrac{3y + 2}{y + 8}$$    Combine like terms.

Be careful not to use $y + 2$ as the LCD. Because $y$ appears in two denominators, it must be a factor in the LCD.

**(b)** $\dfrac{1 - \dfrac{2}{x} - \dfrac{3}{x^2}}{1 - \dfrac{5}{x} + \dfrac{6}{x^2}}$    There are sums and differences in the numerator and denominator. Use Method 2.

$$= \dfrac{\left(1 - \dfrac{2}{x} - \dfrac{3}{x^2}\right) x^2}{\left(1 - \dfrac{5}{x} + \dfrac{6}{x^2}\right) x^2}$$    Multiply numerator and denominator by the LCD, $x^2$.

$$= \dfrac{x^2 - 2x - 3}{x^2 - 5x + 6}$$    Distributive property

$$= \dfrac{(x-3)(x+1)}{(x-3)(x-2)}$$    Factor.

$$= \dfrac{x+1}{x-2}$$    Divide out the common factor.

NOW TRY
EXERCISE 6

Simplify each complex fraction.

**(a)** $\dfrac{1 - \dfrac{2}{x} - \dfrac{15}{x^2}}{1 + \dfrac{5}{x} + \dfrac{6}{x^2}}$

**(b)** $\dfrac{\dfrac{9y^2 - 16}{y^2 - 100}}{\dfrac{3y - 4}{y + 10}}$

NOW TRY ANSWERS

6. **(a)** $\dfrac{x - 5}{x + 2}$  **(b)** $\dfrac{3y + 4}{y - 10}$

**(c)** $\dfrac{\dfrac{x + 2}{x - 3}}{\dfrac{x^2 - 4}{x^2 - 9}}$   This is a quotient of two rational expressions. Use Method 1.

$= \dfrac{x + 2}{x - 3} \div \dfrac{x^2 - 4}{x^2 - 9}$   Write as a division problem.

$= \dfrac{x + 2}{x - 3} \cdot \dfrac{x^2 - 9}{x^2 - 4}$   Multiply by the reciprocal.

$= \dfrac{(x + 2)(x + 3)(x - 3)}{(x - 3)(x + 2)(x - 2)}$   Multiply and then factor.

$= \dfrac{x + 3}{x - 2}$   Divide out the common factors.   NOW TRY

---

## 7.5 EXERCISES

MyMathLab   Math XL PRACTICE   WATCH   DOWNLOAD   READ   REVIEW

*Complete solution available on the Video Resources on DVD*

**1.** *Concept Check*  Consider the complex fraction $\dfrac{\frac{3}{2} - \frac{4}{3}}{\frac{1}{6} - \frac{5}{12}}$. Answer each part, outlining Method 1 for simplifying this complex fraction.

  **(a)** To combine the terms in the numerator, we must find the LCD of $\frac{3}{2}$ and $\frac{4}{3}$. What is this LCD? Determine the simplified form of the numerator of the complex fraction.

  **(b)** To combine the terms in the denominator, we must find the LCD of $\frac{1}{6}$ and $\frac{5}{12}$. What is this LCD? Determine the simplified form of the denominator of the complex fraction.

  **(c)** Now use the results from parts (a) and (b) to write the complex fraction as a division problem using the symbol $\div$.

  **(d)** Perform the operation from part (c) to obtain the final simplification.

**2.** *Concept Check*  Consider the complex fraction given in **Exercise 1:** $\dfrac{\frac{3}{2} - \frac{4}{3}}{\frac{1}{6} - \frac{5}{12}}$. Answer each part, outlining Method 2 for simplifying this complex fraction.

  **(a)** We must determine the LCD of all the fractions within the complex fraction. What is this LCD?

  **(b)** Multiply every term in the complex fraction by the LCD found in part (a), but do not yet combine the terms in the numerator and the denominator.

  **(c)** Combine the terms from part (b) to obtain the simplified form of the complex fraction.

**3.** Which complex fraction is equivalent to $\dfrac{2 - \frac{1}{4}}{3 - \frac{1}{2}}$? Answer this question without showing any work, and explain your reasoning.

  **A.** $\dfrac{2 + \frac{1}{4}}{3 + \frac{1}{2}}$   **B.** $\dfrac{2 - \frac{1}{4}}{-3 + \frac{1}{2}}$   **C.** $\dfrac{-2 - \frac{1}{4}}{-3 - \frac{1}{2}}$   **D.** $\dfrac{-2 + \frac{1}{4}}{-3 + \frac{1}{2}}$

**4.** Only one of these choices is equal to $\dfrac{\frac{1}{3} + \frac{1}{12}}{\frac{1}{2} + \frac{1}{4}}$. Which one is it? Answer this question without showing any work, and explain your reasoning.

  **A.** $\dfrac{5}{9}$   **B.** $-\dfrac{5}{9}$   **C.** $-\dfrac{9}{5}$   **D.** $-\dfrac{1}{12}$

*Simplify each complex fraction. Use either method.* **See Examples 1–6.**

**5.** $\dfrac{-\dfrac{4}{3}}{\dfrac{2}{9}}$

**6.** $\dfrac{-\dfrac{5}{6}}{\dfrac{5}{4}}$

**7.** $\dfrac{\dfrac{x}{y^2}}{\dfrac{x^2}{y}}$

**8.** $\dfrac{\dfrac{p^4}{r}}{\dfrac{p^2}{r^2}}$

**9.** $\dfrac{\dfrac{4a^4b^3}{3a}}{\dfrac{2ab^4}{b^2}}$

**10.** $\dfrac{\dfrac{2r^4t^2}{3t}}{\dfrac{5r^2t^5}{3r}}$

**11.** $\dfrac{\dfrac{m+2}{3}}{\dfrac{m-4}{m}}$

**12.** $\dfrac{\dfrac{q-5}{q}}{\dfrac{q+5}{3}}$

**13.** $\dfrac{\dfrac{2}{x}-3}{\dfrac{2-3x}{2}}$

**14.** $\dfrac{6+\dfrac{2}{r}}{\dfrac{3r+1}{4}}$

**15.** $\dfrac{\dfrac{1}{x}+x}{\dfrac{x^2+1}{8}}$

**16.** $\dfrac{\dfrac{3}{m}-m}{\dfrac{3-m^2}{4}}$

**17.** $\dfrac{a-\dfrac{5}{a}}{a+\dfrac{1}{a}}$

**18.** $\dfrac{q+\dfrac{1}{q}}{q+\dfrac{4}{q}}$

**19.** $\dfrac{\dfrac{5}{8}+\dfrac{2}{3}}{\dfrac{7}{3}-\dfrac{1}{4}}$

**20.** $\dfrac{\dfrac{6}{5}-\dfrac{1}{9}}{\dfrac{2}{5}+\dfrac{5}{3}}$

**21.** $\dfrac{\dfrac{1}{x^2}+\dfrac{1}{y^2}}{\dfrac{1}{x}-\dfrac{1}{y}}$

**22.** $\dfrac{\dfrac{1}{a^2}-\dfrac{1}{b^2}}{\dfrac{1}{a}-\dfrac{1}{b}}$

**23.** $\dfrac{\dfrac{2}{p^2}-\dfrac{3}{5p}}{\dfrac{4}{p}+\dfrac{1}{4p}}$

**24.** $\dfrac{\dfrac{2}{m^2}-\dfrac{3}{m}}{\dfrac{2}{5m^2}+\dfrac{1}{3m}}$

**25.** $\dfrac{\dfrac{5}{x^2y}-\dfrac{2}{xy^2}}{\dfrac{3}{x^2y^2}+\dfrac{4}{xy}}$

**26.** $\dfrac{\dfrac{1}{m^3p}+\dfrac{2}{mp^2}}{\dfrac{4}{mp}+\dfrac{1}{m^2p}}$

**27.** $\dfrac{\dfrac{1}{4}-\dfrac{1}{a^2}}{\dfrac{1}{2}+\dfrac{1}{a}}$

**28.** $\dfrac{\dfrac{1}{9}-\dfrac{1}{m^2}}{\dfrac{1}{3}+\dfrac{1}{m}}$

**29.** $\dfrac{\dfrac{1}{z+5}}{\dfrac{4}{z^2-25}}$

**30.** $\dfrac{\dfrac{1}{a+1}}{\dfrac{2}{a^2-1}}$

**31.** $\dfrac{\dfrac{1}{m+1}-1}{\dfrac{1}{m+1}+1}$

**32.** $\dfrac{\dfrac{2}{x-1}+2}{\dfrac{2}{x-1}-2}$

**33.** $\dfrac{\dfrac{1}{m-1}+\dfrac{2}{m+2}}{\dfrac{2}{m+2}-\dfrac{1}{m-3}}$

**34.** $\dfrac{\dfrac{5}{r+3}-\dfrac{1}{r-1}}{\dfrac{2}{r+2}+\dfrac{3}{r+3}}$

**35.** $\dfrac{2+\dfrac{1}{x}-\dfrac{28}{x^2}}{3+\dfrac{13}{x}+\dfrac{4}{x^2}}$

**36.** $\dfrac{4-\dfrac{11}{x}-\dfrac{3}{x^2}}{2-\dfrac{1}{x}-\dfrac{15}{x^2}}$

**37.** $\dfrac{\dfrac{y+8}{y-4}}{\dfrac{y^2-64}{y^2-16}}$

**38.** $\dfrac{\dfrac{t+5}{t-8}}{\dfrac{t^2-25}{t^2-64}}$

*Brain Busters*  *Simplify each fraction.*

**39.** $\dfrac{1 + x^{-1} - 12x^{-2}}{1 - x^{-1} - 20x^{-2}}$

**40.** $\dfrac{1 + t^{-1} - 56t^{-2}}{1 - t^{-1} - 72t^{-2}}$

**41.** *Concept Check*  In a fraction, what operation does the fraction bar represent?

**42.** *Concept Check*  What property of real numbers justifies Method 2 of simplifying complex fractions?

---

**RELATING CONCEPTS**  EXERCISES 43–46

**FOR INDIVIDUAL OR GROUP WORK**

*To find the average of two numbers, we add them and divide by 2. Suppose that we wish to find the average of $\frac{3}{8}$ and $\frac{5}{6}$.* **Work Exercises 43–46 in order,** *to see how a complex fraction occurs in a problem like this.*

**43.** Write in symbols:  The sum of $\frac{3}{8}$ and $\frac{5}{6}$, divided by 2. Your result should be a complex fraction.

**44.** Use Method 1 to simplify the complex fraction from **Exercise 43.**

**45.** Use Method 2 to simplify the complex fraction from **Exercise 43.**

**46.** Your answers in **Exercises 44 and 45** should be the same. Which method did you prefer? Why?

---

*Brain Busters*  *The fractions in Exercises 47–52 are called* **continued fractions.** *Simplify by starting at "the bottom" and working upward.*

**47.** $1 + \dfrac{1}{1 + \dfrac{1}{1 + 1}}$

**48.** $5 + \dfrac{5}{5 + \dfrac{5}{5 + 5}}$

**49.** $7 - \dfrac{3}{5 + \dfrac{2}{4 - 2}}$

**50.** $3 - \dfrac{2}{4 + \dfrac{2}{4 - 2}}$

**51.** $r + \dfrac{r}{4 - \dfrac{2}{6 + 2}}$

**52.** $\dfrac{2q}{7} - \dfrac{q}{6 + \dfrac{8}{4 + 4}}$

---

**PREVIEW EXERCISES**

*Simplify.* **See Section 1.8.**

**53.** $9\left(\dfrac{4x}{3} + \dfrac{2}{9}\right)$

**54.** $8\left(\dfrac{3r}{4} + \dfrac{9}{8}\right)$

**55.** $-12\left(\dfrac{11p^2}{3} - \dfrac{9p}{4}\right)$

**56.** $6\left(\dfrac{5z^2}{2} - \dfrac{8z}{3}\right)$

*Solve each equation.* **See Sections 2.3 and 6.5.**

**57.** $3x + 5 = 7x + 3$

**58.** $9z + 2 = 7z + 6$

**59.** $6(z - 3) + 5 = 8z - 3$

**60.** $k^2 + 3k - 4 = 0$

## 7.6  Solving Equations with Rational Expressions

### OBJECTIVES

1. Distinguish between operations with rational expressions and equations with terms that are rational expressions.
2. Solve equations with rational expressions.
3. Solve a formula for a specified variable.

**OBJECTIVE 1** **Distinguish between operations with rational expressions and equations with terms that are rational expressions.** Before solving equations with rational expressions, you must understand the difference between sums and differences of terms with rational coefficients, or rational *expressions*, and *equations* with terms that are rational expressions.

***Sums and differences are expressions to simplify. Equations are solved.***

### EXAMPLE 1   Distinguishing between Expressions and Equations

Identify each of the following as an *expression* or an *equation*. Then simplify the expression or solve the equation.

**(a)** $\dfrac{3}{4}x - \dfrac{2}{3}x$

This is a difference of two terms. It represents an *expression* to simplify since there is no equals symbol.

$$= \frac{3 \cdot 3}{3 \cdot 4}x - \frac{4 \cdot 2}{4 \cdot 3}x$$

The LCD is 12. Write each coefficient with this LCD.

$$= \frac{9}{12}x - \frac{8}{12}x$$

Multiply.

$$= \frac{1}{12}x$$

Combine like terms, using the distributive property: $\frac{9}{12}x - \frac{8}{12}x = \left(\frac{9}{12} - \frac{8}{12}\right)x.$

**(b)**

$$\frac{3}{4}x - \frac{2}{3}x = \frac{1}{2}$$

Because there is an equals symbol, this is an *equation* to be solved.

$$12\left(\frac{3}{4}x - \frac{2}{3}x\right) = 12\left(\frac{1}{2}\right)$$

Use the multiplication property of equality to clear fractions. Multiply by 12, the LCD.

Multiply *each* term by 12.

$$12\left(\frac{3}{4}x\right) - 12\left(\frac{2}{3}x\right) = 12\left(\frac{1}{2}\right)$$

Distributive property

$$9x - 8x = 6$$

Multiply.

$$x = 6$$

Combine like terms.

CHECK

$$\frac{3}{4}x - \frac{2}{3}x = \frac{1}{2}$$

Original equation

$$\frac{3}{4}(6) - \frac{2}{3}(6) \overset{?}{=} \frac{1}{2}$$

Let $x = 6$.

$$\frac{9}{2} - 4 \overset{?}{=} \frac{1}{2}$$

Multiply.

$$\frac{1}{2} = \frac{1}{2} \checkmark$$

True

Since a true statement results, {6} is the solution set of the equation.   NOW TRY

---

**NOW TRY**
**EXERCISE 1**

Identify each of the following as an *expression* or an *equation*. Then simplify the expression or solve the equation.

**(a)** $\dfrac{3}{2}t - \dfrac{5}{7}t = \dfrac{11}{7}$

**(b)** $\dfrac{3}{2}t - \dfrac{5}{7}t$

**NOW TRY ANSWERS**
1. **(a)** equation; {2}
   **(b)** expression; $\frac{11}{14}t$

The ideas of **Example 1** can be summarized as follows.

> **Uses of the LCD**
>
> When adding or subtracting rational expressions, keep the LCD throughout the simplification. (See **Example 1(a)**.)
>
> When solving an equation, multiply each side by the LCD so that denominators are eliminated. (See **Example 1(b)**.)

**OBJECTIVE 2** Solve equations with rational expressions. When an equation involves fractions, as in **Example 1(b)**, we use the multiplication property of equality to clear the fractions. Choose as multiplier the LCD of all denominators in the fractions of the equation.

*NOW TRY*
*EXERCISE 2*

Solve, and check the solution.

$$\frac{x + 5}{5} - \frac{x}{7} = \frac{3}{7}$$

**EXAMPLE 2** Solving an Equation with Rational Expressions

Solve, and check the solution.

$$\frac{p}{2} - \frac{p - 1}{3} = 1$$

$$6\left(\frac{p}{2} - \frac{p - 1}{3}\right) = 6(1) \quad \text{Multiply each side by the LCD, 6.}$$

$$6\left(\frac{p}{2}\right) - 6\left(\frac{p - 1}{3}\right) = 6(1) \quad \text{Distributive property}$$

$$3p - 2(p - 1) = 6 \quad \boxed{\text{Use parentheses around } p - 1 \text{ to avoid errors.}}$$

$$3p - 2(p) - 2(-1) = 6 \quad \text{Distributive property}$$
$$\boxed{\text{Be careful with signs.}}$$
$$3p - 2p + 2 = 6 \quad \text{Multiply.}$$

$$p + 2 = 6 \quad \text{Combine like terms.}$$

$$p = 4 \quad \text{Subtract 2.}$$

Check to see that $\{4\}$ is the solution set by replacing $p$ with 4 in the original equation.

*NOW TRY*

⚠ **CAUTION** In **Example 2**, we used the multiplication property of equality to multiply each side of an *equation* by the LCD. In **Section 7.5**, we used the fundamental property to multiply a *fraction* by another fraction that had the LCD as both its numerator and denominator. Be careful not to confuse these procedures.

Recall from **Section 7.1** that the denominator of a rational expression cannot equal 0, since division by 0 is undefined. *Therefore, when solving an equation with rational expressions that have variables in the denominator, the solution cannot be a number that makes the denominator equal 0.*

A value of the variable that appears to be a solution after both sides of a rational equation are multiplied by a variable expression is called a **proposed solution.** *All proposed solutions must be checked in the original equation.*

*NOW TRY ANSWER*
**2.** $\{-10\}$

NOW TRY
EXERCISE 3
Solve, and check the proposed solution.

$$4 + \frac{6}{x-3} = \frac{2x}{x-3}$$

### EXAMPLE 3    Solving an Equation with Rational Expressions

Solve, and check the proposed solution.

$$\frac{x}{x-2} = \frac{2}{x-2} + 2$$

*x cannot* equal 2, since 2 causes both denominators to equal 0.

$$(x-2)\left(\frac{x}{x-2}\right) = (x-2)\left(\frac{2}{x-2} + 2\right)$$

Multiply each side by the LCD, $x - 2$.

$$(x-2)\left(\frac{x}{x-2}\right) = (x-2)\left(\frac{2}{x-2}\right) + (x-2)(2)$$

Distributive property

$$x = 2 + 2x - 4$$    Simplify.

$$x = -2 + 2x$$    Combine like terms.

$$-x = -2$$    Subtract 2x.

$$x = 2$$    Multiply by −1.

As noted, $x$ cannot equal 2, since replacing $x$ with 2 in the original equation causes the denominators to equal 0.

CHECK    $$\frac{x}{x-2} = \frac{2}{x-2} + 2$$    Original equation

$$\frac{2}{2-2} \overset{?}{=} \frac{2}{2-2} + 2$$    Let $x = 2$.

Division by 0 is undefined.    $$\frac{2}{0} \overset{?}{=} \frac{2}{0} + 2$$    Subtract in the denominators.

Thus, 2 must be rejected as a solution, and the solution set is $\varnothing$.    NOW TRY

A proposed solution that is not an actual solution of the original equation, such as 2 in **Example 3**, is called an **extraneous solution**, or **extraneous value**. Some students like to determine which numbers cannot be solutions *before* solving the equation, as we did in **Example 3.**

> ### Solving an Equation with Rational Expressions
>
> *Step 1*    **Multiply each side of the equation by the LCD** to clear the equation of fractions. Be sure to distribute to *every* term on *both* sides.
>
> *Step 2*    **Solve** the resulting equation.
>
> *Step 3*    **Check** each proposed solution by substituting it into the original equation. Reject any that cause a denominator to equal 0.

### EXAMPLE 4    Solving an Equation with Rational Expressions

Solve, and check the proposed solution.

$$\frac{2}{x^2 - x} = \frac{1}{x^2 - 1}$$

NOW TRY ANSWER
3. $\varnothing$

*Step 1*    $$\frac{2}{x(x-1)} = \frac{1}{(x+1)(x-1)}$$    Factor the denominators to find the LCD, $x(x+1)(x-1)$.

NOW TRY
EXERCISE 4
Solve, and check the proposed solution.

$$\frac{3}{2x^2 - 8x} = \frac{1}{x^2 - 16}$$

Notice that 0, 1, and $-1$ cannot be solutions. Otherwise a denominator will equal 0.

$$\frac{2}{x(x - 1)} = \frac{1}{(x + 1)(x - 1)} \qquad \text{The LCD is } x(x + 1)(x - 1).$$

$$x(x + 1)(x - 1)\frac{2}{x(x - 1)} = x(x + 1)(x - 1)\frac{1}{(x + 1)(x - 1)} \qquad \begin{array}{l}\text{Multiply by} \\ \text{the LCD.}\end{array}$$

***Step 2***
$$2(x + 1) = x \qquad \text{Divide out the common factors.}$$
$$2x + 2 = x \qquad \text{Distributive property}$$
$$x + 2 = 0 \qquad \text{Subtract } x.$$
$$x = -2 \qquad \text{Subtract 2.}$$

***Step 3***  The proposed solution is $-2$, which does not make any denominator equal 0.

CHECK
$$\frac{2}{x^2 - x} = \frac{1}{x^2 - 1} \qquad \text{Original equation}$$

$$\frac{2}{(-2)^2 - (-2)} \overset{?}{=} \frac{1}{(-2)^2 - 1} \qquad \text{Let } x = -2.$$

$$\frac{2}{4 + 2} \overset{?}{=} \frac{1}{4 - 1} \qquad \text{Apply the exponents.}$$

$$\frac{1}{3} = \frac{1}{3} \checkmark \qquad \text{True}$$

The solution set is $\{-2\}$.  NOW TRY

NOW TRY
EXERCISE 5
Solve, and check the proposed solution.

$$\frac{2y}{y^2 - 25} = \frac{8}{y + 5} - \frac{1}{y - 5}$$

**EXAMPLE 5**  Solving an Equation with Rational Expressions

Solve, and check the proposed solution.

$$\frac{2m}{m^2 - 4} + \frac{1}{m - 2} = \frac{2}{m + 2}$$

$$\frac{2m}{(m + 2)(m - 2)} + \frac{1}{m - 2} = \frac{2}{m + 2} \qquad \begin{array}{l}\text{Factor the first denominator} \\ \text{on the left to find the LCD,} \\ (m + 2)(m - 2).\end{array}$$

Notice that $-2$ and 2 cannot be solutions of this equation.

$$(m + 2)(m - 2)\left(\frac{2m}{(m + 2)(m - 2)} + \frac{1}{m - 2}\right) \qquad \text{Multiply by the LCD.}$$
$$= (m + 2)(m - 2)\frac{2}{m + 2}$$

$$(m + 2)(m - 2)\frac{2m}{(m + 2)(m - 2)} + (m + 2)(m - 2)\frac{1}{m - 2}$$
$$= (m + 2)(m - 2)\frac{2}{m + 2} \qquad \text{Distributive property}$$

$$2m + m + 2 = 2(m - 2) \qquad \text{Divide out the common factors.}$$
$$3m + 2 = 2m - 4 \qquad \text{Combine like terms; distributive property}$$
$$m + 2 = -4 \qquad \text{Subtract } 2m.$$
$$m = -6 \qquad \text{Subtract 2.}$$

NOW TRY ANSWERS
4. $\{-12\}$  5. $\{9\}$

A check verifies that $\{-6\}$ is the solution set.  NOW TRY

*NOW TRY*
*EXERCISE 6*

Solve, and check the proposed solution(s).

$$\frac{3}{m^2 - 9} = \frac{1}{2(m - 3)} - \frac{1}{4}$$

**EXAMPLE 6** Solving an Equation with Rational Expressions

Solve, and check the proposed solution(s).

$$\frac{1}{x - 1} + \frac{1}{2} = \frac{2}{x^2 - 1}$$

$\boxed{x \neq 1, -1 \text{ or a denominator is } 0.}$ $\quad \dfrac{1}{x - 1} + \dfrac{1}{2} = \dfrac{2}{(x + 1)(x - 1)}$

Factor the denominator on the right. The LCD is $2(x + 1)(x - 1)$.

$$2(x + 1)(x - 1)\left(\frac{1}{x - 1} + \frac{1}{2}\right) = 2(x + 1)(x - 1)\frac{2}{(x + 1)(x - 1)}$$

Multiply by the LCD.

$$2(x + 1)(x - 1)\frac{1}{x - 1} + 2(x + 1)(x - 1)\frac{1}{2} = 2(x + 1)(x - 1)\frac{2}{(x + 1)(x - 1)}$$

Distributive property

$$2(x + 1) + (x + 1)(x - 1) = 4 \qquad \text{Divide out the common factors.}$$

$$2x + 2 + x^2 - 1 = 4 \qquad \text{Distributive property}$$

$\boxed{\text{Write in standard form.}}$ $\quad x^2 + 2x - 3 = 0 \qquad$ Subtract 4. Combine like terms.

$$(x + 3)(x - 1) = 0 \qquad \text{Factor.}$$

$$x + 3 = 0 \quad \text{or} \quad x - 1 = 0 \qquad \text{Zero-factor property}$$

$$x = -3 \quad \text{or} \qquad x = 1 \leftarrow \text{Proposed solutions}$$

Since 1 makes a denominator equal 0, 1 is *not* a solution. Check that $-3$ is a solution.

CHECK $\qquad \dfrac{1}{x - 1} + \dfrac{1}{2} = \dfrac{2}{x^2 - 1} \qquad$ Original equation

$$\frac{1}{-3 - 1} + \frac{1}{2} \overset{?}{=} \frac{2}{(-3)^2 - 1} \qquad \text{Let } x = -3.$$

$$\frac{1}{-4} + \frac{1}{2} \overset{?}{=} \frac{2}{9 - 1} \qquad \text{Simplify.}$$

$$\frac{1}{4} = \frac{1}{4} \ \checkmark \qquad \text{True}$$

The solution set is $\{-3\}$.

*NOW TRY*

**EXAMPLE 7** Solving an Equation with Rational Expressions

Solve, and check the proposed solution.

$$\frac{1}{k^2 + 4k + 3} + \frac{1}{2k + 2} = \frac{3}{4k + 12}$$

$$\frac{1}{(k + 1)(k + 3)} + \frac{1}{2(k + 1)} = \frac{3}{4(k + 3)} \qquad \text{Factor each denominator. The LCD is } 4(k + 1)(k + 3).$$

$\boxed{k \neq -1, -3}$ $\quad 4(k + 1)(k + 3)\left(\dfrac{1}{(k + 1)(k + 3)} + \dfrac{1}{2(k + 1)}\right)$

$$= 4(k + 1)(k + 3)\frac{3}{4(k + 3)} \qquad \text{Multiply by the LCD.}$$

*NOW TRY ANSWER*
**6.** $\{-1\}$

NOW TRY
EXERCISE 7

Solve, and check the proposed solution.

$$\frac{5}{k^2 + k - 2} = \frac{1}{3k - 3} - \frac{1}{k + 2}$$

$$4(k + 1)(k + 3)\frac{1}{(k + 1)(k + 3)} + 2 \cdot 2(k + 1)(k + 3)\frac{1}{2(k + 1)}$$

$$= 4(k + 1)(k + 3)\frac{3}{4(k + 3)} \qquad \text{Distributive property}$$

$\boxed{\text{Do } \textit{not} \text{ add} \atop 4 + 2 \text{ here.}}$ $4 + 2(k + 3) = 3(k + 1)$    Simplify.

$$4 + 2k + 6 = 3k + 3 \qquad \text{Distributive property}$$

$$2k + 10 = 3k + 3 \qquad \text{Combine like terms.}$$

$$10 = k + 3 \qquad \text{Subtract } 2k.$$

$$7 = k \qquad \text{Subtract 3.}$$

The proposed solution, 7, does not make an original denominator equal 0. A check shows that the algebra is correct (see **Exercise 78**), so {7} is the solution set.    *NOW TRY*

**OBJECTIVE 3** **Solve a formula for a specified variable.** When solving a formula for a specified variable, *remember to treat the variable for which you are solving as if it were the only variable, and all others as if they were constants.*

NOW TRY
EXERCISE 8

Solve each formula for the specified variable.

**(a)** $p = \dfrac{x - y}{z}$ for $x$

**(b)** $a = \dfrac{b}{c + d}$ for $d$

**EXAMPLE 8** **Solving for a Specified Variable**

Solve each formula for the specified variable.

**(a)** $a = \dfrac{v - w}{t}$ for $v$

$$a = \frac{v - w}{t} \qquad \boxed{\text{Our goal is to isolate } v.}$$

$$at = v - w \qquad \text{Multiply by } t.$$

$$at + w = v, \quad \text{or} \quad v = at + w \qquad \text{Add } w.$$

**(b)** $F = \dfrac{k}{d - D}$ for $d$

$$\boxed{\text{We must isolate } d.} \quad F = \frac{k}{d - D} \qquad \text{Given equation}$$

$$F(d - D) = \frac{k}{d - D}(d - D) \qquad \text{Multiply by } d - D \text{ to clear the fraction.}$$

$$F(d - D) = k \qquad \text{Simplify.}$$

$$Fd - FD = k \qquad \text{Distributive property}$$

$$Fd = k + FD \qquad \text{Add } FD.$$

$$d = \frac{k + FD}{F} \qquad \text{Divide by } F.$$

We can write an equivalent form of this answer as follows.

$$d = \frac{k + FD}{F} \qquad \text{Answer from above}$$

$$d = \frac{k}{F} + \frac{FD}{F} \qquad \text{Definition of addition of fractions: } \frac{a + b}{c} = \frac{a}{c} + \frac{b}{c}.$$

$$d = \frac{k}{F} + D \qquad \text{Divide out the common factor from } \frac{FD}{F}.$$

Either answer is correct.    *NOW TRY*

NOW TRY ANSWERS
7. {−5}
8. **(a)** $x = pz + y$
   **(b)** $d = \frac{b - ac}{a}$

NOW TRY
EXERCISE 9

Solve the following formula for $x$.

$$\frac{2}{w} = \frac{1}{x} - \frac{3}{y}$$

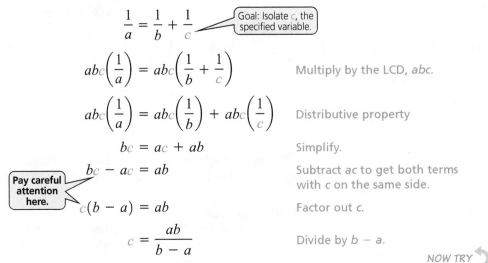

**EXAMPLE 9** Solving for a Specified Variable

Solve the following formula for $c$.

$$\frac{1}{a} = \frac{1}{b} + \frac{1}{c}$$

Goal: Isolate $c$, the specified variable.

$$abc\left(\frac{1}{a}\right) = abc\left(\frac{1}{b} + \frac{1}{c}\right) \qquad \text{Multiply by the LCD, } abc.$$

$$abc\left(\frac{1}{a}\right) = abc\left(\frac{1}{b}\right) + abc\left(\frac{1}{c}\right) \qquad \text{Distributive property}$$

$$bc = ac + ab \qquad \text{Simplify.}$$

$$bc - ac = ab \qquad \text{Subtract } ac \text{ to get both terms with } c \text{ on the same side.}$$

Pay careful attention here.

$$c(b - a) = ab \qquad \text{Factor out } c.$$

$$c = \frac{ab}{b - a} \qquad \text{Divide by } b - a.$$

NOW TRY

⚠ **CAUTION** Students often have trouble in the step that involves factoring out the variable for which they are solving. In **Example 9,** we needed to get both terms with $c$ on the same side of the equation. This allowed us to factor out $c$ on the left, and then isolate it by dividing each side by $b - a$.

*When solving an equation for a specified variable, be sure that the specified variable appears alone on only one side of the equals symbol in the final equation.*

NOW TRY ANSWER

9. $x = \frac{wy}{2y + 3w}$

---

## 7.6 EXERCISES

**MyMathLab** | Math XL PRACTICE | WATCH | DOWNLOAD | READ | REVIEW

🌐 Complete solution available on the Video Resources on DVD

Identify each of the following as an expression or an equation. Then simplify the expression or solve the equation. **See Example 1.**

🌐 **1.** $\frac{7}{8}x + \frac{1}{5}x$

**2.** $\frac{4}{7}x + \frac{4}{5}x$

**3.** $\frac{7}{8}x + \frac{1}{5}x = 1$

**4.** $\frac{4}{7}x + \frac{4}{5}x = 1$

**5.** $\frac{3}{5}x - \frac{7}{10}x$

**6.** $\frac{2}{3}x - \frac{9}{4}x$

**7.** $\frac{3}{5}x - \frac{7}{10}x = 1$

**8.** $\frac{2}{3}x - \frac{9}{4}x = -19$

**9.** $\frac{3}{4}x - \frac{1}{2}x = 0$

✏ **10.** Explain why the equation in **Exercise 9** is easy to check.

When solving an equation with variables in denominators, we must determine the values that cause these denominators to equal 0, so that we can reject these extraneous values if they appear as potential solutions. Find all values for which at least one denominator is equal to 0. Write answers using the symbol $\neq$. Do not solve. **See Examples 3–7.**

**11.** $\frac{3}{x + 2} - \frac{5}{x} = 1$

**12.** $\frac{7}{x} + \frac{9}{x - 4} = 5$

**13.** $\frac{-1}{(x + 3)(x - 4)} = \frac{1}{2x + 1}$

**14.** $\frac{8}{(x - 7)(x + 3)} = \frac{7}{3x - 10}$

15. $\dfrac{4}{x^2 + 8x - 9} + \dfrac{1}{x^2 - 4} = 0$     16. $\dfrac{-3}{x^2 + 9x - 10} - \dfrac{12}{x^2 - 49} = 0$

📝 **17.** What is wrong with the following problem? "Solve $\dfrac{2}{3x} + \dfrac{1}{5x}$."

📝 **18.** Explain how the LCD is used in a different way when adding and subtracting rational expressions as compared to solving equations with rational expressions.

*Solve each equation, and check your solutions.* ***See Examples 1(b), 2, and 3.***

19. $\dfrac{5}{m} - \dfrac{3}{m} = 8$     20. $\dfrac{4}{y} + \dfrac{1}{y} = 2$     21. $\dfrac{5}{y} + 4 = \dfrac{2}{y}$

22. $\dfrac{11}{q} - 3 = \dfrac{1}{q}$     23. $\dfrac{3x}{5} - 6 = x$     24. $\dfrac{5t}{4} + t = 9$

25. $\dfrac{4m}{7} + m = 11$     26. $a - \dfrac{3a}{2} = 1$     27. $\dfrac{z - 1}{4} = \dfrac{z + 3}{3}$

28. $\dfrac{r - 5}{2} = \dfrac{r + 2}{3}$     29. $\dfrac{3p + 6}{8} = \dfrac{3p - 3}{16}$     30. $\dfrac{2z + 1}{5} = \dfrac{7z + 5}{15}$

31. $\dfrac{2x + 3}{x} = \dfrac{3}{2}$     32. $\dfrac{7 - 2x}{x} = \dfrac{-17}{5}$

💿 33. $\dfrac{k}{k - 4} - 5 = \dfrac{4}{k - 4}$     34. $\dfrac{-5}{a + 5} - 2 = \dfrac{a}{a + 5}$

35. $\dfrac{q + 2}{3} + \dfrac{q - 5}{5} = \dfrac{7}{3}$     36. $\dfrac{x - 6}{6} + \dfrac{x + 2}{8} = \dfrac{11}{4}$

37. $\dfrac{x}{2} = \dfrac{5}{4} + \dfrac{x - 1}{4}$     38. $\dfrac{8p}{5} = \dfrac{3p - 4}{2} + \dfrac{5}{2}$

39. $x + \dfrac{17}{2} = \dfrac{x}{2} + x + 6$     40. $t + \dfrac{8}{3} = \dfrac{t}{3} + t + \dfrac{14}{3}$

41. $\dfrac{9}{3x + 4} = \dfrac{36 - 27x}{16 - 9x^2}$     42. $\dfrac{25}{5x - 6} = \dfrac{-150 - 125x}{36 - 25x^2}$

*Solve each equation, and check your solutions.* ***Be careful with signs. See Example 2.***

💿 43. $\dfrac{a + 7}{8} - \dfrac{a - 2}{3} = \dfrac{4}{3}$     44. $\dfrac{x + 3}{7} - \dfrac{x + 2}{6} = \dfrac{1}{6}$

45. $\dfrac{p}{2} - \dfrac{p - 1}{4} = \dfrac{5}{4}$     46. $\dfrac{r}{6} - \dfrac{r - 2}{3} = -\dfrac{4}{3}$

47. $\dfrac{3x}{5} - \dfrac{x - 5}{7} = 3$     48. $\dfrac{8k}{5} - \dfrac{3k - 4}{2} = \dfrac{5}{2}$

*Solve each equation, and check your solutions.* ***See Examples 3–7.***

💿 49. $\dfrac{4}{x^2 - 3x} = \dfrac{1}{x^2 - 9}$     50. $\dfrac{2}{t^2 - 4} = \dfrac{3}{t^2 - 2t}$

51. $\dfrac{2}{m} = \dfrac{m}{5m + 12}$     52. $\dfrac{x}{4 - x} = \dfrac{2}{x}$

53. $\dfrac{-2}{z + 5} + \dfrac{3}{z - 5} = \dfrac{20}{z^2 - 25}$     54. $\dfrac{3}{r + 3} - \dfrac{2}{r - 3} = \dfrac{-12}{r^2 - 9}$

55. $\dfrac{3}{x - 1} + \dfrac{2}{4x - 4} = \dfrac{7}{4}$     56. $\dfrac{2}{p + 3} + \dfrac{3}{8} = \dfrac{5}{4p + 12}$

**57.** $\dfrac{x}{3x + 3} = \dfrac{2x - 3}{x + 1} - \dfrac{2x}{3x + 3}$

**58.** $\dfrac{2k + 3}{k + 1} - \dfrac{3k}{2k + 2} = \dfrac{-2k}{2k + 2}$

**59.** $\dfrac{2p}{p^2 - 1} = \dfrac{2}{p + 1} - \dfrac{1}{p - 1}$

**60.** $\dfrac{2x}{x^2 - 16} - \dfrac{2}{x - 4} = \dfrac{4}{x + 4}$

**61.** $\dfrac{5x}{14x + 3} = \dfrac{1}{x}$

**62.** $\dfrac{m}{8m + 3} = \dfrac{1}{3m}$

**63.** $\dfrac{2}{x - 1} - \dfrac{2}{3} = \dfrac{-1}{x + 1}$

**64.** $\dfrac{5}{p - 2} = 7 - \dfrac{10}{p + 2}$

**65.** $\dfrac{x}{2x + 2} = \dfrac{-2x}{4x + 4} + \dfrac{2x - 3}{x + 1}$

**66.** $\dfrac{5t + 1}{3t + 3} = \dfrac{5t - 5}{5t + 5} + \dfrac{3t - 1}{t + 1}$

**67.** $\dfrac{8x + 3}{x} = 3x$

**68.** $\dfrac{10x - 24}{x} = x$

**69.** $\dfrac{1}{x + 4} + \dfrac{x}{x - 4} = \dfrac{-8}{x^2 - 16}$

**70.** $\dfrac{x}{x - 3} + \dfrac{4}{x + 3} = \dfrac{18}{x^2 - 9}$

**71.** $\dfrac{4}{3x + 6} - \dfrac{3}{x + 3} = \dfrac{8}{x^2 + 5x + 6}$

**72.** $\dfrac{-13}{t^2 + 6t + 8} + \dfrac{4}{t + 2} = \dfrac{3}{2t + 8}$

**73.** $\dfrac{3x}{x^2 + 5x + 6} = \dfrac{5x}{x^2 + 2x - 3} - \dfrac{2}{x^2 + x - 2}$

**74.** $\dfrac{m}{m^2 + m - 2} + \dfrac{m}{m^2 - 1} = \dfrac{m}{m^2 + 3m + 2}$

**75.** $\dfrac{x + 4}{x^2 - 3x + 2} - \dfrac{5}{x^2 - 4x + 3} = \dfrac{x - 4}{x^2 - 5x + 6}$

**76.** $\dfrac{3}{r^2 + r - 2} - \dfrac{1}{r^2 - 1} = \dfrac{7}{2(r^2 + 3r + 2)}$

**77.** *Concept Check* If you are solving a formula for the letter $k$, and your steps lead to the equation $kr - mr = km$, what would be your next step?

**78.** Refer to **Example 7,** and show that 7 is a solution.

*Solve each formula for the specified variable.* ***See Examples 8 and 9.***

**79.** $m = \dfrac{kF}{a}$ for $F$

**80.** $I = \dfrac{kE}{R}$ for $E$

**81.** $m = \dfrac{kF}{a}$ for $a$

**82.** $I = \dfrac{kE}{R}$ for $R$

**83.** $I = \dfrac{E}{R + r}$ for $R$

**84.** $I = \dfrac{E}{R + r}$ for $r$

**85.** $h = \dfrac{2\mathcal{A}}{B + b}$ for $\mathcal{A}$

**86.** $d = \dfrac{2S}{n(a + L)}$ for $S$

**87.** $d = \dfrac{2S}{n(a + L)}$ for $a$

**88.** $h = \dfrac{2\mathcal{A}}{B + b}$ for $B$

**89.** $\dfrac{1}{x} = \dfrac{1}{y} - \dfrac{1}{z}$ for $y$

**90.** $\dfrac{3}{k} = \dfrac{1}{p} + \dfrac{1}{q}$ for $q$

**91.** $\dfrac{2}{r} + \dfrac{3}{s} + \dfrac{1}{t} = 1$ for $t$

**92.** $\dfrac{5}{p} + \dfrac{2}{q} + \dfrac{3}{r} = 1$ for $r$

**93.** $9x + \dfrac{3}{z} = \dfrac{5}{y}$ for $z$

**94.** $-3t - \dfrac{4}{p} = \dfrac{6}{s}$ for $p$

**95.** $\dfrac{t}{x - 1} - \dfrac{2}{x + 1} = \dfrac{1}{x^2 - 1}$ for $t$

**96.** $\dfrac{5}{y + 2} - \dfrac{r}{y - 2} = \dfrac{3}{y^2 - 4}$ for $r$

PREVIEW EXERCISES

*Write a mathematical expression for each exercise. **See Section 2.7.***

**97.** Andrew drives from Pittsburgh to Philadelphia, a distance of 288 mi, in $t$ hours. Find his rate in miles per hour.

**98.** Tyler drives for 20 hr, traveling from City $A$ to City $B$, a distance of $d$ kilometers. Find his rate in kilometers per hour.

**99.** Jack flies his small plane from St. Louis to Chicago, a distance of 289 mi, at $z$ miles per hour. Find his time in hours.

**100.** Joshua can do a job in $r$ hours. What portion of the job is done in 1 hr?

## SUMMARY EXERCISES on Rational Expressions and Equations

Students often confuse *simplifying expressions* with *solving equations*. We review the four operations to simplify the rational expressions $\frac{1}{x}$ and $\frac{1}{x-2}$ as follows.

***Add:*** $\dfrac{1}{x} + \dfrac{1}{x-2}$

$= \dfrac{1(x-2)}{x(x-2)} + \dfrac{x(1)}{x(x-2)}$     Write with a common denominator.

$= \dfrac{x-2+x}{x(x-2)}$     Add numerators.
Keep the same denominator.

$= \dfrac{2x-2}{x(x-2)}$     Combine like terms.

***Subtract:*** $\dfrac{1}{x} - \dfrac{1}{x-2}$

$= \dfrac{1(x-2)}{x(x-2)} - \dfrac{x(1)}{x(x-2)}$     Write with a common denominator.

$= \dfrac{x-2-x}{x(x-2)}$     Subtract numerators.
Keep the same denominator.

$= \dfrac{-2}{x(x-2)}$     Combine like terms.

***Multiply:*** $\dfrac{1}{x} \cdot \dfrac{1}{x-2}$

$= \dfrac{1}{x(x-2)}$     Multiply numerators and multiply denominators.

***Divide:*** $\dfrac{1}{x} \div \dfrac{1}{x-2}$

$= \dfrac{1}{x} \cdot \dfrac{x-2}{1}$     Multiply by the reciprocal of the divisor.

$= \dfrac{x-2}{x}$     Multiply numerators and multiply denominators.

(continued)

By contrast, consider the following *equation*.

$$\frac{1}{x} + \frac{1}{x-2} = \frac{3}{4} \qquad \begin{array}{l} x \neq 0 \text{ and } x \neq 2 \\ \text{since a denominator} \\ \text{is 0 for these values.} \end{array}$$

$$4x(x-2)\frac{1}{x} + 4x(x-2)\frac{1}{x-2} = 4x(x-2)\frac{3}{4} \qquad \text{Multiply each side by the LCD,} \\ 4x(x-2), \text{ to clear fractions.}$$

$$4(x-2) + 4x = 3x(x-2) \qquad \text{Divide out common factors.}$$

$$4x - 8 + 4x = 3x^2 - 6x \qquad \text{Distributive property}$$

$$3x^2 - 14x + 8 = 0 \qquad \text{Get 0 on one side.}$$

$$(3x-2)(x-4) = 0 \qquad \text{Factor.}$$

$$3x - 2 = 0 \quad \text{or} \quad x - 4 = 0 \qquad \text{Zero-factor property}$$

$$x = \frac{2}{3} \quad \text{or} \qquad x = 4 \qquad \text{Solve for } x.$$

Both $\frac{2}{3}$ and 4 are solutions, since neither makes a denominator equal 0. Check to confirm that the solution set is $\left\{\frac{2}{3}, 4\right\}$.

> ### Points to Remember When Working with Rational Expressions and Equations
>
> 1. When simplifying rational expressions, the fundamental property is applied only after numerators and denominators have been *factored*.
>
> 2. When adding and subtracting rational expressions, the common denominator must be kept throughout the problem and in the final result.
>
> 3. When simplifying rational expressions, always check to see if the answer is in lowest terms. If it is not, use the fundamental property.
>
> 4. When solving equations with rational expressions, the LCD is used to clear the equation of fractions. Multiply each side by the LCD. (Notice how this use differs from that of the LCD in Point 2.)
>
> 5. When solving equations with rational expressions, reject any proposed solution that causes an original denominator to equal 0.

*For each exercise, indicate "expression" if an expression is to be simplified or "equation" if an equation is to be solved. Then simplify the expression or solve the equation.*

**1.** $\dfrac{4}{p} + \dfrac{6}{p}$

**2.** $\dfrac{x^3 y^2}{x^2 y^4} \cdot \dfrac{y^5}{x^4}$

**3.** $\dfrac{1}{x^2 + x - 2} \div \dfrac{4x^2}{2x - 2}$

**4.** $\dfrac{8}{t - 5} = 2$

**5.** $\dfrac{2y^2 + y - 6}{2y^2 - 9y + 9} \cdot \dfrac{y^2 - 2y - 3}{y^2 - 1}$

**6.** $\dfrac{2}{k^2 - 4k} + \dfrac{3}{k^2 - 16}$

**7.** $\dfrac{x - 4}{5} = \dfrac{x + 3}{6}$

**8.** $\dfrac{3t^2 - t}{6t^2 + 15t} \div \dfrac{6t^2 + t - 1}{2t^2 - 5t - 25}$

**9.** $\dfrac{4}{p + 2} + \dfrac{1}{3p + 6}$

**10.** $\dfrac{1}{x} + \dfrac{1}{x - 3} = -\dfrac{5}{4}$

11. $\dfrac{3}{t-1} + \dfrac{1}{t} = \dfrac{7}{2}$

12. $\dfrac{6}{k} - \dfrac{2}{3k}$

13. $\dfrac{5}{4z} - \dfrac{2}{3z}$

14. $\dfrac{x+2}{3} = \dfrac{2x-1}{5}$

15. $\dfrac{1}{m^2+5m+6} + \dfrac{2}{m^2+4m+3}$

16. $\dfrac{2k^2-3k}{20k^2-5k} \div \dfrac{2k^2-5k+3}{4k^2+11k-3}$

17. $\dfrac{2}{x+1} + \dfrac{5}{x-1} = \dfrac{10}{x^2-1}$

18. $\dfrac{3}{x+3} + \dfrac{4}{x+6} = \dfrac{9}{x^2+9x+18}$

19. $\dfrac{4t^2-t}{6t^2+10t} \div \dfrac{8t^2+2t-1}{3t^2+11t+10}$

20. $\dfrac{x}{x-2} + \dfrac{3}{x+2} = \dfrac{8}{x^2-4}$

## 7.7  Applications of Rational Expressions

### OBJECTIVES

1  Solve problems about numbers.

2  Solve problems about distance, rate, and time.

3  Solve problems about work.

NOW TRY
EXERCISE 1

In a certain fraction, the numerator is 4 less than the denominator. If 7 is added to both the numerator and denominator, the resulting fraction is equivalent to $\frac{7}{8}$. What is the original fraction?

For applications that lead to rational equations, the six-step problem-solving method of **Section 2.4** still applies.

**OBJECTIVE 1**  Solve problems about numbers.

**EXAMPLE 1**  Solving a Problem about an Unknown Number

If the same number is added to both the numerator and the denominator of the fraction $\frac{2}{5}$, the result is equivalent to $\frac{2}{3}$. Find the number.

*Step 1*  **Read** the problem carefully. We are trying to find a number.

*Step 2*  **Assign a variable.**

Let $x =$ the number added to the numerator and the denominator.

*Step 3*  **Write an equation.** The fraction $\frac{2+x}{5+x}$ represents the result of adding the same number to both the numerator and the denominator. Since this result is equivalent to $\frac{2}{3}$, the equation is written as follows.

$$\frac{2+x}{5+x} = \frac{2}{3}$$

*Step 4*  **Solve** this equation.

$$3(5+x)\frac{2+x}{5+x} = 3(5+x)\frac{2}{3} \quad \text{Multiply by the LCD, } 3(5+x).$$

$$3(2+x) = 2(5+x) \quad \text{Divide out common factors.}$$

$$6+3x = 10+2x \quad \text{Distributive property}$$

$$x = 4 \quad \text{Subtract } 2x. \text{ Subtract } 6.$$

*Step 5*  **State the answer.** The number is 4.

*Step 6*  **Check** the solution in the words of the original problem. If 4 is added to both the numerator and the denominator of $\frac{2}{5}$, the result is $\frac{6}{9} = \frac{2}{3}$, as required.

NOW TRY ANSWER
1. $\frac{21}{25}$

NOW TRY

**OBJECTIVE 2** Solve problems about distance, rate, and time. Recall from **Chapter 2** the following formulas relating distance, rate, and time. You may wish to refer to **Example 5** in **Section 2.7** to review the basic use of these formulas.

---

**Distance, Rate, and Time Relationship**

$$d = rt \qquad r = \frac{d}{t} \qquad t = \frac{d}{r}$$

---

**EXAMPLE 2** Solving a Problem about Distance, Rate, and Time

The Tickfaw River has a current of 3 mph. A motorboat takes as long to go 12 mi downstream as to go 8 mi upstream. What is the rate of the boat in still water?

***Step 1*** **Read** the problem again. We must find the rate (speed) of the boat in still water.

***Step 2*** **Assign a variable.** Let $x =$ the rate of the boat in still water.

Because the current pushes the boat when the boat is going downstream, the rate of the boat downstream will be the *sum* of the rate of the boat and the rate of the current, $(x + 3)$ mph.

Because the current slows down the boat when the boat is going upstream, the boat's rate going upstream is given by the *difference* between the rate of the boat and the rate of the current, $(x - 3)$ mph. See **FIGURE 1**.

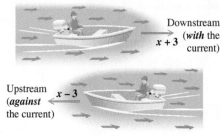

**FIGURE 1**

This information is summarized in the following table.

| | d | r | t |
|---|---|---|---|
| Downstream | 12 | x + 3 | |
| Upstream | 8 | x − 3 | |

Fill in the times by using the formula $t = \frac{d}{r}$.

The time downstream is the distance divided by the rate.

$$t = \frac{d}{r} = \frac{12}{x + 3} \qquad \text{Time downstream}$$

The time upstream is that distance divided by that rate.

$$t = \frac{d}{r} = \frac{8}{x - 3} \qquad \text{Time upstream}$$

| | d | r | t |
|---|---|---|---|
| Downstream | 12 | x + 3 | $\frac{12}{x + 3}$ |
| Upstream | 8 | x − 3 | $\frac{8}{x - 3}$ |

Times are equal.

*NOW TRY*
*EXERCISE 2*

In her small boat, Jennifer can travel 12 mi downstream in the same amount of time that she can travel 4 mi upstream. The rate of the current is 2 mph. Find the rate of Jennifer's boat in still water.

*Step 3*  **Write an equation.**

$$\frac{12}{x+3} = \frac{8}{x-3}$$

The time downstream equals the time upstream, so the two times from the table must be equal.

*Step 4*  **Solve.**

$$(x+3)(x-3)\frac{12}{x+3} = (x+3)(x-3)\frac{8}{x-3}$$  Multiply by the LCD, $(x+3)(x-3)$.

$$12(x-3) = 8(x+3)$$  Divide out the common factors.

$$12x - 36 = 8x + 24$$  Distributive property

$$4x = 60$$  Subtract 8x and add 36.

$$x = 15$$  Divide by 4.

*Step 5*  **State the answer.** The rate of the boat in still water is 15 mph.

*Step 6*  **Check.** First we find the rate of the boat going downstream, which is $15 + 3 = 18$ mph. Divide 12 mi by 18 mph to find the time.

$$t = \frac{d}{r} = \frac{12}{18} = \frac{2}{3} \text{ hr}$$

The rate of the boat going upstream is $15 - 3 = 12$ mph. Divide 8 mi by 12 mph to find the time.

$$t = \frac{d}{r} = \frac{8}{12} = \frac{2}{3} \text{ hr}$$

The time upstream equals the time downstream, as required.

*NOW TRY*

**OBJECTIVE 3**  **Solve problems about work.** Suppose that you can mow your lawn in 4 hr. Then after 1 hr, you will have mowed $\frac{1}{4}$ of the lawn. After 2 hr, you will have mowed $\frac{2}{4}$, or $\frac{1}{2}$, of the lawn, and so on. This idea is generalized as follows.

**Rate of Work**

If a job can be completed in $t$ units of time, then the rate of work is

$$\frac{1}{t} \text{ job per unit of time.}$$

**PROBLEM-SOLVING HINT**

Recall that the formula $d = rt$ says that distance traveled is equal to rate of travel multiplied by time traveled. Similarly, the fractional part of a job accomplished is equal to the rate of work multiplied by the time worked. In the lawn-mowing example, after 3 hr, the fractional part of the job done is as follows.

$$\underbrace{\frac{1}{4}}_{\substack{\text{Rate of} \\ \text{work}}} \cdot \underbrace{3}_{\substack{\text{Time} \\ \text{worked}}} = \underbrace{\frac{3}{4}}_{\substack{\text{Fractional part} \\ \text{of job done}}}$$

After 4 hr, $\frac{1}{4}(4) = 1$ whole job has been done.

*NOW TRY ANSWER*
**2.** 4 mph

NOW TRY
EXERCISE 3

Sarah can proofread a manuscript in 10 hr, while Joyce can proofread the same manuscript in 12 hr. How long will it take them to proofread the manuscript if they work together?

**EXAMPLE 3** Solving a Problem about Work Rates

"If Joe can paint a house in 3 hr and Sam can paint the same house in 5 hr, how long does it take for them to do it together?" (*Source:* The movie *Little Big League.*)

***Step 1*** **Read** the problem again. We are looking for time working together.

***Step 2*** **Assign a variable.** Let $x$ = the number of hours it takes Joe and Sam to paint the house, working together.

Certainly, $x$ will be less than 3, since Joe alone can complete the job in 3 hr. We begin by making a table. Based on the preceding discussion, Joe's rate alone is $\frac{1}{3}$ job per hour, and Sam's rate is $\frac{1}{5}$ job per hour.

| | Rate | Time Working Together | Fractional Part of the Job Done When Working Together | |
|---|---|---|---|---|
| Joe | $\frac{1}{3}$ | $x$ | $\frac{1}{3}x$ | Sum is 1 whole job. |
| Sam | $\frac{1}{5}$ | $x$ | $\frac{1}{5}x$ | |

***Step 3*** **Write an equation.**

$$\underbrace{\frac{1}{3}x}_{\substack{\text{Fractional part}\\\text{done by Joe}}} + \underbrace{\frac{1}{5}x}_{\substack{\text{Fractional part}\\\text{done by Sam}}} = \underbrace{1}_{\text{1 whole job.}}$$

Together, Joe and Sam complete 1 whole job. Add their individual fractional parts and set the sum equal to 1.

***Step 4*** **Solve.**

$$15\left(\frac{1}{3}x + \frac{1}{5}x\right) = 15(1) \qquad \text{Multiply by the LCD, 15.}$$

$$15\left(\frac{1}{3}x\right) + 15\left(\frac{1}{5}x\right) = 15(1) \qquad \text{Distributive property}$$

$$5x + 3x = 15$$

$$8x = 15 \qquad \text{Combine like terms.}$$

$$x = \frac{15}{8} \qquad \text{Divide by 8.}$$

***Step 5*** **State the answer.** Working together, Joe and Sam can paint the house in $\frac{15}{8}$ hr, or $1\frac{7}{8}$ hr.

***Step 6*** **Check** to be sure the answer is correct.

NOW TRY

**From *Little Big League***

---

**NOTE** An alternative approach in work problems is to consider the part of the job that can be done in 1 hr. For instance, in **Example 3** Joe can do the entire job in 3 hr and Sam can do it in 5 hr. Thus, their work rates, as we saw in **Example 3,** are $\frac{1}{3}$ and $\frac{1}{5}$, respectively. Since it takes them $x$ hours to complete the job working together, in 1 hr they can paint $\frac{1}{x}$ of the house.

NOW TRY ANSWER
**3.** $\frac{60}{11}$ hr, or $5\frac{5}{11}$ hr

(continued)

The amount painted by Joe in 1 hr plus the amount painted by Sam in 1 hr must equal the amount they can do together. This relationship leads to the equation

Amount by Sam
↓

Amount by Joe → $\dfrac{1}{3} + \dfrac{1}{5} = \dfrac{1}{x}$. ← Amount together

Compare this equation with the one in **Example 3.** Multiplying each side by $15x$ leads to

$$5x + 3x = 15,$$

the same equation found in the third line of Step 4 in the example. The same solution results.

---

## 7.7 EXERCISES

MyMathLab | Math XL PRACTICE  WATCH  DOWNLOAD  READ  REVIEW

*Complete solution available on the Video Resources on DVD*

*Concept Check    Use Steps 2 and 3 of the six-step method to set up the equation you would use to solve each problem. (Remember that Step 1 is to read the problem carefully.) Do not actually solve the equation. **See Example 1.***

1. The numerator of the fraction $\frac{5}{6}$ is increased by an amount so that the value of the resulting fraction is equivalent to $\frac{13}{3}$. By what amount was the numerator increased?

   **(a)** Let $x =$ _____. (*Step 2*)

   **(b)** Write an expression for "the numerator of the fraction $\frac{5}{6}$ is increased by an amount."

   **(c)** Set up an equation to solve the problem. (*Step 3*)

2. If the same number is added to the numerator and subtracted from the denominator of $\frac{23}{12}$, the resulting fraction is equivalent to $\frac{3}{2}$. What is the number?

   **(a)** Let $x =$ _____. (*Step 2*)

   **(b)** Write an expression for "a number is added to the numerator of $\frac{23}{12}$." Then write an expression for "the same number is subtracted from the denominator of $\frac{23}{12}$."

   **(c)** Set up an equation to solve the problem. (*Step 3*)

*Solve each problem. **See Example 1.***

3. In a certain fraction, the denominator is 6 more than the numerator. If 3 is added to both the numerator and the denominator, the resulting fraction is equivalent to $\frac{5}{7}$. What was the original fraction (*not* written in lowest terms)?

4. In a certain fraction, the denominator is 4 less than the numerator. If 3 is added to both the numerator and the denominator, the resulting fraction is equivalent to $\frac{3}{2}$. What was the original fraction?

5. The numerator of a certain fraction is four times the denominator. If 6 is added to both the numerator and the denominator, the resulting fraction is equivalent to 2. What was the original fraction (*not* written in lowest terms)?

6. The denominator of a certain fraction is three times the numerator. If 2 is added to the numerator and subtracted from the denominator, the resulting fraction is equivalent to 1. What was the original fraction (*not* written in lowest terms)?

7. One-third of a number is 2 greater than one-sixth of the same number. What is the number?

8. One-seventh of a number is 6 greater than the same number. What is the number?

**9.** A quantity, $\frac{2}{3}$ of it, $\frac{1}{2}$ of it, and $\frac{1}{7}$ of it, added together, equals 33. What is the quantity? (*Source:* Rhind Mathematical Papyrus.)

**10.** A quantity, $\frac{3}{4}$ of it, $\frac{1}{2}$ of it, and $\frac{1}{3}$ of it, added together, equals 93. What is the quantity? (*Source:* Rhind Mathematical Papyrus.)

*Solve each problem. **See Example 5** in **Section 2.7** (pages 143 and 144).*

**11.** In 2007, British explorer and endurance swimmer Lewis Gordon Pugh became the first person to swim at the North Pole. He swam 0.6 mi at 0.0319 mi per min in waters created by melted sea ice. What was his time (to three decimal places)? (*Source: The Gazette.*)

**12.** In the 2008 Summer Olympics, Britta Steffen of Germany won the women's 100-m freestyle swimming event. Her rate was 1.8825 m per sec. What was her time (to two decimal places)? (*Source: World Almanac and Book of Facts.*)

**13.** Tirunesh Dibaba of Ethiopia won the women's 5000-m race in the 2008 Olympics with a time of 15.911 min. What was her rate (to three decimal places)? (*Source: World Almanac and Book of Facts.*)

**14.** The winner of the women's 1500-m run in the 2008 Olympics was Nancy Jebet Langat of Kenya with a time of 4.004 min. What was her rate (to three decimal places)? (*Source: World Almanac and Book of Facts.*)

**15.** The winner of the 2008 Daytona 500 (mile) race was Ryan Newman, who drove his Dodge to victory with a rate of 152.672 mph. What was his time (to the nearest thousandth of an hour)? (*Source: World Almanac and Book of Facts.*)

**16.** In 2008, Kasey Kahne drove his Dodge to victory in the Coca-Cola 600 (mile) race. His rate was 135.722 mph. What was his time (to the nearest thousandth of an hour)? (*Source: World Almanac and Book of Facts.*)

*Concept Check*  Solve each problem.

**17.** Suppose Stephanie walks $D$ miles at $R$ mph in the same time that Wally walks $d$ miles at $r$ mph. Give an equation relating $D$, $R$, $d$, and $r$.

**18.** If a migrating hawk travels $m$ mph in still air, what is its rate when it flies into a steady headwind of 6 mph?    What is its rate with a tailwind of 6 mph?

*Set up the equation you would use to solve each problem. Do not actually solve the equation.* **See Example 2.**

**19.** Mitch Levy flew his airplane 500 mi against the wind in the same time it took him to fly 600 mi with the wind. If the speed of the wind was 10 mph, what was the rate of his plane in still air? (Let $x$ = rate of the plane in still air.)

| | d | r | t |
|---|---|---|---|
| Against the Wind | 500 | $x - 10$ | |
| With the Wind | 600 | $x + 10$ | |

**20.** Janet Sturdy can row 4 mph in still water. She takes as long to row 8 mi upstream as 24 mi downstream. How fast is the current? (Let $x$ = rate of the current.)

| | d | r | t |
|---|---|---|---|
| Upstream | 8 | $4 - x$ | |
| Downstream | 24 | $4 + x$ | |

*Solve each problem.* **See Example 2.**

🌐 **21.** A boat can go 20 mi against a current in the same time that it can go 60 mi with the current. The current is 4 mph. Find the rate of the boat in still water.

**22.** Vince Grosso can fly his plane 200 mi against the wind in the same time it takes him to fly 300 mi with the wind. The wind blows at 30 mph. Find the rate of his plane in still air.

**23.** The sanderling is a small shorebird about 6.5 in. long, with a thin, dark bill and a wide, white wing stripe. If a sanderling can fly 30 mi with the wind in the same time it can fly 18 mi against the wind when the wind speed is 8 mph, what is the rate of the bird in still air? (*Source:* U.S. Geological Survey.)

**24.** Airplanes usually fly faster from west to east than from east to west because the prevailing winds go from west to east. The air distance between Chicago and London is about 4000 mi, while the air distance between New York and London is about 3500 mi. If a jet can fly eastbound from Chicago to London in the same time it can fly westbound from London to New York in a 35-mph wind, what is the rate of the plane in still air? (*Source:* *Encyclopaedia Britannica.*)

**25.** An airplane maintaining a constant airspeed takes as long to go 450 mi with the wind as it does to go 375 mi against the wind. If the wind is blowing at 15 mph, what is the rate of the plane in still air?

**26.** A river has a current of 4 km per hr. Find the rate of Jai Singh's boat in still water if it goes 40 km downstream in the same time that it takes to go 24 km upstream.

**27.** Connie McNair's boat goes 12 mph. Find the rate of the current of the river if she can go 6 mi upstream in the same amount of time she can go 10 mi downstream.

**28.** Howie Sorkin can travel 8 mi upstream in the same time it takes him to go 12 mi downstream. His boat goes 15 mph in still water. What is the rate of the current?

**29.** The distance from Seattle, Washington, to Victoria, British Columbia, is about 148 mi by ferry. It takes about 4 hr less to travel by the same ferry from Victoria to Vancouver, British Columbia, a distance of about 74 mi. What is the average rate of the ferry?

**30.** Driving from Tulsa to Detroit, Dean Loring averaged 50 mph. He figured that if he had averaged 60 mph, his driving time would have decreased 3 hr. How far is it from Tulsa to Detroit?

*Concept Check*   *Solve each problem.*

**31.** If it takes Elayn 10 hr to do a job, what is her rate?

**32.** If it takes Clay 12 hr to do a job, how much of the job does he do in 8 hr?

*In Exercises 33 and 34, set up the equation you would use to solve each problem. Do not actually solve the equation.* **See Example 3.**

**33.** Working alone, Edward Good can paint a room in 8 hr. Abdalla Elusta can paint the same room working alone in 6 hr. How long will it take them if they work together? (Let *t* represent the time they work together.)

| | r | t | w |
|---|---|---|---|
| Edward | | t | |
| Abdalla | | t | |

**34.** Donald Bridgewater can tune up his Chevy in 2 hr working alone. Jeff Bresner can do the job in 3 hr working alone. How long would it take them if they worked together? (Let *t* represent the time they work together.)

| | r | t | w |
|---|---|---|---|
| Donald | | t | |
| Jeff | | t | |

*Solve each problem.* **See Example 3.**

**35.** Heather Schaefer, a high school mathematics teacher, gave a test on perimeter, area, and volume to her geometry classes. Working alone, it would take her 4 hr to grade the tests. Her student teacher, Courtney Slade, would take 6 hr to grade the same tests. How long would it take them to grade these tests if they work together?

**36.** Zachary and Samuel are brothers who share a bedroom. By himself, Zachary can completely mess up their room in 20 min, while it would take Samuel only 12 min to do the same thing. How long would it take them to mess up the room together?

**37.** A pump can pump the water out of a flooded basement in 10 hr. A smaller pump takes 12 hr. How long would it take to pump the water from the basement with both pumps?

**38.** Lou Viggiano's copier can do a printing job in 7 hr. Nora Demosthenes' copier can do the same job in 12 hr. How long would it take to do the job with both copiers?

**39.** An experienced employee can enter tax data into a computer twice as fast as a new employee. Working together, it takes the employees 2 hr. How long would it take the experienced employee working alone?

**40.** One roofer can put a new roof on a house three times faster than another. Working together, they can roof a house in 4 days. How long would it take the faster roofer working alone?

41. One pipe can fill a swimming pool in 6 hr, and another pipe can do it in 9 hr. How long will it take the two pipes working together to fill the pool $\frac{3}{4}$ full?

42. An inlet pipe can fill a swimming pool in 9 hr, and an outlet pipe can empty the pool in 12 hr. Through an error, both pipes are left open. How long will it take to fill the pool?

*Brain Busters*   *Extend the concepts of **Example 3** to solve each problem.*

43. A cold-water faucet can fill a sink in 12 min, and a hot-water faucet can fill it in 15 min. The drain can empty the sink in 25 min. If both faucets are on and the drain is open, how long will it take to fill the sink?

44. Refer to **Exercise 42.** Assume that the error was discovered after both pipes had been running for 3 hr and the outlet pipe was then closed. How much more time would then be required to fill the pool? (*Hint:* Consider how much of the job had been done when the error was discovered.)

## PREVIEW EXERCISES

*Solve each equation for k. **See Section 2.2.***

**45.** $200 = 15k$     **46.** $25 = 9k$     **47.** $180 = \dfrac{k}{20}$     **48.** $92 = \dfrac{k}{2}$

*Solve each formula for k. **See Section 2.5.***

**49.** $y = kx$     **50.** $y = kx^2$     **51.** $y = \dfrac{k}{x}$     **52.** $y = \dfrac{k}{x^2}$

# 7.8  Variation

**OBJECTIVES**

1  Solve direct variation problems.

2  Solve inverse variation problems.

**OBJECTIVE 1**  Solve direct variation problems. Suppose that gasoline costs $3.00 per gal. Then 1 gal costs $3.00, 2 gal costs 2($3.00) = $6.00, 3 gal costs 3($3.00) = $9.00, and so on. Each time, the total cost is obtained by multiplying the number of gallons by the price per gallon. In general, if $k$ equals the price per gallon and $x$ equals the number of gallons, then the total cost $y$ is given by $y = kx$.

As the *number of gallons **increases,*** the *total cost **increases.***

The following is also true.

As the *number of gallons **decreases,*** the *total cost **decreases.***

The preceding discussion presents an example of *variation.* As in the gasoline example, ***two variables vary directly if one is a constant multiple of the other.***

## Direct Variation

**$y$ varies directly as $x$** if there exists a constant $k$ such that the following is true.

$$y = kx$$

Also, $y$ is said to be *proportional to x*. The constant $k$ in the equation for direct variation is a numerical value, such as 3.00 in the gasoline price discussion. This value is called the **constant of variation.**

*NOW TRY*
*EXERCISE 1*

If $W$ varies directly as $r$, and $W = 40$ when $r = 5$, find $W$ when $r = 10$.

### EXAMPLE 1 Using Direct Variation

Suppose $y$ varies directly as $x$, and $y = 20$ when $x = 4$. Find $y$ when $x = 9$.

Since $y$ varies directly as $x$, there is a constant $k$ such that $y = kx$. We know that $y = 20$ when $x = 4$. We substitute these values into $y = kx$ and solve for $k$.

$$y = kx \qquad \text{Equation for direct variation}$$
$$20 = k \cdot 4 \qquad \text{Substitute the given values.}$$
$$k = 5 \qquad \leftarrow \text{Constant of variation}$$

Since $y = kx$ and $k = 5$, we have the following.

$$y = 5x \qquad \text{Let } k = 5.$$

Now find the value of $y$ when $x = 9$.

$$y = 5x = 5 \cdot 9 = 45 \qquad \text{Let } x = 9.$$

Thus, $y = 45$ when $x = 9$.  *NOW TRY*

### Solving a Variation Problem

*Step 1* Write the variation equation.

*Step 2* Substitute the appropriate given values and solve for $k$.

*Step 3* Rewrite the variation equation with the value of $k$ from Step 2.

*Step 4* Substitute the remaining values, solve for the unknown, and find the required answer.

The direct variation equation $y = kx$ is a linear equation. However, other kinds of variation involve other types of equations.

## Direct Variation as a Power

**$y$ varies directly as the *n*th power of $x$** if there exists a real number $k$ such that the following is true.

$$y = kx^n$$

An example of direct variation as a power is the formula for the area of a circle, $\mathcal{A} = \pi r^2$. Here, $\pi$ is the constant of variation, and the area varies directly as the square of the radius. See **FIGURE 2**.

$\mathcal{A} = \pi r^2$

**FIGURE 2**

*NOW TRY ANSWER*
1. 80

*NOW TRY*
*EXERCISE 2*
If the height is constant, the volume of a right circular cylinder varies directly as the square of the radius of its base. If the volume is 80 ft³ when the radius is 4 ft, find the volume when the radius is 5 ft.

**EXAMPLE 2** Solving a Direct Variation Problem

The distance a body falls from rest varies directly as the square of the time it falls (disregarding air resistance). If a sky diver falls 64 ft in 2 sec, how far will she fall in 8 sec?

**Step 1** If $d$ represents the distance the sky diver falls and $t$ the time it takes to fall, then $d$ is a function of $t$, and, for some constant $k$, the following holds true.

$$d = kt^2$$

**Step 2** To find the value of $k$, use the fact that the sky diver falls 64 ft in 2 sec.

$d = kt^2$     Variation equation

$64 = k(2)^2$     Let $d = 64$ and $t = 2$.

$64 = 4k$     Apply the exponent.

$k = 16$     Divide by 4.

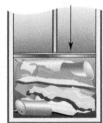

**Step 3** Substitute 16 for $k$ to find the variation equation.

$$d = 16t^2$$

**Step 4** Now let $t = 8$ to find the number of feet the sky diver will fall in 8 sec.

$$d = 16(8)^2 = 16 \cdot 64 = 1024 \quad \text{Let } t = 8.$$

The sky diver will fall 1024 ft in 8 sec.     *NOW TRY*

**OBJECTIVE 2** Solve inverse variation problems. In direct variation, where $k > 0$, as $x$ increases, $y$ increases. Similarly, as $x$ decreases, $y$ decreases. Another type of variation is *inverse variation*. With inverse variation, where $k > 0$,

> As one variable *increases,*
> the other variable *decreases.*

For example, in a closed space, volume decreases as pressure increases, as illustrated by a trash compactor. See **FIGURE 3**. As the compactor presses down, the pressure on the trash increases. As a result, the trash occupies a smaller space.

As pressure increases, volume decreases.

**FIGURE 3**

---

**Inverse Variation**

*y* **varies inversely as** *x* if there exists a real number $k$ such that the following is true.

$$y = \frac{k}{x}$$

Also, *y* **varies inversely as the** *n*th **power of** *x* if there exists a real number $k$ such that the following is true.

$$y = \frac{k}{x^n}$$

*NOW TRY ANSWER*
**2.** 125 ft³

Another example of inverse variation comes from the distance formula.

$$d = rt \quad \text{Distance formula}$$

$$t = \frac{d}{r} \quad \text{Divide each side by } r.$$

In the form $t = \frac{d}{r}$, $t$ (time) varies inversely as $r$ (rate or speed), with $d$ (distance) serving as the constant of variation. For example, if the distance between two cities is 300 mi, then

$$t = \frac{300}{r}$$

and the values of $r$ and $t$ might be any of the following.

$$r = 50, t = 6$$
$$r = 60, t = 5 \quad \text{As } r \text{ increases,}$$
$$r = 75, t = 4 \quad t \text{ decreases.}$$

$$r = 30, t = 10$$
$$r = 25, t = 12 \quad \text{As } r \text{ decreases,}$$
$$r = 20, t = 15 \quad t \text{ increases.}$$

If we *increase* the rate (speed) at which we drive, the time *decreases*. If we *decrease* the rate (speed) at which we drive, the time *increases*.

**NOW TRY**
**EXERCISE 3**

If $t$ varies inversely as $r$, and $t = 12$ when $r = 3$, find $t$ when $r = 6$.

**EXAMPLE 3** Using Inverse Variation

Suppose $y$ varies inversely as $x$, and $y = 3$ when $x = 8$. Find $y$ when $x = 6$.

Since $y$ varies inversely as $x$, there is a constant $k$ such that $y = \frac{k}{x}$. We know that $y = 3$ when $x = 8$, so we can find $k$.

$$y = \frac{k}{x} \quad \text{Equation for inverse variation}$$

$$3 = \frac{k}{8} \quad \text{Substitute the given values.}$$

$$k = 24 \quad \text{Multiply by 8. Rewrite } 24 = k \text{ as } k = 24.$$

Since $y = \frac{24}{x}$, we let $x = 6$ and find $y$.

$$y = \frac{24}{x} = \frac{24}{6} = 4$$

Therefore, when $x = 6$, $y = 4$.

NOW TRY

**EXAMPLE 4** Using Inverse Variation

In the manufacturing of a certain medical syringe, the cost of producing the syringe varies inversely as the number produced. If 10,000 syringes are produced, the cost is $2 per syringe. Find the cost per syringe to produce 25,000 syringes.

Let     $x =$ the number of syringes produced,

and     $c =$ the cost per unit.

Here, as production increases, cost decreases, and as production decreases, cost increases. Since $c$ varies inversely as $x$, there is a constant $k$ such that the following holds true.

**NOW TRY ANSWER**
**3.** 6

NOW TRY
EXERCISE 4

If the area is constant, the height of a triangle varies inversely as the base. If the height is 6 ft when the base is 4 ft, find the height when the base is 12 ft.

NOW TRY ANSWER
**4.** 2 ft

$$c = \frac{k}{x} \qquad \text{Equation for inverse variation}$$

$$2 = \frac{k}{10,000} \qquad \text{Substitute the given values.}$$

$$k = 20,000 \qquad \text{Multiply by 10,000. Rewrite.}$$

Now use $c = \frac{k}{x}$.

$$c = \frac{20,000}{25,000} = 0.80 \qquad \text{Let } k = 20,000 \text{ and } x = 25,000.$$

The cost per syringe to make 25,000 syringes is \$0.80.  NOW TRY

## 7.8 EXERCISES

Complete solution available on the Video Resources on DVD

*Concept Check*  Use personal experience or intuition to determine whether the situation suggests direct *or* inverse variation.*

1. The number of candy bars you buy and your total price for the candy
2. The rate and the distance traveled by a moving van in 3 hr
3. The amount of pressure put on the accelerator of a truck and the speed of the truck
4. The surface area of a beach ball and its diameter
5. The number of days until the end of the baseball season and the number of home runs that Evan Longoria has
6. "The more I see you, the more I want you." (Opening line from a 1966 song by Chris Montez)
7. The number of days from now until December 25 and the magnitude of the frenzy of Christmas shopping
8. Your age and the likelihood that you believe in Santa Claus

*Concept Check*  Determine whether each equation represents direct *or* inverse *variation.*

**9.** $y = \frac{3}{x}$ **10.** $y = \frac{5}{x}$ **11.** $y = 10x^2$ **12.** $y = 3x^3$

**13.** $y = 50x$ **14.** $y = 200x$ **15.** $y = \frac{12}{x^2}$ **16.** $y = \frac{8}{x^3}$

**17.** *Concept Check*  Fill in each blank with the correct response.

  **(a)** If the constant of variation is positive and $y$ varies directly as $x$, then as $x$ increases, $y$ _____.
  (increases/decreases)

  **(b)** If the constant of variation is positive and $y$ varies inversely as $x$, then as $x$ increases, $y$ _____.
  (increases/decreases)

*The authors thank Linda Kodama for suggesting the inclusion of exercises of this type.

✏ **18.** Bill Veeck was the owner of several major league baseball teams in the 1950s and 1960s. He was known to often sit in the stands and enjoy games with his paying customers. Here is a quote attributed to him:

> *I have discovered in 20 years of moving around a ballpark, that the knowledge of the game is usually in inverse proportion to the price of the seats.*

Explain in your own words the meaning of his statement. (To prove his point, Veeck once allowed the fans to vote on managerial decisions.)

*Solve each problem involving direct or inverse variation.* ***See Examples 1 and 3.***

🌐 **19.** If $x$ varies directly as $y$, and $x = 27$ when $y = 6$, find $x$ when $y = 2$.

**20.** If $z$ varies directly as $x$, and $z = 30$ when $x = 8$, find $z$ when $x = 4$.

**21.** If $d$ varies directly as $t$, and $d = 150$ when $t = 3$, find $d$ when $t = 5$.

**22.** If $d$ varies directly as $r$, and $d = 200$ when $r = 40$, find $d$ when $r = 60$.

🌐 **23.** If $x$ varies inversely as $y$, and $x = 3$ when $y = 8$, find $y$ when $x = 4$.

**24.** If $z$ varies inversely as $x$, and $z = 50$ when $x = 2$, find $z$ when $x = 25$.

**25.** If $p$ varies inversely as $q$, and $p = 7$ when $q = 6$, find $p$ when $q = 2$.

**26.** If $m$ varies inversely as $r$, and $m = 12$ when $r = 8$, find $m$ when $r = 16$.

**27.** If $m$ varies inversely as $p^2$, and $m = 20$ when $p = 2$, find $m$ when $p = 5$.

**28.** If $a$ varies inversely as $b^2$, and $a = 48$ when $b = 4$, find $a$ when $b = 7$.

**29.** If $p$ varies inversely as $q^2$, and $p = 4$ when $q = \frac{1}{2}$, find $p$ when $q = \frac{3}{2}$.

**30.** If $z$ varies inversely as $x^2$, and $z = 9$ when $x = \frac{2}{3}$, find $z$ when $x = \frac{5}{4}$.

*Solve each variation problem.* ***See Examples 1–4.***

**31.** The interest on an investment varies directly as the rate of interest. If the interest is $48 when the interest rate is 5%, find the interest when the rate is 4.2%.

**32.** For a given base, the area of a triangle varies directly as its height. Find the area of a triangle with a height of 6 in., if the area is 10 in.$^2$ when the height is 4 in.

**33.** Hooke's law for an elastic spring states that the distance a spring stretches varies directly with the force applied. If a force of 75 lb stretches a certain spring 16 in., how much will a force of 200 lb stretch the spring?

**34.** The pressure exerted by water at a given point varies directly with the depth of the point beneath the surface of the water. Water exerts 4.34 lb per in.$^2$ for every 10 ft traveled below the water's surface. What is the pressure exerted on a scuba diver at 20 ft?

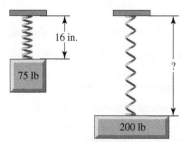

**35.** Over a specified distance, rate varies inversely with time. If a Nissan 370Z on a test track goes a certain distance in one-half minute at 160 mph, what rate is needed to go the same distance in three-fourths minute?

**36.** For a constant area, the length of a rectangle varies inversely as the width. The length of a rectangle is 27 ft when the width is 10 ft. Find the width of a rectangle with the same area if the length is 18 ft.

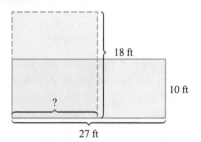

**37.** The current in a simple electrical circuit varies inversely as the resistance. If the current is 20 amps when the resistance is 5 ohms, find the current when the resistance is 8 ohms.

**38.** If the temperature is constant, the pressure of a gas in a container varies inversely as the volume of the container. If the pressure is 10 lb per ft$^2$ in a container with volume 3 ft$^3$, what is the pressure in a container with volume 1.5 ft$^3$?

**39.** The force required to compress a spring varies directly as the change in the length of the spring. If a force of 12 lb is required to compress a certain spring 3 in., how much force is required to compress the spring 5 in.?

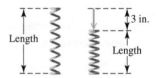

**40.** In the inversion of raw sugar, the rate of change of the amount of raw sugar varies directly as the amount of raw sugar remaining. The rate is 200 kg per hr when there are 800 kg left. What is the rate of change per hour when only 100 kg are left?

**41.** The area of a circle varies directly as the square of its radius. A circle with radius 3 in. has area 28.278 in.$^2$. What is the area of a circle with radius 4.1 in. (to the nearest thousandth)?

**42.** For a body falling freely from rest (disregarding air resistance), the distance the body falls varies directly as the square of the time. If an object is dropped from the top of a tower 400 ft high and hits the ground in 5 sec, how far did it fall in the first 3 sec?

**43.** The amount of light (measured in *footcandles*) produced by a light source varies inversely as the square of the distance from the source. If the amount of light produced 4 ft from a light source is 75 footcandles, find the amount of light produced 9 ft from the same source.

**44.** The force with which Earth attracts an object above Earth's surface varies inversely as the square of the object's distance from the center of Earth. If an object 4000 mi from the center of Earth is attracted with a force of 160 lb, find the force of attraction on an object 6000 mi from the center of Earth.

**PREVIEW EXERCISES**

*Find each power. See Sections 1.2 and 5.1.*

**45.** $8^2$      **46.** $(-3)^2$      **47.** $-12^2$      **48.** $3.5^2$

*Find the value of $a^2 + b^2$ for the given values of a and b. See Section 1.3.*

**49.** $a = 5, b = 12$      **50.** $a = 7, b = 24$

STUDY SKILLS

# Preparing for Your Math Final Exam

Your math final exam is likely to be a comprehensive exam, which means it will cover material from the entire term.

1. **Figure out the grade you need to earn on the final exam to get the course grade you want.** Check your course syllabus for grading policies, or ask your instructor if you are not sure.

   *How many points do you need to earn on your math final exam to get the grade you want?*

2. **Create a final exam week plan.** Set priorities that allow you to spend extra time studying. This may mean making adjustments, in advance, in your work schedule or enlisting extra help with family responsibilities.

   *What adjustments do you need to make for final exam week?*

3. **Use the following suggestions to guide your studying and reviewing.**

   ▶ **Begin reviewing several days before the final exam.** DON'T wait until the last minute.

   ▶ **Know exactly which chapters and sections will be covered on the exam.**

   ▶ **Divide up the chapters.** Decide how much you will review each day.

   ▶ **Use returned quizzes and tests to review earlier material.**

   ▶ **Practice all types of problems. Use the Cumulative Reviews** that are at the end of each chapter in your textbook. All answers, with section references, are given in the answer section.

   ▶ **Review or rewrite your notes** to create summaries of important information.

   ▶ **Make study cards for all types of problems.** Carry the cards with you, and review them whenever you have a few minutes.

   ▶ **Take plenty of short breaks to reduce physical and mental stress.** Exercising, listening to music, and enjoying a favorite activity are effective stress busters.

   **Finally, *DON'T* stay up all night the night before an exam—*get a good night's sleep.***

   *Select several suggestions to use as you study for your math final exam.*

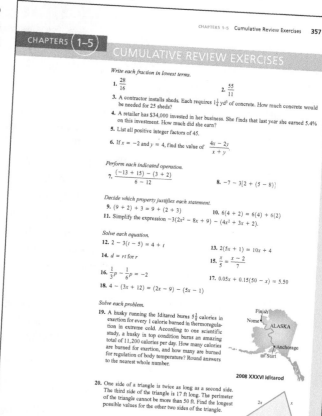

# CHAPTER ( 7 ) SUMMARY

## KEY TERMS

**7.1**

rational expression
lowest terms

**7.3**

least common
  denominator (LCD)

**7.5**

complex fraction

**7.6**

proposed solution
extraneous solution (value)

**7.8**

direct variation
constant of variation
inverse variation

## TEST YOUR WORD POWER

*See how well you have learned the vocabulary in this chapter.*

1. A **rational expression** is
   A. an algebraic expression made up of a term or the sum of a finite number of terms with real coefficients and whole number exponents
   B. a polynomial equation of degree 2
   C. an expression with one or more fractions in the numerator, or denominator, or both
   D. the quotient of two polynomials with denominator not 0.

2. A **complex fraction** is
   A. an algebraic expression made up of a term or the sum of a finite number of terms with real coefficients and whole number exponents
   B. a polynomial equation of degree 2
   C. a quotient with one or more fractions in the numerator, or denominator, or both
   D. the quotient of two polynomials with denominator not 0.

3. If two positive quantities $x$ and $y$ are in **direct variation,** and the constant of variation is positive, then
   A. as $x$ increases, $y$ decreases
   B. as $x$ increases, $y$ increases
   C. as $x$ increases, $y$ remains constant
   D. as $x$ decreases, $y$ remains constant.

4. If two positive quantities $x$ and $y$ are in **inverse variation,** and the constant of variation is positive, then
   A. as $x$ increases, $y$ decreases
   B. as $x$ increases, $y$ increases
   C. as $x$ increases, $y$ remains constant
   D. as $x$ decreases, $y$ remains constant.

### ANSWERS

1. D; *Examples:* $-\dfrac{3}{4y}, \dfrac{5x^3}{x+2}, \dfrac{a+3}{a^2-4a-5}$    2. C; *Examples:* $\dfrac{\frac{2}{3}}{\frac{4}{7}}, \dfrac{x-\frac{1}{y}}{x+\frac{1}{y}}, \dfrac{\frac{2}{a+1}}{a^2-1}$

3. B; *Example:* The equation $y = 3x$ represents direct variation. When $x = 2$, $y = 6$. If $x$ increases to 3, then $y$ increases to $3(3) = 9$.

4. A; *Example:* The equation $y = \frac{3}{x}$ represents inverse variation. When $x = 1$, $y = 3$. If $x$ increases to 2, then $y$ decreases to $\frac{3}{2}$, or $1\frac{1}{2}$.

## QUICK REVIEW

### CONCEPTS

**7.1**  The Fundamental Property of Rational Expressions

To find the value(s) for which a rational expression is undefined, set the denominator equal to 0 and solve the equation.

### EXAMPLES

Find the values for which the expression $\dfrac{x-4}{x^2-16}$ is undefined.

$$x^2 - 16 = 0$$
$$(x-4)(x+4) = 0 \qquad \text{Factor.}$$
$$x - 4 = 0 \quad \text{or} \quad x + 4 = 0 \qquad \text{Zero-factor property}$$
$$x = 4 \quad \text{or} \qquad x = -4 \qquad \text{Solve for } x.$$

The rational expression is undefined for 4 and $-4$, so $x \neq 4$ and $x \neq -4$.

(continued)

| CONCEPTS | EXAMPLES |
|---|---|

**Writing a Rational Expression in Lowest Terms**

**Step 1**   Factor the numerator and denominator.

**Step 2**   Use the fundamental property to divide out common factors.

Write in lowest terms.   $\dfrac{x^2 - 1}{(x - 1)^2}$

$$= \dfrac{(x - 1)(x + 1)}{(x - 1)(x - 1)}$$

$$= \dfrac{x + 1}{x - 1}$$

---

## 7.2   Multiplying and Dividing Rational Expressions

**Multiplying or Dividing Rational Expressions**

**Step 1**   Note the operation. If the operation is division, use the definition of division to rewrite as multiplication.

**Step 2**   Multiply numerators and multiply denominators.

**Step 3**   Factor numerators and denominators completely.

**Step 4**   Write in lowest terms, using the fundamental property.

*Note: Steps 2 and 3 may be interchanged based on personal preference.*

Multiply.   $\dfrac{3x + 9}{x - 5} \cdot \dfrac{x^2 - 3x - 10}{x^2 - 9}$

$$= \dfrac{(3x + 9)(x^2 - 3x - 10)}{(x - 5)(x^2 - 9)} \quad \text{Multiply numerators and denominators.}$$

$$= \dfrac{3(x + 3)(x - 5)(x + 2)}{(x - 5)(x + 3)(x - 3)} \quad \text{Factor.}$$

$$= \dfrac{3(x + 2)}{x - 3} \quad \text{Lowest terms}$$

Divide.   $\dfrac{2x + 1}{x + 5} \div \dfrac{6x^2 - x - 2}{x^2 - 25}$

$$= \dfrac{2x + 1}{x + 5} \cdot \dfrac{x^2 - 25}{6x^2 - x - 2} \quad \text{Multiply by the reciprocal of the divisor.}$$

$$= \dfrac{(2x + 1)(x^2 - 25)}{(x + 5)(6x^2 - x - 2)} \quad \text{Multiply numerators and denominators.}$$

$$= \dfrac{(2x + 1)(x + 5)(x - 5)}{(x + 5)(2x + 1)(3x - 2)} \quad \text{Factor.}$$

$$= \dfrac{x - 5}{3x - 2} \quad \text{Lowest terms}$$

---

## 7.3   Least Common Denominators

**Finding the LCD**

**Step 1**   Factor each denominator into prime factors.

**Step 2**   List each different factor the greatest number of times it appears.

**Step 3**   Multiply the factors from Step 2 to get the LCD.

**Writing a Rational Expression with a Specified Denominator**

**Step 1**   Factor both denominators.

**Step 2**   Decide what factor(s) the denominator must be multiplied by in order to equal the specified denominator.

**Step 3**   Multiply the rational expression by that factor divided by itself. (That is, multiply by 1.)

Find the LCD for   $\dfrac{3}{k^2 - 8k + 16}$   and   $\dfrac{1}{4k^2 - 16k}$.

$$\left. \begin{array}{l} k^2 - 8k + 16 = (k - 4)^2 \\ 4k^2 - 16k = 4k(k - 4) \end{array} \right\} \quad \begin{array}{l}\text{Factor each} \\ \text{denominator.}\end{array}$$

$$\text{LCD} = (k - 4)^2 \cdot 4 \cdot k$$

$$= 4k(k - 4)^2$$

Find the numerator.   $\dfrac{5}{2z^2 - 6z} = \dfrac{?}{4z^3 - 12z^2}$

$$\dfrac{5}{2z(z - 3)} = \dfrac{?}{4z^2(z - 3)}$$

$2z(z - 3)$ must be multiplied by $2z$ in order to obtain $4z^2(z - 3)$.

$$\dfrac{5}{2z(z - 3)} \cdot \dfrac{2z}{2z} = \dfrac{10z}{4z^2(z - 3)} = \dfrac{10z}{4z^3 - 12z^2}$$

*(continued)*

| CONCEPTS | EXAMPLES |
|---|---|

### 7.4 Adding and Subtracting Rational Expressions

**Adding Rational Expressions**

**Step 1** Find the LCD.

**Step 2** Rewrite each rational expression with the LCD as denominator.

**Step 3** Add the numerators to get the numerator of the sum. The LCD is the denominator of the sum.

**Step 4** Write in lowest terms.

**Subtracting Rational Expressions**

Follow the same steps as for addition, but subtract in Step 3.

---

Add. $\dfrac{2}{3m+6} + \dfrac{m}{m^2-4}$

$3m + 6 = 3(m+2)$ — The LCD is
$m^2 - 4 = (m+2)(m-2)$ — $3(m+2)(m-2)$.

$= \dfrac{2(m-2)}{3(m+2)(m-2)} + \dfrac{3m}{3(m+2)(m-2)}$   Write with the LCD.

$= \dfrac{2m-4+3m}{3(m+2)(m-2)}$   Add numerators and keep the same denominator.

$= \dfrac{5m-4}{3(m+2)(m-2)}$   Combine like terms.

Subtract. $\dfrac{6}{k+4} - \dfrac{2}{k}$   The LCD is $k(k+4)$.

$= \dfrac{6k}{(k+4)k} - \dfrac{2(k+4)}{k(k+4)}$   Write with the LCD.

$= \dfrac{6k - 2(k+4)}{k(k+4)}$   Subtract numerators and keep the same denominator.

$= \dfrac{6k - 2k - 8}{k(k+4)}$   Distributive property

$= \dfrac{4k - 8}{k(k+4)}$   Combine like terms.

---

### 7.5 Complex Fractions

**Simplifying Complex Fractions**

**Method 1** Simplify the numerator and denominator separately. Then divide the simplified numerator by the simplified denominator.

**Method 2** Multiply the numerator and denominator of the complex fraction by the LCD of all the denominators in the complex fraction. Write in lowest terms.

---

Simplify.

**Method 1**   $\dfrac{\frac{1}{a} - a}{1-a} = \dfrac{\frac{1}{a} - \frac{a^2}{a}}{1-a} = \dfrac{\frac{1-a^2}{a}}{1-a}$

$= \dfrac{1-a^2}{a} \div (1-a)$

$= \dfrac{1-a^2}{a} \cdot \dfrac{1}{1-a}$   Multiply by the reciprocal of the divisor.

$= \dfrac{(1-a)(1+a)}{a(1-a)} = \dfrac{1+a}{a}$

**Method 2**   $\dfrac{\frac{1}{a} - a}{1-a} = \dfrac{\left(\frac{1}{a} - a\right)a}{(1-a)a} = \dfrac{\frac{a}{a} - a^2}{(1-a)a}$

$= \dfrac{1-a^2}{(1-a)a} = \dfrac{(1+a)(1-a)}{(1-a)a}$

$= \dfrac{1+a}{a}$

(continued)

| CONCEPTS | EXAMPLES |
|---|---|

### 7.6 Solving Equations with Rational Expressions

**Solving Equations with Rational Expressions**

**Step 1** Multiply each side of the equation by the LCD to clear the equation of fractions. Be sure to distribute to *every* term on *both* sides.

Solve. $\dfrac{x}{x-3} + \dfrac{4}{x+3} = \dfrac{18}{x^2-9}$

$\dfrac{x}{x-3} + \dfrac{4}{x+3} = \dfrac{18}{(x-3)(x+3)}$  Factor.

The LCD is $(x-3)(x+3)$. Note that 3 and $-3$ cannot be solutions, as they cause a denominator to equal 0.

$$(x-3)(x+3)\left(\dfrac{x}{x-3} + \dfrac{4}{x+3}\right)$$
$$= (x-3)(x+3)\dfrac{18}{(x-3)(x+3)}$$  Multiply by the LCD.

**Step 2** Solve the resulting equation.

$x(x+3) + 4(x-3) = 18$  Distributive property
$x^2 + 3x + 4x - 12 = 18$  Distributive property
$x^2 + 7x - 30 = 0$  Standard form
$(x-3)(x+10) = 0$  Factor.
$x - 3 = 0$ or $x + 10 = 0$  Zero-factor property

**Step 3** Check each proposed solution.

Reject $\rightarrow x = 3$ or $x = -10$  Solve for $x$.

Since 3 causes denominators to equal 0, the only solution is $-10$. Thus, $\{-10\}$ is the solution set.

### 7.7 Applications of Rational Expressions

**Solving Problems about Distance, Rate, and Time**
Use the formulas relating $d$, $r$, and $t$.

$$d = rt, \quad r = \dfrac{d}{t}, \quad t = \dfrac{d}{r}$$

**Solving Problems about Work**

It takes the regular mail carrier 6 hr to cover her route. A substitute takes 8 hr to cover the same route. How long would it take them to cover the route together?

**Step 1** Read the problem carefully.

Let $x$ = the number of hours required to cover the route together.

**Step 2** Assign a variable. State what the variable represents. Put the information from the problem into a table. If a job is done in $t$ units of time, the rate is $\frac{1}{t}$.

|  | Rate | Time | Part of the Job Done |
|---|---|---|---|
| Regular | $\dfrac{1}{6}$ | $x$ | $\dfrac{1}{6}x$ |
| Substitute | $\dfrac{1}{8}$ | $x$ | $\dfrac{1}{8}x$ |

**Step 3** Write an equation. The sum of the fractional parts should equal 1 (whole job).

$$\dfrac{1}{6}x + \dfrac{1}{8}x = 1$$

**Step 4** Solve the equation.

$24\left(\dfrac{1}{6}x + \dfrac{1}{8}x\right) = 24(1)$  The LCD is 24.

$4x + 3x = 24$  Distributive property
$7x = 24$  Combine like terms.
$x = \dfrac{24}{7}$  Divide by 7.

**Steps 5 and 6** State the answer and check the solution.

It would take them $\frac{24}{7}$ hr, or $3\frac{3}{7}$ hr, to cover the route together.
The solution checks because $\frac{1}{6}\left(\frac{24}{7}\right) + \frac{1}{8}\left(\frac{24}{7}\right) = 1$.

(continued)

| CONCEPTS | EXAMPLES |
|---|---|
| **7.8** Variation | If $y$ varies inversely as $x$, and $y = 4$ when $x = 9$, find $y$ when $x = 6$. |

**Solving Variation Problems**

*Step 1* Write the variation equation.

$y = kx$ or $y = kx^n$    Direct variation

$y = \dfrac{k}{x}$ or $y = \dfrac{k}{x^n}$    Inverse variation

*Step 2* Find $k$ by substituting the appropriate given values of $x$ and $y$ into the equation.

*Step 3* Rewrite the variation equation with the value of $k$ from Step 2.

*Step 4* Substitute the remaining values, and solve for the unknown.

The equation for inverse variation is as follows.

$$y = \frac{k}{x}$$

$$4 = \frac{k}{9} \qquad \text{Substitute given values.}$$

$$k = 36 \qquad \text{Multiply by 9. Rewrite.}$$

$$y = \frac{36}{x} \qquad k = 36$$

$$y = \frac{36}{6} = 6 \qquad \text{Let } x = 6.$$

# CHAPTER 7 REVIEW EXERCISES

**7.1** *Find the numerical value of each rational expression for **(a)** $x = -2$ and **(b)** $x = 4$.*

**1.** $\dfrac{4x - 3}{5x + 2}$

**2.** $\dfrac{3x}{x^2 - 4}$

*Find any values of the variable for which each rational expression is undefined. Write answers with the symbol $\neq$.*

**3.** $\dfrac{4}{x - 3}$

**4.** $\dfrac{y + 3}{2y}$

**5.** $\dfrac{2k + 1}{3k^2 + 17k + 10}$

**6.** How do you determine the values of the variable for which a rational expression is undefined?

*Write each rational expression in lowest terms.*

**7.** $\dfrac{5a^3b^3}{15a^4b^2}$

**8.** $\dfrac{m - 4}{4 - m}$

**9.** $\dfrac{4x^2 - 9}{6 - 4x}$

**10.** $\dfrac{4p^2 + 8pq - 5q^2}{10p^2 - 3pq - q^2}$

*Write four equivalent forms for each rational expression.*

**11.** $-\dfrac{4x - 9}{2x + 3}$

**12.** $-\dfrac{8 - 3x}{3 - 6x}$

**7.2**   *Multiply or divide, and write each answer in lowest terms.*

**13.** $\dfrac{18p^3}{6} \cdot \dfrac{24}{p^4}$

**14.** $\dfrac{8x^2}{12x^5} \cdot \dfrac{6x^4}{2x}$

**15.** $\dfrac{x-3}{4} \cdot \dfrac{5}{2x-6}$

**16.** $\dfrac{2r+3}{r-4} \cdot \dfrac{r^2-16}{6r+9}$

**17.** $\dfrac{6a^2+7a-3}{2a^2-a-6} \div \dfrac{a+5}{a-2}$

**18.** $\dfrac{y^2-6y+8}{y^2+3y-18} \div \dfrac{y-4}{y+6}$

**19.** $\dfrac{2p^2+13p+20}{p^2+p-12} \cdot \dfrac{p^2+2p-15}{2p^2+7p+5}$

**20.** $\dfrac{3z^2+5z-2}{9z^2-1} \cdot \dfrac{9z^2+6z+1}{z^2+5z+6}$

**7.3**   *Find the least common denominator for the fractions in each list.*

**21.** $\dfrac{4}{9y}, \dfrac{7}{12y^2}, \dfrac{5}{27y^4}$

**22.** $\dfrac{3}{x^2+4x+3}, \dfrac{5}{x^2+5x+4}$

*Rewrite each rational expression with the given denominator.*

**23.** $\dfrac{3}{2a^3} = \dfrac{?}{10a^4}$

**24.** $\dfrac{9}{x-3} = \dfrac{?}{18-6x}$

**25.** $\dfrac{-3y}{2y-10} = \dfrac{?}{50-10y}$

**26.** $\dfrac{4b}{b^2+2b-3} = \dfrac{?}{(b+3)(b-1)(b+2)}$

**7.4**   *Add or subtract, and write each answer in lowest terms.*

**27.** $\dfrac{10}{x} + \dfrac{5}{x}$

**28.** $\dfrac{6}{3p} - \dfrac{12}{3p}$

**29.** $\dfrac{9}{k} - \dfrac{5}{k-5}$

**30.** $\dfrac{4}{y} + \dfrac{7}{7+y}$

**31.** $\dfrac{m}{3} - \dfrac{2+5m}{6}$

**32.** $\dfrac{12}{x^2} - \dfrac{3}{4x}$

**33.** $\dfrac{5}{a-2b} + \dfrac{2}{a+2b}$

**34.** $\dfrac{4}{k^2-9} - \dfrac{k+3}{3k-9}$

**35.** $\dfrac{8}{z^2+6z} - \dfrac{3}{z^2+4z-12}$

**36.** $\dfrac{11}{2p-p^2} - \dfrac{2}{p^2-5p+6}$

**7.5**   *Simplify each complex fraction.*

**37.** $\dfrac{\dfrac{y-3}{y}}{\dfrac{y+3}{4y}}$

**38.** $\dfrac{\dfrac{2}{3} - \dfrac{1}{6}}{\dfrac{1}{4} + \dfrac{2}{5}}$

**39.** $\dfrac{x + \dfrac{1}{w}}{x - \dfrac{1}{w}}$

**40.** $\dfrac{\dfrac{1}{p} - \dfrac{1}{q}}{\dfrac{1}{q-p}}$

**41.** $\dfrac{\dfrac{x^2-25}{x+3}}{\dfrac{x+5}{x^2-9}}$

**42.** $\dfrac{\dfrac{1}{r+t} - 1}{\dfrac{1}{r+t} + 1}$

**7.6**   *Solve each equation, and check your solutions.*

**43.** $\dfrac{3x-1}{x-2} = \dfrac{5}{x-2} + 1$

**44.** $\dfrac{4-z}{z} + \dfrac{3}{2} = \dfrac{-4}{z}$

**45.** $\dfrac{3}{x+4} - \dfrac{2x}{5} = \dfrac{3}{x+4}$

**46.** $\dfrac{3}{m-2} + \dfrac{1}{m-1} = \dfrac{7}{m^2-3m+2}$

*Solve each formula for the specified variable.*

**47.** $m = \dfrac{Ry}{t}$ for $t$

**48.** $x = \dfrac{3y-5}{4}$ for $y$

**49.** $p^2 = \dfrac{4}{3m-q}$ for $m$

**7.7**   *Solve each problem.*

**50.** In a certain fraction, the denominator is 5 less than the numerator. If 5 is added to both the numerator and the denominator, the resulting fraction is equivalent to $\frac{5}{4}$. Find the original fraction (*not* written in lowest terms).

**51.** The denominator of a certain fraction is six times the numerator. If 3 is added to the numerator and subtracted from the denominator, the resulting fraction is equivalent to $\frac{2}{5}$. Find the original fraction (*not* written in lowest terms).

**52.** A plane flies 350 mi with the wind in the same time that it can fly 310 mi against the wind. The plane has a speed of 165 mph in still air. Find the speed of the wind.

**53.** Susan Costa can plant her garden in 5 hr working alone. A friend can do the same job in 8 hr. How long would it take them if they worked together?

**54.** The head gardener can mow the lawns in the city park twice as fast as his assistant. Working together, they can complete the job in $1\frac{1}{3}$ hr. How long would it take the head gardener working alone?

**7.8**   *Solve each problem.*

**55.** *Concept Check*   The longer the term of your subscription to *Entertainment Weekly*, the less you will have to pay per year. Is this an example of direct or inverse variation?

**56.** If a parallelogram has a fixed area, the height varies inversely as the base. A parallelogram has a height of 8 cm and a base of 12 cm. Find the height if the base is changed to 24 cm.

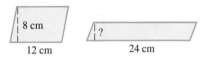

**57.** If $y$ varies directly as $x$, and $x = 12$ when $y = 5$, find $x$ when $y = 3$.

## MIXED REVIEW EXERCISES

*Perform each indicated operation.*

**58.** $\dfrac{4}{m-1} - \dfrac{3}{m+1}$

**59.** $\dfrac{8p^5}{5} \div \dfrac{2p^3}{10}$

**60.** $\dfrac{r-3}{8} \div \dfrac{3r-9}{4}$

**61.** $\dfrac{\dfrac{5}{x}-1}{\dfrac{5-x}{3x}}$

**62.** $\dfrac{4}{z^2-2z+1} - \dfrac{3}{z^2-1}$

**63.** $\dfrac{1}{t^2-4} + \dfrac{1}{2-t}$

*Solve.*

**64.** $\dfrac{2}{z} - \dfrac{z}{z+3} = \dfrac{1}{z+3}$

**65.** $a = \dfrac{v-w}{t}$ for $v$

**66.** Rob Fusco flew his plane 400 km with the wind in the same time it took him to go 200 km against the wind. The speed of the wind is 50 km per hr. Find the rate of the plane in still air.

**67.** With spraying equipment, Lizette Foley can paint the woodwork in a small house in 8 hr. Seyed Sadati needs 14 hr to complete the same job painting by hand. If Lizette and Seyed work together, how long will it take them to paint the woodwork?

**68.** If $w$ varies inversely as $z$, and $w = 16$ when $z = 3$, find $w$ when $z = 2$.

**69.** In a rectangle of constant area, the length and the width vary inversely. When the length is 24, the width is 2. What is the width when the length is 12?

**70.** If $x$ varies directly as the cube of $y$, and $x = 54$ when $y = 3$, find $x$ when $y = -2$.

RELATING CONCEPTS EXERCISES 71–80

**FOR INDIVIDUAL OR GROUP WORK**

*In these exercises, we summarize the various concepts involving rational expressions.*
**Work Exercises 71–80 in order.**

Let $P$, $Q$, and $R$ be rational expressions defined as follows:

$$P = \frac{6}{x + 3}, \qquad Q = \frac{5}{x + 1}, \qquad R = \frac{4x}{x^2 + 4x + 3}.$$

**71.** Find the value or values for which the expression is undefined.

    **(a)** $P$     **(b)** $Q$     **(c)** $R$

**72.** Find and express $(P \cdot Q) \div R$ in lowest terms.

**73.** Why is $(P \cdot Q) \div R$ not defined if $x = 0$?

**74.** Find the LCD for $P$, $Q$, and $R$.

**75.** Perform the operations and express $P + Q - R$ in lowest terms.

**76.** Simplify the complex fraction $\frac{P + Q}{R}$.

**77.** Solve the equation $P + Q = R$.

**78.** How does your answer to **Exercise 71** help you work **Exercise 77?**

**79.** Suppose that a car travels 6 miles in $(x + 3)$ minutes. Explain why $P$ represents the rate of the car (in miles per minute).

**80.** For what value or values of $x$ is $R = \frac{40}{77}$?

---

# CHAPTER 7

# TEST

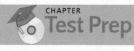

Step-by-step test solutions are found on the Chapter Test Prep Videos available via the Video Resources on DVD, in *MyMathLab*, or on YouTube (search "LialBeginningAlgebra").

*View the complete solutions to all Chapter Test exercises on the Video Resources on DVD.*

**1.** Find the numerical value of $\dfrac{6r + 1}{2r^2 - 3r - 20}$ for **(a)** $r = -2$ and **(b)** $r = 4$.

**2.** Find any values for which $\dfrac{3x - 1}{x^2 - 2x - 8}$ is undefined. Write your answer with the symbol $\neq$.

**3.** Write four rational expressions equivalent to $-\dfrac{6x - 5}{2x + 3}$.

*Write each rational expression in lowest terms.*

**4.** $\dfrac{-15x^6 y^4}{5x^4 y}$

**5.** $\dfrac{6a^2 + a - 2}{2a^2 - 3a + 1}$

*Multiply or divide. Write each answer in lowest terms.*

**6.** $\dfrac{5(d - 2)}{9} \div \dfrac{3(d - 2)}{5}$

**7.** $\dfrac{6k^2 - k - 2}{8k^2 + 10k + 3} \cdot \dfrac{4k^2 + 7k + 3}{3k^2 + 5k + 2}$

**8.** $\dfrac{4a^2 + 9a + 2}{3a^2 + 11a + 10} \div \dfrac{4a^2 + 17a + 4}{3a^2 + 2a - 5}$

**9.** $\dfrac{x^2 - 10x + 25}{9 - 6x + x^2} \cdot \dfrac{x - 3}{5 - x}$

*Find the least common denominator for the fractions in each list.*

**10.** $\dfrac{-3}{10p^2}, \dfrac{21}{25p^3}, \dfrac{-7}{30p^5}$

**11.** $\dfrac{r + 1}{2r^2 + 7r + 6}, \dfrac{-2r + 1}{2r^2 - 7r - 15}$

*Rewrite each rational expression with the given denominator.*

**12.** $\dfrac{15}{4p} = \dfrac{?}{64p^3}$

**13.** $\dfrac{3}{6m - 12} = \dfrac{?}{42m - 84}$

*Add or subtract. Write each answer in lowest terms.*

**14.** $\dfrac{4x + 2}{x + 5} + \dfrac{-2x + 8}{x + 5}$

**15.** $\dfrac{-4}{y + 2} + \dfrac{6}{5y + 10}$

**16.** $\dfrac{x + 1}{3 - x} + \dfrac{x^2}{x - 3}$

**17.** $\dfrac{3}{2m^2 - 9m - 5} - \dfrac{m + 1}{2m^2 - m - 1}$

*Simplify each complex fraction.*

**18.** $\dfrac{\dfrac{2p}{k^2}}{\dfrac{3p^2}{k^3}}$

**19.** $\dfrac{\dfrac{1}{x + 3} - 1}{1 + \dfrac{1}{x + 3}}$

*Solve.*

**20.** $\dfrac{3x}{x + 1} = \dfrac{3}{2x}$

**21.** $\dfrac{2x}{x - 3} + \dfrac{1}{x + 3} = \dfrac{-6}{x^2 - 9}$

**22.** $F = \dfrac{k}{d - D}$ for $D$

*Solve each problem.*

**23.** A boat goes 7 mph in still water. It takes as long to go 20 mi upstream as 50 mi downstream. Find the rate of the current.

**24.** Sanford Geraci can paint a room in his house, working alone, in 5 hr. His neighbor can do the job in 4 hr. How long will it take them to paint the room if they work together?

**25.** If $x$ varies directly as $y$, and $x = 12$ when $y = 4$, find $x$ when $y = 9$.

**26.** Under certain conditions, the length of time that it takes for fruit to ripen during the growing season varies inversely as the average maximum temperature during the season. If it takes 25 days for fruit to ripen with an average maximum temperature of 80°, find the number of days it would take at 75°. Round your answer to the nearest whole number.

# CHAPTERS (1–7)

# CUMULATIVE REVIEW EXERCISES

**1.** Use the order of operations to evaluate $3 + 4\left(\frac{1}{2} - \frac{3}{4}\right)$.

*Solve.*

**2.** $3(2y - 5) = 2 + 5y$

**3.** $\mathscr{A} = \dfrac{1}{2}bh$ for $b$

**4.** $\dfrac{2 + m}{2 - m} = \dfrac{3}{4}$

**5.** $5y \le 6y + 8$

**6.** Consider the graph of $4x + 3y = -12$.

    **(a)** What is the $x$-intercept?    **(b)** What is the $y$-intercept?

*Sketch each graph.*

**7.** $y = -3x + 2$

**8.** $y = -x^2 + 1$

*Solve each system.*

**9.** $4x - y = -7$
    $5x + 2y = 1$

**10.** $5x + 2y = 7$
    $10x + 4y = 12$

*Simplify each expression. Write with only positive exponents.*

**11.** $\dfrac{(2x^3)^{-1} \cdot x}{2^3 x^5}$

**12.** $\dfrac{(m^{-2})^3 m}{m^5 m^{-4}}$

*Perform each indicated operation.*

**13.** $(2k^2 + 3k) - (k^2 + k - 1)$

**14.** $(2a - b)^2$

**15.** $(y^2 + 3y + 5)(3y - 1)$

**16.** $\dfrac{12p^3 + 2p^2 - 12p + 4}{2p - 2}$

*Factor completely.*

**17.** $8t^2 + 10tv + 3v^2$

**18.** $8r^2 - 9rs + 12s^2$

**19.** $16x^4 - 1$

*Solve each equation.*

**20.** $r^2 = 2r + 15$

**21.** $(r - 5)(2r + 1)(3r - 2) = 0$

*Solve each problem.*

**22.** One number is 4 greater than another. The product of the numbers is 2 less than the lesser number. Find the lesser number.

**23.** The length of a rectangle is 2 m less than twice the width. The area is 60 m². Find the width of the rectangle.

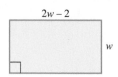

**24.** Which one of the following is equal to 1 for *all* real numbers?

**A.** $\dfrac{k^2 + 2}{k^2 + 2}$    **B.** $\dfrac{4 - m}{4 - m}$    **C.** $\dfrac{2x + 9}{2x + 9}$    **D.** $\dfrac{x^2 - 1}{x^2 - 1}$

**25.** Which one of the following rational expressions is *not* equivalent to $\dfrac{4 - 3x}{7}$?

**A.** $-\dfrac{-4 + 3x}{7}$    **B.** $-\dfrac{4 - 3x}{-7}$    **C.** $\dfrac{-4 + 3x}{-7}$    **D.** $\dfrac{-(3x + 4)}{7}$

*Perform each operation and write the answer in lowest terms.*

**26.** $\dfrac{5}{q} - \dfrac{1}{q}$

**27.** $\dfrac{3}{7} + \dfrac{4}{r}$

**28.** $\dfrac{4}{5q - 20} - \dfrac{1}{3q - 12}$

**29.** $\dfrac{2}{k^2 + k} - \dfrac{3}{k^2 - k}$

**30.** $\dfrac{7z^2 + 49z + 70}{16z^2 + 72z - 40} \div \dfrac{3z + 6}{4z^2 - 1}$

**31.** $\dfrac{\dfrac{4}{a} + \dfrac{5}{2a}}{\dfrac{7}{6a} - \dfrac{1}{5a}}$

*Solve each equation. Check your solutions.*

**32.** $\dfrac{r + 2}{5} = \dfrac{r - 3}{3}$

**33.** $\dfrac{1}{x} = \dfrac{1}{x + 1} + \dfrac{1}{2}$

*Solve each problem.*

**34.** Jody Harris can weed the yard in 3 hr. Pat Tabler can weed the same yard in 2 hr. How long will it take them if they work together?

**35.** The circumference of a circle varies directly as its radius. A circle with circumference 9.42 in. has radius approximately 1.5 in. Find the circumference of a circle with radius 5.25 in. Give the answer to the nearest hundredth.

$C = 9.42$ in.

# Roots and Radicals

The London Eye is a unique Ferris wheel that features 32 observation capsules and has a diameter of 135 m. Located on the bank of the Thames River, it faces the Houses of Parliament. (*Source:* www.londoneye.com)

The formula

$$\text{sight distance} = 111.7\sqrt{\text{height of structure in kilometers}}$$

can be used to determine how far one can see (in kilometers) from the top of a structure on a clear day. (*Source: A Sourcebook of Applications of School Mathematics,* NCTM.) In **Exercise 75** of **Section 8.6,** we use this formula to determine the truth of the claim that passengers on the London Eye can see Windsor Castle, 25 mi away.

493

## 8.1 Evaluating Roots

**OBJECTIVE 1** Find square roots. In **Section 1.2,** we discussed the idea of the *square* of a number. Recall that squaring a number means multiplying the number by itself.

$$7^2 = 7 \cdot 7 = 49 \qquad \text{The square of 7 is 49.}$$

The opposite (inverse) of squaring a number is taking its *square root.* This is equivalent to asking

"What number when multiplied by itself equals 49?"

From the example above, one answer is 7, since $7 \cdot 7 = 49$.

This discussion can be generalized.

**Square Root**

A number $b$ is a **square root** of $a$ if $b^2 = a.$

**EXAMPLE 1** Finding All Square Roots of a Number

Find all square roots of 49.

We ask, "What number when multiplied by itself equals 49?" As mentioned above, one square root is 7, because $7 \cdot 7 = 49$. Another square root of 49 is $-7$, because

$$(-7)(-7) = 49.$$

Thus, the number 49 has *two* square roots: 7 and $-7$. One square root is positive, and one is negative. NOW TRY

The **positive** or **principal square root** of a number is written with the symbol $\sqrt{\phantom{x}}$. For example, the positive square root of 121 is 11.

$$\sqrt{121} = 11$$

The symbol $-\sqrt{\phantom{x}}$ is used for the **negative square root** of a number. For example, the negative square root of 121 is $-11$.

$$-\sqrt{121} = -11$$

The symbol $\sqrt{\phantom{x}}$, called a **radical symbol,** always represents the positive square root $\left(\text{except that } \sqrt{0} = 0\right)$. The number inside the radical symbol is called the **radicand,** and the entire expression—radical symbol and radicand—is called a **radical.**

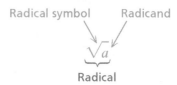

Radical symbol     Radicand

$\sqrt{a}$

Radical

An algebraic expression containing a radical is called a **radical expression.**

The radical symbol $\sqrt{\phantom{x}}$ has been used since 16th-century Germany and was probably derived from the letter $R$. The radical symbol in the margin comes from the Latin word *radix,* for *root.* It was first used by Leonardo of Pisa (Fibonacci) in 1220.

NOW TRY
EXERCISE 1
Find all square roots of 81.

**Early radical symbol**

NOW TRY ANSWER
1. 9, −9

We summarize our discussion of square roots as follows.

---

**Square Roots of *a***

If *a* is a positive real number, then

$$\sqrt{a} \text{ is the positive or principal square root of } a,$$

and $\quad -\sqrt{a}$ is the negative square root of *a*.

For nonnegative *a*,

$$\sqrt{a} \cdot \sqrt{a} = \left(\sqrt{a}\right)^2 = a \quad \text{and} \quad -\sqrt{a} \cdot \left(-\sqrt{a}\right) = \left(-\sqrt{a}\right)^2 = a.$$

Also, $\sqrt{0} = 0$.

---

**NOW TRY
EXERCISE 2**

Find each square root.

(a) $\sqrt{400}$ (b) $-\sqrt{169}$

(c) $\sqrt{\dfrac{100}{121}}$

**EXAMPLE 2** Finding Square Roots

Find each square root.

(a) $\sqrt{144}$

The radical $\sqrt{144}$ represents the positive or principal square root of 144. Think of a positive number whose square is 144.

$$12^2 = 144, \quad \text{so} \quad \sqrt{144} = 12.$$

(b) $-\sqrt{1024}$

This symbol represents the negative square root of 1024. A calculator with a square root key can be used to find $\sqrt{1024} = 32$. Therefore,

$$-\sqrt{1024} = -32.$$

(c) $\sqrt{\dfrac{4}{9}} = \dfrac{2}{3}$ (d) $-\sqrt{\dfrac{16}{49}} = -\dfrac{4}{7}$ (e) $\sqrt{0.81} = 0.9$ NOW TRY

As shown in the preceding definition, when the square root of a positive real number is squared, the result is that positive real number. $\left(\text{Also, } \left(\sqrt{0}\right)^2 = 0.\right)$

**NOW TRY
EXERCISE 3**

Find the square of each radical expression.

(a) $\sqrt{15}$ (b) $-\sqrt{23}$

(c) $\sqrt{2k^2 + 5}$

**EXAMPLE 3** Squaring Radical Expressions

Find the *square* of each radical expression.

(a) $\sqrt{13}$

$$\left(\sqrt{13}\right)^2 = 13 \qquad \text{Definition of square root}$$

(b) $-\sqrt{29}$

$$\left(-\sqrt{29}\right)^2 = 29 \qquad \text{The square of a \textit{negative} number is positive.}$$

(c) $\sqrt{p^2 + 1}$

$$\left(\sqrt{p^2 + 1}\right)^2 = p^2 + 1$$

NOW TRY

NOW TRY ANSWERS
**2.** (a) 20 (b) $-13$ (c) $\frac{10}{11}$
**3.** (a) 15 (b) 23 (c) $2k^2 + 5$

**OBJECTIVE 2** **Decide whether a given root is rational, irrational, or not a real number.** Numbers with square roots that are rational are called **perfect squares**.

Perfect squares ↓            Rational square roots ↓

| 25 | | $\sqrt{25} = 5$ |
| 144 | are perfect squares since | $\sqrt{144} = 12$ |
| $\dfrac{4}{9}$ | | $\sqrt{\dfrac{4}{9}} = \dfrac{2}{3}$ |

A number that is not a perfect square has a square root that is not a rational number. For example, $\sqrt{5}$ is not a rational number because it cannot be written as the ratio of two integers. Its decimal equivalent neither terminates nor repeats. However, $\sqrt{5}$ is a real number and corresponds to a point on the number line.

As mentioned in **Section 1.4,** a real number that is not rational is called an **irrational number.** The number $\sqrt{5}$ is irrational. *Many square roots of integers are irrational.*

If $a$ is a positive real number that is *not* a perfect square, then $\sqrt{a}$ is irrational.

*Not every number has a real number square root.* For example, there is no real number that can be squared to get $-36$. (The square of a real number can never be negative.) Because of this, $\sqrt{-36}$ *is not a real number.*

If $a$ is a *negative* real number, then $\sqrt{a}$ is *not* a real number.

⚠ **CAUTION** Do not confuse $\sqrt{-36}$ and $-\sqrt{36}$. $\sqrt{-36}$ is not a real number, since there is no real number that can be squared to obtain $-36$. However, $-\sqrt{36}$ is the negative square root of 36, which is $-6$.

**NOW TRY EXERCISE 4**

Tell whether each square root is *rational, irrational,* or *not a real number.*

(a) $\sqrt{31}$    (b) $\sqrt{900}$

(c) $\sqrt{-16}$

**EXAMPLE 4** Identifying Types of Square Roots

Tell whether each square root is *rational, irrational,* or *not a real number.*

(a) $\sqrt{17}$   Because 17 is not a perfect square, $\sqrt{17}$ is irrational.

(b) $\sqrt{64}$   The number 64 is a perfect square, $8^2$, so $\sqrt{64} = 8$, a rational number.

(c) $\sqrt{-25}$   There is no real number whose square is $-25$. Therefore, $\sqrt{-25}$ is not a real number.    NOW TRY ↻

**NOTE** Not all irrational numbers are square roots of integers. For example, $\pi$ (approximately 3.14159) is an irrational number that is not a square root of any integer.

**OBJECTIVE 3** **Find decimal approximations for irrational square roots.** Even if a number is irrational, a decimal that *approximates* the number can be found using a calculator.

*NOW TRY ANSWERS*
**4.** (a) irrational   (b) rational
    (c) not a real number

NOW TRY
EXERCISE 5

Find a decimal approximation for each square root. Round answers to the nearest thousandth.

(a) $\sqrt{51}$     (b) $-\sqrt{360}$

EXAMPLE 5   Approximating Irrational Square Roots

Find a decimal approximation for each square root. Round answers to the nearest thousandth.

(a) $\sqrt{11}$

   Using the square root key on a calculator gives $3.31662479 \approx 3.317$, where the symbol $\approx$ means "**is approximately equal to.**"

(b) $\sqrt{39} \approx 6.245$     Use a calculator.     (c) $-\sqrt{740} \approx -27.203$     *NOW TRY*

**OBJECTIVE 4**   Use the Pythagorean theorem. Many applications of square roots require the use of the Pythagorean theorem. Recall from **Section 6.6** and **FIGURE 1** that if $c$ is the length of the hypotenuse of a right triangle, and $a$ and $b$ are the lengths of the two legs, then

$$a^2 + b^2 = c^2.$$

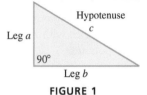

**FIGURE 1**

   In the next example, we use the fact that if $k > 0$, then the positive solution of the equation $x^2 = k$ is $\sqrt{k}$. (See **page 554.**)

NOW TRY
EXERCISE 6

Find the length of the unknown side in each right triangle with sides $a$, $b$, and $c$, where $c$ is the hypotenuse. Give any decimal approximations to the nearest thousandth.

(a) $a = 5, b = 12$
(b) $a = 9, c = 14$

EXAMPLE 6   Using the Pythagorean Theorem

Find the length of the unknown side in each right triangle with sides $a$, $b$, and $c$, where $c$ is the hypotenuse.

(a) $a = 3, b = 4$

$$\begin{aligned} a^2 + b^2 &= c^2 & \text{Use the Pythagorean theorem.} \\ 3^2 + 4^2 &= c^2 & \text{Let } a = 3 \text{ and } b = 4. \\ 9 + 16 &= c^2 & \text{Square.} \\ 25 &= c^2 & \text{Add.} \end{aligned}$$

Since the length of a side of a triangle must be a positive number, find the positive square root of 25 to get $c$.

$$c = \sqrt{25} = 5$$

(b) $b = 5, c = 9$

$$\begin{aligned} a^2 + b^2 &= c^2 & \text{Use the Pythagorean theorem.} \\ \text{Solve for } a^2. \rightarrow a^2 + 5^2 &= 9^2 & \text{Let } b = 5 \text{ and } c = 9. \\ a^2 + 25 &= 81 & \text{Square.} \\ a^2 &= 56 & \text{Subtract 25.} \end{aligned}$$

Use a calculator to approximate the positive square root of 56.

$$a = \sqrt{56} \approx 7.483$$     *NOW TRY*

⚠ **CAUTION**   Be careful not to make the common mistake of thinking that $\sqrt{a^2 + b^2}$ equals $a + b$. Consider the following.

$$\sqrt{9 + 16} = \sqrt{25} = 5, \quad \text{but} \quad \sqrt{9} + \sqrt{16} = 3 + 4 = 7.$$

In general,     $$\sqrt{a^2 + b^2} \neq a + b.$$

NOW TRY ANSWERS
5. (a) 7.141   (b) −18.974
6. (a) $c = 13$   (b) $b \approx 10.724$

*NOW TRY*
*EXERCISE 7*

The length of a rectangle is 48 ft, and the width is 14 ft. Find the measure of the diagonal of the rectangle.

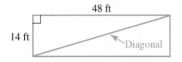

(Note that the diagonal divides the rectangle into two right triangles with itself as the hypotenuse.)

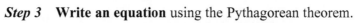

**EXAMPLE 7** Using the Pythagorean Theorem to Solve an Application

A ladder 10 ft long leans against a wall. The foot of the ladder is 6 ft from the base of the wall. How high up the wall does the top of the ladder rest?

*Step 1* **Read** the problem again.

*Step 2* **Assign a variable.** As shown in **FIGURE 2**, a right triangle is formed with the ladder as the hypotenuse. Let *a* represent the height of the top of the ladder, measured straight down to the ground.

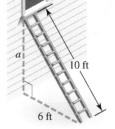

**FIGURE 2**

*Step 3* **Write an equation** using the Pythagorean theorem.

$$a^2 + b^2 = c^2 \quad \text{(Substitute carefully.)}$$
$$a^2 + 6^2 = 10^2 \qquad \text{Let } c = 10 \text{ and } b = 6.$$

*Step 4* **Solve.**
$$a^2 + 36 = 100 \qquad \text{Square.}$$
$$a^2 = 64 \qquad \text{Subtract 36.}$$
$$a = \sqrt{64} \qquad \text{Solve for } a.$$
$$a = 8 \qquad \sqrt{64} = 8$$

We choose the positive square root of 64 because *a* represents a length.

*Step 5* **State the answer.** The top of the ladder rests 8 ft up the wall.

*Step 6* **Check.** From **FIGURE 2**, we must have the following.
$$8^2 + 6^2 \overset{?}{=} 10^2 \qquad a^2 + b^2 = c^2$$
$$64 + 36 = 100 \quad \checkmark \quad \text{True}$$

The check confirms that the top of the ladder rests 8 ft up the wall.

*NOW TRY*

---

**CONNECTIONS**

Although Pythagoras may have written the first proof of the Pythagorean relationship, there is evidence that the Babylonians knew the concept quite well. The figure illustrates the theorem with a tile pattern. The side of the square along the hypotenuse measures 5 units, while the sides along the legs measure 3 and 4 units. If we let $a = 3$, $b = 4$, and $c = 5$, the Pythagorean theorem is satisfied.

$$a^2 + b^2 = c^2$$
$$3^2 + 4^2 \overset{?}{=} 5^2$$
$$25 = 25 \quad \checkmark \quad \text{True}$$

**For Discussion or Writing**

The diagram to the right can be used to verify the Pythagorean theorem, as follows.

1. Find the area of the large square.

2. Find the sum of the areas of the smaller square and the four right triangles.

3. Set the areas equal and simplify the equation.

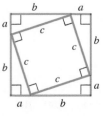

*NOW TRY ANSWER*
**7.** 50 ft

**OBJECTIVE 5** Use the distance formula. Consider **FIGURE 3**. The distance between the points $(x_2, y_2)$ and $(x_2, y_1)$ is $a = y_2 - y_1$, and the distance between the points $(x_1, y_1)$ and $(x_2, y_1)$ is $b = x_2 - x_1$. From the Pythagorean theorem,

$$d^2 = (x_2 - x_1)^2 + (y_2 - y_1)^2.$$

Taking the square root of each side gives the **distance formula.**

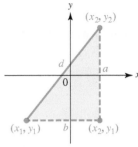

**FIGURE 3**

---

**Distance Formula**

The distance between the points $(x_1, y_1)$ and $(x_2, y_2)$ is

$$d = \sqrt{(x_2 - x_1)^2 + (y_2 - y_1)^2}.$$

---

⌐ NOW TRY
↳ EXERCISE 8

Find the distance between $(-4, 3)$ and $(-7, 1)$.

**EXAMPLE 8** Using the Distance Formula

Find the distance between $(-3, 4)$ and $(2, 5)$.

$$d = \sqrt{(x_2 - x_1)^2 + (y_2 - y_1)^2} \quad \text{Distance formula}$$

$$= \sqrt{(2 - (-3))^2 + (5 - 4)^2} \quad \begin{array}{l}\text{Let } (x_1, y_1) = (-3, 4) \\ \text{and } (x_2, y_2) = (2, 5).\end{array}$$

Start with the x-value and the y-value of the *same* point.

$$= \sqrt{5^2 + 1^2}$$

$$= \sqrt{26}$$

NOW TRY ↻

**OBJECTIVE 6** Find cube, fourth, and other roots. Finding the square root of a number is the opposite (inverse) of squaring a number. In a similar way, there are inverses to finding the cube of a number or to finding the fourth or greater power of a number. These inverses are, respectively, the **cube root**, written $\sqrt[3]{a}$, and the **fourth root**, written $\sqrt[4]{a}$. Similar symbols are used for other roots.

---

$\sqrt[n]{a}$

The $n$th root of $a$, written $\sqrt[n]{a}$, is a number whose $n$th power equals $a$. That is,

$$\sqrt[n]{a} = b \quad \text{means} \quad b^n = a.$$

---

In $\sqrt[n]{a}$, the number $n$ is the **index** or **order** of the radical.

We could write $\sqrt[2]{a}$ instead of $\sqrt{a}$, but the simpler symbol $\sqrt{a}$ is customary, since the square root is the most commonly used root.

---

NOW TRY ANSWER

8. $\sqrt{13}$

**NOTE** When working with cube roots or fourth roots, it is helpful to memorize the first few **perfect cubes** ($2^3 = 8$, $3^3 = 27$, and so on) and the first few **perfect fourth powers** ($2^4 = 16$, $3^4 = 81$, and so on). See **Exercises 93 and 94.**

NOW TRY
EXERCISE 9

Find each cube root.

(a) $\sqrt[3]{343}$   (b) $\sqrt[3]{-1000}$

(c) $\sqrt[3]{27}$

---

**EXAMPLE 9** Finding Cube Roots

Find each cube root.

(a) $\sqrt[3]{8}$   What number can be cubed to give 8? Because $2^3 = 8$, $\sqrt[3]{8} = 2$.

(b) $\sqrt[3]{-8} = -2$, because $(-2)^3 = -8$.

(c) $\sqrt[3]{216} = 6$, because $6^3 = 216$.   NOW TRY

Notice in **Example 9(b)** that we can find the cube root of a negative number. (Contrast this with the square root of a negative number, which is not real.) In fact, the cube root of a positive number is positive, and the cube root of a negative number is negative. *There is only one real number cube root for each real number.*

When a radical has an *even index* (square root, fourth root, and so on), *the radicand must be nonnegative* to yield a real number root. Also, for $a > 0$,

$$\sqrt{a}, \ \sqrt[4]{a}, \ \sqrt[6]{a}, \text{ and so on are positive (principal) roots.}$$
$$-\sqrt{a}, \ -\sqrt[4]{a}, \ -\sqrt[6]{a}, \text{ and so on are negative roots.}$$

---

NOW TRY
EXERCISE 10

Find each root.

(a) $\sqrt[4]{625}$   (b) $\sqrt[4]{-625}$

(c) $\sqrt[5]{3125}$   (d) $\sqrt[5]{-3125}$

---

**EXAMPLE 10** Finding Other Roots

Find each root.

(a) $\sqrt[4]{16} = 2$, because 2 is positive and $2^4 = 16$.

(b) $-\sqrt[4]{16}$   From part (a), $\sqrt[4]{16} = 2$, so the negative root is $-\sqrt[4]{16} = -2$.

(c) $\sqrt[4]{-16}$   For a fourth root to be a real number, the radicand must be nonnegative. There is no real number that equals $\sqrt[4]{-16}$.

(d) $-\sqrt[5]{32}$
First find $\sqrt[5]{32}$. Because 2 is the number whose fifth power is 32, $\sqrt[5]{32} = 2$. Since $\sqrt[5]{32} = 2$, it follows that

$$-\sqrt[5]{32} = -2.$$

(e) $\sqrt[5]{-32} = -2$, because $(-2)^5 = -32$.   NOW TRY

NOW TRY ANSWERS
9. (a) 7  (b) −10  (c) 3
10. (a) 5  (b) not a real number
   (c) 5  (d) −5

---

## 8.1 EXERCISES

*MyMathLab*  PRACTICE  WATCH  DOWNLOAD  READ  REVIEW

🌐 *Complete solution available on the Video Resources on DVD*

*Concept Check* *Decide whether each statement is* true *or* false. *If false, tell why.*

1. Every positive number has two real square roots.

2. A negative number has negative real square roots.

3. Every nonnegative number has two real square roots.

4. The positive square root of a positive number is its principal square root.

5. The cube root of every nonzero real number has the same sign as the number itself.

6. Every positive number has three real cube roots.

*Find all square roots of each number.* **See Example 1.**

🌐 **7.** 9      **8.** 16      **9.** 64      **10.** 100      **11.** 169

**12.** 225   **13.** $\dfrac{25}{196}$   **14.** $\dfrac{81}{400}$   **15.** 900   **16.** 1600

*Find each square root.* **See Examples 2 and 4(c).**

**17.** $\sqrt{1}$　　**18.** $\sqrt{4}$　　🌐 **19.** $\sqrt{49}$　　**20.** $\sqrt{81}$　　**21.** $-\sqrt{256}$

**22.** $-\sqrt{196}$　　**23.** $-\sqrt{\dfrac{144}{121}}$　　**24.** $-\sqrt{\dfrac{49}{36}}$　　**25.** $\sqrt{0.64}$　　**26.** $\sqrt{0.16}$

**27.** $\sqrt{-121}$　　　**28.** $\sqrt{-64}$　　　**29.** $-\sqrt{-49}$　　**30.** $-\sqrt{-100}$

*Find the square of each radical expression.* **See Example 3.**

🌐 **31.** $\sqrt{19}$　　**32.** $\sqrt{59}$　　**33.** $-\sqrt{19}$　　**34.** $-\sqrt{59}$

**35.** $\sqrt{\dfrac{2}{3}}$　　**36.** $\sqrt{\dfrac{5}{7}}$　　**37.** $\sqrt{3x^2 + 4}$　　**38.** $\sqrt{9y^2 + 3}$

*Concept Check*　*What must be true about the variable a for each statement to be true?*

**39.** $\sqrt{a}$ represents a positive number.　　**40.** $-\sqrt{a}$ represents a negative number.

**41.** $\sqrt{a}$ is not a real number.　　　　**42.** $-\sqrt{a}$ is not a real number.

*Determine whether each number is* rational, irrational, *or* not a real number. *If a number is rational, give its exact value. If a number is irrational, give a decimal approximation to the nearest thousandth. Use a calculator as necessary.* **See Examples 4 and 5.**

🌐 **43.** $\sqrt{25}$　　**44.** $\sqrt{169}$　　**45.** $\sqrt{29}$　　**46.** $\sqrt{33}$

**47.** $-\sqrt{64}$　　**48.** $-\sqrt{81}$　　🌐 **49.** $-\sqrt{300}$　　**50.** $-\sqrt{500}$

**51.** $\sqrt{-29}$　　**52.** $\sqrt{-47}$　　**53.** $\sqrt{1200}$　　**54.** $\sqrt{1500}$

*Concept Check*　*Without using a calculator, determine between which two consecutive integers each square root lies. For example,*

$$\sqrt{75} \text{ is between 8 and 9, because } \sqrt{64} = 8, \sqrt{81} = 9, \text{ and } 64 < 75 < 81.$$

**55.** $\sqrt{94}$　　**56.** $\sqrt{43}$　　**57.** $\sqrt{51}$　　**58.** $\sqrt{30}$

**59.** $-\sqrt{40}$　　**60.** $-\sqrt{63}$　　**61.** $\sqrt{23.2}$　　**62.** $\sqrt{10.3}$

*Work Exercises 63 and 64 without using a calculator.*

**63.** Choose the best estimate for the length and width (in meters) of this rectangle.

　**A.** 11 by 6　　**B.** 11 by 7

　**C.** 10 by 7　　**D.** 10 by 6

**64.** Choose the best estimate for the base and height (in feet) of this triangle.

　**A.** $b = 8, h = 5$　　**B.** $b = 8, h = 4$

　**C.** $b = 9, h = 5$　　**D.** $b = 9, h = 4$

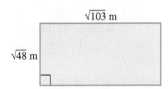

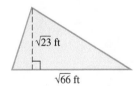

*Find the length of the unknown side of each right triangle with sides a, b, and c, where c is the hypotenuse. Give any decimal approximations to the nearest thousandth.* **See FIGURE 1 and Example 6.**

🌐 **65.** $a = 8, b = 15$　　**66.** $a = 24, b = 10$　　**67.** $a = 6, c = 10$

**68.** $a = 5, c = 13$　　　**69.** $a = 11, b = 4$　　　**70.** $a = 13, b = 9$

*Solve each problem. Give any decimal approximations to the nearest tenth.* ***See Example 7.***

**71.** The diagonal of a rectangle measures 25 cm. The width of the rectangle is 7 cm. Find the length of the rectangle.

**72.** The length of a rectangle is 40 m, and the width is 9 m. Find the measure of the diagonal of the rectangle.

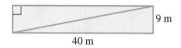

**73.** Tyler is flying a kite on 100 ft of string. How high is it above his hand (vertically) if the horizontal distance between Tyler and the kite is 60 ft?

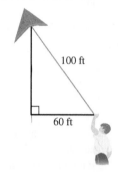

**74.** A guy wire is attached to the mast of a shortwave transmitting antenna at a point 96 ft above ground level. If the wire is staked to the ground 72 ft from the base of the mast, how long is the wire?

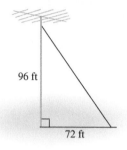

**75.** A surveyor measured the distances shown in the figure. Find the distance across the lake between points *R* and *S*.

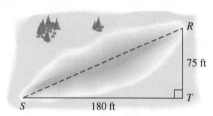

**76.** A boat is being pulled toward a dock with a rope attached at water level. When the boat is 24 ft from the dock, 30 ft of rope is extended. What is the height of the dock above the water?

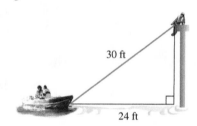

**77.** Following Hurricane Katrina in 2005, thousands of pine trees in southeastern Louisiana formed right triangles as shown in the photo. Suppose that, for a small such tree, the vertical distance from the base of the broken tree to the point of the break is 4.5 ft. The length of the broken part is 12 ft. How far along the ground is it from the base of the tree to the point where the broken part touches the ground?

**78.** One of the authors of this text purchased a rear-projection Toshiba 51H84 television. A television set is "sized" according to the diagonal measurement of the viewing screen. The author purchased a 51-in. TV, so the TV measures 51 in. from one corner of the viewing screen diagonally to the other corner. The viewing screen is 44.5 in. wide. Find the height of the viewing screen.

**79.** A surveyor wants to find the height of a building. At a point 110.0 ft from the base of the building, he sights to the top of the building and finds the distance to be 193.0 ft. How tall is the building?

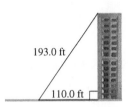

193.0 ft

110.0 ft

**80.** Two towns are separated by dense woods. To go from Town B to Town A, it is necessary to travel due west for 19.0 mi and then turn due north and travel for 14.0 mi. How far apart are the towns?

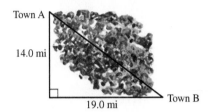

Town A

14.0 mi

19.0 mi

Town B

**81.** What is the value of $x$ (to the nearest thousandth) in the figure?

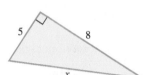

5

8

$x$

**82.** What is the value of $y$ (to the nearest thousandth) in the figure?

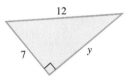

12

7

$y$

*One of the many proofs of the Pythagorean theorem was given in the **Connections box** in this section. Two more are given in Exercises 83 and 84.*

**83.** Another proof of the Pythagorean theorem, attributed to the Hindu mathematician Bhaskara, is based on the figures shown here. The figure on the left is made up of the same square and triangles as the figure on the right. Use this information to derive the Pythagorean theorem.

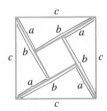

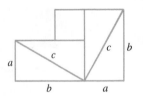

**84.** James A. Garfield, the twentieth president of the United States, provided a proof of the Pythagorean theorem using the given figure. Supply the required information in each of parts (a)–(c) in order to follow his proof.

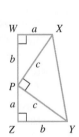

**(a)** Find the area of the trapezoid *WXYZ* using the formula for the area of a trapezoid.

**(b)** Find the area of each of the right triangles *PWX*, *PZY*, and *PXY*.

**(c)** Since the sum of the areas of the three right triangles must equal the area of the trapezoid, set the expression from part (a) equal to the sum of the three expressions from part (b). Simplify the equation as much as possible.

*Find the distance between each pair of points. Express the answer as a whole number or as a square root. Do not use a calculator. See Example 8.*

**85.** $(5, 7)$ and $(1, 4)$

**86.** $(8, 13)$ and $(3, 1)$

**87.** $(2, 9)$ and $(-3, -3)$

**88.** $(4, 6)$ and $(-4, -9)$

**89.** $(-1, -2)$ and $(-3, 1)$

**90.** $(-3, -6)$ and $(-4, 0)$

**91.** $\left(-\frac{1}{4}, \frac{2}{3}\right)$ and $\left(\frac{3}{4}, -\frac{1}{3}\right)$

**92.** $\left(\frac{2}{5}, \frac{3}{2}\right)$ and $\left(-\frac{8}{5}, \frac{1}{2}\right)$

**93.** *Concept Check* To help find cube roots, complete this list of perfect cubes.

$1^3 =$ _____ $\quad 2^3 =$ _____ $\quad 3^3 =$ _____ $\quad 4^3 =$ _____ $\quad 5^3 =$ _____

$6^3 =$ _____ $\quad 7^3 =$ _____ $\quad 8^3 =$ _____ $\quad 9^3 =$ _____ $\quad 10^3 =$ _____

**94.** *Concept Check* To help find fourth roots, complete this list of perfect fourth powers.

$1^4 =$ _____ $\quad 2^4 =$ _____ $\quad 3^4 =$ _____ $\quad 4^4 =$ _____ $\quad 5^4 =$ _____

$6^4 =$ _____ $\quad 7^4 =$ _____ $\quad 8^4 =$ _____ $\quad 9^4 =$ _____ $\quad 10^4 =$ _____

*Find each root.* **See Examples 9 and 10.**

**95.** $\sqrt[3]{1}$ $\qquad$ **96.** $\sqrt[3]{27}$ $\qquad$ **97.** $\sqrt[3]{125}$ $\qquad$ **98.** $\sqrt[3]{1000}$

**99.** $\sqrt[3]{-27}$ $\qquad$ **100.** $\sqrt[3]{-64}$ $\qquad$ **101.** $\sqrt[3]{-216}$ $\qquad$ **102.** $\sqrt[3]{-343}$

**103.** $-\sqrt[3]{-8}$ $\qquad$ **104.** $-\sqrt[3]{-343}$ $\qquad$ **105.** $\sqrt[4]{625}$ $\qquad$ **106.** $\sqrt[4]{256}$

**107.** $\sqrt[4]{1296}$ $\qquad$ **108.** $\sqrt[4]{10,000}$ $\qquad$ **109.** $\sqrt[4]{-1}$ $\qquad$ **110.** $\sqrt[4]{-625}$

**111.** $-\sqrt[4]{81}$ $\qquad$ **112.** $-\sqrt[4]{256}$ $\qquad$ **113.** $\sqrt[5]{-1024}$ $\qquad$ **114.** $\sqrt[5]{-100,000}$

*Use a calculator with a cube root key to find each root. Round to the nearest thousandth.*

**115.** $\sqrt[3]{12}$ $\qquad\qquad$ **116.** $\sqrt[3]{74}$ $\qquad\qquad$ **117.** $\sqrt[3]{130.6}$

**118.** $\sqrt[3]{251.8}$ $\qquad\qquad$ **119.** $\sqrt[3]{-87}$ $\qquad\qquad$ **120.** $\sqrt[3]{-95}$

### PREVIEW EXERCISES

*Write each number in prime factored form.* **See Section 6.1.**

**121.** 72 $\qquad$ **122.** 100 $\qquad$ **123.** 40 $\qquad$ **124.** 242 $\qquad$ **125.** 23 $\qquad$ **126.** 41

---

## 8.2 Multiplying, Dividing, and Simplifying Radicals

**OBJECTIVES**

1. Multiply square root radicals.
2. Simplify radicals by using the product rule.
3. Simplify radicals by using the quotient rule.
4. Simplify radicals involving variables.
5. Simplify other roots.

**OBJECTIVE 1** **Multiply square root radicals.** In this section, we develop several rules for finding products and quotients of radicals. Notice that

$$\sqrt{4} \cdot \sqrt{9} = 2 \cdot 3 = 6 \quad \text{and} \quad \sqrt{4 \cdot 9} = \sqrt{36} = 6,$$

showing that $\quad \sqrt{4} \cdot \sqrt{9} = \sqrt{4 \cdot 9}.$

This result is a particular case of the **product rule for radicals.**

---

**Product Rule for Radicals**

For nonnegative real numbers $a$ and $b$,

$$\sqrt{a} \cdot \sqrt{b} = \sqrt{a \cdot b} \quad \text{and} \quad \sqrt{a \cdot b} = \sqrt{a} \cdot \sqrt{b}.$$

That is, the product of two square roots is the square root of the product, and the square root of a product is the product of the two square roots.

---

⚠ **CAUTION** In general, $\sqrt{x + y} \neq \sqrt{x} + \sqrt{y}$. To see why this is so, let $x = 16$ and $y = 9$.

$$\sqrt{16 + 9} = \sqrt{25} = 5, \quad \text{but} \quad \sqrt{16} + \sqrt{9} = 4 + 3 = 7.$$

**NOW TRY
EXERCISE 1**

Find each product.

(a) $\sqrt{5} \cdot \sqrt{11}$

(b) $\sqrt{11} \cdot \sqrt{11}$

(c) $\sqrt{7} \cdot \sqrt{k}, \quad k \geq 0$

---

**EXAMPLE 1** Using the Product Rule to Multiply Radicals

Use the product rule for radicals to find each product.

(a) $\sqrt{2} \cdot \sqrt{3}$
$= \sqrt{2 \cdot 3}$
$= \sqrt{6}$

(b) $\sqrt{7} \cdot \sqrt{5}$
$= \sqrt{35}$

(c) $\sqrt{11} \cdot \sqrt{a}$
$= \sqrt{11a}$
Assume $a \geq 0$.

(d) $\sqrt{31} \cdot \sqrt{31}$
$= 31$

NOW TRY

---

**OBJECTIVE 2** Simplify radicals by using the product rule. *A square root radical is simplified when no perfect square factor other than 1 remains under the radical symbol.*

**NOW TRY
EXERCISE 2**

Simplify each radical.

(a) $\sqrt{28}$ (b) $\sqrt{99}$

(c) $\sqrt{85}$

---

**EXAMPLE 2** Using the Product Rule to Simplify Radicals

Simplify each radical.

(a) $\sqrt{20}$ — 20 has a perfect square factor of 4.

$= \sqrt{4 \cdot 5}$ Factor; 4 is a perfect square.

$= \sqrt{4} \cdot \sqrt{5}$ Product rule in the form $\sqrt{a \cdot b} = \sqrt{a} \cdot \sqrt{b}$

$= 2\sqrt{5}$ $\sqrt{4} = 2$

Thus, $\sqrt{20} = 2\sqrt{5}$. Because 5 has no perfect square factor (other than 1), $2\sqrt{5}$ is called the **simplified form** of $\sqrt{20}$. Note that $2\sqrt{5}$ represents a product whose factors are 2 and $\sqrt{5}$.

We could also factor 20 into prime factors and look for pairs of like factors. Each pair of like factors produces one factor outside the radical in the simplified form.

$$\sqrt{20} = \sqrt{2 \cdot 2 \cdot 5} = 2\sqrt{5}$$

(b) $\sqrt{72}$ — Look for the *greatest* perfect square factor of 72.

$= \sqrt{36 \cdot 2}$ Factor; 36 is a perfect square.

$= \sqrt{36} \cdot \sqrt{2}$ Product rule

$= 6\sqrt{2}$ $\sqrt{36} = 6$

We could also factor 72 into its prime factors and look for pairs of like factors.

$$\sqrt{72} = \sqrt{2 \cdot 2 \cdot 2 \cdot 3 \cdot 3} = 2 \cdot 3 \cdot \sqrt{2} = 6\sqrt{2}$$

In either case, we obtain $6\sqrt{2}$ as the simplified form of $\sqrt{72}$.

(c) $\sqrt{300}$

$= \sqrt{100 \cdot 3}$ Factor; 100 is a perfect square.

$= \sqrt{100} \cdot \sqrt{3}$ Product rule

$= 10\sqrt{3}$ $\sqrt{100} = 10$

(d) $\sqrt{15}$ The number 15 has no perfect square factors (except 1), so $\sqrt{15}$ cannot be simplified further.

NOW TRY

---

**NOW TRY ANSWERS**

1. (a) $\sqrt{55}$ (b) 11 (c) $\sqrt{7k}$

2. (a) $2\sqrt{7}$ (b) $3\sqrt{11}$
   (c) It cannot be simplified further.

NOW TRY
EXERCISE 3

Find each product and simplify.

**(a)** $\sqrt{16} \cdot \sqrt{50}$

**(b)** $\sqrt{6} \cdot \sqrt{30}$

---

**EXAMPLE 3** Multiplying and Simplifying Radicals

Find each product and simplify.

**(a)** $\sqrt{9} \cdot \sqrt{75}$

$= 3\sqrt{75}$      $\sqrt{9} = 3$

$= 3\sqrt{25 \cdot 3}$      Factor; 25 is a perfect square.

$= 3\sqrt{25} \cdot \sqrt{3}$      Product rule

$= 3 \cdot 5\sqrt{3}$      $\sqrt{25} = 5$

$= 15\sqrt{3}$      Multiply.

We could have used the product rule to get $\sqrt{9} \cdot \sqrt{75} = \sqrt{675}$ and then simplified. However, the product rule as used here allows us to obtain the final answer without using a large number like 675.

**(b)** $\sqrt{8} \cdot \sqrt{12}$

$= \sqrt{8 \cdot 12}$      Product rule

$= \sqrt{4 \cdot 2 \cdot 4 \cdot 3}$      Factor; 4 is a perfect square.

$= \sqrt{4} \cdot \sqrt{4} \cdot \sqrt{2 \cdot 3}$      Product rule

$= 2 \cdot 2 \cdot \sqrt{6}$      $\sqrt{4} = 2$; Multiply.

$= 4\sqrt{6}$      Multiply.

**(c)** $2\sqrt{3} \cdot 3\sqrt{6}$

$= 2 \cdot 3 \cdot \sqrt{3 \cdot 6}$      Commutative property; product rule

$= 6\sqrt{18}$      Multiply.

$= 6\sqrt{9 \cdot 2}$      Factor; 9 is a perfect square.

$= 6\sqrt{9} \cdot \sqrt{2}$      Product rule

$= 6 \cdot 3 \cdot \sqrt{2}$      $\sqrt{9} = 3$

$= 18\sqrt{2}$      Multiply.      NOW TRY

---

**NOTE** We could also simplify the product in **Example 3(b)** as follows.

$$\sqrt{8} \cdot \sqrt{12}$$

$$= \sqrt{4 \cdot 2} \cdot \sqrt{4 \cdot 3} \qquad \text{Factor.}$$

$$= \sqrt{4} \cdot \sqrt{2} \cdot \sqrt{4} \cdot \sqrt{3} \qquad \text{Product rule}$$

$$= 2\sqrt{2} \cdot 2\sqrt{3} \qquad \sqrt{4} = 2$$

$$= 2 \cdot 2 \cdot \sqrt{2} \cdot \sqrt{3} \qquad \text{Commutative property}$$

$$\text{Same result} \rightarrow = 4\sqrt{6} \qquad \text{Multiply.}$$

There is often more than one way to find such a product.

NOW TRY ANSWERS
**3. (a)** $20\sqrt{2}$ **(b)** $6\sqrt{5}$

**OBJECTIVE 3** Simplify radicals by using the quotient rule. The **quotient rule for radicals** is similar to the product rule.

### Quotient Rule for Radicals

If $a$ and $b$ are nonnegative real numbers and $b \neq 0$, then

$$\sqrt{\frac{a}{b}} = \frac{\sqrt{a}}{\sqrt{b}} \quad \text{and} \quad \frac{\sqrt{a}}{\sqrt{b}} = \sqrt{\frac{a}{b}}.$$

That is, the square root of a quotient is the quotient of the two square roots, and the quotient of two square roots is the square root of the quotient.

*NOW TRY*
*EXERCISE 4*
Simplify each radical.

**(a)** $\sqrt{\dfrac{81}{100}}$   **(b)** $\dfrac{\sqrt{245}}{\sqrt{5}}$

**(c)** $\sqrt{\dfrac{11}{49}}$

**EXAMPLE 4** Using the Quotient Rule to Simplify Radicals

Use the quotient rule to simplify each radical.

**(a)** $\sqrt{\dfrac{25}{9}}$

$= \dfrac{\sqrt{25}}{\sqrt{9}}$

$= \dfrac{5}{3}$

**(b)** $\dfrac{\sqrt{288}}{\sqrt{2}}$

$= \sqrt{\dfrac{288}{2}}$

$= \sqrt{144}$

$= 12$

**(c)** $\sqrt{\dfrac{3}{4}}$

$= \dfrac{\sqrt{3}}{\sqrt{4}}$

$= \dfrac{\sqrt{3}}{2}$   *NOW TRY*

*NOW TRY*
*EXERCISE 5*
Simplify.

$$\frac{24\sqrt{39}}{4\sqrt{13}}$$

**EXAMPLE 5** Using the Quotient Rule to Divide Radicals

Simplify.

$$\frac{27\sqrt{15}}{9\sqrt{3}}$$

$= \dfrac{27}{9} \cdot \dfrac{\sqrt{15}}{\sqrt{3}}$   Multiplication of fractions

$= \dfrac{27}{9} \cdot \sqrt{\dfrac{15}{3}}$   Quotient rule

$= 3\sqrt{5}$   Divide.   *NOW TRY*

*NOW TRY*
*EXERCISE 6*
Simplify.

$$\sqrt{\frac{1}{2}} \cdot \sqrt{\frac{5}{18}}$$

**EXAMPLE 6** Using Both the Product and Quotient Rules

Simplify.

$$\sqrt{\frac{3}{5}} \cdot \sqrt{\frac{1}{5}}$$

$= \sqrt{\dfrac{3}{5} \cdot \dfrac{1}{5}}$   Product rule

$= \sqrt{\dfrac{3}{25}}$   Multiply fractions.

$= \dfrac{\sqrt{3}}{\sqrt{25}}$, or $\dfrac{\sqrt{3}}{5}$   Quotient rule; $\sqrt{25} = 5$   *NOW TRY*

*NOW TRY ANSWERS*

**4. (a)** $\dfrac{9}{10}$ **(b)** 7 **(c)** $\dfrac{\sqrt{11}}{7}$

**5.** $6\sqrt{3}$ **6.** $\dfrac{\sqrt{5}}{6}$

**OBJECTIVE 4** Simplify radicals involving variables. Simplifying radicals with variable radicands, such as $\sqrt{x^2}$, can get a little tricky.

If $x$ represents a nonnegative number, then $\sqrt{x^2} = x$.

If $x$ represents a negative number, then $\sqrt{x^2} = -x$, the *opposite* of $x$ (which is positive).

For example, $\sqrt{5^2} = 5$, but $\sqrt{(-5)^2} = \sqrt{25} = 5$, the *opposite* of $-5$.

This means that the square root of a squared number is always nonnegative. We can use absolute value to express this.

---

$\sqrt{a^2}$

For any real number $a$, $\qquad \sqrt{a^2} = |a|.$

---

The product and quotient rules apply when variables appear under radical symbols, as long as the variables represent *nonnegative* real numbers. ***To avoid negative radicands, we assume variables under radical symbols are nonnegative in this text.*** In such cases, absolute value bars are not necessary, since, for $x \geq 0$, $|x| = x$.

**NOW TRY**
**EXERCISE 7**
Simplify each radical. Assume that all variables represent nonnegative real numbers.

**(a)** $\sqrt{16y^8}$ **(b)** $\sqrt{x^5}$

**(c)** $\sqrt{\dfrac{13}{t^2}}, \quad t \neq 0$

**EXAMPLE 7** Simplifying Radicals Involving Variables

Simplify each radical. Assume that all variables represent nonnegative real numbers.

**(a)** $\sqrt{x^4} = x^2$, since $(x^2)^2 = x^4$.

**(b)** $\sqrt{25m^6}$
$= \sqrt{25} \cdot \sqrt{m^6}$    Product rule
$= 5m^3$    $(m^3)^2 = m^6$

**(c)** $\sqrt{8p^{10}}$
$= \sqrt{4 \cdot 2 \cdot p^{10}}$    Factor; 4 is a perfect square.
$= \sqrt{4} \cdot \sqrt{2} \cdot \sqrt{p^{10}}$    Product rule
$= 2 \cdot \sqrt{2} \cdot p^5$    $\sqrt{4} = 2; (p^5)^2 = p^{10}$
$= 2p^5\sqrt{2}$    Commutative property

**(d)** $\sqrt{r^9}$
$= \sqrt{r^8 \cdot r}$
$= \sqrt{r^8} \cdot \sqrt{r}$    Product rule
$= r^4\sqrt{r}$    $(r^4)^2 = r^8$

**(e)** $\sqrt{\dfrac{5}{x^2}}, \quad x \neq 0$
$= \dfrac{\sqrt{5}}{\sqrt{x^2}}$    Quotient rule
$= \dfrac{\sqrt{5}}{x}$    NOW TRY

---

**NOTE** A quick way to find the square root of a variable raised to an even power is to divide the exponent by the index, 2. For example,

$$\sqrt{x^6} = x^3 \quad \text{and} \quad \sqrt{x^{10}} = x^5.$$

$6 \div 2 = 3 \qquad\qquad 10 \div 2 = 5$

**NOW TRY ANSWERS**
**7. (a)** $4y^4$ **(b)** $x^2\sqrt{x}$
**(c)** $\dfrac{\sqrt{13}}{t}$

**OBJECTIVE 5**   Simplify other roots.   The product and quotient rules for radicals also apply to other roots.

### Properties of Radicals

For all real numbers for which the indicated roots exist,

$$\sqrt[n]{a} \cdot \sqrt[n]{b} = \sqrt[n]{ab} \quad \text{and} \quad \frac{\sqrt[n]{a}}{\sqrt[n]{b}} = \sqrt[n]{\frac{a}{b}} \quad (b \neq 0).$$

⌐ **NOW TRY**
  **EXERCISE 8**

Simplify each radical.

**(a)** $\sqrt[3]{250}$     **(b)** $\sqrt[4]{48}$

**(c)** $\sqrt[3]{\dfrac{1}{125}}$

**EXAMPLE 8**   Simplifying Other Roots

Simplify each radical.

**(a)**              $\sqrt[3]{32}$

| Remember to write the root index 3 in each radical. | $= \sqrt[3]{8 \cdot 4}$ | Factor; 8 is a perfect cube. |

$= \sqrt[3]{8} \cdot \sqrt[3]{4}$     Product rule

$= 2\sqrt[3]{4}$     Take the cube root.

**(b)**              $\sqrt[4]{32}$

| Remember to write the root index 4 in each radical. | $= \sqrt[4]{16 \cdot 2}$ | Factor; 16 is a perfect fourth power. |

$= \sqrt[4]{16} \cdot \sqrt[4]{2}$     Product rule

$= 2\sqrt[4]{2}$     Take the fourth root.

**(c)** $\sqrt[3]{\dfrac{27}{125}}$

$= \dfrac{\sqrt[3]{27}}{\sqrt[3]{125}}$     Quotient rule

$= \dfrac{3}{5}$     Take cube roots.     **NOW TRY** ⌐

Other roots of radicals involving variables can also be simplified. To simplify cube roots with variables, use the fact that for any real number $a$,

$$\sqrt[3]{a^3} = a.$$

This is true whether $a$ is positive, negative, or 0.

**EXAMPLE 9**   Simplifying Cube Roots Involving Variables

Simplify each radical.

**(a)** $\sqrt[3]{m^6}$

$= m^2$     $(m^2)^3 = m^6$

**(b)** $\sqrt[3]{27x^{12}}$

$= \sqrt[3]{27} \cdot \sqrt[3]{x^{12}}$     Product rule

$= 3x^4$     $3^3 = 27; (x^4)^3 = x^{12}$

**NOW TRY ANSWERS**
**8.** **(a)** $5\sqrt[3]{2}$   **(b)** $2\sqrt[4]{3}$   **(c)** $\dfrac{1}{5}$

**NOW TRY**
**EXERCISE 9**

Simplify each radical.

**(a)** $\sqrt[3]{x^{12}}$   **(b)** $\sqrt[3]{64t^3}$

**(c)** $\sqrt[3]{40a^7}$   **(d)** $\sqrt[3]{\dfrac{x^{15}}{1000}}$

**NOW TRY ANSWERS**

9. **(a)** $x^4$   **(b)** $4t$

  **(c)** $2a^2\sqrt[3]{5a}$   **(d)** $\dfrac{x^5}{10}$

**(c)** $\sqrt[3]{32a^4}$

$= \sqrt[3]{8a^3 \cdot 4a}$     Factor; $8a^3$ is a perfect cube.

$= \sqrt[3]{8a^3} \cdot \sqrt[3]{4a}$     Product rule

$= 2a\sqrt[3]{4a}$     $(2a)^3 = 8a^3$

**(d)** $\sqrt[3]{\dfrac{y^3}{125}}$

$= \dfrac{\sqrt[3]{y^3}}{\sqrt[3]{125}}$     Quotient rule

$= \dfrac{y}{5}$     Take cube roots.     NOW TRY

---

## 8.2 EXERCISES

MyMathLab | Math XL PRACTICE | WATCH | DOWNLOAD | READ | REVIEW

◉ *Complete solution available on the Video Resources on DVD*

*Find each product.* **See Example 1.**

◉ **1.** $\sqrt{3} \cdot \sqrt{5}$      **2.** $\sqrt{3} \cdot \sqrt{7}$      **3.** $\sqrt{2} \cdot \sqrt{11}$

**4.** $\sqrt{2} \cdot \sqrt{15}$      **5.** $\sqrt{6} \cdot \sqrt{7}$      **6.** $\sqrt{5} \cdot \sqrt{6}$

**7.** $\sqrt{3} \cdot \sqrt{27}$      **8.** $\sqrt{2} \cdot \sqrt{8}$      **9.** $\sqrt{13} \cdot \sqrt{13}$

**10.** $\sqrt{17} \cdot \sqrt{17}$      **11.** $\sqrt{13} \cdot \sqrt{r}, \quad r \geq 0$      **12.** $\sqrt{19} \cdot \sqrt{k}, \quad k \geq 0$

**13.** Which one of the following radicals is simplified? **See Example 2.**

    **A.** $\sqrt{47}$     **B.** $\sqrt{45}$     **C.** $\sqrt{48}$     **D.** $\sqrt{44}$

**14.** *Concept Check* If $p$ is a prime number, is $\sqrt{p}$ in simplified form?

*Simplify each radical.* **See Example 2.**

**15.** $\sqrt{45}$      **16.** $\sqrt{27}$      **17.** $\sqrt{24}$      **18.** $\sqrt{44}$

**19.** $\sqrt{90}$      **20.** $\sqrt{56}$      **21.** $\sqrt{75}$      **22.** $\sqrt{18}$

**23.** $\sqrt{125}$      **24.** $\sqrt{80}$      ◉ **25.** $\sqrt{145}$      **26.** $\sqrt{110}$

**27.** $\sqrt{160}$      **28.** $\sqrt{128}$      **29.** $-\sqrt{700}$      **30.** $-\sqrt{600}$

**31.** $3\sqrt{27}$      **32.** $9\sqrt{8}$      **33.** $5\sqrt{50}$      **34.** $6\sqrt{40}$

*Use the Pythagorean theorem to find the length of the unknown side of each right triangle. Express answers as simplified radicals.* **See Section 8.1.**

**35.**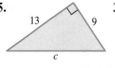

**36.**

**37.**

**38.**

*Use the distance formula to find the length of each line segment. Express answers as simplified radicals.* ***See Section 8.1.***

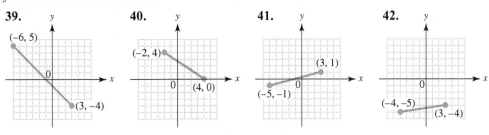

*Find each product and simplify.* ***See Example 3.***

**43.** $\sqrt{9} \cdot \sqrt{32}$     **44.** $\sqrt{9} \cdot \sqrt{50}$     **45.** $\sqrt{3} \cdot \sqrt{18}$

**46.** $\sqrt{3} \cdot \sqrt{21}$     **47.** $\sqrt{12} \cdot \sqrt{48}$     **48.** $\sqrt{50} \cdot \sqrt{72}$

**49.** $\sqrt{12} \cdot \sqrt{30}$     **50.** $\sqrt{30} \cdot \sqrt{24}$     **51.** $2\sqrt{10} \cdot 3\sqrt{2}$

**52.** $5\sqrt{6} \cdot 2\sqrt{10}$     **53.** $5\sqrt{3} \cdot 2\sqrt{15}$     **54.** $4\sqrt{6} \cdot 3\sqrt{2}$

**55.** Simplify the product $\sqrt{8} \cdot \sqrt{32}$ in two ways. First, multiply 8 by 32 and simplify the square root of this product. Second, simplify $\sqrt{8}$, simplify $\sqrt{32}$, and then multiply. How do the answers compare? Make a conjecture (an educated guess) about whether the correct answer can always be obtained using either method when simplifying a product such as this.

**56.** Simplify the radical $\sqrt{288}$ in two ways. First, factor 288 as $144 \cdot 2$ and then simplify. Second, factor 288 as $48 \cdot 6$ and then simplify. How do the answers compare? Make a conjecture concerning the quickest way to simplify such a radical.

*Simplify each radical expression.* ***See Examples 4–6.***

**57.** $\sqrt{\dfrac{16}{225}}$     **58.** $\sqrt{\dfrac{9}{100}}$     **59.** $\sqrt{\dfrac{7}{16}}$     **60.** $\sqrt{\dfrac{13}{25}}$

**61.** $\sqrt{\dfrac{4}{50}}$     **62.** $\sqrt{\dfrac{14}{72}}$     **63.** $\dfrac{\sqrt{75}}{\sqrt{3}}$     **64.** $\dfrac{\sqrt{200}}{\sqrt{2}}$

**65.** $\dfrac{30\sqrt{10}}{5\sqrt{2}}$     **66.** $\dfrac{50\sqrt{20}}{2\sqrt{10}}$     **67.** $\sqrt{\dfrac{5}{2}} \cdot \sqrt{\dfrac{125}{8}}$     **68.** $\sqrt{\dfrac{8}{3}} \cdot \sqrt{\dfrac{512}{27}}$

*Simplify each radical. Assume that all variables represent nonnegative real numbers.* ***See Example 7.***

**69.** $\sqrt{m^2}$     **70.** $\sqrt{k^2}$     **71.** $\sqrt{y^4}$     **72.** $\sqrt{s^4}$

**73.** $\sqrt{36z^2}$     **74.** $\sqrt{49n^2}$     **75.** $\sqrt{400x^6}$     **76.** $\sqrt{900y^8}$

**77.** $\sqrt{18x^8}$     **78.** $\sqrt{20r^{10}}$     **79.** $\sqrt{45c^{14}}$     **80.** $\sqrt{50d^{20}}$

**81.** $\sqrt{z^5}$     **82.** $\sqrt{y^3}$     **83.** $\sqrt{a^{13}}$     **84.** $\sqrt{p^{17}}$

**85.** $\sqrt{64x^7}$     **86.** $\sqrt{25t^{11}}$     **87.** $\sqrt{x^6y^{12}}$     **88.** $\sqrt{a^8b^{10}}$

**89.** $\sqrt{81m^4n^2}$     **90.** $\sqrt{100c^4d^6}$     **91.** $\sqrt{\dfrac{7}{x^{10}}}, \quad x \neq 0$     **92.** $\sqrt{\dfrac{14}{z^{12}}}, \quad z \neq 0$

**93.** $\sqrt{\dfrac{y^4}{100}}$     **94.** $\sqrt{\dfrac{w^8}{144}}$     **95.** $\sqrt{\dfrac{x^4y^6}{169}}$     **96.** $\sqrt{\dfrac{w^8z^{10}}{400}}$

*Simplify each radical. See Example 8.*

**97.** $\sqrt[3]{40}$       **98.** $\sqrt[3]{48}$       **99.** $\sqrt[3]{54}$       **100.** $\sqrt[3]{135}$

**101.** $\sqrt[3]{128}$       **102.** $\sqrt[3]{192}$       **103.** $\sqrt[4]{80}$       **104.** $\sqrt[4]{243}$

**105.** $\sqrt[3]{\dfrac{8}{27}}$       **106.** $\sqrt[3]{\dfrac{64}{125}}$       **107.** $\sqrt[3]{-\dfrac{216}{125}}$       **108.** $\sqrt[3]{-\dfrac{1}{64}}$

*Simplify each radical. See Example 9.*

**109.** $\sqrt[3]{p^3}$       **110.** $\sqrt[3]{w^3}$       **111.** $\sqrt[3]{x^9}$       **112.** $\sqrt[3]{y^{18}}$

**113.** $\sqrt[3]{64z^6}$       **114.** $\sqrt[3]{125a^{15}}$       **115.** $\sqrt[3]{343a^9b^3}$       **116.** $\sqrt[3]{216m^3n^6}$

**117.** $\sqrt[3]{16t^5}$       **118.** $\sqrt[3]{24x^4}$       **119.** $\sqrt[3]{\dfrac{m^{12}}{8}}$       **120.** $\sqrt[3]{\dfrac{n^9}{27}}$

*The volume of a cube is found with the formula $V = s^3$, where s is the length of an edge of the cube. Use this information in Exercises 121 and 122.*

**121.** A container in the shape of a cube has a volume of 216 cm³. What is the length of each side of the container?

**122.** A cube-shaped box must be constructed to contain 128 ft³. What should the dimensions (height, width, and length) of the box be?

*The volume of a sphere is found with the formula $V = \frac{4}{3}\pi r^3$, where r is the length of the radius of the sphere. Use this information in Exercises 123 and 124.*

**123.** A ball in the shape of a sphere has a volume of 288π in.³. What is the radius of the ball?

**124.** Suppose that the volume of the ball described in **Exercise 123** is multiplied by 8. How is the radius affected?

*Work Exercises 125 and 126 without using a calculator.*

**125.** Choose the best estimate for the area (in square inches) of this rectangle.

    **A.** 45    **B.** 72    **C.** 80    **D.** 90

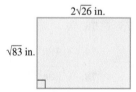

$2\sqrt{26}$ in.

$\sqrt{83}$ in.

**126.** Choose the best estimate for the area (in square feet) of this triangle.

    **A.** 20    **B.** 40    **C.** 60    **D.** 80

$\sqrt{97}$ ft

$2\sqrt{17}$ ft

**PREVIEW EXERCISES**

*Combine like terms. See Section 1.8.*

**127.** $4x + 7 - 9x + 12$       **128.** $9x^2 + 3x^2 - 2x + 4x - 8 + 1$

**129.** $2xy + 3x^2y - 9xy + 8x^2y$       **130.** $x + 3y + 12z$

## 8.3 Adding and Subtracting Radicals

**OBJECTIVE 1**  **Add and subtract radicals.**  We add or subtract radicals as shown.

$$8\sqrt{3} + 6\sqrt{3}$$

$$= (8 + 6)\sqrt{3}$$  Distributive property

$$= 14\sqrt{3}$$  Add.

$$2\sqrt{11} - 7\sqrt{11}$$

$$= (2 - 7)\sqrt{11}$$  Distributive property

$$= -5\sqrt{11}$$  Subtract.

Only **like radicals**—those that are *multiples of the same root of the same number*—can be combined in this way. By contrast, examples of **unlike radicals** are

$$2\sqrt{5} \quad \text{and} \quad 2\sqrt{3}, \quad \text{Radicands are different.}$$

as well as

$$2\sqrt{3} \quad \text{and} \quad 2\sqrt[3]{3}. \quad \text{Indexes are different.}$$

**EXAMPLE 1**  Adding and Subtracting Like Radicals

Add or subtract, as indicated.

**(a)** $3\sqrt{6} + 5\sqrt{6}$

$$= (3 + 5)\sqrt{6} \quad \text{We are factoring out } \sqrt{6} \text{ here.}$$

$$= 8\sqrt{6}$$

**(b)** $5\sqrt{10} - 7\sqrt{10}$

$$= (5 - 7)\sqrt{10}$$

$$= -2\sqrt{10}$$

**(c)** $\sqrt{7} + 2\sqrt{7}$

$$= 1\sqrt{7} + 2\sqrt{7}$$

$$= (1 + 2)\sqrt{7}$$

$$= 3\sqrt{7}$$

**(d)** $\sqrt{5} + \sqrt{5}$

$$= 1\sqrt{5} + 1\sqrt{5}$$

$$= (1 + 1)\sqrt{5}$$

$$= 2\sqrt{5}$$

**(e)** $\sqrt{3} + \sqrt{7}$ cannot be added by the distributive property. They are unlike radicals.

NOW TRY

**NOW TRY**
**EXERCISE 1**

Add or subtract, as indicated.

**(a)** $4\sqrt{3} + \sqrt{3}$

**(b)** $2\sqrt{11} - 6\sqrt{11}$

**(c)** $\sqrt{5} + \sqrt{14}$

**OBJECTIVE 2**  **Simplify radical sums and differences.**

**EXAMPLE 2**  Simplifying Radicals to Add or Subtract

Add or subtract, as indicated.

**(a)** $3\sqrt{2} + \sqrt{8}$

$$= 3\sqrt{2} + \sqrt{4 \cdot 2} \quad \text{Factor; 4 is a perfect square.}$$

$$= 3\sqrt{2} + \sqrt{4} \cdot \sqrt{2} \quad \text{Product rule}$$

$$= 3\sqrt{2} + 2\sqrt{2} \quad \sqrt{4} = 2$$

$$= (3 + 2)\sqrt{2} \quad \text{Distributive property}$$

$$= 5\sqrt{2} \quad \text{Add.}$$

**(b)**

$$\sqrt{18} - \sqrt{27}$$

$$= \sqrt{9 \cdot 2} - \sqrt{9 \cdot 3} \quad \text{Factor; 9 is a perfect square.}$$

$$= \sqrt{9} \cdot \sqrt{2} - \sqrt{9} \cdot \sqrt{3} \quad \text{Product rule}$$

These are unlike radicals. They cannot be combined.

$$= 3\sqrt{2} - 3\sqrt{3} \quad \sqrt{9} = 3$$

**NOW TRY ANSWERS**
**1. (a)** $5\sqrt{3}$ **(b)** $-4\sqrt{11}$
**(c)** It cannot be added by the distributive property.

NOW TRY
EXERCISE 2

Add or subtract, as indicated.

**(a)** $\sqrt{2} + \sqrt{18}$

**(b)** $3\sqrt{48} - 2\sqrt{75}$

**(c)** $8\sqrt[3]{5} + 10\sqrt[3]{40}$

**(c)** $2\sqrt{12} + 3\sqrt{75}$

$\quad = 2\left(\sqrt{4} \cdot \sqrt{3}\right) + 3\left(\sqrt{25} \cdot \sqrt{3}\right)$     Product rule

$\quad = 2\left(2\sqrt{3}\right) + 3\left(5\sqrt{3}\right)$     $\sqrt{4} = 2;\ \sqrt{25} = 5$

$\quad = 4\sqrt{3} + 15\sqrt{3}$     Multiply.

$\quad = 19\sqrt{3}$     Think: $(4 + 15)\sqrt{3}$     Add like radicals.

**(d)** $3\sqrt[3]{16} + 5\sqrt[3]{2}$

$\quad = 3\left(\sqrt[3]{8} \cdot \sqrt[3]{2}\right) + 5\sqrt[3]{2}$     Product rule

$\quad = 3\left(2\sqrt[3]{2}\right) + 5\sqrt[3]{2}$     $\sqrt[3]{8} = 2$

$\quad = 6\sqrt[3]{2} + 5\sqrt[3]{2}$     Multiply.

$\quad = 11\sqrt[3]{2}$     Add like radicals.     NOW TRY

---

**OBJECTIVE 3** Simplify more complicated radical expressions.

---

**EXAMPLE 3** Simplifying Radical Expressions

Simplify. Assume that all variables represent nonnegative real numbers.

**(a)** $\sqrt{5} \cdot \sqrt{15} + 4\sqrt{3}$

$\quad = \sqrt{5 \cdot 15} + 4\sqrt{3}$     Product rule

$\quad = \sqrt{75} + 4\sqrt{3}$     Multiply.

$\quad = \sqrt{25 \cdot 3} + 4\sqrt{3}$     Factor; 25 is a perfect square.

$\quad = \sqrt{25} \cdot \sqrt{3} + 4\sqrt{3}$     Product rule

$\quad = 5\sqrt{3} + 4\sqrt{3}$     $\sqrt{25} = 5$

$\quad = 9\sqrt{3}$     Add like radicals.

**(b)** $\sqrt{12k} + \sqrt{27k}$

$\quad = \sqrt{4 \cdot 3k} + \sqrt{9 \cdot 3k}$     Factor.

$\quad = \sqrt{4} \cdot \sqrt{3k} + \sqrt{9} \cdot \sqrt{3k}$     Product rule

$\quad = 2\sqrt{3k} + 3\sqrt{3k}$     $\sqrt{4} = 2;\ \sqrt{9} = 3$

$\quad = 5\sqrt{3k}$     Add like radicals.

**(c)** $3x\sqrt{50} + \sqrt{2x^2}$

$\quad = 3x\sqrt{25 \cdot 2} + \sqrt{x^2 \cdot 2}$     Factor.

$\quad = 3x\sqrt{25} \cdot \sqrt{2} + \sqrt{x^2} \cdot \sqrt{2}$     Product rule

$\quad = 3x \cdot 5\sqrt{2} + x\sqrt{2}$     $\sqrt{25} = 5;\ \sqrt{x^2} = x$

$\quad = 15x\sqrt{2} + x\sqrt{2}$     Multiply.

$\quad = 16x\sqrt{2}$     Think: $(15x + 1x)\sqrt{2}$     Add like radicals.

NOW TRY ANSWERS
**2. (a)** $4\sqrt{2}$ **(b)** $2\sqrt{3}$
**(c)** $28\sqrt[3]{5}$

**NOW TRY
EXERCISE 3**

Simplify. Assume that all variables represent nonnegative real numbers.

**(a)** $\sqrt{7} \cdot \sqrt{14} + 5\sqrt{2}$

**(b)** $\sqrt{150x} + 2\sqrt{24x}$

**(c)** $5k^2\sqrt{12} - 4\sqrt{27k^4}$

**(d)** $\sqrt[3]{128y^5} + 5y\sqrt[3]{16y^2}$

**NOW TRY ANSWERS**

3. **(a)** $12\sqrt{2}$  **(b)** $9\sqrt{6x}$

   **(c)** $-2k^2\sqrt{3}$  **(d)** $14y\sqrt[3]{2y^2}$

**(d)** $2\sqrt[3]{32m^3} - \sqrt[3]{108m^3}$

$\qquad = 2\sqrt[3]{8m^3 \cdot 4} - \sqrt[3]{27m^3 \cdot 4}$  Factor.

$\qquad = 2 \cdot 2m\sqrt[3]{4} - 3m\sqrt[3]{4}$  $\sqrt[3]{8m^3} = 2m;\ \sqrt[3]{27m^3} = 3m$

$\qquad = 4m\sqrt[3]{4} - 3m\sqrt[3]{4}$  Multiply.

$\qquad = m\sqrt[3]{4}$  Subtract like radicals.  NOW TRY

---

⚠ **CAUTION** *A sum or difference of radicals can be simplified only if the radicals are like radicals.*

$\left.\begin{array}{l} \sqrt{5} + 3\sqrt{5} \\ = 4\sqrt{5} \end{array}\right\}$ Add like radicals.  $\qquad$  $\left.\begin{array}{l} \sqrt{5} + 5\sqrt{3} \\ 2\sqrt{3} + 5\sqrt[3]{3} \end{array}\right\}$ Unlike radicals cannot be simplified.

---

## 8.3 EXERCISES

**MyMathLab**  Math XL PRACTICE  WATCH  DOWNLOAD  READ  REVIEW

⊕ *Complete solution available on the Video Resources on DVD*

*Concept Check*  *Fill in each blank with the correct response.*

**1.** Simplifying the expression $5\sqrt{2} + 6\sqrt{2}$ as $(5 + 6)\sqrt{2}$, or $11\sqrt{2}$, is an application of the _____ property.

**2.** The radicals $\sqrt[4]{3xy^3}$ and $-6\sqrt[4]{3xy^3}$ are examples of like radicals because both radicals have the same root index, _____, and the same radicand, _____.

**3.** $\sqrt{2} - 2\sqrt{3}$ cannot be simplified because the _____ are different.

**4.** $4\sqrt[3]{2} + 3\sqrt{2}$ cannot be simplified because the _____ are different.

*Add or subtract wherever possible.* **See Examples 1, 2, and 3(a).**

⊙ **5.** $2\sqrt{3} + 5\sqrt{3}$  **6.** $6\sqrt{5} + 8\sqrt{5}$  **7.** $4\sqrt{7} - 9\sqrt{7}$

**8.** $6\sqrt{2} - 8\sqrt{2}$  **9.** $\sqrt{6} + \sqrt{6}$  **10.** $\sqrt{11} + \sqrt{11}$

**11.** $\sqrt{17} + 2\sqrt{17}$  **12.** $\sqrt{19} + 3\sqrt{19}$  ⊙ **13.** $5\sqrt{3} + \sqrt{12}$

**14.** $3\sqrt{2} + \sqrt{50}$  **15.** $\sqrt{6} + \sqrt{7}$  **16.** $\sqrt{14} + \sqrt{17}$

**17.** $2\sqrt{75} - \sqrt{12}$  **18.** $2\sqrt{27} - \sqrt{300}$  **19.** $2\sqrt{50} - 5\sqrt{72}$

**20.** $6\sqrt{18} - 4\sqrt{32}$  **21.** $5\sqrt{7} - 2\sqrt{28} + 6\sqrt{63}$  **22.** $3\sqrt{11} - 3\sqrt{99} + 5\sqrt{44}$

**23.** $9\sqrt{24} - 2\sqrt{54} + 3\sqrt{20}$  **24.** $2\sqrt{8} - 5\sqrt{32} + 2\sqrt{48}$

**25.** $5\sqrt{72} - 3\sqrt{48} - 4\sqrt{128}$  **26.** $4\sqrt{50} - 3\sqrt{12} - 5\sqrt{200}$

**27.** $\frac{1}{4}\sqrt{288} + \frac{1}{6}\sqrt{72}$  **28.** $\frac{2}{3}\sqrt{27} + \frac{3}{4}\sqrt{48}$

**29.** $\frac{3}{5}\sqrt{75} - \frac{2}{3}\sqrt{45}$  **30.** $\frac{5}{8}\sqrt{128} - \frac{3}{4}\sqrt{160}$

⊕ **31.** $\sqrt{3} \cdot \sqrt{7} + 2\sqrt{21}$  **32.** $\sqrt{13} \cdot \sqrt{2} + 3\sqrt{26}$

**33.** $\sqrt{6} \cdot \sqrt{2} + 3\sqrt{3}$  **34.** $\sqrt{15} \cdot \sqrt{3} + 2\sqrt{5}$

**35.** $4\sqrt[3]{16} - 3\sqrt[3]{54}$  **36.** $3\sqrt[3]{250} - 4\sqrt[3]{128}$

**37.** $3\sqrt[3]{24} + 6\sqrt[3]{81}$

**38.** $2\sqrt[4]{48} - \sqrt[4]{243}$

**39.** $5\sqrt[4]{32} + 2\sqrt[4]{32} \cdot \sqrt[4]{4}$

**40.** $8\sqrt[3]{48} + 10\sqrt[3]{3} \cdot \sqrt[3]{18}$

*Perform each indicated operation. Assume that all variables represent nonnegative real numbers. **See Example 3.***

**41.** $\sqrt{32x} - \sqrt{18x}$

**42.** $\sqrt{125t} - \sqrt{80t}$

**43.** $\sqrt{27r} + \sqrt{48r}$

**44.** $\sqrt{24x} + \sqrt{54x}$

**45.** $\sqrt{75x^2} + x\sqrt{300}$

**46.** $\sqrt{20y^2} + y\sqrt{125}$

**47.** $3\sqrt{8x^2} - 4x\sqrt{2}$

**48.** $2\sqrt{18b^2} - 3b\sqrt{2}$

**49.** $5\sqrt{75p^2} - 4\sqrt{27p^2}$

**50.** $4\sqrt{32k^2} - 6\sqrt{8k^2}$

**51.** $2\sqrt{125x^2z} + 8x\sqrt{80z}$

**52.** $4p\sqrt{63m} + 6\sqrt{28mp^2}$

**53.** $3k\sqrt{24k^2h^2} + 9h\sqrt{54k^3}$

**54.** $6r\sqrt{27r^2s^2} + 3r\sqrt{12s^3}$

**55.** $6\sqrt[3]{8p^2} - 2\sqrt[3]{27p^2}$

**56.** $5\sqrt[3]{27x^2} + 8\sqrt[3]{8x^2}$

**57.** $5\sqrt[4]{m^3} + 8\sqrt[4]{16m^3}$

**58.** $5\sqrt[4]{x^3} + 3\sqrt[4]{81x^3}$

**59.** $2\sqrt[4]{p^5} - 5p\sqrt[4]{16p}$

**60.** $8k\sqrt[3]{54k} + 6\sqrt[3]{16k^4}$

**61.** $-5\sqrt[3]{256z^4} - 2z\sqrt[3]{32z}$

**62.** $-10\sqrt[3]{4m^4} - 3m\sqrt[3]{32m}$

**63.** $2\sqrt[4]{6k^7} - k\sqrt[4]{96k^3}$

**64.** $\dfrac{3}{2}\sqrt[3]{16a^4b^5} - ab\sqrt[3]{54ab^2}$

*Find the perimeter of each figure.*

**65.**

$7\sqrt{2}$ / $4\sqrt{2}$

**66.**
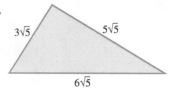
$3\sqrt{5}$ / $5\sqrt{5}$ / $6\sqrt{5}$

*Perform the indicated operations. Express all answers in simplest form.*

**67.** $\sqrt{(-3-1)^2 + (1-4)^2}$

**68.** $\sqrt{(-9-3)^2 + (3-8)^2}$

**69.** $\sqrt{(2-1)^2 + (6-(-3))^2}$

**70.** $\sqrt{(3-1)^2 + (2-(-1))^2}$

**71.** $\sqrt{(-5)^2 - 4(1)(-6)}$

**72.** $\sqrt{(-7)^2 - 4(1)(-8)}$

**73.** $\sqrt{(-10)^2 - 4(3)(-8)}$

**74.** $\sqrt{(-2)^2 - 4(5)(-3)}$

**75.** $\sqrt{(-4)^2 - 4(2)(1)}$

**76.** $\sqrt{(-6)^2 - 4(1)(-3)}$

## PREVIEW EXERCISES

*Perform each operation. **See Section 8.1.***

**77.** $\left(\sqrt{6}\right)^2$

**78.** $\left(\sqrt{25}\right)^2$

**79.** $\sqrt[3]{2} \cdot \sqrt[3]{4}$

*Simplify each radical. **See Section 8.2.***

**80.** $\sqrt{288}$

**81.** $\sqrt{7500}$

**82.** $\sqrt{x^2y^6}, x \geq 0, y \geq 0$

## 8.4  Rationalizing the Denominator

**OBJECTIVE 1** **Rationalize denominators with square roots.** Although calculators now make it fairly easy to divide by a radical in an expression such as $\dfrac{1}{\sqrt{2}}$, it is sometimes easier to work with radical expressions if the denominators do not contain any radicals.

For example, the radical in the denominator of $\dfrac{1}{\sqrt{2}}$ can be eliminated by multiplying the numerator and denominator by $\sqrt{2}$, since $\sqrt{2} \cdot \sqrt{2} = \sqrt{4} = 2$.

$$\frac{1}{\sqrt{2}} = \frac{1 \cdot \sqrt{2}}{\sqrt{2} \cdot \sqrt{2}} = \frac{\sqrt{2}}{2} \qquad \text{Multiply by } \frac{\sqrt{2}}{\sqrt{2}} = 1.$$

This process of changing the denominator from a radical (an irrational number) to a rational number is called **rationalizing the denominator.** *The value of the radical expression is not changed. Only the form is changed, because the expression has been multiplied by 1 in the form* $\dfrac{\sqrt{2}}{\sqrt{2}}$.

> **NOW TRY**
> **EXERCISE 1**
> Rationalize each denominator.
> **(a)** $\dfrac{15}{\sqrt{5}}$ **(b)** $\dfrac{3}{\sqrt{24}}$

**EXAMPLE 1** Rationalizing Denominators

Rationalize each denominator.

**(a)** $\dfrac{9}{\sqrt{6}}$

$$= \frac{9 \cdot \sqrt{6}}{\sqrt{6} \cdot \sqrt{6}} \qquad \text{Multiply by } \frac{\sqrt{6}}{\sqrt{6}} = 1.$$

$$= \frac{9\sqrt{6}}{6} \qquad \begin{array}{l}\text{In the denominator,}\\ \sqrt{6} \cdot \sqrt{6} = \sqrt{36} = 6.\end{array}$$

$$= \frac{3\sqrt{6}}{2} \qquad \text{Lowest terms}$$

**(b)** $\dfrac{12}{\sqrt{8}}$  The denominator could be rationalized by multiplying by $\sqrt{8}$. However, simplifying the denominator first is more direct.

$$\frac{12}{\sqrt{8}}$$

$$= \frac{12}{2\sqrt{2}} \qquad \sqrt{8} = \sqrt{4} \cdot \sqrt{2} = 2\sqrt{2}$$

$$= \frac{12 \cdot \sqrt{2}}{2\sqrt{2} \cdot \sqrt{2}} \qquad \text{Multiply by } \frac{\sqrt{2}}{\sqrt{2}} = 1.$$

$$= \frac{12 \cdot \sqrt{2}}{2 \cdot 2} \qquad \sqrt{2} \cdot \sqrt{2} = \sqrt{4} = 2$$

$$= \frac{12\sqrt{2}}{4} \qquad \text{Multiply.}$$

$$= 3\sqrt{2} \qquad \tfrac{12}{4} = 3; \text{ lowest terms} \qquad \text{NOW TRY}$$

**NOW TRY ANSWERS**
**1.** **(a)** $3\sqrt{5}$ **(b)** $\dfrac{\sqrt{6}}{4}$

NOTE In **Example 1(b),** we could also have rationalized the original denominator, $\sqrt{8}$, by multiplying by $\sqrt{2}$, since $\sqrt{8} \cdot \sqrt{2} = \sqrt{16} = 4.$

$$\frac{12}{\sqrt{8}} = \frac{12 \cdot \sqrt{2}}{\sqrt{8} \cdot \sqrt{2}} = \frac{12\sqrt{2}}{\sqrt{16}} = \frac{12\sqrt{2}}{4} = 3\sqrt{2}$$

Either approach yields the same correct answer.

**OBJECTIVE 2** **Write radicals in simplified form.** A radical is considered to be in simplified form if the following three conditions are met.

---

**Conditions for Simplified Form of a Radical**

1. The radicand contains no factor (except 1) that is a perfect square (when dealing with square roots), a perfect cube (when dealing with cube roots), and so on.

2. The radicand has no fractions.

3. No denominator contains a radical.

---

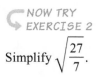
NOW TRY
EXERCISE 2

Simplify $\sqrt{\dfrac{27}{7}}$.

**EXAMPLE 2** Simplifying a Radical

Simplify.

$$\sqrt{\frac{27}{5}}$$

$$= \frac{\sqrt{27}}{\sqrt{5}} \qquad \text{Quotient rule}$$

$$= \frac{\sqrt{27} \cdot \sqrt{5}}{\sqrt{5} \cdot \sqrt{5}} \qquad \text{Rationalize the denominator.}$$

$$= \frac{\sqrt{27} \cdot \sqrt{5}}{5} \qquad \sqrt{5} \cdot \sqrt{5} = 5$$

$$= \frac{\sqrt{9 \cdot 3} \cdot \sqrt{5}}{5} \qquad \text{Factor.}$$

$$= \frac{\sqrt{9} \cdot \sqrt{3} \cdot \sqrt{5}}{5} \qquad \text{Product rule}$$

$$= \frac{3 \cdot \sqrt{3} \cdot \sqrt{5}}{5} \qquad \sqrt{9} = 3$$

$$= \frac{3\sqrt{15}}{5} \qquad \text{Product rule} \qquad \text{NOW TRY}$$

NOW TRY ANSWER

2. $\dfrac{3\sqrt{21}}{7}$

NOW TRY
EXERCISE 3

Simplify.

$$\sqrt{\frac{1}{6}} \cdot \sqrt{\frac{3}{10}}$$

Simplifying a Product of Radicals

Simplify.

$$\sqrt{\frac{5}{8}} \cdot \sqrt{\frac{1}{6}}$$

$$= \sqrt{\frac{5}{8} \cdot \frac{1}{6}} \qquad \text{Product rule}$$

$$= \sqrt{\frac{5}{48}} \qquad \text{Multiply fractions.}$$

$$= \frac{\sqrt{5}}{\sqrt{48}} \qquad \text{Quotient rule}$$

$$= \frac{\sqrt{5}}{\sqrt{16} \cdot \sqrt{3}} \qquad \text{Product rule}$$

$$= \frac{\sqrt{5}}{4\sqrt{3}} \qquad \sqrt{16} = 4$$

$$= \frac{\sqrt{5} \cdot \sqrt{3}}{4\sqrt{3} \cdot \sqrt{3}} \qquad \text{Rationalize the denominator.}$$

$$= \frac{\sqrt{15}}{4 \cdot 3} \qquad \text{Product rule; } \sqrt{3} \cdot \sqrt{3} = 3$$

$$= \frac{\sqrt{15}}{12} \qquad \text{Multiply.} \qquad \text{NOW TRY}$$

NOW TRY
EXERCISE 4

Simplify. Assume that $m$ and $n$ represent positive real numbers.

**(a)** $\dfrac{\sqrt{9m}}{\sqrt{n}}$  **(b)** $\sqrt{\dfrac{16m^2n}{5}}$

Simplifying Quotients Involving Radicals

Simplify. Assume that $x$ and $y$ represent positive real numbers.

**(a)** $\dfrac{\sqrt{4x}}{\sqrt{y}}$

$$= \frac{\sqrt{4x} \cdot \sqrt{y}}{\sqrt{y} \cdot \sqrt{y}} \qquad \begin{array}{l}\text{Rationalize the} \\ \text{denominator.}\end{array}$$

$$= \frac{\sqrt{4xy}}{y} \qquad \begin{array}{l}\text{Product rule;} \\ \sqrt{y} \cdot \sqrt{y} = y\end{array}$$

$$= \frac{2\sqrt{xy}}{y} \qquad \sqrt{4} = 2$$

**(b)** $\sqrt{\dfrac{2x^2y}{3}}$

$$= \frac{\sqrt{2x^2y}}{\sqrt{3}} \qquad \text{Quotient rule}$$

$$= \frac{\sqrt{2x^2y} \cdot \sqrt{3}}{\sqrt{3} \cdot \sqrt{3}} \qquad \begin{array}{l}\text{Rationalize the} \\ \text{denominator.}\end{array}$$

$$= \frac{\sqrt{6x^2y}}{3} \qquad \begin{array}{l}\text{Product rule;} \\ \sqrt{3} \cdot \sqrt{3} = 3\end{array}$$

$$= \frac{\sqrt{x^2}\sqrt{6y}}{3} \qquad \text{Product rule}$$

$$= \frac{x\sqrt{6y}}{3} \qquad \begin{array}{l}\sqrt{x^2} = x, \\ \text{since } x > 0.\end{array}$$

NOW TRY

NOW TRY ANSWERS

**3.** $\dfrac{\sqrt{5}}{10}$

**4. (a)** $\dfrac{3\sqrt{mn}}{n}$  **(b)** $\dfrac{4m\sqrt{5n}}{5}$

**OBJECTIVE 3** Rationalize denominators with cube roots. To rationalize a denominator with a cube root, we change the radicand in the denominator to a perfect cube.

NOW TRY
EXERCISE 5
Rationalize each denominator.

(a) $\sqrt[3]{\dfrac{2}{7}}$  (b) $\dfrac{\sqrt[3]{2}}{\sqrt[3]{5}}$

(c) $\dfrac{\sqrt[3]{4}}{\sqrt[3]{9t}}$, $t \neq 0$

**EXAMPLE 5** Rationalizing Denominators with Cube Roots

Rationalize each denominator.

(a) $\sqrt[3]{\dfrac{3}{2}}$

First write the expression as a quotient of radicals. Then multiply numerator and denominator by a sufficient number of factors of 2 to make the radicand in the denominator a perfect cube. This will eliminate the radical in the denominator. Here, multiply by $\sqrt[3]{2 \cdot 2}$, or $\sqrt[3]{2^2}$.

$$\sqrt[3]{\dfrac{3}{2}} = \dfrac{\sqrt[3]{3}}{\sqrt[3]{2}} = \dfrac{\sqrt[3]{3} \cdot \sqrt[3]{2 \cdot 2}}{\sqrt[3]{2} \cdot \sqrt[3]{2 \cdot 2}} = \dfrac{\sqrt[3]{3 \cdot 2 \cdot 2}}{\sqrt[3]{2 \cdot 2 \cdot 2}} = \dfrac{\sqrt[3]{12}}{2}$$

We need 3 factors of 2 in the radicand in the denominator.

$\sqrt[3]{2 \cdot 2 \cdot 2} = \sqrt[3]{2^3} = 2$
Denominator radicand is a perfect cube.

(b) $\dfrac{\sqrt[3]{3}}{\sqrt[3]{4}}$

Since $\sqrt[3]{4} = \sqrt[3]{2 \cdot 2}$, multiply numerator and denominator by a sufficient number of factors of 2 to get a perfect cube in the radicand in the denominator.

$$\dfrac{\sqrt[3]{3}}{\sqrt[3]{4}} = \dfrac{\sqrt[3]{3} \cdot \sqrt[3]{2}}{\sqrt[3]{2 \cdot 2} \cdot \sqrt[3]{2}} = \dfrac{\sqrt[3]{6}}{\sqrt[3]{2 \cdot 2 \cdot 2}} = \dfrac{\sqrt[3]{6}}{2}$$

(c) $\dfrac{\sqrt[3]{2}}{\sqrt[3]{3x^2}}$, $x \neq 0$

Multiply numerator and denominator by a sufficient number of factors of 3 and of $x$ to get a perfect cube in the radicand in the denominator.

$$\dfrac{\sqrt[3]{2}}{\sqrt[3]{3x^2}} = \dfrac{\sqrt[3]{2} \cdot \sqrt[3]{3 \cdot 3 \cdot x}}{\sqrt[3]{3 \cdot x \cdot x} \cdot \sqrt[3]{3 \cdot 3 \cdot x}} = \dfrac{\sqrt[3]{18x}}{\sqrt[3]{(3x)^3}} = \dfrac{\sqrt[3]{18x}}{3x}$$

We need 3 factors of 3 and 3 factors of $x$ in the radicand in the denominator.

$\sqrt[3]{3 \cdot x \cdot x} \cdot \sqrt[3]{3 \cdot 3 \cdot x} = \sqrt[3]{(3x)^3}$
$= 3x$
Denominator radicand is a perfect cube.

NOW TRY

NOW TRY ANSWERS
5. (a) $\dfrac{\sqrt[3]{98}}{7}$ (b) $\dfrac{\sqrt[3]{50}}{5}$

(c) $\dfrac{\sqrt[3]{12t^2}}{3t}$

⚠ **CAUTION** A common error in a problem like the one in **Example 5(a)** is to multiply by $\sqrt[3]{2}$ instead of $\sqrt[3]{2^2}$. Doing this would give a denominator of

$$\sqrt[3]{2} \cdot \sqrt[3]{2} = \sqrt[3]{4}.$$

Because 4 is not a perfect cube, the denominator is still not rationalized.

**8.4 EXERCISES** **MyMathLab**   WATCH  DOWNLOAD  READ REVIEW

● *Complete solution available on the Video Resources on DVD*

*Rationalize each denominator.* ***See Examples 1 and 2.***

**1.** $\dfrac{6}{\sqrt{5}}$

**2.** $\dfrac{3}{\sqrt{2}}$

**3.** $\dfrac{5}{\sqrt{5}}$

**4.** $\dfrac{15}{\sqrt{15}}$

● **5.** $\dfrac{4}{\sqrt{6}}$

**6.** $\dfrac{15}{\sqrt{10}}$

**7.** $\dfrac{8\sqrt{3}}{\sqrt{5}}$

**8.** $\dfrac{9\sqrt{6}}{\sqrt{5}}$

**9.** $\dfrac{12\sqrt{10}}{8\sqrt{3}}$

**10.** $\dfrac{9\sqrt{15}}{6\sqrt{2}}$

**11.** $\dfrac{8}{\sqrt{27}}$

**12.** $\dfrac{12}{\sqrt{18}}$

**13.** $\dfrac{6}{\sqrt{200}}$

**14.** $\dfrac{10}{\sqrt{300}}$

**15.** $\dfrac{12}{\sqrt{72}}$

**16.** $\dfrac{21}{\sqrt{45}}$

**17.** $\dfrac{\sqrt{10}}{\sqrt{5}}$

**18.** $\dfrac{\sqrt{6}}{\sqrt{3}}$

● **19.** $\sqrt{\dfrac{40}{3}}$

**20.** $\sqrt{\dfrac{5}{8}}$

**21.** $\sqrt{\dfrac{1}{32}}$

**22.** $\sqrt{\dfrac{1}{8}}$

**23.** $\sqrt{\dfrac{9}{5}}$

**24.** $\sqrt{\dfrac{16}{7}}$

**25.** $\dfrac{-3}{\sqrt{50}}$

**26.** $\dfrac{-5}{\sqrt{75}}$

**27.** $\dfrac{63}{\sqrt{45}}$

**28.** $\dfrac{27}{\sqrt{32}}$

**29.** $\dfrac{\sqrt{8}}{\sqrt{24}}$

**30.** $\dfrac{\sqrt{5}}{\sqrt{10}}$

**31.** $-\sqrt{\dfrac{1}{5}}$

**32.** $-\sqrt{\dfrac{1}{6}}$

**33.** $\sqrt{\dfrac{13}{5}}$

**34.** $\sqrt{\dfrac{17}{11}}$

**35.** *Concept Check* To rationalize the denominator of an expression such as $\dfrac{4}{\sqrt{3}}$, we multiply both the numerator and denominator by $\sqrt{3}$. By what number are we actually multiplying the given expression, and what property of real numbers justifies the fact that our result is equal to the given expression?

**36.** In **Example 1(a),** we showed algebraically that $\dfrac{9}{\sqrt{6}} = \dfrac{3\sqrt{6}}{2}$. Support this result numerically by finding the decimal approximation of $\dfrac{9}{\sqrt{6}}$ on your calculator and then finding the decimal approximation of $\dfrac{3\sqrt{6}}{2}$. What do you notice?

*Simplify.* ***See Example 3.***

**37.** $\sqrt{\dfrac{7}{13}} \cdot \sqrt{\dfrac{13}{3}}$

**38.** $\sqrt{\dfrac{19}{20}} \cdot \sqrt{\dfrac{20}{3}}$

**39.** $\sqrt{\dfrac{21}{7}} \cdot \sqrt{\dfrac{21}{8}}$

**40.** $\sqrt{\dfrac{5}{8}} \cdot \sqrt{\dfrac{5}{6}}$

**41.** $\sqrt{\dfrac{1}{12}} \cdot \sqrt{\dfrac{1}{3}}$

**42.** $\sqrt{\dfrac{1}{8}} \cdot \sqrt{\dfrac{1}{2}}$

**43.** $\sqrt{\dfrac{2}{9}} \cdot \sqrt{\dfrac{9}{2}}$

**44.** $\sqrt{\dfrac{4}{3}} \cdot \sqrt{\dfrac{3}{4}}$

● **45.** $\sqrt{\dfrac{3}{4}} \cdot \sqrt{\dfrac{1}{5}}$

**46.** $\sqrt{\dfrac{1}{10}} \cdot \sqrt{\dfrac{10}{3}}$

**47.** $\sqrt{\dfrac{17}{3}} \cdot \sqrt{\dfrac{17}{6}}$

**48.** $\sqrt{\dfrac{1}{11}} \cdot \sqrt{\dfrac{33}{16}}$

**49.** $\sqrt{\dfrac{2}{5}} \cdot \sqrt{\dfrac{3}{10}}$

**50.** $\sqrt{\dfrac{9}{8}} \cdot \sqrt{\dfrac{7}{16}}$

**51.** $\sqrt{\dfrac{16}{27}} \cdot \sqrt{\dfrac{1}{9}}$

**52.** $\sqrt{\dfrac{256}{125}} \cdot \sqrt{\dfrac{1}{16}}$

*Simplify each radical. Assume that all variables represent positive real numbers.* **See Example 4.**

**53.** $\sqrt{\dfrac{6}{p}}$     **54.** $\sqrt{\dfrac{5}{x}}$     **55.** $\sqrt{\dfrac{3}{y}}$     **56.** $\sqrt{\dfrac{9}{k}}$

**57.** $\sqrt{\dfrac{16}{m}}$     **58.** $\sqrt{\dfrac{2z^2}{x}}$     ◉ **59.** $\dfrac{\sqrt{3p^2}}{\sqrt{q}}$     **60.** $\dfrac{\sqrt{5a^3}}{\sqrt{b}}$

**61.** $\dfrac{\sqrt{7x^3}}{\sqrt{y}}$     **62.** $\dfrac{\sqrt{4r^3}}{\sqrt{s}}$     **63.** $\sqrt{\dfrac{6p^3}{3m}}$     **64.** $\sqrt{\dfrac{a^3b}{6}}$

**65.** $\sqrt{\dfrac{x^2}{4y}}$     **66.** $\sqrt{\dfrac{m^2n}{2}}$     ◉ **67.** $\sqrt{\dfrac{9a^2r}{5}}$     **68.** $\sqrt{\dfrac{2x^2z^4}{3y}}$

**69.** *Concept Check*   Which one of the following would be an appropriate choice for multiplying the numerator and the denominator of $\dfrac{\sqrt[3]{2}}{\sqrt[3]{5}}$ in order to rationalize the denominator?

   **A.** $\sqrt[3]{5}$     **B.** $\sqrt[3]{25}$     **C.** $\sqrt[3]{2}$     **D.** $\sqrt[3]{3}$

**70.** *Concept Check*   In **Example 5(b),** we multiplied the numerator and denominator of $\dfrac{\sqrt[3]{3}}{\sqrt[3]{4}}$ by $\sqrt[3]{2}$ to rationalize the denominator. Suppose we had chosen to multiply by $\sqrt[3]{16}$ instead. Would we have obtained the correct answer after all simplifications were done?

*Rationalize each denominator. Assume that variables in denominators are nonzero.* **See Example 5.**

**71.** $\sqrt[3]{\dfrac{1}{2}}$     **72.** $\sqrt[3]{\dfrac{1}{4}}$     **73.** $\sqrt[3]{\dfrac{1}{32}}$     **74.** $\sqrt[3]{\dfrac{1}{5}}$

**75.** $\sqrt[3]{\dfrac{1}{11}}$     **76.** $\sqrt[3]{\dfrac{3}{2}}$     ◉ **77.** $\sqrt[3]{\dfrac{2}{5}}$     **78.** $\sqrt[3]{\dfrac{4}{9}}$

**79.** $\dfrac{\sqrt[3]{4}}{\sqrt[3]{7}}$     **80.** $\dfrac{\sqrt[3]{5}}{\sqrt[3]{10}}$     **81.** $\sqrt[3]{\dfrac{3}{4y^2}}$     **82.** $\sqrt[3]{\dfrac{3}{25x^2}}$

**83.** $\dfrac{\sqrt[3]{7m}}{\sqrt[3]{36n}}$     **84.** $\dfrac{\sqrt[3]{11p}}{\sqrt[3]{49q}}$     **85.** $\sqrt[4]{\dfrac{1}{8}}$     **86.** $\sqrt[4]{\dfrac{1}{27}}$

*In Exercises 87 and 88,* **(a)** *give the answer as a simplified radical and* **(b)** *use a calculator to give the answer correct to the nearest thousandth.*

**87.** The period $p$ of a pendulum is the time it takes for it to swing from one extreme to the other and back again. The value of $p$ in seconds is given by

$$p = k \cdot \sqrt{\dfrac{L}{g}},$$

where $L$ is the length of the pendulum, $g$ is the acceleration due to gravity, and $k$ is a constant. Find the period when $k = 6$, $L = 9$ ft, and $g = 32$ ft per sec$^2$.

**88.** The velocity $v$ of a meteor approaching Earth is given by

$$v = \dfrac{k}{\sqrt{d}}$$

kilometers per second, where $d$ is the distance of the meteor from the center of Earth and $k$ is a constant. What is the velocity of a meteor that is 6000 km away from the center of Earth if $k = 450$?

*PREVIEW EXERCISES*

Find each product. *See Sections 5.5 and 5.6.*

**89.** $(4x + 7)(8x - 3)$

**90.** $ab(3a^2b - 2ab^2 + 7)$

**91.** $(6x - 1)(6x + 1)$

**92.** $(r + 7)(r - 7)$

**93.** $(p + q)(a - m)$

**94.** $(3w - 8)^2$

## 8.5  More Simplifying and Operations with Radicals

**OBJECTIVES**

1. Simplify products of radical expressions.
2. Use conjugates to rationalize denominators of radical expressions.
3. Write radical expressions with quotients in lowest terms.

A set of guidelines to use when you are simplifying radical expressions follows.

**Guidelines for Simplifying Radical Expressions**

1. If a radical represents a rational number, use that rational number in place of the radical.

   *Examples:*  $\sqrt{49} = 7$,  $\sqrt{\dfrac{169}{9}} = \dfrac{13}{3}$

2. If a radical expression contains products of radicals, use the product rule for radicals, $\sqrt[n]{a} \cdot \sqrt[n]{b} = \sqrt[n]{ab}$, to get a single radical.

   *Examples:*  $\sqrt{5} \cdot \sqrt{x} = \sqrt{5x}$,  $\sqrt[3]{3} \cdot \sqrt[3]{2} = \sqrt[3]{6}$

3. If a radicand of a square root radical has a factor that is a perfect square, express the radical as the product of the positive square root of the perfect square and the remaining radical factor. A similar statement applies to higher roots.

   *Examples:*  $\sqrt{20} = \sqrt{4 \cdot 5} = \sqrt{4} \cdot \sqrt{5} = 2\sqrt{5}$

   $\sqrt[3]{16} = \sqrt[3]{8 \cdot 2} = \sqrt[3]{8} \cdot \sqrt[3]{2} = 2\sqrt[3]{2}$

4. If a radical expression contains sums or differences of radicals, use the distributive property to combine like radicals.

   *Examples:*  $3\sqrt{2} + 4\sqrt{2}$ can be combined to get $7\sqrt{2}$.

   $3\sqrt{2} + 4\sqrt{3}$ cannot be simplified further.

5. Rationalize any denominator containing a radical.

   *Examples:*  $\dfrac{5}{\sqrt{3}} = \dfrac{5 \cdot \sqrt{3}}{\sqrt{3} \cdot \sqrt{3}} = \dfrac{5\sqrt{3}}{3}$

   $\sqrt[3]{\dfrac{1}{4}} = \dfrac{\sqrt[3]{1}}{\sqrt[3]{4}} = \dfrac{\sqrt[3]{1} \cdot \sqrt[3]{2}}{\sqrt[3]{4} \cdot \sqrt[3]{2}} = \dfrac{\sqrt[3]{2}}{\sqrt[3]{8}} = \dfrac{\sqrt[3]{2}}{2}$

**OBJECTIVE 1** Simplify products of radical expressions.

*NOW TRY*
*EXERCISE 1*

Find each product and simplify.

**(a)** $\sqrt{3}\left(\sqrt{45} - \sqrt{20}\right)$

**(b)** $\left(2\sqrt{3} + \sqrt{7}\right)\left(\sqrt{3} + 3\sqrt{7}\right)$

**(c)** $\left(\sqrt{10} - 8\right)\left(2\sqrt{10} + 3\sqrt{2}\right)$

**EXAMPLE 1** Multiplying Radical Expressions

Find each product and simplify.

**(a)**
$$\sqrt{5}\left(\sqrt{8} - \sqrt{32}\right) \quad \boxed{\text{Simplify inside the parentheses.}}$$

$$= \sqrt{5}\left(2\sqrt{2} - 4\sqrt{2}\right) \qquad \sqrt{8} = 2\sqrt{2}; \; \sqrt{32} = 4\sqrt{2}$$

$$= \sqrt{5}\left(-2\sqrt{2}\right) \qquad \text{Subtract like radicals.}$$

$$= -2\sqrt{5 \cdot 2} \qquad \text{Product rule}$$

$$= -2\sqrt{10} \qquad \text{Multiply.}$$

**(b)**
$$\left(\sqrt{3} + 2\sqrt{5}\right)\left(\sqrt{3} - 4\sqrt{5}\right) \quad \boxed{\text{Use the FOIL method to multiply.}}$$

$$= \underbrace{\sqrt{3}\left(\sqrt{3}\right)}_{\text{First}} + \underbrace{\sqrt{3}\left(-4\sqrt{5}\right)}_{\text{Outer}} + \underbrace{2\sqrt{5}\left(\sqrt{3}\right)}_{\text{Inner}} + \underbrace{2\sqrt{5}\left(-4\sqrt{5}\right)}_{\text{Last}}$$

$$= 3 - 4\sqrt{15} + 2\sqrt{15} - 8 \cdot 5 \qquad \text{Product rule}$$

$$= 3 - 2\sqrt{15} - 40 \qquad \text{Add like radicals. Multiply.}$$

$$\boxed{\text{This does } \textbf{\textit{not}} \text{ equal } -39\sqrt{15}.} = -37 - 2\sqrt{15} \qquad \text{Combine like terms.}$$

**(c)** $\left(\sqrt{3} + \sqrt{21}\right)\left(\sqrt{3} - \sqrt{7}\right)$

$$= \sqrt{3}\left(\sqrt{3}\right) + \sqrt{3}\left(-\sqrt{7}\right) + \sqrt{21}\left(\sqrt{3}\right) + \sqrt{21}\left(-\sqrt{7}\right) \qquad \text{FOIL}$$

$$= 3 - \sqrt{21} + \sqrt{63} - \sqrt{147} \qquad \text{Product rule}$$

$$= 3 - \sqrt{21} + \sqrt{9} \cdot \sqrt{7} - \sqrt{49} \cdot \sqrt{3} \qquad \text{Factor; 9 and 49 are perfect squares.}$$

$$= 3 - \sqrt{21} + 3\sqrt{7} - 7\sqrt{3} \qquad \sqrt{9} = 3; \; \sqrt{49} = 7$$

Since there are no like radicals, no terms can be combined. *NOW TRY*

**Example 2** uses the rules for the square of a binomial from **Section 5.6.**

$$(x + y)^2 = x^2 + 2xy + y^2 \quad \text{and} \quad (x - y)^2 = x^2 - 2xy + y^2$$

**EXAMPLE 2** Using Special Products with Radicals

Find each product. Assume that $x \geq 0$.

**(a)**
$$\left(\sqrt{10} - 7\right)^2$$

$$= \left(\sqrt{10}\right)^2 - 2\left(\sqrt{10}\right)(7) + 7^2 \qquad \begin{array}{l}(x - y)^2 = x^2 - 2xy + y^2\\ \text{Let } x = \sqrt{10} \text{ and } y = 7.\end{array}$$

$$= 10 - 14\sqrt{10} + 49 \qquad \left(\sqrt{10}\right)^2 = 10; \; 7^2 = 49$$

$$\boxed{\text{Do } \textbf{\textit{not}} \text{ try to combine further here.}} = 59 - 14\sqrt{10} \qquad \text{Combine like terms.}$$

NOW TRY ANSWERS
1. **(a)** $\sqrt{15}$
   **(b)** $27 + 7\sqrt{21}$
   **(c)** $20 + 6\sqrt{5} - 16\sqrt{10} - 24\sqrt{2}$

NOW TRY
EXERCISE 2

Find each product. Assume that $y \geq 0$.

**(a)** $\left(\sqrt{7} - 4\right)^2$

**(b)** $\left(3 + \sqrt{y}\right)^2$

**(b)** $$\left(2\sqrt{3} + 4\right)^2$$

$$= \left(2\sqrt{3}\right)^2 + 2\left(2\sqrt{3}\right)(4) + 4^2 \qquad \begin{array}{l}(x + y)^2 = x^2 + 2xy + y^2 \\ \text{Let } x = 2\sqrt{3} \text{ and } y = 4.\end{array}$$

$$= 12 + 16\sqrt{3} + 16 \qquad \left(2\sqrt{3}\right)^2 = 4 \cdot 3 = 12$$

Do **not** try to combine further here.

$$= 28 + 16\sqrt{3}$$

**(c)** $\left(5 - \sqrt{x}\right)^2$

$$= 5^2 - 2(5)\left(\sqrt{x}\right) + \left(\sqrt{x}\right)^2 \qquad \text{Square the binomial.}$$

$$= 25 - 10\sqrt{x} + x \qquad \qquad \textit{NOW TRY}$$

---

⚠ **CAUTION** *Only like radicals can be combined.* In **Examples 2(a) and (b)**,

$$59 - 14\sqrt{10} \neq 45\sqrt{10} \quad \text{and} \quad 28 + 16\sqrt{3} \neq 44\sqrt{3}.$$

---

**Example 3** uses the rule for the product of the sum and difference of two terms.

$$(x + y)(x - y) = x^2 - y^2$$

NOW TRY
EXERCISE 3

Find each product. Assume that $x \geq 0$.

**(a)** $\left(8 + \sqrt{10}\right)\left(8 - \sqrt{10}\right)$

**(b)** $\left(\sqrt{x} + 2\sqrt{3}\right)\left(\sqrt{x} - 2\sqrt{3}\right)$

**EXAMPLE 3** Using a Special Product with Radicals

Find each product. Assume that $x \geq 0$.

**(a)** $\left(4 + \sqrt{3}\right)\left(4 - \sqrt{3}\right)$

$$= 4^2 - \left(\sqrt{3}\right)^2 \qquad \begin{array}{l}(x + y)(x - y) = x^2 - y^2 \\ \text{Let } x = 4 \text{ and } y = \sqrt{3}.\end{array}$$

$$= 16 - 3 \qquad \qquad 4^2 = 16; \left(\sqrt{3}\right)^2 = 3$$

$$= 13$$

**(b)** $\left(\sqrt{x} - \sqrt{6}\right)\left(\sqrt{x} + \sqrt{6}\right)$

$$= \left(\sqrt{x}\right)^2 - \left(\sqrt{6}\right)^2$$

$$= x - 6 \qquad \qquad \left(\sqrt{x}\right)^2 = x; \left(\sqrt{6}\right)^2 = 6 \qquad \textit{NOW TRY}$$

In **Example 3,** the pairs of expressions $4 + \sqrt{3}$ and $4 - \sqrt{3}$ and $\sqrt{x} - \sqrt{6}$ and $\sqrt{x} + \sqrt{6}$ are called **conjugates** of each other.

**OBJECTIVE 2** Use conjugates to rationalize denominators of radical expressions. To rationalize the denominator in a quotient such as

$$\frac{2}{4 - \sqrt{3}},$$

we multiply the numerator and denominator by the conjugate of the denominator, here $4 + \sqrt{3}$, to obtain

NOW TRY ANSWERS

2. **(a)** $23 - 8\sqrt{7}$
   **(b)** $9 + 6\sqrt{y} + y$
3. **(a)** $54$
   **(b)** $x - 12$

$$\frac{2\left(4 + \sqrt{3}\right)}{\left(4 - \sqrt{3}\right)\left(4 + \sqrt{3}\right)}, \quad \text{or} \quad \frac{2\left(4 + \sqrt{3}\right)}{13}.$$

The denominator contains no radicals. It has been rationalized.

### Using Conjugates to Rationalize a Binomial Denominator

To rationalize a binomial denominator, where at least one of those terms is a square root radical, multiply numerator and denominator by the conjugate of the denominator.

**NOW TRY**
**EXERCISE 4**

Simplify by rationalizing each denominator. Assume that $k \geq 0$.

**(a)** $\dfrac{6}{4 + \sqrt{3}}$  **(b)** $\dfrac{5 + \sqrt{7}}{\sqrt{7} - 2}$

**(c)** $\dfrac{9}{\sqrt{k} - 6}$, $k \neq 36$

**EXAMPLE 4** Using Conjugates to Rationalize Denominators

Simplify by rationalizing each denominator. Assume that $x \geq 0$.

**(a)** $\dfrac{5}{3 + \sqrt{5}}$

$$= \dfrac{5(3 - \sqrt{5})}{(3 + \sqrt{5})(3 - \sqrt{5})}$$  Multiply the numerator and denominator by the conjugate of the denominator.

$$= \dfrac{5(3 - \sqrt{5})}{3^2 - (\sqrt{5})^2}$$  $(x + y)(x - y) = x^2 - y^2$

$$= \dfrac{5(3 - \sqrt{5})}{9 - 5}$$  $3^2 = 9$; $(\sqrt{5})^2 = 5$

$$= \dfrac{5(3 - \sqrt{5})}{4}$$  Subtract.

**(b)** $\dfrac{6 + \sqrt{2}}{\sqrt{2} - 5}$

$$= \dfrac{(6 + \sqrt{2})(\sqrt{2} + 5)}{(\sqrt{2} - 5)(\sqrt{2} + 5)}$$  Multiply the numerator and denominator by the conjugate of the denominator.

$$= \dfrac{6\sqrt{2} + 30 + 2 + 5\sqrt{2}}{2 - 25}$$  FOIL; $(x + y)(x - y) = x^2 - y^2$

$$= \dfrac{11\sqrt{2} + 32}{-23}$$  Combine like terms.

$$= \dfrac{-11\sqrt{2} - 32}{23}$$  $\dfrac{x}{-y} = \dfrac{-x}{y}$

**(c)** $\dfrac{4}{3 + \sqrt{x}}$

$$= \dfrac{4(3 - \sqrt{x})}{(3 + \sqrt{x})(3 - \sqrt{x})}$$  Multiply by $\dfrac{3 - \sqrt{x}}{3 - \sqrt{x}} = 1$.

We assume here that $x \geq 0$ and $x \neq 9$.

$$= \dfrac{4(3 - \sqrt{x})}{9 - x}$$  $3^2 = 9$; $(\sqrt{x})^2 = x$   **NOW TRY**

**NOW TRY ANSWERS**

**4. (a)** $\dfrac{6(4 - \sqrt{3})}{13}$

**(b)** $\dfrac{17 + 7\sqrt{7}}{3}$

**(c)** $\dfrac{9(\sqrt{k} + 6)}{k - 36}$

**OBJECTIVE 3** Write radical expressions with quotients in lowest terms.

*NOW TRY*
*EXERCISE 5*
Write the quotient in lowest terms.

$$\frac{12\sqrt{6} + 28}{20}$$

**EXAMPLE 5** Writing a Radical Quotient in Lowest Terms

Write the quotient in lowest terms.

$$\frac{3\sqrt{3} + 9}{12} \quad \boxed{\text{Don't simplify yet!}}$$

$$= \frac{3\left(\sqrt{3} + 3\right)}{3(4)} \qquad \text{Factor first.}$$

$$= 1 \cdot \frac{\sqrt{3} + 3}{4} \qquad \text{Now divide out the common factor; } \tfrac{3}{3} = 1$$

$$= \frac{\sqrt{3} + 3}{4} \qquad \text{Identity property; lowest terms} \qquad \textit{NOW TRY}$$

*NOW TRY ANSWER*

**5.** $\dfrac{3\sqrt{6} + 7}{5}$

⚠ **CAUTION**   An expression like the one in **Example 5** can be simplified only by factoring a common factor from the denominator and *each* term of the numerator. For example, *first factor*

$$\frac{4 + 8\sqrt{5}}{4} \quad \text{as} \quad \frac{4\left(1 + 2\sqrt{5}\right)}{4} \quad \text{to obtain} \quad 1 + 2\sqrt{5}.$$

---

## 8.5 EXERCISES

**MyMathLab**   Math XL PRACTICE   WATCH   DOWNLOAD   READ   REVIEW

🌐 *Complete solution available on the Video Resources on DVD*

*In this exercise set, we assume that variables are such that no negative numbers appear as radicals in square roots and such that no denominators are zero.*

*In Exercises 1–4, perform the operations mentally, and write the answers without doing intermediate steps.*

**1.** $\sqrt{25} + \sqrt{64}$     **2.** $\sqrt{100} - \sqrt{49}$     **3.** $\sqrt{8} \cdot \sqrt{2}$     **4.** $\sqrt{6} \cdot \sqrt{6}$

*Simplify each expression. Use the five guidelines given in this section.* ***See Examples 1–3.***

🌐 **5.** $\sqrt{5}\left(\sqrt{3} - \sqrt{7}\right)$     **6.** $\sqrt{7}\left(\sqrt{10} + \sqrt{3}\right)$     **7.** $2\sqrt{5}\left(3\sqrt{5} + \sqrt{2}\right)$

**8.** $3\sqrt{7}\left(2\sqrt{7} + 4\sqrt{5}\right)$     **9.** $3\sqrt{14} \cdot \sqrt{2} - \sqrt{28}$     **10.** $7\sqrt{6} \cdot \sqrt{3} - 2\sqrt{18}$

**11.** $\left(2\sqrt{6} + 3\right)\left(3\sqrt{6} + 7\right)$         **12.** $\left(4\sqrt{5} - 2\right)\left(2\sqrt{5} - 4\right)$

**13.** $\left(5\sqrt{7} - 2\sqrt{3}\right)\left(3\sqrt{7} + 4\sqrt{3}\right)$     **14.** $\left(2\sqrt{10} + 5\sqrt{2}\right)\left(3\sqrt{10} - 3\sqrt{2}\right)$

🌐 **15.** $\left(8 - \sqrt{7}\right)^2$         **16.** $\left(6 - \sqrt{11}\right)^2$

**17.** $\left(2\sqrt{7} + 3\right)^2$         **18.** $\left(4\sqrt{5} + 5\right)^2$

**19.** $\left(\sqrt{6} + 1\right)^2$         **20.** $\left(\sqrt{7} + 2\right)^2$

🌐 **21.** $\left(5 - \sqrt{2}\right)\left(5 + \sqrt{2}\right)$         **22.** $\left(3 - \sqrt{5}\right)\left(3 + \sqrt{5}\right)$

**23.** $\left(\sqrt{8} - \sqrt{7}\right)\left(\sqrt{8} + \sqrt{7}\right)$     **24.** $\left(\sqrt{12} - \sqrt{11}\right)\left(\sqrt{12} + \sqrt{11}\right)$

**25.** $\left(\sqrt{78} - \sqrt{76}\right)\left(\sqrt{78} + \sqrt{76}\right)$ **26.** $\left(\sqrt{85} - \sqrt{82}\right)\left(\sqrt{85} + \sqrt{82}\right)$

**27.** $\left(\sqrt{2} + \sqrt{3}\right)\left(\sqrt{6} - \sqrt{2}\right)$ **28.** $\left(\sqrt{3} + \sqrt{5}\right)\left(\sqrt{15} - \sqrt{5}\right)$

**29.** $\left(\sqrt{10} - \sqrt{5}\right)\left(\sqrt{5} + \sqrt{20}\right)$ **30.** $\left(\sqrt{6} - \sqrt{3}\right)\left(\sqrt{3} + \sqrt{18}\right)$

**31.** $\left(\sqrt{5} + \sqrt{30}\right)\left(\sqrt{6} + \sqrt{3}\right)$ **32.** $\left(\sqrt{10} - \sqrt{20}\right)\left(\sqrt{2} - \sqrt{5}\right)$

**33.** $\left(5\sqrt{7} - 2\sqrt{3}\right)^2$ **34.** $\left(8\sqrt{2} - 3\sqrt{3}\right)^2$

**35.** *Concept Check* In **Example 1(b)**, a student simplified $-37 - 2\sqrt{15}$ by combining the $-37$ and the $-2$ to get $-39\sqrt{15}$, which is incorrect. *WHAT WENT WRONG?*

**36.** *Concept Check* Find each product mentally.

    **(a)** $\left(\sqrt{x} + \sqrt{y}\right)\left(\sqrt{x} - \sqrt{y}\right)$    **(b)** $\left(\sqrt{28} - \sqrt{14}\right)\left(\sqrt{28} + \sqrt{14}\right)$

*Simplify each radical expression. See Examples 1–3.*

**37.** $\left(7 + \sqrt{x}\right)^2$             **38.** $\left(12 - \sqrt{r}\right)^2$

**39.** $\left(3\sqrt{t} + \sqrt{7}\right)\left(2\sqrt{t} - \sqrt{14}\right)$    **40.** $\left(2\sqrt{z} - \sqrt{3}\right)\left(\sqrt{z} - \sqrt{5}\right)$

**41.** $\left(\sqrt{3m} + \sqrt{2n}\right)\left(\sqrt{3m} - \sqrt{2n}\right)$    **42.** $\left(\sqrt{4p} - \sqrt{3k}\right)\left(\sqrt{4p} + \sqrt{3k}\right)$

**43.** *Concept Check* Determine the expression by which you should multiply the numerator and denominator to rationalize each denominator.

    **(a)** $\dfrac{1}{\sqrt{5} + \sqrt{3}}$      **(b)** $\dfrac{3}{\sqrt{6} - \sqrt{5}}$

**44.** *Concept Check* If you try to rationalize the denominator of $\dfrac{2}{4 + \sqrt{3}}$ by multiplying by $\dfrac{4 + \sqrt{3}}{4 + \sqrt{3}}$, what problem arises? By what should you multiply?

*Rationalize each denominator. Write quotients in lowest terms. See Example 4.*

**45.** $\dfrac{1}{2 + \sqrt{5}}$   **46.** $\dfrac{1}{4 + \sqrt{15}}$   🌐 **47.** $\dfrac{7}{2 - \sqrt{11}}$   **48.** $\dfrac{38}{5 - \sqrt{6}}$

**49.** $\dfrac{\sqrt{12}}{\sqrt{3} + 1}$   **50.** $\dfrac{\sqrt{18}}{\sqrt{2} - 1}$   **51.** $\dfrac{2\sqrt{3}}{\sqrt{3} + 5}$   **52.** $\dfrac{2\sqrt{3}}{2 - \sqrt{10}}$

**53.** $\dfrac{\sqrt{2} + 3}{\sqrt{3} - 1}$   **54.** $\dfrac{\sqrt{5} + 2}{2 - \sqrt{3}}$   **55.** $\dfrac{6 - \sqrt{5}}{\sqrt{2} + 2}$   **56.** $\dfrac{3 + \sqrt{2}}{\sqrt{2} + 1}$

**57.** $\dfrac{2\sqrt{6} + 1}{\sqrt{2} + 5}$   **58.** $\dfrac{3\sqrt{2} - 4}{\sqrt{3} + 2}$   **59.** $\dfrac{\sqrt{7} + \sqrt{2}}{\sqrt{3} - \sqrt{2}}$   **60.** $\dfrac{\sqrt{6} + \sqrt{5}}{\sqrt{3} + \sqrt{5}}$

**61.** $\dfrac{\sqrt{5}}{\sqrt{2} + \sqrt{3}}$   **62.** $\dfrac{\sqrt{3}}{\sqrt{2} + \sqrt{3}}$   **63.** $\dfrac{\sqrt{108}}{3 + 3\sqrt{3}}$   **64.** $\dfrac{9\sqrt{8}}{6\sqrt{2} - 6}$

**65.** $\dfrac{8}{4 - \sqrt{x}}$   **66.** $\dfrac{12}{6 + \sqrt{y}}$   **67.** $\dfrac{1}{\sqrt{x} + \sqrt{y}}$   **68.** $\dfrac{2}{\sqrt{x} - \sqrt{y}}$

*Write each quotient in lowest terms. See Example 5.*

🌐 **69.** $\dfrac{5\sqrt{7} - 10}{5}$   **70.** $\dfrac{6\sqrt{5} - 9}{3}$   **71.** $\dfrac{2\sqrt{3} + 10}{8}$   **72.** $\dfrac{4\sqrt{6} + 6}{10}$

**73.** $\dfrac{12 - 2\sqrt{10}}{4}$   **74.** $\dfrac{9 - 6\sqrt{2}}{12}$   **75.** $\dfrac{16 + \sqrt{128}}{24}$   **76.** $\dfrac{25 + \sqrt{75}}{10}$

*Brain Busters*   *Perform each operation and express the answer in simplest form.*

**77.** $\sqrt[3]{4}\left(\sqrt[3]{2} - 3\right)$

**78.** $\sqrt[3]{5}\left(4\sqrt[3]{5} - \sqrt[3]{25}\right)$

**79.** $2\sqrt[4]{2}\left(3\sqrt[4]{8} + 5\sqrt[4]{4}\right)$

**80.** $6\sqrt[4]{9}\left(2\sqrt[4]{9} - \sqrt[4]{27}\right)$

**81.** $\left(\sqrt[3]{2} - 1\right)\left(\sqrt[3]{4} + 3\right)$

**82.** $\left(\sqrt[3]{9} + 5\right)\left(\sqrt[3]{3} - 4\right)$

**83.** $\left(\sqrt[3]{5} - \sqrt[3]{4}\right)\left(\sqrt[3]{25} + \sqrt[3]{20} + \sqrt[3]{16}\right)$

**84.** $\left(\sqrt[3]{4} + \sqrt[3]{2}\right)\left(\sqrt[3]{16} - \sqrt[3]{8} + \sqrt[3]{4}\right)$

*Solve each problem.*

**85.** The radius of the circular top or bottom of a tin can with surface area $S$ and height $h$ is given by

$$r = \frac{-h + \sqrt{h^2 + 0.64S}}{2}.$$

What radius should be used to make a can with height 12 in. and surface area 400 in.²?

**86.** If an investment of $P$ dollars grows to $A$ dollars in 2 yr, the annual rate of return on the investment is given by

$$r = \frac{\sqrt{A} - \sqrt{P}}{\sqrt{P}}.$$

First rationalize the denominator, and then find the annual rate of return (as a percent) if $50,000 increases to $54,080.

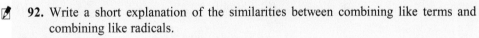

*RELATING CONCEPTS*   **EXERCISES 87–92**

**FOR INDIVIDUAL OR GROUP WORK**

*Work Exercises 87–92 in order,* *to see why a common student error is indeed an error.*

**87.** Use the distributive property to write $6(5 + 3x)$ as a sum.

**88.** Your answer in **Exercise 87** should be $30 + 18x$. Why can we not combine these two terms to get $48x$?

**89.** Repeat **Exercise 14** from earlier in this exercise set.

**90.** Your answer in **Exercise 89** should be $30 + 18\sqrt{5}$. Many students will, in error, try to combine these terms to get $48\sqrt{5}$. Why is this wrong?

**91.** Write the expression similar to $30 + 18x$ that simplifies to $48x$. Then write the expression similar to $30 + 18\sqrt{5}$ that simplifies to $48\sqrt{5}$.

**92.** Write a short explanation of the similarities between combining like terms and combining like radicals.

*PREVIEW EXERCISES*

*Solve each equation. **See Section 6.5.***

**93.** $(2x - 1)(4x - 3) = 0$

**94.** $(5x + 6)^2 = 0$

**95.** $x^2 + 4x + 3 = 0$

**96.** $x^2 - 6x + 9 = 0$

**97.** $x(x + 2) = 3$

**98.** $x(x + 4) = 21$

## SUMMARY EXERCISES on Operations with Radicals

*Perform all indicated operations and express each answer in simplest form. Assume that all variables represent positive numbers.*

**1.** $5\sqrt{10} - 8\sqrt{10}$

**2.** $\sqrt{5}(\sqrt{5} - \sqrt{3})$

**3.** $(1 + \sqrt{3})(2 - \sqrt{6})$

**4.** $\sqrt{98} - \sqrt{72} + \sqrt{50}$

**5.** $(3\sqrt{5} - 2\sqrt{7})^2$

**6.** $\dfrac{3}{\sqrt{6}}$

**7.** $\dfrac{1 + \sqrt{2}}{1 - \sqrt{2}}$

**8.** $\dfrac{8}{\sqrt{7} - \sqrt{5}}$

**9.** $(\sqrt{3} + 6)(\sqrt{3} - 6)$

**10.** $\dfrac{1}{\sqrt{t} + \sqrt{3}}$

**11.** $\sqrt[3]{8x^3y^5z^6}$

**12.** $\dfrac{12}{\sqrt[3]{9}}$

**13.** $\dfrac{5}{\sqrt{6} - 1}$

**14.** $\sqrt{\dfrac{2}{3x}}$

**15.** $\dfrac{6\sqrt{3}}{5\sqrt{12}}$

**16.** $\dfrac{8\sqrt{50}}{2\sqrt{25}}$

**17.** $\dfrac{-4}{\sqrt[3]{4}}$

**18.** $\dfrac{\sqrt{6} - \sqrt{5}}{\sqrt{6} + \sqrt{5}}$

**19.** $\sqrt{75x} - \sqrt{12x}$

**20.** $(5 + 3\sqrt{3})^2$

**21.** $\sqrt[3]{\dfrac{16}{81}}$

**22.** $(\sqrt{107} - \sqrt{106})(\sqrt{107} + \sqrt{106})$

**23.** $x\sqrt[4]{x^5} - 3\sqrt[4]{x^9} + x^2\sqrt[4]{x}$

**24.** $\sqrt[3]{16t^2} - \sqrt[3]{54t^2} + \sqrt[3]{128t^2}$

**25.** $(1 + \sqrt[3]{3})(1 - \sqrt[3]{3} + \sqrt[3]{9})$

*Students often have trouble distinguishing between the following two types of problems:*

| | |
|---|---|
| **Simplifying a Radical Involving a Square Root** | **Solving an Equation by Using Square Roots** |
| *Exercise:* Simplify $\sqrt{25}$. | *Exercise:* Solve $x^2 = 25$. |
| *Answer:* 5 | *Answer:* $\{-5, 5\}$ |
| In this situation, $\sqrt{25}$ represents the positive square root of 25, namely, 5. | In this situation, $x^2 = 25$ has either of two solutions: the negative square root of 25 or the positive square root of 25—that is, $-5$ or 5. (See **Exercise 36.**) |

*Use the preceding information to work Exercises 26–35.*

**26. (a)** Simplify $\sqrt{36}$.
   **(b)** Solve $x^2 = 36$.

**27. (a)** Simplify $\sqrt{81}$.
   **(b)** Solve $x^2 = 81$.

**28. (a)** Solve $x^2 = 4$.
   **(b)** Simplify $-\sqrt{4}$.

**29. (a)** Solve $x^2 = 9$.
   **(b)** Simplify $-\sqrt{9}$.

**30. (a)** Solve $x^2 = \frac{1}{4}$.
   **(b)** Simplify $\sqrt{\frac{1}{4}}$.

**31. (a)** Solve $x^2 = \frac{1}{49}$.
   **(b)** Simplify $\sqrt{\frac{1}{49}}$.

**32. (a)** Simplify $-\sqrt{\frac{16}{25}}$.
   **(b)** Solve $x^2 = \frac{16}{25}$.

**33. (a)** Simplify $-\sqrt{\frac{49}{100}}$.
   **(b)** Solve $x^2 = \frac{49}{100}$.

**34. (a)** Solve $x^2 = 0.04$.
   **(b)** Simplify $\sqrt{0.04}$.

**35. (a)** Solve $x^2 = 0.16$.
   **(b)** Simplify $\sqrt{0.16}$.

**36.** Use the zero-factor property **(Section 6.5)** to show that the solution set of $x^2 = 25$ is $\{-5, 5\}$.

## 8.6  Solving Equations with Radicals

**OBJECTIVES**

1. Solve radical equations having square root radicals.
2. Identify equations with no solutions.
3. Solve equations by squaring a binomial.
4. Solve radical equations having cube root radicals.

A **radical equation** is an equation having a variable in the radicand.

$$\sqrt{x+1} = 3 \quad \text{and} \quad 3\sqrt{x} = \sqrt{8x+9} \quad \text{Radical equations}$$

**OBJECTIVE 1** Solve radical equations having square root radicals. To solve radical equations having square root radicals, we need a new property, called the **squaring property of equality.**

**Squaring Property of Equality**

If each side of a given equation is squared, then all solutions of the original equation are *among* the solutions of the squared equation.

⚠ **CAUTION** Using the squaring property can give a new equation with *more* solutions than the original equation. For example, starting with $x = 4$ and squaring each side gives

$$x^2 = 4^2, \quad \text{or} \quad x^2 = 16.$$

This last equation, $x^2 = 16$, has either of *two* solutions, 4 or $-4$, while the original equation, $x = 4$, has only *one* solution, 4.

Because of this possibility, checking is more than just a guard against algebraic errors when solving an equation with radicals. It is an essential part of the solution process. ***All proposed solutions from the squared equation must be checked in the original equation.***

*NOW TRY*
*EXERCISE 1*

Solve $\sqrt{x-5} = 6$.

**EXAMPLE 1** Using the Squaring Property of Equality

Solve $\sqrt{x+1} = 3$.

$$\sqrt{x+1} = 3$$
$$\left(\sqrt{x+1}\right)^2 = 3^2 \quad \text{Use the squaring property to square each side.}$$
$$x+1 = 9 \quad \text{On the left, } \left(\sqrt{a}\right)^2 = a.$$
$$x = 8 \quad \text{Subtract 1.}$$

CHECK  $\sqrt{x+1} = 3$  Original equation

A check is essential.

$$\sqrt{8+1} \overset{?}{=} 3 \quad \text{Let } x = 8.$$
$$\sqrt{9} \overset{?}{=} 3 \quad \text{Add.}$$
$$3 = 3 \checkmark \quad \text{True}$$

Because this statement is true, $\{8\}$ is the solution set of $\sqrt{x+1} = 3$. Here, the equation obtained by squaring had just one solution, which also satisfied the original equation.

*NOW TRY*

*NOW TRY ANSWER*
1. $\{41\}$

NOW TRY
EXERCISE 2
Solve $4\sqrt{x} = \sqrt{10x + 12}$.

**EXAMPLE 2** Using the Squaring Property with a Radical on Each Side

Solve $3\sqrt{x} = \sqrt{x + 8}$.

$$3\sqrt{x} = \sqrt{x + 8}$$

$$\left(3\sqrt{x}\right)^2 = \left(\sqrt{x + 8}\right)^2 \quad \text{Squaring property}$$

$$3^2\left(\sqrt{x}\right)^2 = \left(\sqrt{x + 8}\right)^2 \quad (ab)^2 = a^2b^2$$

*Be careful here.*

$$9x = x + 8 \quad \left(\sqrt{x}\right)^2 = x; \left(\sqrt{x + 8}\right)^2 = x + 8$$

$$8x = 8 \quad \text{Subtract } x.$$

$$x = 1 \quad \text{Divide by 8.}$$

CHECK

$$3\sqrt{x} = \sqrt{x + 8} \quad \text{Original equation}$$

$$3\sqrt{1} \stackrel{?}{=} \sqrt{1 + 8} \quad \text{Let } x = 1.$$

$$3(1) \stackrel{?}{=} \sqrt{9}$$

*This is not the solution*

$$3 = 3 \quad ✓ \quad \text{True}$$

The solution set of $3\sqrt{x} = \sqrt{x + 8}$ is $\{1\}$.

NOW TRY

---

⚠ **CAUTION** Do not write the final result obtained in the check in the solution set. In **Example 2,** the solution set is $\{1\}$, *not* $\{3\}$.

---

**OBJECTIVE 2** **Identify equations with no solutions.** Not all radical equations have solutions.

NOW TRY
EXERCISE 3
Solve $\sqrt{x} = -6$.

**EXAMPLE 3** Using the Squaring Property When One Side Is Negative

Solve $\sqrt{x} = -3$.

$$\sqrt{x} = -3$$

$$\left(\sqrt{x}\right)^2 = (-3)^2 \quad \text{Squaring property}$$

$$x = 9 \longleftarrow \text{Proposed solution}$$

CHECK

$$\sqrt{x} = -3 \quad \text{Original equation}$$

$$\sqrt{9} \stackrel{?}{=} -3 \quad \text{Let } x = 9.$$

$$3 = -3 \quad \text{False}$$

Because the statement $3 = -3$ is false, the number 9 is *not* a solution of the given equation. Recall from **Section 7.6** that a proposed solution that is not an actual solution of the original equation is called an **extraneous solution** and must be rejected. In fact, $\sqrt{x} = -3$ has no solution. The solution set is $\emptyset$.

NOW TRY

NOW TRY ANSWERS
**2.** $\{2\}$ **3.** $\emptyset$

---

**NOTE** Because $\sqrt{x}$ represents the *principal* or *nonnegative* square root of $x$ in **Example 3,** we might have seen immediately that there is no solution.

| Solving a Radical Equation |
|---|

*Step 1* **Isolate a radical.** Arrange the terms so that a radical is isolated on one side of the equation.

*Step 2* **Square each side.**

*Step 3* **Combine like terms.**

*Step 4* **Repeat Steps 1–3,** if there is still a term with a radical.

*Step 5* **Solve the equation.** Find all proposed solutions.

*Step 6* **Check all proposed solutions** in the original equation.

NOW TRY
EXERCISE 4

Solve $t = \sqrt{t^2 + 3t + 9}$.

**EXAMPLE 4**  Using the Squaring Property with a Quadratic Expression

Solve $x = \sqrt{x^2 + 5x + 10}$.

*Step 1*  The radical is already isolated on the right side of the equation.

*Step 2*  Square each side.

$$x^2 = \left(\sqrt{x^2 + 5x + 10}\right)^2 \qquad \text{Squaring property}$$
$$x^2 = x^2 + 5x + 10 \qquad \left(\sqrt{x^2 + 5x + 10}\right)^2 = x^2 + 5x + 10$$

*Step 3*  $\qquad 0 = 5x + 10 \qquad \text{Subtract } x^2.$

*Step 4*  This step is not needed.

*Step 5*  $\quad -10 = 5x \qquad \text{Subtract 10.}$

$\qquad\qquad -2 = x \longleftarrow \text{Proposed solution}$

*Step 6*  CHECK  $\qquad x = \sqrt{x^2 + 5x + 10} \qquad \text{Original equation}$

$$-2 \stackrel{?}{=} \sqrt{(-2)^2 + 5(-2) + 10} \qquad \text{Let } x = -2.$$

The principal square root of a quantity *cannot* be negative.

$$-2 \stackrel{?}{=} \sqrt{4 - 10 + 10} \qquad \text{Multiply.}$$
$$-2 = 2 \qquad \text{False}$$

Since substituting $-2$ for $x$ leads to a false result, the equation has no solution, and the solution set is $\emptyset$.  NOW TRY

**OBJECTIVE 3**  Solve equations by squaring a binomial. Recall the rules for squaring binomials from **Section 5.6.**

$$(x + y)^2 = x^2 + 2xy + y^2 \quad \text{and} \quad (x - y)^2 = x^2 - 2xy + y^2$$

We apply the second pattern in **Example 5** when finding $(x - 3)^2$.

$$(x - 3)^2 \qquad \text{Remember the middle term when squaring.}$$
$$= x^2 - 2x(3) + 3^2$$
$$= x^2 - 6x + 9$$

**EXAMPLE 5**  Using the Squaring Property when One Side Has Two Terms

Solve $\sqrt{2x - 3} = x - 3$.

$$\sqrt{2x - 3} = x - 3$$
$$\left(\sqrt{2x - 3}\right)^2 = (x - 3)^2 \qquad \text{Square each side.}$$
$$2x - 3 = x^2 - 6x + 9 \qquad (x - y)^2 = x^2 - 2xy + y^2$$

NOW TRY ANSWER
4. $\emptyset$

NOW TRY
EXERCISE 5
Solve.

$$\sqrt{4x + 1} = x - 5$$

The equation $2x - 3 = x^2 - 6x + 9$ is quadratic because of the $x^2$-term. To solve it, as shown in **Section 6.5,** we must write the equation in standard form.

$$\text{Standard form} \rightarrow x^2 - 8x + 12 = 0 \qquad \text{Subtract } 2x, \text{ add 3, and interchange sides.}$$

$$(x - 6)(x - 2) = 0 \qquad \text{Factor.}$$

$$x - 6 = 0 \quad \text{or} \quad x - 2 = 0 \qquad \text{Zero-factor property}$$

$$x = 6 \quad \text{or} \qquad x = 2 \leftarrow \text{Proposed solutions}$$

CHECK
$$\sqrt{2x - 3} = x - 3 \qquad\qquad \sqrt{2x - 3} = x - 3$$
$$\sqrt{2(6) - 3} \overset{?}{=} 6 - 3 \quad \text{Let } x = 6. \qquad \sqrt{2(2) - 3} \overset{?}{=} 2 - 3 \quad \text{Let } x = 2.$$
$$\sqrt{12 - 3} \overset{?}{=} 3 \qquad\qquad\qquad \sqrt{4 - 3} \overset{?}{=} -1$$
$$\sqrt{9} \overset{?}{=} 3 \qquad\qquad\qquad\quad \sqrt{1} \overset{?}{=} -1$$
$$3 = 3 \ \checkmark \quad \text{True} \qquad\qquad\quad 1 \overset{?}{=} -1 \qquad \text{False}$$

Only 6 is a valid solution. (2 is extraneous.) The solution set is $\{6\}$. NOW TRY

NOW TRY
EXERCISE 6
Solve $\sqrt{27x} - 3 = 2x$.

**EXAMPLE 6** Rewriting an Equation before Using the Squaring Property

Solve $\sqrt{9x} - 1 = 2x$.

We must apply Step 1 here, and isolate the radical *before* squaring each side. If we skip Step 1 and begin by squaring instead, we obtain

$$\left(\sqrt{9x} - 1\right)^2 = (2x)^2$$

$$9x - 2\sqrt{9x} + 1 = 4x^2,$$

a more complicated equation that still contains a radical. Follow the steps below.

$$\sqrt{9x} - 1 = 2x$$

This is a key step. $\quad \sqrt{9x} = 2x + 1 \qquad$ Add 1 to isolate the radical. (Step 1)

$$\left(\sqrt{9x}\right)^2 = (2x + 1)^2 \qquad \text{Square both sides. (Step 2)}$$

$$9x = 4x^2 + 4x + 1 \qquad (x + y)^2 = x^2 + 2xy + y^2 \\ \text{No terms contain radicals.}$$

$$4x^2 - 5x + 1 = 0 \qquad \text{Standard form (Step 3)}$$

$$(4x - 1)(x - 1) = 0 \qquad \text{Factor. (Step 5; Step 4 is not needed.)}$$

$$4x - 1 = 0 \quad \text{or} \quad x - 1 = 0 \qquad \text{Zero-factor property}$$

$$x = \frac{1}{4} \quad \text{or} \qquad x = 1 \longleftarrow \text{Proposed solutions}$$

CHECK
$$\sqrt{9x} - 1 = 2x \qquad \text{(Step 6)} \qquad\qquad \sqrt{9x} - 1 = 2x \qquad \text{(Step 6)}$$
$$\sqrt{9\left(\frac{1}{4}\right)} - 1 \overset{?}{=} 2\left(\frac{1}{4}\right) \quad \text{Let } x = \tfrac{1}{4}. \qquad \sqrt{9(1)} - 1 \overset{?}{=} 2(1) \quad \text{Let } x = 1.$$
$$\frac{1}{2} = \frac{1}{2} \ \checkmark \quad \text{True} \qquad\qquad\qquad 2 = 2 \ \checkmark \quad \text{True}$$

NOW TRY ANSWERS
5. $\{12\}$    6. $\left\{\frac{3}{4}, 3\right\}$

Both proposed solutions check, so the solution set is $\left\{\frac{1}{4}, 1\right\}$. NOW TRY

---

⚠️ **CAUTION**  When squaring each side of

$$\sqrt{9x} = 2x + 1$$

in **Example 6,** the *entire* binomial $2x + 1$ must be squared to get $4x^2 + 4x + 1$. It is incorrect to square the $2x$ and the 1 separately to get $4x^2 + 1$.

---

⟳ NOW TRY
↪ EXERCISE 7

Solve.

$$\sqrt{x} + 2 = \sqrt{x + 8}$$

**EXAMPLE 7**  Using the Squaring Property Twice

Solve $\sqrt{21 + x} = 3 + \sqrt{x}$.

$$\sqrt{21 + x} = 3 + \sqrt{x}$$

$$\left(\sqrt{21 + x}\right)^2 = \left(3 + \sqrt{x}\right)^2 \qquad \text{Square each side.}$$

$$21 + x = 9 + 6\sqrt{x} + x \qquad \boxed{\text{Be careful here.}}$$

$$12 = 6\sqrt{x} \qquad \text{Subtract 9. Subtract } x.$$

$$2 = \sqrt{x} \qquad \text{Divide by 6.}$$

$$2^2 = \left(\sqrt{x}\right)^2 \qquad \text{Square each side again.}$$

$$4 = x \qquad \text{Apply the exponents.}$$

CHECK

$$\sqrt{21 + x} = 3 + \sqrt{x} \qquad \text{Original equation}$$

$$\sqrt{21 + 4} \stackrel{?}{=} 3 + \sqrt{4} \qquad \text{Let } x = 4.$$

$$\sqrt{25} \stackrel{?}{=} 3 + 2$$

$$5 = 5 \ \checkmark \qquad \text{True}$$

The solution set is $\{4\}$.

NOW TRY ⟳

---

**OBJECTIVE 4**  **Solve radical equations having cube root radicals.** We do this by extending the concept of raising both sides of an equation to a power.

**EXAMPLE 8**  Solving Equations with Cube Root Radicals

Solve each equation.

**(a)**

$$\sqrt[3]{5x} = \sqrt[3]{3x + 1}$$

$$\left(\sqrt[3]{5x}\right)^3 = \left(\sqrt[3]{3x + 1}\right)^3 \qquad \text{Cube each side.}$$

$$5x = 3x + 1 \qquad \text{Apply the exponents.}$$

$$2x = 1 \qquad \text{Subtract } 3x.$$

$$x = \frac{1}{2} \qquad \text{Divide by 2.}$$

CHECK

$$\sqrt[3]{5x} = \sqrt[3]{3x + 1} \qquad \text{Original equation}$$

$$\sqrt[3]{5\left(\frac{1}{2}\right)} \stackrel{?}{=} \sqrt[3]{3\left(\frac{1}{2}\right) + 1} \qquad \text{Let } x = \frac{1}{2}.$$

$$\sqrt[3]{\frac{5}{2}} = \sqrt[3]{\frac{5}{2}} \ \checkmark \qquad \text{True}$$

NOW TRY ANSWER
**7.** $\{1\}$

The solution set is $\left\{\frac{1}{2}\right\}$.

NOW TRY
EXERCISE 8

Solve each equation.

(a) $\sqrt[3]{8x - 3} = \sqrt[3]{4x}$

(b) $\sqrt[3]{2x^2} = \sqrt[3]{10x - 12}$

**(b)**

$$\sqrt[3]{x^2} = \sqrt[3]{26x + 27}$$

$$\left(\sqrt[3]{x^2}\right)^3 = \left(\sqrt[3]{26x + 27}\right)^3 \qquad \text{Cube each side.}$$

$$x^2 = 26x + 27 \qquad \text{Apply the exponents.}$$

$$x^2 - 26x - 27 = 0 \qquad \text{Standard form}$$

$$(x + 1)(x - 27) = 0 \qquad \text{Factor.}$$

$$x + 1 = 0 \quad \text{or} \quad x - 27 = 0 \qquad \text{Zero-factor property}$$

$$x = -1 \quad \text{or} \quad x = 27 \qquad \text{Solve.}$$

CHECK $\qquad \sqrt[3]{x^2} = \sqrt[3]{26x + 27}$ $\qquad\qquad\qquad \sqrt[3]{x^2} = \sqrt[3]{26x + 27}$

$\qquad \sqrt[3]{(-1)^2} \stackrel{?}{=} \sqrt[3]{26(-1) + 27}$ $\qquad\qquad \sqrt[3]{(27)^2} \stackrel{?}{=} \sqrt[3]{26(27) + 27}$

$\qquad\qquad\qquad\qquad\qquad$ Let $x = -1$. $\qquad\qquad\qquad\qquad\qquad\qquad$ Let $x = 27$.

$\qquad\qquad \sqrt[3]{1} \stackrel{?}{=} \sqrt[3]{1}$ $\qquad\qquad\qquad\qquad \sqrt[3]{729} \stackrel{?}{=} \sqrt[3]{729}$

NOW TRY ANSWERS

8. **(a)** $\left\{\frac{3}{4}\right\}$ **(b)** $\{2, 3\}$

$\qquad\qquad 1 = 1 \checkmark \quad \text{True}$ $\qquad\qquad\qquad\qquad 9 = 9 \checkmark \quad \text{True}$

Both proposed solutions check, so the solution set is $\{-1, 27\}$. NOW TRY

---

## 8.6 EXERCISES

*MyMathLab* | Math XL PRACTICE | WATCH | DOWNLOAD | READ | REVIEW

🌐 *Complete solution available on the Video Resources on DVD*

*Solve each equation.* **See Examples 1–4.**

**1.** $\sqrt{x} = 7$ $\qquad$ **2.** $\sqrt{x} = 10$ $\qquad$ 🌐 **3.** $\sqrt{x + 2} = 3$ $\qquad$ **4.** $\sqrt{x + 7} = 5$

**5.** $\sqrt{r - 4} = 9$ $\qquad$ **6.** $\sqrt{x - 12} = 3$ $\qquad$ **7.** $\sqrt{4 - t} = 7$ $\qquad$ **8.** $\sqrt{9 - s} = 5$

**9.** $\sqrt{2t + 3} = 0$ $\qquad$ **10.** $\sqrt{5x - 4} = 0$ $\qquad$ 🌐 **11.** $\sqrt{t} = -5$ $\qquad$ **12.** $\sqrt{p} = -8$

**13.** $\sqrt{w - 4} = 7$ $\qquad$ **14.** $\sqrt{t + 3} = 10$ $\qquad$ 🌐 **15.** $\sqrt{10x - 8} = 3\sqrt{x}$

**16.** $\sqrt{17t - 4} = 4\sqrt{t}$ $\qquad$ **17.** $5\sqrt{x} = \sqrt{10x + 15}$ $\qquad$ **18.** $4\sqrt{x} = \sqrt{20x - 16}$

**19.** $\sqrt{3x - 5} = \sqrt{2x + 1}$ $\qquad$ **20.** $\sqrt{5x + 2} = \sqrt{3x + 8}$ $\qquad$ 🌐 **21.** $k = \sqrt{k^2 - 5k - 15}$

**22.** $x = \sqrt{x^2 - 2x - 6}$ $\qquad$ **23.** $7x = \sqrt{49x^2 + 2x - 10}$ $\qquad$ **24.** $6x = \sqrt{36x^2 + 5x - 5}$

**25.** $\sqrt{2x + 2} = \sqrt{3x - 5}$ $\qquad$ **26.** $\sqrt{x + 2} = \sqrt{2x - 5}$ $\qquad$ **27.** $\sqrt{5x - 5} = \sqrt{4x + 1}$

**28.** $\sqrt{3m + 3} = \sqrt{5m - 1}$ $\qquad$ **29.** $\sqrt{3x - 8} = -2$ $\qquad$ **30.** $\sqrt{6t + 4} = -3$

**31.** *Concept Check* Consider the following "solution." *WHAT WENT WRONG?*

$$-\sqrt{x - 1} = -4$$

$$-(x - 1) = 16 \qquad \text{Square each side.}$$

$$-x + 1 = 16 \qquad \text{Distributive property}$$

$$-x = 15 \qquad \text{Subtract 1.}$$

$$x = -15 \qquad \text{Multiply by } -1.$$

Solution set: $\{-15\}$

**32.** *Concept Check* The first step in solving the equation

$$\sqrt{2x + 1} = x - 7$$

is to square each side of the equation. Errors often occur in solving equations such as this one when the right side of the equation is squared incorrectly. What is the square of the right side?

*Solve each equation.* ***See Examples 5 and 6.***

**33.** $\sqrt{5x + 11} = x + 3$      **34.** $\sqrt{5x + 1} = x + 1$

**35.** $\sqrt{2x + 1} = x - 7$      **36.** $\sqrt{3x + 10} = 2x - 5$

**37.** $\sqrt{x + 2} - 2 = x$      **38.** $\sqrt{x + 1} - 1 = x$

**39.** $\sqrt{12x + 12} + 10 = 2x$      **40.** $\sqrt{4x + 5} + 5 = 2x$

**41.** $\sqrt{6x + 7} - 1 = x + 1$      **42.** $\sqrt{8x + 8} - 1 = 2x + 1$

**43.** $2\sqrt{x + 7} = x - 1$      **44.** $3\sqrt{x + 13} = x + 9$

**45.** $\sqrt{2x + 4} = x$      **46.** $\sqrt{3x + 6} = x$

**47.** $\sqrt{x + 9} = x + 3$      **48.** $\sqrt{x + 3} = x - 9$

**49.** $3\sqrt{x - 2} = x - 2$      **50.** $2\sqrt{x + 4} = x + 1$

**51.** *Concept Check*   Consider the following "solution." *WHAT WENT WRONG?*

$$\sqrt{3x + 4} + \sqrt{x + 5} = 7$$

$$3x + 4 + x + 5 = 49 \qquad \text{Square each side.}$$

$$4x + 9 = 49 \qquad \text{Combine terms.}$$

$$4x = 40 \qquad \text{Subtract 9.}$$

$$x = 10 \qquad \text{Divide by 4.}$$

**52.** Explain how you can tell that the equation $\sqrt{x} = -8$ has no real number solution without performing any algebraic steps.

*Solve each equation.* ***See Example 7.***

**53.** $\sqrt{3x + 3} + \sqrt{x + 2} = 5$      **54.** $\sqrt{2x + 1} + \sqrt{x + 4} = 3$

**55.** $\sqrt{x + 6} = \sqrt{x + 72}$      **56.** $\sqrt{x - 4} = \sqrt{x - 32}$

**57.** $\sqrt{3x + 4} - \sqrt{2x - 4} = 2$      **58.** $\sqrt{1 - x} + \sqrt{x + 9} = 4$

**59.** $\sqrt{2x + 11} + \sqrt{x + 6} = 2$      **60.** $\sqrt{x + 9} + \sqrt{x + 16} = 7$

*Solve each equation. (Hint: In Exercises 67 and 68, extend the concepts to fourth root radicals.)* ***See Example 8.***

**61.** $\sqrt[3]{2x} = \sqrt[3]{5x + 2}$      **62.** $\sqrt[3]{4x + 3} = \sqrt[3]{2x - 1}$

**63.** $\sqrt[3]{x^2} = \sqrt[3]{8 + 7x}$      **64.** $\sqrt[3]{x^2} = \sqrt[3]{8 - 7x}$

**65.** $\sqrt[3]{3x^2 - 9x + 8} = \sqrt[3]{x}$      **66.** $\sqrt[3]{5x^2 - 6x + 2} = \sqrt[3]{x}$

**67.** $\sqrt[4]{x^2 + 24x} = 3$      **68.** $\sqrt[4]{x^2 + 6x} = 2$

*Solve each problem.*

**69.** The square root of the sum of a number and 4 is 5. Find the number.

**70.** A certain number is the same as the square root of the product of 8 and the number. Find the number.

**71.** Three times the square root of 2 equals the square root of the sum of some number and 10. Find the number.

**72.** The negative square root of a number equals that number decreased by 2. Find the number.

*Solve each problem. Give answers to the nearest tenth.*

**73.** To estimate the speed at which a car was traveling at the time of an accident, a police officer drives the car under conditions similar to those during which the accident took place and then skids to a stop. If the car is driven at 30 mph, then the speed $s$ at the time of the accident is given by

$$s = 30\sqrt{\frac{a}{p}},$$

where $a$ is the length of the skid marks left at the time of the accident and $p$ is the length of the skid marks in the police test. Find $s$ for the following values of $a$ and $p$.

**(a)** $a = 862$ ft; $p = 156$ ft   **(b)** $a = 382$ ft; $p = 96$ ft   **(c)** $a = 84$ ft; $p = 26$ ft

**74.** A formula for calculating the distance $d$ one can see from an airplane to the horizon on a clear day is

$$d = 1.22\sqrt{x},$$

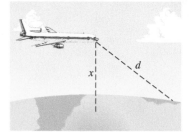

where $x$ is the altitude of the plane in feet and $d$ is given in miles. How far can one see to the horizon in a plane flying at the following altitudes?

**(a)** 15,000 ft   **(b)** 18,000 ft   **(c)** 24,000 ft

*On a clear day, the maximum distance in kilometers that you can see from a tall building is given by the formula*

$$\text{sight distance} = 111.7\sqrt{\text{height of building in kilometers}}.$$

*(Source: A Sourcebook of Applications of School Mathematics, NCTM, 1980.)*

*Use the conversion equations* 1 ft ≈ 0.3048 m *and* 1 km ≈ 0.621371 mi *as necessary to solve each problem. Round your answers to the nearest mile.*

**75.** As mentioned in the chapter opener, the London Eye is a unique form of a Ferris wheel that features 32 observation capsules and has a diameter of 135 m. (*Source:* www.londoneye.com) Does the formula justify the claim that on a clear day passengers on the London Eye can see Windsor Castle, 25 mi away?

**76.** The Empire State Building in New York City is 1250 ft high. (The antenna reaches to 1454 ft.) The observation deck, located on the 102nd floor, is at a height of 1050 ft. (*Source:* www.esbnyc.com) How far could you see on a clear day from the observation deck?

**77.** The twin Petronas Towers in Kuala Lumpur, Malaysia, are 1483 ft high (including the spires). (*Source: World Almanac and Book of Facts.*) How far would one of the builders have been able to see on a clear day from the top of a spire?

**78.** The Khufu Pyramid in Giza (also known as the Cheops Pyramid) was built in about 2566 B.C. to a height, at that time, of 481 ft. It is now only 449 ft high. How far would one of the original builders of the pyramid have been able to see from the top of the pyramid? (*Source:* www.archaeology.com)

**FOR INDIVIDUAL OR GROUP WORK**

The most common formula for the area of a triangle is $\mathcal{A} = \frac{1}{2}bh$, where $b$ is the length of the base and $h$ is the height. What if the height is not known?

**Heron's formula** allows us to calculate the area of a triangle if we know the lengths of the sides $a$, $b$, and $c$. First, let $s$ equal the **semiperimeter,** which is one-half the perimeter.

$$s = \frac{1}{2}(a + b + c)$$

The area $\mathcal{A}$ is given by the formula

$$\mathcal{A} = \sqrt{s(s - a)(s - b)(s - c)}.$$

The familiar 3-4-5 right triangle has area $\mathcal{A} = \frac{1}{2}(3)(4) = 6$ square units, calculated with the familiar formula. From Heron's formula, $s = \frac{1}{2}(3 + 4 + 5) = 6$, and

$$\mathcal{A} = \sqrt{6(6 - 3)(6 - 4)(6 - 5)} = \sqrt{36} = 6 \text{ square units,} \quad \text{as expected.}$$

Consider the figure below, and *work Exercises 79–84 in order.*

**79.** The lengths of the sides of the entire triangle are 7, 7, and 12. Find the semiperimeter $s$.

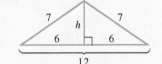

**80.** Now use Heron's formula to find the area of the entire triangle. Write it as a simplified radical.

**81.** Find the value of $h$ by using the Pythagorean theorem.

**82.** Find the area of each of the congruent right triangles forming the entire triangle by using the formula $\mathcal{A} = \frac{1}{2}bh$.

**83.** Double your result from **Exercise 82** to determine the area of the entire triangle.

**84.** How do your answers in **Exercises 80 and 83** compare?

**PREVIEW EXERCISES**

*Simplify each expression. Write the answer in exponential form with only positive exponents.*
***See Sections 5.1 and 5.2.***

**85.** $(5^2)^3$

**86.** $3^{-4} \cdot 3^{-1}$

**87.** $\dfrac{a^{-2}a^3}{a^4}$

**88.** $(2x^3)^{-1}$

**89.** $\left(\dfrac{p}{3}\right)^{-2}$

**90.** $\left(\dfrac{2y^3}{y^{-1}}\right)^{-2}$

**91.** $\dfrac{(c^3)^2 c^4}{(c^{-1})^3}$

**92.** $\dfrac{(m^2)^4 m^{-1}}{(m^3)^{-1}}$

## 8.7 Using Rational Numbers as Exponents

**OBJECTIVE 1** Define and use expressions of the form $a^{1/n}$. We now consider how an expression such as $5^{1/2}$ should be defined so that all the rules for exponents developed earlier still hold. Consider the following.

$$5^{1/2} \cdot 5^{1/2} = 5^{1/2+1/2} = 5^1 = 5$$

This agrees with the product rule for exponents from **Section 5.1.** By definition,

$$(\sqrt{5})(\sqrt{5}) = 5.$$

Since both $5^{1/2} \cdot 5^{1/2}$ and $\sqrt{5} \cdot \sqrt{5}$ equal 5,

$$5^{1/2} \text{ should equal } \sqrt{5}.$$

Similarly,

$$5^{1/3} \cdot 5^{1/3} \cdot 5^{1/3} = 5^{1/3+1/3+1/3} = 5^{3/3} = 5,$$

and

$$\sqrt[3]{5} \cdot \sqrt[3]{5} \cdot \sqrt[3]{5} = \sqrt[3]{5^3} = 5,$$

so

$$5^{1/3} \text{ should equal } \sqrt[3]{5}.$$

These examples suggest the following definition.

> **$a^{1/n}$**
>
> If $a$ is a nonnegative number and $n$ is a positive integer, then
>
> $$a^{1/n} = \sqrt[n]{a}.$$

*Notice that the denominator of the rational exponent is the index of the radical.*

**EXAMPLE 1** Using the Definition of $a^{1/n}$

Simplify by first writing in radical form.

**(a)** $16^{1/2}$   By the definition of $a^{1/n}$,   $16^{1/2} = \sqrt{16} = 4.$

**(b)** $27^{1/3} = \sqrt[3]{27} = 3$   **(c)** $216^{1/3} = \sqrt[3]{216} = 6$   **(d)** $64^{1/6} = \sqrt[6]{64} = 2$

> The denominator is the index.

NOW TRY

**OBJECTIVE 2** Define and use expressions of the form $a^{m/n}$. A more general exponential expression, such as $16^{3/4}$, can be defined using the power rule, $(a^m)^n = a^{mn}$.

$$16^{3/4} = (16^{1/4})^3 = (\sqrt[4]{16})^3 = 2^3 = 8$$

However, $16^{3/4}$ can also be written as follows.

$$16^{3/4} = (16^3)^{1/4} = (4096)^{1/4} = \sqrt[4]{4096} = 8$$

— Same answer

Either way, the answer is the same. Taking the root first involves smaller numbers and is often easier.

This example suggests the following definition for $a^{m/n}$.

---

**$a^{m/n}$**

If $a$ is a nonnegative number and $m$ and $n$ are integers with $n > 0$, then

$$a^{m/n} = (a^{1/n})^m = \left(\sqrt[n]{a}\right)^m.$$

---

NOW TRY
EXERCISE 2
Evaluate.
**(a)** $27^{4/3}$   **(b)** $16^{3/2}$
**(c)** $-16^{7/4}$

**EXAMPLE 2**   Using the Definition of $a^{m/n}$

Evaluate.

**(a)** $9^{3/2} = (9^{1/2})^3 = 3^3 = 27$

**(b)** $64^{2/3} = (64^{1/3})^2 = 4^2 = 16$

**(c)** $-32^{4/5} = -(32^{1/5})^4 = -2^4 = -16$

The base is 32, not $-32$.

Be careful with signs here.

NOW TRY

Earlier, $a^{-n}$ was defined as $a^{-n} = \frac{1}{a^n}$ for nonzero numbers $a$ and integers $n$. This same result applies to negative rational exponents.

---

**$a^{-m/n}$**

If $a$ is a positive number and $m$ and $n$ are integers with $n > 0$, then

$$a^{-m/n} = \frac{1}{a^{m/n}}.$$

---

NOW TRY
EXERCISE 3
Evaluate.
**(a)** $16^{-3/4}$   **(b)** $8^{-2/3}$

**EXAMPLE 3**   Using the Definition of $a^{-m/n}$

Evaluate.

**(a)** $32^{-3/5} = \frac{1}{32^{3/5}} = \frac{1}{(32^{1/5})^3} = \frac{1}{2^3} = \frac{1}{8}$   **(b)** $27^{-4/3} = \frac{1}{27^{4/3}} = \frac{1}{(27^{1/3})^4} = \frac{1}{3^4} = \frac{1}{81}$

Think: $32^{1/5} = \sqrt[5]{32} = 2$.

This is *not* the same as $-27^{4/3}$.

NOW TRY

⚠ **CAUTION**   In **Example 3(b)**, do *not* write $27^{-4/3}$ as $-27^{3/4}$. ***This is incorrect. The negative exponent does not indicate a negative number.*** Also, the negative exponent indicates to use the reciprocal of the *base*, not the reciprocal of the *exponent*.

---

**OBJECTIVE 3**   **Apply the rules for exponents using rational exponents.**
All the rules for exponents given earlier still hold when the exponents are fractions.

---

**EXAMPLE 4**   Using the Rules for Exponents with Fractional Exponents

Simplify. Write each answer in exponential form with only positive exponents.

Keep the same base.

Keep the same base.

NOW TRY ANSWERS
**2. (a)** 81 **(b)** 64 **(c)** $-128$
**3. (a)** $\frac{1}{8}$ **(b)** $\frac{1}{4}$

**(a)** $3^{2/3} \cdot 3^{5/3} = 3^{2/3+5/3} = 3^{7/3}$   **(b)** $\dfrac{5^{1/4}}{5^{3/4}} = 5^{1/4-3/4} = 5^{-2/4} = 5^{-1/2} = \dfrac{1}{5^{1/2}}$

**NOW TRY**
**EXERCISE 4**

Simplify. Write each answer in exponential form with only positive exponents.

**(a)** $7^{1/4} \cdot 7^{5/4}$   **(b)** $\dfrac{11^{1/3}}{11^{2/3}}$

**(c)** $\left(\dfrac{64}{125}\right)^{2/3}$   **(d)** $\dfrac{5^{1/3} \cdot 5^{-2/3}}{5^{-4/3}}$

**(c)** $(9^{1/4})^2 = 9^{2(1/4)} = 9^{2/4} = 9^{1/2} = \sqrt{9} = 3$

**(d)** $\left(\dfrac{9}{4}\right)^{5/2} = \dfrac{9^{5/2}}{4^{5/2}} = \dfrac{(9^{1/2})^5}{(4^{1/2})^5} = \dfrac{(\sqrt{9})^5}{(\sqrt{4})^5} = \dfrac{3^5}{2^5}$
*Use parentheses to avoid errors.*

**(e)** $\dfrac{2^{1/2} \cdot 2^{-1}}{2^{-3/2}} = \dfrac{2^{1/2+(-1)}}{2^{-3/2}} = \dfrac{2^{-1/2}}{2^{-3/2}} = 2^{-1/2-(-3/2)} = 2^{2/2} = 2^1 = 2$   NOW TRY

---

**NOW TRY**
**EXERCISE 5**

Simplify. Write each answer in exponential form with only positive exponents. Assume that all variables represent positive numbers.

**(a)** $\left(x^{2/3}y^{3/2}\right)^6$   **(b)** $\left(\dfrac{p^{1/5}}{q^{3/4}}\right)^3$

**(c)** $\dfrac{t^{-1} \cdot t^{3/4}}{t^{7/4}}$

**EXAMPLE 5** Using Fractional Exponents with Variables

Simplify. Write each answer in exponential form with only positive exponents. Assume that all variables represent positive numbers.

**(a)** $m^{1/5} \cdot m^{3/5} = m^{1/5+3/5} = m^{4/5}$   **(b)** $\dfrac{p^{5/3}}{p^{4/3}} = p^{5/3-4/3} = p^{1/3}$

**(c)** $(x^2y^{1/2})^4 = (x^2)^4(y^{1/2})^4 = x^8y^2$   **(d)** $\left(\dfrac{z^{1/4}}{w^{1/3}}\right)^5 = \dfrac{(z^{1/4})^5}{(w^{1/3})^5} = \dfrac{z^{5/4}}{w^{5/3}}$

**(e)** $\dfrac{k^{2/3} \cdot k^{-1/3}}{k^{5/3}} = k^{2/3+(-1/3)-5/3} = k^{-4/3} = \dfrac{1}{k^{4/3}}$
*Use parentheses to avoid errors.*   NOW TRY

---

⚠ **CAUTION** Errors often occur in problems like those in **Examples 4 and 5** because students try to convert the expressions to radicals. Remember that the *rules of exponents* apply here.

---

**NOW TRY**
**EXERCISE 6**

Simplify each radical by first writing it in exponential form.

**(a)** $\sqrt[6]{64^2}$   **(b)** $\left(\sqrt[10]{y}\right)^5$

**OBJECTIVE 4** Use rational exponents to simplify radicals.

**EXAMPLE 6** Simplifying Radicals by Using Rational Exponents

Simplify each radical by first writing it in exponential form.

**(a)** $\sqrt[6]{9^3} = (9^3)^{1/6} = 9^{3/6} = 9^{1/2} = \sqrt{9} = 3$

**(b)** $\left(\sqrt[4]{m}\right)^2 = (m^{1/4})^2 = m^{2/4} = m^{1/2} = \sqrt{m}, \quad m \geq 0$   NOW TRY

**NOW TRY ANSWERS**

4. **(a)** $7^{3/2}$ **(b)** $\dfrac{1}{11^{1/3}}$
   **(c)** $\dfrac{16}{25}$ **(d)** 5

5. **(a)** $x^4y^9$ **(b)** $\dfrac{p^{3/5}}{q^{9/4}}$ **(c)** $\dfrac{1}{t^2}$

6. **(a)** 4 **(b)** $\sqrt{y}, \ y \geq 0$

---

## 8.7 EXERCISES

**MyMathLab** | Math XL PRACTICE |  WATCH |  DOWNLOAD |  READ |  REVIEW

🌐 *Complete solution available on the Video Resources on DVD*

*Concept Check*   *Decide which one of the four choices is* not *equal to the given expression.*

**1.** $49^{1/2}$

   **A.** $-7$   **B.** 7   **C.** $\sqrt{49}$   **D.** $49^{0.5}$

**2.** $81^{1/2}$

   **A.** 9   **B.** $\sqrt{81}$   **C.** $81^{0.5}$   **D.** $\dfrac{81}{2}$

**3.** $-64^{1/3}$

   **A.** $-\sqrt{16}$   **B.** $-4$   **C.** 4   **D.** $-\sqrt[3]{64}$

**4.** $-125^{1/3}$

    **A.** $-\sqrt{25}$     **B.** $-5$     **C.** $-\sqrt[3]{125}$     **D.** $5$

*Simplify by first writing in radical form. **See Examples 1–3.***

**5.** $25^{1/2}$      **6.** $121^{1/2}$      **7.** $64^{1/3}$      **8.** $125^{1/3}$      **9.** $16^{1/4}$

**10.** $81^{1/4}$      **11.** $32^{1/5}$      **12.** $243^{1/5}$      **13.** $4^{3/2}$      **14.** $9^{5/2}$

**15.** $27^{2/3}$      **16.** $8^{5/3}$      **17.** $16^{3/4}$      **18.** $64^{5/3}$

**19.** $32^{2/5}$      **20.** $144^{3/2}$      **21.** $-8^{2/3}$      **22.** $-27^{5/3}$

**23.** $-64^{1/3}$      **24.** $-125^{5/3}$      **25.** $49^{-3/2}$      **26.** $9^{-5/2}$

**27.** $216^{-2/3}$      **28.** $32^{-4/5}$      **29.** $-16^{-5/4}$      **30.** $-81^{-3/4}$

*Simplify. Write answers in exponential form with only positive exponents. Assume that all variables represent positive numbers. **See Examples 4 and 5.***

**31.** $2^{1/3} \cdot 2^{7/3}$      **32.** $5^{2/3} \cdot 5^{5/3}$      **33.** $6^{1/4} \cdot 6^{-3/4}$      **34.** $12^{-2/5} \cdot 12^{1/5}$

**35.** $\dfrac{15^{3/4}}{15^{5/4}}$      **36.** $\dfrac{7^{2/5}}{7^{3/5}}$      **37.** $\dfrac{11^{-2/7}}{11^{-3/7}}$

**38.** $\dfrac{4^{-4/9}}{4^{-5/9}}$      **39.** $\left(8^{3/2}\right)^2$      **40.** $\left(5^{2/5}\right)^{10}$

**41.** $\left(6^{1/3}\right)^{3/2}$      **42.** $\left(7^{2/5}\right)^{5/3}$      **43.** $\left(\dfrac{25}{4}\right)^{3/2}$

**44.** $\left(\dfrac{8}{27}\right)^{2/3}$      **45.** $\dfrac{2^{2/5} \cdot 2^{-3/5}}{2^{7/5}}$      **46.** $\dfrac{3^{-3/4} \cdot 3^{5/4}}{3^{-1/4}}$

**47.** $\dfrac{6^{-2/9}}{6^{1/9} \cdot 6^{-5/9}}$      **48.** $\dfrac{8^{6/7}}{8^{2/7} \cdot 8^{-1/7}}$      **49.** $x^{2/5} \cdot x^{7/5}$

**50.** $y^{2/3} \cdot y^{5/3}$      **51.** $\dfrac{r^{4/9}}{r^{3/9}}$      **52.** $\dfrac{s^{5/6}}{s^{4/6}}$

**53.** $\left(m^3 n^{1/4}\right)^{2/3}$      **54.** $\left(p^4 q^{1/2}\right)^{4/3}$      **55.** $\left(\dfrac{a^{2/3}}{b^{1/4}}\right)^6$

**56.** $\left(\dfrac{t^{3/7}}{s^{1/3}}\right)^{21}$      **57.** $\dfrac{m^{3/4} \cdot m^{-1/4}}{m^{1/3}}$      **58.** $\dfrac{q^{5/6} \cdot q^{-1/6}}{q^{1/3}}$

*Simplify each radical by first writing it in exponential form. Give the answer as an integer or a radical in simplest form. Assume that all variables represent nonnegative numbers. **See Example 6.***

**59.** $\sqrt[6]{4^3}$      **60.** $\sqrt[9]{8^3}$      **61.** $\sqrt[8]{16^2}$      **62.** $\sqrt[9]{27^3}$

**63.** $\sqrt[4]{a^2}$      **64.** $\sqrt[9]{b^3}$      **65.** $\sqrt[6]{k^4}$      **66.** $\sqrt[8]{m^4}$

### PREVIEW EXERCISES

*Find the real square roots of each number. Simplify where possible. **See Section 8.1.***

**67.** $121$      **68.** $0.49$      **69.** $\dfrac{1}{4}$      **70.** $\dfrac{4}{25}$

*Find and simplify the positive square root of each number. **See Section 8.2.***

**71.** $236$      **72.** $160$      **73.** $147$      **74.** $320$

# CHAPTER 8 SUMMARY

## KEY TERMS

**8.1**

square root
principal square root
negative square root
radicand
radical
radical expression

perfect square
cube root
fourth root
index (order)
perfect cube
perfect fourth
    power

**8.3**

like radicals
unlike radicals

**8.4**

rationalizing the
    denominator

**8.5**

conjugate

**8.6**

radical equation
squaring property of equality
extraneous solution

## NEW SYMBOLS

$\sqrt{\phantom{x}}$    radical symbol

$\approx$    is approximately
    equal to

$\sqrt[3]{a}$   cube root of $a$
$\sqrt[n]{a}$   $n$th root of $a$

$a^{1/n}$   $n$th root of $a$

## TEST YOUR WORD POWER

*See how well you have learned the vocabulary in this chapter.*

**1.** The **square root** of a number is
  **A.** the number raised to the second power
  **B.** the number under a radical sign
  **C.** a number that, when multiplied by itself, gives the original number
  **D.** the inverse of the number.

**2.** A **radical** is
  **A.** a symbol that indicates the $n$th root
  **B.** an algebraic expression containing a square root
  **C.** the positive $n$th root of a number
  **D.** a radical sign and the number or expression under it.

**3.** The **principal root** of a positive number with even index $n$ is
  **A.** the positive $n$th root of the number
  **B.** the negative $n$th root of the number
  **C.** the square root of the number
  **D.** the cube root of the number.

**4.** **Like radicals** are
  **A.** radicals in simplest form
  **B.** algebraic expressions containing radicals
  **C.** multiples of the same root of the same number
  **D.** radicals with the same index.

**5.** **Rationalizing the denominator** is the process of
  **A.** eliminating fractions from a radical expression
  **B.** changing the denominator of a fraction from a radical to a rational number
  **C.** clearing a radical expression of radicals
  **D.** multiplying radical expressions.

**6.** The **conjugate** of $a + b$ is
  **A.** $a - b$
  **B.** $a \cdot b$
  **C.** $a \div b$
  **D.** $(a + b)^2$.

### ANSWERS

**1.** C; *Examples:* 6 is a square root of 36, since $6^2 = 6 \cdot 6 = 36$. $-6$ is also a square root of 36.    **2.** D; *Examples:* $\sqrt{144}$, $\sqrt{4xy^2}$, $\sqrt{4 + t^2}$
**3.** A; *Examples:* $\sqrt{36} = 6$, $\sqrt[4]{81} = 3$, $\sqrt[6]{64} = 2$    **4.** C; *Examples:* $\sqrt{7}$ and $3\sqrt{7}$ are like radicals, as are $2\sqrt[3]{6k}$ and $5\sqrt[3]{6k}$.    **5.** B; *Example:*
To rationalize the denominator of $\dfrac{5}{\sqrt{3} + 1}$, multiply numerator and denominator by $\sqrt{3} - 1$ to get $\dfrac{5(\sqrt{3} - 1)}{2}$.    **6.** A; *Example:* The conjugate of
$\sqrt{3} + 1$ is $\sqrt{3} - 1$.

| CONCEPTS | EXAMPLES |
|---|---|

## 8.1 Evaluating Roots

If $a$ is a positive real number, then

$\sqrt{a}$ is the positive square root of $a$;

$-\sqrt{a}$ is the negative square root of $a$; $\sqrt{0} = 0$.

If $a$ is a negative real number, then $\sqrt{a}$ is not a real number.

If $a$ is a positive rational number, then $\sqrt{a}$ is rational if $a$ is a perfect square and $\sqrt{a}$ is irrational if $a$ is not a perfect square.

$\sqrt{49} = 7$

$-\sqrt{81} = -9$

$\sqrt{-25}$ is not a real number.

$\sqrt{\dfrac{4}{9}}, \sqrt{16}$ are rational.　　$\sqrt{\dfrac{2}{3}}, \sqrt{21}$ are irrational.

**Distance Formula**
The distance between $(x_1, y_1)$ and $(x_2, y_2)$ is

$$d = \sqrt{(x_2 - x_1)^2 + (y_2 - y_1)^2}.$$

The distance between $(0, -2)$ and $(-1, 1)$ is

$$\sqrt{(-1 - 0)^2 + [1 - (-2)]^2}$$
$$= \sqrt{(-1)^2 + 3^2}$$
$$= \sqrt{1 + 9}$$
$$= \sqrt{10}.$$

Each real number has exactly one real cube root.

$\sqrt[3]{27} = 3$　　$\sqrt[3]{-8} = -2$

## 8.2 Multiplying, Dividing, and Simplifying Radicals

**Product Rule for Radicals**
For nonnegative real numbers $a$ and $b$,

$$\sqrt{a} \cdot \sqrt{b} = \sqrt{ab} \quad \text{and} \quad \sqrt{a \cdot b} = \sqrt{a} \cdot \sqrt{b}.$$

$\sqrt{5} \cdot \sqrt{7} = \sqrt{35}$

$\sqrt{48} = \sqrt{16 \cdot 3} = \sqrt{16} \cdot \sqrt{3} = 4\sqrt{3}$

**Quotient Rule for Radicals**
If $a$ and $b$ are nonnegative real numbers and $b \neq 0$, then

$$\frac{\sqrt{a}}{\sqrt{b}} = \sqrt{\frac{a}{b}} \quad \text{and} \quad \sqrt{\frac{a}{b}} = \frac{\sqrt{a}}{\sqrt{b}}.$$

If all indicated roots are real, then

$$\sqrt[n]{a} \cdot \sqrt[n]{b} = \sqrt[n]{ab} \quad \text{and} \quad \frac{\sqrt[n]{a}}{\sqrt[n]{b}} = \sqrt[n]{\frac{a}{b}} \ (b \neq 0).$$

$\dfrac{\sqrt{8}}{\sqrt{2}} = \sqrt{\dfrac{8}{2}} = \sqrt{4} = 2$　　$\sqrt{\dfrac{25}{64}} = \dfrac{\sqrt{25}}{\sqrt{64}} = \dfrac{5}{8}$

$\sqrt[3]{5} \cdot \sqrt[3]{3} = \sqrt[3]{15}$　　$\dfrac{\sqrt[4]{12}}{\sqrt[4]{4}} = \sqrt[4]{\dfrac{12}{4}} = \sqrt[4]{3}$

## 8.3 Adding and Subtracting Radicals

Add and subtract like radicals by using the distributive property. ***Only like radicals can be combined in this way.***

$2\sqrt{5} + 4\sqrt{5}$
$= (2 + 4)\sqrt{5}$
$= 6\sqrt{5}$

$\sqrt{8} - \sqrt{32}$
$= 2\sqrt{2} - 4\sqrt{2}$
$= -2\sqrt{2}$

## 8.4 Rationalizing the Denominator

The denominator of a radical can be rationalized by multiplying both the numerator and denominator by a number that will eliminate the radical from the denominator.

$\dfrac{2}{\sqrt{3}} = \dfrac{2 \cdot \sqrt{3}}{\sqrt{3} \cdot \sqrt{3}} = \dfrac{2\sqrt{3}}{3}$

$\sqrt[3]{\dfrac{5}{6}} = \dfrac{\sqrt[3]{5} \cdot \sqrt[3]{6^2}}{\sqrt[3]{6} \cdot \sqrt[3]{6^2}} = \dfrac{\sqrt[3]{180}}{6}$

(continued)

| CONCEPTS | EXAMPLES |
|---|---|

### 8.5 More Simplifying and Operations with Radicals

When appropriate, use the rules for adding and multiplying polynomials to simplify radical expressions.

$$\sqrt{6}\left(\sqrt{5} - \sqrt{7}\right) = \sqrt{30} - \sqrt{42} \quad \text{Distributive property}$$

$$\left(\sqrt{3} + 1\right)\left(\sqrt{3} - 2\right)$$
$$= 3 - 2\sqrt{3} + \sqrt{3} - 2 \quad \text{FOIL}$$
$$= 1 - \sqrt{3} \quad \text{Combine like terms.}$$

The formulas

$$(a + b)^2 = a^2 + 2ab + b^2,$$
$$(a - b)^2 = a^2 - 2ab + b^2,$$

and $$(a + b)(a - b) = a^2 - b^2$$

are useful when simplifying radical expressions.

$$\left(\sqrt{13} - \sqrt{2}\right)^2$$
$$= \left(\sqrt{13}\right)^2 - 2\left(\sqrt{13}\right)\left(\sqrt{2}\right) + \left(\sqrt{2}\right)^2$$
$$= 13 - 2\sqrt{26} + 2$$
$$= 15 - 2\sqrt{26}$$

$$\left(\sqrt{5} + \sqrt{3}\right)\left(\sqrt{5} - \sqrt{3}\right)$$
$$= 5 - 3, \quad \text{or} \quad 2$$

Any denominators with radicals should be rationalized.

$$\frac{3}{\sqrt{6}} = \frac{3 \cdot \sqrt{6}}{\sqrt{6} \cdot \sqrt{6}} = \frac{3\sqrt{6}}{6} = \frac{\sqrt{6}}{2}$$

If a radical expression contains two terms in the denominator and at least one of those terms is a square root radical, multiply both numerator and denominator by the conjugate of the denominator.

$$\frac{6}{\sqrt{7} - \sqrt{2}}$$

$$= \frac{6\left(\sqrt{7} + \sqrt{2}\right)}{\left(\sqrt{7} - \sqrt{2}\right)\left(\sqrt{7} + \sqrt{2}\right)} \quad \begin{array}{l}\text{Multiply by the}\\\text{conjugate of the}\\\text{denominator.}\end{array}$$

$$= \frac{6\left(\sqrt{7} + \sqrt{2}\right)}{7 - 2} \quad \text{Multiply fractions.}$$

$$= \frac{6\left(\sqrt{7} + \sqrt{2}\right)}{5} \quad \text{Subtract.}$$

### 8.6 Solving Equations with Radicals

**Solving a Radical Equation**

*Step 1*  Isolate a radical.

*Step 2*  Square each side. (By the squaring property of equality, all solutions of the original equation are *among* the solutions of the squared equation.)

*Step 3*  Combine like terms.

*Step 4*  If there is still a term with a radical, repeat Steps 1–3.

*Step 5*  Solve the equation for proposed solutions.

*Step 6*  Check all proposed solutions from Step 5 in the original equation.

Solve $\sqrt{2x - 3} + x = 3$.

$$\sqrt{2x - 3} = 3 - x \quad \text{Isolate the radical.}$$

$$\left(\sqrt{2x - 3}\right)^2 = (3 - x)^2 \quad \text{Square each side.}$$

$$2x - 3 = 9 - 6x + x^2 \quad \begin{array}{l}\text{Remember the middle}\\\text{term when squaring the}\\\text{binomial on the right.}\end{array}$$

$$0 = x^2 - 8x + 12 \quad \text{Standard form}$$

$$0 = (x - 2)(x - 6) \quad \text{Factor.}$$

$$x - 2 = 0 \quad \text{or} \quad x - 6 = 0 \longleftarrow \text{Zero-factor property}$$

$$x = 2 \quad \text{or} \quad x = 6 \quad \text{Proposed solutions}$$

Verify that 2 is the only solution (6 is extraneous). The solution set is $\{2\}$.

(continued)

| CONCEPTS | EXAMPLES |
|---|---|
| **8.7** **Using Rational Numbers as Exponents**<br><br>Assume that $a \geq 0$, $m$ and $n$ are integers, and $n > 0$.<br><br>$a^{1/n} = \sqrt[n]{a}$<br><br>$a^{m/n} = \sqrt[n]{a^m} = \left(\sqrt[n]{a}\right)^m$<br><br>$a^{-m/n} = \dfrac{1}{a^{m/n}} \quad (a \neq 0)$ | $8^{1/3} = \sqrt[3]{8} = 2$<br><br>$(81)^{3/4} = \sqrt[4]{81^3} = \left(\sqrt[4]{81}\right)^3 = 3^3 = 27$<br><br>$36^{-3/2} = \dfrac{1}{36^{3/2}} = \dfrac{1}{(36^{1/2})^3} = \dfrac{1}{6^3} = \dfrac{1}{216}$ |

# CHAPTER 8 REVIEW EXERCISES

**8.1** *Find all square roots of each number.*

**1.** 49 **2.** 81 **3.** 196 **4.** 121 **5.** 225 **6.** 729

*Find each indicated root. If the root is not a real number, say so.*

**7.** $\sqrt{16}$ **8.** $-\sqrt{36}$ **9.** $\sqrt[3]{1000}$ **10.** $\sqrt[4]{81}$

**11.** $\sqrt{-8100}$ **12.** $-\sqrt{4225}$ **13.** $\sqrt{\dfrac{49}{36}}$ **14.** $\sqrt{\dfrac{100}{81}}$

**15.** Find the distance between $(-3, -5)$ and $(4, -3)$.

**16.** Find the value of $x$ in the figure.

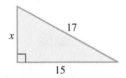

**17.** An HP f1905 computer monitor has viewing screen dimensions as shown in the figure. Find the diagonal measure of the viewing screen to the nearest tenth. (*Source:* Author's computer.)

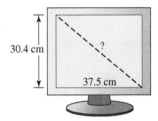

30.4 cm

37.5 cm

*Determine whether each number is* rational, irrational, *or* not a real number. *If the number is rational, give its exact value. If the number is irrational, give a decimal approximation rounded to the nearest thousandth.*

**18.** $\sqrt{111}$ **19.** $-\sqrt{25}$ **20.** $\sqrt{-4}$

**8.2** *Simplify each expression.*

**21.** $\sqrt{5} \cdot \sqrt{15}$ **22.** $-\sqrt{27}$ **23.** $\sqrt{160}$ **24.** $\sqrt[3]{-1331}$

**25.** $\sqrt[3]{1728}$ **26.** $\sqrt{12} \cdot \sqrt{27}$ **27.** $\sqrt{32} \cdot \sqrt{48}$ **28.** $\sqrt{50} \cdot \sqrt{125}$

*Use the product rule, the quotient rule, or both to simplify each expression.*

**29.** $-\sqrt{\dfrac{121}{400}}$ **30.** $\sqrt{\dfrac{3}{49}}$ **31.** $\sqrt{\dfrac{7}{169}}$ **32.** $\sqrt{\dfrac{1}{6}} \cdot \sqrt{\dfrac{5}{6}}$

**33.** $\sqrt{\dfrac{2}{5}} \cdot \sqrt{\dfrac{2}{45}}$  **34.** $\dfrac{3\sqrt{10}}{\sqrt{5}}$  **35.** $\dfrac{24\sqrt{12}}{6\sqrt{3}}$  **36.** $\dfrac{8\sqrt{150}}{4\sqrt{75}}$

*Simplify each expression. Assume that all variables represent nonnegative real numbers.*

**37.** $\sqrt{p} \cdot \sqrt{p}$  **38.** $\sqrt{k} \cdot \sqrt{m}$  **39.** $\sqrt{r^{18}}$

**40.** $\sqrt{x^{10}y^{16}}$  **41.** $\sqrt{a^{15}b^{21}}$  **42.** $\sqrt{121x^6y^{10}}$

**8.3** *Simplify, and combine terms where possible.*

**43.** $7\sqrt{11} + \sqrt{11}$  **44.** $3\sqrt{2} + 6\sqrt{2}$  **45.** $3\sqrt{75} + 2\sqrt{27}$

**46.** $4\sqrt{12} + \sqrt{48}$  **47.** $4\sqrt{24} - 3\sqrt{54} + \sqrt{6}$  **48.** $2\sqrt{7} - 4\sqrt{28} + 3\sqrt{63}$

**49.** $\dfrac{2}{5}\sqrt{75} + \dfrac{3}{4}\sqrt{160}$  **50.** $\dfrac{1}{3}\sqrt{18} + \dfrac{1}{4}\sqrt{32}$  **51.** $\sqrt{15} \cdot \sqrt{2} + 5\sqrt{30}$

*Simplify each expression. Assume that all variables represent nonnegative real numbers.*

**52.** $\sqrt{4x} + \sqrt{36x} - \sqrt{9x}$  **53.** $\sqrt{20m^2} - m\sqrt{45}$  **54.** $3k\sqrt{8k^2n} + 5k^2\sqrt{2n}$

**8.4** *Perform each indicated operation and write answers in simplest form. Assume that all variables represent positive real numbers.*

**55.** $\dfrac{8\sqrt{2}}{\sqrt{5}}$  **56.** $\dfrac{5}{\sqrt{5}}$  **57.** $\dfrac{12}{\sqrt{24}}$  **58.** $\dfrac{\sqrt{2}}{\sqrt{15}}$  **59.** $\sqrt{\dfrac{2}{5}}$

**60.** $\sqrt{\dfrac{5}{14}} \cdot \sqrt{28}$  **61.** $\sqrt{\dfrac{2}{7}} \cdot \sqrt{\dfrac{1}{3}}$  **62.** $\sqrt{\dfrac{r^2}{16x}}$  **63.** $\sqrt[3]{\dfrac{1}{3}}$  **64.** $\sqrt[3]{\dfrac{2}{7}}$

**8.5** *Simplify each expression.*

**65.** $-\sqrt{3}\left(\sqrt{5} + \sqrt{27}\right)$  **66.** $3\sqrt{2}\left(\sqrt{3} + 2\sqrt{2}\right)$

**67.** $\left(2\sqrt{3} - 4\right)\left(5\sqrt{3} + 2\right)$  **68.** $\left(5\sqrt{7} + 2\right)^2$

**69.** $\left(\sqrt{5} - \sqrt{7}\right)\left(\sqrt{5} + \sqrt{7}\right)$  **70.** $\left(2\sqrt{3} + 5\right)\left(2\sqrt{3} - 5\right)$

*Rationalize each denominator.*

**71.** $\dfrac{1}{2 + \sqrt{5}}$  **72.** $\dfrac{\sqrt{8}}{\sqrt{2} + 6}$  **73.** $\dfrac{2 + \sqrt{6}}{\sqrt{3} - 1}$

*Write each quotient in lowest terms.*

**74.** $\dfrac{15 + 10\sqrt{6}}{15}$  **75.** $\dfrac{3 + 9\sqrt{7}}{12}$  **76.** $\dfrac{6 + \sqrt{192}}{2}$

**8.6** *Solve each equation.*

**77.** $\sqrt{m} - 5 = 0$  **78.** $\sqrt{p} + 4 = 0$  **79.** $\sqrt{x + 1} = 7$

**80.** $\sqrt{5m + 4} = 3\sqrt{m}$  **81.** $\sqrt{2p + 3} = \sqrt{5p - 3}$  **82.** $\sqrt{-2t - 4} = t + 2$

**83.** $\sqrt{13 + 4t} = t + 4$  **84.** $\sqrt{2 - x} + 3 = x + 7$

**85.** $\sqrt[3]{x + 4} = \sqrt[3]{16 - 2x}$  **86.** $\sqrt{5x + 6} + \sqrt{3x + 4} = 2$

**8.7** *Simplify each expression. Assume that all variables represent positive real numbers.*

**87.** $81^{1/2}$

**88.** $-125^{1/3}$

**89.** $7^{2/3} \cdot 7^{7/3}$

**90.** $\dfrac{13^{4/5}}{13^{-3/5}}$

**91.** $\dfrac{x^{1/4} \cdot x^{5/4}}{x^{3/4}}$

**92.** $\sqrt[8]{49^4}$

## MIXED REVIEW EXERCISES

*Simplify each expression. Assume that all variables represent positive real numbers.*

**93.** $64^{2/3}$

**94.** $\sqrt{\dfrac{1}{3}} \cdot \sqrt{\dfrac{24}{5}}$

**95.** $\dfrac{1}{5 + \sqrt{2}}$

**96.** $\sqrt[3]{-125}$

**97.** $\sqrt{50y^2}$

**98.** $\sqrt{\dfrac{16r^3}{3s}}$

**99.** $-\sqrt{5}\left(\sqrt{2} + \sqrt{75}\right)$

**100.** $-\sqrt{162} + \sqrt{8}$

**101.** $\dfrac{12 + 6\sqrt{13}}{12}$

**102.** $\left(6\sqrt{7} + 2\right)\left(4\sqrt{7} - 1\right)$

**103.** $\left(\sqrt{5} - \sqrt{2}\right)^2$

**104.** $\dfrac{x^{8/3}}{x^{2/3}}$

**105.** $-\sqrt{121}$

**106.** $2\sqrt{27} + 3\sqrt{75} - \sqrt{300}$

*Solve.*

**107.** $\sqrt{x + 2} = x - 4$

**108.** $\sqrt{x} + 3 = 0$

**109.** $\sqrt{1 + 3t} - t = -3$

**110.** A biologist has shown that the number of different plant species $S$ on a Galápagos island is related to the area $\mathcal{A}$ (in square miles) of the island by

$$S = 28.6\sqrt[3]{\mathcal{A}}.$$

How many plant species would exist on such an island with the following areas?

**(a)** 8 mi$^2$    **(b)** 1790 mi$^2$

---

## CHAPTER **8**

## TEST

Step-by-step test solutions are found on the Chapter Test Prep Videos available via the Video Resources on DVD, in *MyMathLab*, or on YouTube (search "LialBeginningAlgebra").

*View the complete solutions to all Chapter Test exercises on the Video Resources on DVD.*

**1.** Find all square roots of 196.

**2.** Consider $\sqrt{142}$.

   **(a)** Determine whether it is rational or irrational.

   **(b)** Find a decimal approximation to the nearest thousandth.

**3.** Match each radical in Column I with the equivalent choice in Column II. Choices may be used once, more than once, or not at all.

| I | | II | |
|---|---|---|---|
| **(a)** $\sqrt{64}$ | **(b)** $-\sqrt{64}$ | **A.** 4 | **B.** 8 |
| **(c)** $\sqrt{-64}$ | **(d)** $\sqrt[3]{64}$ | **C.** $-4$ | **D.** Not a real number |
| **(e)** $\sqrt[3]{-64}$ | **(f)** $-\sqrt[3]{-64}$ | **E.** 16 | **F.** $-8$ |

*Simplify where possible.*

**4.** $\sqrt{\dfrac{128}{25}}$

**5.** $\sqrt[3]{32}$

**6.** $\dfrac{20\sqrt{18}}{5\sqrt{3}}$

**7.** $3\sqrt{28} + \sqrt{63}$

**8.** $3\sqrt{27x} - 4\sqrt{48x} + 2\sqrt{3x}$

**9.** $\sqrt[3]{32x^2y^3}$

**10.** $\left(6 - \sqrt{5}\right)\left(6 + \sqrt{5}\right)$

**11.** $\left(2 - \sqrt{7}\right)\left(3\sqrt{2} + 1\right)$

**12.** $\left(\sqrt{5} + \sqrt{6}\right)^2$

**13.** $\sqrt[3]{16x^4} - 2\sqrt[3]{128x^4}$

**14.** $\sqrt[3]{\dfrac{2}{3}}$

*Solve each problem.*

**15.** Find the measure of the unknown leg of this right triangle.

    **(a)** Give its length in simplified radical form.

    **(b)** Give the length to the nearest thousandth.

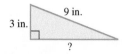

**16.** In electronics, the impedance $Z$ of an alternating series circuit is given by the formula

$$Z = \sqrt{R^2 + X^2},$$

where $R$ is the resistance and $X$ is the reactance, both in ohms. Find the value of the impedance $Z$ if $R = 40$ ohms and $X = 30$ ohms. (*Source:* Cooke, Nelson M., and Orleans, Joseph B., *Mathematics Essential to Electricity and Radio,* McGraw-Hill.)

*Rationalize each denominator.*

**17.** $\dfrac{5\sqrt{2}}{\sqrt{7}}$

**18.** $\sqrt{\dfrac{2}{3x}}$

**19.** $\dfrac{-2}{\sqrt[3]{4}}$

**20.** $\dfrac{-3}{4 - \sqrt{3}}$

**21.** Write $\dfrac{2 + \sqrt{8}}{4}$ in lowest terms.

*Solve each equation.*

**22.** $\sqrt{2x + 6} + 4 = 2$

**23.** $\sqrt{x + 1} = 5 - x$

**24.** $3\sqrt{x - 1} = 2x$

**25.** $\sqrt{2x + 9} + \sqrt{x + 5} = 2$

**26.** *Concept Check*    Consider the following "solution." **WHAT WENT WRONG?**

$$\sqrt{2x + 1} + 5 = 0$$

$$\sqrt{2x + 1} = -5 \qquad \text{Subtract 5.}$$

$$2x + 1 = 25 \qquad \text{Square both sides.}$$

$$2x = 24 \qquad \text{Subtract 1.}$$

$$x = 12 \qquad \text{Divide by 2.}$$

The solution set is $\{12\}$.

*Simplify each expression.*

**27.** $8^{4/3}$

**28.** $-125^{2/3}$

**29.** $5^{3/4} \cdot 5^{1/4}$

**30.** $\dfrac{\left(3^{1/4}\right)^3}{3^{7/4}}$

*Simplify each expression.*

**1.** $3(6 + 7) + 6 \cdot 4 - 3^2$

**2.** $\dfrac{3(6 + 7) + 3}{2(4) - 1}$

**3.** $|-6| - |-3|$

*Solve each equation or inequality.*

**4.** $5(k - 4) - k = k - 11$

**5.** $-\dfrac{3}{4}x \le 12$

**6.** $5z + 3 - 4 > 2z + 9 + z$

**7.** Trevor Brazile won the ProRodeo All-Around Championship in both 2006 and 2007. He set a new record for winnings in 2006 and then broke his own record by $95,191 in 2007. He won a total of $755,039 in these two years. How much did he win each year? (*Source: The World Almanac and Book of Facts.*)

*Graph.*

**8.** $-4x + 5y = -20$

**9.** $x = 2$

**10.** $2x - 5y > 10$

**11.** The graph shows a line that models the number of cell phone subscribers in millions in the United States from 2002 to 2008.

   **(a)** Use the ordered pairs shown on the graph to find the slope of the line to the nearest tenth. Interpret the slope.

   **(b)** Use the slope from part (a) and the ordered pair $(0, 140.8)$ to find the equation of the line that models the data, where $x = 0$ represents 2002.

   **(c)** Use the equation from part (b) to estimate the number of cell phone subscribers in 2010. Round to the nearest tenth.

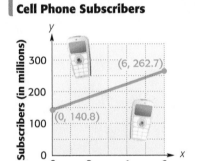

**Cell Phone Subscribers**

*Source: CITA—The Wireless Association.*

*Solve each system of equations.*

**12.** $4x - \phantom{2}y = 19$
$\phantom{4}3x + 2y = -5$

**13.** $2x - y = 6$
$\phantom{2}3y = 6x - 18$

**14.** Des Moines and Chicago are 345 mi apart. Two cars start from these cities, traveling toward each other. They meet after 3 hr. The car from Chicago has an average rate 7 mph faster than the other car. Find the average rate of each car. (*Source: State Farm Road Atlas.*)

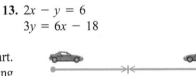

*Simplify and write each expression without negative exponents. Assume that variables represent positive real numbers.*

**15.** $(3x^6)(2x^2y)^2$

**16.** $\left(\dfrac{3^2y^{-2}}{2^{-1}y^3}\right)^{-3}$

**17.** Subtract $7x^3 - 8x^2 + 4$ from $10x^3 + 3x^2 - 9$.

**18.** Divide $\dfrac{8t^3 - 4t^2 - 14t + 15}{2t + 3}$.

*Factor each polynomial completely.*

**19.** $m^2 + 12m + 32$        **20.** $12a^2 + 4ab - 5b^2$       **21.** $81z^2 + 72z + 16$

*Perform each indicated operation. Express answers in lowest terms.*

**22.** $\dfrac{x^2 - 3x - 4}{x^2 + 3x} \cdot \dfrac{x^2 + 2x - 3}{x^2 - 5x + 4}$        **23.** $\dfrac{t^2 + 4t - 5}{t + 5} \div \dfrac{t - 1}{t^2 + 8t + 15}$

**24.** $\dfrac{y}{y^2 - 1} + \dfrac{y}{y + 1}$       **25.** $\dfrac{2}{x + 3} - \dfrac{4}{x - 1}$       **26.** $\dfrac{\frac{2}{3} + \frac{1}{2}}{\frac{1}{9} - \frac{1}{6}}$

*Solve each equation.*

**27.** $x^2 - 7x = -12$        **28.** $(x + 4)(x - 1) = -6$

**29.** $\dfrac{x}{x + 8} - \dfrac{3}{x - 8} = \dfrac{128}{x^2 - 64}$        **30.** $A = \dfrac{B + CD}{BC + D}$ for $B$

**31.** $\sqrt{x} + 2 = x - 10$

*Simplify each expression. Assume that all variables represent nonnegative real numbers.*

**32.** $\sqrt{27} - 2\sqrt{12} + 6\sqrt{75}$     **33.** $\dfrac{2}{\sqrt{3} + \sqrt{5}}$       **34.** $\left(3\sqrt{2} + 1\right)\left(4\sqrt{2} - 3\right)$

**35.** Evaluate $16^{5/4}$.

# Quadratic Equations

Recreational fishing is big business in the United States. In 2006, nearly 40 million anglers generated over $45.3 billion in retail sales and had a $125.0 billion impact on the U.S. economy. The sportfishing industry created employment for over one million people. If sportfishing were a corporation, it would rank 47th on the 2007 Fortune 500 list of largest American companies based on total sales, ahead of such global giants as Time Warner, IBM, and Microsoft. More Americans fish than play golf and tennis combined. (*Source:* American Sportfishing Association.)

In **Example 6** of **Section 9.1,** we apply the *square root property,* a topic of this chapter, to a formula for calculating the length of a bass.

## 9.1

# Solving Quadratic Equations by the Square Root Property

In **Section 6.5,** we solved quadratic equations by factoring. Since not all quadratic equations can easily be solved by factoring, we must develop other methods.

**OBJECTIVE 1** Review the zero-factor property. Recall that a **quadratic equation** is an equation that can be written in the form

$$ax^2 + bx + c = 0, \quad \text{Standard form}$$

for real numbers $a$, $b$, and $c$, with $a \neq 0$. As seen in **Section 6.5,** we can solve the quadratic equation $x^2 + 4x + 3 = 0$ by factoring, using the zero-factor property.

**Zero-Factor Property**

If $a$ and $b$ are real numbers and if $ab = 0$, then $a = 0$ or $b = 0$.

NOW TRY
EXERCISE 1

Solve each equation by the zero-factor property.

(a) $x^2 - x - 20 = 0$

(b) $x^2 = 36$

**EXAMPLE 1** Solving Quadratic Equations by the Zero-Factor Property

Solve each equation by the zero-factor property.

(a)
$$x^2 + 4x + 3 = 0$$
$$(x + 3)(x + 1) = 0 \qquad \text{Factor.}$$
$$x + 3 = 0 \quad \text{or} \quad x + 1 = 0 \qquad \text{Zero-factor property}$$
$$x = -3 \quad \text{or} \qquad x = -1 \qquad \text{Solve each equation.}$$

The solution set is $\{-3, -1\}$.

(b)
$$x^2 = 9$$
$$x^2 - 9 = 0 \qquad \text{Subtract 9.}$$
$$(x + 3)(x - 3) = 0 \qquad \text{Factor.}$$
$$x + 3 = 0 \quad \text{or} \quad x - 3 = 0 \qquad \text{Zero-factor property}$$
$$x = -3 \quad \text{or} \qquad x = 3 \qquad \text{Solve each equation.}$$

The solution set is $\{-3, 3\}$.

NOW TRY

**OBJECTIVE 2** Solve equations of the form $x^2 = k$, where $k > 0$. In **Example 1(b),** we might also have solved $x^2 = 9$ by noticing that $x$ must be a number whose square is 9. Thus, $x = \sqrt{9} = 3$ or $x = -\sqrt{9} = -3$. This is generalized as the **square root property.**

**Square Root Property**

If $k$ is a positive number and if $x^2 = k$, then

$$x = \sqrt{k} \quad \text{or} \quad x = -\sqrt{k}.$$

The solution set is $\left\{-\sqrt{k}, \sqrt{k}\right\}$, which can be written $\left\{\pm\sqrt{k}\right\}$. ($\pm$ is read "positive or negative" or "plus or minus.")

NOW TRY ANSWERS
1. (a) $\{-4, 5\}$   (b) $\{-6, 6\}$

**NOTE**  When we solve an equation, we must find *all* values of the variable that satisfy the equation. Therefore, we want both the positive and negative square roots of $k$.

*NOW TRY*
*EXERCISE 2*

Solve each equation. Write radicals in simplified form.

**(a)** $t^2 = 25$

**(b)** $x^2 = 13$

**(c)** $x^2 = -144$

**(d)** $2x^2 - 5 = 35$

**EXAMPLE 2**   Solving Quadratic Equations of the Form $x^2 = k$

Solve each equation. Write radicals in simplified form.

**(a)** $x^2 = 16$

By the square root property, if $x^2 = 16$, then

$$x = \sqrt{16} = 4 \quad \text{or} \quad x = -\sqrt{16} = -4.$$

*Check* each solution by substituting it for $x$ in the original equation. The solution set is

$$\{-4, 4\}, \quad \text{or} \quad \{\pm 4\}.$$

> This notation indicates *two* solutions, one positive and one negative.

**(b)** $z^2 = 5$

The solutions are $z = \sqrt{5}$ or $z = -\sqrt{5}$, so the solution set is $\left\{\pm\sqrt{5}\right\}$.

**(c)**

$$5m^2 - 32 = 8$$

$$5m^2 = 40 \qquad \text{Add 32.}$$

$$m^2 = 8 \qquad \text{Divide by 5.}$$

> Don't stop here. Simplify the radicals.

$$m = \sqrt{8} \quad \text{or} \quad m = -\sqrt{8} \qquad \text{Square root property}$$

$$m = 2\sqrt{2} \quad \text{or} \quad m = -2\sqrt{2} \qquad \sqrt{8} = \sqrt{4} \cdot \sqrt{2} = 2\sqrt{2}$$

The solution set is $\left\{\pm 2\sqrt{2}\right\}$.

**(d)** $p^2 = -4$

Since $-4$ is a negative number and since the square of a real number cannot be negative, ***there is no real number solution*** of this equation. (At this point, we are only concerned with *real number* solutions.) The solution set is $\emptyset$.

**(e)**

$$3x^2 + 5 = 11$$

$$3x^2 = 6 \qquad \text{Subtract 5.}$$

$$x^2 = 2 \qquad \text{Divide by 3.}$$

$$x = \sqrt{2} \quad \text{or} \quad x = -\sqrt{2} \qquad \text{Square root property}$$

The solution set is $\left\{\pm\sqrt{2}\right\}$.

*NOW TRY*

**OBJECTIVE 3**   **Solve equations of the form $(ax + b)^2 = k$, where $k > 0$.**
In each equation above, the exponent 2 appeared with a single variable as its base. We can extend the square root property to solve equations in which the base is a binomial.

**EXAMPLE 3**   Solving Quadratic Equations of the Form $(x + b)^2 = k$

Solve each equation.

**(a)**

> Use $(x - 3)$ as the base.

$$(x - 3)^2 = 16$$

$$x - 3 = \sqrt{16} \quad \text{or} \quad x - 3 = -\sqrt{16} \qquad \text{Square root property}$$

$$x - 3 = 4 \quad \text{or} \quad x - 3 = -4 \qquad \sqrt{16} = 4$$

$$x = 7 \quad \text{or} \quad x = -1 \qquad \text{Add 3.}$$

*NOW TRY ANSWERS*

**2. (a)** $\{\pm 5\}$   **(b)** $\left\{\pm\sqrt{13}\right\}$

**(c)** $\emptyset$   **(d)** $\left\{\pm 2\sqrt{5}\right\}$

NOW TRY
EXERCISE 3
Solve $(x - 2)^2 = 32$.

**CHECK** Substitute each solution in the original equation.

$$(x - 3)^2 = 16 \qquad\qquad\qquad (x - 3)^2 = 16$$
$$(7 - 3)^2 \overset{?}{=} 16 \quad \text{Let } x = 7. \qquad (-1 - 3)^2 \overset{?}{=} 16 \quad \text{Let } x = -1.$$
$$4^2 \overset{?}{=} 16 \quad \text{Subtract.} \qquad\qquad (-4)^2 \overset{?}{=} 16 \quad \text{Subtract.}$$
$$16 = 16 \; \checkmark \; \text{True} \qquad\qquad\qquad 16 = 16 \; \checkmark \; \text{True}$$

The solution set is $\{-1, 7\}$.

**(b)** $$(x - 1)^2 = 6$$

$$x - 1 = \sqrt{6} \qquad \text{or} \qquad x - 1 = -\sqrt{6} \qquad \text{Square root property}$$
$$x = 1 + \sqrt{6} \qquad \text{or} \qquad x = 1 - \sqrt{6} \qquad \text{Add 1.}$$

**CHECK** $\left(1 + \sqrt{6} - 1\right)^2 = \left(\sqrt{6}\right)^2 = 6 \; \checkmark \qquad \text{Let } x = 1 + \sqrt{6}.$

$\left(1 - \sqrt{6} - 1\right)^2 = \left(-\sqrt{6}\right)^2 = 6 \; \checkmark \qquad \text{Let } x = 1 - \sqrt{6}.$

The solution set is $\left\{1 + \sqrt{6}, 1 - \sqrt{6}\right\}$, or $\left\{1 \pm \sqrt{6}\right\}$. **NOW TRY**

NOW TRY
EXERCISE 4
Solve $(2t - 4)^2 = 50$.

**EXAMPLE 4** Solving a Quadratic Equation of the Form $(ax + b)^2 = k$

Solve $(3r - 2)^2 = 27$.

$$(3r - 2)^2 = 27$$

$$3r - 2 = \sqrt{27} \qquad \text{or} \qquad 3r - 2 = -\sqrt{27} \qquad \text{Square root property}$$
$$3r - 2 = 3\sqrt{3} \qquad \text{or} \qquad 3r - 2 = -3\sqrt{3} \qquad \sqrt{27} = \sqrt{9} \cdot \sqrt{3} = 3\sqrt{3}$$
$$3r = 2 + 3\sqrt{3} \qquad \text{or} \qquad 3r = 2 - 3\sqrt{3} \qquad \text{Add 2.}$$
$$r = \frac{2 + 3\sqrt{3}}{3} \qquad \text{or} \qquad r = \frac{2 - 3\sqrt{3}}{3} \qquad \text{Divide by 3.}$$

**CHECK** $\left(3 \cdot \dfrac{2 + 3\sqrt{3}}{3} - 2\right)^2 \overset{?}{=} 27 \qquad \text{Let } r = \frac{2 + 3\sqrt{3}}{3}.$

$\left(2 + 3\sqrt{3} - 2\right)^2 \overset{?}{=} 27 \qquad \text{Multiply.}$

$\left(3\sqrt{3}\right)^2 \overset{?}{=} 27 \qquad \text{Subtract.}$

$(ab)^2 = a^2b^2$

$27 = 27 \; \checkmark \qquad \text{True}$

The check of the other solution is similar. The solution set is $\left\{\dfrac{2 \pm 3\sqrt{3}}{3}\right\}$.

**NOW TRY**

⚠ **CAUTION** The solutions in **Example 4** are fractions that cannot be simplified, since 3 is *not* a common factor in the numerator.

NOW TRY
EXERCISE 5
Solve $(2x + 1)^2 = -5$.

**EXAMPLE 5** Recognizing a Quadratic Equation with No Real Solutions

Solve $(x + 3)^2 = -9$.

Because the square root of $-9$ is not a real number, the solution set is $\emptyset$.

**NOW TRY**

NOW TRY ANSWERS
3. $\left\{2 \pm 4\sqrt{2}\right\}$  4. $\left\{\dfrac{4 \pm 5\sqrt{2}}{2}\right\}$
5. $\emptyset$

**NOW TRY**
**EXERCISE 6**

Use the formula in **Example 6** to approximate the length of a bass weighing 2.10 lb and having girth 9 in.

**OBJECTIVE 4** Use formulas involving squared variables.

**EXAMPLE 6** Finding the Length of a Bass

We can approximate the weight of a bass, in pounds, given its length $L$ and its girth $g$, both measured in inches, using the formula

$$w = \frac{L^2 g}{1200}.$$

Approximate the length of a bass weighing 2.20 lb and having girth 10 in. (*Source: Sacramento Bee.*)

| | |
|---|---|
| $w = \dfrac{L^2 g}{1200}$ | Given formula |
| $2.20 = \dfrac{L^2 \cdot 10}{1200}$ | $w = 2.20$, $g = 10$ |
| $2640 = 10L^2$ | Multiply by 1200. |
| $L^2 = 264$ | Divide by 10. Interchange the sides. |
| $L = \pm\sqrt{264}$ | Square root property |

**NOW TRY ANSWER**
**6.** approximately 16.73 in.

A calculator shows that $\sqrt{264} \approx 16.25$, so the length of the bass is a little more than 16 in. (We reject the negative solution $-\sqrt{264} \approx -16.25$, since $L$ represents length.)

NOW TRY

---

# 9.1 EXERCISES

**MyMathLab** | Math XL PRACTICE |  WATCH |  DOWNLOAD |  READ |  REVIEW

🌐 *Complete solution available on the Video Resources on DVD*

*Concept Check* Match each equation in Column I with the correct description of its solution in Column II.

| **I** | **II** |
|---|---|
| **1.** $x^2 = 12$ | **A.** No real number solutions |
| **2.** $x^2 = -9$ | **B.** Two integer solutions |
| **3.** $x^2 = \dfrac{25}{36}$ | **C.** Two irrational solutions |
| **4.** $x^2 = 16$ | **D.** Two rational solutions that are not integers |

*Solve each equation by the zero-factor property.* **See Example 1.**

**5.** $x^2 - x - 56 = 0$    **6.** $x^2 - 2x - 99 = 0$    **7.** $x^2 = 121$

**8.** $x^2 = 144$    **9.** $3x^2 - 13x = 30$    **10.** $5x^2 - 14x = 3$

*Solve each equation by using the square root property. Simplify all radicals.* **See Example 2.**

🌐 **11.** $x^2 = 81$    **12.** $z^2 = 169$    **13.** $x^2 = 14$

**14.** $m^2 = 22$    **15.** $t^2 = 48$    **16.** $x^2 = 54$

**17.** $x^2 = -100$    **18.** $m^2 = -64$    **19.** $x^2 = \dfrac{25}{4}$

**20.** $m^2 = \dfrac{36}{121}$   **21.** $x^2 = 2.25$   **22.** $w^2 = 56.25$

**23.** $r^2 - 3 = 0$   **24.** $x^2 - 13 = 0$   **25.** $7x^2 = 4$

**26.** $3p^2 = 10$   **27.** $3n^2 - 72 = 0$   **28.** $5z^2 - 200 = 0$

**29.** $5x^2 + 4 = 8$   **30.** $4p^2 - 3 = 7$   **31.** $2t^2 + 7 = 61$

**32.** $3x^2 + 8 = 80$   **33.** $-8x^2 = -64$   **34.** $-12x^2 = -144$

**35.** *Concept Check*   When a student was asked to solve $x^2 = 81$, she wrote $\{9\}$ as her answer. Her teacher did not give her full credit. The student argued that because $9^2 = 81$, her answer had to be correct. *WHAT WENT WRONG?* Give the correct solution set.

**36.** Explain the square root property for solving equations, and illustrate with an example.

*Solve each equation by using the square root property. Simplify all radicals.* ***See Examples 3–5.***

**37.** $(x - 3)^2 = 25$   **38.** $(x - 7)^2 = 16$   **39.** $(z + 5)^2 = -13$

**40.** $(m + 2)^2 = -17$   **41.** $(x - 8)^2 = 27$   **42.** $(p - 5)^2 = 40$

**43.** $(3x + 2)^2 = 49$   **44.** $(5t + 3)^2 = 36$   **45.** $(4x - 3)^2 = 9$

**46.** $(7z - 5)^2 = 25$   **47.** $(5 - 2x)^2 = 30$   **48.** $(3 - 2x)^2 = 70$

**49.** $(3k + 1)^2 = 18$   **50.** $(5z + 6)^2 = 75$   **51.** $\left(\dfrac{1}{2}x + 5\right)^2 = 12$

**52.** $\left(\dfrac{1}{3}m + 4\right)^2 = 27$   **53.** $(4x - 1)^2 - 48 = 0$   **54.** $(2x - 5)^2 - 180 = 0$

**55.** Jeff solved the equation in **Exercise 47** and wrote his answer as $\left\{\dfrac{5 + \sqrt{30}}{2}, \dfrac{5 - \sqrt{30}}{2}\right\}$. Linda solved the same equation and wrote her answer as $\left\{\dfrac{-5 + \sqrt{30}}{-2}, \dfrac{-5 - \sqrt{30}}{-2}\right\}$. The teacher gave them both full credit. Explain why both students were correct.

**56.** In the solutions $\dfrac{2 \pm 3\sqrt{3}}{3}$ found in **Example 4** of this section, why is it not valid to simplify the answers by dividing out the 3's in the numerator and denominator?

*Use a calculator with a square root key to solve each equation. Round your answers to the nearest hundredth.*

**57.** $(k + 2.14)^2 = 5.46$   **58.** $(r - 3.91)^2 = 9.28$

**59.** $(2.11p + 3.42)^2 = 9.58$   **60.** $(1.71m - 6.20)^2 = 5.41$

*Solve each problem.* ***See Example 6.***

**61.** One expert at marksmanship can hold a silver dollar at forehead level, drop it, draw his gun, and shoot the coin as it passes waist level. The distance traveled by a falling object is given by

$$d = 16t^2,$$

where $d$ is the distance (in feet) the object falls in $t$ seconds. If the coin falls about 4 ft, use the formula to estimate the time that elapses between the dropping of the coin and the shot.

**62.** The illumination produced by a light source depends on the distance from the source. For a particular light source, this relationship can be expressed as

$$I = \frac{4050}{d^2},$$

where $I$ is the amount of illumination in footcandles and $d$ is the distance from the light source (in feet). How far from the source is the illumination equal to 50 footcandles?

**63.** The area $\mathcal{A}$ of a circle with radius $r$ is given by the formula

$$\mathcal{A} = \pi r^2.$$

If a circle has area $81\pi$ in.$^2$, what is its radius?

$$\mathcal{A} = \pi r^2$$

**64.** The surface area $S$ of a sphere with radius $r$ is given by the formula

$$S = 4\pi r^2.$$

If a sphere has surface area $36\pi$ ft$^2$, what is its radius?

$$S = 4\pi r^2$$

*The amount A that P dollars invested at an annual rate of interest r will grow to in 2 yr is*

$$A = P(1 + r)^2.$$

**65.** At what interest rate will \$100 grow to \$104.04 in 2 yr?

**66.** At what interest rate will \$500 grow to \$530.45 in 2 yr?

### PREVIEW EXERCISES

*Simplify all radicals, and combine like terms. Express fractions in lowest terms.* ***See Sections 8.3 and 8.4.***

**67.** $\dfrac{4}{5} + \sqrt{\dfrac{48}{25}}$

**68.** $\dfrac{12 - \sqrt{27}}{9}$

**69.** $\dfrac{6 + \sqrt{24}}{8}$

*Factor each perfect square trinomial.* ***See Section 6.4.***

**70.** $z^2 + 4z + 4$

**71.** $x^2 - 10x + 25$

**72.** $z^2 + z + \dfrac{1}{4}$

## 9.2 Solving Quadratic Equations by Completing the Square

**OBJECTIVES**

1 Solve quadratic equations by completing the square when the coefficient of the second-degree term is 1.

2 Solve quadratic equations by completing the square when the coefficient of the second-degree term is not 1.

3 Simplify the terms of an equation before solving.

4 Solve applied problems that require quadratic equations.

**OBJECTIVE 1** Solve quadratic equations by completing the square when the coefficient of the second-degree term is 1. The methods we have studied so far are not enough to solve an equation such as

$$x^2 + 6x + 7 = 0.$$

If we could write the equation in the form $(x + 3)^2$ equals a constant, we could solve it with the square root property discussed in **Section 9.1.** To do that, we need to have a perfect square trinomial on one side of the equation.

Recall from **Section 6.4** that a perfect square trinomial has the form

$$x^2 + 2kx + k^2 \quad \text{or} \quad x^2 - 2kx + k^2,$$

where $k$ represents a number.

**NOW TRY**
**EXERCISE 1**

Complete each trinomial so that it is a perfect square. Then factor the trinomial.

**(a)** $x^2 + 4x +$ _____

**(b)** $x^2 - 22x +$ _____

**EXAMPLE 1** Creating Perfect Square Trinomials

Complete each trinomial so that it is a perfect square. Then factor the trinomial.

**(a)** $x^2 + 8x +$ _____

The perfect square trinomial will have the form $x^2 + 2kx + k^2$. Thus, the middle term, $8x$, must equal $2kx$.

$$8x = 2kx \quad \longleftarrow \text{Solve this equation for } k.$$

$$4 = k \qquad \text{Divide each side by } 2x.$$

Therefore, $k = 4$ and $k^2 = 4^2 = 16$. The required perfect square trinomial is

$$x^2 + 8x + 16, \quad \text{which factors as} \quad (x + 4)^2.$$

**(b)** $x^2 - 18x +$ _____

Here the perfect square trinomial will have the form $x^2 - 2kx + k^2$. The middle term, $-18x$, must equal $-2kx$.

$$-18x = -2kx \quad \longleftarrow \text{Solve this equation for } k.$$

$$9 = k \qquad \text{Divide each side by } -2x.$$

Thus, $k = 9$ and $k^2 = 9^2 = 81$. The required perfect square trinomial is

$$x^2 - 18x + 81, \quad \text{which factors as} \quad (x - 9)^2. \qquad \text{NOW TRY}$$

**EXAMPLE 2** Rewriting an Equation to Use the Square Root Property

Solve $x^2 + 6x + 7 = 0$.

$$x^2 + 6x = -7 \qquad \text{Subtract 7 from each side.}$$

To solve this equation with the square root property, the quantity on the left side, $x^2 + 6x$, must be written as a perfect square trinomial in the form $x^2 + 2kx + k^2$.

$$x^2 + 6x + \underline{\quad\quad} \quad \text{A square must go here.}$$

Here, $2kx = 6x$, so $k = 3$ and $k^2 = 9$. The required perfect square trinomial is

$$x^2 + 6x + 9, \quad \text{which factors as} \quad (x + 3)^2.$$

*NOW TRY ANSWERS*
1. **(a)** $4; (x + 2)^2$
   **(b)** $121; (x - 11)^2$

NOW TRY
EXERCISE 2
Solve $x^2 + 10x + 8 = 0$.

Therefore, if we add 9 to each side of $x^2 + 6x = -7$, the equation will have a perfect square trinomial on the left side, as needed.

$$x^2 + 6x = -7$$

This is a key step. → $x^2 + 6x + 9 = -7 + 9$     Add 9.

$$(x + 3)^2 = 2$$     Factor. Add.

Now use the square root property to complete the solution.

$$x + 3 = \sqrt{2} \qquad \text{or} \qquad x + 3 = -\sqrt{2}$$
$$x = -3 + \sqrt{2} \qquad \text{or} \qquad x = -3 - \sqrt{2}$$

*Check* by substituting $-3 + \sqrt{2}$ and $-3 - \sqrt{2}$ for $x$ in the original equation. The solution set is $\left\{-3 \pm \sqrt{2}\right\}$.                                    NOW TRY

The process of changing the form of the equation in **Example 2** from

$$x^2 + 6x + 7 = 0 \qquad \text{to} \qquad (x + 3)^2 = 2$$

is called **completing the square.** Completing the square changes only the form of the equation. To see this, multiply out the left side of $(x + 3)^2 = 2$ and combine like terms. Then subtract 2 from each side to see that the result is $x^2 + 6x + 7 = 0$.

Look again at the original equation in **Example 2.**

$$x^2 + 6x + 7 = 0$$

If we take half the coefficient of $x$, which is 6 here, and square it, we get 9.

$$\frac{1}{2} \cdot 6 = 3 \qquad \text{and} \qquad 3^2 = 9$$

Coefficient of $x$            Quantity added to each side

To complete the square in **Example 2,** we added 9 to each side.

NOW TRY
EXERCISE 3
Solve $x^2 - 6x = 9$.

**EXAMPLE 3**  Completing the Square to Solve a Quadratic Equation

Solve $x^2 - 8x = 5$.

To complete the square on $x^2 - 8x$, take half the coefficient of $x$ and square it.

$$\frac{1}{2}(-8) = -4 \qquad \text{and} \qquad (-4)^2 = 16$$

Coefficient of $x$

Add the result, 16, to each side of the equation.

$$x^2 - 8x = 5 \qquad\qquad \text{Given equation}$$
$$x^2 - 8x + 16 = 5 + 16 \qquad \text{Add 16.}$$
$$(x - 4)^2 = 21 \qquad\qquad \text{Factor on the left. Add on the right.}$$
$$x - 4 = \pm\sqrt{21} \qquad\qquad \text{Square root property}$$
$$x = 4 \pm \sqrt{21} \qquad\qquad \text{Add 4.}$$

NOW TRY ANSWERS
**2.** $\left\{-5 \pm \sqrt{17}\right\}$
**3.** $\left\{3 \pm 3\sqrt{2}\right\}$

A check indicates that the solution set is $\left\{4 \pm \sqrt{21}\right\}$.                    NOW TRY

**OBJECTIVE 2** Solve quadratic equations by completing the square when the coefficient of the second-degree term is not 1. If a quadratic equation has the form

$$ax^2 + bx + c = 0, \quad \text{where} \quad a \neq 1,$$

we obtain 1 as the coefficient of $x^2$ by dividing each side of the equation by $a$.

The steps used to solve a quadratic equation $ax^2 + bx + c = 0$ by completing the square are summarized here.

---

**Solving a Quadratic Equation by Completing the Square**

*Step 1* **Be sure the second-degree term has coefficient 1.** If the coefficient of the second-degree term is 1, go to Step 2. If it is not 1, but some other nonzero number $a$, divide each side of the equation by $a$.

*Step 2* **Write in correct form.** Make sure that all variable terms are on one side of the equation and that all constant terms are on the other side.

*Step 3* **Complete the square.** Take half the coefficient of the first-degree term, and square it. Add the square to each side of the equation. Factor the variable side, and combine like terms on the other side.

*Step 4* **Solve** the equation by using the square root property.

---

NOW TRY
EXERCISE 4
Solve $4t^2 - 4t - 3 = 0$.

**EXAMPLE 4** Solving a Quadratic Equation by Completing the Square

Solve $4x^2 + 16x - 9 = 0$.

*Step 1* **Before completing the square, the coefficient of $x^2$ must be 1,** not 4. We get 1 as the coefficient of $x^2$ here by dividing each side by 4.

$$4x^2 + 16x - 9 = 0 \qquad \text{Given equation}$$

The coefficient of $x^2$ must be 1. $\longrightarrow x^2 + 4x - \dfrac{9}{4} = 0 \qquad$ Divide by 4.

*Step 2* Write the equation so that all variable terms are on one side of the equation and all constant terms are on the other side.

$$x^2 + 4x = \dfrac{9}{4} \qquad \text{Add } \tfrac{9}{4}.$$

*Step 3* Complete the square by taking half the coefficient of $x$, and squaring it.

$$\dfrac{1}{2}(4) = 2 \qquad \text{and} \qquad 2^2 = 4$$

We add the result, 4, to each side of the equation.

$$x^2 + 4x + 4 = \dfrac{9}{4} + 4 \qquad \text{Add 4.}$$

$$(x + 2)^2 = \dfrac{25}{4} \qquad \text{Factor; } \tfrac{9}{4} + 4 = \tfrac{9}{4} + \tfrac{16}{4} = \tfrac{25}{4}.$$

NOW TRY ANSWER
**4.** $\left\{-\tfrac{1}{2}, \tfrac{3}{2}\right\}$

***Step 4***   Solve the equation by using the square root property.

$$x + 2 = \sqrt{\frac{25}{4}} \quad \text{or} \quad x + 2 = -\sqrt{\frac{25}{4}} \qquad \text{Square root property}$$

$$x + 2 = \frac{5}{2} \quad \text{or} \quad x + 2 = -\frac{5}{2} \qquad \text{Take square roots.}$$

$$x = -2 + \frac{5}{2} \quad \text{or} \quad x = -2 - \frac{5}{2} \qquad \text{Subtract 2.}$$

$$x = \frac{1}{2} \quad \text{or} \quad x = -\frac{9}{2} \qquad -2 = -\frac{4}{2}$$

CHECK

$$4x^2 + 16x - 9 = 0$$

$$4\left(\frac{1}{2}\right)^2 + 16\left(\frac{1}{2}\right) - 9 \stackrel{?}{=} 0 \qquad \text{Let } x = \frac{1}{2}.$$

$$4\left(\frac{1}{4}\right) + 8 - 9 \stackrel{?}{=} 0$$

$$1 + 8 - 9 \stackrel{?}{=} 0$$

$$0 = 0 \checkmark \quad \text{True}$$

$$4x^2 + 16x - 9 = 0$$

$$4\left(-\frac{9}{2}\right)^2 + 16\left(-\frac{9}{2}\right) - 9 \stackrel{?}{=} 0 \qquad \text{Let } x = -\frac{9}{2}.$$

$$4\left(\frac{81}{4}\right) - 72 - 9 \stackrel{?}{=} 0$$

$$81 - 72 - 9 \stackrel{?}{=} 0$$

$$0 = 0 \checkmark \quad \text{True}$$

The two solutions, $\frac{1}{2}$ and $-\frac{9}{2}$, check, so the solution set is $\left\{-\frac{9}{2}, \frac{1}{2}\right\}$.   NOW TRY

---

**EXAMPLE 5**   **Solving a Quadratic Equation by Completing the Square**

Solve $2x^2 - 7x - 9 = 0$.

***Step 1***   Get 1 as the coefficient of the $x^2$-term.

$$x^2 - \frac{7}{2}x - \frac{9}{2} = 0 \qquad \text{Divide by 2.}$$

***Step 2***   Add $\frac{9}{2}$ to each side to get the variable terms on the left and the constant on the right.

$$x^2 - \frac{7}{2}x = \frac{9}{2} \qquad \text{Add } \frac{9}{2}.$$

***Step 3***   To complete the square, take half the coefficient of $x$ and square it.

$$\left[\frac{1}{2}\left(-\frac{7}{2}\right)\right]^2 = \left(-\frac{7}{4}\right)^2 = \frac{49}{16}$$

Add the result, $\frac{49}{16}$, to each side of the equation.

$$x^2 - \frac{7}{2}x + \frac{49}{16} = \frac{9}{2} + \frac{49}{16} \qquad \boxed{\text{Be sure to add } \frac{49}{16} \text{ to } \textit{each} \text{ side.}}$$

$$\left(x - \frac{7}{4}\right)^2 = \frac{121}{16} \qquad \text{Factor; } \frac{9}{2} + \frac{49}{16} = \frac{72}{16} + \frac{49}{16} = \frac{121}{16}.$$

NOW TRY
EXERCISE 5
Solve $4x^2 + 9x - 9 = 0$.

**Step 4**    Solve by using the square root property.

$$x - \frac{7}{4} = \sqrt{\frac{121}{16}} \quad \text{or} \quad x - \frac{7}{4} = -\sqrt{\frac{121}{16}} \qquad \text{Square root property}$$

$$x = \frac{7}{4} + \frac{11}{4} \quad \text{or} \quad x = \frac{7}{4} - \frac{11}{4} \qquad \text{Add } \tfrac{7}{4}; \sqrt{\tfrac{121}{16}} = \tfrac{11}{4}.$$

$$x = \frac{18}{4} \quad \text{or} \quad x = -\frac{4}{4} \qquad \text{Simplify.}$$

$$x = \frac{9}{2} \quad \text{or} \quad x = -1 \qquad \text{Lowest terms}$$

A check confirms that the solution set is $\left\{-1, \frac{9}{2}\right\}$.    NOW TRY

NOW TRY
EXERCISE 6
Solve $3t^2 - 12t + 15 = 0$.

**EXAMPLE 6**    Solving a Quadratic Equation by Completing the Square

Solve $4p^2 + 8p + 5 = 0$.

$$4p^2 + 8p + 5 = 0$$

The coefficient of the second-degree term must be 1. $\longrightarrow$
$$p^2 + 2p + \frac{5}{4} = 0 \qquad \text{Divide by 4.}$$

$$p^2 + 2p = -\frac{5}{4} \qquad \text{Add } -\tfrac{5}{4} \text{ to each side.}$$

The coefficient of $p$ is 2. Take half of 2, square the result, and add it to each side.

$$p^2 + 2p + 1 = -\frac{5}{4} + 1 \qquad \left[\tfrac{1}{2}(2)\right]^2 = 1^2 = 1; \text{ Add 1.}$$

$$(p + 1)^2 = -\frac{1}{4} \qquad \begin{array}{l}\text{Factor on the left.}\\ \text{Add on the right.}\end{array}$$

If we apply the square root property to solve this equation, we get the square root of $-\frac{1}{4}$, which is not a real number. The solution set is $\emptyset$.    NOW TRY

**OBJECTIVE 3**    Simplify the terms of an equation before solving.

NOW TRY
EXERCISE 7
Solve $(x - 5)(x + 1) = 2$.

**EXAMPLE 7**    Simplifying the Terms of an Equation before Solving

Solve $(x + 3)(x - 1) = 2$.

$$(x + 3)(x - 1) = 2$$

$$x^2 + 2x - 3 = 2 \qquad \text{Multiply by using the FOIL method.}$$

$$x^2 + 2x = 5 \qquad \text{Add 3.}$$

$$x^2 + 2x + 1 = 5 + 1 \qquad \text{Add } \left[\tfrac{1}{2}(2)\right]^2 = 1^2 = 1.$$

$$(x + 1)^2 = 6 \qquad \text{Factor on the left. Add on the right.}$$

$$x + 1 = \sqrt{6} \quad \text{or} \quad x + 1 = -\sqrt{6} \qquad \text{Square root property}$$

$$x = -1 + \sqrt{6} \quad \text{or} \quad x = -1 - \sqrt{6} \qquad \text{Subtract 1.}$$

The solution set is $\left\{-1 \pm \sqrt{6}\right\}$.    NOW TRY

NOW TRY ANSWERS
**5.** $\left\{-3, \frac{3}{4}\right\}$  **6.** $\emptyset$
**7.** $\left\{2 \pm \sqrt{11}\right\}$

NOTE The solutions $-1 \pm \sqrt{6}$ given in **Example 7** are *exact*. In applications, decimal solutions are more appropriate. Using the square root key of a calculator yields $\sqrt{6} \approx 2.449$. Approximating the two solutions gives

$$x \approx 1.449 \quad \text{and} \quad x \approx -3.449.$$

**OBJECTIVE 4** Solve applied problems that require quadratic equations.

NOW TRY
EXERCISE 8
At what times will the ball in **Example 8** be 28 ft above the ground?

**EXAMPLE 8** Solving a Velocity Problem

If a ball is projected into the air from ground level with an initial velocity of 64 ft per sec, its altitude (height) $s$ in feet in $t$ seconds is given by the formula

$$s = -16t^2 + 64t.$$

At what times will the ball be 48 ft above the ground?

Since $s$ represents the height, we let $s = 48$ in the formula and solve this equation for the time $t$ by completing the square.

| | |
|---|---|
| $48 = -16t^2 + 64t$ | Let $s = 48$. |
| $-3 = t^2 - 4t$ | Divide by $-16$. |
| $t^2 - 4t = -3$ | Interchange the sides. |
| $t^2 - 4t + 4 = -3 + 4$ | Add $\left[\frac{1}{2}(-4)\right]^2 = (-2)^2 = 4$. |
| $(t - 2)^2 = 1$ | Factor. Add. |
| $t - 2 = 1 \quad \text{or} \quad t - 2 = -1$ | Square root property |
| $t = 3 \quad \text{or} \quad t = 1$ | Add 2. |

The ball reaches a height of 48 ft twice, once on the way up and again on the way down. It takes 1 sec to reach 48 ft on the way up, and then after 3 sec, the ball reaches 48 ft again on the way down. NOW TRY

NOW TRY ANSWER
**8.** 0.5 sec and 3.5 sec

---

**9.2 EXERCISES** **MyMathLab** Math XL PRACTICE  WATCH  DOWNLOAD  READ  REVIEW

🌐 *Complete solution available on the Video Resources on DVD*

Complete each trinomial so that it is a perfect square. Then factor the trinomial. **See Example 1.**

🌐 **1.** $x^2 + 10x + \underline{\hspace{1cm}}$     **2.** $x^2 + 16x + \underline{\hspace{1cm}}$     🌐 **3.** $z^2 - 20z + \underline{\hspace{1cm}}$

**4.** $a^2 - 32a + \underline{\hspace{1cm}}$     **5.** $x^2 + 2x + \underline{\hspace{1cm}}$     **6.** $m^2 - 2m + \underline{\hspace{1cm}}$

**7.** $p^2 - 5p + \underline{\hspace{1cm}}$     **8.** $x^2 + 3x + \underline{\hspace{1cm}}$

**9.** *Concept Check* Which step is an appropriate way to begin solving the quadratic equation $2x^2 - 4x = 9$ by completing the square?

    **A.** Add 4 to each side of the equation.     **B.** Factor the left side as $2x(x - 2)$.

    **C.** Factor the left side as $x(2x - 4)$.     **D.** Divide each side by 2.

**10.** *Concept Check* In **Example 3** of **Section 6.5**, we solved the quadratic equation $4p^2 + 40 = 26p$ by factoring. If we were to solve by completing the square, would we get the same solution set, $\left\{\frac{5}{2}, 4\right\}$?

*Solve each equation by completing the square.* **See Examples 2 and 3.**

🌐 **11.** $x^2 - 4x = -3$      **12.** $p^2 - 2p = 8$      🌐 **13.** $x^2 + 2x - 5 = 0$

**14.** $r^2 + 4r + 1 = 0$      **15.** $x^2 - 8x = -4$      **16.** $m^2 - 4m = 14$

**17.** $x^2 + 6x + 9 = 0$      **18.** $x^2 - 8x + 16 = 0$

*Solve each equation by completing the square.* **See Examples 4–7.**

🌐 **19.** $4x^2 + 4x = 3$      **20.** $9x^2 + 3x = 2$      🌐 **21.** $2p^2 - 2p + 3 = 0$

**22.** $3q^2 - 3q + 4 = 0$      **23.** $3x^2 - 9x + 5 = 0$      **24.** $6x^2 - 8x - 3 = 0$

**25.** $3x^2 + 7x = 4$      **26.** $2x^2 + 5x = 1$      🌐 **27.** $(x + 3)(x - 1) = 5$

**28.** $(x - 8)(x + 2) = 24$      **29.** $(r - 3)(r - 5) = 2$      **30.** $(x - 1)(x - 7) = 1$

**31.** $-x^2 + 2x = -5$      **32.** $-x^2 + 4x = 1$

*Solve each equation by completing the square. Give* **(a)** *exact solutions and* **(b)** *solutions rounded to the nearest thousandth.*

**33.** $3r^2 - 2 = 6r + 3$          **34.** $4p + 3 = 2p^2 + 2p$

**35.** $(x + 1)(x + 3) = 2$         **36.** $(x - 3)(x + 1) = 1$

*Solve each problem.* **See Example 8.**

🌐 **37.** If an object is projected upward on the surface of Mars from ground level with an initial velocity of 104 ft per sec, its altitude (height) $s$ in feet in $t$ seconds is given by the formula $s = -13t^2 + 104t$. At what times will the object be 195 ft above the ground?

**38.** After how many seconds will the object in **Exercise 37** return to the surface? (*Hint:* When it returns to the surface, $s = 0$.)

**39.** If an object is projected upward from ground level on Earth with an initial velocity of 96 ft per sec, its altitude (height) $s$ in feet in $t$ seconds is given by the formula $s = -16t^2 + 96t$. At what times will the object be at a height of 80 ft? (*Hint:* Let $s = 80$.)

**40.** At what times will the object described in **Exercise 39** be at a height of 100 ft? Round your answers to the nearest tenth.

**41.** A farmer has a rectangular cattle pen with perimeter 350 ft and area 7500 ft². What are the dimensions of the pen? (*Hint:* Use the figure to set up the equation.)

**42.** The base of a triangle measures 1 m more than three times the height of the triangle. The area of the triangle is 15 m². Find the lengths of the base and the height.

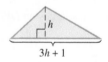

**43.** Two cars travel at right angles to each other from an intersection until they are 17 mi apart. At that point, one car has gone 7 mi farther than the other. How far did the slower car travel? (*Hint:* Use the Pythagorean theorem.)

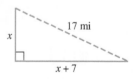

**44.** Two painters are painting a house in a development of new homes. One of the painters takes 2 hr longer to paint the house working alone than the other painter takes. When they do the job together, they can complete it in 4.8 hr. How long would it take the faster painter alone to paint the house? (Give your answer to the nearest tenth.)

**FOR INDIVIDUAL OR GROUP WORK**

*We have discussed "completing the square" in an algebraic sense. This procedure can literally be applied to a geometric figure so that it becomes a square.*

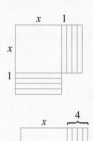

*For example, to complete the square for $x^2 + 8x$, begin with a square having a side of length x. Add four rectangles of width 1 to the right side and to the bottom, as shown in the top figure. To "complete the square," fill in the bottom right corner with 16 squares of area 1, as shown in the bottom figure.*

**Work Exercises 45–48 in order.**

**45.** What is the area of the original square?

**46.** What is the area of the figure after the 8 rectangles are added?

**47.** What is the area of the figure after the 16 small squares are added?

**48.** At what point did we "complete the square"?

*PREVIEW EXERCISES*

*Write each quotient in lowest terms. Simplify the radicals. **See Section 8.5.***

**49.** $\dfrac{8 - 6\sqrt{3}}{6}$  **50.** $\dfrac{4 + \sqrt{28}}{2}$  **51.** $\dfrac{6 - \sqrt{45}}{6}$  **52.** $\dfrac{8 + \sqrt{32}}{4}$

*Evaluate the expression $\sqrt{b^2 - 4ac}$ for the given values of a, b, and c. Simplify the radicals. **See Sections 1.3, 8.1, and 8.2.***

**53.** $a = 1, b = 2, c = -4$  **54.** $a = 9, b = 30, c = 25$

---

## 9.3  Solving Quadratic Equations by the Quadratic Formula

**OBJECTIVES**

**1** Identify the values of *a*, *b*, and *c* in a quadratic equation.

**2** Use the quadratic formula to solve quadratic equations.

**3** Solve quadratic equations with only one solution.

**4** Solve quadratic equations with fractions.

We can solve any quadratic equation by completing the square, but the method can be tedious. In this section, we complete the square on the general quadratic equation

$$ax^2 + bx + c = 0, \quad \text{with } a \neq 0, \qquad \text{Standard form}$$

to obtain the *quadratic formula,* which gives the solution(s) of *any* quadratic equation.

---

NOTE  In $ax^2 + bx + c = 0$, there is a restriction that *a* is not zero. If it were, the equation would be linear, not quadratic.

---

**OBJECTIVE 1**  Identify the values of *a*, *b*, and *c* in a quadratic equation. To solve a quadratic equation with the quadratic formula, we must first identify the values of *a*, *b*, and *c* in the standard form.

NOW TRY
EXERCISE 1

Write the equation in standard form, if necessary, with 0 on the right side. Then identify the values of $a$, $b$, and $c$.

(a) $3x^2 - 7x + 4 = 0$

(b) $x^2 - 3 = -2x$

(c) $2x^2 - 4x = 0$

(d) $2(2x + 1)(x - 5) = -3$

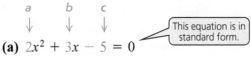 Determining Values of $a$, $b$, and $c$ in Quadratic Equations

Identify the values of $a$, $b$, and $c$ in each quadratic equation $ax^2 + bx + c = 0$.

(a) $\underset{\underset{a}{\downarrow}}{2}x^2 + \underset{\underset{b}{\downarrow}}{3}x - \underset{\underset{c}{\downarrow}}{5} = 0$    This equation is in standard form.

Here, $a = 2$, $b = 3$, and $c = -5$.

(b) $-x^2 + 2 = 6x$

First write the equation in standard form $ax^2 + bx + c = 0$.

$$-x^2 + 2 = 6x$$

$-x^2$ means $-1x^2$.

$$-x^2 - 6x + 2 = 0 \qquad \text{Subtract } 6x.$$

Here, $a = -1$, $b = -6$, and $c = 2$.

(c) $5x^2 - 12 = 0$

The $x$-term is missing, so write the equation as follows.

$$5x^2 + 0x - 12 = 0$$

Then $a = 5$, $b = 0$, and $c = -12$.

(d)   The equation is not in standard form.

$$(2x - 7)(x + 4) = -23$$
$$2x^2 + x - 28 = -23 \qquad \text{Use the FOIL method.}$$
$$2x^2 + x - 5 = 0 \qquad \text{Add 23; standard form}$$

Now, identify the required values:   $a = 2$, $b = 1$, and $c = -5$.    NOW TRY

**OBJECTIVE 2**   **Use the quadratic formula to solve quadratic equations.** To develop the quadratic formula, we follow the steps given in **Section 9.2** for completing the square on $ax^2 + bx + c = 0$. For comparison, we also show the corresponding steps for solving $2x^2 + x - 5 = 0$ (from **Example 1(d)**).

***Step 1***   Transform so that the coefficient of the second-degree term is equal to 1.

$$2x^2 + x - 5 = 0 \qquad\qquad\qquad ax^2 + bx + c = 0 \quad (a > 0)$$
$$x^2 + \frac{1}{2}x - \frac{5}{2} = 0 \quad \text{Divide by 2.} \qquad x^2 + \frac{b}{a}x + \frac{c}{a} = 0 \quad \text{Divide by } a.$$

***Step 2***   Write the equation so that the variable terms with $x$ are alone on the left side.

$$x^2 + \frac{1}{2}x = \frac{5}{2} \quad \text{Add } \tfrac{5}{2}. \qquad\qquad x^2 + \frac{b}{a}x = -\frac{c}{a} \quad \text{Subtract } \tfrac{c}{a}.$$

***Step 3***   Add the square of half the coefficient of $x$ to each side, factor the left side, and combine like terms on the right.

$$x^2 + \frac{1}{2}x + \frac{1}{16} = \frac{5}{2} + \frac{1}{16} \quad \text{Add } \tfrac{1}{16}. \qquad x^2 + \frac{b}{a}x + \frac{b^2}{4a^2} = -\frac{c}{a} + \frac{b^2}{4a^2} \quad \text{Add } \tfrac{b^2}{4a^2}.$$

$$\left(x + \frac{1}{4}\right)^2 = \frac{41}{16} \quad \begin{array}{l}\text{Factor.}\\ \text{Add on}\\ \text{right.}\end{array} \qquad \left(x + \frac{b}{2a}\right)^2 = \frac{b^2 - 4ac}{4a^2} \quad \begin{array}{l}\text{Factor.}\\ \text{Add on}\\ \text{right.}\end{array}$$

NOW TRY ANSWERS
1. (a) $a = 3$, $b = -7$, $c = 4$
   (b) $a = 1$, $b = 2$, $c = -3$
   (c) $a = 2$, $b = -4$, $c = 0$
   (d) $a = 4$, $b = -18$, $c = -7$

***Step 4***   Use the square root property to complete the solution.

$$x + \frac{1}{4} = \pm\sqrt{\frac{41}{16}}$$

$$x + \frac{1}{4} = \pm\frac{\sqrt{41}}{4}$$

$$x = -\frac{1}{4} \pm \frac{\sqrt{41}}{4}$$

$$x = \frac{-1 \pm \sqrt{41}}{4}$$

$$x + \frac{b}{2a} = \pm\sqrt{\frac{b^2 - 4ac}{4a^2}}$$

$$x + \frac{b}{2a} = \pm\frac{\sqrt{b^2 - 4ac}}{2a}$$

$$x = -\frac{b}{2a} \pm \frac{\sqrt{b^2 - 4ac}}{2a}$$

$$x = \frac{-b \pm \sqrt{b^2 - 4ac}}{2a}$$

The final result on the right (which is also valid for $a < 0$) is called the **quadratic formula.** *It gives two values: one for the + sign and one for the − sign.*

---

**Quadratic Formula**

The solutions of the quadratic equation $ax^2 + bx + c = 0$, $a \neq 0$, are

$$x = \frac{-b + \sqrt{b^2 - 4ac}}{2a} \quad \text{and} \quad x = \frac{-b - \sqrt{b^2 - 4ac}}{2a}$$

or, in compact form, $\quad x = \dfrac{-b \pm \sqrt{b^2 - 4ac}}{2a}.$

---

*NOW TRY*
*EXERCISE 2*
Solve $3x^2 + 5x - 2 = 0$.

**EXAMPLE 2**   Solving a Quadratic Equation by the Quadratic Formula

Solve $2x^2 - 7x - 9 = 0$.

In this equation, $a = 2$, $b = -7$, and $c = -9$.

$$x = \frac{-b \pm \sqrt{b^2 - 4ac}}{2a} \qquad \text{Quadratic formula}$$

Be sure to write $-b$ in the numerator.

$$x = \frac{-(-7) \pm \sqrt{(-7)^2 - 4(2)(-9)}}{2(2)} \qquad \begin{array}{l}\text{Substitute } a = 2,\\ b = -7, \text{ and } c = -9.\end{array}$$

$$x = \frac{7 \pm \sqrt{49 + 72}}{4} \qquad \text{Simplify.}$$

$$x = \frac{7 \pm \sqrt{121}}{4} \qquad \text{Add.}$$

This represents **two** solutions.

$$x = \frac{7 \pm 11}{4} \qquad \sqrt{121} = 11$$

Find the two solutions by first using the plus sign and then using the minus sign.

$$x = \frac{7 + 11}{4} = \frac{18}{4} = \frac{9}{2} \quad \text{or} \quad x = \frac{7 - 11}{4} = \frac{-4}{4} = -1$$

*Check* each solution. The solution set is $\left\{-1, \frac{9}{2}\right\}$.   *NOW TRY*

⚠ **CAUTION** Notice in the quadratic formula that the fraction bar is under $-b$ as well as the radical. ***Be sure to find the values of $-b \pm \sqrt{b^2 - 4ac}$ first. Then divide those results by the value of $2a$.***

---

**NOW TRY**
**EXERCISE 3**
Solve $x^2 + 2 = 6x$.

**EXAMPLE 3** Rewriting a Quadratic Equation before Solving

Solve $x^2 = 2x + 1$.

Write the given equation in standard form as $x^2 - 2x - 1 = 0$.

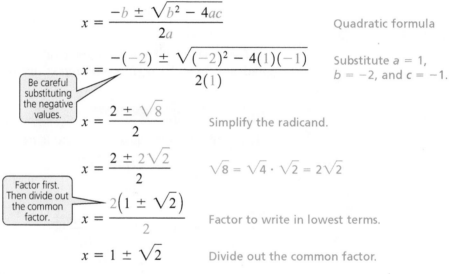

$$x = \frac{-b \pm \sqrt{b^2 - 4ac}}{2a}$$     Quadratic formula

$$x = \frac{-(-2) \pm \sqrt{(-2)^2 - 4(1)(-1)}}{2(1)}$$     Substitute $a = 1$, $b = -2$, and $c = -1$.

*Be careful substituting the negative values.*

$$x = \frac{2 \pm \sqrt{8}}{2}$$     Simplify the radicand.

$$x = \frac{2 \pm 2\sqrt{2}}{2}$$     $\sqrt{8} = \sqrt{4} \cdot \sqrt{2} = 2\sqrt{2}$

*Factor first. Then divide out the common factor.*

$$x = \frac{2\left(1 \pm \sqrt{2}\right)}{2}$$     Factor to write in lowest terms.

$$x = 1 \pm \sqrt{2}$$     Divide out the common factor.

The solution set is $\left\{1 \pm \sqrt{2}\right\}$.     NOW TRY

---

**OBJECTIVE 3** **Solve quadratic equations with only one solution.** In the quadratic formula, the quantity under the radical,

$$b^2 - 4ac, \quad \text{Discriminant}$$

is called the **discriminant.** When the discriminant for $ax^2 + bx + c = 0$ equals 0 and $a$, $b$, and $c$ are integers, the equation has just one rational number solution. Furthermore, the trinomial $ax^2 + bx + c$ is a perfect square.

---

**NOW TRY**
**EXERCISE 4**
Solve $16x^2 = 8x - 1$.

**EXAMPLE 4** Solving a Quadratic Equation with Only One Solution

Solve $4x^2 + 25 = 20x$.

$$4x^2 - 20x + 25 = 0 \quad \text{Subtract 20x; standard form}$$

Here, $a = 4$, $b = -20$, and $c = 25$. By the quadratic formula,

$$x = \frac{-(-20) \pm \sqrt{(-20)^2 - 4(4)(25)}}{2(4)} = \frac{20 \pm 0}{8} = \frac{5}{2}.$$

In this case, the discriminant $b^2 - 4ac$ is 0, and the trinomial $4x^2 - 20x + 25$ is a perfect square, $(2x - 5)^2$. There is just one solution, $\frac{5}{2}$. A check confirms that the solution set is $\left\{\frac{5}{2}\right\}$.     NOW TRY

**NOW TRY ANSWERS**
**3.** $\left\{3 \pm \sqrt{7}\right\}$   **4.** $\left\{\frac{1}{4}\right\}$

**NOTE** The single solution of the equation in **Example 4** is a rational number. If all solutions of a quadratic equation are rational, the equation can be solved by factoring.

---

**OBJECTIVE 4**  Solve quadratic equations with fractions.

**NOW TRY**
**EXERCISE 5**
Solve $\frac{1}{12}x^2 = \frac{1}{2}x - \frac{1}{3}$.

**EXAMPLE 5**  Solving a Quadratic Equation with Fractions

Solve $\dfrac{1}{10}t^2 = \dfrac{2}{5}t + \dfrac{1}{5}$.

$$10\left(\frac{1}{10}t^2\right) = 10\left(\frac{2}{5}t + \frac{1}{5}\right)$$   Clear fractions. Multiply by the LCD, 10.

$$t^2 = 10\left(\frac{2}{5}t\right) + 10\left(\frac{1}{5}\right)$$   Distributive property

$$t^2 = 4t + 2$$   Multiply.

$$t^2 - 4t - 2 = 0$$   Subtract 4t and 2 to write in standard form.

Identify $a = 1$, $b = -4$, and $c = -2$.

$$t = \frac{-(-4) \pm \sqrt{(-4)^2 - 4(1)(-2)}}{2(1)}$$   Substitute into the quadratic formula.

$$t = \frac{4 \pm \sqrt{16 + 8}}{2}$$   Simplify.

$$t = \frac{4 \pm \sqrt{24}}{2}$$   Add.

$$t = \frac{4 \pm 2\sqrt{6}}{2}$$   $\sqrt{24} = \sqrt{4 \cdot 6} = 2\sqrt{6}$

$$t = \frac{2\left(2 \pm \sqrt{6}\right)}{2}$$   Factor.

Be careful here.

$$t = 2 \pm \sqrt{6}$$   Divide to write in lowest terms.

**NOW TRY ANSWER**
**5.** $\left\{3 \pm \sqrt{5}\right\}$

The solution set is $\left\{2 \pm \sqrt{6}\right\}$.   NOW TRY

---

## 9.3 EXERCISES   *MyMathLab*   Math XL PRACTICE    WATCH    DOWNLOAD    READ    REVIEW

⊙ *Complete solution available on the Video Resources on DVD*

*If necessary, write each equation in standard form $ax^2 + bx + c = 0$. Then identify the values of a, b, and c. Do not actually solve the equation.* **See Example 1.**

⊙ **1.** $3x^2 + 4x - 8 = 0$     **2.** $9x^2 + 2x - 3 = 0$     **3.** $-8x^2 - 2x - 3 = 0$

**4.** $-2x^2 + 3x - 8 = 0$     **5.** $3x^2 = 4x + 2$     **6.** $5x^2 = 3x - 6$

**7.** $3x^2 = -7x$          **8.** $9x^2 = 8x$

**9.** $(x - 3)(x + 4) = 0$     **10.** $(x + 7)(x - 2) = 0$

**11.** $9(x - 1)(x + 2) = 8$     **12.** $2(3x - 1)(2x + 5) = 5$

**13.** *Concept Check* A student writes the quadratic formula as

$$x = -b \pm \frac{\sqrt{b^2 - 4ac}}{2a}.$$

*WHAT WENT WRONG?* Explain the error, and give the correct formula.

**14.** To solve the quadratic equation $-2x^2 - 4x + 3 = 0$, we might choose to use $a = -2$, $b = -4$, and $c = 3$. Or, we might decide to first multiply both sides by $-1$, obtaining the equation $2x^2 + 4x - 3 = 0$, and then use $a = 2$, $b = 4$, and $c = -3$. Show that in either case we obtain the same solution set.

*Use the quadratic formula to solve each equation. Simplify all radicals, and write all answers in lowest terms.* **See Examples 2–4.**

**15.** $k^2 + 12k - 13 = 0$   **16.** $r^2 - 8r - 9 = 0$   **17.** $2x^2 + 12x = -5$

**18.** $5m^2 + m = 1$   **19.** $p^2 - 4p + 4 = 0$   **20.** $x^2 - 10x + 25 = 0$

**21.** $2x^2 = 5 + 3x$   **22.** $2z^2 = 30 + 7z$   **23.** $6x^2 + 6x = 0$

**24.** $4n^2 - 12n = 0$   **25.** $7x^2 = 12x$   **26.** $9r^2 = 11r$

**27.** $x^2 - 24 = 0$   **28.** $z^2 - 96 = 0$   **29.** $25x^2 - 4 = 0$

**30.** $16x^2 - 9 = 0$   **31.** $3x^2 - 2x + 5 = 10x + 1$   **32.** $4x^2 - x + 4 = x + 7$

**33.** $-2x^2 = -3x + 2$   **34.** $-x^2 = -5x + 20$   **35.** $2x^2 + x + 5 = 0$

**36.** $3x^2 + 2x + 8 = 0$   **37.** $(x + 3)(x + 2) = 15$   **38.** $(2x + 1)(x + 1) = 7$

*Use the quadratic formula to solve each equation.* **(a)** *Give solutions in exact form, and* **(b)** *use a calculator to give solutions correct to the nearest thousandth.*

**39.** $2x^2 = 5 - 2x$   **40.** $5x^2 = 3 - x$   **41.** $x^2 = 1 + x$   **42.** $x^2 = 2 + 4x$

*Use the quadratic formula to solve each equation.* **See Example 5.**

**43.** $\frac{3}{2}k^2 - k - \frac{4}{3} = 0$   **44.** $\frac{2}{5}x^2 - \frac{3}{5}x - 1 = 0$   **45.** $\frac{1}{2}x^2 + \frac{1}{6}x = 1$

**46.** $\frac{2}{3}z^2 - \frac{4}{9}z = \frac{1}{3}$   **47.** $\frac{3}{8}x^2 - x + \frac{17}{24} = 0$   **48.** $\frac{1}{3}x^2 + \frac{8}{9}x + \frac{7}{9} = 0$

**49.** $0.5x^2 = x + 0.5$   **50.** $0.25x^2 = -1.5x - 1$

**51.** $0.6x - 0.4x^2 = -1$   **52.** $0.25x + 0.5x^2 = 1.5$

*Solve each problem.*

**53.** Solve the formula $S = 2\pi rh + \pi r^2$ for $r$ by writing it in the form $ar^2 + br + c = 0$ and then using the quadratic formula. (Leave $\pm$ in your answer.)

**54.** Solve the formula $V = \pi r^2 h + \pi R^2 h$ for $r$, using the method described in **Exercise 53**. (Leave $\pm$ in your answer.)

**55.** A frog is sitting on a stump 3 ft above the ground. He hops off the stump and lands on the ground 4 ft away. During his leap, his height $h$ with respect to the ground is given by

(0, 3)

(4, 0)

$$h = -0.5x^2 + 1.25x + 3,$$

where $x$ is the distance in feet from the base of the stump and $h$ is in feet. How far was the frog from the base of the stump when he was 1.25 ft above the ground?

**56.** An astronaut on the moon throws a baseball upward. The altitude (height) $h$ of the ball, in feet, $x$ seconds after he throws it, is given by the equation

$$h = -2.7x^2 + 30x + 6.5.$$

At what times is the ball 12 ft above the moon's surface?

**57.** A rule for estimating the number of board feet of lumber that can be cut from a log depends on the diameter of the log. To find the diameter $d$ required to get 9 board feet of lumber, we use the equation

$$\left(\frac{d-4}{4}\right)^2 = 9.$$

Solve this equation for $d$. Are both answers reasonable?

**58.** A Babylonian problem asks for the length of the side of a square, where the area of the square minus the length of a side is 870. Find the length of the side. (*Source:* Eves, Howard, *An Introduction to the History of Mathematics,* Sixth Edition, Saunders College Publishing.)

## PREVIEW EXERCISES

*Perform the indicated operations. **See Sections 5.4, 5.5, and 5.6.***

**59.** $(4 + 6z) + (-9 + 2z)$   **60.** $(10 - 3t) - (5 - 7t)$   **61.** $4 - (6 - 3k)$

**62.** $7x(3 - 4x)$   **63.** $(4 + 3r)(6 - 5r)$   **64.** $(5 + 2x)(5 - 2x)$

## SUMMARY EXERCISES on Quadratic Equations

The table summarizes methods for solving a quadratic equation $ax^2 + bx + c = 0$.

| Method | Advantages | Disadvantages |
|---|---|---|
| **1. Factoring** | It is usually the fastest method. | Not all equations can be solved by factoring. Some factorable polynomials are difficult to factor. |
| **2. Square root property** | It is the simplest method for solving equations of the form $(ax + b)^2 =$ a number. | Few equations are given in this form. |
| **3. Completing the square** | It can always be used. (Also, the procedure is useful in other areas of mathematics.) | It requires more steps than other methods. |
| **4. Quadratic formula** | It can always be used. | Sign errors are common because of the $\sqrt{b^2 - 4ac}$ expression. |

*Solve each quadratic equation by the method of your choice.*

**1.** $s^2 = 36$   **2.** $x^2 + 3x = -1$   **3.** $(x + 2)(x - 4) = 16$

**4.** $81t^2 = 49$   **5.** $z^2 - 4z + 3 = 0$   **6.** $w^2 + 3w + 2 = 0$

**7.** $z(z - 9) = -20$

**8.** $x^2 + 3x - 2 = 0$

**9.** $(3x - 2)^2 = 9$

**10.** $(2s - 1)^2 = 10$

**11.** $(x + 6)^2 = 121$

**12.** $(5x + 1)^2 = 36$

**13.** $(3r - 7)^2 = 24$

**14.** $(7p - 1)^2 = 32$

**15.** $(5x - 8)^2 = -6$

**16.** $2t^2 + 1 = t$

**17.** $-2x^2 = -3x - 2$

**18.** $-2x^2 + x = -1$

**19.** $8z^2 = 15 + 2z$

**20.** $3x^2 = 3 - 8x$

**21.** $0.1x^2 - 0.2x = 0.1$

**22.** $0.3x^2 + 0.5x = -0.1$

**23.** $5z^2 - 22z = -8$

**24.** $z(z + 6) + 4 = 0$

**25.** $(x + 2)(x + 1) = 10$

**26.** $16x^2 + 40x + 25 = 0$

**27.** $4x^2 = -1 + 5x$

**28.** $2p^2 = 2p + 1$

**29.** $3m(3m + 4) = 7$

**30.** $5x - 1 + 4x^2 = 0$

**31.** $\dfrac{r^2}{2} + \dfrac{7r}{4} + \dfrac{11}{8} = 0$

**32.** $\dfrac{1}{5}x^2 + x + 1 = 0$

**33.** $9x^2 = 16(3x + 4)$

**34.** $t(15t + 58) = -48$

**35.** $x^2 - x + 3 = 0$

**36.** $4m^2 - 11m + 8 = -2$

**37.** $-3x^2 + 4x = -4$

**38.** $z^2 - \dfrac{5}{12}z = \dfrac{1}{6}$

**39.** $5x^2 + 19x = 2x + 12$

**40.** $\dfrac{1}{2}n^2 - n = \dfrac{15}{2}$

**41.** $x^2 - \dfrac{4}{15} = -\dfrac{4}{15}x$

**42.** $x^2 - \dfrac{100}{81} = 0$

---

## 9.4  Complex Numbers

**OBJECTIVES**

**1** Write complex numbers as multiples of $i$.

**2** Add and subtract complex numbers.

**3** Multiply complex numbers.

**4** Divide complex numbers.

**5** Solve quadratic equations with complex number solutions.

Some quadratic equations have no real number solutions. For example, solving the equation from **Example 6** of **Section 9.2,** $4p^2 + 8p + 5 = 0$, by the quadratic formula leads to the values

$$\frac{-8 \pm \sqrt{-16}}{8}.$$

← These are not real numbers, since the radicand is $-16$.

To ensure that every quadratic equation has a solution, we need a new set of numbers that includes the real numbers. This new set of numbers is defined with a new number $i$, called the **imaginary unit,** such that

$$i = \sqrt{-1}, \quad \text{and thus,} \quad i^2 = -1.$$

**OBJECTIVE 1** **Write complex numbers as multiples of $i$.** We can write numbers such as $\sqrt{-4}$, $\sqrt{-5}$, and $\sqrt{-8}$ as multiples of $i$, using the properties of $i$ to define any square root of a negative number as follows.

$\boxed{\sqrt{-b}}$

For any positive real number $b$, $\quad \sqrt{-b} = i\sqrt{b}.$

*NOW TRY*
*EXERCISE 1*
Write $\sqrt{-12}$ as a multiple of $i$.

EXAMPLE 1    Simplifying Square Roots of Negative Numbers

Write each number as a multiple of $i$.

**(a)** $\sqrt{-5}$
  $= i\sqrt{5}$

**(b)** $\sqrt{-4}$
  $= i\sqrt{4}$
  $= i \cdot 2$
  $= 2i$

**(c)** $\sqrt{-8}$
  $= i\sqrt{8}$
  $= i \cdot \sqrt{4} \cdot \sqrt{2}$
  $= i \cdot 2 \cdot \sqrt{2}$, or $2i\sqrt{2}$

NOW TRY

⚠ **CAUTION**  It is easy to mistake $\sqrt{2}i$ for $\sqrt{2i}$, with the $i$ under the radical. For this reason, it is customary to write the factor $i$ first when it is multiplied by a radical. For example, we usually write $i\sqrt{2}$ rather than $\sqrt{2}i$.

Numbers that are nonzero multiples of $i$ are *pure imaginary numbers*. The *complex numbers* include all real numbers and all imaginary numbers.

**Complex Number**

A **complex number** is a number of the form $a + bi$, where $a$ and $b$ are real numbers. If $a = 0$ and $b \neq 0$, then the number $bi$ is a **pure imaginary number**.

For example, the real number 2 is a complex number, since it can be written as $2 + 0i$. Also, the pure imaginary number $3i = 0 + 3i$ is a complex number.

$$3 - 2i, \quad 1 + i\sqrt{2}, \quad \text{and} \quad -5 + 4i \qquad \text{Other complex numbers}$$

In the complex number $a + bi$, $a$ is called the **real part** and $b$ is called the **imaginary part**.* A complex number written in the form $a + bi$ (or $a + ib$) is in **standard form**. **FIGURE 1** shows the relationships among the various types of numbers. (Compare this figure with **FIGURE 7** in **Section 1.4**.)

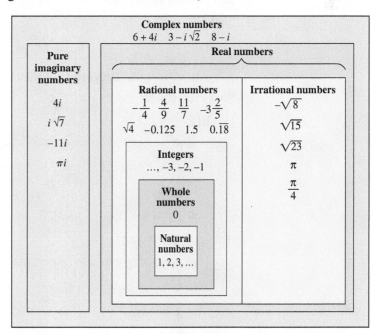

**FIGURE 1**

*NOW TRY ANSWER*
**1.**  $2i\sqrt{3}$

*Some texts refer to $bi$ as the imaginary part.

**OBJECTIVE 2** **Add and subtract complex numbers.** Adding and subtracting complex numbers is similar to adding and subtracting binomials. To add complex numbers, add their real parts and add their imaginary parts. To subtract complex numbers, use the definition of subtraction and add.

↱ *NOW TRY*
*EXERCISE 2*
Add or subtract.
**(a)** $(3 + 5i) + (-4 - 2i)$
**(b)** $(-2 - i) - (1 - 3i)$

**EXAMPLE 2** Adding and Subtracting Complex Numbers

Add or subtract.

**(a)** $(2 - 6i) + (7 + 4i)$

$= (2 + 7) + (-6 + 4)i$     Add real parts.
                                Add imaginary parts.

$= 9 - 2i$               Standard form

**(b)** $3i + (-2 - i)$

$= -2 + (3 - 1)i$       $-i = -1i$

$= -2 + 2i$

**(c)** $(2 + 6i) - (-4 + i)$

$= (2 + 6i) + (4 - i)$     Definition of subtraction

$= (2 + 4) + (6 - 1)i$     Properties of real numbers

$= 6 + 5i$                 Add and subtract.

**(d)** $(-1 + 2i) - 4$

$= (-1 - 4) + 2i$       Properties of real numbers

$= -5 + 2i$            Subtract real parts.      *NOW TRY* ↻

**OBJECTIVE 3** **Multiply complex numbers.** We multiply complex numbers as we do polynomials. Since $i^2 = -1$ by definition, *whenever $i^2$ appears, we replace it with $-1$.*

**EXAMPLE 3** Multiplying Complex Numbers

Find each product.

**(a)** $3i(2 - 5i)$

$= 6i - 15i^2$        Distributive property

$= 6i - 15(-1)$      $i^2 = -1$

$= 6i + 15$          Multiply.

$= 15 + 6i$         Standard form

**(b)** $(4 - 3i)(2 + 5i)$

$= 4(2) + 4(5i) + (-3i)2 + (-3i)5i$     Use the FOIL method.

$= 8 + 20i - 6i - 15i^2$            Multiply.

$= 8 + 14i - 15(-1)$            Combine terms; $i^2 = -1$

$= 8 + 14i + 15$               Multiply.

$= 23 + 14i$                  Add.

*NOW TRY ANSWERS*
**2. (a)** $-1 + 3i$ **(b)** $-3 + 2i$

NOW TRY
EXERCISE 3
Find each product.

**(a)** $8i(1 - 3i)$

**(b)** $(2 - 4i)(3 + 2i)$

**(c)** $(5 - 7i)(5 + 7i)$

**(c)** $(1 + 2i)(1 - 2i)$

$\quad = 1^2 - (2i)^2 \qquad (x + y)(x - y) = x^2 - y^2$

$\quad = 1 - 4i^2 \qquad (xy)^2 = x^2y^2$

$\quad = 1 - 4(-1) \qquad i^2 = -1$

$\quad = 1 + 4 \qquad$ Multiply.

$\quad = 5 \qquad$ Add.

NOW TRY

---

**OBJECTIVE 4**  **Divide complex numbers.** The quotient of two complex numbers, such as

$$\frac{8 + i}{1 + 2i},$$

is expressed in standard form by changing the denominator into a real number.

As seen in **Example 3(c),** the product $(1 + 2i)(1 - 2i)$ is 5, a real number. This suggests multiplying the numerator and denominator of the given quotient by $1 - 2i$ as follows.

$$\frac{8 + i}{1 + 2i}$$

$$= \frac{8 + i}{1 + 2i} \cdot \frac{1 - 2i}{1 - 2i} \qquad \frac{1 - 2i}{1 - 2i} = 1$$

$$= \frac{8 - 16i + i - 2i^2}{1 - 4i^2} \qquad \text{Multiply.}$$

$$= \frac{8 - 16i + i - 2(-1)}{1 - 4(-1)} \qquad \boxed{\text{Use parentheses around } -1 \text{ to avoid errors.}}$$

$$= \frac{10 - 15i}{5} \qquad \text{Combine like terms.}$$

$\boxed{\text{Factor first. Then divide out the common factor.}} = \dfrac{5(2 - 3i)}{5} \qquad \text{Factor out 5.}$

$$= 2 - 3i \qquad \text{Divide out the common factor.}$$

The complex numbers $1 + 2i$ and $1 - 2i$ are *conjugates.* That is, the **conjugate** of the complex number **$a + bi$** is **$a - bi$.** Multiplying the complex number $a + bi$ by its conjugate $a - bi$ gives the real number $a^2 + b^2$.

---

**Product of Conjugates**

$$(a + bi)(a - bi) = a^2 + b^2$$

That is, the product of a complex number and its conjugate is the sum of the squares of the real and imaginary parts.

---

To divide complex numbers, multiply both the numerator and denominator by the conjugate of the denominator. We used a similar method to rationalize some radical expressions in **Chapter 8.**

NOW TRY ANSWERS
3. **(a)** $24 + 8i$  **(b)** $14 - 8i$
   **(c)** 74

NOW TRY
EXERCISE 4

Write each quotient in standard form.

(a) $\dfrac{3 - i}{2 + 3i}$  (b) $\dfrac{5 + i}{-i}$

**EXAMPLE 4** Dividing Complex Numbers

Write each quotient in standard form.

(a) $\dfrac{-4 + i}{2 - i}$

$= \dfrac{-4 + i}{2 - i} \cdot \dfrac{2 + i}{2 + i}$    Multiply numerator and denominator by the conjugate of the denominator.

$= \dfrac{-8 - 4i + 2i + i^2}{4 - i^2}$    Multiply.

$= \dfrac{-8 - 4i + 2i - 1}{4 - (-1)}$    [Be careful with signs.]

$= \dfrac{-9 - 2i}{5}, \quad \text{or} \quad -\dfrac{9}{5} - \dfrac{2}{5}i$    Combine like terms; $\dfrac{a - b}{c} = \dfrac{a}{c} - \dfrac{b}{c}$

(b) $\dfrac{3 + i}{-i}$

$= \dfrac{3 + i}{-i} \cdot \dfrac{i}{i}$    The conjugate of $0 - i$ is $0 + i$, or $i$.

$= \dfrac{3i + i^2}{-i^2}$    Multiply.

$= \dfrac{-1 + 3i}{-(-1)}$    $i^2 = -1$; commutative property

$= -1 + 3i$    [Be careful with signs.]    NOW TRY

**OBJECTIVE 5** Solve quadratic equations with complex number solutions.

NOW TRY
EXERCISE 5

Solve $(x - 1)^2 = -49$ for complex solutions.

**EXAMPLE 5** Solving a Quadratic Equation with Complex Solutions (Square Root Property)

Solve $(x + 3)^2 = -25$ for complex solutions.

$$(x + 3)^2 = -25$$

$x + 3 = \sqrt{-25}$   or   $x + 3 = -\sqrt{-25}$    [Extend the square root property for $k < 0$.]

$x + 3 = 5i$   or   $x + 3 = -5i$    $\sqrt{-25} = 5i$

$x = -3 + 5i$   or   $x = -3 - 5i$    Add $-3$.

The solution set is $\{-3 \pm 5i\}$.    NOW TRY

**EXAMPLE 6** Solving a Quadratic Equation with Complex Solutions (Quadratic Formula)

Solve $2x^2 = 4x - 5$ for complex solutions.

Write the equation in standard form as $2x^2 - 4x + 5 = 0$.

$$x = \dfrac{-b \pm \sqrt{b^2 - 4ac}}{2a}$$    Quadratic formula

$$x = \dfrac{-(-4) \pm \sqrt{(-4)^2 - 4(2)(5)}}{2(2)}$$    Substitute $a = 2$, $b = -4$, and $c = 5$.

NOW TRY ANSWERS

4. (a) $\dfrac{3}{13} - \dfrac{11}{13}i$   (b) $-1 + 5i$
5. $\{1 \pm 7i\}$

*NOW TRY*
*EXERCISE 6*
Solve $3t^2 = 2t - 1$ for complex solutions.

$$x = \frac{4 \pm \sqrt{16 - 40}}{4}$$     Simplify.

$$x = \frac{4 \pm \sqrt{-24}}{4}$$     Subtract in the radicand.

$$x = \frac{4 \pm 2i\sqrt{6}}{4}$$     $\sqrt{-24} = i\sqrt{24} = i \cdot \sqrt{4} \cdot \sqrt{6}$
$$= i \cdot 2 \cdot \sqrt{6} = 2i\sqrt{6}$$

> Factor first. Then divide out the common factor.

$$x = \frac{2\left(2 \pm i\sqrt{6}\right)}{2(2)}$$     Factor out 2.

$$x = \frac{2 \pm i\sqrt{6}}{2}$$     Divide out the common factor.

$$x = \frac{2}{2} \pm \frac{i\sqrt{6}}{2}$$     $\frac{a \pm b}{c} = \frac{a}{c} \pm \frac{b}{c}$; Separate into real and imaginary parts.

$$x = 1 \pm \frac{\sqrt{6}}{2}i$$     Standard form

*NOW TRY ANSWER*
**6.** $\left\{ \frac{1}{3} \pm \frac{\sqrt{2}}{3}i \right\}$

The solution set is $\left\{ 1 \pm \frac{\sqrt{6}}{2}i \right\}$.     *NOW TRY*

---

# 9.4 EXERCISES

*MyMathLab*   Math XL PRACTICE   WATCH   DOWNLOAD   READ   REVIEW

🌐 *Complete solution available on the Video Resources on DVD*

*Write each number as a multiple of i.* **See Example 1.**

🌐 **1.** $\sqrt{-9}$     **2.** $\sqrt{-36}$     **3.** $\sqrt{-20}$     **4.** $\sqrt{-27}$

**5.** $\sqrt{-18}$     **6.** $\sqrt{-50}$     **7.** $\sqrt{-125}$     **8.** $\sqrt{-98}$

*Add or subtract as indicated.* **See Example 2.**

🌐 **9.** $(2 + 8i) + (3 - 5i)$     **10.** $(4 + 5i) + (7 - 2i)$     **11.** $(8 - 3i) - (2 + 6i)$

**12.** $(1 + i) - (3 - 2i)$     **13.** $4i + (-6 - 2i)$     **14.** $-3i + (-8 + 6i)$

**15.** $(-3 + 6i) - 5$     **16.** $(12 - 3i) - 8$

**17.** $(3 - 4i) + (6 - i) - (3 + 2i)$     **18.** $(5 + 8i) - (4 + 2i) + (3 - i)$

*Find each product.* **See Example 3.**

**19.** $(2i)(i)$     **20.** $(3i)(i)$     **21.** $(-6i)(-i)$

**22.** $(-5i)(-i)$     **23.** $2i(4 - 3i)$     **24.** $7i(7 - 4i)$

🌐 **25.** $(3 + 2i)(4 - i)$     **26.** $(9 - 2i)(3 + i)$     **27.** $(5 - 4i)(3 - 2i)$

**28.** $(10 + 6i)(8 - 4i)$     **29.** $(3 + 6i)(3 - 6i)$     **30.** $(11 - 2i)(11 + 2i)$

*Write each quotient in standard form.* **See Example 4.**

**31.** $\dfrac{1}{1 - i}$     **32.** $\dfrac{1}{1 + i}$     **33.** $\dfrac{40}{2 + 6i}$

**34.** $\dfrac{13}{3 + 2i}$     **35.** $\dfrac{i}{4 - 3i}$     **36.** $\dfrac{-i}{1 + 2i}$

**37.** $\dfrac{7 + 3i}{1 - i}$

**38.** $\dfrac{-4 + 2i}{1 + i}$

**39.** $\dfrac{17 + i}{5 + 2i}$

**40.** $\dfrac{21 + i}{4 + i}$

**41.** $\dfrac{-5 + 10i}{6 + 12i}$

**42.** $\dfrac{13 - 14i}{12 + 24i}$

*Solve each quadratic equation for complex solutions by the square root property, with $k < 0$. Write solutions in standard form.* **See Example 5.**

**43.** $(x + 1)^2 = -4$

**44.** $(x - 5)^2 = -36$

**45.** $(x - 3)^2 = -5$

**46.** $(x + 6)^2 = -7$

**47.** $(3x + 2)^2 = -18$

**48.** $(4x + 1)^2 = -48$

*Solve each quadratic equation for complex solutions by the quadratic formula. Write solutions in standard form.* **See Example 6.**

**49.** $m^2 - 2m + 2 = 0$

**50.** $x^2 - 4x + 5 = 0$

**51.** $2r^2 + 3r + 5 = 0$

**52.** $3x^2 - 2x + 3 = 0$

**53.** $p^2 - 3p + 4 = 0$

**54.** $2x^2 + x + 3 = 0$

**55.** $5x^2 + 3 = 2x$

**56.** $6x^2 + 1 = -2x$

**57.** $2m^2 + 7 = -2m$

**58.** $4x^2 + 3 = -2x$

**59.** $x^2 - x + 3 = 0$

**60.** $4q^2 - 2q + 3 = 0$

*Concept Check* *Answer* true *or* false *to each statement. If false, say why.*

**61.** Every real number is a complex number.

**62.** Every pure imaginary number is a complex number.

**63.** Every complex number is a real number.

**64.** Every complex number is a pure imaginary number.

## PREVIEW EXERCISES

*Graph each linear equation.* **See Section 3.2.**

**65.** $2x - 3y = 6$

**66.** $y = 4x - 3$

*Evaluate each expression for $x = 3$.* **See Section 1.3.**

**67.** $2x^2 - x + 1$

**68.** $(x - 1)^2$

## 9.5 More on Graphing Quadratic Equations; Quadratic Functions

### OBJECTIVES

**1** Graph quadratic equations of the form $y = ax^2 + bx + c$ $(a \neq 0)$.

**2** Use a graph to determine the number of real solutions of a quadratic equation.

In **Section 5.4,** we graphed the quadratic equation $y = x^2$. By plotting points, we obtained the graph of a **parabola,** shown here in **FIGURE 2.**

Recall that the lowest point on this graph is called the **vertex** of the parabola. (If the parabola opens downward, the vertex is the highest point.) The vertical line through the vertex is called the **axis,** or **axis of symmetry.** The two halves of the parabola are mirror images of each other across this axis.

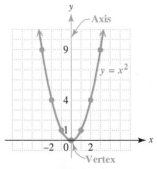

| $x$ | $y$ |
|-----|-----|
| 3 | 9 |
| 2 | 4 |
| 1 | 1 |
| 0 | 0 |
| −1 | 1 |
| −2 | 4 |
| −3 | 9 |

**FIGURE 2**

**OBJECTIVE 1** Graph quadratic equations of the form $y = ax^2 + bx + c$ ($a \neq 0$). Every equation of the form

$$y = ax^2 + bx + c,$$

with $a \neq 0$, has a graph that is a parabola. The vertex is an important point to locate when graphing a quadratic equation.

NOW TRY
EXERCISE 1
Graph $y = x^2 - x - 2$.

**EXAMPLE 1**   Graphing a Parabola by Finding the Vertex and Intercepts

Graph $y = x^2 - 2x - 3$.

We must find the vertex of the graph. **Because of its symmetry, if a parabola has two x-intercepts, the x-value of the vertex is exactly halfway between them.** Therefore, we begin by finding the $x$-intercepts. Let $y = 0$ in the equation and solve for $x$.

$$0 = x^2 - 2x - 3$$

| | |
|---|---|
| $x^2 - 2x - 3 = 0$ | Interchange sides. |
| $(x + 1)(x - 3) = 0$ | Factor. |
| $x + 1 = 0$ or $x - 3 = 0$ | Zero-factor property |
| $x = -1$ or $x = 3$ | Solve each equation. |

There are two $x$-intercepts, $(-1, 0)$ and $(3, 0)$.

Since the $x$-value of the vertex is halfway between the $x$-values of the two $x$-intercepts, it is half their sum.

$$x = \frac{1}{2}(-1 + 3) = 1 \longleftarrow x\text{-value of the vertex}$$

Find the corresponding $y$-value by substituting 1 for $x$ in $y = x^2 - 2x - 3$.

$$y = 1^2 - 2(1) - 3 = -4 \longleftarrow y\text{-value of the vertex}$$

The vertex is $(1, -4)$. The axis is the line $x = 1$.

To find the $y$-intercept, substitute $x = 0$ in the equation.

$$y = 0^2 - 2(0) - 3 = -3$$

The $y$-intercept is $(0, -3)$.

Plot the three intercepts and the vertex. Find additional ordered pairs as needed. For example, if $x = 2$, then

$$y = 2^2 - 2(2) - 3 = -3,$$

leading to the ordered pair $(2, -3)$. A table with all these ordered pairs is shown with the graph in **FIGURE 3**.

NOW TRY ANSWER

1.

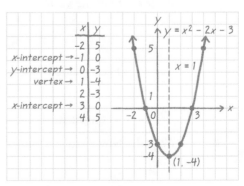

| $x$ | $y$ | |
|---|---|---|
| -2 | 5 | |
| -1 | 0 | x-intercept |
| 0 | -3 | y-intercept |
| 1 | -4 | vertex |
| 2 | -3 | |
| 3 | 0 | x-intercept |
| 4 | 5 | |

**FIGURE 3**

NOW TRY

We can generalize from **Example 1.** The $x$-coordinates of the $x$-intercepts for the equation $y = ax^2 + bx + c$, by the quadratic formula, are

$$x = \frac{-b + \sqrt{b^2 - 4ac}}{2a} \quad \text{and} \quad x = \frac{-b - \sqrt{b^2 - 4ac}}{2a}.$$

Thus, the $x$-value of the vertex is half their sum.

$$x = \frac{1}{2}\left( \frac{-b + \sqrt{b^2 - 4ac}}{2a} + \frac{-b - \sqrt{b^2 - 4ac}}{2a} \right)$$

$$x = \frac{1}{2}\left( \frac{-b + \sqrt{b^2 - 4ac} - b - \sqrt{b^2 - 4ac}}{2a} \right)$$

$$x = \frac{1}{2}\left( \frac{-2b}{2a} \right) \qquad \text{Combine like terms.}$$

$$x = -\frac{b}{2a} \qquad \text{Multiply; lowest terms}$$

For the equation in **Example 1**, $y = x^2 - 2x - 3$, we have $a = 1$, and $b = -2$. Thus, the $x$-value of the vertex is

$$x = -\frac{b}{2a} = -\frac{-2}{2(1)} = 1,$$

which is the same $x$-value for the vertex we found in **Example 1.** (It can be shown that the $x$-value of the vertex is $x = -\frac{b}{2a}$, even if the graph has no $x$-intercepts.)

---

### Graphing the Parabola $y = ax^2 + bx + c$

*Step 1*   **Find the vertex.** Let $x = -\frac{b}{2a}$, and find the corresponding $y$-value by substituting for $x$ in the equation.

*Step 2*   **Find the $y$-intercept.** Let $x = 0$ and solve for $y$.

*Step 3*   **Find the $x$-intercepts** (if they exist). Let $y = 0$ and solve for $x$.

*Step 4*   **Plot** the intercepts and the vertex.

*Step 5*   **Find and plot additional ordered pairs** near the vertex and intercepts as needed, using symmetry about the axis of the parabola.

---

#### EXAMPLE 2   Graphing a Parabola

Graph $y = x^2 - 4x + 1$.

*Step 1*   Find the vertex. The $x$-value of the vertex is

$$x = -\frac{b}{2a} = -\frac{-4}{2(1)} = 2. \qquad a = 1, b = -4$$

The $y$-value of the vertex is

$$y = 2^2 - 4(2) + 1 = -3,$$

so the vertex is $(2, -3)$. The axis is the line $x = 2$.

*Step 2*   Now find the $y$-intercept. Let $x = 0$ in $y = x^2 - 4x + 1$.

$$y = 0^2 - 4(0) + 1 = 1$$

The $y$-intercept is $(0, 1)$.

NOW TRY
EXERCISE 2
Graph $y = -x^2 + 4x + 2$.

**Step 3**   Let $y = 0$ to determine the $x$-intercepts. The equation is $0 = x^2 - 4x + 1$, which cannot be solved by factoring, so we use the quadratic formula.

$$x = \frac{-(-4) \pm \sqrt{(-4)^2 - 4(1)(1)}}{2(1)}$$   Let $a = 1$, $b = -4$, $c = 1$ in the quadratic formula.

$$x = \frac{4 \pm \sqrt{12}}{2}$$   Simplify.

$$x = \frac{4 \pm 2\sqrt{3}}{2}$$   $\sqrt{12} = \sqrt{4} \cdot \sqrt{3} = 2\sqrt{3}$

Factor first. Then divide out the common factor.

$$x = \frac{2(2 \pm \sqrt{3})}{2}$$   Factor.

$$x = 2 \pm \sqrt{3}$$   Divide out 2.

Using a calculator, we find that the $x$-intercepts are $(3.7, 0)$ and $(0.3, 0)$ to the nearest tenth.

**Steps 4 and 5**   Plot the intercepts, vertex, and the additional points shown in the table. Connect these points with a smooth curve. The graph is shown in **FIGURE 4**.

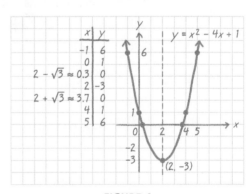

**FIGURE 4**

NOW TRY

**OBJECTIVE 2**   **Use a graph to determine the number of real solutions of a quadratic equation.**   Using the vertical line test **(Section 3.6)**, we see that the graph of an equation of the form

$$y = ax^2 + bx + c$$

is the graph of a function. A function defined by an equation of the form

$$f(x) = ax^2 + bx + c \quad (a \neq 0)$$

is called a **quadratic function.** The **domain** (possible $x$-values) of a quadratic function is the set of all real numbers, or $(-\infty, \infty)$. The **range** (the resulting $y$-values) can be determined after the function is graphed. In **Example 2**, the domain is $(-\infty, \infty)$, and from **FIGURE 4**, we see that the range is $[-3, \infty)$.

In **Example 2**, we found that the $x$-intercepts of the graph of $y = x^2 - 4x + 1$ (where $y = 0$) have $x$-values

$$2 - \sqrt{3} \approx 0.3 \quad \text{and} \quad 2 + \sqrt{3} \approx 3.7.$$

This means that $2 - \sqrt{3} \approx 0.3$ and $2 + \sqrt{3} \approx 3.7$ are also the solutions of the equation $0 = x^2 - 4x + 1$.

NOW TRY ANSWER
2. $y = -x^2 + 4x + 2$

### x-Intercepts of the Graph of a Quadratic Function

The real number solutions of a quadratic equation $ax^2 + bx + c = 0$ are the $x$-values of the $x$-intercepts of the graph of the corresponding quadratic function defined by $f(x) = ax^2 + bx + c$.

The fact that the graph of a quadratic function can intersect the $x$-axis in two, one, or no points justifies why some quadratic equations have two, some have one, and some have no real solutions.

*NOW TRY*
*EXERCISE 3*

Decide from the graph how many real number solutions there are of the corresponding equation $f(x) = 0$. Give the solution set.

**EXAMPLE 3** Determining the Number of Real Solutions from Graphs

Decide from the graphs in **FIGURES 5-7** how many real number solutions there are of the corresponding equation $f(x) = 0$. Give the solution set for the domain of real numbers.

**(a) FIGURE 5** shows the graph of $f(x) = x^2 - 3$. The corresponding equation,

$$x^2 - 3 = 0,$$

has two real solutions, $\sqrt{3}$ and $-\sqrt{3}$, which correspond to the $x$-intercepts. The solution set is $\left\{\pm\sqrt{3}\right\}$.

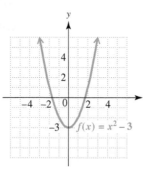

**FIGURE 5**          **FIGURE 6**

**(b) FIGURE 6** shows the graph of $f(x) = x^2 - 4x + 4$. The corresponding equation,

$$x^2 - 4x + 4 = 0,$$

has one real solution, 2, which is the $x$-value of the $x$-intercept of the graph. The solution set is $\{2\}$.

**(c) FIGURE 7** shows the graph of $f(x) = x^2 + 2$. The equation

$$x^2 + 2 = 0$$

has no real solutions, since there are no $x$-intercepts. The solution set over the domain of real numbers is $\emptyset$. (The equation *does* have two pure imaginary solutions: $i\sqrt{2}$ and $-i\sqrt{2}$.)

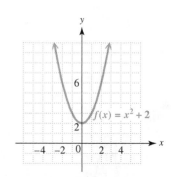

**FIGURE 7**

NOW TRY

*NOW TRY ANSWER*
**3.** one real solution; $\{2\}$

## 9.5 EXERCISES

    MyMathLab  Math XL PRACTICE  WATCH  DOWNLOAD  READ  REVIEW

🌐 *Complete solution available on the Video Resources on DVD*

*Give the coordinates of the vertex and sketch the graph of each equation.* **See Examples 1 and 2.**

**1.** $y = x^2 - 6$  **2.** $y = -x^2 + 2$  **3.** $y = (x + 3)^2$

**4.** $y = (x - 4)^2$  🌐 **5.** $y = x^2 + 2x + 3$  **6.** $y = x^2 - 4x + 3$

🌐 **7.** $y = x^2 - 8x + 16$  **8.** $y = x^2 + 6x + 9$  **9.** $y = -x^2 + 6x - 5$

**10.** $y = -x^2 - 4x - 3$  **11.** $y = x^2 + 4x$  **12.** $y = x^2 - 2x$

*Decide from each graph how many real solutions $f(x) = 0$ has. Then give the solution set (of real solutions).* **See Example 3.**

🌐 **13.**

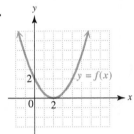

**14.**

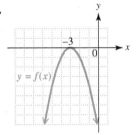

**15.**

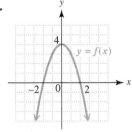

**16.**

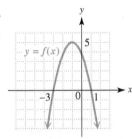

**17.**

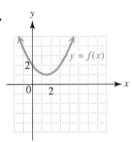

**18.**

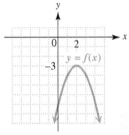

**19.** *Concept Check* Based on your work in **Exercises 1–12,** what seems to be the direction in which the parabola $y = ax^2 + bx + c$ opens if $a > 0$? If $a < 0$?

**20.** *Concept Check* How many real solutions does a quadratic equation have if its corresponding graph has **(a)** no $x$-intercepts, **(b)** one $x$-intercept, **(c)** two $x$-intercepts? (See **Examples 1–3.**)

### TECHNOLOGY INSIGHTS   EXERCISES 21–22

*The connection between the solutions of an equation and the $x$-intercepts of its graph enables us to solve quadratic equations with a graphing calculator. With the equation in the form $ax^2 + bx + c = 0$, enter $ax^2 + bx + c$ as $Y_1$, and then direct the calculator to find the $x$-intercepts of the graph. (These are also referred to as **zeros** of the function.)*

*For example, to solve $x^2 - 5x - 6 = 0$ graphically, refer to the three screens shown here. The displays at the bottoms of the lower two screens show the two solutions: $-1$ and 6.*

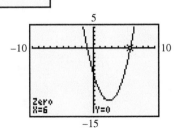

*Determine the solution set of each quadratic equation by observing the corresponding screens. Then use the method of your choice to verify your answers by solving the quadratic equation.*

**21.** $x^2 - x - 6 = 0$

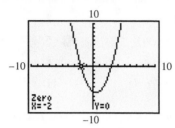
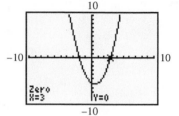

**22.** $2x^2 - x - 3 = 0$

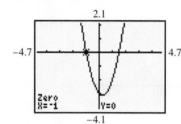
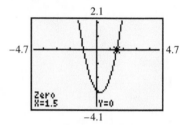

---

*Find the domain and range of each function graphed in the indicated exercise.*

**23.** Exercise 13     **24.** Exercise 14     **25.** Exercise 15

**26.** Exercise 16     **27.** Exercise 17     **28.** Exercise 18

*Given $f(x) = 2x^2 - 5x + 3$, find each of the following.*

**29.** $f(0)$     **30.** $f(1)$     **31.** $f(-2)$     **32.** $f(-1)$

*Solve each problem.*

**33.** Find two numbers whose sum is 80 and whose product is a maximum. (*Hint:* Let $x$ represent one of the numbers. Then $80 - x$ represents the other. A quadratic function represents their product.)

**34.** Find two numbers whose sum is 300 and whose product is a maximum.

**35.** The U.S. Naval Research Laboratory designed a giant radio telescope that had a diameter of 300 ft and a maximum depth of 44 ft. The graph depicts a cross section of that telescope. Find the equation of this parabola. (*Source:* Mar, J., and H. Liebowitz, *Structure Technology for Large Radio and Radar Telescope Systems*, The MIT Press.)

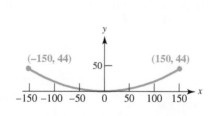

**36.** Suppose the telescope in **Exercise 35** had a diameter of 400 ft and a maximum depth of 50 ft. Find the equation of this parabola.

**RELATING CONCEPTS**  EXERCISES 37–42

FOR INDIVIDUAL OR GROUP WORK

*We can use a graphing calculator to illustrate how the graph of $y = x^2$ can be transformed through arithmetic operations.* **Work Exercises 37–42 in order.**

**37.** In the standard viewing window of your calculator, graph the following one at a time, leaving the previous graphs on the screen as you move along.

$$Y_1 = x^2 \qquad Y_2 = 2x^2 \qquad Y_3 = 3x^2 \qquad Y_4 = 4x^2$$

Describe the effect the successive coefficients have on the parabola.

**38.** Repeat **Exercise 37** for the following.

$$Y_1 = x^2 \qquad Y_2 = \frac{1}{2}x^2 \qquad Y_3 = \frac{1}{4}x^2 \qquad Y_4 = \frac{1}{8}x^2$$

**39.** In the standard viewing window of your calculator, graph the following pair of parabolas on the same screen.

$$Y_1 = x^2 \qquad Y_2 = -x^2$$

Describe how the graph of $Y_2$ can be obtained from the graph of $Y_1$.

**40.** In the standard viewing window of your calculator, graph the following parabolas on the same screen.

$$Y_1 = -x^2 \qquad Y_2 = -2x^2 \qquad Y_3 = -3x^2 \qquad Y_4 = -4x^2$$

Make a conjecture about what happens when the coefficient of $x^2$ is negative.

**41.** In the standard viewing window of your calculator, graph the following one at a time, leaving the previous graphs on the screen as you move along.

$$Y_1 = x^2 \qquad Y_2 = x^2 + 3 \qquad Y_3 = x^2 - 6$$

Describe the effect that adding or subtracting a constant has on the parabola.

**42.** Repeat **Exercise 41** for the following.

$$Y_1 = x^2 \qquad Y_2 = (x + 3)^2 \qquad Y_3 = (x - 6)^2$$

# CHAPTER ⑨ SUMMARY

## KEY TERMS

**9.1**
quadratic equation

**9.2**
completing the square

**9.3**
quadratic formula
discriminant

**9.4**
complex number
pure imaginary number

real part
imaginary part
standard form (of a complex number)
conjugate (of a complex number)

**9.5**
parabola
vertex
axis (of symmetry)
quadratic function

$\pm$   positive or negative
  ( plus or minus)

$i$   imaginary unit

**TEST YOUR WORD POWER**

*See how well you have learned the vocabulary in this chapter.*

1. A **quadratic equation** is an
   equation that can be written in the
   form
   **A.** $Ax + By = C$
   **B.** $ax^2 + bx + c = 0$
   **C.** $Ax + B = 0$
   **D.** $y = mx + b$.

2. A **complex number** is
   **A.** a real number that includes a
     complex fraction
   **B.** a nonzero multiple of $i$
   **C.** a number of the form $a + bi$,
     where $a$ and $b$ are real numbers
   **D.** the square root of $-1$.

3. A **pure imaginary number** is
   **A.** a complex number $a + bi$, where
     $a = 0, b \neq 0$
   **B.** a number that does not exist
   **C.** a complex number $a + bi$, where
     $b = 0$
   **D.** any real number.

4. A **parabola** is the graph of
   **A.** any equation in two variables
   **B.** a linear equation
   **C.** an equation of degree three
   **D.** a quadratic equation in two
     variables.

5. The **vertex** of a parabola is
   **A.** the point where the graph
     intersects the $y$-axis
   **B.** the point where the graph
     intersects the $x$-axis
   **C.** the lowest point on a parabola
     that opens up or the highest point
     on a parabola that opens down
   **D.** the origin.

6. The **axis** of a vertical parabola is
   **A.** either the $x$-axis or the $y$-axis
   **B.** the vertical line through the vertex
   **C.** the horizontal line through the vertex
   **D.** the $x$-axis.

**ANSWERS**

**1.** B; *Examples:* $z^2 + 6z + 9 = 0$, $y^2 - 2y = 8$, $(x + 3)(x - 1) = 5$   **2.** C; *Examples:* $-5$ (or $-5 + 0i$), $7i$ (or $0 + 7i$), $\sqrt{2} - 4i$
**3.** A; *Examples:* $2i, -13i, i\sqrt{6}$   **4.** D; *Examples:* See **FIGURES 2–7** in **Section 9.5**.   **5.** C; *Example:* The graph of $y = (x + 3)^2$ has vertex
$(-3, 0)$, which is the lowest point on the graph.   **6.** B; *Example:* The axis of the graph of $y = (x + 3)^2$ is the line $x = -3$.

**QUICK REVIEW**

| CONCEPTS | EXAMPLES |
|---|---|

### 9.1 Solving Quadratic Equations by the Square Root Property

**Square Root Property**
If $k$ is positive and if $x^2 = k$, then

$$x = \sqrt{k} \quad \text{or} \quad x = -\sqrt{k}.$$

The solution set, $\{-\sqrt{k}, \sqrt{k}\}$, can be written $\{\pm\sqrt{k}\}$.

Solve $(2x + 1)^2 = 5$.

| | | |
|---|---|---|
| $2x + 1 = \sqrt{5}$ | or | $2x + 1 = -\sqrt{5}$ |
| $2x = -1 + \sqrt{5}$ | or | $2x = -1 - \sqrt{5}$ |
| $x = \dfrac{-1 + \sqrt{5}}{2}$ | or | $x = \dfrac{-1 - \sqrt{5}}{2}$ |

The solution set is $\left\{\dfrac{-1 \pm \sqrt{5}}{2}\right\}$.

### 9.2 Solving Quadratic Equations by Completing the Square

**Solving a Quadratic Equation by Completing the Square**

*Step 1*   If the coefficient of the second-degree term is
   1, go to Step 2. If it is not 1, divide each side of
   the equation by this coefficient.

*Step 2*   Make sure that all variable terms are on one
   side of the equation and all constant terms are
   on the other.

Solve $2x^2 + 4x - 1 = 0$.

$$x^2 + 2x - \frac{1}{2} = 0 \qquad \text{Divide by 2.}$$

$$x^2 + 2x = \frac{1}{2} \qquad \text{Add } \tfrac{1}{2}.$$

(continued)

| CONCEPTS | EXAMPLES |
|---|---|
| **Step 3** Take half the coefficient of $x$, square it, and add the square to each side of the equation. Factor the variable side and combine terms on the other side. | $x^2 + 2x + 1 = \dfrac{1}{2} + 1$    Add $\left[\frac{1}{2}(2)\right]^2 = 1^2 = 1.$ <br><br> $(x + 1)^2 = \dfrac{3}{2}$    Factor. Add. |
| **Step 4** Use the square root property to solve the equation. | $x + 1 = \sqrt{\dfrac{3}{2}}$    or    $x + 1 = -\sqrt{\dfrac{3}{2}}$ <br><br> $x + 1 = \dfrac{\sqrt{6}}{2}$    or    $x + 1 = -\dfrac{\sqrt{6}}{2}$ <br><br> $x = -1 + \dfrac{\sqrt{6}}{2}$    or    $x = -1 - \dfrac{\sqrt{6}}{2}$ <br><br> $x = \dfrac{-2 + \sqrt{6}}{2}$    or    $x = \dfrac{-2 - \sqrt{6}}{2}$ <br><br> The solution set is $\left\{\dfrac{-2 \pm \sqrt{6}}{2}\right\}.$ |

## 9.3  Solving Quadratic Equations by the Quadratic Formula

| | |
|---|---|
| **Quadratic Formula** <br> The solutions of $ax^2 + bx + c = 0$, $a \neq 0$, are <br><br> $$x = \dfrac{-b \pm \sqrt{b^2 - 4ac}}{2a}.$$ <br><br><br> The discriminant of the quadratic equation is <br> $$b^2 - 4ac.$$ | Solve $3x^2 - 4x - 2 = 0.$ <br><br> $x = \dfrac{-(-4) \pm \sqrt{(-4)^2 - 4(3)(-2)}}{2(3)}$    $a = 3, b = -4,$ $c = -2$ <br><br> $x = \dfrac{4 \pm \sqrt{40}}{6}$    Simplify. <br><br> $x = \dfrac{4 \pm 2\sqrt{10}}{6}$    $\sqrt{40} = \sqrt{4 \cdot 10}$ $= 2\sqrt{10}$ <br><br> $x = \dfrac{2(2 \pm \sqrt{10})}{2 \cdot 3}$    Factor out 2. <br><br> $x = \dfrac{2 \pm \sqrt{10}}{3}$    Divide out 2. <br><br> The solution set is $\left\{\dfrac{2 \pm \sqrt{10}}{3}\right\}.$ |

## 9.4  Complex Numbers

| | |
|---|---|
| The imaginary unit is $i$, where <br> $$i = \sqrt{-1}, \quad \text{and thus,} \quad i^2 = -1.$$ <br> For the positive number $b$, $\sqrt{-b} = i\sqrt{b}.$ | $\sqrt{-19} = i\sqrt{19}$ |
| **Addition** <br> Add complex numbers by adding the real parts and adding the imaginary parts. | Add.    $(3 + 6i) + (-9 + 2i)$ <br><br> $= (3 - 9) + (6 + 2)i$ <br><br> $= -6 + 8i$ |

(continued)

| CONCEPTS | EXAMPLES |
|---|---|

**Subtraction**

To subtract complex numbers, change the number following the subtraction sign to its negative and add.

Subtract. $(5 + 4i) - (2 - 4i)$

$$= (5 + 4i) + (-2 + 4i) \qquad \text{Definition of subtraction}$$

$$= (5 - 2) + (4 + 4)i \qquad \text{Add real parts and add imaginary parts.}$$

$$= 3 + 8i$$

**Multiplication**

Multiply complex numbers in the same way polynomials are multiplied. Replace $i^2$ with $-1$.

Multiply. $(7 + i)(3 - 4i)$

$$= 7(3) + 7(-4i) + i(3) + i(-4i) \qquad \text{FOIL method}$$

$$= 21 - 28i + 3i - 4i^2 \qquad \text{Multiply.}$$

$$= 21 - 25i - 4(-1) \qquad i^2 = -1$$

$$= 21 - 25i + 4 \qquad \text{Multiply.}$$

$$= 25 - 25i \qquad \text{Add.}$$

**Division**

Divide complex numbers by multiplying the numerator and the denominator by the conjugate of the denominator.

Divide. $\dfrac{2}{6 + i}$

$$= \frac{2}{6 + i} \cdot \frac{6 - i}{6 - i} \qquad 6 - i \text{ is the conjugate of } 6 + i.$$

$$= \frac{2(6 - i)}{36 - i^2} \qquad \text{Multiply.}$$

$$= \frac{12 - 2i}{36 - (-1)} \qquad \text{Multiply; } i^2 = -1$$

$$= \frac{12 - 2i}{37} \qquad \text{Subtract.}$$

$$= \frac{12}{37} - \frac{2}{37}i \qquad \text{Standard form}$$

**Complex Solutions**

A quadratic equation may have nonreal complex solutions. This occurs when the discriminant is negative. The quadratic formula will give complex solutions in such cases.

Solve for all complex solutions of $x^2 + x + 1 = 0$.

$$x = \frac{-1 \pm \sqrt{1^2 - 4(1)(1)}}{2(1)} \qquad a = 1, b = 1, c = 1$$

$$x = \frac{-1 \pm \sqrt{1 - 4}}{2} \qquad \text{Simplify.}$$

$$x = \frac{-1 \pm \sqrt{-3}}{2}$$

$$x = \frac{-1 \pm i\sqrt{3}}{2}, \quad \text{or} \quad -\frac{1}{2} \pm \frac{i\sqrt{3}}{2}$$

The solution set is $\left\{ -\dfrac{1}{2} \pm \dfrac{\sqrt{3}}{2}i \right\}$.

*(continued)*

## CONCEPTS

**9.5** More on Graphing Quadratic Equations; Quadratic Functions

**To graph $y = ax^2 + bx + c$,**

**Step 1** Find the vertex: $x = -\frac{b}{2a}$. Find $y$ by substituting this value for $x$ in the equation.

**Step 2** Find the $y$-intercept. Let $x = 0$ and solve for $y$.

**Step 3** Find the $x$-intercepts (if they exist). Let $y = 0$ and solve for $x$.

**Step 4** Plot the intercepts and the vertex.

**Step 5** Find and plot additional ordered pairs near the vertex and intercepts as needed.

## EXAMPLES

Graph $y = 2x^2 - 5x - 3$.

$$x = -\frac{b}{2a}$$

$$x = -\frac{-5}{2(2)}$$

$$x = \frac{5}{4}$$

$$y = 2\left(\frac{5}{4}\right)^2 - 5\left(\frac{5}{4}\right) - 3$$

$$y = 2\left(\frac{25}{16}\right) - \frac{25}{4} - 3$$

$$y = \frac{25}{8} - \frac{50}{8} - \frac{24}{8}$$

$$y = -\frac{49}{8}$$

The vertex is $\left(\frac{5}{4}, -\frac{49}{8}\right)$.

$$y = 2(0)^2 - 5(0) - 3 = -3$$

The $y$-intercept is $(0, -3)$.

$$0 = 2x^2 - 5x - 3$$
$$0 = (2x + 1)(x - 3)$$

$2x + 1 = 0 \qquad \text{or} \qquad x - 3 = 0$

$2x = -1 \qquad \text{or} \qquad x = 3$

$x = -\frac{1}{2} \qquad \text{or} \qquad x = 3$

The $x$-intercepts are $\left(-\frac{1}{2}, 0\right)$ and $(3, 0)$.

| $x$ | $y$ |
|---|---|
| $-\frac{1}{2}$ | $0$ |
| $0$ | $-3$ |
| $\frac{5}{4}$ | $-\frac{49}{8}$ |
| $2$ | $-5$ |
| $3$ | $0$ |

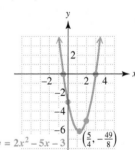

## CHAPTER 9 REVIEW EXERCISES

**9.1** *Solve each equation by using the square root property. Give only real number solutions. Express all radicals in simplest form.*

**1.** $z^2 = 144$  **2.** $x^2 = 37$  **3.** $m^2 = 128$  **4.** $(x + 2)^2 = 25$

**5.** $(r - 3)^2 = 10$  **6.** $(2p + 1)^2 = 14$  **7.** $(3x + 2)^2 = -3$  **8.** $(3 - 5x)^2 = 8$

**9.2**    *Solve each equation by completing the square. Give only real number solutions.*

**9.** $m^2 + 6m + 5 = 0$ 

**10.** $p^2 + 4p = 7$

**11.** $-x^2 + 5 = 2x$ 

**12.** $2z^2 - 3 = -8z$

**13.** $5x^2 - 3x - 2 = 0$ 

**14.** $(4x + 1)(x - 1) = -7$

*Solve each problem.*

**15.** If an object is projected upward on Earth from a height of 50 ft, with an initial velocity of 32 ft per sec, then its altitude (height) after $t$ seconds is given by $h = -16t^2 + 32t + 50$, where $h$ is in feet. At what times will the object be at a height of 30 ft?

**16.** Find the lengths of the three sides of the right triangle shown.

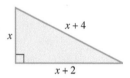

**17.** *Concept Check*    What must be added to $x^2 + 3x$ to make it a perfect square?

**9.3**

**18.** Consider the equation $x^2 - 9 = 0$.

**(a)** Solve the equation by factoring.

**(b)** Solve the equation by the square root property.

**(c)** Solve the equation by the quadratic formula.

**(d)** Compare your answers. If a quadratic equation can be solved by both factoring and the quadratic formula, should you always get the same results? Explain.

*Solve each equation by using the quadratic formula. Give only real number solutions.*

**19.** $x^2 - 2x - 4 = 0$ 

**20.** $3k^2 + 2k = -3$ 

**21.** $2p^2 + 8 = 4p + 11$

**22.** $-4x^2 + 7 = 2x$ 

**23.** $\frac{1}{4}p^2 = 2 - \frac{3}{4}p$ 

**24.** $3x^2 - x - 2 = 0$

**25.** *Concept Check*    How many real solutions are there for a quadratic equation that has a negative number as its radicand in the quadratic formula?

**9.4**    *Perform each indicated operation.*

**26.** $(3 + 5i) + (2 - 6i)$ 

**27.** $(-2 - 8i) - (4 - 3i)$ 

**28.** $(6 - 2i)(3 + i)$

**29.** $(2 + 3i)(2 - 3i)$ 

**30.** $\dfrac{1 + i}{1 - i}$ 

**31.** $\dfrac{5 + 6i}{2 + 3i}$

**32.** *Concept Check*    What is the conjugate of the real number $a$?

**33.** Is it possible to multiply a complex number by its conjugate and get a product that is not a real number? Explain.

*Find the complex solutions of each quadratic equation.*

**34.** $(m + 2)^2 = -3$ 

**35.** $(3p - 2)^2 = -8$ 

**36.** $3x^2 = 2x - 1$

**37.** $x^2 + 3x = -8$ 

**38.** $4q^2 + 2 = 3q$ 

**39.** $9z^2 + 2z + 1 = 0$

**9.5**    *Identify the vertex and sketch the graph of each equation.*

**40.** $y = -3x^2$ 

**41.** $y = -x^2 + 5$ 

**42.** $y = (x + 4)^2$

**43.** $y = x^2 - 2x + 1$ 

**44.** $y = -x^2 + 2x + 3$ 

**45.** $y = x^2 + 4x + 2$

*Decide from the graph how many real number solutions there are of the equation $f(x) = 0$. Determine the solution set (of real solutions) for $f(x) = 0$ from the graph. Give the domain and range of each function.*

**46.**

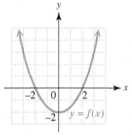

**47.**

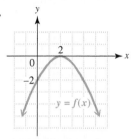

**48.**

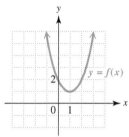

## MIXED REVIEW EXERCISES

*Solve by any method. Give only real number solutions.*

**49.** $(2t - 1)(t + 1) = 54$    **50.** $(2p + 1)^2 = 100$    **51.** $(x + 2)(x - 1) = 3$

**52.** $6t^2 + 7t - 3 = 0$    **53.** $2x^2 + 3x + 2 = x^2 - 2x$    **54.** $x^2 + 2x + 5 = 7$

**55.** $m^2 - 4m + 10 = 0$    **56.** $k^2 - 9k + 10 = 0$    **57.** $(3x + 5)^2 = 0$

**58.** $0.5r^2 = 3.5 - r$    **59.** $x^2 + 4x = 1$    **60.** $7x^2 - 8 = 5x^2 + 8$

**61.** The owners of Cole's Baseball Cards have found that the price $p$, in dollars, of a particular Jim "Mudcat" Grant card depends on the demand $d$, in hundreds, for the card, according to the function defined by

$$p = -(d - 6)^2 + 10.$$

What demand produces a price of $6 for the card?

**62.** Find the vertex of the parabola from **Exercise 61.** Give the corresponding demand and price.

---

CHAPTER **9**

TEST

CHAPTER Test Prep VIDEOS

Step-by-step test solutions are found on the Chapter Test Prep Videos available via the Video Resources on DVD, in *MyMathLab*, or on You Tube (search "LialBeginningAlgebra").

*View the complete solutions to all Chapter Test exercises on the Video Resources on DVD.*

*Items marked * require knowledge of complex numbers.*

*Solve by using the square root property.*

  **1.** $x^2 = 39$      **2.** $(z + 3)^2 = 64$      **3.** $(4x + 3)^2 = 24$

*Solve by completing the square.*

  **4.** $x^2 - 4x = 6$          **5.** $2x^2 + 12x - 3 = 0$

*Solve by the quadratic formula.*

  **6.** $5x^2 + 2x = 0$      **7.** $2x^2 + 5x - 3 = 0$      **8.** $3w^2 + 2 = 6w$

**\*9.** $4x^2 + 8x + 11 = 0$          **10.** $t^2 - \dfrac{5}{3}t + \dfrac{1}{3} = 0$

*Solve by the method of your choice.*

**11.** $p^2 - 2p - 1 = 0$

**12.** $(2x + 1)^2 = 18$

**13.** $(x - 5)(2x - 1) = 1$

**14.** $t^2 + 25 = 10t$

*Solve each problem.*

**15.** If an object is projected vertically into the air from ground level on Earth with an initial velocity of 64 ft per sec, its altitude (height) $s$ in feet after $t$ seconds is given by the formula

$$s = -16t^2 + 64t.$$

At what time will the object be at a height of 64 ft?

**16.** Find the lengths of the three sides of the right triangle.

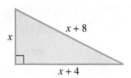

*\*Perform each indicated operation.*

**17.** $(3 + i) + (-2 + 3i) - (6 - i)$

**18.** $(6 + 5i)(-2 + i)$

**19.** $(3 - 8i)(3 + 8i)$

**20.** $\dfrac{15 - 5i}{7 + i}$

*Identify the vertex and sketch the graph of each equation.*

**21.** $y = x^2 - 6x + 9$

**22.** $y = -x^2 - 2x - 4$

**23.** $f(x) = x^2 + 6x + 7$

**24.** Refer to the equation in **Exercise 23.**

(a) Determine the number of real solutions of $x^2 + 6x + 7 = 0$ by looking at the graph.

(b) Use the quadratic formula to find the exact values of the real solutions. Give the solution set.

(c) Use a calculator to find approximations for the solutions. Round your answers to the nearest thousandth.

**25.** Find two numbers whose sum is 400 and whose product is a maximum.

# CHAPTERS (1–9)   CUMULATIVE REVIEW EXERCISES

*Perform each indicated operation.*

**1.** $\dfrac{-4 \cdot 3^2 + 2 \cdot 3}{2 - 4 \cdot 1}$

**2.** $-9 - (-8)(2) + 6 - (6 + 2)$

**3.** $-4r + 14 + 3r - 7$

**4.** $5(4m - 2) - (m + 7)$

*Solve each equation.*

**5.** $x - 5 = 13$

**6.** $3k - 9k - 8k + 6 = -64$

**7.** $\dfrac{3}{5}t - \dfrac{1}{10} = \dfrac{3}{2}$

**8.** $2(m - 1) - 6(3 - m) = -4$

*Solve each problem.*

**9.** Find the measures of the marked angles.

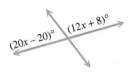

**10.** The perimeter of a basketball court is 288 ft. The width of the court is 44 ft less than the length. What are the dimensions of the court?

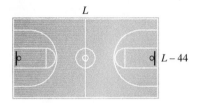

**11.** Solve the formula $P = 2L + 2W$ for $L$.

*Solve each inequality, and graph the solution set.*

**12.** $-8m < 16$

**13.** $-9p + 2(8 - p) - 6 \geq 4p - 50$

*Graph each equation.*

**14.** $2x + 3y = 6$

**15.** $y = 3$

**16.** Find the slope of the line through $(-1, 4)$ and $(5, 2)$.

**17.** Write an equation of a line with slope 2 and $y$-intercept $(0, 3)$. Give the equation in the form $Ax + By = C$.

*Solve each system of equations.*

**18.** $2x + y = -4$
$-3x + 2y = 13$

**19.** $3x - 5y = 8$
$-6x + 10y = 16$

**20.** In September 2009, the cost of three AT&T Trimline® corded phones and two jWIN corded speakerphones was $84.95. Two of the AT&T phones and three of the jWIN phones cost $89.95. Find the price for a single phone of each model. (*Source:* www.radioshack.com)

**21.** Graph the solution set of the system of inequalities.

$2x + y \leq 4$
$x - y > 2$

*Simplify each expression. Write answers with positive exponents.*

**22.** $(3^2 \cdot x^{-4})^{-1}$

**23.** $\left(\dfrac{b^{-3}c^4}{b^5c^3}\right)^{-2}$

*Perform each indicated operation.*

**24.** $(5x^5 - 9x^4 + 8x^2) - (9x^2 + 8x^4 - 3x^5)$

**25.** $(2x - 5)(x^3 + 3x^2 - 2x - 4)$

**26.** $\dfrac{3x^3 + 10x^2 - 7x + 4}{x + 4}$

**27. (a)** The number of possible hands in contract bridge is about 6,350,000,000. Write this number in scientific notation.

**(b)** The body of a 150-lb person contains about $2.3 \times 10^{-4}$ lb of copper. Write this number without using exponents.

*Factor.*

**28.** $16x^3 - 48x^2y$

**29.** $2a^2 - 5a - 3$

**30.** $16x^4 - 1$

**31.** $25m^2 - 20m + 4$

*Solve.*

**32.** $x^2 + 3x - 54 = 0$

**33.** The length of a rectangle is 2.5 times its width. The area is 1000 m². Find the length.

*Simplify each expression as much as possible.*

**34.** $\dfrac{2}{a - 3} \div \dfrac{5}{2a - 6}$

**35.** $\dfrac{1}{k} - \dfrac{2}{k - 1}$

**36.** $\dfrac{2}{a^2 - 4} + \dfrac{3}{a^2 - 4a + 4}$

**37.** $\dfrac{\dfrac{1}{a} + \dfrac{1}{b}}{\dfrac{1}{a} - \dfrac{1}{b}}$

**38.** Solve $\dfrac{1}{x + 3} + \dfrac{1}{x} = \dfrac{7}{10}$.

*Simplify each expression as much as possible.*

**39.** $\sqrt{100}$

**40.** $\dfrac{6\sqrt{6}}{\sqrt{5}}$

**41.** $\sqrt[3]{\dfrac{7}{16}}$

**42.** $3\sqrt{5} - 2\sqrt{20} + \sqrt{125}$

**43.** Solve $\sqrt{x + 2} = x - 4$.

**44.** Simplify.

    **(a)** $8^{2/3}$    **(b)** $-16^{1/4}$

*Solve each quadratic equation, using the method indicated. Give only real solutions.*

**45.** $(3x + 2)^2 = 12$ (square root property)    **46.** $-x^2 + 5 = 2x$ (completing the square)

**47.** $2x(x - 2) - 3 = 0$ (quadratic formula)

*Solve each problem. (Items marked \* require knowledge of complex numbers.)*

**\*48.** Perform the indicated operations. Give answers in standard form.

    **(a)** $(-9 + 3i) + (4 + 2i) - (-5 - 3i)$    **(b)** $\dfrac{-17 - i}{-3 + i}$

**\*49.** Find the complex solutions of $2x^2 + 2x = -9$.

**50.** Graph the quadratic function defined by $f(x) = -x^2 - 2x + 1$, and identify the vertex. Give the domain and range.

# Sets

**OBJECTIVES**

1 Learn the vocabulary and symbols used to discuss sets.

2 Decide whether a set is finite or infinite.

3 Decide whether a given set is a subset of another set.

4 Find the complement of a set.

5 Find the union and the intersection of two sets.

**OBJECTIVE 1** Learn the vocabulary and symbols used to discuss sets. A **set** is a collection of objects. These objects are called the **elements** of the set. A set is represented by listing its elements between **braces,** $\{\quad\}$.* The order in which the elements of a set are listed is unimportant.

Capital letters are used to name sets. To state that 5 is an element of

$$S = \{1, 2, 3, 4, 5\},$$

write $5 \in S$. The statement $6 \notin S$ means that 6 is not an element of $S$.

The set with no elements is called the **empty set,** or the **null set.** The symbol $\emptyset$ or $\{\quad\}$ is used for the empty set. If we let $A$ be the set of all negative natural numbers, then $A$ is the empty set.

$$A = \emptyset \quad \text{or} \quad A = \{\quad\}$$

⚠ **CAUTION** Do not make the common error of writing the empty set as $\{\emptyset\}$.

**EXAMPLE 1** Listing the Elements of Sets

Represent each set by listing its elements.

**(a)** The set of states in the United States that border the Pacific Ocean is

$$\{\text{California, Oregon, Washington, Hawaii, Alaska}\}.$$

**(b)** The set of all counting numbers less than $6 = \{1, 2, 3, 4, 5\}$.

**(c)** The set of all counting numbers less than $0 = \emptyset$     NOW TRY

NOW TRY
EXERCISE 1

List the elements of the set of odd natural numbers less than 13.

In any discussion of sets, there is some set that includes all the elements under consideration. This set is called the **universal set** for that situation. For example, if the discussion is about presidents of the United States, then the set of all presidents of the United States is the universal set. The universal set is denoted $U$.

**OBJECTIVE 2** Decide whether a set is finite or infinite. In **Example 1,** there are five elements in the set in part (a) and five in part (b). If the number of elements in a set is either 0 or a counting number, then the set is **finite.** By contrast, the set of natural numbers is an **infinite** set, because there is no final natural number. We can list the elements of the set of natural numbers as

$$N = \{1, 2, 3, 4, \dots\},$$

where the three dots indicate that the set continues indefinitely. Not all infinite sets can be listed in this way. For example, there is no way to list the elements in the set of all real numbers between 1 and 2.

*NOW TRY ANSWER*
1. $\{1, 3, 5, 7, 9, 11\}$

*Some people refer to this convention as *roster notation.*

NOW TRY
EXERCISE 2

List the elements of each set if possible. Decide whether each set is finite or infinite.

(a) The set of negative integers

(b) The set of even natural numbers between 11 and 19

---

NOW TRY
EXERCISE 3

Let

$$A = \{1, 3, 5, 7, 9, 11\},$$
$$B = \{1, 5, 7, 9\}, \text{ and}$$
$$C = \{1, 9, 11\}.$$

Tell whether each statement is *true* or *false*.

(a) $B \subseteq A$    (b) $C \subseteq B$

(c) $C \not\subseteq A$

---

NOW TRY ANSWERS

2. (a) $\{-1, -2, -3, -4, \ldots\}$; infinite

(b) $\{12, 14, 16, 18\}$; finite

3. (a) true  (b) false  (c) false

---

**EXAMPLE 2**  Distinguishing between Finite and Infinite Sets

List the elements of each set if possible. Decide whether each set is finite or infinite.

(a) The set of all integers
One way to list the elements is $\{\ldots, -2, -1, 0, 1, 2, \ldots\}$. The set is infinite.

(b) The set of all natural numbers between 0 and 5
$\{1, 2, 3, 4\}$   The set is finite.

(c) The set of all irrational numbers
This is an infinite set whose elements cannot be listed.   NOW TRY

Two sets are equal if they have exactly the same elements. Thus, the set of natural numbers and the set of positive integers are equal sets. Also, the sets

$$\{1, 2, 4, 7\} \quad \text{and} \quad \{4, 2, 7, 1\} \quad \text{are equal.}$$

The order of the elements does not make a difference.

**OBJECTIVE 3**  **Decide whether a given set is a subset of another set.**  If all elements of a set $A$ are also elements of another set $B$, then we say that $A$ is a **subset** of $B$, written $A \subseteq B$. We use the symbol $A \not\subseteq B$ to mean that $A$ is not a subset of $B$.

**EXAMPLE 3**  Using Subset Notation

Let $A = \{1, 2, 3, 4\}$, $B = \{1, 4\}$, and $C = \{1\}$. Then

$$B \subseteq A, \quad C \subseteq A, \quad \text{and} \quad C \subseteq B,$$

but

$$A \not\subseteq B, \quad A \not\subseteq C, \quad \text{and} \quad B \not\subseteq C.$$   NOW TRY

The empty set is defined to be a subset of any set. Thus, the set $M = \{a, b\}$ has four subsets:

$$\{a, b\}, \quad \{a\}, \quad \{b\}, \quad \text{and} \quad \emptyset.$$

How many subsets does $N = \{a, b, c\}$ have? There is one subset with three elements: $\{a, b, c\}$. There are three subsets with two elements:

$$\{a, b\}, \quad \{a, c\}, \quad \text{and} \quad \{b, c\}.$$

There are three subsets with one element:

$$\{a\}, \quad \{b\}, \quad \text{and} \quad \{c\}.$$

There is one subset with no elements: $\emptyset$. Thus, set $N$ has eight subsets.
The following generalization can be made and proved in more advanced courses.

**Number of Subsets of a Set**

A set with $n$ elements has $2^n$ subsets.

To illustrate the relationships between sets, **Venn diagrams** are often used. A rectangle represents the universal set, $U$. The sets under discussion are represented by regions within the rectangle. The Venn diagram in **FIGURE 1** on the next page shows that $B \subseteq A$.

$B \subseteq A$

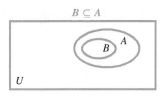

**FIGURE 1**

**OBJECTIVE 4** Find the complement of a set. For every set $A$, there is a set $A'$, the **complement** of $A$, that contains all the elements of $U$ that are not in $A$. The shaded region in the Venn diagram in **FIGURE 2** represents $A'$.

$A'$ is shaded.

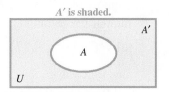

**FIGURE 2**

> NOW TRY
> EXERCISE 4
>
> Let
>
> $U = \{2, 4, 6, 8, 10, 12, 14\}$
>
> and $M = \{2, 10, 12, 14\}$.
>
> List the elements in $M'$.

**EXAMPLE 4**   Determining Complements of a Set

Given $U = \{a, b, c, d, e, f, g\}$, $A = \{a, b, c\}$, $B = \{a, d, f, g\}$, and $C = \{d, e\}$, list the elements of $A'$, $B'$, and $C'$.

$$A' = \{d, e, f, g\}, \quad B' = \{b, c, e\}, \quad \text{and} \quad C' = \{a, b, c, f, g\}. \quad \text{NOW TRY}$$

**OBJECTIVE 5** Find the union and the intersection of two sets. The **union** of two sets $A$ and $B$, written $A \cup B$, is the set of all elements of $A$ together with all elements of $B$. Thus, for the sets in **Example 4,**

$$A \cup B = \{a, b, c, d, f, g\} \quad \text{and} \quad A \cup C = \{a, b, c, d, e\}.$$

In **FIGURE 3**, the shaded region is the union of sets $A$ and $B$.

$A \cup B$ is shaded.

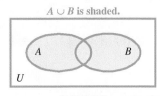

**FIGURE 3**

> NOW TRY
> EXERCISE 5
>
> If $M = \{1, 3, 5, 7, 9\}$ and $N = \{0, 3, 6, 9\}$, find $M \cup N$.

**EXAMPLE 5**   Finding the Union of Two Sets

If $M = \{2, 5, 7\}$ and $N = \{1, 2, 3, 4, 5\}$, find $M \cup N$.

$$M \cup N = \{1, 2, 3, 4, 5, 7\} \quad \text{NOW TRY}$$

The **intersection** of two sets $A$ and $B$, written $A \cap B$, is the set of all elements that belong to both $A$ and $B$. For example, if

$$A = \{\text{José, Ellen, Marge, Kevin}\}$$

and

$$B = \{\text{José, Patrick, Ellen, Sue}\},$$

then

$$A \cap B = \{\text{José, Ellen}\}.$$

> NOW TRY ANSWERS
> 4. $\{4, 6, 8\}$
> 5. $\{0, 1, 3, 5, 6, 7, 9\}$

The shaded region in **FIGURE 4** represents the intersection of the two sets $A$ and $B$.

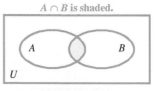

$A \cap B$ is shaded.

**FIGURE 4**

NOW TRY
EXERCISE 6
If $M = \{1, 3, 5, 7, 9\}$ and
$N = \{0, 3, 6, 9\}$, find $M \cap N$.

**EXAMPLE 6** Finding the Intersection of Two Sets

Suppose that $P = \{3, 9, 27\}$, $Q = \{2, 3, 10, 18, 27, 28\}$, and $R = \{2, 10, 28\}$. Find each of the following.

**(a)** $P \cap Q = \{3, 27\}$    **(b)** $Q \cap R = \{2, 10, 28\} = R$    **(c)** $P \cap R = \emptyset$

NOW TRY

Sets like $P$ and $R$ in **Example 6** that have no elements in common are called **disjoint sets.** The Venn diagram in **FIGURE 5** shows a pair of disjoint sets.

NOW TRY
EXERCISE 7
Let
$U = \{1, 2, 4, 5, 7, 8, 9, 10\}$,
$A = \{1, 4, 7, 9, 10\}$,
$B = \{2, 5, 8\}$, and
$C = \{5\}$.

Find each of the following.
**(a)** $B \cup C$   **(b)** $A \cap B$   **(c)** $C'$

Disjoint sets; $A \cap B = \emptyset$

**FIGURE 5**

**EXAMPLE 7** Using Set Operations

Let $U = \{2, 5, 7, 10, 14, 20\}$, $A = \{2, 10, 14, 20\}$, $B = \{5, 7\}$, and $C = \{2, 5, 7\}$. Find each of the following.

**(a)** $A \cup B = \{2, 5, 7, 10, 14, 20\} = U$    **(b)** $A \cap B = \emptyset$

**(c)** $B \cup C = \{2, 5, 7\} = C$           **(d)** $B \cap C = \{5, 7\} = B$

**(e)** $A' = \{5, 7\} = B$

NOW TRY

NOW TRY ANSWERS
**6.** $\{3, 9\}$
**7. (a)** $\{2, 5, 8\} = B$   **(b)** $\emptyset$
   **(c)** $\{1, 2, 4, 7, 8, 9, 10\}$

**EXERCISES**                  

*List the elements of each set.* ***See Examples 1 and 2.***

**1.** The set of all natural numbers less than 8

**2.** The set of all integers between 4 and 10

**3.** The set of seasons

**4.** The set of months of the year

**5.** The set of women presidents of the United States before 2008

**6.** The set of all living humans who are more than 200 years old

**7.** The set of letters of the alphabet between K and M

**8.** The set of letters of the alphabet between D and H

   **9.** The set of positive even integers

   **10.** The set of all multiples of 5

   **11.** Which of the sets described in **Exercises 1–10** are infinite sets?

   **12.** Which of the sets described in **Exercises 1–10** are finite sets?

*Concept Check*   *Tell whether each statement is* true *or* false.

**13.** $5 \in \{1, 2, 5, 8\}$                    **14.** $6 \in \{1, 2, 3, 4, 5\}$

**15.** $2 \in \{1, 3, 5, 7, 9\}$                **16.** $1 \in \{6, 2, 5, 1\}$

**17.** $7 \notin \{2, 4, 6, 8\}$                **18.** $7 \notin \{1, 3, 5, 7\}$

**19.** $\{2, 4, 9, 12, 13\} = \{13, 12, 9, 4, 2\}$     **20.** $\{7, 11, 4\} = \{7, 11, 4, 0\}$

*Let*

$$A = \{1, 3, 4, 5, 7, 8\}, \quad B = \{2, 4, 6, 8\}, \quad C = \{1, 3, 5, 7\}, \quad D = \{1, 2, 3\},$$
$$E = \{3, 7\}, \quad \text{and} \quad U = \{1, 2, 3, 4, 5, 6, 7, 8, 9, 10\}.$$

*Tell whether each statement is* true *or* false. ***See Examples 3, 5, 6, and 7.***

**21.** $A \subseteq U$     **22.** $D \subseteq A$     **23.** $\emptyset \subseteq A$     **24.** $\{1, 2\} \subseteq D$     **25.** $C \subseteq A$

**26.** $A \subseteq C$     **27.** $D \subseteq B$     **28.** $E \subseteq C$     **29.** $D \nsubseteq E$     **30.** $E \nsubseteq A$

**31.** There are exactly 4 subsets of $E$.     **32.** There are exactly 8 subsets of $D$.

**33.** There are exactly 12 subsets of $C$.     **34.** There are exactly 16 subsets of $B$.

**35.** $\{4, 6, 8, 12\} \cap \{6, 8, 14, 17\} = \{6, 8\}$     **36.** $\{2, 5, 9\} \cap \{1, 2, 3, 4, 5\} = \{2, 5\}$

**37.** $\{3, 1, 0\} \cap \{0, 2, 4\} = \{0\}$     **38.** $\{4, 2, 1\} \cap \{1, 2, 3, 4\} = \{1, 2, 3\}$

**39.** $\{3, 9, 12\} \cap \emptyset = \{3, 9, 12\}$     **40.** $\{3, 9, 12\} \cup \emptyset = \emptyset$

**41.** $\{3, 5, 7, 9\} \cup \{4, 6, 8\} = \emptyset$     **42.** $\{1, 2, 3\} \cup \{1, 2, 3\} = \{1, 2, 3\}$

**43.** $\{4, 9, 11, 7, 3\} \cup \{1, 2, 3, 4, 5\} = \{1, 2, 3, 4, 5, 7, 9, 11\}$

**44.** $\{5, 10, 15, 20\} \cup \{5, 15, 30\} = \{5, 15\}$

*Let*

$$U = \{a, b, c, d, e, f, g, h\}, \quad A = \{a, b, c, d, e, f\},$$
$$B = \{a, c, e\}, \quad C = \{a, f\}, \quad \text{and} \quad D = \{d\}.$$

*List the elements in each set.* ***See Examples 4–7.***

**45.** $A'$          **46.** $B'$          **47.** $C'$          **48.** $D'$

**49.** $A \cap B$      **50.** $B \cap A$      **51.** $A \cap D$      **52.** $B \cap D$

**53.** $B \cap C$      **54.** $A \cup B$      **55.** $B \cup D$      **56.** $B \cup C$

**57.** $C \cup B$      **58.** $C \cup D$      **59.** $A \cap \emptyset$      **60.** $B \cup \emptyset$

**61.** Name every pair of disjoint sets among sets $A$–$D$ in the directions for **Exercises 45–60**.

**62.** Show that for sets $B$ and $D$ in the directions for **Exercises 45–60**,

$$(B \cup D)' = B' \cap D'.$$

# An Introduction to Calculators

There is little doubt that the appearance of handheld calculators more than three decades ago and the later development of scientific and graphing calculators have changed the methods of learning and studying mathematics forever. For example, computations with tables of logarithms and slide rules made up an important part of mathematics courses prior to 1970. Today, with the widespread availability of calculators, these topics are studied only for their historical significance.

Calculators come in a large array of different types, sizes, and prices. ***For the course for which this textbook is intended, the most appropriate type is the scientific calculator,*** which costs $10–$20.

In this introduction, we explain some of the features of scientific and graphing calculators. However, remember that calculators vary among manufacturers and models and that, while the methods explained here apply to many of them, they may not apply to your specific calculator. ***This introduction is only a guide and is not intended to take the place of your owner's manual.*** Always refer to the manual whenever you need an explanation of how to perform a particular operation.

## Scientific Calculators

Scientific calculators are capable of much more than the typical four-function calculator that you might use for balancing your checkbook. Most scientific calculators use *algebraic logic.* (Models sold by Texas Instruments, Sharp, Casio, and Radio Shack, for example, use algebraic logic.) A notable exception is Hewlett-Packard, a company whose calculators use *Reverse Polish Notation* (RPN). In this introduction, we explain the use of calculators with algebraic logic.

**Arithmetic Operations**   To perform an operation of arithmetic, simply enter the first number, press the operation key $+$, $-$, $\times$, or $\div$, enter the second number, and then press the $=$ key. For example, to add 4 and 3, use the following keystrokes.

$$4 \quad + \quad 3 \quad = \quad 7$$

**Change Sign Key**   The key marked $+/-$ allows you to change the sign of a display. This is particularly useful when you wish to enter a negative number. For example, to enter $-3$, use the following keystrokes.

$$3 \quad +/- \quad -3$$

**Memory Key** Scientific calculators can hold a number in memory for later use. The label of the memory key varies among models; two of these are (M) and (STO). The (M+) and (M−) keys allow you to add to or subtract from the value currently in memory. The memory recall key, labeled (MR), (RM), or (RCL), allows you to retrieve the value stored in memory.

Suppose that you wish to store the number 5 in memory. Enter 5, and then press the key for memory. You can then perform other calculations. When you need to retrieve the 5, press the key for memory recall.

If a calculator has a constant memory feature, the value in memory will be retained even after the power is turned off. Some advanced calculators have more than one memory. Read the owner's manual for your model to see exactly how memory is activated.

**Clearing/Clear Entry Keys** The key (C) or (CE) allows you to clear the display or clear the last entry entered into the display. In some models, pressing the (C) key once will clear the last entry, while pressing it twice will clear the entire operation in progress.

**Second Function Key** This key, usually marked (2nd), is used in conjunction with another key to activate a function that is printed *above* an operation key (and not on the key itself). For example, suppose you wish to find the square of a number, and the squaring function (explained in more detail later) is printed above another key. You would need to press (2nd) before the desired squaring function can be activated.

**Square Root Key** Pressing (√) or (√x) will give the square root (or an approximation of the square root) of the number in the display. On some scientific calculators, the square root key is pressed *before* entering the number, while other calculators use the opposite order. Experiment with your calculator to see which method it uses. For example, to find the square root of 36, use the following keystrokes.

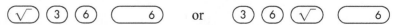

$(√)$ $(3)$ $(6)$ ⟨ 6 ⟩    or    $(3)$ $(6)$ $(√)$ ⟨ 6 ⟩

The square root of 2 is an example of an irrational number (**Chapter 8**). The calculator will give an approximation of its value, since the decimal for $\sqrt{2}$ never terminates and never repeats. The number of digits shown will vary among models. To find an approximation for $\sqrt{2}$, use the following keystrokes.

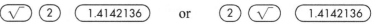

$(√)$ $(2)$ ⟨ 1.4142136 ⟩    or    $(2)$ $(√)$ ⟨ 1.4142136 ⟩

An approximation for $\sqrt{2}$

**Squaring Key** The $(x^2)$ key allows you to square the entry in the display. For example, to square 35.7, use the following keystrokes.

$(3)$ $(5)$ $(.)$ $(7)$ $(x^2)$ ⟨ 1274.49 ⟩

The squaring key and the square root key are often found together, with one of them being a second function (that is, activated by the second function key previously described).

**Reciprocal Key** The key marked $(1/x)$ is the reciprocal key. (When two numbers have a product of 1, they are called *reciprocals*. See **Chapter 1**.) Suppose that you wish to find the reciprocal of 5. Use the following keystrokes.

$(5)$ $(1/x)$ ⟨ 0.2 ⟩

**Inverse Key**   Some calculators have an inverse key, marked ⬭INV⬭. Inverse operations are operations that "undo" each other. For example, the operations of squaring and taking the square root are inverse operations. The use of the ⬭INV⬭ key varies among different models of calculators, so read your owner's manual carefully.

**Exponential Key**   The key marked ⬭$x^y$⬭ or ⬭$y^x$⬭ allows you to raise a number to a power. For example, if you wish to raise 4 to the fifth power (that is, find $4^5$, as explained in **Chapter 1**), use the following keystrokes.

⬭4⬭ ⬭$x^y$⬭ ⬭5⬭ ⬭=⬭ ⬭ 1024 ⬭

**Root Key**   Some calculators have a key specifically marked ⬭$\sqrt[x]{x}$⬭ or ⬭$\sqrt[x]{y}$⬭; with others, the operation of taking roots is accomplished by using the inverse key in conjunction with the exponential key. Suppose, for example, your calculator is of the latter type and you wish to find the fifth root of 1024. Use the following keystrokes.

⬭1⬭ ⬭0⬭ ⬭2⬭ ⬭4⬭ ⬭INV⬭ ⬭$x^y$⬭ ⬭5⬭ ⬭=⬭ ⬭ 4 ⬭

Notice how this "undoes" the operation explained in the discussion of the exponential key.

**Pi Key**   The number $\pi$ is an important number in mathematics. It occurs, for example, in the area and circumference formulas for a circle. One popular model gives the following display when the ⬭$\pi$⬭ key is pressed. (Because $\pi$ is irrational, the display shows only an approximation.)

⬭ 3.1415927 ⬭   An approximation for $\pi$

**Methods of Display**   When decimal approximations are shown on scientific calculators, they are either *truncated* or *rounded*. To see how a particular model is programmed, evaluate 1/18 as an example. If the display shows 0.0555555 (last digit 5), the calculator truncates the display. If the display shows 0.0555556 (last digit 6), the calculator rounds the display.

When very large or very small numbers are obtained as answers, scientific calculators often express these numbers in scientific notation (**Chapter 5**). For example, if you multiply 6,265,804 by 8,980,591, the display might look like this:

⬭ 5.6270623 13 ⬭

The 13 at the far right means that the number on the left is multiplied by $10^{13}$. This means that the decimal point must be moved 13 places to the right if the answer is to be expressed in its usual form. Even then, the value obtained will only be an approximation: 56,270,623,000,000.

## Graphing Calculators

While you are not expected to have a graphing calculator to study from this book, we include the following as background information and reference should your course or future courses require the use of graphing calculators.

**Basic Features**  In addition to possessing the typical keys found on scientific calculators, graphing calculators have keys that can be used to create graphs, make tables, analyze data, and change settings. One of the major differences between graphing and scientific calculators is that a graphing calculator has a larger viewing screen with graphing capabilities. The following screens illustrate the graphs of $Y = X$ and $Y = X^2$. (We use screens from a Texas Instruments calculator in our illustrations.)

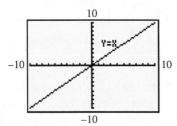 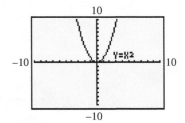

If you look closely at the screens, you will see that the graphs appear to be jagged rather than smooth. The reason for this is that graphing calculators have much lower resolution than computer screens. Because of this, graphs generated by graphing calculators must be interpreted carefully.

**Editing Input**  The screen of a graphing calculator can display several lines of text at a time. This feature allows you to view both previous and current expressions. If an incorrect expression is entered, an error message is displayed. The erroneous expression can be viewed and corrected by using various editing keys, much like a word-processing program. You do not need to enter the entire expression again. Many graphing calculators can also recall past expressions for editing or updating. The screen on the left shows how two expressions are evaluated. The final line is entered incorrectly, and the resulting error message is shown in the screen on the right.

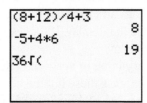 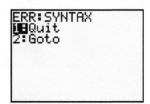

**Order of Operations**  Arithmetic operations on graphing calculators are usually entered as they are written in mathematical expressions. For example, to evaluate $\sqrt{36}$ you would first press the square root key and then enter 36. See the left screen below. The order of operations on a graphing calculator is also important, and current models assist the user by inserting parentheses when typical errors might occur. The open parenthesis that follows the square root symbol is automatically entered by the calculator so that an expression such as $\sqrt{2 \times 8}$ will not be calculated incorrectly as $\sqrt{2} \times 8$. Compare the two entries and their results in the screen on the right.

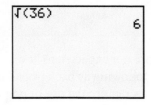 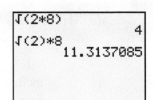

**Viewing Windows**   The viewing window for a graphing calculator is similar to the viewfinder in a camera. A camera usually cannot take a photograph of an entire view of a scene. The camera must be centered on some object and can capture only a portion of the available scenery. A camera with a zoom lens can photograph different views of the same scene by zooming in and out. Graphing calculators have similar capabilities. The *xy*-coordinate plane is infinite. The calculator screen can show only a finite, rectangular region in the plane, and it must be specified before the graph can be drawn. This is done by setting both minimum and maximum values for the *x*- and *y*-axes. The scale (distance between tick marks) is usually specified as well. Determining an appropriate viewing window for a graph is often a challenge, and many times it will take a few attempts before a satisfactory window is found.

The screen on the left shows a standard viewing window, and the graph of $Y = 2X + 1$ is shown on the right. Using a different window would give a different view of the line.

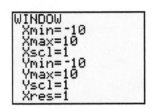

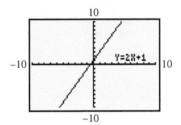

**Locating Points on a Graph: Tracing and Tables**   Graphing calculators allow you to trace along the graph of an equation and display the coordinates of points on the graph. For example, the screen on the left below indicates that the point $(2, 5)$ lies on the graph of $Y = 2X + 1$. Tables for equations can also be displayed. The screen on the right shows a partial table for this same equation. Note the middle of the screen, which indicates that when $X = 2$, $Y = 5$.

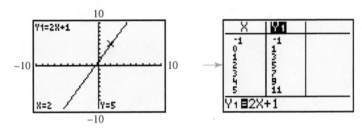

**Additional Features**   There are many features of graphing calculators that go far beyond the scope of this book. These calculators can be programmed, much like computers. Many of them can solve equations at the stroke of a key, analyze statistical data, and perform symbolic algebraic manipulations. Calculators also provide the opportunity to ask "What if . . . ?" more easily. Values in algebraic expressions can be altered and conjectures tested quickly.

**Final Comments**   Despite the power of today's calculators, they cannot replace human thought. ***In the entire problem-solving process, your brain is the most important component.*** Calculators are only tools, and like any tool, they must be used appropriately in order to enhance our ability to understand mathematics. Mathematical insight may often be the quickest and easiest way to solve a problem; a calculator may be neither needed nor appropriate. By applying mathematical concepts, you can make the decision whether to use a calculator.

In this section we provide the answers that we think most students will obtain when they work the exercises using the methods explained in the text. If your answer does not look exactly like the one given here, it is not necessarily wrong. In many cases, there are equivalent forms of the answer that are correct. For example, if the answer section shows $\frac{3}{4}$ and your answer is 0.75, you have obtained the right answer, but written it in a different (yet equivalent) form. Unless the directions specify otherwise, 0.75 is just as valid an answer as $\frac{3}{4}$.

In general, if your answer does not agree with the one given in the text, see whether it can be transformed into the other form. If it can, then it is the correct answer. If you still have doubts, talk with your instructor. You might also want to obtain a copy of the *Student's Solutions Manual* that goes with this book. Your college bookstore either has this manual or can order it for you.

## 1 THE REAL NUMBER SYSTEM

### Section 1.1 (pages 10–13)

**1.** true **3.** false; This is an improper fraction. Its value is 1. **5.** false; The fraction $\frac{13}{39}$ is written in lowest terms as $\frac{1}{3}$. **7.** false; *Product* refers to multiplication, so the product of 10 and 2 is 20. **9.** prime
**11.** composite; $2 \cdot 3 \cdot 5$ **13.** composite; $2 \cdot 2 \cdot 2 \cdot 2 \cdot 2$
**15.** neither **17.** composite; $3 \cdot 19$ **19.** prime **21.** composite; $2 \cdot 2 \cdot 31$ **23.** composite; $2 \cdot 2 \cdot 5 \cdot 5 \cdot 5$ **25.** composite; $2 \cdot 7 \cdot 13 \cdot 19$ **27.** $\frac{1}{2}$ **29.** $\frac{5}{6}$ **31.** $\frac{16}{25}$ **33.** $\frac{1}{5}$ **35.** $\frac{6}{5}$ **37.** C **39.** $\frac{24}{35}$
**41.** $\frac{5}{8}$ **43.** $\frac{6}{25}$ **45.** $\frac{6}{5}$, or $1\frac{1}{5}$ **47.** 9 **49.** $\frac{65}{12}$, or $5\frac{5}{12}$ **51.** $\frac{38}{5}$, or $7\frac{3}{5}$
**53.** $\frac{10}{3}$, or $3\frac{1}{3}$ **55.** 12 **57.** $\frac{1}{16}$ **59.** 10 **61.** 18 **63.** $\frac{35}{24}$, or $1\frac{11}{24}$
**65.** $\frac{84}{47}$, or $1\frac{37}{47}$ **67.** A **69.** $\frac{11}{15}$ **71.** $\frac{2}{3}$ **73.** $\frac{8}{9}$ **75.** $\frac{29}{24}$, or $1\frac{5}{24}$ **77.** $\frac{43}{8}$, or $5\frac{3}{8}$ **79.** $\frac{101}{20}$, or $5\frac{1}{20}$ **81.** $\frac{5}{9}$ **83.** $\frac{2}{3}$ **85.** $\frac{1}{4}$ **87.** $\frac{17}{36}$ **89.** $\frac{67}{20}$, or $3\frac{7}{20}$
**91.** $\frac{11}{12}$ **93.** 6 cups **95.** $1\frac{1}{8}$ in. **97.** $\frac{9}{16}$ in. **99.** $618\frac{3}{4}$ ft **101.** $5\frac{5}{24}$ in.
**103.** 8 cakes (There will be some sugar left over.) **105.** $16\frac{5}{8}$ yd
**107.** $3\frac{3}{8}$ in. **109.** $\frac{1}{20}$ **111.** about $5\frac{8}{25}$ million, or 5,320,000
**113. (a)** $\frac{1}{2}$ **(b)** $\frac{1}{4}$ **(c)** $\frac{1}{3}$ **(d)** $\frac{1}{6}$

### Section 1.2 (pages 19–21)

**1.** false; $6^2$ means that 6 is used as a factor 2 times; so $6^2 = 6 \cdot 6 = 36$.
**3.** false; 1 raised to *any* power is 1. Here, $1^3 = 1 \cdot 1 \cdot 1 = 1$.
**5.** false; $4 + 3(8 - 2)$ means $4 + 3 \cdot 6$, which simplifies to $4 + 18$, or 22. The common error leading to 42 is adding 4 to 3 and then multiplying by 6. One must follow the order of operations. **7.** 9 **9.** 49
**11.** 144 **13.** 64 **15.** 1000 **17.** 81 **19.** 1024 **21.** $\frac{1}{36}$ **23.** $\frac{16}{81}$
**25.** 0.064 **27.** 32 **29.** 58 **31.** 22.2 **33.** $\frac{49}{30}$, or $1\frac{19}{30}$ **35.** 12
**37.** 13 **39.** 26 **41.** 4 **43.** 42 **45.** 5 **47.** 41 **49.** 95 **51.** 90
**53.** 14 **55.** 9 **57.** $16 \le 16$; true **59.** $61 \le 60$; false **61.** $0 \ge 0$; true **63.** $45 \ge 46$; false **65.** $66 > 72$; false **67.** $2 \ge 3$; false

**69.** $3 \ge 3$; true **71.** $3 \cdot (6 + 4) \cdot 2 = 60$ **73.** $10 - (7 - 3) = 6$
**75.** $(8 + 2)^2 = 100$ **77.** Five is less than seventeen; true **79.** Five is not equal to eight; true **81.** Seven is greater than or equal to fourteen; false **83.** Fifteen is less than or equal to 15; true **85.** $15 = 5 + 10$
**87.** $9 > 5 - 4$ **89.** $16 \ne 19$ **91.** $\frac{1}{2} \le \frac{2}{4}$ **93.** $20 > 5$
**95.** $1.3 \le 2.5$ **97. (a)** $14.7 - 40 \cdot 0.13$ **(b)** 9.5 **(c)** 8.075; walking (5 mph) **99.** Answers will vary.

### Section 1.3 (pages 26–27)

**1.** B **3.** A **5.** $2x^3 = 2 \cdot x \cdot x \cdot x$, while $2x \cdot 2x \cdot 2x = (2x)^3$.
**7.** The exponent 2 applies only to its base, which is $x$. **9. (a)** 11
**(b)** 13 **11. (a)** 16 **(b)** 24 **13. (a)** 64 **(b)** 144 **15. (a)** $\frac{5}{3}$
**(b)** $\frac{7}{3}$ **17. (a)** $\frac{7}{8}$ **(b)** $\frac{13}{12}$ **19. (a)** 52 **(b)** 114 **21. (a)** 25.836
**(b)** 38.754 **23. (a)** 24 **(b)** 28 **25. (a)** 12 **(b)** 33 **27. (a)** 6
**(b)** $\frac{9}{5}$ **29. (a)** $\frac{4}{3}$ **(b)** $\frac{13}{6}$ **31. (a)** $\frac{2}{7}$ **(b)** $\frac{16}{27}$ **33. (a)** 12 **(b)** 55
**35. (a)** 1 **(b)** $\frac{28}{17}$ **37. (a)** 3.684 **(b)** 8.841 **39.** $12x$ **41.** $x + 9$
**43.** $x - 4$ **45.** $7 - x$ **47.** $x - 8$ **49.** $\frac{18}{x}$ **51.** $6(x - 4)$ **53.** An expression cannot be solved—it indicates a series of operations to perform. An expression is simplified. An equation is solved. **55.** yes
**57.** no **59.** yes **61.** yes **63.** yes **65.** no **67.** $x + 8 = 18$; 10
**69.** $16 - \frac{3}{4}x = 13$; 4 **71.** $2x + 1 = 5$; 2 **73.** $3x = 2x + 8$; 8
**75.** expression **77.** equation **79.** equation **81.** 64.9 yr **83.** 73.8 yr
**85.** Life expectancy has increased over 13 yr during this time.

### Section 1.4 (pages 34–36)

**1.** 2,866,000 **3.** −52,000 **5.** −11.2; 8.6 **7.** 82.60 **9.** 4 **11.** 0
**13.** One example is $\sqrt{13}$. There are others. **15.** true **17.** true
**19.** false

*In Exercises 21–25, answers will vary.*

**21.** $\frac{1}{2}, \frac{5}{8}, 1\frac{3}{4}$ **23.** $-3\frac{1}{2}, -\frac{2}{3}, \frac{3}{7}$ **25.** $\sqrt{5}, \pi, -\sqrt{3}$ **27. (a)** 3, 7
**(b)** 0, 3, 7 **(c)** −9, 0, 3, 7 **(d)** $-9, -1\frac{1}{4}, -\frac{3}{5}, 0, 0.\overline{1}, 3, 5.9, 7$
**(e)** $-\sqrt{7}, \sqrt{5}$ **(f)** All are real numbers. **29.** [number line graph with points at −6, −4, −2, 0, 2]

**31.** [number line graph from −6 to 4] **33.** [number line graph labeled $-3\frac{4}{5}, -1\frac{5}{8}, \frac{1}{4}, 2\frac{1}{2}$ from −4 to 4] **35. (a)** A
**(b)** A **(c)** B **(d)** B **37. (a)** 7 **(b)** 7 **39. (a)** −8 **(b)** 8
**41. (a)** $\frac{3}{4}$ **(b)** $\frac{3}{4}$ **43.** 6 **45.** −12 **47.** $-\frac{2}{3}$ **49.** 3 **51.** This is not true. The absolute value of 0 is 0, and 0 is not positive. A more accurate way of describing absolute value is to say that *absolute value is never negative,* or *absolute value is always nonnegative.* **53.** −11 **55.** −7
**57.** 4 **59.** $|-3.5|$, or 3.5 **61.** $-|-6|$, or −6 **63.** $|5 - 3|$, or 2
**65.** true **67.** true **69.** true **71.** false **73.** true **75.** false
**77.** fuel and other utilities, 2004 to 2005 **79.** apparel and upkeep, 2006 to 2007

## Section 1.5 (pages 44–48)

**1.** negative **3.** negative

**5.** $-8$; $-6$; 2  **7.** positive  **9.** negative  **11.** $-8$  **13.** $-12$  **15.** 2
**17.** $-2$  **19.** 8.9  **21.** 12  **23.** 5  **25.** 2  **27.** $-9$  **29.** 0  **31.** $\frac{1}{2}$
**33.** $-\frac{19}{24}$  **35.** $-\frac{3}{4}$  **37.** $-7.7$  **39.** $-8$  **41.** 0  **43.** $-20$  **45.** $-3$
**47.** $-4$  **49.** $-8$  **51.** $-14$  **53.** 9  **55.** $-4$  **57.** 4  **59.** $\frac{3}{4}$
**61.** $-\frac{11}{8}$, or $-1\frac{3}{8}$  **63.** $\frac{15}{8}$, or $1\frac{7}{8}$  **65.** 11.6  **67.** $-9.9$  **69.** 10
**71.** $-5$  **73.** 11  **75.** $-10$  **77.** 22  **79.** $-2$  **81.** $-\frac{17}{8}$, or $-2\frac{1}{8}$
**83.** $-\frac{1}{4}$, or $-0.25$  **85.** $-6$  **87.** $-12$  **89.** $-5.90617$
**91.** $-5 + 12 + 6$; 13  **93.** $[-19 + (-4)] + 14$; $-9$
**95.** $[-4 + (-10)] + 12$; $-2$  **97.** $\left[\frac{5}{7} + \left(-\frac{9}{7}\right)\right] + \frac{2}{7}$; $-\frac{2}{7}$
**99.** $4 - (-8)$; 12  **101.** $-2 - 8$; $-10$  **103.** $[9 + (-4)] - 7$; $-2$
**105.** $[8 - (-5)] - 12$; 1  **107.** $-12$  **109.** $-56°F$  **111.** $-69°F$
**113.** $-184$ m  **115. (a)** 7.4%  **(b)** Americans spent more money than
they earned, which means they had to dip into savings or increase borrowing.
**117.** $3173  **119.** 17  **121.** $1045.55  **123.** $323.83
**125.** 30.4 billion dollars  **127.** 3.1 billion dollars  **129.** 50,395 ft
**131.** 1345 ft  **133.** 136 ft

## Section 1.6 (pages 56–59)

**1.** greater than 0  **3.** less than 0  **5.** greater than 0  **7.** equal to 0
**9.** undefined; 0; Examples include $\frac{1}{0}$, which is undefined, and $\frac{0}{1}$, which
equals 0.  **11.** $-30$  **13.** 30  **15.** 120  **17.** $-33$  **19.** 0  **21.** $-2.38$
**23.** $\frac{5}{12}$  **25.** $-\frac{1}{6}$  **27.** 6  **29.** $-32, -16, -8, -4, -2, -1, 1, 2, 4, 8,$
$16, 32$  **31.** $-40, -20, -10, -8, -5, -4, -2, -1, 1, 2, 4, 5, 8, 10,$
$20, 40$  **33.** $-31, -1, 1, 31$  **35.** 3  **37.** $-7$  **39.** 8  **41.** $-6$
**43.** $\frac{32}{3}$, or $10\frac{2}{3}$  **45.** $-4$  **47.** 0  **49.** undefined  **51.** $-11$  **53.** $-2$
**55.** 35  **57.** 13  **59.** $-22$  **61.** 6  **63.** $-18$  **65.** 67  **67.** $-8$
**69.** 3  **71.** 7  **73.** 4  **75.** $-1$  **77.** 4  **79.** $-3$  **81.** 47  **83.** 72
**85.** $-\frac{78}{25}$  **87.** 0  **89.** $-23$  **91.** 2  **93.** $9 + (-9)(2)$; $-9$
**95.** $-4 - 2(-1)(6)$; 8  **97.** $(1.5)(-3.2) - 9$; $-13.8$
**99.** $12[9 - (-8)]$; 204  **101.** $\frac{-12}{-5 + (-1)}$; 2  **103.** $\frac{15 + (-3)}{4(-3)}$; $-1$
**105.** $\frac{2}{3}[8 - (-1)]$; 6  **107.** $0.20(-5 \cdot 6)$; $-6$
**109.** $\left(\frac{1}{2} + \frac{5}{8}\right)\left(\frac{3}{5} - \frac{1}{3}\right)$; $\frac{3}{10}$  **111.** $\frac{-\frac{1}{2}\left(\frac{3}{4}\right)}{-\frac{2}{3}}$; $\frac{9}{16}$  **113.** $\frac{x}{3} = -3$; $-9$
**115.** $x - 6 = 4$; 10  **117.** $x + 5 = -5$; $-10$  **119.** $8\frac{2}{5}$  **121.** 4
**123.** 2  **125. (a)** 6 is divisible by 2.  **(b)** 9 is not divisible by 2.
**127. (a)** 64 is divisible by 4.  **(b)** 35 is not divisible by 4.
**129. (a)** 2 is divisible by 2 and $1 + 5 + 2 + 4 + 8 + 2 + 2 = 24$
is divisible by 3.  **(b)** Although 0 is divisible by 2,
$2 + 8 + 7 + 3 + 5 + 9 + 0 = 34$ is not divisible by 3.
**131. (a)** $4 + 1 + 1 + 4 + 1 + 0 + 7 = 18$ is divisible by 9.
**(b)** $2 + 2 + 8 + 7 + 3 + 2 + 1 = 25$ is not divisible by 9.

## Summary Exercises on Operations with Real Numbers (pages 59–60)

**1.** $-16$  **2.** 4  **3.** 0  **4.** $-24$  **5.** $-17$  **6.** 76  **7.** $-18$  **8.** 90
**9.** 38  **10.** 4  **11.** $-5$  **12.** 5  **13.** $-\frac{7}{2}$, or $-3\frac{1}{2}$  **14.** 4  **15.** 13

**16.** $\frac{5}{4}$, or $1\frac{1}{4}$  **17.** 9  **18.** $\frac{37}{10}$, or $3\frac{7}{10}$  **19.** 0  **20.** 25  **21.** 14
**22.** undefined  **23.** $-4$  **24.** $\frac{6}{5}$, or $1\frac{1}{5}$  **25.** $-1$  **26.** $\frac{52}{37}$, or $1\frac{15}{37}$
**27.** $\frac{17}{16}$, or $1\frac{1}{16}$  **28.** $-\frac{2}{3}$  **29.** 3.33  **30.** 1.02  **31.** $-13$  **32.** 0
**33.** 24  **34.** $-7$  **35.** 37  **36.** $-3$  **37.** $-1$  **38.** $\frac{1}{2}$  **39.** $-\frac{5}{13}$
**40.** 5  **41.** $-\frac{8}{27}$  **42.** 4

## Section 1.7 (pages 67–69)

**1. (a)** B  **(b)** F  **(c)** C  **(d)** I  **(e)** B  **(f)** D, F  **(g)** B  **(h)** A
**(i)** G  **(j)** H  **3.** yes  **5.** no  **7.** no  **9.** (foreign sales) clerk; foreign
(sales clerk)  **11.** $-15$; commutative property  **13.** 3; commutative
property  **15.** 6; associative property  **17.** 7; associative property
**19.** Subtraction is not associative.  **21.** row 1: $-5, \frac{1}{5}$; row 2: $10, -\frac{1}{10}$;
row 3: $\frac{1}{2}$, $-2$; row 4: $-\frac{3}{8}, \frac{8}{3}$; row 5: $-x, \frac{1}{x}$; row 6: $y, -\frac{1}{y}$; opposite;
the same  **23.** commutative property  **25.** associative property
**27.** associative property  **29.** inverse property  **31.** inverse property
**33.** identity property  **35.** commutative property  **37.** distributive
property  **39.** identity property  **41.** distributive property
**43.** 150  **45.** 2010  **47.** 400  **49.** 1400  **51.** 470
**53.** $-9300$  **55.** 11  **57.** 0  **59.** $-0.38$  **61.** 1  **63.** The expression
following the first equals symbol should be $-3(4) - 3(-6)$.
$-3(4 - 6)$ means $-3(4) - 3(-6)$, which simplifies to $-12 + 18$, or 6.
**65.** 85  **67.** $4t + 12$  **69.** $7z - 56$  **71.** $-8r - 24$  **73.** $-2x - \frac{3}{4}$
**75.** $-5y + 20$  **77.** $-16y - 20z$  **79.** $8(z + w)$  **81.** $7(2v + 5r)$
**83.** $24r + 32s - 40y$  **85.** $-24x - 9y - 12z$  **87.** $5(x + 3)$
**89.** $-4t - 3m$  **91.** $5c + 4d$  **93.** $q - 5r + 8s$

## Section 1.8 (pages 72–74)

**1.** B  **3.** C  **5.** $4r + 11$  **7.** $5 + 2x - 6y$  **9.** $-7 + 3p$
**11.** $2 - 3x$  **13.** $-12$  **15.** 3  **17.** 1  **19.** $-1$  **21.** $\frac{1}{2}$  **23.** $\frac{2}{5}$
**25.** 10  **27.** like  **29.** unlike  **31.** like  **33.** unlike  **35.** The
student made a sign error when applying the distributive property:
$7x - 2(3 - 2x)$ means $7x - 2(3) - 2(-2x)$, which simplifies to
$7x - 6 + 4x$, or $11x - 6$.  **37.** $13y$  **39.** $-9x$  **41.** $13b$
**43.** $7k + 15$  **45.** $-4y$  **47.** $2x + 6$  **49.** $14 - 7m$  **51.** $-17 + x$
**53.** $23x$  **55.** $-\frac{1}{3}t - \frac{28}{3}$  **57.** $9y^2$  **59.** $-14p^3 + 5p^2$  **61.** $8x + 15$
**63.** $5x + 15$  **65.** $-4y + 22$  **67.** $-\frac{3}{2}y + 16$  **69.** $-16y + 63$
**71.** $4r + 15$  **73.** $12k - 5$  **75.** $-2k - 3$  **77.** $4x - 7$
**79.** $-23.7y - 12.6$  **81.** $(x + 3) + 5x$; $6x + 3$
**83.** $(13 + 6x) - (-7x)$; $13 + 13x$  **85.** $2(3x + 4) - (-4 + 6x)$; 12
**87.** $1000 + 5x$ (dollars)  **88.** $750 + 3y$ (dollars)
**89.** $1000 + 5x + 750 + 3y$ (dollars)  **90.** $1750 + 5x + 3y$ (dollars)

## Chapter 1 Review Exercises (pages 79–83)

**1.** $\frac{3}{4}$  **2.** $\frac{7}{2}$, or $3\frac{1}{2}$  **3.** $\frac{11}{24}$  **4.** $\frac{59}{16}$, or $3\frac{11}{16}$  **5.** about 1270 thousand
**6.** about 5079 thousand  **7.** 625  **8.** $\frac{27}{125}$  **9.** 0.0004  **10.** 0.001
**11.** 27  **12.** 17  **13.** 4  **14.** 399  **15.** 39  **16.** 5  **17.** true  **18.** true
**19.** false  **20.** $13 < 17$  **21.** $5 + 2 \neq 10$  **22.** $\frac{2}{3} \geq \frac{4}{6}$  **23.** 30
**24.** 60  **25.** 14  **26.** 13  **27.** $x + 6$  **28.** $8 - x$  **29.** $6x - 9$
**30.** $12 + \frac{3}{5}x$  **31.** yes  **32.** no  **33.** $2x - 6 = 10$; 8  **34.** $4x = 8$; 2

**35.**   **36.**

**37.** rational numbers, real numbers   **38.** rational numbers, real numbers
**39.** natural numbers, whole numbers, integers, rational numbers, real numbers   **40.** irrational numbers, real numbers   **41.** $-10$   **42.** $-9$
**43.** $-\frac{3}{4}$   **44.** $-|23|$   **45.** true   **46.** true   **47.** true   **48.** true
**49.** (a) 9   (b) 9   **50.** (a) 0   (b) 0   **51.** (a) $-6$   (b) 6
**52.** (a) $\frac{5}{7}$   (b) $\frac{5}{7}$   **53.** 12   **54.** $-3$   **55.** $-19$   **56.** $-7$   **57.** $-6$
**58.** $-4$   **59.** $-17$   **60.** $-\frac{29}{36}$   **61.** $-21.8$   **62.** $-14$   **63.** $-10$
**64.** $-19$   **65.** $-11$   **66.** $-1$   **67.** 7   **68.** $-\frac{43}{35}$, or $-1\frac{8}{35}$   **69.** 10.31
**70.** $-12$   **71.** 2   **72.** $-3$   **73.** $(-31 + 12) + 19; 0$
**74.** $[-4 + (-8)] + 13; 1$   **75.** $-4 - (-6); 2$
**76.** $[4 + (-8)] - 5; -9$   **77.** $-2$   **78.** $-1$   **79.** \$26.25
**80.** $-10°F$   **81.** $-\$29$   **82.** $-10°$   **83.** 38   **84.** 9544.2
**85.** 36   **86.** $-105$   **87.** $\frac{1}{2}$   **88.** 10.08   **89.** $-20$   **90.** $-10$
**91.** $-24$   **92.** $-35$   **93.** 4   **94.** $-20$   **95.** $-\frac{3}{4}$   **96.** 11.3   **97.** $-1$
**98.** 2   **99.** 1   **100.** 0.5   **101.** $-18$   **102.** $-18$   **103.** 125
**104.** $-423$   **105.** $-4(5) - 9; -29$   **106.** $\frac{5}{6}[12 + (-6)]; 5$
**107.** $\frac{12}{8 + (-4)}; 3$   **108.** $\frac{-20(12)}{15 - (-15)}; -8$   **109.** $8x = -24; -3$
**110.** $\frac{x}{3} = -2; -6$   **111.** 32   **112.** $-3$   **113.** identity property
**114.** identity property   **115.** inverse property   **116.** inverse property
**117.** associative property   **118.** associative property   **119.** distributive property   **120.** commutative property   **121.** $7(y + 2)$
**122.** $-48 + 12t$   **123.** $3(2s + 5y)$   **124.** $4r - 5s$   **125.** $11m$
**126.** $16p^2$   **127.** $16p^2 + 2p$   **128.** $-4k + 12$   **129.** $-2m + 29$
**130.** $-5k - 1$   **131.** $-2(3x) - 7x; -13x$
**132.** $(5 + 4x) + 8x; 5 + 12x$   **133.** $\frac{8}{3}$, or $2\frac{2}{3}$   **134.** $-\frac{1}{24}$
**135.** 2   **136.** $-\frac{28}{15}$, or $-1\frac{13}{15}$   **137.** $-\frac{3}{2}$, or $-1\frac{1}{2}$   **138.** $\frac{25}{36}$   **139.** 16
**140.** 77.6   **141.** 11   **142.** $16t - 36$   **143.** $8x^2 - 21y^2$   **144.** 24
**145.** Dividing 0 *by* a nonzero number gives a quotient of 0. However, dividing a number *by* 0 is undefined.   **146.** $-47°F$   **147.** $-0.84$ million students   **148.** $-1.05$ million students   **149.** 1.02 million students
**150.** 1.39 million students

## Chapter 1 Test (pages 83–84)

[1.1] **1.** $\frac{7}{11}$   **2.** $\frac{241}{120}$, or $2\frac{1}{120}$   **3.** $\frac{19}{18}$, or $1\frac{1}{18}$   [1.2] **4.** true
[1.4] **5.**   **6.** rational numbers, real numbers

**7.** If $-8$ and $-1$ are both graphed on a number line, we see that the point for $-8$ is to the *left* of the point for $-1$. This indicates $-8 < -1$.
[1.6] **8.** $\frac{-6}{2 + (-8)}; 1$   [1.1, 1.4–1.6] **9.** 4   **10.** $-\frac{17}{6}$, or $-2\frac{5}{6}$   **11.** 2
**12.** 6   **13.** 108   **14.** $\frac{30}{7}$, or $4\frac{2}{7}$   [1.3, 1.5, 1.6] **15.** 6   **16.** 4
[1.6] **17.** $-70$   **18.** 3   [1.4–1.6] **19.** 7000 m   **20.** 15
**21.** $-\$1.42$ trillion   [1.7] **22.** B   **23.** D   **24.** E   **25.** A   **26.** C
**27.** distributive property   **28.** (a) $-18$   (b) $-18$   (c) The distributive property assures us that the answers must be the same, because $a(b + c) = ab + ac$ for all $a, b, c$.   [1.8] **29.** $21x$   **30.** $15x - 3$

**2**   **LINEAR EQUATIONS AND INEQUALITIES IN ONE VARIABLE**

## Section 2.1 (pages 90–92)

**1.** (a) expression; $x + 15$   (b) expression; $y + 7$   (c) equation; $\{-1\}$
(d) equation; $\{-17\}$   **3.** A and B   **5.** $\{12\}$   **7.** $\{31\}$   **9.** $\{-3\}$
**11.** $\{4\}$   **13.** $\{-9\}$   **15.** $\left\{-\frac{3}{4}\right\}$   **17.** $\{-10\}$   **19.** $\{-13\}$
**21.** $\{10\}$   **23.** $\left\{\frac{4}{15}\right\}$   **25.** $\{6.3\}$   **27.** $\{-16.9\}$   **29.** $\{7\}$   **31.** $\{-4\}$
**33.** $\{-3\}$   **35.** $\{0\}$   **37.** $\{2\}$   **39.** $\{-6\}$   **41.** $\{-2\}$   **43.** $\{3\}$
**45.** $\{0\}$   **47.** $\{0\}$   **49.** $\{-5\}$   **51.** $\{-7\}$   **53.** $\{13\}$   **55.** $\{-4\}$
**57.** $\{0\}$   **59.** $\left\{\frac{7}{15}\right\}$   **61.** $\{7\}$   **63.** $\{-4\}$   **65.** $\{13\}$   **67.** $\{29\}$
**69.** $\{18\}$   **71.** $\{12\}$   **73.** Answers will vary. One example is $x - 6 = -8$.   **75.** $3x = 2x + 17; \{17\}$   **77.** $7x - 6x = -9; \{-9\}$
**79.** 1   **81.** $x$   **83.** $r$

## Section 2.2 (pages 96–97)

**1.** (a) multiplication property of equality   (b) addition property of equality   (c) multiplication property of equality   (d) addition property of equality   **3.** To find the solution of $-x = 5$, multiply (or divide) each side by $-1$, or use the rule "If $-x = a$, then $x = -a$."   **5.** $\frac{5}{4}$   **7.** 10
**9.** $-\frac{2}{9}$   **11.** $-1$   **13.** 6   **15.** $-4$   **17.** 0.12   **19.** $-1$   **21.** $\{6\}$
**23.** $\left\{\frac{15}{2}\right\}$   **25.** $\{-5\}$   **27.** $\{-4\}$   **29.** $\left\{-\frac{18}{5}\right\}$, or $\{-3.6\}$
**31.** $\{12\}$   **33.** $\{0\}$   **35.** $\{-12\}$   **37.** $\left\{\frac{3}{4}\right\}$   **39.** $\{40\}$
**41.** $\{-12.2\}$   **43.** $\{-48\}$   **45.** $\{72\}$   **47.** $\{-35\}$   **49.** $\{14\}$
**51.** $\{18\}$   **53.** $\left\{-\frac{27}{35}\right\}$   **55.** $\{-30\}$   **57.** $\{3\}$   **59.** $\{-5\}$   **61.** $\{20\}$
**63.** $\{7\}$   **65.** $\{0\}$   **67.** $\left\{-\frac{3}{5}\right\}$   **69.** $\{18\}$   **71.** Answers will vary. One example is $\frac{3}{2}x = -6$.   **73.** $4x = 6; \left\{\frac{3}{2}\right\}$   **75.** $\frac{x}{-5} = 2; \{-10\}$
**77.** $-3m - 5$   **79.** $-8 + 5p$   **81.** $\{5\}$

## Section 2.3 (pages 104–106)

**1.** Use the addition property of equality to subtract 8 from each side.
**3.** Clear parentheses by using the distributive property.   **5.** Clear fractions by multiplying by the LCD, 6.   **7.** D   **9.** $\{4\}$   **11.** $\{-5\}$   **13.** $\left\{\frac{5}{2}\right\}$
**15.** $\{-1\}$   **17.** $\left\{-\frac{1}{2}\right\}$   **19.** $\{-3\}$   **21.** $\{5\}$   **23.** $\{0\}$   **25.** $\left\{\frac{4}{3}\right\}$
**27.** $\left\{-\frac{5}{3}\right\}$   **29.** $\{5\}$   **31.** $\{0\}$   **33.** $\emptyset$   **35.** {all real numbers}
**37.** $\emptyset$   **39.** $\{5\}$   **41.** $\{12\}$   **43.** $\{11\}$   **45.** $\{0\}$   **47.** $\{18\}$
**49.** $\{120\}$   **51.** $\{6\}$   **53.** $\{15,000\}$   **55.** $\{8\}$   **57.** $\{4\}$   **59.** $\{20\}$
**61.** {all real numbers}   **63.** $\emptyset$   **65.** $11 - q$   **67.** $\frac{9}{x}$   **69.** $x + 9$
**71.** $65 - h$   **73.** $x + 15; x - 5$   **75.** $25r$   **77.** $\frac{t}{5}$   **79.** $3x + 2y$
**81.** $-6 + x$   **83.** $-5 - x$   **85.** $12(x - 9)$

## Summary Exercises on Solving Linear Equations (pages 106–107)

**1.** $\{-5\}$   **2.** $\{4\}$   **3.** $\{-5.1\}$   **4.** $\{12\}$   **5.** $\{-25\}$   **6.** $\{-6\}$
**7.** $\{0\}$   **8.** $\{-16\}$   **9.** $\{-6\}$   **10.** $\left\{-\frac{96}{5}\right\}$   **11.** {all real numbers}

**12.** $\left\{\frac{7}{3}\right\}$   **13.** $\{7\}$   **14.** $\{1\}$   **15.** $\{5\}$   **16.** $\{23.7\}$   **17.** $\{6\}$
**18.** $\{3\}$   **19.** $\emptyset$   **20.** $\emptyset$   **21.** $\{25\}$   **22.** $\{-10.8\}$   **23.** $\{3\}$
**24.** $\{7\}$   **25.** $\{2\}$   **26.** {all real numbers}   **27.** $\{-2\}$   **28.** $\{70\}$
**29.** $\left\{\frac{14}{17}\right\}$   **30.** $\{0\}$

## Section 2.4 (pages 115–119)

**1.** D; There cannot be a fractional number of cars.   **3.** A; Distance cannot
be negative.   **5.** 7   **7.** 3   **9.** 6   **11.** $-3$   **13.** Pennsylvania: 35 screens;
Ohio: 33 screens   **15.** Democrats: 58; Republicans: 40   **17.** Bon Jovi:
$210.7 million; Bruce Springsteen: $204.6 million   **19.** wins: 62;
losses: 20   **21.** orange: 97 mg; pineapple: 25 mg   **23.** 168 DVDs
**25.** onions: 81.3 kg; grilled steak: 536.3 kg   **27.** 1950 Denver nickel:
$16.00; 1945 Philadelphia nickel: $8.00   **29.** whole wheat: 25.6 oz;
rye: 6.4 oz   **31.** American: 18; United: 11; Southwest: 26   **33.** shortest
piece: 15 in.; middle piece: 20 in.; longest piece: 24 in.   **35.** 36 million mi
**37.** $A$ and $B$: 40°; $C$: 100°   **39.** 68, 69   **41.** 101, 102   **43.** 10, 12
**45.** 10, 11   **47.** 18   **49.** 15, 17, 19   **51.** 18°   **53.** 20°   **55.** 39°
**57.** 50°   **59.** 24   **61.** 20

## Section 2.5 (pages 125–129)

**1. (a)** The perimeter of a plane geometric figure is the distance around
the figure.   **(b)** The area of a plane geometric figure is the measure of
the surface covered or enclosed by the figure.   **3.** 180°; the same
**5.** area   **7.** perimeter   **9.** area   **11.** area   **13.** $P = 26$   **15.** $\mathcal{A} = 64$
**17.** $b = 4$   **19.** $t = 5.6$   **21.** $I = 1575$   **23.** $B = 14$   **25.** $r = 2.6$
**27.** $r = 10$   **29.** $\mathcal{A} = 50.24$   **31.** $r = 6$   **33.** $V = 150$   **35.** $V = 52$
**37.** $V = 7234.56$   **39.** length: 18 in.; width: 9 in.   **41.** length: 14 m;
width: 4 m   **43.** shortest: 5 in.; medium: 7 in.; longest: 8 in.
**45.** two equal sides: 7 m; third side: 10 m   **47.** about 154,000 ft$^2$
**49.** perimeter: 5.4 m; area: 1.8 m$^2$   **51.** 10 ft   **53.** 194.48 ft$^2$; 49.42 ft
**55.** 23,800.10 ft$^2$   **57.** length: 36 in.; volume: 11,664 in.$^3$   **59.** 48°, 132°
**61.** 55°, 35°   **63.** 51°, 51°   **65.** 105°, 105°   **67.** $t = \dfrac{d}{r}$   **69.** $b = \dfrac{\mathcal{A}}{h}$
**71.** $d = \dfrac{C}{\pi}$   **73.** $H = \dfrac{V}{LW}$   **75.** $r = \dfrac{I}{pt}$   **77.** $h = \dfrac{2\mathcal{A}}{b}$   **79.** $h = \dfrac{3V}{\pi r^2}$
**81.** $b = P - a - c$   **83.** $W = \dfrac{P - 2L}{2}$   **85.** $m = \dfrac{y - b}{x}$
**87.** $y = \dfrac{C - Ax}{B}$   **89.** $r = \dfrac{M - C}{C}$, or $r = \dfrac{M}{C} - 1$   **91.** $a = \dfrac{P - 2b}{2}$,
or $a = \dfrac{P}{2} - b$   **93.** $\{5000\}$   **95.** $\{28\}$   **97.** $\left\{-\frac{1}{12}\right\}$

## Section 2.6 (pages 135–139)

**1. (a)** C   **(b)** D   **(c)** B   **(d)** A   **3.** $\frac{4}{3}$   **5.** $\frac{4}{3}$   **7.** $\frac{15}{2}$   **9.** $\frac{1}{5}$   **11.** $\frac{5}{6}$
**13.** 10 lb; $0.429   **15.** 32 oz; $0.093   **17.** 128 oz; $0.051   **19.** 36 oz;
$0.049   **21.** 263 oz; $0.076   **23.** true   **25.** false   **27.** true   **29.** $\{35\}$
**31.** $\{7\}$   **33.** $\left\{\frac{45}{2}\right\}$   **35.** $\{2\}$   **37.** $\{-1\}$   **39.** $\{5\}$   **41.** $\left\{-\frac{31}{5}\right\}$
**43.** $30.00   **45.** $8.75   **47.** $67.50   **49.** $48.90   **51.** 4 ft
**53.** 2.7 in.   **55.** 2.0 in.   **57.** $2\frac{5}{8}$ cups   **59.** $428.82   **61.** 50,000 fish
**63.** $x = 4$   **65.** $x = 2$   **67.** $x = 1; y = 4$

**69. (a)**

**(b)** 54 ft   **71.** $237   **73.** $272
**75.** 0.53   **77.** 0.96   **79.** 0.09
**81.** 1.29   **83.** 80%   **85.** 2%
**87.** 12.5%   **89.** 220%   **91.** 109.2
**93.** 700   **95.** 425   **97.** 8%
**99.** 120%   **101.** $119.25; $675.75
**103.** 80%   **105.** $3000   **107.** $\{6\}$   **109.** $\{4\}$

## Section 2.7 (pages 145–150)

**1.** 45 L   **3.** $750   **5.** $17.50   **7.** A   **9. (a)** 532,000   **(b)** 798,000
**(c)** 494,000   **11.** D   **13.** 160 L   **15.** $13\frac{1}{3}$ L   **17.** 4 L   **19.** 20 mL
**21.** 4 L   **23.** $2100 at 5%; $900 at 4%   **25.** $2500 at 6%; $13,500
at 5%   **27.** 10 nickels   **29.** 44-cent stamps: 25; 17-cent stamps: 20
**31.** Arabian Mocha: 7 lb; Colombian Decaf: 3.5 lb   **33.** A   **35.** 530 mi
**37.** 3.483 hr   **39.** 7.97 m per sec   **41.** 8.47 m per sec   **43.** 5 hr
**45.** $1\frac{3}{4}$ hr   **47.** $7\frac{1}{2}$ hr   **49.** eastbound: 300 mph; westbound: 450 mph
**51.** 40 mph; 60 mph   **53.** Bob: 7 yr old; Kevin: 21 yr old
**55.** width: 3 ft; length: 9 ft   **57.** $650   **59.** false   **61.** true   **63.** true

## Section 2.8 (pages 159–162)

**1.** $>, <$ (or $<, >$); $\geq, \leq$ (or $\leq, \geq$)   **3.** $(0, \infty)$   **5.** $x > -4$
**7.** $x \leq 4$   **9.** $(-\infty, 4]$

**11.** $(-\infty, -3)$

**13.** $(4, \infty)$

**15.** $(-\infty, 0]$

**17.** $\left[-\frac{1}{2}, \infty\right)$

**19.** $[1, \infty)$

**21.** $[5, \infty)$

**23.** $(-\infty, -11)$

**25.** It must be reversed when one is multiplying or dividing by a negative
number.

**27.** $(-\infty, 6)$

**29.** $[-10, \infty)$

**31.** $(-\infty, -3)$

**33.** $(-\infty, 0]$

**35.** $(20, \infty)$

**37.** $[-3, \infty)$

**39.** $(-\infty, -3]$

**41.** $(-1, \infty)$

**43.** $[-5, \infty)$

**45.** $(-\infty, 1)$

**47.** $(-\infty, 0]$

**49.** $\left(-\frac{1}{2}, \infty\right)$

**51.** $[4, \infty)$

**53.** $(-\infty, 32)$

**55.** $\left[\frac{5}{12}, \infty\right)$

**57.** $(-21, \infty)$

**59.** $\{4\}$

**60.** $(4, \infty)$

**61.** $(-\infty, 4)$

**62.** The graph is the set of all real numbers.   **63.** $x \geq 18$   **65.** $x > 5$
**67.** $x \leq 20$   **69.** 83 or greater   **71.** all numbers greater than 16
**73.** It is never less than $-13°$F.   **75.** 32 or greater   **77.** 15 min
**79.** $R = 5x - 100$   **81.** $P = (5x - 100) - (125 + 4x) = x - 225$;
$x > 225$   **83.** $-1 < x < 2$   **85.** $-1 < x \leq 2$

**87.** $[8, 10]$

**89.** $(0, 10]$

**91.** $(-3, 4)$

**93.** $[-1, 6]$

**95.** $\left(-\frac{11}{6}, -\frac{2}{3}\right)$

**97.** $(1, 3)$

**99.** $[-26, 6]$

**101.** $[-3, 6]$

**103.** $\left[-\frac{24}{5}, 0\right]$

**105. (a)** $-7$  **(b)** 23   **107. (a)** $-14$  **(b)** 22
**109. (a)** $-\frac{14}{5}$  **(b)** $-\frac{2}{5}$

## Chapter 2 Review Exercises (pages 167–171)

**1.** $\{6\}$   **2.** $\{-12\}$   **3.** $\{7\}$   **4.** $\left\{\frac{2}{3}\right\}$   **5.** $\{11\}$   **6.** $\{17\}$
**7.** $\{5\}$   **8.** $\{-4\}$   **9.** $\{5\}$   **10.** $\{-12\}$   **11.** $\left\{\frac{64}{5}\right\}$   **12.** $\{4\}$

**13.** {all real numbers}   **14.** $\{-19\}$   **15.** {all real numbers}
**16.** $\{20\}$   **17.** $\emptyset$   **18.** $\{-1\}$   **19.** $-\frac{7}{2}$   **20.** Democrats: 70;
Republicans: 48   **21.** Hawaii: 6425 mi$^2$; Rhode Island: 1212 mi$^2$
**22.** Seven Falls: 300 ft; Twin Falls: 120 ft   **23.** $80°$   **24.** 11, 13
**25.** $h = 11$   **26.** $\mathcal{A} = 28$   **27.** $r = 4.75$   **28.** $V = 904.32$
**29.** $h = \frac{\mathcal{A}}{b}$   **30.** $h = \frac{2\mathcal{A}}{b + B}$   **31.** $135°$; $45°$   **32.** $100°$; $100°$
**33.** 2 cm   **34.** diameter: approximately 19.9 ft; radius: approximately
9.95 ft; area: approximately 311 ft$^2$   **35.** $42.2°$; $92.8°$   **36.** $\frac{3}{2}$
**37.** $\frac{5}{14}$   **38.** $\frac{3}{4}$   **39.** $\left\{\frac{7}{2}\right\}$   **40.** $\left\{-\frac{8}{3}\right\}$   **41.** \$3.06   **42.** 375 km
**43.** 10 bronze medals   **44.** 25.5 oz; \$0.137   **45.** 6   **46.** 175%
**47.** 2500   **48.** 3.75 L   **49.** \$5000 at 5%; \$5000 at 6%
**50.** 8.2 mph   **51.** 13 hr   **52.** $2\frac{1}{2}$ hr

**53.** $[-4, \infty)$

**54.** $(-\infty, 7)$

**55.** $[-5, 6)$

**56.** B   **57.** $[-3, \infty)$

**58.** $(-\infty, 2)$

**59.** $[3, \infty)$

**60.** $[46, \infty)$

**61.** $(-\infty, -5)$

**62.** $(-\infty, -4)$

**63.** $\left[-2, \frac{3}{2}\right]$

**64.** $\left(\frac{4}{3}, 5\right]$

**65.** 88 or more   **66.** all numbers less than or equal to $-\frac{1}{3}$   **67.** $\{7\}$
**68.** $r = \frac{I}{pt}$   **69.** $(-\infty, 2)$   **70.** $\{-9\}$   **71.** $\{70\}$   **72.** $\left\{\frac{13}{4}\right\}$   **73.** $\emptyset$
**74.** {all real numbers}   **75.** \$304   **76.** 4000 calories   **77.** Golden
Gate Bridge: 4200 ft; Brooklyn Bridge: 1596 ft   **78.** 100 oz; \$0.060
**79.** 8 qt   **80.** faster train: 80 mph; slower train: 50 mph   **81.** 44 m
**82.** 50 m or less

## Chapter 2 Test (pages 171–172)

[2.1–2.3] **1.** $\{-6\}$   **2.** $\{21\}$   **3.** $\emptyset$   **4.** $\{30\}$   **5.** {all real numbers}
[2.4] **6.** wins: 100; losses: 62   **7.** Hawaii: 4021 mi$^2$; Maui: 728 mi$^2$;
Kauai: 551 mi$^2$   **8.** $50°$   [2.5] **9. (a)** $W = \frac{P - 2L}{2}$   **(b)** 18
**10.** $75°$, $75°$   [2.6] **11.** $\{6\}$   **12.** $\{-29\}$   **13.** 32 oz; \$0.250
**14.** 2300 mi   [2.7] **15.** \$8000 at 3%; \$14,000 at 4.5%   **16.** 4 hr
[2.8] **17.** $(-\infty, 4]$

**18.** $(-2, 6]$

**19.** 83 or more   **20.** When an inequality is multiplied or divided by a negative number, the direction of the inequality symbol must be reversed.

## Chapters 1–2 Cumulative Review Exercises (pages 172–173)

[1.1] **1.** $\frac{37}{60}$   **2.** $\frac{48}{5}$   [1.2] **3.** $\frac{1}{2}x - 18$   **4.** $\frac{6}{x + 12} = 2$   [1.4] **5.** true

[1.5–1.6] **6.** $-8$   **7.** 28   [1.3] **8.** $-\frac{19}{3}$   [1.7] **9.** distributive property

**10.** commutative property   [2.1–2.3] **11.** $\{-1\}$   **12.** $\{-1\}$

**13.** $\{-12\}$   [2.6] **14.** $\{26\}$   [2.5] **15.** $y = \frac{24 - 3x}{4}$

[2.8] **16.** $(-\infty, 1]$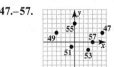

**17.** $(-1, 2]$

[2.4] **18.** 4 cm; 9 cm; 27 cm   [2.5] **19.** 12.42 cm

[2.7] **20.** 40 mph; 60 mph

**3** **LINEAR EQUATIONS AND INEQUALITIES IN TWO VARIABLES; FUNCTIONS**

## Section 3.1 (pages 183–187)

**1.** between 2003 and 2004, 2004 and 2005, and 2005 and 2006
**3.** 2003: 6.0%; 2004: 5.5%; decline: 0.5%   **5.** does; do not   **7.** II
**9.** 3   **11.** yes   **13.** yes   **15.** no   **17.** yes   **19.** yes   **21.** no
**23.** 17   **25.** $-5$   **27.** $-1$   **29.** $-7$   **31.** 8; 6; 3; $(0, 8)$; $(6, 0)$; $(3, 4)$
**33.** $-9$; 4; 9; $(-9, 0)$; $(0, 4)$; $(9, 8)$   **35.** 12; 12; 12; $(12, 3)$;
$(12, 8)$; $(12, 0)$   **37.** $-10$; $-10$; $-10$; $(4, -10)$; $(0, -10)$; $(-4, -10)$
**39.** $-2$; $-2$; $-2$; $(9, -2)$; $(2, -2)$; $(0, -2)$   **41.** 4; 4; 4; $(4, 4)$; $(4, 0)$;
$(4, -4)$   **43.** No, the ordered pair $(3, 4)$ represents the point 3 units to the right of the origin and 4 units up from the $x$-axis. The ordered pair $(4, 3)$ represents the point 4 units to the right of the origin and 3 units up from the $x$-axis.   **45.** $A$: $(2, 4)$, I; $B$: $(-3, 2)$, II; $C$: $(-5, 4)$, II; $D$: $(-5, -2)$, III; $E$: $(3, 0)$, no quadrant; $F$: $(0, -2)$, no quadrant
**47.–57.**    **59.** negative; negative
**61.** positive; negative

**63.** If $xy < 0$, then either $x < 0$ and $y > 0$ or $x > 0$ and $y < 0$. If $x < 0$ and $y > 0$, then the point lies in quadrant II. If $x > 0$ and $y < 0$, then the point lies in quadrant IV.

**65.** $-3$; 6; $-2$; 4    **67.** $-3$; 4; $-6$; $-\frac{4}{3}$

**69.** $-4$; $-4$; $-4$; $-4$

**71.** The points in each graph appear to lie on a straight line.

**73. (a)** $(5, 45)$   **(b)** $(6, 50)$   **75. (a)** $(2002, 31.6)$, $(2003, 30.1)$, $(2004, 29.0)$, $(2005, 27.5)$, $(2006, 26.6)$, $(2007, 26.9)$   **(b)** $(2007, 26.9)$ means that 26.9 percent of 2-year college students in 2007 received a degree within 3 years.

**(c)** 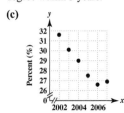   **(d)** With the exception of the point for 2007, the points lie approximately on a straight line. Rates at which 2-year college students complete a degree within 3 years were generally decreasing.

**77. (a)** 130; 117; 104; 91   **(b)** $(20, 130)$, $(40, 117)$, $(60, 104)$, $(80, 91)$
**(c)** yes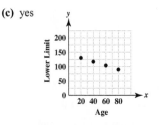

**79.** between 130 and 170 beats per minute; between 117 and 153 beats per minute   **81.** $\{-2\}$   **83.** $\{13\}$

**Connections** **(page 195)** **1.** $3x + 4 - 2x - 7 - 4x - 3 = 0$
**2.** $5x - 15 - 3(x - 2) = 0$

## Section 3.2 (pages 195–199)

**1.** 5; 5; 3    **3.** 1; 3; $-1$    **5.** $-6$; $-2$; $-5$

**7. (a)** A   **(b)** C   **(c)** D   **(d)** B   **9.** $x$-intercept: $(4, 0)$; $y$-intercept: $(0, -4)$   **11.** $x$-intercept: $(-2, 0)$; $y$-intercept: $(0, -3)$
**13.** $(8, 0)$; $(0, -8)$   **15.** $(4, 0)$; $(0, -10)$   **17.** $(0, 0)$; $(0, 0)$
**19.** $(2, 0)$; $(0, 4)$   **21.** $(6, 0)$; $(0, -2)$   **23.** $(0, 0)$; $(0, 0)$
**25.** $(4, 0)$; none   **27.** none; $(0, 2.5)$   **29. (a)** D   **(b)** C   **(c)** B   **(d)** A
**31.** 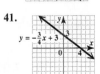   **33.**   **35.**

**37.**   **39.**   **41.**

**43.**  **45.**  **47.**

**49.**  **51.**  **53.**

*In Exercises 55–61, descriptions may vary.*

**55.** The graph is a line with $x$-intercept $(-3, 0)$ and $y$-intercept $(0, 9)$.

**57.** The graph is a vertical line with $x$-intercept $(11, 0)$.

**59.** The graph is a horizontal line with $y$-intercept $(0, -2)$.

**61.** The graph has $x$- and $y$-intercepts $(0, 0)$. It passes through the points $(2, 1)$ and $(4, 2)$.

**63.** $x = 3$  **65.** $y = -3$

**67. (a)** 121 lb; 143 lb; 176 lb **(b)** $(62, 121), (66, 143), (72, 176)$

**(c)** 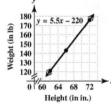 **(d)** 68 in.; 68 in.

**69. (a)** $62.50; $100 **(b)** 200 **(c)** $(50, 62.50), (100, 100), (200, 175)$

**(d)**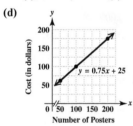

**71. (a)** $30,000 **(b)** $15,000 **(c)** $5000 **(d)** After 5 yr, the SUV has a value of $5000. **73. (a)** 2000: $73 billion; 2004: $85 billion; 2006: $91 billion **(b)** 2000: $74 billion; 2004: $86 billion; 2006: $91 billion **(c)** The values are quite close. **75.** $\frac{2}{3}$ **77.** $\frac{1}{2}$

## Section 3.3 (pages 206–210)

**1.** 4 **3.** $-\frac{1}{2}$ **5.** 0 **7.** Rise is the vertical change between two different points on a line. Run is the horizontal change between two different points on a line. **9. (a)** C **(b)** A **(c)** D **(d)** B

*In Exercises 11 and 13, sketches will vary.*

**11.** The line must fall from left to right. **13.** The line must be vertical.

**15. (a)** negative **(b)** zero **17. (a)** positive **(b)** negative

**19. (a)** zero **(b)** negative **21.** $\frac{8}{27}$ **23.** $-\frac{2}{3}$ **25.** Because he found the difference $3 - 5 = -2$ in the numerator, he should have subtracted

in the same order in the denominator to get $-1 - 2 = -3$. The correct slope is $\frac{-2}{-3} = \frac{2}{3}$. **27.** $\frac{5}{4}$ **29.** $\frac{3}{2}$ **31.** 0 **33.** $-3$ **35.** undefined

**37.** $\frac{1}{4}$ **39.** $-\frac{1}{2}$ **41.** 5 **43.** $\frac{1}{4}$ **45.** $\frac{3}{2}$ **47.** $\frac{3}{2}$ **49.** 0 **51.** undefined

**53.** $-3; \frac{1}{3}$ **55.** A **57.** $-\frac{2}{5}; -\frac{2}{5};$ parallel **59.** $\frac{8}{9}; -\frac{4}{3};$ neither

**61.** $\frac{3}{2}; -\frac{2}{3};$ perpendicular **63.** $5; \frac{1}{5};$ neither **65.** 232 thousand, or 232,000

**66.** positive; increased **67.** 232,000 students **68.** $-0.95$

**69.** negative; decreased **70.** 0.95 students per computer

**71. (a)** $(2004, 817), (2008, 1513)$ **(b)** 174 **(c)** Music purchases increased by 696 million units in 4 yr, or 174 million units per year.

**73.** 0.4 **75.** $(0, 4)$ **77.** $y = -\frac{2}{5}x + 3$ **79.** $y = \frac{10}{3}x - 10$

**81.** $y = 2x - 16$

## Section 3.4 (pages 218–222)

**1.** E **3.** B **5.** C **7.** A **9.** slope: $\frac{5}{2}$; $y$-intercept: $(0, -4)$

**11.** slope: $-1$; $y$-intercept: $(0, 9)$ **13.** slope: $\frac{1}{5}$; $y$-intercept: $\left(0, -\frac{3}{10}\right)$

**15.** $y = 3x - 3$ **17.** $y = -x + 3$ **19.** $y = -\frac{1}{2}x + 2$

**21.** $y = 4x - 3$ **23.** $y = -x - 7$ **25.** $y = 3$ **27.** $x = 0$

**29.**  **31.**  **33.**

**35.**  **37.**  **39.**

**41.**  **43.**  **45.**

**47.**  **49.** the $y$-axis **51.** $y = 2x - 7$

**53.** $y = -4x - 1$ **55.** $y = x - 6$

**57.** $y = \frac{3}{4}x + 4$ **59.** $y = \frac{2}{3}x + \frac{19}{3}$

**61.** $y = -\frac{4}{5}x + \frac{9}{5}$ **63.** A, B, D

**65. (a)** $y = x + 6$ **(b)** $x - y = -6$ **67. (a)** $y = \frac{1}{2}x + 2$

**(b)** $x - 2y = -4$ **69. (a)** $y = -\frac{3}{5}x - \frac{11}{5}$ **(b)** $3x + 5y = -11$

**71. (a)** $y = -\frac{1}{3}x + \frac{22}{9}$ **(b)** $3x + 9y = 22$ **73.** $y = -2x - 3$

**75.** $y = 4x - 5$ **77.** $y = \frac{3}{4}x - \frac{9}{2}$ **79. (a)** $400 **(b)** $0.25

**(c)** $y = 0.25x + 400$ **(d)** $425 **(e)** 1500

**81. (a)** $(1, 2079), (2, 2182), (3, 2272), (4, 2361), (5, 2402)$

**(b)** yes **(c)** $y = 94x + 1985$ **(d)** $2549

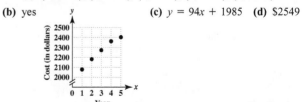

**83.** $y = 15x - 29,978$ **85.** $y = -3x + 6$

**87.** $(-3, \infty)$ **89.** $[5, \infty)$

## Summary Exercises on Linear Equations and Graphs (pages 222–223)

**1.**   **2.**   **3.**

**4.**   **5.**   **6.**

**7.** 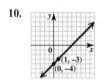  **8.**   **9.**

**10.**   **11.**   **12.**

**13.**   **14.**   **15.**

**16.**   **17.**   **18.**

**19. (a)** B **(b)** D **(c)** A **(d)** C **20.** A, B **21.** $y = -3x - 6$
**22.** $y = \frac{3}{2}x + 12$ **23.** $y = -4x - 3$ **24.** $y = \frac{3}{5}x$ **25.** $x = 0$
**26.** $y = x - 3$ **27.** $y = \frac{2}{3}x$ **28.** $y = -2x - 4$ **29.** $y = x - 5$
**30.** $y = 0$ **31.** $y = \frac{5}{3}x + 5$ **32.** $y = -5x - 8$

Connections **(page 227)** **1.** $(5, \infty)$ **2.** $(-\infty, 5)$ **3.** $(3, 5]$

## Section 3.5 (pages 227–229)

**1.** $>, >$ **3.** $\leq$ **5.** $<$ **7.** false **9.** true

**11.**   **13.** (graph)  **15.** (graph)

**17.** Use a dashed line if the symbol is $<$ or $>$. Use a solid line if the symbol is $\leq$ or $\geq$.

**19.**   **21.** (graph)  **23.** (graph)

**25.**   **27.**   **29.**

**31.** Every point in quadrant IV has a positive $x$-value and a negative $y$-value. Substituting into $y > x$ would imply that a negative number is greater than a positive number, which is always false. Thus, the graph of $y > x$ cannot lie in quadrant IV.

**33. (a)** 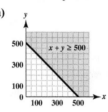  **(b)** $(500, 0), (200, 400)$
(Other answers are possible.)

**35.** 5 **37.** 85 **39.** 16

## Section 3.6 (pages 234–236)

**1.** 3; 3; $(1, 3)$ **3.** 5; 5; $(3, 5)$ **5.** The graph consists of the four points $(0, 2), (1, 3), (2, 4),$ and $(3, 5)$. **7.** not a function; domain: $\{-4, -2, 0\}$; range: $\{3, 1, 5, -8\}$ **9.** function; domain: $\{A, B, C, D, E\}$; range: $\{2, 3, 6, 4\}$ **11.** not a function; domain: $\{-4, -2, 0, 2, 3\}$; range: $\{-2, 0, 1, 2, 3\}$ **13.** function **15.** not a function
**17.** function **19.** function **21.** not a function
**23.** domain: $(-\infty, \infty)$; range: $(-\infty, \infty)$ **25.** domain: $(-\infty, \infty)$; range: $[2, \infty)$ **27.** domain: $[0, \infty)$; range: $[0, \infty)$ **29.** $(2, 4)$
**30.** $(-1, -4)$ **31.** $\frac{8}{3}$ **32.** $f(x) = \frac{8}{3}x - \frac{4}{3}$ **33. (a)** 11 **(b)** 3 **(c)** $-9$
**35. (a)** 4 **(b)** 2 **(c)** 14 **37. (a)** 2 **(b)** 0 **(c)** 3
**39.** $\{(1970, 9.6), (1980, 14.1), (1990, 19.8), (2000, 28.4),$ $(2007, 37.3)\}$; yes **41.** $g(1980) = 14.1; g(2000) = 28.4$ **43.** 2007
**45. (a)** 4 **(b)** 2 **47.** 4 **49.** 1 **51. (a)** 1 **(b)** $(0, 1)$
**53.** (graph)  **55.** (graph)

## Chapter 3 Review Exercises (pages 241–244)

**1. (a)** from 2002 to 2005 and 2006 to 2007 **(b)** from 2005 to 2006
**(c)** 2005: about 33 million; 2006: about 29 million **(d)** about 4 million
**2.** $-1; 2; 1$ **3.** $2; \frac{3}{2}, \frac{14}{3}$ **4.** $0; \frac{8}{3}; -9$ **5.** 7; 7; 7 **6.** yes **7.** no
**8.** yes **9.** I **10.** II **11.** none **12.** none **13.** I or III

*Graph for Exercises 9–12*

(graph)

**14.** $\left(-\frac{5}{2}, 0\right); (0, 5)$   **15.** $\left(\frac{8}{3}, 0\right); (0, 4)$   **16.** $(-4, 0); (0, -2)$

**17.** $-\frac{1}{2}$   **18.** undefined   **19.** 3   **20.** 0   **21.** $\frac{3}{2}$   **22.** $-\frac{1}{3}$   **23.** $\frac{3}{2}$

**24. (a)** 2   **(b)** $\frac{1}{3}$   **25.** parallel   **26.** perpendicular   **27.** neither

**28.** $y = -x + \frac{2}{3}$   **29.** $y = -\frac{1}{2}x + 4$   **30.** $y = x - 7$   **31.** $y = \frac{2}{3}x + \frac{14}{3}$

**32.** $y = -\frac{3}{4}x - \frac{1}{4}$   **33.** $y = -\frac{1}{4}x + \frac{3}{2}$   **34.** $y = 1$   **35.** $x = \frac{1}{3}$;
It is not possible to express this equation in the form $y = mx + b$.

**36.**     **37.**    **38.**

**39.** not a function; domain: $\{-2, 0, 2\}$; range: $\{4, 8, 5, 3\}$

**40.** function; domain: $\{8, 7, 6, 5, 4\}$; range: $\{3, 4, 5, 6, 7\}$

**41.** not a function   **42.** function   **43.** function   **44.** function

**45. (a)** 8   **(b)** $-1$   **46. (a)** 7   **(b)** 1   **47. (a)** 5   **(b)** 2   **48.** A

**49.** C, D   **50.** A, B, D   **51.** D   **52.** C   **53.** B

**54.** $\left(-\frac{5}{2}, 0\right); (0, -5); -2$   **55.** $(0, 0); (0, 0); -\frac{1}{3}$

**56.** no $x$-intercept; $(0, 5); 0$   **57.** $y = -\frac{1}{4}x - \frac{5}{4}$   **58.** $y = -3x + 30$

**59.** $y = -\frac{4}{7}x - \frac{23}{7}$   **60.** $y = -5$

**61.**    **62.**

**63.** Since the graph rises from left to right, the slope is positive.

**64.** $(2002, 41.2), (2007, 43.7)$   **65.** $y = 0.5x - 959.8$

**66.** 2003: 41.7; 2004: 42.2; 2005: 42.7; 2006: 43.2

## Chapter 3 Test (pages 244–245)

[3.1] **1.** $-6, -10, -5$   **2.** no   [3.2] **3.** To find the $x$-intercept, let $y = 0$, and to find the $y$-intercept, let $x = 0$.

**4.** $x$-intercept: $(2, 0)$;   **5.** $x$-intercept: $(0, 0)$;
   $y$-intercept: $(0, 6)$      $y$-intercept: $(0, 0)$

**6.** $x$-intercept: $(-3, 0)$;   **7.** $x$-intercept: none;
   $y$-intercept: none         $y$-intercept: $(0, 1)$

**8.** $x$-intercept: $(4, 0)$;   [3.3] **9.** $-\frac{8}{3}$   **10.** $-2$   **11.** undefined
   $y$-intercept: $(0, -4)$   **12.** 0   **13.** $\frac{5}{2}$

   [3.4] **14.** $y = 2x + 6$   **15.** $y = \frac{5}{2}x - 4$

   **16.** $y = -9x + 12$

[3.5] **17.**    **18.**

[3.1–3.4] **19.** The slope is negative, since sales are decreasing.

**20.** $(0, 209), (7, 160); y = -7x + 209$

**21.** 174 thousand; The equation gives a good approximation of the actual sales.   **22.** In 2007, worldwide snowmobile sales were 160 thousand.

[3.6] **23. (a)** not a function   **(b)** function; domain: $\{0, 1, 2\}$;
range: $\{2\}$   **24.** not a function   **25.** 1

## Chapters 1–3 Cumulative Review Exercises (page 246)

[1.1] **1.** $\frac{301}{40}$, or $7\frac{21}{40}$   **2.** 6   [1.5] **3.** 7   [1.6] **4.** $\frac{73}{18}$, or $4\frac{1}{18}$

[1.2–1.6] **5.** true   **6.** $-43$   [1.7] **7.** distributive property

[1.8] **8.** $-p + 2$   [2.5] **9.** $h = \dfrac{3V}{\pi r^2}$   [2.3] **10.** $\{-1\}$   **11.** $\{2\}$

[2.6] **12.** $\{-13\}$   [2.8] **13.** $(-2.6, \infty)$

[graph]   $-2.6$  $-1$   $0$

**14.** $(0, \infty)$   [graph]   **15.** $(-\infty, -4]$   [graph]

[2.4] **16.** high school diploma: \$30,732; bachelor's degree: \$50,856

[1.1, 2.6] **17. (a)** \$7000   **(b)** \$10,000   **18.** about \$30,000

[3.2] **19.** $(-4, 0); (0, 3)$   [3.3] **20.** $\frac{3}{4}$

[3.2] **21.** [graph]   [3.3] **22.** perpendicular

   [3.4] **23.** $y = 3x - 11$   **24.** $y = 4$

4   **SYSTEMS OF LINEAR EQUATIONS AND INEQUALITIES**

**Connections**   **(page 253)**   **1.** $\{(-1, 5)\}$   **2.** $\{(0.25, -0.5)\}$

**3.** $\{(1.5, -1.5)\}$

## Section 4.1 (pages 253–257)

**1.** A; The ordered-pair solution must be in quadrant II, and $(-4, -4)$ is in quadrant III.   **3.** no   **5.** yes   **7.** yes   **9.** no

**11.** yes **13. (a)** B **(b)** C **(c)** D **(d)** A

**15.** $\{(4, 2)\}$ **17.** $\{(0, 4)\}$ **19.** $\{(4, -1)\}$

*In Exercises 21–31, we do not show the graphs.*

**21.** $\{(1, 3)\}$ **23.** $\{(0, 2)\}$ **25.** $\emptyset$ (inconsistent system)
**27.** $\{(x, y) \mid 3x + y = 5\}$ (dependent equations) **29.** $\{(4, -3)\}$
**31.** $\emptyset$ (inconsistent system) **33.** It is difficult to read the exact
coordinates of the solution. Thus, the solution cannot be checked.
**35. (a)** neither **(b)** intersecting lines **(c)** one solution
**37. (a)** dependent **(b)** one line **(c)** infinite number of solutions
**39. (a)** neither **(b)** intersecting lines **(c)** one solution
**41. (a)** inconsistent **(b)** parallel lines **(c)** no solution
**43. (a)** 1980–2000 **(b)** 2001; about 750 newspapers
**45. (a)** 1997–2002 **(b)** 2001 **(c)** 2002 **(d)** (1998, 30) (The $y$-value
is approximate.) **47.** 30 **49.** B **51.** A **53.** $y = -3x + 4$
**55.** $y = \frac{9}{2}x - 2$ **57.** $\{2\}$ **59.** $\left\{\frac{4}{5}\right\}$

## Section 4.2 (pages 262–264)

**1.** The student must find the value of $y$ and write the solution as
an ordered pair. The solution set is $\{(3, 0)\}$. **3.** $\{(3, 9)\}$
**5.** $\{(7, 3)\}$ **7.** $\{(-4, 8)\}$ **9.** $\{(3, -2)\}$ **11.** $\{(0, 5)\}$
**13.** $\{(x, y) \mid 3x - y = 5\}$ **15.** $\left\{\left(\frac{1}{4}, -\frac{1}{2}\right)\right\}$ **17.** $\emptyset$
**19.** $\{(x, y) \mid 2x - y = -12\}$ **21.** $\{(2, 6)\}$ **23.** $\{(2, -4)\}$
**25.** $\{(-2, 1)\}$ **27.** $\{(x, y) \mid x + 2y = 48\}$ **29.** $\{(10, 4)\}$
**31.** $\{(4, -9)\}$ **33.** To find the total cost, multiply the number of
bicycles ($x$) by the cost per bicycle ($\$400$), and add the fixed cost ($\$5000$).
Thus, $y_1 = 400x + 5000$ gives this total cost (in dollars). **34.** $y_2 = 600x$
**35.** $y_1 = 400x + 5000, y_2 = 600x$; solution set: $\{(25, 15,000)\}$
**36.** 25; 15,000; 15,000
**37.** $\{(2, 4)\}$ **39.** $\{(1, 5)\}$

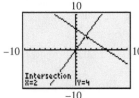 

**41.** $\{(5, -3)\}$; The equations to input are $Y_1 = \dfrac{5 - 4X}{5}$ and
$Y_2 = \dfrac{1 - 2X}{3}$.

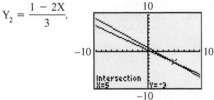

**43.** $16x$ **45.** $10y$ **47.** $4x$ **49.** $-2$

## Section 4.3 (pages 268–270)

**1.** false; The solution set is $\emptyset$. **3.** $\{(4, 6)\}$ **5.** $\{(-1, -3)\}$
**7.** $\{(-2, 3)\}$ **9.** $\left\{\left(\frac{1}{2}, 4\right)\right\}$ **11.** $\{(3, -6)\}$ **13.** $\{(0, 4)\}$
**15.** $\{(0, 0)\}$ **17.** $\{(7, 4)\}$ **19.** $\{(0, 3)\}$ **21.** $\{(3, 0)\}$
**23.** $\{(x, y) \mid x - 3y = -4\}$ **25.** $\emptyset$ **27.** $\{(-3, 2)\}$ **29.** $\{(11, 15)\}$
**31.** $\left\{\left(13, -\frac{7}{5}\right)\right\}$ **33.** $\{(6, -4)\}$ **35.** $\{(x, y) \mid x + 3y = 6\}$ **37.** $\emptyset$
**39.** $\left\{\left(-\frac{5}{7}, -\frac{2}{7}\right)\right\}$ **41.** $\left\{\left(\frac{1}{8}, -\frac{5}{6}\right)\right\}$ **43.** $5.39 = 2000a + b$
**44.** $7.18 = 2008a + b$ **45.** $2000a + b = 5.39, 2008a + b = 7.18$;
solution set: $\{(0.22375, -442.11)\}$ **46. (a)** $y = 0.22375x - 442.11$
**(b)** 6.96 ($\$6.96$); This is a bit more ($\$0.08$) than the actual figure.
**47.** goals: 894; assists: 1963 **49.** 13 twenties

## Summary Exercises on Solving Systems of Linear Equations (pages 270–271)

**1. (a)** Use substitution, since the second equation is solved for $y$.
**(b)** Use elimination, since the coefficients of the $y$-terms are opposites.
**(c)** Use elimination, since the equations are in standard form with no
coefficients of 1 or $-1$. Solving by substitution would involve fractions.
**2.** System B is easier to solve by substitution because the second equation
is already solved for $y$. **3. (a)** $\{(1, 4)\}$ **(b)** $\{(1, 4)\}$ **(c)** Answers
will vary. **4. (a)** $\{(-5, 2)\}$ **(b)** $\{(-5, 2)\}$ **(c)** Answers will vary.
**5.** $\{(3, 12)\}$ **6.** $\{(-3, 2)\}$ **7.** $\left\{\left(\frac{1}{3}, \frac{1}{2}\right)\right\}$ **8.** $\emptyset$ **9.** $\{(3, -2)\}$
**10.** $\{(-1, -11)\}$ **11.** $\{(x, y) \mid 2x - 3y = 5\}$ **12.** $\{(9, 4)\}$
**13.** $\left\{\left(\frac{45}{31}, \frac{4}{31}\right)\right\}$ **14.** $\{(4, -5)\}$ **15.** $\emptyset$ **16.** $\{(-4, 6)\}$
**17.** $\{(-3, 2)\}$ **18.** $\left\{\left(\frac{22}{13}, -\frac{23}{13}\right)\right\}$ **19.** $\{(0, 0)\}$ **20.** $\{(2, -3)\}$
**21.** $\{(24, -12)\}$ **22.** $\{(3, 2)\}$ **23.** $\{(10, -12)\}$
**24.** $\{(-4, 2)\}$ **25.** $\{(5, 3)\}$

## Section 4.4 (pages 276–281)

**1.** D **3.** B **5.** D **7.** C **9.** the second number; $x - y = 48$;
The two numbers are 73 and 25. **11.** *The Phantom of the Opera:* 8603;
*Cats:* 7485 **13.** *Avatar*: $\$429.0$ million; *Transformers 2*: $\$402.1$ million
**15. (a)** 45 units **(b)** Do not produce; the product will lead to a loss.
**17.** quarters: 24; dimes: 15 **19.** 2 DVDs of *The Blind Side;*
5 Beyoncé CDs **21.** $\$2500$ at 4%; $\$5000$ at 5% **23.** The Police: $\$102$;
Madonna: $\$137$ **25.** 40% solution: 80 L; 70% solution: 40 L
**27.** 30 lb at $\$6$ per lb; 60 lb at $\$3$ per lb **29.** nuts: 40 lb; raisins: 20 lb
**31.** 60 mph; 50 mph **33.** 35 mph; 65 mph **35.** bicycle: 13.5 mph;
car: 49.3 mph **37.** boat: 10 mph; current: 2 mph **39.** plane: 470 mph;
wind: 30 mph **41.** Yady: 17.5 mph; Dane: 12.5 mph
**43.** **45.**

## Section 4.5 (pages 284–285)

**1.** C  **3.** B  **5.**   **7.**

**9.** 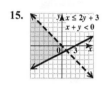  **11.**   **13.**

**15.** 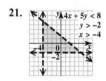  **17.** 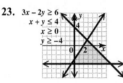  **19.**

**21.**   **23.**

**25.** D  **27.** A  **29.** 64  **31.** 625  **33.** $\frac{8}{27}$

## Chapter 4 Review Exercises (pages 288–291)

**1.** yes  **2.** no  **3.** $\{(3, 1)\}$  **4.** $\{(0, -2)\}$  **5.** $\emptyset$
**6.** $\{(x, y) \mid x - 2y = 2\}$  **7.** It would be easiest to solve for $x$ in the second equation because its coefficient is $-1$. No fractions would be involved.  **8.** The true statement $0 = 0$ is an indication that the system has an infinite number of solutions. Write the solution set using set-builder notation and the equation of the system that is in standard form with integer coefficients having greatest common factor 1.  **9.** $\{(2, 1)\}$
**10.** $\{(3, 5)\}$  **11.** $\{(6, 4)\}$  **12.** $\{(x, y) \mid x + 3y = 6\}$  **13.** C
**14.** (a) 2  (b) 9  **15.** $\{(7, 1)\}$  **16.** $\{(-4, 3)\}$
**17.** $\{(x, y) \mid 3x - 4y = 9\}$  **18.** $\emptyset$  **19.** $\{(-4, 1)\}$
**20.** $\{(x, y) \mid 2x - 3y = 0\}$  **21.** $\{(9, 2)\}$  **22.** $\{(8, 9)\}$
**23.** $\{(2, 1)\}$  **24.** $\{(-3, 2)\}$  **25.** Pizza Hut: 14,759 locations;
Domino's: 8641 locations  **26.** *Reader's Digest:* 9.3 million;
*People:* 3.6 million  **27.** length: 27 m; width: 18 m  **28.** twenties: 13;
tens: 7  **29.** 25 lb of $1.30 candy; 75 lb of $0.90 candy
**30.** 40% solution: 60 L; 70% solution: 30 L  **31.** $7000 at 3%;
$11,000 at 4%  **32.** plane: 250 mph; wind: 20 mph

**33.**   **34.**   **35.**

**36.**   **37.** (a) years 0 to 6  (b) year 6; about $650
**38.** In System B, the bottom equation is already
solved for $y$.  **39.** B  **40.** $\{(4, 8)\}$
**41.** $\{(x, y) \mid x - y = 6\}$  **42.** $\{(2, 0)\}$

**43.** $\{(4, 1)\}$  **44.**   **45.**

**46.** 8 in., 8 in., 13 in.  **47.** Statue of Liberty: 3.4 million; National
World War II Memorial: 4.1 million  **48.** slower car: 38 mph;
faster car: 68 mph

## Chapter 4 Test (pages 291–292)

[4.1] **1.** (a) no  (b) no  (c) yes  **2.** $\{(4, 1)\}$  [4.2] **3.** $\{(1, -6)\}$
**4.** $\{(-35, 35)\}$  [4.3] **5.** $\{(5, 6)\}$  **6.** $\{(-1, 3)\}$  **7.** $\{(-1, 3)\}$
**8.** $\emptyset$  **9.** $\{(0, 0)\}$  [4.1–4.3] **10.** $\{(x, y) \mid 3x + 4y = 5\}$
**11.** $\{(-15, 6)\}$  [4.4] **12.** Memphis and Atlanta: 394 mi;
Minneapolis and Houston: 1176 mi  **13.** Magic Kingdom: 17.1 million;
Disneyland: 14.7 million  **14.** 25% solution: $33\frac{1}{3}$ L; 40% solution: $16\frac{2}{3}$ L
**15.** slower car: 45 mph; faster car: 60 mph

[4.5] **16.**   **17.**   **18.** B

## Chapters 1–4 Cumulative Review Exercises (pages 292–293)

[1.6] **1.** $-1, 1, -2, 2, -4, 4, -5, 5, -8, 8, -10, 10, -20, 20, -40, 40$
**2.** 46  [1.3] **3.** 1  [1.7] **4.** distributive property  [2.3] **5.** $\left\{-\frac{13}{11}\right\}$
**6.** $\left\{\frac{9}{11}\right\}$  [2.5] **7.** $T = \dfrac{PV}{k}$  [2.8] **8.** $(-18, \infty)$  **9.** $\left(-\frac{11}{2}, \infty\right)$
[2.6] **10.** 2010; 1813; 62.8%; 57.2%  [2.4] **11.** in favor: 68; against: 31
[2.5] **12.** 46°, 46°, 88°
[3.2] **13.**   **14.**

[3.3] **15.** $-\frac{4}{3}$  **16.** $-\frac{1}{4}$  [3.4] **17.** $y = \frac{1}{2}x + 3$  **18.** $y = 2x + 1$
**19.** (a) $x = 9$  (b) $y = -1$  [4.1–4.3] **20.** $\{(-1, 6)\}$
**21.** $\{(3, -4)\}$  **22.** $\emptyset$  [4.4] **23.** 405 adults tickets; 49 child tickets
**24.** 20% solution: 4 L; 50% solution: 8 L

[4.5] **25.**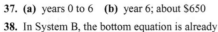

**5  EXPONENTS AND POLYNOMIALS**

## Section 5.1 (pages 301–303)

**1.** false; $3^3 = 3 \cdot 3 \cdot 3 = 27$  **3.** false; $(x^2)^3 = x^{2 \cdot 3} = x^6$  **5.** $w^6$
**7.** $\left(\frac{1}{2}\right)^6$  **9.** $(-4)^4$  **11.** $(-7y)^4$  **13.** In $(-3)^4$, $-3$ is the base; in $-3^4$,
3 is the base. $(-3)^4 = 81$; $-3^4 = -81$.  **15.** base: 3; exponent: 5; 243

**17.** base: $-3$; exponent: 5; $-243$   **19.** base: $-6x$; exponent: 4
**21.** base: $x$; exponent: 4   **23.** $5^2 + 5^3$ is a sum, not a product;
$5^2 + 5^3 = 25 + 125 = 150$.   **25.** $5^8$   **27.** $4^{12}$   **29.** $(-7)^9$   **31.** $t^{24}$
**33.** $-56r^7$   **35.** $42p^{10}$   **37.** $-30x^9$   **39.** The product rule does not
apply.   **41.** The product rule does not apply.   **43.** $4^6$   **45.** $t^{20}$   **47.** $7^3 r^3$
**49.** $5^5 x^5 y^5$   **51.** $5^{12}$   **53.** $-8^{15}$   **55.** $8q^3 r^3$   **57.** $\dfrac{9^8}{5^8}$   **59.** $\dfrac{1}{2^3}$   **61.** $\dfrac{a^3}{b^3}$

**63.** $\dfrac{x^3}{2^3}$   **65.** $\dfrac{5^5}{2^5}$   **67.** $\dfrac{9^5}{8^3}$   **69.** $2^{12} x^{12}$   **71.** $-6^5 p^5$   **73.** $6^5 x^{10} y^{15}$

**75.** $x^{21}$   **77.** $4w^4 x^{26} y^7$   **79.** $-r^{18} s^{17}$   **81.** $\dfrac{5^3 a^6 b^{15}}{c^{18}}$, or $\dfrac{125 a^6 b^{15}}{c^{18}}$

**83.** Using the product rule, it is simplified as follows: $(10^2)^3 = 10^{2 \cdot 3} =$
$10^6 = 1,000,000$.   **85.** $12x^5$   **87.** $6p^7$   **89.** $125x^6$   **91.** $-a^4, -a^3,$
$-(-a)^3, (-a)^4$; One way is to choose a positive number greater than 1
and substitute it for $a$ in each expression. Then arrange the terms from
least to greatest.   **93.** \$304.16   **95.** \$1843.88   **97.** $\frac{1}{9}$   **99.** $-8$
**101.** 12   **103.** 3

## Section 5.2 (pages 308–310)

**1.** 1   **3.** 1   **5.** $-1$   **7.** $-1$   **9.** 0   **11.** 0   **13.** 0   **15.** 0   **17.** **(a)** B
**(b)** C   **(c)** D   **(d)** B   **(e)** E   **(f)** B   **19.** 2   **21.** $\frac{1}{64}$   **23.** 16

**25.** $\frac{49}{36}$   **27.** $\frac{1}{81}$   **29.** $\frac{8}{15}$   **31.** $-\frac{7}{18}$   **33.** $\frac{7}{2}$   **35.** $5^3$, or 125   **37.** $\dfrac{5^3}{3^2}$, or

$\dfrac{125}{9}$   **39.** $5^2$, or 25   **41.** $x^{15}$   **43.** $6^3$, or 216   **45.** $2r^4$   **47.** $\dfrac{5^2}{4^3}$, or $\dfrac{25}{64}$

**49.** $\dfrac{p^5}{q^8}$   **51.** $r^9$   **53.** $\dfrac{yz^2}{4x^3}$   **55.** $a + b$   **57.** $(x + 2y)^2$   **59.** 1   **60.** $\dfrac{5^2}{5^2}$

**61.** $5^0$   **62.** $1 = 5^0$; This supports the definition of 0 as an exponent.

**63.** $7^3$, or 343   **65.** $\dfrac{1}{x^2}$   **67.** $\dfrac{64x}{9}$   **69.** $\dfrac{x^2 z^4}{y^2}$   **71.** $6x$   **73.** $\dfrac{1}{m^{10} n^5}$

**75.** $\dfrac{1}{xyz}$   **77.** $x^3 y^9$   **79.** $\dfrac{a^{11}}{2b^5}$   **81.** $\dfrac{108}{y^5 z^3}$   **83.** $\dfrac{9z^2}{400x^3}$   **85.** The student

attempted to use the quotient rule with unequal bases. The correct way to

simplify is $\dfrac{16^3}{2^2} = \dfrac{(2^4)^3}{2^2} = \dfrac{2^{12}}{2^2} = 2^{10} = 1024$.   **87.** 64,280   **89.** 1530

**91.** 3.8   **93.** 0.277

## Summary Exercises on the Rules for Exponents (page 311)

**1.** $10^5 x^7 y^{14}$   **2.** $-128 a^{10} b^{15} c^4$   **3.** $\dfrac{729 w^3 x^9}{y^{12}}$   **4.** $\dfrac{x^4 y^6}{16}$   **5.** $c^{22}$   **6.** $\dfrac{1}{k^4 t^{12}}$

**7.** $\frac{11}{30}$   **8.** $y^{12} z^3$   **9.** $\dfrac{x^6}{y^5}$   **10.** 0   **11.** $\dfrac{1}{z^2}$   **12.** $\dfrac{9}{r^2 s^2 t^{10}}$   **13.** $\dfrac{300 x^3}{y^3}$

**14.** $\dfrac{3}{5x^6}$   **15.** $x^8$   **16.** $\dfrac{y^{11}}{x^{11}}$   **17.** $\dfrac{a^6}{b^4}$   **18.** $6ab$   **19.** $\frac{61}{900}$   **20.** 1

**21.** $\dfrac{343 a^6 b^9}{8}$   **22.** 1   **23.** $-1$   **24.** 0   **25.** $\dfrac{27 y^{18}}{4x^8}$   **26.** $\dfrac{1}{a^8 b^{12} c^{16}}$

**27.** $\dfrac{x^{15}}{216 z^9}$   **28.** $\dfrac{q}{8p^6 r^3}$   **29.** $x^6 y^6$   **30.** 0   **31.** $\dfrac{343}{x^{15}}$   **32.** $\dfrac{9}{x^6}$

**33.** $5p^{10} q^9$   **34.** $\frac{7}{24}$   **35.** $\dfrac{r^{14} t}{2s^2}$   **36.** 1   **37.** $8p^{10} q$   **38.** $\dfrac{1}{mn^3 p^3}$

**39.** $-1$   **40.** **(a)** D   **(b)** D   **(c)** E   **(d)** B   **(e)** J   **(f)** F   **(g)** I
**(h)** B   **(i)** E   **(j)** F

**Connections**   **(page 316)**   **1.** The Indonesia earthquake was 10 times
as powerful as the Peru earthquake.   **2.** The Afghanistan earthquake had
one-hundredth the power of the China earthquake.   **3.** The Alaska
earthquake was about 19.95 times as powerful as the China earthquake.
**4.** "+3.0" corresponds to a factor of 1000 times stronger; "−1.0"
corresponds to a factor of one-tenth as strong.

## Section 5.3 (pages 316–319)

**1.** **(a)** C   **(b)** A   **(c)** B   **(d)** D   **3.** in scientific notation
**5.** not in scientific notation; $5.6 \times 10^6$   **7.** not in scientific notation;
$8 \times 10^1$   **9.** not in scientific notation; $4 \times 10^{-3}$   **11.** It is written as
the product of a power of 10 and a number whose absolute value is
between 1 and 10 (inclusive of 1). Some examples are $2.3 \times 10^{-4}$ and
$6.02 \times 10^{23}$.   **13.** $5.876 \times 10^9$   **15.** $8.235 \times 10^4$   **17.** $7 \times 10^{-6}$
**19.** $2.03 \times 10^{-3}$   **21.** $-1.3 \times 10^7$   **23.** $-6 \times 10^{-3}$   **25.** 750,000
**27.** 5,677,000,000,000   **29.** 1,000,000,000,000   **31.** 6.21
**33.** 0.00078   **35.** 0.000000005134   **37.** $-0.004$   **39.** $-810,000$
**41.** **(a)** $6 \times 10^{11}$   **(b)** 600,000,000,000   **43.** **(a)** $1.5 \times 10^7$
**(b)** 15,000,000   **45.** **(a)** $-6 \times 10^4$   **(b)** $-60,000$
**47.** **(a)** $2.4 \times 10^2$   **(b)** 240   **49.** **(a)** $6.3 \times 10^{-2}$   **(b)** 0.063
**51.** **(a)** $3 \times 10^{-4}$   **(b)** 0.0003   **53.** **(a)** $-4 \times 10$   **(b)** $-40$
**55.** **(a)** $1.3 \times 10^{-5}$   **(b)** 0.000013   **57.** **(a)** $5 \times 10^2$   **(b)** 500
**59.** **(a)** $-3 \times 10^6$   **(b)** $-3,000,000$   **61.** **(a)** $2 \times 10^{-7}$
**(b)** 0.0000002   **63.** 4.7E-7   **65.** 2E7   **67.** 1E1   **69.** $1.04 \times 10^8$
**71.** $9.2 \times 10^{-3}$   **73.** $6 \times 10^9$   **75.** $1 \times 10^{10}$   **77.** 2,000,000,000
**79.** $3.305 \times 10^9$   **81.** \$2.81 $\times 10^{10}$   **83.** about $2.76 \times 10^{-1}$, or
0.276, lb   **85.** $3.59 \times 10^2$, or 359, sec   **87.** \$76.26   **89.** \$40,000
**91.** $1.5 \times 10^{17}$ mi   **93.** about \$1,220,000,000,000   **95.** \$3252
**97.** $2x - 36$   **99.** 19   **101.** 64

## Section 5.4 (pages 325–329)

**1.** 4; 6   **3.** 9   **5.** 19   **7.** 0   **9.** 1; 6   **11.** 1; 1   **13.** 2; $-19, -1$
**15.** 3; 1, 8, 5   **17.** $2m^5$   **19.** $-r^5$   **21.** It cannot be simplified.
**23.** $-5x^5$   **25.** $5p^9 + 4p^7$   **27.** $-2xy^2$   **29.** already simplified; 4;
binomial   **31.** $11m^4 - 7m^3 - 3m^2$; 4; trinomial   **33.** $x^4$; 4; monomial
**35.** 7; 0; monomial   **37.** **(a)** $-3$   **(b)** 0   **39.** **(a)** 14   **(b)** $-19$
**41.** **(a)** 36   **(b)** $-12$   **43.** $5x^2 - 2x$   **45.** $5m^2 + 3m + 2$
**47.** $\frac{7}{6}x^2 - \frac{2}{15}x + \frac{5}{6}$   **49.** $6m^3 + m^2 + 4m - 14$   **51.** $3y^3 - 11y^2$
**53.** $4x^4 - 4x^2 + 4x$   **55.** $15m^3 - 13m^2 + 8m + 11$
**57.** Answers will vary.   **59.** $5m^2 - 14m + 6$   **61.** $4x^3 + 2x^2 + 5x$
**63.** $-11y^4 + 8y^2 + y$   **65.** $a^4 - a^2 + 1$   **67.** $5m^2 + 8m - 10$
**69.** $-6x^2 - 12x + 12$   **71.** $-10$   **73.** $4b - 5c$   **75.** $6x - xy - 7$
**77.** $-3x^2 y - 15xy - 3xy^2$   **79.** $8x^2 + 8x + 6$   **81.** $2x^2 + 8x$
**83.** $8t^2 + 8t + 13$   **85.** **(a)** $23y + 5t$   **(b)** $25°, 67°, 88°$   **87.** $-7x - 1$
**89.** $0, -3, -4, -3, 0$   **91.** 7, 1, $-1$, 1, 7   **93.** 0, 3, 4, 3, 0

$y = x^2 - 4$

$y = 2x^2 - 1$

$y = -x^2 + 4$

**95.** 4, 1, 0, 1, 4

$y = (x + 3)^2$

**97.** 63; If a dog is 9 in dog years, then it is 63 in human years.   **98.** about 26   **99.** 2.5; 130   **100.** 6; \$27   **101.** $5x + 20$   **103.** $8a + 24b$   **105.** $-10a^2b$   **107.** $-m^7$

## Section 5.5 (pages 333–334)

**1.** (a) B   (b) D   (c) A   (d) C   **3.** $15y^{11}$   **5.** $30a^9$   **7.** $15pq^2$   **9.** $-18m^3n^2$   **11.** $9y^{10}$   **13.** $-8x^{10}$   **15.** $6m^2 + 4m$   **17.** $-6p^4 + 12p^3$   **19.** $-16z^2 - 24z^3 - 24z^4$   **21.** $6y^3 + 4y^4 + 10y^7$   **23.** $28r^5 - 32r^4 + 36r^3$   **25.** $6a^4 - 12a^3b + 15a^2b^2$   **27.** $21m^5n^2 + 14m^4n^3 - 7m^3n^5$   **29.** $12x^3 + 26x^2 + 10x + 1$   **31.** $72y^3 - 70y^2 + 21y - 2$   **33.** $20m^4 - m^3 - 8m^2 - 17m - 15$   **35.** $6x^6 - 3x^5 - 4x^4 + 4x^3 - 5x^2 + 8x - 3$   **37.** $5x^4 - 13x^3 + 20x^2 + 7x + 5$   **39.** $3x^5 + 18x^4 - 2x^3 - 8x^2 + 24x$   **41.** $m^2 + 12m + 35$   **43.** $n^2 + 3n - 4$   **45.** $x^2 - 25$   **47.** $12x^2 + 10x - 12$   **49.** $81 - t^2$   **51.** $9x^2 - 12x + 4$   **53.** $10a^2 + 37a + 7$   **55.** $12 + 8m - 15m^2$   **57.** $20 - 7x - 3x^2$   **59.** $3t^2 + 5st - 12s^2$   **61.** $8xy - 4x + 6y - 3$   **63.** $15x^2 + xy - 6y^2$   **65.** $6y^5 - 21y^4 - 45y^3$   **67.** $-200r^7 + 32r^3$   **69.** (a) $3y^2 + 10y + 7$   (b) $8y + 16$   **71.** $6p^2 - \frac{5}{2}pq - \frac{25}{12}q^2$   **73.** $x^2 + 14x + 49$   **75.** $a^2 - 16$   **77.** $4p^2 - 20p + 25$   **79.** $25k^2 + 30kq + 9q^2$   **81.** $m^3 - 15m^2 + 75m - 125$   **83.** $8a^3 + 12a^2 + 6a + 1$   **85.** $-9a^3 + 33a^2 + 12a$   **87.** $56m^2 - 14m - 21$   **89.** $81r^4 - 216r^3s + 216r^2s^2 - 96rs^3 + 16s^4$   **91.** $6p^8 + 15p^7 + 12p^6 + 36p^5 + 15p^4$   **93.** $-24x^8 - 28x^7 + 32x^6 + 20x^5$   **95.** $14x + 49$   **97.** $\pi x^2 - 9$   **99.** $9m^2$   **101.** $4r^2$   **103.** $16x^4$

## Section 5.6 (pages 338–340)

**1.** (a) $16x^2$   (b) $24x$   (c) 9   (d) $16x^2 + 24x + 9$   **3.** $m^2 + 4m + 4$   **5.** $r^2 - 6r + 9$   **7.** $x^2 + 4xy + 4y^2$   **9.** $25p^2 + 20pq + 4q^2$   **11.** $16a^2 + 40ab + 25b^2$   **13.** $36m^2 - \frac{48}{5}mn + \frac{16}{25}n^2$   **15.** $9t^3 - 6t^2 + t$   **17.** $48t^3 + 24t^2 + 3t$   **19.** $-16r^2 + 16r - 4$   **21.** (a) $49x^2$   (b) 0   (c) $-9y^2$   (d) $49x^2 - 9y^2$; Because 0 is the identity element for addition, it is not necessary to write " $+ 0$."   **23.** $k^2 - 25$   **25.** $16 - 9t^2$   **27.** $25x^2 - 4$   **29.** $25y^2 - 9x^2$   **31.** $100x^2 - 9y^2$   **33.** $4x^4 - 25$   **35.** $\frac{9}{16} - x^2$   **37.** $81y^2 - \frac{4}{9}$   **39.** $25q^3 - q$   **41.** No. In general, $(a + b)^2$ equals $a^2 + 2ab + b^2$, which is not equivalent to $a^2 + b^2$.   **43.** $x^3 + 3x^2 + 3x + 1$   **45.** $t^3 - 9t^2 + 27t - 27$   **47.** $r^3 + 15r^2 + 75r + 125$   **49.** $8a^3 + 12a^2 + 6a + 1$   **51.** $256x^4 - 256x^3 + 96x^2 - 16x + 1$   **53.** $81r^4 - 216r^3t + 216r^2t^2 - 96rt^3 + 16t^4$   **55.** $2x^4 + 6x^3 + 6x^2 + 2x$   **57.** $-4t^4 - 36t^3 - 108t^2 - 108t$   **59.** $x^4 - 2x^2y^2 + y^4$   **61.** $(a + b)^2$   **62.** $a^2$   **63.** $2ab$   **64.** $b^2$   **65.** $a^2 + 2ab + b^2$   **66.** They both represent the area of the entire large square.   **67.** 1225   **68.** $30^2 + 2(30)(5) + 5^2$   **69.** 1225   **70.** They are equal.   **71.** 9999   **73.** 39,999   **75.** $399\frac{3}{4}$   **77.** $\frac{1}{2}m^2 - 2n^2$   **79.** $9a^2 - 4$   **81.** $\pi x^2 + 4\pi x + 4\pi$   **83.** $x^3 + 6x^2 + 12x + 8$   **85.** $2p + 1 + \frac{4}{p}$

**87.** $\frac{m^2}{3} + 3m - 2$   **89.** $-24k^3 + 36k^2 - 6k$   **91.** $-16k^3 - 10k^2 + 3k + 3$   **93.** $5t + 3$

## Section 5.7 (pages 346–348)

**1.** $10x^2 + 8$; 2; $5x^2 + 4$   **3.** $5x^2 + 4$; 2 (These may be reversed.); $10x^2 + 8$   **5.** The first is a polynomial divided by a monomial, covered in Objective 1. This section does not cover dividing a monomial by a polynomial of several terms.   **7.** $30x^3 - 10x + 5$   **9.** $4m^3 - 2m^2 + 1$   **11.** $4t^4 - 2t^2 + 2t$   **13.** $a^4 - a + \frac{2}{a}$   **15.** $-3p^2 - 2 + \frac{1}{p}$   **17.** $7r^2 - 6 + \frac{1}{r}$   **19.** $4x^3 - 3x^2 + 2x$   **21.** $-9x^2 + 5x + 1$   **23.** $2x + 8 + \frac{12}{x}$   **25.** $\frac{4x^2}{3} + x + \frac{2}{3x}$   **27.** $-27x^3 + 10x^2 + 4$   **29.** $9r^3 - 12r^2 + 2r + \frac{26}{3} - \frac{2}{3r}$   **31.** $-m^2 + 3m - \frac{4}{m}$   **33.** $-3a + 4 + \frac{5}{a}$   **35.** $\frac{12}{x} - \frac{6}{x^2} + \frac{14}{x^3} - \frac{10}{x^4}$   **37.** $6x^4y^2 - 4xy + 2xy^2 - x^4y$   **39.** 1423   **40.** $(1 \times 10^3) + (4 \times 10^2) + (2 \times 10^1) + (3 \times 10^0)$   **41.** $x^3 + 4x^2 + 2x + 3$   **42.** They are similar in that the coefficients of powers of 10 are equal to the coefficients of the powers of $x$. They are different in that one is a constant while the other is a polynomial. They are equal if $x = 10$ (the base of our decimal system).   **43.** $x + 2$   **45.** $2y - 5$   **47.** $p - 4 + \frac{44}{p + 6}$   **49.** $6m - 1$   **51.** $2a - 14 + \frac{74}{2a + 3}$   **53.** $4x^2 - 7x + 3$   **55.** $4k^3 - k + 2$   **57.** $5y^3 + 2y - 3 + \frac{-5}{y + 1}$   **59.** $3k^2 + 2k - 2 + \frac{6}{k - 2}$   **61.** $2p^3 - 6p^2 + 7p - 4 + \frac{14}{3p + 1}$   **63.** $x^2 + 3x + 3$   **65.** $2x^2 - 2x + 3 + \frac{-1}{x + 1}$   **67.** $r^2 - 1 + \frac{4}{r^2 - 1}$   **69.** $3x^2 + 3x - 1 + \frac{1}{x - 1}$   **71.** $y^2 - y + 1$   **73.** $a^2 + 1$   **75.** $x^2 - 4x + 2 + \frac{9x - 4}{x^2 + 3}$   **77.** $x^3 + 3x^2 - x + 5$   **79.** $\frac{3}{2}a - 10 + \frac{77}{2a + 6}$   **81.** $x^2 + \frac{8}{3}x - \frac{1}{3} + \frac{4}{3x - 3}$   **83.** $x^2 + x - 3$   **85.** $48m^2 + 96m + 24$   **87.** $5x^2 - 11x + 14$   **89.** 1, 2, 3, 6, 9, 18   **91.** 1, 2, 3, 4, 6, 8, 12, 16, 24, 48

## Chapter 5 Review Exercises (pages 352–355)

**1.** $4^{11}$   **2.** $(-5)^{11}$   **3.** $-72x^7$   **4.** $10x^{14}$   **5.** $19^5x^5$   **6.** $(-4)^7y^7$   **7.** $5p^4t^4$   **8.** $\frac{7^6}{5^6}$   **9.** $3^3x^6y^9$   **10.** $t^{42}$   **11.** $6^2x^{16}y^4z^{16}$   **12.** $\frac{2^3m^9n^3}{p^6}$   **13.** The expression is a *sum* of powers of 7, not a *product*.   **14.** 2   **15.** $-1$   **16.** $-1$   **17.** $-\frac{1}{49}$   **18.** $\frac{64}{25}$   **19.** $5^8$   **20.** $\frac{1}{81}$   **21.** $\frac{3}{4}$   **22.** $\frac{1}{36}$   **23.** $x^2$   **24.** $y^7$   **25.** $\frac{r^8}{81}$   **26.** $\frac{3^5}{p^3}$   **27.** $\frac{1}{a^3b^5}$   **28.** $72r^5$   **29.** $4.8 \times 10^7$   **30.** $2.8988 \times 10^{10}$   **31.** $8.24 \times 10^{-8}$   **32.** 24,000   **33.** 78,300,000   **34.** 0.000000897   **35.** 800   **36.** 4,000,000   **37.** 0.025   **38.** 0.000002   **39.** 0.0000000000016   **40.** $4.2 \times 10^{42}$   **41.** $9.7 \times 10^4$; $5 \times 10^3$

**42.** $1 \times 10^{100}$ **43.** $1 \times 10^3; 2 \times 10^3; 5 \times 10^4; 1 \times 10^5$ **44.** $22m^2$; degree 2; monomial **45.** $p^3 - p^2 + 4p + 2$; degree 3; none of these **46.** already in descending powers; degree 5; none of these **47.** $-8y^5 - 7y^4 + 9y$; degree 5; trinomial **48.** $7r^4 - 4r^3 + 1$; degree 4; trinomial **49.** $13x^3y^2 - 5xy^5 + 21x^2$ **50.** $a^3 + 4a^2$ **51.** $y^2 - 10y + 9$ **52.** $-13k^4 - 15k^2 + 18k$

**53.** 1, 4, 5, 4, 1  **54.** 10, 1, −2, 1, 10

**55.** $a^3 - 2a^2 - 7a + 2$ **56.** $6r^3 + 8r^2 - 17r + 6$ **57.** $5p^5 - 2p^4 - 3p^3 + 25p^2 + 15p$ **58.** $m^2 - 7m - 18$ **59.** $6k^2 - 9k - 6$ **60.** $2a^2 + 5ab - 3b^2$ **61.** $12k^2 - 32kq - 35q^2$ **62.** $s^3 - 3s^2 + 3s - 1$ **63.** $a^2 + 8a + 16$ **64.** $4r^2 + 20rt + 25t^2$ **65.** $36m^2 - 25$ **66.** $25a^2 - 36b^2$ **67.** $r^3 + 6r^2 + 12r + 8$ **68.** $25t^3 - 30t^2 + 9t$ **69. (a)** Answers will vary. For example, let $x = 1$ and $y = 2$. $(1 + 2)^2 \neq 1^2 + 2^2$, because $9 \neq 5$. **(b)** Answers will vary. For example, let $x = 1$ and $y = 2$. $(1 + 2)^3 \neq 1^3 + 2^3$, because $27 \neq 9$. **70.** To find the third power of a binomial, such as $(a + b)^3$, first square the binomial and then multiply that result by the binomial. $(a + b)^3 = (a + b)^2(a + b) = (a^2 + 2ab + b^2)(a + b) = a^3 + 3a^2b + 3ab^2 + b^3$ **71.** In both cases, $x = 0$ and $y = 1$ lead to 1 on each side of the inequality. This would not be sufficient to show that, *in general,* the inequality is true. It would be necessary to choose other values of $x$ and $y$. **72.** $x^6 + 6x^4 + 12x^2 + 8$ **73.** $\frac{4}{3}\pi(x + 1)^3$, or $\frac{4}{3}\pi x^3 + 4\pi x^2 + 4\pi x + \frac{4}{3}\pi$ **74.** $\frac{-5y^2}{3}$ **75.** $y^3 - 2y + 3$ **76.** $-2m^2n + mn + \frac{6n^3}{5}$ **77.** $2mn + 3m^4n^2 - 4n$ **78.** The friend wrote the second term of the quotient as $-12x$ rather than $-2x$. Here is the correct method. $\frac{6x^2 - 12x}{6} = \frac{6x^2}{6} - \frac{12x}{6} = x^2 - 2x$ **79.** $2r + 7$ **80.** $2a^2 + 3a - 1 + \frac{6}{5a - 3}$ **81.** $x^2 + 3x - 4$ **82.** $m^2 + 4m - 2$ **83.** $4x - 5$ **84.** $5y - 10$ **85.** $y^2 + 2y + 4$ **86.** $100x^4 - 10x^2 + 1$ **87.** $2y^2 - 5y + 4 + \frac{-5}{3y^2 + 1}$ **88.** $x^3 - 2x^2 + 4 + \frac{-3}{4x^2 - 3}$ **89.** 2 **90.** $\frac{63r^6p^3}{5^3}$ **91.** $144a^2 - 1$ **92.** $\frac{1}{16}$ **93.** $\frac{1}{8^{12}}$ **94.** $p - 3 + \frac{5}{2p}$ **95.** $\frac{2}{3m^3}$ **96.** $6k^3 - 21k - 6$ **97.** $r^{13}$ **98.** $4r^2 + 20rs + 25s^2$ **99.** $-y^2 - 4y + 4$ **100.** $10r^2 + 21r - 10$ **101.** $y^2 + 5y + 1$ **102.** $\frac{5}{2} - \frac{4}{5xy} + \frac{3x}{2y^2}$ **103.** $10p^2 - 3p - 5$ **104.** $3x^2 + 9x + 25 + \frac{80}{x - 3}$ **105.** $49 - 28k + 4k^2$ **106.** $\frac{1}{x^4y^{12}}$ **107. (a)** $6x - 2$ **(b)** $2x^2 + x - 6$ **108. (a)** $20x^4 + 8x^2$ **(b)** $25x^8 + 20x^6 + 4x^4$

## Chapter 5 Test (pages 355–356)

[5.1, 5.2] **1.** $\frac{1}{625}$ **2.** 2 **3.** $\frac{7}{12}$ **4.** $9x^3y^5$ **5.** $8^5$ **6.** $x^2y^6$ **7. (a)** positive **(b)** positive **(c)** negative **(d)** positive **(e)** zero **(f)** negative [5.3] **8. (a)** $4.5 \times 10^{10}$ **(b)** 0.0000036 **(c)** 0.00019 **9. (a)** $1 \times 10^3; 5.89 \times 10^{12}$ **(b)** $5.89 \times 10^{15}$ mi

[5.4] **10.** $-7x^2 + 8x$; 2; binomial **11.** $4n^4 + 13n^3 - 10n^2$; 4; trinomial **12.** 4, −2, −4, −2, 4 **13.** $-2y^2 - 9y + 17$ 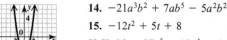 **14.** $-21a^3b^2 + 7ab^5 - 5a^2b^2$ **15.** $-12t^2 + 5t + 8$ [5.5] **16.** $-27x^5 + 18x^4 - 6x^3 + 3x^2$ **17.** $t^2 - 5t - 24$ **18.** $8x^2 + 2xy - 3y^2$ [5.6] **19.** $25x^2 - 20xy + 4y^2$ **20.** $100v^2 - 9w^2$ [5.5] **21.** $2r^3 + r^2 - 16r + 15$ [5.6] **22.** $12x + 36; 9x^2 + 54x + 81$ [5.7] **23.** $4y^2 - 3y + 2 + \frac{5}{y}$ **24.** $-3xy^2 + 2x^3y^2 + 4y^2$ **25.** $x - 2$ **26.** $3x^2 + 6x + 11 + \frac{26}{x - 2}$

## Chapters 1–5 Cumulative Review Exercises (pages 357–358)

[1.1] **1.** $\frac{7}{4}$ **2.** 5 **3.** $31\frac{1}{4}$ yd$^3$ [1.6] **4.** \$1836 **5.** 1, 3, 5, 9, 15, 45 **6.** −8 **7.** $\frac{1}{2}$ [1.5] **8.** −4 [1.7] **9.** associative property **10.** distributive property [1.8] **11.** $-10x^2 + 21x - 29$ [2.1–2.3] **12.** $\left\{\frac{13}{4}\right\}$ **13.** ∅ [2.5] **14.** $r = \frac{d}{t}$ [2.6] **15.** $\{-5\}$ [2.1–2.3] **16.** $\{-12\}$ **17.** $\{20\}$ **18.** {all real numbers} [2.4] **19.** exertion: 9443 calories; regulating body temperature: 1757 calories [2.8] **20.** 11 ft and 22 ft **21.** $\left(-\infty, -\frac{14}{5}\right)$ **22.** $[-4, 2)$ [3.2] **23.** 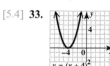 [3.3, 3.4] **24. (a)** 1 **(b)** $y = x + 6$ [3.5] **25.** no [3.6] **26.** −1 [4.2] **27.** $\{(-3, -1)\}$ [4.3] **28.** $\{(4, -5)\}$ [5.1, 5.2] **29.** $\frac{5}{4}$ **30.** 1 **31.** $\frac{2b}{a^{10}}$ [5.3] **32.** about 10,800,000 km [5.4] **33.** **34.** $11x^3 - 14x^2 - x + 14$ [5.5] **35.** $63x^2 + 57x + 12$ [5.7] **36.** $y^2 - 2y + 6$

## 6   FACTORING AND APPLICATIONS

## Section 6.1 (pages 365–367)

**1.** 4 **3.** 6 **5.** 1 **7.** 8 **9.** $10x^3$ **11.** $xy^2$ **13.** $6m^3n^2$ **15.** factored **17.** not factored **19.** $3m^2$ **21.** $2z^4$ **23.** $2mn^4$ **25.** $y + 2$ **27.** $a - 2$ **29.** $2 + 3xy$ **31.** First, verify that you have factored completely. Then multiply the factors. The product should be the original polynomial. **33.** $x(x - 4)$ **35.** $3t(2t + 5)$ **37.** $9m(3m^2 - 1)$ **39.** $8z^2(2z^2 + 3)$ **41.** $6x^2(2x + 1)$ **43.** $5y^6(13y^4 + 7)$ **45.** in factored form **47.** $8mn^3(1 + 3m)$ **49.** $13y^2(y^6 + 2y^2 - 3)$ **51.** $9p^3q(4p^3 + 5p^2q^3 + 9q)$ **53.** $a^3(a^2 + 2b^2 - 3a^2b^2 + 4ab^3)$ **55.** $(x + 2)(c - d)$ **57.** $(m + 2n)(m + n)$ **59.** $(p - 4)(q^2 + 1)$ **61.** not in factored form; $(7t + 4)(8 + x)$ **63.** in factored form **65.** not in factored form **67.** The quantities in parentheses are not the same, so there is no common factor of the two terms $18x^2(y + 4)$ and $7(y - 4)$. **69.** $(p + 4)(p + q)$ **71.** $(a - 2)(a + b)$

**73.** $(z + 2)(7z - a)$   **75.** $(3r + 2y)(6r - x)$

**77.** $(a^2 + b^2)(3a + 2b)$   **79.** $(3 - a)(4 - b)$

**81.** $(4m - p^2)(4m^2 - p)$   **83.** $(y + 3)(y + x)$

**85.** $(5 - 2p)(m + 3)$   **87.** $(3r + 2y)(6r - t)$

**89.** $(1 + 2b)(a^5 - 3)$   **91.** commutative property

**92.** $2x(y - 4) - 3(y - 4)$   **93.** No, because it is not a product.

It is the difference between $2x(y - 4)$ and $3(y - 4)$.

**94.** $(2x - 3)(y - 4)$; yes   **95.** $x^2 - 3x - 54$   **97.** $x^2 + 9x + 14$

**99.** $2x^4 + 6x^3 + 10x^2$

## Section 6.2 (pages 371–373)

**1.** 1 and 48, −1 and −48, 2 and 24, −2 and −24, 3 and 16, −3 and −16, 4 and 12, −4 and −12, 6 and 8, −6 and −8; The pair with a sum of −19 is −3 and −16.   **3.** 1 and −24, −1 and 24, 2 and −12, −2 and 12, 3 and −8, −3 and 8, 4 and −6, −4 and 6; The pair with a sum of −5 is 3 and −8.   **5.** $a$ and $b$ must have different signs, one positive and one negative.   **7.** A prime polynomial is a polynomial that cannot be factored by using only integers in the factors.   **9.** C   **11.** $a^2 + 13a + 36$

**13.** $p + 6$   **15.** $x + 11$   **17.** $x - 8$   **19.** $y - 5$   **21.** $x + 11$

**23.** $y - 9$   **25.** $(y + 8)(y + 1)$   **27.** $(b + 3)(b + 5)$

**29.** $(m + 5)(m - 4)$   **31.** $(y - 5)(y - 3)$   **33.** prime

**35.** $(z - 7)(z - 8)$   **37.** $(r - 6)(r + 5)$   **39.** $(a + 4)(a - 12)$

**41.** prime   **43.** $(x + 16)(x - 2)$   **45.** $(r + 2a)(r + a)$

**47.** $(t + 2z)(t - 3z)$   **49.** $(x + y)(x + 3y)$   **51.** $(v - 5w)(v - 6w)$

**53.** $4(x + 5)(x - 2)$   **55.** $2t(t + 1)(t + 3)$   **57.** $2x^4(x - 3)(x + 7)$

**59.** $5m^2(m^3 + 5m^2 - 8)$   **61.** $mn(m - 6n)(m - 4n)$

**63.** $a^3(a + 4b)(a - b)$   **65.** $yz(y + 3z)(y - 2z)$

**67.** $z^8(z - 7y)(z + 3y)$   **69.** $(a + b)(x + 4)(x - 3)$

**71.** $(2p + q)(r - 9)(r - 3)$   **73.** $2y^2 + y - 28$   **75.** $15z^2 - 4z - 4$

## Section 6.3 (pages 378–380)

**1.** $(2t + 1)(5t + 2)$   **3.** $(3z - 2)(5z - 3)$   **5.** $(2s - t)(4s + 3t)$

**7. (a)** 2, 12, 24, 11   **(b)** 3, 8 (Order is irrelevant.)   **(c)** $3m, 8m$

**(d)** $2m^2 + 3m + 8m + 12$   **(e)** $(2m + 3)(m + 4)$

**(f)** $(2m + 3)(m + 4) = 2m^2 + 11m + 12$   **9.** B   **11.** B   **13.** A

**15.** $2a + 5b$   **17.** $x^2 + 3x - 4; x + 4, x - 1,$ or $x - 1, x + 4$

**19.** $2z^2 - 5z - 3; 2z + 1, z - 3,$ or $z - 3, 2z + 1$

**21.** The binomial $2x - 6$ cannot be a factor because its terms have a common factor of 2, which the polynomial terms do not have.

**23.** $(3a + 7)(a + 1)$   **25.** $(2y + 3)(y + 2)$

**27.** $(3m - 1)(5m + 2)$   **29.** $(3s - 1)(4s + 5)$

**31.** $(5m - 4)(2m - 3)$   **33.** $(4w - 1)(2w - 3)$

**35.** $(4y + 1)(5y - 11)$   **37.** prime   **39.** $2(5x + 3)(2x + 1)$

**41.** $3(4x - 1)(2x - 3)$   **43.** $q(5m + 2)(8m - 3)$

**45.** $3n^2(5n - 3)(n - 2)$   **47.** $y^2(5x - 4)(3x + 1)$

**49.** $(5a + 3b)(a - 2b)$   **51.** $(4s + 5t)(3s - t)$

**53.** $m^4n(3m + 2n)(2m + n)$   **55.** $(x - 5)(x - 1)$

**57.** $(3x + 4)(x + 4)$   **59.** $-5x(2x + 7)(x - 4)$

**61.** $(12x + 1)(x - 4)$   **63.** $(24y + 7x)(y - 2x)$

**65.** $(18x^2 - 5y)(2x^2 - 3y)$   **67.** $2(24a + b)(a - 2b)$

**69.** $x^2y^5(10x - 1)(x + 4)$   **71.** $4ab^2(9a + 1)(a - 3)$

**73.** $(12x - 5)(2x - 3)$   **75.** $(8x^2 - 3)(3x^2 + 8)$

**77.** $(4x + 3y)(6x + 5y)$   **79.** $-1(x + 7)(x - 3)$

**81.** $-1(3x + 4)(x - 1)$   **83.** $-1(a + 2b)(2a + b)$

**85.** $(m + 1)^3(5q - 2)(5q + 1)$   **87.** $(r + 3)^3(3x + 2y)^2$   **89.** $-4, 4$

**91.** $-11, -7, 7, 11$   **93.** $49p^2 - 9$   **95.** $x^2 + 12x + 36$

## Section 6.4 (pages 387–389)

**1.** 1; 4; 9; 16; 25; 36; 49; 64; 81; 100; 121; 144; 169; 196; 225; 256; 289; 324; 361; 400   **3.** 1; 8; 27; 64; 125; 216; 343; 512; 729; 1000

**5. (a)** both of these   **(b)** perfect cube   **(c)** perfect square

**(d)** perfect square   **7.** $(y + 5)(y - 5)$   **9.** $(x + 12)(x - 12)$

**11.** prime   **13.** $4(m^2 + 4)$   **15.** $(3r + 2)(3r - 2)$

**17.** $4(3x + 2)(3x - 2)$   **19.** $(14p + 15)(14p - 15)$

**21.** $(4r + 5a)(4r - 5a)$   **23.** prime   **25.** $(p^2 + 7)(p^2 - 7)$

**27.** $(x^2 + 1)(x + 1)(x - 1)$   **29.** $(p^2 + 16)(p + 4)(p - 4)$

**31.** $k^2 - 9$ can be factored as $(k + 3)(k - 3)$. The completely factored form is $(k^2 + 9)(k + 3)(k - 3)$.   **33.** 10   **35.** 9   **37.** $(w + 1)^2$

**39.** $(x - 4)^2$   **41.** $2(x + 6)^2$   **43.** $(4x - 5)^2$   **45.** $(7x - 2y)^2$

**47.** $(8x + 3y)^2$   **49.** $2(5h - 2y)^2$   **51.** $k(4k^2 - 4k + 9)$

**53.** $z^2(25z^2 + 5z + 1)$   **55.** $(a - 1)(a^2 + a + 1)$

**57.** $(m + 2)(m^2 - 2m + 4)$   **59.** $(k + 10)(k^2 - 10k + 100)$

**61.** $(3x - 4)(9x^2 + 12x + 16)$   **63.** $6(p + 1)(p^2 - p + 1)$

**65.** $5(x + 2)(x^2 - 2x + 4)$   **67.** $(y - 2x)(y^2 + 2yx + 4x^2)$

**69.** $2(x - 2y)(x^2 + 2xy + 4y^2)$

**71.** $(2p + 9q)(4p^2 - 18pq + 81q^2)$

**73.** $(3a + 4b)(9a^2 - 12ab + 16b^2)$

**75.** $(5t + 2s)(25t^2 - 10ts + 4s^2)$

**77.** $(2x - 5y^2)(4x^2 + 10xy^2 + 25y^4)$

**79.** $(3m^2 + 2n)(9m^4 - 6m^2n + 4n^2)$

**81.** $(x + y)(x^2 - xy + y^2)(x^6 - x^3y^3 + y^6)$   **83.** $\left(p + \frac{1}{3}\right)\left(p - \frac{1}{3}\right)$

**85.** $\left(6m + \frac{4}{5}\right)\left(6m - \frac{4}{5}\right)$   **87.** $(x + 0.8)(x - 0.8)$   **89.** $\left(t + \frac{1}{2}\right)^2$

**91.** $(x - 0.5)^2$   **93.** $\left(x + \frac{1}{2}\right)\left(x^2 - \frac{1}{2}x + \frac{1}{4}\right)$   **95.** $4mn$

**97.** $(m - p + 2)(m + p)$   **99.** $\{4\}$   **101.** $\{-5\}$

## Summary Exercises on Factoring (pages 390–391)

**1.** G   **2.** H   **3.** A   **4.** B   **5.** E   **6.** I   **7.** C   **8.** F   **9.** I   **10.** E

**11.** $(a - 6)(a + 2)$   **12.** $(a + 8)(a + 9)$   **13.** $6(y - 2)(y + 1)$

**14.** $7y^4(y + 6)(y - 4)$   **15.** $6(a + 2b + 3c)$

**16.** $(m - 4n)(m + n)$   **17.** $(p - 11)(p - 6)$   **18.** $(z + 7)(z - 6)$

**19.** $(5z - 6)(2z + 1)$   **20.** $2(m - 8)(m + 3)$   **21.** $17xy(x^2y + 3)$

**22.** $5(3y + 1)$   **23.** $8a^3(a - 3)(a + 2)$   **24.** $(4k + 1)(2k - 3)$

**25.** $(z - 5a)(z + 2a)$   **26.** $50(z^2 - 2)$   **27.** $(x - 5)(x - 4)$

**28.** $10nr(10nr + 3r^2 - 5n)$   **29.** $(3n - 2)(2n - 5)$

**30.** $(3y - 1)(3y + 5)$   **31.** $4(4x + 5)$   **32.** $(m + 5)(m - 3)$

**33.** $(3y - 4)(2y + 1)$   **34.** $(m + 9)(m - 9)$   **35.** $(6z + 1)(z + 5)$

**36.** $(12x - 1)(x + 4)$   **37.** $(2k - 3)^2$   **38.** $(8p - 1)(p + 3)$

**39.** $6(3m + 2z)(3m - 2z)$   **40.** $(4m - 3)(2m + 1)$

**41.** $(3k - 2)(k + 2)$   **42.** $15a^3b^2(3b^3 - 4a + 5a^3b^2)$

**43.** $7k(2k + 5)(k - 2)$   **44.** $(5 + r)(1 - s)$

**45.** $(y^2 + 4)(y + 2)(y - 2)$  **46.** $10y^4(2y - 3)$  **47.** $8m(1 - 2m)$
**48.** $(k + 4)(k - 4)$  **49.** $(z - 2)(z^2 + 2z + 4)$
**50.** $(y - 8)(y + 7)$  **51.** prime  **52.** $9p^8(3p + 7)(p - 4)$
**53.** $8m^3(4m^6 + 2m^2 + 3)$  **54.** $(2m + 5)(4m^2 - 10m + 25)$
**55.** $(4r + 3m)^2$  **56.** $(z - 6)^2$  **57.** $(5h + 7g)(3h - 2g)$
**58.** $5z(z - 7)(z - 2)$  **59.** $(k - 5)(k - 6)$
**60.** $4(4p - 5m)(4p + 5m)$  **61.** $3k(k - 5)(k + 1)$
**62.** $(y - 6k)(y + 2k)$  **63.** $(10p + 3)(100p^2 - 30p + 9)$
**64.** $(4r - 7)(16r^2 + 28r + 49)$  **65.** $(2 + m)(3 + p)$
**66.** $(2m - 3n)(m + 5n)$  **67.** $(4z - 1)^2$
**68.** $5m^2(5m - 3n)(5m - 13n)$  **69.** $3(6m - 1)^2$
**70.** $(10a + 9y)(10a - 9y)$  **71.** prime  **72.** $(2y + 5)(2y - 5)$
**73.** $8z(4z - 1)(z + 2)$  **74.** $5(2m - 3)(m + 4)$
**75.** $(4 + m)(5 + 3n)$  **76.** $(2 - q)(2 - 3p)$
**77.** $2(3a - 1)(a + 2)$  **78.** $6y^4(3y + 4)(2y - 5)$
**79.** $(a - b)(a^2 + ab + b^2 + 2)$  **80.** $4(2k - 3)^2$
**81.** $(8m - 5n)^2$  **82.** $12y^2(6yz^2 + 1 - 2y^2z^2)$
**83.** $(4k - 3h)(2k + h)$  **84.** $(2a + 5)(a - 6)$
**85.** $2(x + 4)(x^2 - 4x + 16)$  **86.** $(2a - 3)(4a^2 + 6a + 9)$
**87.** $(5y - 6z)(2y + z)$  **88.** $(m - 2)^2$  **89.** $(8a - b)(a + 3b)$
**90.** $(a^2 + 25)(a + 5)(a - 5)$  **91.** $(x^3 - 1)(x^3 + 1)$
**92.** $(x - 1)(x^2 + x + 1)(x + 1)(x^2 - x + 1)$
**93.** $(x^2 - 1)(x^4 + x^2 + 1)$  **94.** $(x - 1)(x + 1)(x^4 + x^2 + 1)$
**95.** The result in **Exercise 92** is factored completely.  **96.** Show that
$x^4 + x^2 + 1 = (x^2 + x + 1)(x^2 - x + 1)$.  **97.** difference of squares
**98.** $(x - 3)(x^2 + 3x + 9)(x + 3)(x^2 - 3x + 9)$

## Section 6.5 (pages 397–400)

**1.** $ax^2 + bx + c$  **3.** factor  **5.** $0; x$  **7.** To solve $2x(3x - 4) = 0$, set
each *variable* factor equal to 0 to get $x = 0$ or $3x - 4 = 0$. The *constant*
factor 2 does not introduce solutions into the equation. The solution set is
$\left\{0, \frac{4}{3}\right\}$.  **9.** The variable $x$ is another factor to set equal to 0, so the
solution set is $\left\{0, \frac{1}{7}\right\}$.  **11.** $\{-5, 2\}$  **13.** $\left\{3, \frac{7}{2}\right\}$  **15.** $\left\{-\frac{1}{2}, \frac{1}{6}\right\}$
**17.** $\left\{-\frac{5}{6}, 0\right\}$  **19.** $\left\{0, \frac{4}{3}\right\}$  **21.** $\{6\}$  **23.** $\{-2, -1\}$  **25.** $\{1, 2\}$
**27.** $\{-8, 3\}$  **29.** $\{-1, 3\}$  **31.** $\{-2, -1\}$  **33.** $\{-4\}$  **35.** $\left\{-2, \frac{1}{3}\right\}$
**37.** $\left\{-\frac{4}{3}, \frac{1}{2}\right\}$  **39.** $\left\{-\frac{2}{3}\right\}$  **41.** $\{-3, 3\}$  **43.** $\left\{-\frac{7}{4}, \frac{7}{4}\right\}$
**45.** $\{-11, 11\}$  **47.** $\{0, 7\}$  **49.** $\left\{0, \frac{1}{2}\right\}$  **51.** $\{2, 5\}$  **53.** $\left\{-4, \frac{1}{2}\right\}$
**55.** $\{-17, 4\}$  **57.** $\left\{-\frac{5}{2}, \frac{1}{3}, 5\right\}$  **59.** $\left\{-\frac{7}{2}, -3, 1\right\}$  **61.** $\left\{-\frac{7}{3}, 0, \frac{7}{3}\right\}$
**63.** $\{-2, 0, 4\}$  **65.** $\{-5, 0, 4\}$  **67.** $\{-3, 0, 5\}$  **69.** $\{-1, 3\}$
**71.** $\{-1, 3\}$  **73.** $\{3\}$  **75.** $\left\{-\frac{2}{3}, 4\right\}$  **77.** $\left\{-\frac{4}{3}, -1, \frac{1}{2}\right\}$
**79. (a)** 64; 144; 4; 6  **(b)** No time has elapsed, so the object hasn't
fallen (been released) yet.  **81.** $\{-0.5, 0.1\}$  **83.** 1845  **85.** 9, 10

## Section 6.6 (pages 405–410)

**1.** Read; variable; equation; Solve; answer; Check, original
**3.** *Step 3:* $45 = (2x + 1)(x + 1)$; *Step 4:* $x = 4$ or $x = -\frac{11}{2}$;
*Step 5:* base: 9 units; height: 5 units; *Step 6:* $9 \cdot 5 = 45$
**5.** *Step 3:* $80 = (x + 8)(x - 8)$; *Step 4:* $x = 12$ or $x = -12$;
*Step 5:* length: 20 units; width: 4 units; *Step 6:* $20 \cdot 4 = 80$

**7.** length: 14 cm; width: 12 cm  **9.** base: 12 in.; height: 5 in.
**11.** height: 13 in.; width: 10 in.  **13.** length: 15 in.; width: 12 in.
**15.** mirror: 7 ft; painting: 9 ft  **17.** 20, 21  **19.** 0, 1, 2 or 7, 8, 9
**21.** 7, 9, 11  **23.** $-2, 0, 2$ or 6, 8, 10  **25.** 12 cm  **27.** 12 mi  **29.** 8 ft
**31.** 112 ft  **33.** 256 ft  **35. (a)** 1 sec  **(b)** $\frac{1}{2}$ sec and $1\frac{1}{2}$ sec  **(c)** 3 sec
**(d)** The negative solution, $-1$, does not make sense, since $t$ represents
time, which cannot be negative.  **37. (a)** 104.4 million; The result obtained from the model is less than 109 million, the actual number for 2000.
**(b)** 18  **(c)** 272.7 million; The result is more than 263 million.
**(d)** 326.6 million  **39.** $\frac{25}{36}$  **41.** $\frac{16}{-9}$, or $-\frac{16}{9}$

## Chapter 6 Review Exercises (pages 413–415)

**1.** $7(t + 2)$  **2.** $30z(2z^2 + 1)$  **3.** $(2y + 3)(x - 4)$
**4.** $(3y + 2x)(2y + 3)$  **5.** $(x + 3)(x + 2)$  **6.** $(y - 5)(y - 8)$
**7.** $(q + 9)(q - 3)$  **8.** $(r - 8)(r + 7)$  **9.** $(r + 8s)(r - 12s)$
**10.** $(p + 12q)(p - 10q)$  **11.** $8p(p + 2)(p - 5)$
**12.** $3x^2(x + 2)(x + 8)$  **13.** $p^5(p - 2q)(p + q)$
**14.** $3r^3(r + 3s)(r - 5s)$  **15.** $9x^2y(x + 2)(x - 3)$
**16.** $2x^5(x - 2y)(x + 3y)$  **17.** $r$ and $6r$, $2r$ and $3r$  **18.** Factor out $z$.
**19.** $(2k - 1)(k - 2)$  **20.** $(3r - 1)(r + 4)$  **21.** $(3r + 2)(2r - 3)$
**22.** $(5z + 1)(2z - 1)$  **23.** $(v + 3)(8v - 7)$
**24.** $4x^3(3x - 1)(2x - 1)$  **25.** $-3(x + 2)(2x - 5)$
**26.** $rs(5r + 6s)(2r + s)$  **27.** $4x^2y(3x + y)(4x - y)$  **28.** The
student stopped too soon. He needs to factor out the common factor
$4x - 1$ to get $(4x - 1)(4x - 5)$ as the correct answer.  **29.** B
**30.** D  **31.** $(n + 7)(n - 7)$  **32.** $(5b + 11)(5b - 11)$
**33.** $(7y + 5w)(7y - 5w)$  **34.** $36(2p + q)(2p - q)$  **35.** prime
**36.** $(r - 6)^2$  **37.** $(3t - 7)^2$  **38.** $(m + 10)(m^2 - 10m + 100)$
**39.** $(5k + 4x)(25k^2 - 20kx + 16x^2)$
**40.** $(7x - 4)(49x^2 + 28x + 16)$
**41.** $(10 - 3x^2)(100 + 30x^2 + 9x^4)$
**42.** $(x - y)(x + y)(x^2 + xy + y^2)(x^2 - xy + y^2)$
**43.** $\left\{-\frac{3}{4}, 1\right\}$  **44.** $\{-7, -3, 4\}$  **45.** $\left\{0, \frac{5}{2}\right\}$  **46.** $\{-3, -1\}$
**47.** $\{1, 4\}$  **48.** $\{3, 5\}$  **49.** $\left\{-\frac{4}{3}, 5\right\}$  **50.** $\left\{-\frac{8}{9}, \frac{8}{9}\right\}$  **51.** $\{0, 8\}$
**52.** $\{-1, 6\}$  **53.** $\{7\}$  **54.** $\{6\}$  **55.** $\left\{-2, -1, -\frac{2}{3}\right\}$  **56.** $\{-3, 3\}$
**57.** length: 10 ft; width: 4 ft  **58.** 5 ft  **59.** 6, 7 or $-5, -4$  **60.** 26 mi
**61. (a)** 256 ft  **(b)** 1024 ft  **62. (a)** 601,000 vehicles; The result is
slightly higher than the actual number for 2005.  **(b)** 655,000 vehicles
**(c)** The estimate may be unreliable because the conditions that prevailed
in the years 2001–2006 may have changed, causing either a greater increase
or a decrease predicted by the model for the number of alternative-
fueled vehicles.  **63.** D  **64.** The factor $(2x + 8)$ has a factor of 2.
The completely factored form is $2(x + 4)(3x - 4)$.
**65.** $(3k + 5)(k + 2)$  **66.** $(z - x)(z - 10x)$
**67.** $(y^2 + 25)(y + 5)(y - 5)$  **68.** $(3m + 4)(5m - 4p)$
**69.** $8abc(3b^2c - 7ac^2 + 9ab)$  **70.** $3m(2m + 3)(m - 5)$
**71.** $6xyz(2xz^2 + 2y - 5x^2yz^3)$  **72.** prime  **73.** $(2r + 3q)(6r - 5)$
**74.** $2a^3(a + 2)(a - 6)$  **75.** $(7t + 4)^2$
**76.** $(10a + 3)(100a^2 - 30a + 9)$  **77.** $\{0, 7\}$  **78.** $\{-5, 2\}$

**79.** $\left\{-\frac{2}{5}\right\}$   **80.** $-5, -4, -3$ or $5, 6, 7$   **81.** length: 6 m; width: 4 m
**82.** 15 m, 36 m, 39 m   **83.** 6 m   **84.** width: 10 m; length: 17 m

## Chapter 6 Test (page 416)

[6.1–6.4] **1.** D   **2.** $6x(2x - 5)$   **3.** $m^2n(2mn + 3m - 5n)$
**4.** $(2x + y)(a - b)$   **5.** $(x + 3)(x - 8)$   **6.** $(2x + 3)(x - 1)$
**7.** $(5z - 1)(2z - 3)$   **8.** prime   **9.** prime   **10.** $(2 - a)(6 + b)$
**11.** $(3y + 8)(3y - 8)$   **12.** $(2x - 7y)^2$   **13.** $-2(x + 1)^2$
**14.** $3t^2(2t + 9)(t - 4)$   **15.** $(r - 5)(r^2 + 5r + 25)$
**16.** $8(k + 2)(k^2 - 2k + 4)$   **17.** $(x^2 + 9)(x + 3)(x - 3)$
**18.** $(3x + 2y)(3x - 2y)(9x^2 + 4y^2)$   **19.** $(3x^3y^2 + 2)^2$
[6.5] **20.** $\left\{\frac{1}{2}, 6\right\}$   **21.** $\left\{-\frac{2}{5}, \frac{2}{5}\right\}$   **22.** $\{0, 9\}$   **23.** $\{10\}$
**24.** $\left\{-8, -\frac{5}{2}, \frac{1}{3}\right\}$   [6.6] **25.** 6 ft by 9 ft   **26.** $-2, -1$   **27.** 17 ft
**28.** $8493 billion

## Chapters 1–6 Cumulative Review Exercises (pages 417–418)

[2.1–2.3] **1.** $\{0\}$   **2.** $\{0.05\}$   **3.** $\{6\}$   [2.5] **4.** $P = \dfrac{A}{1 + rt}$
**5.** $110°$ and $70°$   [2.4] **6.** gold: 11; silver: 12; bronze: 6
[2.6] **7.** 230; 205; 38%; 12%   [3.1] **8. (a)** negative, positive
**(b)** negative, negative
[3.2, 3.3] **9. (a)** $\left(-\frac{1}{4}, 0\right), (0, 3)$   **(b)** 12   **(c)**

[3.3, 3.4] **10. (a)** 16; A slope of (approximately) 16 means that retail
sales of prescription drugs increased by about $16 billion per year.
**(b)** $(2005, 230)$   [4.1–4.3] **11.** $\{(-1, 2)\}$   **12.** $\emptyset$   [5.1, 5.2] **13.** $\frac{16}{9}$
**14.** 256   **15.** $\dfrac{1}{p^2}$   **16.** $\dfrac{1}{m^6}$   [5.4] **17.** $-4k^2 - 4k + 8$
[5.5] **18.** $45x^2 + 3x - 18$   [5.6] **19.** $9p^2 + 12p + 4$
[5.7] **20.** $4x^3 + 6x^2 - 3x + 10$   [5.3] **21.** $5.5 \times 10^4; 2.0 \times 10^6$
[6.2, 6.3] **22.** $(2a - 1)(a + 4)$   **23.** $(2m + 3)(5m + 2)$
**24.** $(4t + 3v)(2t + v)$   [6.4] **25.** $(2p - 3)^2$   **26.** $(5r + 9t)(5r - 9t)$
[6.3] **27.** $2pq(3p + 1)(p + 1)$   [6.5] **28.** $\left\{-\frac{2}{3}, \frac{1}{2}\right\}$   **29.** $\{0, 8\}$
[6.6] **30.** 5 m, 12 m, 13 m

**7**   **RATIONAL EXPRESSIONS AND APPLICATIONS**

**Connections** **(page 425)** **1.** $3x^2 + 11x + 8$ cannot be factored, so
this quotient cannot be simplified. By long division, the quotient is
$3x + 5 + \dfrac{-2}{x + 2}$.   **2.** The numerator factors as $(x - 2)(x^2 + 2x + 4)$,
so, after simplification, the quotient is $x - 2$. Long division gives the
same quotient.

## Section 7.1 (pages 426–428)

**1. (a)** $\frac{7}{10}$   **(b)** $\frac{8}{15}$   **3. (a)** 0   **(b)** $-1$   **5. (a)** $-\frac{64}{15}$   **(b)** undefined
**7. (a)** undefined   **(b)** $\frac{8}{25}$   **9. (a)** 0   **(b)** 0   **11. (a)** 0   **(b)** undefined
**13.** A rational expression is a quotient of two polynomials, such as
$\dfrac{x^2 + 3x - 6}{x + 4}$. One can think of this as an algebraic fraction.   **15.** Division
by 0 is undefined. If the denominator of a rational expression equals 0,
the expression is undefined.   **17.** $y \neq 0$   **19.** $x \neq 6$
**21.** $x \neq -\frac{5}{3}$   **23.** $m \neq -3, m \neq 2$   **25.** It is never undefined.
**27.** It is never undefined.   **29. (a)** numerator: $x^2, 4x$; denominator: $x, 4$
**(b)** First factor the numerator, getting $x(x + 4)$. Then divide the
numerator and denominator by the common factor $x + 4$ to get $\dfrac{x}{1}$, or $x$.
**31.** $3r^2$   **33.** $\frac{2}{5}$   **35.** $\dfrac{x - 1}{x + 1}$   **37.** $\frac{7}{5}$   **39.** $\frac{6}{7}$   **41.** $m - n$   **43.** $\dfrac{2}{t - 3}$
**45.** $\dfrac{3(2m + 1)}{4}$   **47.** $\dfrac{3m}{5}$   **49.** $\dfrac{3r - 2s}{3}$   **51.** $k - 3$   **53.** $\dfrac{x - 3}{x + 1}$
**55.** $\dfrac{x + 1}{x - 1}$   **57.** $\dfrac{x + 2}{x - 4}$   **59.** $-\dfrac{3}{7t}$   **61.** $\dfrac{z - 3}{z + 5}$   **63.** $\dfrac{r + s}{r - s}$   **65.** $\dfrac{a + b}{a - b}$
**67.** $\dfrac{m + n}{2}$   **69.** $\dfrac{x^2 + 1}{x}$   **71.** $1 - p + p^2$   **73.** $x^2 + 3x + 9$
**75.** $-\dfrac{b^2 + ba + a^2}{a + b}$   **77.** $\dfrac{k^2 - 2k + 4}{k - 2}$   **79.** $\dfrac{z + 3}{z}$   **81.** $\dfrac{1 - 2r}{2}$
**83.** B, D   **85.** $-1$   **87.** $-(m + 1)$   **89.** $-1$   **91.** It is already in
lowest terms.   **93.** B

*Answers may vary in Exercises 95, 97, and 99.*   **95.** $\dfrac{-(x + 4)}{x - 3}, \dfrac{-x - 4}{x - 3},$
$\dfrac{x + 4}{-(x - 3)}, \dfrac{x + 4}{-x + 3}$   **97.** $\dfrac{-(2x - 3)}{x + 3}, \dfrac{-2x + 3}{x + 3}, \dfrac{2x - 3}{-(x + 3)}, \dfrac{2x - 3}{-x - 3}$
**99.** $\dfrac{-(3x - 1)}{5x - 6}, \dfrac{-3x + 1}{5x - 6}, \dfrac{3x - 1}{-(5x - 6)}, \dfrac{3x - 1}{-5x + 6}$
**101.** $x^2 + 3$   **103. (a)** 0   **(b)** 1.6   **(c)** 4.1   **(d)** The waiting time
also increases.   **105.** $\frac{5}{9}$   **107.** 4

## Section 7.2 (pages 433–434)

**1. (a)** B   **(b)** D   **(c)** C   **(d)** A   **3.** $\dfrac{3a}{2}$   **5.** $-\dfrac{4x^4}{3}$   **7.** $\dfrac{2}{c + d}$
**9.** $4(x - y)$   **11.** $\dfrac{t^2}{2}$   **13.** $\dfrac{x + 3}{2x}$   **15.** 5   **17.** $-\dfrac{3}{2t^4}$   **19.** $\frac{1}{4}$
**21.** $-\frac{35}{8}$   **23.** $\dfrac{2(x + 2)}{x(x - 1)}$   **25.** $\dfrac{x(x - 3)}{6}$   **27.** $\frac{10}{9}$   **29.** $-\frac{3}{4}$   **31.** $-\frac{9}{2}$
**33.** $\dfrac{p + 4}{p + 2}$   **35.** $-1$   **37.** $\dfrac{(2x - 1)(x + 2)}{x - 1}$   **39.** $\dfrac{(k - 1)^2}{(k + 1)(2k - 1)}$
**41.** $\dfrac{4k - 1}{3k - 2}$   **43.** $\dfrac{m + 4p}{m + p}$   **45.** $\dfrac{m + 6}{m + 3}$   **47.** $\dfrac{y + 3}{y + 4}$   **49.** $\dfrac{m}{m + 5}$
**51.** $\dfrac{r + 6s}{r + s}$   **53.** $\dfrac{(q - 3)^2(q + 2)^2}{q + 1}$   **55.** $\dfrac{x + 10}{10}$   **57.** $\dfrac{3 - a - b}{2a - b}$
**59.** $-\dfrac{(x + y)^2(x^2 - xy + y^2)}{3y(y - x)(x - y)}$, or $\dfrac{(x + y)^2(x^2 - xy + y^2)}{3y(x - y)^2}$   **61.** $\dfrac{5xy^2}{4q}$
**63.** $2 \cdot 3^2$   **65.** $2^2 \cdot 3^3$   **67.** 6   **69.** $6q^3$

## Section 7.3 (pages 438–440)

**1.** C  **3.** C  **5.** 60  **7.** 1800  **9.** $x^5$  **11.** 30p  **13.** $180y^4$  **15.** $84r^5$

**17.** $15a^5b^3$  **19.** $12p(p - 2)$  **21.** $28m^2(3m - 5)$  **23.** $30(b - 2)$

**25.** $18(r - 2)$  **27.** $12p(p + 5)^2$  **29.** $8(y + 2)(y + 1)$

**31.** $c - d$ or $d - c$  **33.** $m - 3$ or $3 - m$  **35.** $p - q$ or $q - p$

**37.** $k(k + 5)(k - 2)$  **39.** $a(a + 6)(a - 3)$

**41.** $(p + 3)(p + 5)(p - 6)$  **43.** $(k + 3)(k - 5)(k + 7)(k + 8)$

**45.** 7  **46.** 1  **47.** identity property of multiplication

**48.** 7  **49.** 1  **50.** identity property of multiplication

**51.** $\frac{20}{55}$  **53.** $\frac{-45}{9k}$  **55.** $\frac{60m^2k^3}{32k^4}$  **57.** $\frac{57z}{6z - 18}$  **59.** $\frac{-4a}{18a - 36}$

**61.** $\frac{6(k + 1)}{k(k - 4)(k + 1)}$  **63.** $\frac{36r(r + 1)}{(r - 3)(r + 2)(r + 1)}$

**65.** $\frac{ab(a + 2b)}{2a^3b + a^2b^2 - ab^3}$  **67.** $\frac{(t - r)(4r - t)}{t^3 - r^3}$

**69.** $\frac{2y(z - y)(y - z)}{y^4 - z^3y}$, or $\frac{-2y(y - z)^2}{y^4 - z^3y}$  **71.** $\frac{11}{8}$  **73.** $\frac{13}{20}$

## Section 7.4 (pages 445–448)

**1.** E  **3.** C  **5.** B  **7.** G  **9.** $\frac{11}{m}$  **11.** $\frac{4}{y + 4}$  **13.** 1  **15.** $\frac{m - 1}{m + 1}$

**17.** $b$  **19.** $x$  **21.** $y - 6$  **23.** $\frac{1}{x - 3}$  **25.** $\frac{3z + 5}{15}$  **27.** $\frac{10 - 7r}{14}$

**29.** $\frac{-3x - 2}{4x}$  **31.** $\frac{57}{10x}$  **33.** $\frac{x + 1}{2}$  **35.** $\frac{5x + 9}{6x}$  **37.** $\frac{7 - 6p}{3p^2}$

**39.** $\frac{-k - 8}{k(k + 4)}$  **41.** $\frac{x + 4}{x + 2}$  **43.** $\frac{6m^2 + 23m - 2}{(m + 2)(m + 1)(m + 5)}$

**45.** $\frac{4y^2 - y + 5}{(y + 1)^2(y - 1)}$  **47.** $\frac{3}{t}$  **49.** $m - 2$, or $2 - m$

**51.** $\frac{-2}{x - 5}$, or $\frac{2}{5 - x}$  **53.** $-4$  **55.** $\frac{-5}{x - y^2}$, or $\frac{5}{y^2 - x}$

**57.** $\frac{x + y}{5x - 3y}$, or $\frac{-x - y}{3y - 5x}$  **59.** $\frac{-6}{4p - 5}$, or $\frac{6}{5 - 4p}$

**61.** $\frac{-m - n}{2(m - n)}$  **63.** $\frac{-x^2 + 6x + 11}{(x + 3)(x - 3)(x + 1)}$

**65.** $\frac{-5q^2 - 13q + 7}{(3q - 2)(q + 4)(2q - 3)}$  **67.** $\frac{9r + 2}{r(r + 2)(r - 1)}$

**69.** $\frac{2(x^2 + 3xy + 4y^2)}{(x + y)(x + y)(x + 3y)}$, or $\frac{2(x^2 + 3xy + 4y^2)}{(x + y)^2(x + 3y)}$

**71.** $\frac{15r^2 + 10ry - y^2}{(3r + 2y)(6r - y)(6r + y)}$  **73.** (a) $\frac{9k^2 + 6k + 26}{5(3k + 1)}$  (b) $\frac{1}{4}$

**75.** $\frac{10x}{49(101 - x)}$  **77.** $\frac{5}{4}$  **79.** $\frac{6}{7}$

## Section 7.5 (pages 453–455)

**1.** (a) $6; \frac{1}{6}$  (b) $12; -\frac{1}{4}$  (c) $\frac{1}{6} \div \left(-\frac{1}{4}\right)$  (d) $-\frac{2}{3}$  **3.** Choice D is correct, because every sign has been changed in the fraction. This means it was multiplied by $\frac{-1}{-1} = 1$.  **5.** $-6$  **7.** $\frac{1}{xy}$  **9.** $\frac{2a^2b}{3}$

**11.** $\frac{m(m + 2)}{3(m - 4)}$  **13.** $\frac{2}{x}$  **15.** $\frac{8}{x}$  **17.** $\frac{a^2 - 5}{a^2 + 1}$  **19.** $\frac{31}{50}$  **21.** $\frac{y^2 + x^2}{xy(y - x)}$

**23.** $\frac{40 - 12p}{85p}$  **25.** $\frac{5y - 2x}{3 + 4xy}$  **27.** $\frac{a - 2}{2a}$  **29.** $\frac{z - 5}{4}$  **31.** $\frac{-m}{m + 2}$

**33.** $\frac{3m(m - 3)}{(m - 1)(m - 8)}$  **35.** $\frac{2x - 7}{3x + 1}$  **37.** $\frac{y + 4}{y - 8}$  **39.** $\frac{x - 3}{x - 5}$

**41.** division  **43.** $\frac{\frac{3}{8} + \frac{5}{6}}{2}$  **44.** $\frac{29}{48}$  **45.** $\frac{29}{48}$  **46.** Answers will vary.

**47.** $\frac{5}{3}$  **49.** $\frac{13}{2}$  **51.** $\frac{19r}{15}$  **53.** $12x + 2$  **55.** $-44p^2 + 27p$

**57.** $\left\{\frac{1}{2}\right\}$  **59.** $\{-5\}$

## Section 7.6 (pages 462–465)

**1.** expression; $\frac{43}{40}x$  **3.** equation; $\left\{\frac{40}{43}\right\}$  **5.** expression; $-\frac{1}{10}x$

**7.** equation; $\{-10\}$  **9.** equation; $\{0\}$  **11.** $x \neq -2, 0$

**13.** $x \neq -3, 4, -\frac{1}{2}$  **15.** $x \neq -9, 1, -2, 2$  **17.** $\frac{2}{3x} + \frac{1}{5x}$ is an

expression, not an equation. Only equations and inequalities are "solved."

**19.** $\left\{\frac{1}{4}\right\}$  **21.** $\left\{-\frac{3}{4}\right\}$  **23.** $\{-15\}$  **25.** $\{7\}$  **27.** $\{-15\}$  **29.** $\{-5\}$

**31.** $\{-6\}$  **33.** $\emptyset$  **35.** $\{5\}$  **37.** $\{4\}$  **39.** $\{5\}$  **41.** $\left\{x | x \neq \pm\frac{4}{3}\right\}$

**43.** $\{1\}$  **45.** $\{4\}$  **47.** $\{5\}$  **49.** $\{-4\}$  **51.** $\{-2, 12\}$  **53.** $\emptyset$

**55.** $\{3\}$  **57.** $\{3\}$  **59.** $\{-3\}$  **61.** $\left\{-\frac{1}{5}, 3\right\}$  **63.** $\left\{-\frac{1}{2}, 5\right\}$  **65.** $\{3\}$

**67.** $\left\{-\frac{1}{3}, 3\right\}$  **69.** $\{-1\}$  **71.** $\{-6\}$  **73.** $\left\{-6, \frac{1}{2}\right\}$  **75.** $\{6\}$

**77.** Transform so that the terms with $k$ are on one side and the remaining

term is on the other.  **79.** $F = \frac{ma}{k}$  **81.** $a = \frac{kF}{m}$  **83.** $R = \frac{E - Ir}{I}$, or

$R = \frac{E}{I} - r$  **85.** $\mathscr{A} = \frac{h(B + b)}{2}$  **87.** $a = \frac{2S - ndL}{nd}$, or $a = \frac{2S}{nd} - L$

**89.** $y = \frac{xz}{x + z}$  **91.** $t = \frac{rs}{rs - 2s - 3r}$, or $t = \frac{-rs}{-rs + 2s + 3r}$

**93.** $z = \frac{3y}{5 - 9xy}$, or $z = \frac{-3y}{9xy - 5}$  **95.** $t = \frac{2x - 1}{x + 1}$, or $t = \frac{-2x + 1}{-x - 1}$

**97.** $\frac{288}{t}$ mph  **99.** $\frac{289}{z}$ hr

## Summary Exercises on Rational Expressions and Equations (pages 466–467)

**1.** expression; $\frac{10}{p}$  **2.** expression; $\frac{y^3}{x^3}$  **3.** expression; $\frac{1}{2x^2(x + 2)}$

**4.** equation; $\{9\}$  **5.** expression; $\frac{y + 2}{y - 1}$  **6.** expression;

$\frac{5k + 8}{k(k - 4)(k + 4)}$  **7.** equation; $\{39\}$  **8.** expression; $\frac{t - 5}{3(2t + 1)}$

**9.** expression; $\frac{13}{3(p + 2)}$  **10.** equation; $\left\{-1, \frac{12}{5}\right\}$  **11.** equation;

$\left\{\frac{1}{7}, 2\right\}$  **12.** expression; $\frac{16}{3k}$  **13.** expression; $\frac{7}{12z}$  **14.** equation; $\{13\}$

**15.** expression; $\frac{3m + 5}{(m + 3)(m + 2)(m + 1)}$  **16.** expression; $\frac{k + 3}{5(k - 1)}$

**17.** equation; ∅  **18.** equation; ∅  **19.** expression; $\dfrac{t+2}{2(2t+1)}$

**20.** equation; $\{-7\}$

## Section 7.7 (pages 471–475)

**1. (a)** the amount  **(b)** $5+x$  **(c)** $\dfrac{5+x}{6}=\dfrac{13}{3}$  **3.** $\frac{12}{18}$  **5.** $\frac{12}{3}$  **7.** 12

**9.** $\frac{1386}{97}$  **11.** 18.809 min  **13.** 314.248 m per min  **15.** 3.275 hr

**17.** $\dfrac{D}{R}=\dfrac{d}{r}$  **19.** $\dfrac{500}{x-10}=\dfrac{600}{x+10}$  **21.** 8 mph  **23.** 32 mph

**25.** 165 mph  **27.** 3 mph  **29.** 18.5 mph  **31.** $\frac{1}{10}$ job per hr

**33.** $\dfrac{1}{8}t+\dfrac{1}{6}t=1$, or $\dfrac{1}{8}+\dfrac{1}{6}=\dfrac{1}{t}$  **35.** $2\frac{2}{5}$ hr  **37.** $5\frac{5}{11}$ hr  **39.** 3 hr

**41.** $2\frac{7}{10}$ hr  **43.** $9\frac{1}{11}$ min  **45.** $\left\{\frac{40}{3}\right\}$  **47.** $\{3600\}$  **49.** $k=\dfrac{y}{x}$

**51.** $k=xy$

## Section 7.8 (pages 479–481)

**1.** direct  **3.** direct  **5.** inverse  **7.** inverse  **9.** inverse  **11.** direct

**13.** direct  **15.** inverse  **17. (a)** increases  **(b)** decreases  **19.** 9

**21.** 250  **23.** 6  **25.** 21  **27.** $\frac{16}{5}$  **29.** $\frac{4}{9}$  **31.** $40.32  **33.** $42\frac{2}{3}$ in.

**35.** $106\frac{2}{3}$ mph  **37.** $12\frac{1}{2}$ amps  **39.** 20 lb  **41.** 52.817 in.$^2$

**43.** $14\frac{22}{27}$ footcandles  **45.** 64  **47.** $-144$  **49.** 169

## Chapter 7 Review Exercises (pages 487–490)

**1. (a)** $\frac{11}{8}$  **(b)** $\frac{13}{22}$  **2. (a)** undefined  **(b)** 1  **3.** $x\neq3$  **4.** $y\neq0$

**5.** $k\neq-5,-\frac{2}{3}$  **6.** Set the denominator equal to 0 and solve the equation. Any solutions are values for which the rational expression is undefined.  **7.** $\dfrac{b}{3a}$  **8.** $-1$  **9.** $\dfrac{-(2x+3)}{2}$  **10.** $\dfrac{2p+5q}{5p+q}$

*Answers may vary in Exercises 11 and 12.*  **11.** $\dfrac{-(4x-9)}{2x+3}$, $\dfrac{-4x+9}{2x+3}$,

$\dfrac{4x-9}{-(2x+3)}$, $\dfrac{4x-9}{-2x-3}$  **12.** $\dfrac{-(8-3x)}{3-6x}$, $\dfrac{-8+3x}{3-6x}$, $\dfrac{8-3x}{-(3-6x)}$,

$\dfrac{8-3x}{-3+6x}$  **13.** $\dfrac{72}{p}$  **14.** 2  **15.** $\frac{5}{8}$  **16.** $\dfrac{r+4}{3}$  **17.** $\dfrac{3a-1}{a+5}$

**18.** $\dfrac{y-2}{y-3}$  **19.** $\dfrac{p+5}{p+1}$  **20.** $\dfrac{3z+1}{z+3}$  **21.** $108y^4$

**22.** $(x+3)(x+1)(x+4)$  **23.** $\dfrac{15a}{10a^4}$  **24.** $\dfrac{-54}{18-6x}$  **25.** $\dfrac{15y}{50-10y}$

**26.** $\dfrac{4b(b+2)}{(b+3)(b-1)(b+2)}$  **27.** $\dfrac{15}{x}$  **28.** $-\dfrac{2}{p}$  **29.** $\dfrac{4k-45}{k(k-5)}$

**30.** $\dfrac{28+11y}{y(7+y)}$  **31.** $\dfrac{-2-3m}{6}$  **32.** $\dfrac{3(16-x)}{4x^2}$

**33.** $\dfrac{7a+6b}{(a-2b)(a+2b)}$  **34.** $\dfrac{-k^2-6k+3}{3(k+3)(k-3)}$  **35.** $\dfrac{5z-16}{z(z+6)(z-2)}$

**36.** $\dfrac{-13p+33}{p(p-2)(p-3)}$  **37.** $\dfrac{4(y-3)}{y+3}$  **38.** $\frac{10}{13}$  **39.** $\dfrac{xw+1}{xw-1}$

**40.** $\dfrac{(q-p)^2}{pq}$  **41.** $(x-5)(x-3)$, or $x^2-8x+15$  **42.** $\dfrac{1-r-t}{1+r+t}$

**43.** ∅  **44.** $\{-16\}$  **45.** $\{0\}$  **46.** $\{3\}$  **47.** $t=\dfrac{Ry}{m}$

**48.** $y=\dfrac{4x+5}{3}$  **49.** $m=\dfrac{4+p^2q}{3p^2}$  **50.** $\frac{20}{15}$  **51.** $\frac{3}{18}$  **52.** 10 mph

**53.** $3\frac{1}{13}$ hr  **54.** 2 hr  **55.** inverse  **56.** 4 cm  **57.** $\frac{36}{5}$

**58.** $\dfrac{m+7}{(m-1)(m+1)}$  **59.** $8p^2$  **60.** $\frac{1}{6}$  **61.** 3  **62.** $\dfrac{z+7}{(z+1)(z-1)^2}$

**63.** $\dfrac{-t-1}{(t+2)(t-2)}$, or $\dfrac{t+1}{(2+t)(2-t)}$  **64.** $\{-2,3\}$

**65.** $v=at+w$  **66.** 150 km per hr  **67.** $5\frac{1}{11}$ hr  **68.** 24  **69.** 4

**70.** $-16$  **71. (a)** $-3$  **(b)** $-1$  **(c)** $-3,-1$  **72.** $\dfrac{15}{2x}$  **73.** If $x=0$,

the divisor $R$ is equal to 0, and division by 0 is undefined.

**74.** $(x+3)(x+1)$  **75.** $\dfrac{7}{x+1}$  **76.** $\dfrac{11x+21}{4x}$  **77.** ∅

**78.** We know that $-3$ is not allowed, because $P$ and $R$ are undefined for $x=-3$.  **79.** Rate is equal to distance divided by time. Here, distance is 6 miles and time is $(x+3)$ minutes, so rate $=\dfrac{6}{x+3}$, which is the expression for $P$.  **80.** $\frac{6}{5},\frac{5}{2}$

## Chapter 7 Test (pages 490–491)

[7.1] **1. (a)** $\frac{11}{6}$  **(b)** undefined  **2.** $x\neq-2,4$  **3.** (Answers may vary.) $\dfrac{-(6x-5)}{2x+3}$, $\dfrac{-6x+5}{2x+3}$, $\dfrac{6x-5}{-(2x+3)}$, $\dfrac{6x-5}{-2x-3}$  **4.** $-3x^2y^3$

**5.** $\dfrac{3a+2}{a-1}$  [7.2] **6.** $\frac{25}{27}$  **7.** $\dfrac{3k-2}{3k+2}$  **8.** $\dfrac{a-1}{a+4}$  **9.** $\dfrac{x-5}{3-x}$

[7.3] **10.** $150p^5$  **11.** $(2r+3)(r+2)(r-5)$  **12.** $\dfrac{240p^2}{64p^3}$

**13.** $\dfrac{21}{42m-84}$  [7.4] **14.** 2  **15.** $\dfrac{-14}{5(y+2)}$  **16.** $\dfrac{-x^2+x+1}{3-x}$, or

$\dfrac{x^2-x-1}{x-3}$  **17.** $\dfrac{-m^2+7m+2}{(2m+1)(m-5)(m-1)}$  [7.5] **18.** $\dfrac{2k}{3p}$

**19.** $\dfrac{-2-x}{4+x}$  [7.6] **20.** $\left\{-\frac{1}{2},1\right\}$  **21.** $\left\{-\frac{1}{2}\right\}$  **22.** $D=\dfrac{dF-k}{F}$, or

$D=d-\dfrac{k}{F}$  [7.7] **23.** 3 mph  **24.** $2\frac{2}{9}$ hr  [7.8] **25.** 27

**26.** 27 days

## Chapters 1–7 Cumulative Review Exercises (pages 491–492)

[1.2, 1.5, 1.6] **1.** 2  [2.3] **2.** $\{17\}$  [2.5] **3.** $b=\dfrac{2\mathcal{A}}{h}$  [2.6] **4.** $\left\{-\frac{2}{7}\right\}$

[2.8] **5.** $[-8,\infty)$  [3.1, 3.2] **6. (a)** $(-3,0)$  **(b)** $(0,-4)$

**7.**   [5.4] **8.**

[4.1–4.3] **9.** $\{(-1, 3)\}$   **10.** $\emptyset$   [5.1, 5.2] **11.** $\dfrac{1}{2^4 x^7}$   **12.** $\dfrac{1}{m^6}$

[5.4] **13.** $k^2 + 2k + 1$   [5.6] **14.** $4a^2 - 4ab + b^2$

[5.5] **15.** $3y^3 + 8y^2 + 12y - 5$   [5.7] **16.** $6p^2 + 7p + 1 + \dfrac{3}{p - 1}$

[6.3] **17.** $(4t + 3v)(2t + v)$   **18.** prime

[6.4] **19.** $(4x^2 + 1)(2x + 1)(2x - 1)$   [6.5] **20.** $\{-3, 5\}$

**21.** $\left\{5, -\frac{1}{2}, \frac{2}{3}\right\}$   [6.6] **22.** $-2$ or $-1$   **23.** 6 m   [7.1] **24.** A   **25.** D

[7.4] **26.** $\dfrac{4}{q}$   **27.** $\dfrac{3r + 28}{7r}$   **28.** $\dfrac{7}{15(q - 4)}$   **29.** $\dfrac{-k - 5}{k(k + 1)(k - 1)}$

[7.2] **30.** $\dfrac{7(2z + 1)}{24}$   [7.5] **31.** $\frac{195}{29}$   [7.6] **32.** $\left\{\frac{21}{2}\right\}$   **33.** $\{-2, 1\}$

[7.7] **34.** $1\frac{1}{5}$ hr   [7.8] **35.** 32.97 in.

---

## 8   ROOTS AND RADICALS

**Connections   (page 498)   1.** $(a + b)^2$, or $a^2 + 2ab + b^2$.
**2.** $c^2 + 2ab$   **3.** Subtract $2ab$ from each side to get $a^2 + b^2 = c^2$.

## Section 8.1 (pages 500–504)

**1.** true   **3.** false; Zero has only one square root.   **5.** true   **7.** $-3, 3$
**9.** $-8, 8$   **11.** $-13, 13$   **13.** $-\frac{5}{14}, \frac{5}{14}$   **15.** $-30, 30$   **17.** 1   **19.** 7
**21.** $-16$   **23.** $-\frac{12}{11}$   **25.** 0.8   **27.** It is not a real number.   **29.** It is not
a real number.   **31.** 19   **33.** 19   **35.** $\frac{2}{3}$   **37.** $3x^2 + 4$   **39.** $a$ must be
positive.   **41.** $a$ must be negative.   **43.** rational; 5   **45.** irrational;
5.385   **47.** rational; $-8$   **49.** irrational; $-17.321$   **51.** It is not a real
number.   **53.** irrational; 34.641   **55.** 9 and 10   **57.** 7 and 8
**59.** $-7$ and $-6$   **61.** 4 and 5   **63.** C   **65.** $c = 17$   **67.** $b = 8$
**69.** $c \approx 11.705$   **71.** 24 cm   **73.** 80 ft   **75.** 195 ft   **77.** 11.1 ft
**79.** 158.6 ft   **81.** 9.434   **83.** The area of the square on the left is $c^2$.
The small square inside that figure has area $(b - a)^2 = b^2 - 2ba + a^2$.
The sum of the areas of the two rectangles in the figure on the right is
$2ab$. Since the areas of the two figures are the same, we have
$c^2 = 2ab + b^2 - 2ba + a^2$, which simplifies to $c^2 = a^2 + b^2$.   **85.** 5
**87.** 13   **89.** $\sqrt{13}$   **91.** $\sqrt{2}$   **93.** 1; 8; 27; 64; 125; 216; 343; 512;
729; 1000   **95.** 1   **97.** 5   **99.** $-3$   **101.** $-6$   **103.** 2   **105.** 5
**107.** 6   **109.** It is not a real number.   **111.** $-3$   **113.** $-4$   **115.** 2.289
**117.** 5.074   **119.** $-4.431$   **121.** $2^3 \cdot 3^2$   **123.** $2^3 \cdot 5$   **125.** 23 is a
prime number.

## Section 8.2 (pages 510–512)

**1.** $\sqrt{15}$   **3.** $\sqrt{22}$   **5.** $\sqrt{42}$   **7.** $\sqrt{81}$, or 9   **9.** 13   **11.** $\sqrt{13r}$
**13.** A   **15.** $3\sqrt{5}$   **17.** $2\sqrt{6}$   **19.** $3\sqrt{10}$   **21.** $5\sqrt{3}$   **23.** $5\sqrt{5}$
**25.** It cannot be simplified.   **27.** $4\sqrt{10}$   **29.** $-10\sqrt{7}$   **31.** $9\sqrt{3}$
**33.** $25\sqrt{2}$   **35.** $5\sqrt{10}$   **37.** $6\sqrt{2}$   **39.** $9\sqrt{2}$   **41.** $2\sqrt{17}$
**43.** $12\sqrt{2}$   **45.** $3\sqrt{6}$   **47.** 24   **49.** $6\sqrt{10}$   **51.** $12\sqrt{5}$   **53.** $30\sqrt{5}$
**55.** $\sqrt{8} \cdot \sqrt{32} = \sqrt{8 \cdot 32} = \sqrt{256} = 16$. Also, $\sqrt{8} = 2\sqrt{2}$ and
$\sqrt{32} = 4\sqrt{2}$, so $\sqrt{8} \cdot \sqrt{32} = 2\sqrt{2} \cdot 4\sqrt{2} = 8 \cdot 2 = 16$. Both
methods give the same answer, and the correct answer can always be
obtained with either method.   **57.** $\frac{4}{15}$   **59.** $\dfrac{\sqrt{7}}{4}$   **61.** $\dfrac{\sqrt{2}}{5}$   **63.** 5

**65.** $6\sqrt{5}$   **67.** $\frac{25}{4}$   **69.** $m$   **71.** $y^2$   **73.** $6z$   **75.** $20x^3$   **77.** $3x^4\sqrt{2}$
**79.** $3c^7\sqrt{5}$   **81.** $z^2\sqrt{z}$   **83.** $a^6\sqrt{a}$   **85.** $8x^3\sqrt{x}$   **87.** $x^3y^6$
**89.** $9m^2n$   **91.** $\dfrac{\sqrt{7}}{x^5}$   **93.** $\dfrac{y^2}{10}$   **95.** $\dfrac{x^2y^3}{13}$   **97.** $2\sqrt[3]{5}$   **99.** $3\sqrt[3]{2}$
**101.** $4\sqrt[3]{2}$   **103.** $2\sqrt[4]{5}$   **105.** $\frac{2}{3}$   **107.** $-\frac{6}{5}$   **109.** $p$   **111.** $x^3$
**113.** $4z^2$   **115.** $7a^3b$   **117.** $2t\sqrt[3]{2t^2}$   **119.** $\dfrac{m^4}{2}$   **121.** 6 cm   **123.** 6 in.
**125.** D   **127.** $-5x + 19$   **129.** $11x^2y - 7xy$

## Section 8.3 (pages 515–516)

**1.** distributive   **3.** radicands   **5.** $7\sqrt{3}$   **7.** $-5\sqrt{7}$   **9.** $2\sqrt{6}$
**11.** $3\sqrt{17}$   **13.** $7\sqrt{3}$   **15.** It cannot be added by the distributive
property.   **17.** $8\sqrt{3}$   **19.** $-20\sqrt{2}$   **21.** $19\sqrt{7}$   **23.** $12\sqrt{6} + 6\sqrt{5}$
**25.** $-2\sqrt{2} - 12\sqrt{3}$   **27.** $4\sqrt{2}$   **29.** $3\sqrt{3} - 2\sqrt{5}$   **31.** $3\sqrt{21}$
**33.** $5\sqrt{3}$   **35.** $-\sqrt[3]{2}$   **37.** $24\sqrt[3]{3}$   **39.** $10\sqrt[4]{2} + 4\sqrt[4]{8}$   **41.** $\sqrt{2x}$
**43.** $7\sqrt{3r}$   **45.** $15x\sqrt{3}$   **47.** $2x\sqrt{2}$   **49.** $13p\sqrt{3}$   **51.** $42x\sqrt{5z}$
**53.** $6k^2h\sqrt{6} + 27hk\sqrt{6k}$   **55.** $6\sqrt[3]{p^2}$   **57.** $21\sqrt[4]{m^3}$   **59.** $-8p\sqrt[4]{p}$
**61.** $-24z\sqrt[3]{4z}$   **63.** 0   **65.** $22\sqrt{2}$   **67.** 5   **69.** $\sqrt{82}$   **71.** 7
**73.** 14   **75.** $2\sqrt{2}$   **77.** 6   **79.** 2   **81.** $50\sqrt{3}$

## Section 8.4 (pages 521–523)

**1.** $\dfrac{6\sqrt{5}}{5}$   **3.** $\sqrt{5}$   **5.** $\dfrac{2\sqrt{6}}{3}$   **7.** $\dfrac{8\sqrt{15}}{5}$   **9.** $\dfrac{\sqrt{30}}{2}$   **11.** $\dfrac{8\sqrt{3}}{9}$
**13.** $\dfrac{3\sqrt{2}}{10}$   **15.** $\sqrt{2}$   **17.** $\sqrt{2}$   **19.** $\dfrac{2\sqrt{30}}{3}$   **21.** $\dfrac{\sqrt{2}}{8}$   **23.** $\dfrac{3\sqrt{5}}{5}$
**25.** $\dfrac{-3\sqrt{2}}{10}$   **27.** $\dfrac{21\sqrt{5}}{5}$   **29.** $\dfrac{\sqrt{3}}{3}$   **31.** $-\dfrac{\sqrt{5}}{5}$   **33.** $\dfrac{\sqrt{65}}{5}$
**35.** 1; identity property for multiplication   **37.** $\dfrac{\sqrt{21}}{3}$   **39.** $\dfrac{3\sqrt{14}}{4}$
**41.** $\frac{1}{6}$   **43.** 1   **45.** $\dfrac{\sqrt{15}}{10}$   **47.** $\dfrac{17\sqrt{2}}{6}$   **49.** $\dfrac{\sqrt{3}}{5}$   **51.** $\dfrac{4\sqrt{3}}{27}$
**53.** $\dfrac{\sqrt{6p}}{p}$   **55.** $\dfrac{\sqrt{3y}}{y}$   **57.** $\dfrac{4\sqrt{m}}{m}$   **59.** $\dfrac{p\sqrt{3q}}{q}$   **61.** $\dfrac{x\sqrt{7xy}}{y}$
**63.** $\dfrac{p\sqrt{2pm}}{m}$   **65.** $\dfrac{x\sqrt{y}}{2y}$   **67.** $\dfrac{3a\sqrt{5r}}{5}$   **69.** B   **71.** $\dfrac{\sqrt[3]{4}}{2}$   **73.** $\dfrac{\sqrt[3]{2}}{4}$
**75.** $\dfrac{\sqrt[3]{121}}{11}$   **77.** $\dfrac{\sqrt[3]{50}}{5}$   **79.** $\dfrac{\sqrt[3]{196}}{7}$   **81.** $\dfrac{\sqrt[3]{6y}}{2y}$   **83.** $\dfrac{\sqrt[3]{42mn^2}}{6n}$
**85.** $\dfrac{\sqrt[4]{2}}{2}$   **87. (a)** $\dfrac{9\sqrt{2}}{4}$ sec   **(b)** 3.182 sec   **89.** $32x^2 + 44x - 21$
**91.** $36x^2 - 1$   **93.** $pa - pm + qa - qm$

## Section 8.5 (pages 527–529)

**1.** 13   **3.** 4   **5.** $\sqrt{15} - \sqrt{35}$   **7.** $30 + 2\sqrt{10}$   **9.** $4\sqrt{7}$
**11.** $57 + 23\sqrt{6}$   **13.** $81 + 14\sqrt{21}$   **15.** $71 - 16\sqrt{7}$
**17.** $37 + 12\sqrt{7}$   **19.** $7 + 2\sqrt{6}$   **21.** 23   **23.** 1   **25.** 2
**27.** $2\sqrt{3} - 2 + 3\sqrt{2} - \sqrt{6}$   **29.** $15\sqrt{2} - 15$
**31.** $\sqrt{30} + \sqrt{15} + 6\sqrt{5} + 3\sqrt{10}$   **33.** $187 - 20\sqrt{21}$
**35.** Because multiplication must be performed before addition, it is
incorrect to add $-37$ and $-2$. Since $-2\sqrt{15}$ cannot be simplified, the
expression cannot be written in a simpler form, and the final answer is
$-37 - 2\sqrt{15}$.   **37.** $49 + 14\sqrt{x} + x$

**39.** $6t - 3\sqrt{14t} + 2\sqrt{7t} - 7\sqrt{2}$ **41.** $3m - 2n$
**43.** (a) $\sqrt{5} - \sqrt{3}$ (b) $\sqrt{6} + \sqrt{5}$ **45.** $-2 + \sqrt{5}$
**47.** $-2 - \sqrt{11}$ **49.** $3 - \sqrt{3}$ **51.** $\dfrac{-3 + 5\sqrt{3}}{11}$
**53.** $\dfrac{\sqrt{6} + \sqrt{2} + 3\sqrt{3} + 3}{2}$ **55.** $\dfrac{-6\sqrt{2} + 12 + \sqrt{10} - 2\sqrt{5}}{2}$
**57.** $\dfrac{-4\sqrt{3} - \sqrt{2} + 10\sqrt{6} + 5}{23}$ **59.** $\sqrt{21} + \sqrt{14} + \sqrt{6} + 2$
**61.** $-\sqrt{10} + \sqrt{15}$ **63.** $3 - \sqrt{3}$ **65.** $\dfrac{8(4 + \sqrt{x})}{16 - x}$
**67.** $\dfrac{\sqrt{x} - \sqrt{y}}{x - y}$ **69.** $\sqrt{7} - 2$ **71.** $\dfrac{\sqrt{3} + 5}{4}$ **73.** $\dfrac{6 - \sqrt{10}}{2}$
**75.** $\dfrac{2 + \sqrt{2}}{3}$ **77.** $2 - 3\sqrt[3]{4}$ **79.** $12 + 10\sqrt[4]{8}$
**81.** $-1 + 3\sqrt[3]{2} - \sqrt[3]{4}$ **83.** $1$ **85.** $4$ in. **87.** $30 + 18x$
**88.** They are not like terms. **89.** $30 + 18\sqrt{5}$ **90.** They are not like radicals. **91.** Make the first term $30x$, so that $30x + 18x = 48x$. Make the first term $30\sqrt{5}$, so that $30\sqrt{5} + 18\sqrt{5} = 48\sqrt{5}$. **92.** When combining like terms, we add (or subtract) the coefficients of the common factors of the terms: $2xy + 5xy = 7xy$. When combining like radicals, we add (or subtract) the coefficients of the common radical terms: $2\sqrt{ab} + 5\sqrt{ab} = 7\sqrt{ab}$. **93.** $\left\{\frac{1}{2}, \frac{3}{4}\right\}$ **95.** $\{-3, -1\}$ **97.** $\{-3, 1\}$

## Summary Exercises on Operations with Radicals (page 530)

**1.** $-3\sqrt{10}$ **2.** $5 - \sqrt{15}$ **3.** $2 - \sqrt{6} + 2\sqrt{3} - 3\sqrt{2}$ **4.** $6\sqrt{2}$
**5.** $73 - 12\sqrt{35}$ **6.** $\dfrac{\sqrt{6}}{2}$ **7.** $-3 - 2\sqrt{2}$ **8.** $4\sqrt{7} + 4\sqrt{5}$
**9.** $-33$ **10.** $\dfrac{\sqrt{t} - \sqrt{3}}{t - 3}$ **11.** $2xyz^2\sqrt[3]{y^2}$ **12.** $4\sqrt[3]{3}$ **13.** $\sqrt{6} + 1$
**14.** $\dfrac{\sqrt{6x}}{3x}$ **15.** $\frac{3}{5}$ **16.** $4\sqrt{2}$ **17.** $-2\sqrt[3]{2}$ **18.** $11 - 2\sqrt{30}$
**19.** $3\sqrt{3x}$ **20.** $52 + 30\sqrt{3}$ **21.** $\dfrac{2\sqrt[3]{18}}{9}$ **22.** $1$ **23.** $-x^2\sqrt[4]{x}$
**24.** $3\sqrt[3]{2t^2}$ **25.** $4$ **26.** (a) $6$ (b) $\{-6, 6\}$ **27.** (a) $9$ (b) $\{-9, 9\}$
**28.** (a) $\{-2, 2\}$ (b) $-2$ **29.** (a) $\{-3, 3\}$ (b) $-3$
**30.** (a) $\left\{-\frac{1}{2}, \frac{1}{2}\right\}$ (b) $\frac{1}{2}$ **31.** (a) $\left\{-\frac{1}{7}, \frac{1}{7}\right\}$ (b) $\frac{1}{7}$ **32.** (a) $-\frac{4}{5}$
(b) $\left\{-\frac{4}{5}, \frac{4}{5}\right\}$ **33.** (a) $-\frac{7}{10}$ (b) $\left\{-\frac{7}{10}, \frac{7}{10}\right\}$ **34.** (a) $\{-0.2, 0.2\}$
(b) $0.2$ **35.** (a) $\{-0.4, 0.4\}$ (b) $0.4$ **36.** $x^2 = 25; x^2 - 25 = 0;$
$(x + 5)(x - 5) = 0; x = -5$ or $x = 5$; Solution set: $\{-5, 5\}$

## Section 8.6 (pages 536–539)

**1.** $\{49\}$ **3.** $\{7\}$ **5.** $\{85\}$ **7.** $\{-45\}$ **9.** $\left\{-\frac{3}{2}\right\}$ **11.** $\varnothing$
**13.** $\{121\}$ **15.** $\{8\}$ **17.** $\{1\}$ **19.** $\{6\}$ **21.** $\varnothing$ **23.** $\{5\}$ **25.** $\{7\}$
**27.** $\{6\}$ **29.** $\varnothing$ **31.** When the left side is squared, the result should be $x - 1$, not $-(x - 1)$. The correct solution set is $\{17\}$. **33.** $\{-2, 1\}$
**35.** $\{12\}$ **37.** $\{-2, -1\}$ **39.** $\{11\}$ **41.** $\{-1, 3\}$ **43.** $\{9\}$
**45.** $\{8\}$ **47.** $\{9\}$ **49.** $\{2, 11\}$ **51.** We cannot square term by term. The left side must be squared as a binomial in the first step. The correct solution set is $\{4\}$. **53.** $\{2\}$ **55.** $\{9\}$ **57.** $\{4, 20\}$ **59.** $\{-5\}$

**61.** $\left\{-\frac{2}{3}\right\}$ **63.** $\{-1, 8\}$ **65.** $\left\{\frac{4}{3}, 2\right\}$ **67.** $\{-27, 3\}$ **69.** $21$ **71.** $8$
**73.** (a) $70.5$ mph (b) $59.8$ mph (c) $53.9$ mph **75.** yes; $26$ mi
**77.** $47$ mi **79.** $s = 13$ units **80.** $6\sqrt{13}$ sq. units **81.** $h = \sqrt{13}$ units
**82.** $3\sqrt{13}$ sq. units **83.** $6\sqrt{13}$ sq. units **84.** They are both $6\sqrt{13}$.
**85.** $5^6$ **87.** $\dfrac{1}{a^3}$ **89.** $\dfrac{3^2}{p^2}$ **91.** $c^{13}$

## Section 8.7 (pages 542–543)

**1.** A **3.** C **5.** $5$ **7.** $4$ **9.** $2$ **11.** $2$ **13.** $8$ **15.** $9$ **17.** $8$ **19.** $4$
**21.** $-4$ **23.** $-4$ **25.** $\frac{1}{343}$ **27.** $\frac{1}{36}$ **29.** $-\frac{1}{32}$ **31.** $2^{8/3}$ **33.** $\dfrac{1}{6^{1/2}}$
**35.** $\dfrac{1}{15^{1/2}}$ **37.** $11^{1/7}$ **39.** $8^3$ **41.** $6^{1/2}$ **43.** $\dfrac{5^3}{2^3}$ **45.** $\dfrac{1}{2^{8/5}}$ **47.** $6^{2/9}$
**49.** $x^{9/5}$ **51.** $r^{1/9}$ **53.** $m^2n^{1/6}$ **55.** $\dfrac{a^4}{b^{3/2}}$ **57.** $m^{1/6}$ **59.** $2$ **61.** $2$
**63.** $\sqrt{a}$ **65.** $\sqrt[3]{k^2}$ **67.** $-11, 11$ **69.** $-\frac{1}{2}, \frac{1}{2}$ **71.** $2\sqrt{59}$
**73.** $7\sqrt{3}$

## Chapter 8 Review Exercises (pages 547–549)

**1.** $-7, 7$ **2.** $-9, 9$ **3.** $-14, 14$ **4.** $-11, 11$ **5.** $-15, 15$
**6.** $-27, 27$ **7.** $4$ **8.** $-6$ **9.** $10$ **10.** $3$ **11.** It is not a real number.
**12.** $-65$ **13.** $\frac{7}{6}$ **14.** $\frac{10}{9}$ **15.** $\sqrt{53}$ **16.** $8$ **17.** $48.3$ cm
**18.** irrational; $10.536$ **19.** rational; $-5$ **20.** It is not a real number.
**21.** $5\sqrt{3}$ **22.** $-3\sqrt{3}$ **23.** $4\sqrt{10}$ **24.** $-11$ **25.** $12$ **26.** $18$
**27.** $16\sqrt{6}$ **28.** $25\sqrt{10}$ **29.** $-\frac{11}{20}$ **30.** $\dfrac{\sqrt{3}}{7}$ **31.** $\dfrac{\sqrt{7}}{13}$ **32.** $\dfrac{\sqrt{5}}{6}$
**33.** $\frac{2}{15}$ **34.** $3\sqrt{2}$ **35.** $8$ **36.** $2\sqrt{2}$ **37.** $p$ **38.** $\sqrt{km}$ **39.** $r^9$
**40.** $x^5y^8$ **41.** $a^7b^{10}\sqrt{ab}$ **42.** $11x^3y^5$ **43.** $8\sqrt{11}$ **44.** $9\sqrt{2}$
**45.** $21\sqrt{3}$ **46.** $12\sqrt{3}$ **47.** $0$ **48.** $3\sqrt{7}$ **49.** $2\sqrt{3} + 3\sqrt{10}$
**50.** $2\sqrt{2}$ **51.** $6\sqrt{30}$ **52.** $5\sqrt{x}$ **53.** $-m\sqrt{5}$ **54.** $11k^2\sqrt{2n}$
**55.** $\dfrac{8\sqrt{10}}{5}$ **56.** $\sqrt{5}$ **57.** $\sqrt[3]{6}$ **58.** $\dfrac{\sqrt{30}}{15}$ **59.** $\dfrac{\sqrt{10}}{5}$ **60.** $\sqrt{10}$
**61.** $\dfrac{\sqrt{42}}{21}$ **62.** $\dfrac{r\sqrt{x}}{4x}$ **63.** $\dfrac{\sqrt[3]{9}}{3}$ **64.** $\dfrac{\sqrt[3]{98}}{7}$ **65.** $-\sqrt{15} - 9$
**66.** $3\sqrt{6} + 12$ **67.** $22 - 16\sqrt{3}$ **68.** $179 + 20\sqrt{7}$ **69.** $-2$
**70.** $-13$ **71.** $-2 + \sqrt{5}$ **72.** $\dfrac{-2 + 6\sqrt{2}}{17}$
**73.** $\dfrac{2\sqrt{3} + 2 + 3\sqrt{2} + \sqrt{6}}{2}$ **74.** $\dfrac{3 + 2\sqrt{6}}{3}$ **75.** $\dfrac{1 + 3\sqrt{7}}{4}$
**76.** $3 + 4\sqrt{3}$ **77.** $\{25\}$ **78.** $\varnothing$ **79.** $\{48\}$ **80.** $\{1\}$ **81.** $\{2\}$
**82.** $\{-2\}$ **83.** $\{-3, -1\}$ **84.** $\{-2\}$ **85.** $\{4\}$ **86.** $\{-1\}$ **87.** $9$
**88.** $-5$ **89.** $7^3$, or $343$ **90.** $13^{7/5}$ **91.** $x^{3/4}$ **92.** $7$ **93.** $16$
**94.** $\dfrac{2\sqrt{10}}{5}$ **95.** $\dfrac{5 - \sqrt{2}}{23}$ **96.** $-5$ **97.** $5y\sqrt{2}$ **98.** $\dfrac{4r\sqrt{3rs}}{3s}$
**99.** $-\sqrt{10} - 5\sqrt{15}$ **100.** $-7\sqrt{2}$ **101.** $\dfrac{2 + \sqrt{13}}{2}$
**102.** $166 + 2\sqrt{7}$ **103.** $7 - 2\sqrt{10}$ **104.** $x^2$ **105.** $-11$
**106.** $11\sqrt{3}$ **107.** $\{7\}$ **108.** $\varnothing$ **109.** $\{8\}$
**110.** (a) $57$ species (b) $347$ species

## Chapter 8 Test (pages 549–550)

[8.1] **1.** $-14, 14$   **2. (a)** irrational   **(b)** $11.916$   **3. (a)** B   **(b)** F
**(c)** D   **(d)** A   **(e)** C   **(f)** A   [8.2] **4.** $\dfrac{8\sqrt{2}}{5}$   **5.** $2\sqrt[3]{4}$   **6.** $4\sqrt{6}$
[8.3] **7.** $9\sqrt{7}$   **8.** $-5\sqrt{3x}$   [8.2] **9.** $2y\sqrt[3]{4x^2}$   [8.5] **10.** $31$
**11.** $6\sqrt{2} + 2 - 3\sqrt{14} - \sqrt{7}$   **12.** $11 + 2\sqrt{30}$   [8.3] **13.** $-6x\sqrt[3]{2x}$
[8.4] **14.** $\dfrac{\sqrt[3]{18}}{3}$   [8.1] **15. (a)** $6\sqrt{2}$ in.   **(b)** $8.485$ in.   **16.** $50$ ohms
[8.4] **17.** $\dfrac{5\sqrt{14}}{7}$   **18.** $\dfrac{\sqrt{6x}}{3x}$   **19.** $-\sqrt[3]{2}$   [8.5] **20.** $\dfrac{-12 - 3\sqrt{3}}{13}$
**21.** $\dfrac{1 + \sqrt{2}}{2}$   [8.6] **22.** $\emptyset$   **23.** $\{3\}$   **24.** $\left\{\frac{1}{4}, 1\right\}$   **25.** $\{-4\}$
**26.** 12 is not a solution. A check shows that it does not satisfy the original equation. The solution set is $\emptyset$.   [8.7] **27.** $16$   **28.** $-25$   **29.** $5$
**30.** $\frac{1}{3}$

## Chapters 1–8 Cumulative Review Exercises (pages 551–552)

[1.2] **1.** $54$   **2.** $6$   [1.4] **3.** $3$   [2.3] **4.** $\{3\}$   [2.8] **5.** $[-16, \infty)$
**6.** $(5, \infty)$   [2.4] **7.** 2006: \$329,924; 2007: \$425,115
[3.2] **8.** 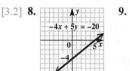   **9.**    [3.5] **10.**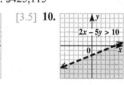

[3.3, 3.4] **11. (a)** 20.3; The number of subscribers increased by an average of 20.3 million per yr.   **(b)** $y = 20.3x + 140.8$   **(c)** 303.2 million
[4.1–4.3] **12.** $\{(3, -7)\}$   **13.** $\{(x, y) \mid 2x - y = 6\}$
[4.4] **14.** from Chicago: 61 mph; from Des Moines: 54 mph
[5.1] **15.** $12x^{10}y^2$   [5.2] **16.** $\dfrac{y^{15}}{2^3 \cdot 3^6}$, or $\dfrac{y^{15}}{5832}$
[5.4] **17.** $3x^3 + 11x^2 - 13$   [5.7] **18.** $4t^2 - 8t + 5$
[6.2–6.4] **19.** $(m + 8)(m + 4)$   **20.** $(6a + 5b)(2a - b)$
**21.** $(9z + 4)^2$   [7.2] **22.** $\dfrac{x + 1}{x}$   **23.** $(t + 5)(t + 3)$, or $t^2 + 8t + 15$
[7.4] **24.** $\dfrac{y^2}{(y + 1)(y - 1)}$   **25.** $\dfrac{-2x - 14}{(x + 3)(x - 1)}$   [7.5] **26.** $-21$
[6.5] **27.** $\{3, 4\}$   **28.** $\{-2, -1\}$   [7.6] **29.** $\{19\}$
**30.** $B = \dfrac{CD - AD}{AC - 1}$   [8.6] **31.** $\{16\}$   [8.3] **32.** $29\sqrt{3}$
[8.5] **33.** $-\sqrt{3} + \sqrt{5}$   **34.** $21 - 5\sqrt{2}$   [8.7] **35.** $32$

## 9 QUADRATIC EQUATIONS

## Section 9.1 (pages 557–559)

**1.** C   **3.** D   **5.** $\{-7, 8\}$   **7.** $\{-11, 11\}$, or $\{\pm 11\}$   **9.** $\left\{-\frac{5}{3}, 6\right\}$
**11.** $\{\pm 9\}$   **13.** $\{\pm\sqrt{14}\}$   **15.** $\{\pm 4\sqrt{3}\}$   **17.** $\emptyset$   **19.** $\left\{\pm\frac{5}{2}\right\}$
**21.** $\{\pm 1.5\}$   **23.** $\{\pm\sqrt{3}\}$   **25.** $\left\{\pm\dfrac{2\sqrt{7}}{7}\right\}$   **27.** $\{\pm 2\sqrt{6}\}$

**29.** $\left\{\pm\dfrac{2\sqrt{5}}{5}\right\}$   **31.** $\{\pm 3\sqrt{3}\}$   **33.** $\{\pm 2\sqrt{2}\}$   **35.** According to the
square root property, $-9$ is also a solution, so her answer was not completely correct. The solution set is $\{\pm 9\}$.   **37.** $\{-2, 8\}$   **39.** $\emptyset$
**41.** $\{8 \pm 3\sqrt{3}\}$   **43.** $\left\{-3, \frac{5}{3}\right\}$   **45.** $\left\{0, \frac{3}{2}\right\}$   **47.** $\left\{\dfrac{5 \pm \sqrt{30}}{2}\right\}$
**49.** $\left\{\dfrac{-1 \pm 3\sqrt{2}}{3}\right\}$   **51.** $\{-10 \pm 4\sqrt{3}\}$   **53.** $\left\{\dfrac{1 \pm 4\sqrt{3}}{4}\right\}$
**55.** Jeff's first solution, $\dfrac{5 + \sqrt{30}}{2}$, is equivalent to Linda's second
solution, $\dfrac{-5 - \sqrt{30}}{-2}$. This can be verified by multiplying $\dfrac{5 + \sqrt{30}}{2}$
by 1 in the form $\frac{-1}{-1}$. Similarly, Jeff's second solution is equivalent to Linda's first one.   **57.** $\{-4.48, 0.20\}$   **59.** $\{-3.09, -0.15\}$
**61.** about $\frac{1}{2}$ sec   **63.** 9 in.   **65.** 2%   **67.** $\dfrac{4 + 4\sqrt{3}}{5}$   **69.** $\dfrac{3 + \sqrt{6}}{4}$
**71.** $(x - 5)^2$

## Section 9.2 (pages 565–567)

**1.** $25; (x + 5)^2$   **3.** $100; (z - 10)^2$   **5.** $1; (x + 1)^2$   **7.** $\frac{25}{4}; \left(p - \frac{5}{2}\right)^2$
**9.** D   **11.** $\{1, 3\}$   **13.** $\{-1 \pm \sqrt{6}\}$   **15.** $\{4 \pm 2\sqrt{3}\}$   **17.** $\{-3\}$
**19.** $\left\{-\frac{3}{2}, \frac{1}{2}\right\}$   **21.** $\emptyset$   **23.** $\left\{\dfrac{9 \pm \sqrt{21}}{6}\right\}$   **25.** $\left\{\dfrac{-7 \pm \sqrt{97}}{6}\right\}$
**27.** $\{-4, 2\}$   **29.** $\{4 \pm \sqrt{3}\}$   **31.** $\{1 \pm \sqrt{6}\}$
**33. (a)** $\left\{\dfrac{3 \pm 2\sqrt{6}}{3}\right\}$   **(b)** $\{-0.633, 2.633\}$   **35. (a)** $\{-2 \pm \sqrt{3}\}$
**(b)** $\{-3.732, -0.268\}$   **37.** 3 sec and 5 sec   **39.** 1 sec and 5 sec
**41.** 75 ft by 100 ft   **43.** 8 mi   **45.** $x^2$   **46.** $x^2 + 8x$
**47.** $x^2 + 8x + 16$   **48.** It occurred when we added the 16 squares.
**49.** $\dfrac{4 - 3\sqrt{3}}{3}$   **51.** $\dfrac{2 - \sqrt{5}}{2}$   **53.** $2\sqrt{5}$

## Section 9.3 (pages 571–573)

**1.** $a = 3, b = 4, c = -8$   **3.** $a = -8, b = -2, c = -3$
**5.** $a = 3, b = -4, c = -2$   **7.** $a = 3, b = 7, c = 0$
**9.** $a = 1, b = 1, c = -12$   **11.** $a = 9, b = 9, c = -26$
**13.** $2a$ should be the denominator for $-b$ as well. The correct
formula is $x = \dfrac{-b \pm \sqrt{b^2 - 4ac}}{2a}$.   **15.** $\{-13, 1\}$
**17.** $\left\{\dfrac{-6 \pm \sqrt{26}}{2}\right\}$   **19.** $\{2\}$   **21.** $\left\{-1, \frac{5}{2}\right\}$   **23.** $\{-1, 0\}$
**25.** $\left\{0, \frac{12}{7}\right\}$   **27.** $\{\pm 2\sqrt{6}\}$   **29.** $\left\{\pm\frac{2}{5}\right\}$   **31.** $\left\{\dfrac{6 \pm 2\sqrt{6}}{3}\right\}$   **33.** $\emptyset$
**35.** $\emptyset$   **37.** $\left\{\dfrac{-5 \pm \sqrt{61}}{2}\right\}$   **39. (a)** $\left\{\dfrac{-1 \pm \sqrt{11}}{2}\right\}$
**(b)** $\{-2.158, 1.158\}$   **41. (a)** $\left\{\dfrac{1 \pm \sqrt{5}}{2}\right\}$   **(b)** $\{-0.618, 1.618\}$
**43.** $\left\{-\frac{2}{3}, \frac{4}{3}\right\}$   **45.** $\left\{\dfrac{-1 \pm \sqrt{73}}{6}\right\}$   **47.** $\emptyset$   **49.** $\{1 \pm \sqrt{2}\}$
**51.** $\left\{-1, \frac{5}{2}\right\}$   **53.** $r = \dfrac{-\pi h \pm \sqrt{\pi^2 h^2 + \pi S}}{\pi}$   **55.** 3.5 ft

**57.** $\{16, -8\}$; Only 16 ft is a reasonable answer. **59.** $-5 + 8z$
**61.** $-2 + 3k$ **63.** $24 - 2r - 15r^2$

## Summary Exercises on Quadratic Equations (pages 573–574)

**1.** $\{\pm 6\}$ **2.** $\left\{\dfrac{-3 \pm \sqrt{5}}{2}\right\}$ **3.** $\{-4, 6\}$ **4.** $\left\{\pm \dfrac{7}{9}\right\}$ **5.** $\{1, 3\}$

**6.** $\{-2, -1\}$ **7.** $\{4, 5\}$ **8.** $\left\{\dfrac{-3 \pm \sqrt{17}}{2}\right\}$ **9.** $\left\{-\dfrac{1}{3}, \dfrac{5}{3}\right\}$

**10.** $\left\{\dfrac{1 \pm \sqrt{10}}{2}\right\}$ **11.** $\{-17, 5\}$ **12.** $\left\{-\dfrac{7}{5}, 1\right\}$ **13.** $\left\{\dfrac{7 \pm 2\sqrt{6}}{3}\right\}$

**14.** $\left\{\dfrac{1 \pm 4\sqrt{2}}{7}\right\}$ **15.** $\varnothing$ **16.** $\varnothing$ **17.** $\left\{-\dfrac{1}{2}, 2\right\}$ **18.** $\left\{-\dfrac{1}{2}, 1\right\}$

**19.** $\left\{-\dfrac{5}{4}, \dfrac{3}{2}\right\}$ **20.** $\left\{-3, \dfrac{1}{3}\right\}$ **21.** $\left\{1 \pm \sqrt{2}\right\}$ **22.** $\left\{\dfrac{-5 \pm \sqrt{13}}{6}\right\}$

**23.** $\left\{\dfrac{2}{5}, 4\right\}$ **24.** $\left\{-3 \pm \sqrt{5}\right\}$ **25.** $\left\{\dfrac{-3 \pm \sqrt{41}}{2}\right\}$ **26.** $\left\{-\dfrac{5}{4}\right\}$

**27.** $\left\{\dfrac{1}{4}, 1\right\}$ **28.** $\left\{\dfrac{1 \pm \sqrt{3}}{2}\right\}$ **29.** $\left\{\dfrac{-2 \pm \sqrt{11}}{3}\right\}$

**30.** $\left\{\dfrac{-5 \pm \sqrt{41}}{8}\right\}$ **31.** $\left\{\dfrac{-7 \pm \sqrt{5}}{4}\right\}$ **32.** $\left\{\dfrac{-5 \pm \sqrt{5}}{2}\right\}$

**33.** $\left\{\dfrac{8 \pm 8\sqrt{2}}{3}\right\}$ **34.** $\left\{-\dfrac{8}{3}, -\dfrac{6}{5}\right\}$ **35.** $\varnothing$ **36.** $\varnothing$ **37.** $\left\{-\dfrac{2}{3}, 2\right\}$

**38.** $\left\{-\dfrac{1}{4}, \dfrac{2}{3}\right\}$ **39.** $\left\{-4, \dfrac{3}{5}\right\}$ **40.** $\{-3, 5\}$ **41.** $\left\{-\dfrac{2}{3}, \dfrac{5}{2}\right\}$ **42.** $\left\{\pm \dfrac{10}{9}\right\}$

## Section 9.4 (pages 579–580)

**1.** $3i$ **3.** $2i\sqrt{5}$ **5.** $3i\sqrt{2}$ **7.** $5i\sqrt{5}$ **9.** $5 + 3i$ **11.** $6 - 9i$
**13.** $-6 + 2i$ **15.** $-8 + 6i$ **17.** $6 - 7i$ **19.** $-2$ **21.** $-6$
**23.** $6 + 8i$ **25.** $14 + 5i$ **27.** $7 - 22i$ **29.** $45$ **31.** $\dfrac{1}{2} + \dfrac{1}{2}i$
**33.** $2 - 6i$ **35.** $-\dfrac{3}{25} + \dfrac{4}{25}i$ **37.** $2 + 5i$ **39.** $3 - i$ **41.** $\dfrac{1}{2} + \dfrac{2}{3}i$
**43.** $\{-1 \pm 2i\}$ **45.** $\left\{3 \pm i\sqrt{5}\right\}$ **47.** $\left\{-\dfrac{2}{3} \pm i\sqrt{2}\right\}$ **49.** $\{1 \pm i\}$
**51.** $\left\{-\dfrac{3}{4} \pm \dfrac{\sqrt{31}}{4}i\right\}$ **53.** $\left\{\dfrac{3}{2} \pm \dfrac{\sqrt{7}}{2}i\right\}$ **55.** $\left\{\dfrac{1}{5} \pm \dfrac{\sqrt{14}}{5}i\right\}$
**57.** $\left\{-\dfrac{1}{2} \pm \dfrac{\sqrt{13}}{2}i\right\}$ **59.** $\left\{\dfrac{1}{2} \pm \dfrac{\sqrt{11}}{2}i\right\}$ **61.** true

**63.** false; For example, $3 + 2i$ is a complex number but it is not real.
**65.**  **67.** $16$

## Section 9.5 (pages 585–587)

**1.** $(0, -6)$ **3.** $(-3, 0)$ **5.** $(-1, 2)$

**7.** $(4, 0)$ **9.** $(3, 4)$ **11.** $(-2, -4)$

**13.** one real solution; $\{2\}$ **15.** two real solutions; $\{\pm 2\}$ **17.** no real
solutions; $\varnothing$ **19.** If $a > 0$, it opens upward, and if $a < 0$, it opens
downward. **21.** $\{-2, 3\}$ *In Exercises 23–27, we give the domain first,
and then the range.* **23.** $(-\infty, \infty)$; $[0, \infty)$ **25.** $(-\infty, \infty)$; $(-\infty, 4]$
**27.** $(-\infty, \infty)$; $[1, \infty)$ **29.** $3$ **31.** $21$ **33.** 40 and 40 **35.** $y = \dfrac{11}{5625}x^2$
**37.** In each case, there is a vertical "stretch" of the parabola. It becomes
narrower as the coefficient gets larger. **38.** In each case, there is a
vertical "shrink" of the parabola. It becomes wider as the coefficient gets
smaller. **39.** The graph of $Y_2$ is obtained by reflecting the graph of
$Y_1$ across the $x$-axis. **40.** When the coefficient of $x^2$ is negative, the
parabola opens downward. **41.** By adding a positive constant $k$, the graph
is shifted $k$ units upward. By subtracting a positive constant $k$, the graph
is shifted $k$ units downward. **42.** Adding a positive constant $k$ before
squaring moves the graph $k$ units to the left. Subtracting a positive
constant $k$ before squaring moves the graph $k$ units to the right.

## Chapter 9 Review Exercises (pages 591–593)

**1.** $\{\pm 12\}$ **2.** $\left\{\pm \sqrt{37}\right\}$ **3.** $\left\{\pm 8\sqrt{2}\right\}$ **4.** $\{-7, 3\}$ **5.** $\left\{3 \pm \sqrt{10}\right\}$
**6.** $\left\{\dfrac{-1 \pm \sqrt{14}}{2}\right\}$ **7.** $\varnothing$ **8.** $\left\{\dfrac{3 \pm 2\sqrt{2}}{5}\right\}$ **9.** $\{-5, -1\}$
**10.** $\left\{-2 \pm \sqrt{11}\right\}$ **11.** $\left\{-1 \pm \sqrt{6}\right\}$ **12.** $\left\{\dfrac{-4 \pm \sqrt{22}}{2}\right\}$
**13.** $\left\{-\dfrac{2}{5}, 1\right\}$ **14.** $\varnothing$ **15.** 2.5 sec **16.** 6, 8, 10 **17.** $\left(\dfrac{3}{2}\right)^2$, or $\dfrac{9}{4}$
**18. (a)** $\{\pm 3\}$ **(b)** $\{\pm 3\}$ **(c)** $\{\pm 3\}$ **(d)** Because there is only one
solution set, we will always get the same results, no matter which method
of solution is used. **19.** $\left\{1 \pm \sqrt{5}\right\}$ **20.** $\varnothing$ **21.** $\left\{\dfrac{2 \pm \sqrt{10}}{2}\right\}$
**22.** $\left\{\dfrac{-1 \pm \sqrt{29}}{4}\right\}$ **23.** $\left\{\dfrac{-3 \pm \sqrt{41}}{2}\right\}$ **24.** $\left\{-\dfrac{2}{3}, 1\right\}$
**25.** There are no real solutions. **26.** $5 - i$ **27.** $-6 - 5i$ **28.** $20$
**29.** $13$ **30.** $i$ **31.** $\dfrac{28}{13} - \dfrac{3}{13}i$ **32.** $a$ (the real number itself)
**33.** No, the product $(a + bi)(a - bi) = a^2 + b^2$ will always be the
sum of the squares of two real numbers, which is a real number.
**34.** $\left\{-2 \pm i\sqrt{3}\right\}$ **35.** $\left\{\dfrac{2}{3} \pm \dfrac{2\sqrt{2}}{3}i\right\}$ **36.** $\left\{\dfrac{1}{3} \pm \dfrac{\sqrt{2}}{3}i\right\}$
**37.** $\left\{-\dfrac{3}{2} \pm \dfrac{\sqrt{23}}{2}i\right\}$ **38.** $\left\{\dfrac{3}{8} \pm \dfrac{\sqrt{23}}{8}i\right\}$ **39.** $\left\{-\dfrac{1}{9} \pm \dfrac{2\sqrt{2}}{9}i\right\}$
**40.** $(0, 0)$ **41.** $(0, 5)$ **42.** $(-4, 0)$

**43.** $(1, 0)$     **44.** $(1, 4)$     **45.** $(-2, -2)$

$y = x^2 - 2x + 1$

$y = -x^2 + 2x + 3$

$y = x^2 + 4x + 2$

**46.** two; $\{\pm 2\}$; $(-\infty, \infty)$; $[-2, \infty)$   **47.** one; $\{2\}$; $(-\infty, \infty)$; $(-\infty, 0]$

**48.** none; $\emptyset$; $(-\infty, \infty)$; $[1, \infty)$   **49.** $\left\{-\frac{11}{2}, 5\right\}$   **50.** $\left\{-\frac{11}{2}, \frac{9}{2}\right\}$

**51.** $\left\{\dfrac{-1 \pm \sqrt{21}}{2}\right\}$   **52.** $\left\{-\frac{3}{2}, \frac{1}{3}\right\}$   **53.** $\left\{\dfrac{-5 \pm \sqrt{17}}{2}\right\}$

**54.** $\left\{-1 \pm \sqrt{3}\right\}$   **55.** $\emptyset$   **56.** $\left\{\dfrac{9 \pm \sqrt{41}}{2}\right\}$   **57.** $\left\{-\frac{5}{3}\right\}$

**58.** $\left\{-1 \pm 2\sqrt{2}\right\}$   **59.** $\left\{-2 \pm \sqrt{5}\right\}$   **60.** $\left\{\pm 2\sqrt{2}\right\}$

**61.** 400 or 800   **62.** $(6, 10)$; demand: 600; price: \$10

## Chapter 9 Test (pages 593–594)

[9.1] **1.** $\left\{\pm \sqrt{39}\right\}$   **2.** $\{-11, 5\}$   **3.** $\left\{\dfrac{-3 \pm 2\sqrt{6}}{4}\right\}$

[9.2] **4.** $\left\{2 \pm \sqrt{10}\right\}$   **5.** $\left\{\dfrac{-6 \pm \sqrt{42}}{2}\right\}$   [9.3] **6.** $\left\{0, -\frac{2}{5}\right\}$

**7.** $\left\{-3, \frac{1}{2}\right\}$   **8.** $\left\{\dfrac{3 \pm \sqrt{3}}{3}\right\}$   [9.4] **9.** $\left\{-1 \pm \dfrac{\sqrt{7}}{2}i\right\}$

[9.3] **10.** $\left\{\dfrac{5 \pm \sqrt{13}}{6}\right\}$   [9.1–9.3] **11.** $\left\{1 \pm \sqrt{2}\right\}$

**12.** $\left\{\dfrac{-1 \pm 3\sqrt{2}}{2}\right\}$   **13.** $\left\{\dfrac{11 \pm \sqrt{89}}{4}\right\}$   **14.** $\{5\}$   **15.** 2 sec

**16.** 12, 16, 20   [9.4] **17.** $-5 + 5i$   **18.** $-17 - 4i$   **19.** 73   **20.** $2 - i$

[9.5] **21.** $(3, 0)$     **22.** $(-1, -3)$     **23.** $(-3, -2)$

$y = x^2 - 6x + 9$

$y = -x^2 - 2x - 4$

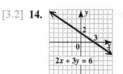
$f(x) = x^2 + 6x + 7$

**24. (a)** two   **(b)** $\left\{-3 \pm \sqrt{2}\right\}$   **(c)** $-3 - \sqrt{2} \approx -4.414$ and $-3 + \sqrt{2} \approx -1.586$   **25.** 200 and 200

## Chapters 1–9 Cumulative Review Exercises (pages 594–596)

[1.6] **1.** 15   **2.** 5   [1.8] **3.** $-r + 7$   **4.** $19m - 17$

[2.1–2.3] **5.** $\{18\}$   **6.** $\{5\}$   **7.** $\left\{\frac{8}{3}\right\}$   **8.** $\{2\}$   [2.5] **9.** 100°, 80°

**10.** width: 50 ft; length: 94 ft   **11.** $L = \dfrac{P - 2W}{2}$, or $L = \dfrac{P}{2} - W$

[2.8] **12.** $(-2, \infty)$

**13.** $(-\infty, 4]$

[3.2] **14.**

**15.**
$y = 3$

$-2x + 3y = 6$

[3.3] **16.** $-\frac{1}{3}$   [3.4] **17.** $2x - y = -3$   [4.1–4.3] **18.** $\{(-3, 2)\}$

**19.** $\emptyset$   [4.4] **20.** AT&T: \$14.99; jWIN: \$19.99

[4.5] **21.**
$2x + y \le 4$
$x - y > 2$

[5.1, 5.2] **22.** $\dfrac{x^4}{3^2}$, or $\dfrac{x^4}{9}$   **23.** $\dfrac{b^{16}}{c^2}$

[5.4] **24.** $8x^5 - 17x^4 - x^2$

[5.5] **25.** $2x^4 + x^3 - 19x^2 + 2x + 20$

[5.7] **26.** $3x^2 - 2x + 1$   [5.3] **27. (a)** $6.35 \times 10^9$   **(b)** $0.00023$

[6.1] **28.** $16x^2(x - 3y)$   [6.3] **29.** $(2a + 1)(a - 3)$

[6.4] **30.** $(4x^2 + 1)(2x + 1)(2x - 1)$   **31.** $(5m - 2)^2$

[6.5] **32.** $\{-9, 6\}$   [6.6] **33.** 50 m   [7.2] **34.** $\frac{4}{5}$   [7.4] **35.** $\dfrac{-k - 1}{k(k - 1)}$

**36.** $\dfrac{5a + 2}{(a - 2)^2(a + 2)}$   [7.5] **37.** $\dfrac{b + a}{b - a}$   [7.6] **38.** $\left\{-\frac{15}{7}, 2\right\}$

[8.1] **39.** 10   [8.4] **40.** $\dfrac{6\sqrt{30}}{5}$   **41.** $\dfrac{\sqrt[3]{28}}{4}$   [8.3] **42.** $4\sqrt{5}$

[8.6] **43.** $\{7\}$   [8.7] **44. (a)** 4   **(b)** $-2$   [9.1] **45.** $\left\{\dfrac{-2 \pm 2\sqrt{3}}{3}\right\}$

[9.2] **46.** $\left\{-1 \pm \sqrt{6}\right\}$   [9.3] **47.** $\left\{\dfrac{2 \pm \sqrt{10}}{2}\right\}$

[9.4] **48. (a)** $8i$   **(b)** $5 + 2i$   **49.** $\left\{-\dfrac{1}{2} \pm \dfrac{\sqrt{17}}{2}i\right\}$

[9.5] **50.**
$f(x) = -x^2 - 2x + 1$

vertex: $(-1, 2)$;
domain: $(-\infty, \infty)$;
range: $(-\infty, 2]$

### APPENDIX A: SETS

## (pages 600–601)

**1.** $\{1, 2, 3, 4, 5, 6, 7\}$   **3.** $\{\text{winter, spring, summer, fall}\}$   **5.** $\emptyset$

**7.** $\{L\}$   **9.** $\{2, 4, 6, 8, 10, \dots\}$   **11.** The sets in **Exercises 9 and 10** are infinite sets.   **13.** true   **15.** false   **17.** true   **19.** true   **21.** true

**23.** true   **25.** true   **27.** false   **29.** true   **31.** true   **33.** false

**35.** true   **37.** true   **39.** false   **41.** false   **43.** true   **45.** $\{g, h\}$

**47.** $\{b, c, d, e, g, h\}$   **49.** $\{a, c, e\} = B$   **51.** $\{d\} = D$   **53.** $\{a\}$

**55.** $\{a, c, d, e\}$   **57.** $\{a, c, e, f\}$   **59.** $\emptyset$   **61.** $B$ and $D$; $C$ and $D$

# Glossary

*For a more complete discussion, see the section(s) in parentheses.*

## A

**absolute value**   The absolute value of a number is the distance between 0 and the number on a number line. (Section 1.4)

**addition property of equality**   The addition property of equality states that the same number can be added to (or subtracted from) both sides of an equation to obtain an equivalent equation. (Section 2.1)

**addition property of inequality**   The addition property of inequality states that the same number can be added to (or subtracted from) both sides of an inequality without changing the solution set. (Section 2.8)

**additive inverse (opposite)**   The additive inverse of a number $x$, symbolized $-x$, is the number that is the same distance from 0 on the number line as $x$, but on the opposite side of 0. The number 0 is its own additive inverse. For all real numbers $x$, $x + (-x) = (-x) + x = 0$. (Section 1.4)

**algebraic expression**   An algebraic expression is a sequence of numbers, variables, operation symbols, and/or grouping symbols (such as parentheses) formed according to the rules of algebra. (Section 1.3)

**area**   Area is a measure of the surface covered by a two-dimensional (flat) figure. (Section 2.5)

**associative property of addition**   The associative property of addition states that the grouping of terms in a sum does not affect the sum. (Section 1.7)

**associative property of multiplication**   The associative property of multiplication states that the grouping of factors in a product does not affect the product. (Section 1.7)

**axis (axis of symmetry)**   The axis of a parabola is the vertical or horizontal line (depending on the orientation of the graph) through the vertex of the parabola. (Sections 5.4, 9.5)

## B

**base**   The base in an exponential expression is the expression that is the repeated factor. In $b^x$, $b$ is the base. (Sections 1.2, 5.1)

**binomial**   A binomial is a polynomial consisting of exactly two terms. (Section 5.4)

**boundary line**   In the graph of a linear inequality, the boundary line separates the region that satisfies the inequality from the region that does not satisfy the inequality. (Section 3.5)

## C

**circle graph (pie chart)**   A circle graph (or pie chart) is a circle divided into sectors, or wedges, whose sizes show the relative magnitudes of the categories of data being represented. (Section 1.1)

**coefficient** (See **numerical coefficient.**)

**combining like terms**   Combining like terms is a method of adding or subtracting terms having exactly the same variable factors by using the properties of real numbers. (Section 1.8)

**common factor**   An integer that is a factor of two or more integers is called a common factor of those integers. (Section 6.1)

**commutative property of addition**   The commutative property of addition states that the order of terms in a sum does not affect the sum. (Section 1.7)

**commutative property of multiplication**   The commutative property of multiplication states that the order of factors in a product does not affect the product. (Section 1.7)

**complement of a set**   The set of elements in the universal set that are not in a set $A$ is the complement of $A$, written $A'$. (Appendix)

**complementary angles (complements)**   Complementary angles are two angles whose measures have a sum of $90°$. (Section 2.4)

**completing the square**   The process of adding to a binomial the expression that makes it a perfect square trinomial is called completing the square. (Section 9.2)

**complex fraction**   A complex fraction is a quotient with one or more fractions in the numerator, denominator, or both. (Section 7.5)

**complex number**   A complex number is any number that can be written in the form $a + bi$, where $a$ and $b$ are real numbers and $i$ is the imaginary unit. (Section 9.4)

**components**   In an ordered pair $(x, y)$, $x$ and $y$ are called the components of the ordered pair. (Section 3.6)

**composite number**   A natural number greater than 1 that is not prime is a composite number. It is composed of prime factors represented in one and only one way. (Section 1.1)

**conditional equation**   A conditional equation is true for some replacements of the variable and false for others. (Section 2.3)

**conjugate**   The conjugate of $a + b$ is $a - b$. (Section 8.5)

**conjugate of a complex number**   The conjugate of a complex number $a + bi$ is $a - bi$. (Section 9.4)

**consecutive integers**   Two integers that differ by 1 are called consecutive integers. (Sections 2.4, 6.6)

**consistent system**   A system of equations with a solution is called a consistent system. (Section 4.1)

**constant of variation**   In the equation $y = kx$ or $y = \frac{k}{x}$, the nonzero real number $k$ is called the constant of variation. (Section 7.8)

**contradiction**   A contradiction is an equation that is never true. It has no solution. (Section 2.3)

**coordinate on a number line**   Every point on a number line is associated with a unique real number, called the coordinate of the point. (Section 1.4)

**coordinates of a point**   The numbers in an ordered pair are called the coordinates of the corresponding point in the plane. (Section 3.1)

**cross products**   The cross products in the proportion $\frac{a}{b} = \frac{c}{d}$ are $ad$ and $bc$. (Section 2.6)

**cube root**   A number $b$ is a cube root of $a$ if $b^3 = a$ is true. (Section 8.1)

## D

**degree**   A degree is a basic unit of measure for angles in which one degree ($1°$) is $\frac{1}{360}$ of a complete revolution. (Section 2.4)

**degree of a polynomial**   The degree of a polynomial is the greatest degree of any of the terms in the polynomial. (Section 5.4)

**degree of a term**   The degree of a term is the sum of the exponents on the variables in the term. (Section 5.4)

**denominator**   The number below the fraction bar in a fraction is called the denominator. It indicates the number of equal parts in a whole. (Section 1.1)

**dependent equations**    Equations of a system that have the same graph (because they are different forms of the same equation) are called dependent equations. (Section 4.1)

**descending powers**    A polynomial in one variable is written in descending powers of the variable if the exponents on the variables of the terms of the polynomial decrease from left to right. (Section 5.4)

**difference**    The answer to a subtraction problem is called the difference. (Section 1.1)

**difference of cubes**    The difference of cubes, $x^3 - y^3$, can be factored as $x^3 - y^3 = (x - y)(x^2 + xy + y^2)$. (Section 6.4)

**difference of squares**    The difference of squares, $x^2 - y^2$, can be factored as $x^2 - y^2 = (x + y)(x - y)$. (Section 6.4)

**direct variation**    $y$ varies directly as $x$ if there exists a nonzero real number (constant) $k$ such that $y = kx$. (Section 7.8)

**discriminant**    The discriminant of the quadratic equation $ax^2 + bx + c = 0$ is the quantity $b^2 - 4ac$ under the radical in the quadratic formula. (Section 9.3)

**disjoint sets**    Sets that have no elements in common are disjoint sets. (Appendix)

**distributive property of multiplication with respect to addition (distributive property)**    For any real numbers $a$, $b$, and $c$, the distributive property states that $a(b + c) = ab + ac$ and $(b + c)a = ba + ca$. (Section 1.7)

**domain**    The set of all first components ($x$-values) in the ordered pairs of a relation is called the domain. (Section 3.6)

### E

**elements (members)**    The elements (members) of a set are the objects that belong to the set. (Section 1.3, Appendix)

**elimination method**    The elimination method is an algebraic method used to solve a system of equations in which the equations of the system are combined so that one or more variables is eliminated. (Section 4.3)

**empty set (null set)**    The empty set, denoted by { } or $\emptyset$, is the set containing no elements. (Section 2.3, Appendix)

**equation**    An equation is a statement that two algebraic expressions are equal. (Section 1.3)

**equivalent equations**    Equivalent equations are equations that have the same solution set. (Section 2.1)

**exponent (power)**    An exponent, or power, is a number that indicates how many times its base is used as a factor. In $b^x$, $x$ is the exponent (power). (Sections 1.2, 5.1)

**exponential expression**    A number or letter (variable) written with an exponent is an exponential expression. (Sections 1.2, 5.1)

**extraneous solution**    A proposed solution to an equation, following any of several procedures in the solution process, that does not satisfy the original equation is called an extraneous solution. (Section 8.6)

**extremes of a proportion**    In the proportion $\frac{a}{b} = \frac{c}{d}$, the $a$- and $d$-terms are called the extremes. (Section 2.6)

### F

**factor**    If $a$, $b$, and $c$ represent numbers and $a \cdot b = c$, than $a$ and $b$ are factors of $c$. (Sections 1.1, 6.1)

**factored**    A number is factored by writing it as the product of two or more numbers. (Section 1.1)

**factored form**    An expression is in factored form when it is written as a product. (Section 6.1)

**factoring**    Writing a polynomial as the product of two or more simpler polynomials is called factoring. (Section 6.1)

**factoring by grouping**    Factoring by grouping is a method for grouping the terms of a polynomial in such a way that the polynomial can be factored. It is used when the greatest common factor of the terms of the polynomial is 1. (Section 6.1)

**factoring out the greatest common factor**    Factoring out the greatest common factor is the process of using the distributive property to write a polynomial as a product of the greatest common factor and a simpler polynomial. (Section 6.1)

**FOIL**    FOIL is a mnemonic device which represents a method for multiplying two binomials $(a + b)(c + d)$. Multiply **F**irst terms $ac$, **O**uter terms $ad$, **I**nner terms $bc$, and **L**ast terms $bd$. Then combine like terms. (Section 5.5)

**formula**    A formula is an equation in which variables are used to describe a relationship among several quantities. (Section 2.5)

**fourth root**    A number $b$ is a fourth root of $a$ if $b^4 = a$ is true. (Section 8.1)

**function**    A function is a set of ordered pairs $(x, y)$ in which each value of the first component $x$ corresponds to exactly one value of the second component $y$. (Section 3.6)

**function notation**    If a function is denoted by $f$, the notation $y = f(x)$ is called function notation. Here $y$, or $f(x)$, represents the value of the function at $x$. (Section 3.6)

### G

**graph of a number**    The point on a number line that corresponds to a number is its graph. (Section 1.4)

**graph of an equation**    The graph of an equation in two variables is the set of all points that correspond to all of the ordered pairs that satisfy the equation. (Section 3.2)

**graphing method**    The graphing method for solving a system of equations requires graphing all equations of the system on the same axes and locating the ordered pair(s) of their intersection. (Section 4.1)

**greatest common factor (GCF)**    The greatest common factor of a list of integers is the largest factor of all those integers. The greatest common factor of the terms of a polynomial is the largest factor of all the terms in the polynomial. (Sections 1.1, 6.1)

**grouping symbols**    Examples of grouping symbols are parentheses ( ), brackets [ ], and fraction bars. (Section 1.2)

### H

**hypotenuse**    The side opposite the right angle in a right triangle is the longest side and is called the hypotenuse. (Section 6.6)

### I

**identity**    An identity is an equation that is true for all valid replacements of the variable. It has an infinite number of solutions. (Section 2.3)

**identity element for addition**    For all real numbers $a$, $a + 0 = 0 + a = a$. The number 0 is called the identity element for addition. (Section 1.7)

**identity element for multiplication**    For all real numbers $a$, $a \cdot 1 = 1 \cdot a = a$. The number 1 is called the identity element for multiplication. (Section 1.7)

**identity property**    The identity property for addition states that the sum of 0 and any number equals the number. The identity property for multiplication states that the product of 1 and any number equals the number. (Section 1.7)

**imaginary part**    The imaginary part of the complex number $a + bi$ is $b$. (Section 9.4)

**inconsistent system**    An inconsistent system of equations is a system with no solution. (Section 4.1)

**independent equations**    Equations of a system that have different graphs are called independent equations. (Section 4.1)

**index (order)**  In a radical of the form $\sqrt[n]{a}$, $n$ is called the index or order. (Section 8.1)

**inequality**  An inequality is a statement that two expressions are not equal. (Section 1.2)

**inner product**  When using the FOIL method to multiply two binomials $(a + b)(c + d)$, the inner product is $bc$. (Section 5.5)

**integers**  The set of integers is $\{\ldots, -3, -2, -1, 0, 1, 2, 3, \ldots\}$. (Section 1.4)

**intersection**  The intersection of two sets $A$ and $B$, written $A \cap B$, is the set of elements that belong to *both A and B*. (Appendix)

**interval**  An interval is a portion of a number line. (Section 2.8)

**interval notation**  Interval notation is a simplified notation that uses parentheses ( ) and/or brackets [ ] and/or the infinity symbol $\infty$ to describe an interval on a number line. (Section 2.8)

**inverse property**  The inverse property for addition states that a number added to its opposite (additive inverse) is 0. The inverse property for multiplication states that a number multiplied by its reciprocal (multiplicative inverse) is 1. (Section 1.7)

**inverse variation**  $y$ varies inversely as $x$ if there exists a nonzero real number (constant) $k$ such that $y = \frac{k}{x}$. (Section 7.8)

**irrational number**  An irrational number cannot be written as the quotient of two integers, but can be represented by a point on a number line. (Section 1.4)

## L

**least common denominator (LCD)**  Given several denominators, the least multiple that is divisible by all the denominators is called the least common denominator. (Sections 1.1, 7.3)

**legs of a right triangle**  The two shorter perpendicular sides of a right triangle are called the legs. (Section 6.6)

**like radicals**  Like radicals are multiples of the same root of the same number or expression. (Section 8.3)

**like terms**  Terms with exactly the same variables raised to exactly the same powers are called like terms. (Sections 1.8, 5.4)

**line graph**  A line graph is a series of line segments in two dimensions that connect points representing data. (Section 3.1)

**linear equation in one variable**  A linear equation in one variable can be written in the form $Ax + B = C$, where $A$, $B$, and $C$ are real numbers, with $A \neq 0$. (Section 2.1)

**linear equation in two variables**  A linear equation in two variables is an equation that can be written in the form $Ax + By = C$, where $A$, $B$, and $C$ are real numbers, and $A$ and $B$ are not both 0. (Section 3.1)

**linear inequality in one variable**  A linear inequality in one variable can be written in the form $Ax + B < C$, $Ax + B \leq C$, $Ax + B > C$, or $Ax + B \geq C$, where $A$, $B$, and $C$ are real numbers, with $A \neq 0$. (Section 2.8)

**linear inequality in two variables**  A linear inequality in two variables can be written in the form $Ax + By < C$, $Ax + By \leq C$, $Ax + By > C$, or $Ax + By \geq C$, where $A$, $B$, and $C$ are real numbers, and $A$ and $B$ are not both 0. (Section 3.5)

**line of symmetry**  The axis of a parabola is a line of symmetry for the graph. It is a line that can be drawn through the vertex of the graph in such a way that the part of the graph on one side of the line is an exact reflection of the part on the opposite side. (Sections 5.4, 9.5)

**lowest terms**  A fraction is in lowest terms if the greatest common factor of the numerator and denominator is 1. (Sections 1.1, 7.1)

## M

**means of a proportion**  In the proportion $\frac{a}{b} = \frac{c}{d}$, the $b$- and $c$-terms are called the means. (Section 2.6)

**mixed number**  A mixed number includes a whole number and a fraction written together and is understood to be the sum of the whole number and the fraction. (Section 1.1)

**monomial**  A monomial is a polynomial consisting of exactly one term. (Section 5.4)

**multiplication property of equality**  The multiplication property of equality states that the same nonzero number can be multiplied by (or divided into) both sides of an equation to obtain an equivalent equation. (Section 2.2)

**multiplication property of inequality**  The multiplication property of inequality states that both sides of an inequality may be multiplied (or divided) by a positive number without changing the direction of the inequality symbol. Multiplying (or dividing) by a negative number reverses the direction of the inequality symbol. (Section 2.8)

**multiplicative inverse (reciprocal)**  The multiplicative inverse (reciprocal) of a nonzero number $x$, symbolized $\frac{1}{x}$, is the real number which has the property that the product of the two numbers is 1. For all nonzero real numbers $x$, $\frac{1}{x} \cdot x = x \cdot \frac{1}{x} = 1$. (Section 1.6)

## N

**natural numbers**  The set of natural numbers is the set of numbers used for counting: $\{1, 2, 3, 4, \ldots\}$. (Sections 1.1, 1.4)

**negative number**  A negative number is located to the left of 0 on a number line. (Section 1.4)

**number line**  A line that has a point designated to correspond to the real number 0, and a standard unit chosen to represent the distance between 0 and 1, is a number line. All real numbers correspond to one and only one number on such a line. (Section 1.4)

**numerator**  The number above the fraction bar in a fraction is called the numerator. It shows how many of the equivalent parts are being considered. (Section 1.1)

**numerical coefficient (coefficient)**  The numerical factor in a term is called the numerical coefficient, or simply, the coefficient. (Sections 1.8, 5.4)

## O

**ordered pair**  An ordered pair is a pair of numbers written within parentheses in the form $(x, y)$. (Section 3.1)

**origin**  The point at which the $x$-axis and $y$-axis of a rectangular coordinate system intersect is called the origin. (Section 3.1)

**outer product**  When using the FOIL method to multiply two binomials $(a + b)(c + d)$, the outer product is $ad$. (Section 5.5)

## P

**parabola**  The graph of a second-degree (quadratic) equation in two variables is called a parabola. (Sections 5.4, 9.5)

**parallel lines**  Parallel lines are two lines in the same plane that never intersect. (Section 3.3)

**percent**  Percent, written with the symbol %, means per one hundred. (Section 2.6)

**percentage**  A percentage is a part of a whole. (Section 2.6)

**perfect cube**  A perfect cube is a number with a rational cube root. (Section 8.1)

**perfect square**  A perfect square is a number with a rational square root. (Section 8.1)

**perfect square trinomial**  A perfect square trinomial is a trinomial that can be factored as the square of a binomial. (Section 6.4)

**perimeter**  The perimeter of a two-dimensional figure is a measure of the distance around the outside edges of the figure—that is, the sum of the lengths of its sides. (Section 2.5)

**perpendicular lines** Perpendicular lines are two lines that intersect to form a right (90°) angle. (Section 3.3)

**plot** To plot an ordered pair is to locate it on a rectangular coordinate system. (Section 3.1)

**point-slope form** A linear equation is written in point-slope form if it is in the form $y - y_1 = m(x - x_1)$, where $m$ is the slope and $(x_1, y_1)$ is a point on the line. (Section 3.4)

**polynomial** A polynomial is a term or a finite sum of terms in which all coefficients are real, all variables have whole number exponents, and no variables appear in denominators. (Section 5.4)

**polynomial in $x$** A polynomial whose only variable is $x$ is called a polynomial in $x$. (Section 5.4)

**positive number** A positive number is located to the right of 0 on a number line. (Section 1.4)

**prime factor** A prime factor of a number is a factor greater than 1 whose only factors are 1 and itself. For example, the prime factors of 12 are $2 \cdot 2 \cdot 3$. (Section 1.1)

**prime number** A natural number greater than 1 is prime if it has only 1 and itself as factors. (Section 1.1)

**prime polynomial** A prime polynomial is a polynomial that cannot be factored into factors having only integer coefficients. (Section 6.2)

**principal root (principal $n$th root)** For even indexes, the symbols $\sqrt{\phantom{x}}$, $\sqrt[4]{\phantom{x}}$, $\sqrt[6]{\phantom{x}}$, ..., $\sqrt[n]{\phantom{x}}$ are used for nonnegative roots, which are called principal roots. (Section 8.1)

**product** The answer to a multiplication problem is called the product. (Section 1.1)

**product of the sum and difference of two terms** The product of the sum and difference of two terms is the difference of the squares of the terms, or $(x + y)(x - y) = x^2 - y^2$. (Section 5.6)

**proportion** A proportion is a statement that two ratios are equal. (Section 2.6)

**proposed solution** A value that appears as an apparent solution after a rational or radical equation has been solved according to standard methods is called a proposed solution for the original equation. It may or may not be an actual solution and must be checked. (Sections 7.7, 8.6)

**pure imaginary number** If $a = 0$ and $b \neq 0$ in the complex number $a + bi$, the complex number is called a pure imaginary number. (Section 9.4)

**Pythagorean theorem** The Pythagorean theorem states that the square of the length of the hypotenuse of a right triangle equals the sum of the squares of the lengths of the two legs. (Section 6.6)

## Q

**quadrant** A quadrant is one of the four regions in the plane determined by the axes in a rectangular coordinate system. (Section 3.1)

**quadratic equation** A quadratic equation is an equation that can be written in the form $ax^2 + bx + c = 0$, where $a$, $b$, and $c$ are real numbers, with $a \neq 0$. (Sections 6.5, 9.1)

**quadratic formula** The quadratic formula is a general formula used to solve a quadratic equation of the form $ax^2 + bx + c = 0$, where $a \neq 0$. It is $x = \dfrac{-b \pm \sqrt{b^2 - 4ac}}{2a}$. (Section 9.3)

**quadratic function** A function defined by an equation of the form $f(x) = ax^2 + bx + c$, for real numbers $a$, $b$, and $c$, with $a \neq 0$, is a quadratic function. (Section 9.5)

**quotient** The answer to a division problem is called the quotient. (Section 1.1)

## R

**radical** An expression consisting of a radical symbol, root index, and radicand is called a radical. (Section 8.1)

**radical equation** A radical equation is an equation with a variable in at least one radicand. (Section 8.6)

**radical expression** A radical expression is an algebraic expression that contains radicals. (Section 8.1)

**radical symbol** The symbol $\sqrt{\phantom{x}}$ is called a radical symbol. (Section 8.1)

**radicand** The number or expression under a radical symbol is called the radicand. (Section 8.1)

**range** The set of all second components ($y$-values) in the ordered pairs of a relation is called the range. (Section 3.6)

**ratio** A ratio is a comparison of two quantities using a quotient. (Section 2.6)

**rational expression** The quotient of two polynomials with denominator not 0 is called a rational expression. (Section 7.1)

**rationalizing the denominator** The process of rewriting a radical expression so that the denominator contains no radicals is called rationalizing the denominator. (Section 8.4)

**rational numbers** Rational numbers can be written as the quotient of two integers, with denominator not 0. (Section 1.4)

**real numbers** Real numbers include all numbers that can be represented by points on the number line—that is, all rational and irrational numbers. (Section 1.4)

**real part** The real part of a complex number $a + bi$ is $a$. (Section 9.4)

**reciprocal (See multiplicative inverse.)**

**rectangular (Cartesian) coordinate system** The $x$-axis and $y$-axis placed at a right angle at their zero points form a rectangular coordinate system. It is also called the Cartesian coordinate system. (Section 3.1)

**relation** A relation is a set of ordered pairs. (Section 3.6)

**right angle** A right angle measures 90°. (Section 2.4)

**rise** Rise refers to the vertical change between two points on a line—that is, the change in $y$-values. (Section 3.3)

**run** Run refers to the horizontal change between two points on a line—that is, the change in $x$-values. (Section 3.3)

## S

**scatter diagram** A scatter diagram is a graph of ordered pairs of data. (Section 3.1)

**scientific notation** A number is written in scientific notation when it is expressed in the form $a \times 10^n$, where $1 \leq |a| < 10$ and $n$ is an integer. (Section 5.3)

**set** A set is a collection of objects. (Section 1.3, Appendix)

**set-builder notation** The special symbolism $\{x \mid x$ has a certain property$\}$ is called set-builder notation. It is used to describe a set of numbers without actually having to list all of the elements. (Section 1.4)

**signed numbers** Signed numbers are numbers that can be written with a positive or negative sign. (Section 1.4)

**simplified radical** A simplified radical meets three conditions:

1. The radicand has no factor (except 1) that is a perfect square (if the radical is a square root), a perfect cube (if the radical is a cube root), and so on.

2. The radicand has no fractions.

3. No denominator contains a radical. (Section 8.4)

**slope** The ratio of the change in $y$ to the change in $x$ for any two points on a line is called the slope of the line. (Section 3.3)

**slope-intercept form** A linear equation is written in slope-intercept form if it is in the form $y = mx + b$, where $m$ is the slope and $(0, b)$ is the $y$-intercept. (Section 3.4)

**solution of an equation** A solution of an equation is any replacement for the variable that makes the equation true. (Section 1.3)

**solution of a system** A solution of a system of equations is an ordered pair $(x, y)$ that makes all equations true at the same time. (Section 4.1)

**solution set** The set of all solutions of an equation is called the solution set. (Section 2.1)

**solution set of a linear system** The set of all ordered pairs that satisfy all equations of a system at the same time is called the solution set. (Section 4.1)

**solution set of a system of linear inequalities** The set of all ordered pairs that make all inequalities of a linear system true at the same time is called the solution set of the system of linear inequalities. (Section 4.5)

**square of a binomial** The square of a binomial is the sum of the square of the first term, twice the product of the two terms, and the square of the last term: $(x + y)^2 = x^2 + 2xy + y^2$ and $(x - y)^2 = x^2 - 2xy + y^2$. (Section 5.6)

**square root** The inverse of squaring a number is called taking its square root. That is, a number $a$ is a square root of $k$ if $a^2 = k$ is true. (Section 8.1)

**square root property** The square root property (for solving equations) states that if $x^2 = k$, with $k > 0$, then $x = \sqrt{k}$ or $x = -\sqrt{k}$. (Section 9.1)

**squaring property** The squaring property (for solving equations) states that if each side of a given equation is squared, then all solutions of the given equation are *among* the solutions of the squared equation. (Section 8.6)

**standard form of a complex number** The standard form of a complex number is $a + bi$. (Section 9.4)

**standard form of a linear equation** A linear equation in two variables written in the form $Ax + By = C$, with $A$ and $B$ not both 0, is in standard form. (Section 3.4)

**standard form of a quadratic equation** A quadratic equation written in the form $ax^2 + bx + c = 0$, where $a$, $b$, and $c$ are real numbers with $a \neq 0$, is in standard form. (Sections 6.5, 9.1)

**straight angle** A straight angle measures $180°$. (Section 2.4)

**subscript notation** Subscript notation is a way of indicating nonspecific values. In $x_1$ and $x_2$, 1 and 2 are subscripts on the variable $x$. (Section 3.3)

**subset** If all elements of set $A$ are in set $B$, then $A$ is a subset of $B$, written $A \subseteq B$. (Appendix)

**substitution method** The substitution method is an algebraic method for solving a system of equations in which one equation is solved for one of the variables, and then the result is substituted into the other equation. (Section 4.2)

**sum** The answer to an addition problem is called the sum. (Section 1.1)

**sum of cubes** The sum of cubes, $x^3 + y^3$, can be factored as $x^3 + y^3 = (x + y)(x^2 - xy + y^2)$. (Section 6.4)

**supplementary angles (supplements)** Supplementary angles are two angles whose measures have a sum of $180°$. (Section 2.4)

**system of linear equations (linear system)** A system of linear equations consists of two or more linear equations to be solved at the same time. (Section 4.1)

**system of linear inequalities** A system of linear inequalities consists of two or more linear inequalities to be solved at the same time. (Section 4.5)

## T

**table of values** A table of values is an organized way of displaying ordered pairs. (Section 3.1)

**term** A term is a number, a variable, or the product or quotient of a number and one or more variables raised to powers. (Section 1.8)

**terms of a proportion** The terms of the proportion $\frac{a}{b} = \frac{c}{d}$ are $a$, $b$, $c$, and $d$. (Section 2.6)

**three-part inequality** An inequality that says that one number is between two other numbers is called a three-part inequality. (Section 2.8)

**trinomial** A trinomial is a polynomial consisting of exactly three terms. (Section 5.4)

## U

**union** The union of two sets $A$ and $B$, written $A \cup B$, is the set of elements that belong to *either A or B*, or both. (Appendix)

**universal set** The set that includes all elements under consideration is the universal set, symbolized $U$. (Appendix)

**unlike terms** Unlike terms are terms that do not have the same variable, or terms with the same variables but whose variables are not raised to the same powers. (Section 1.8)

## V

**variable** A variable is a symbol, usually a letter, used to represent an unknown number. (Section 1.3)

**vary directly (is proportional to)** $y$ varies directly as $x$ if there exists a nonzero real number (constant) $k$ such that $y = kx$. (Section 7.8)

**vary inversely** $y$ varies inversely as $x$ if there exists a nonzero real number (constant) $k$ such that $y = \frac{k}{x}$. (Section 7.8)

**Venn diagram** A Venn diagram consists of geometric figures, such as rectangles and circles, that illustrate the relationships among sets. (Appendix)

**vertex** The point on a parabola that has the least $y$-value (if the parabola opens up) or the greatest $y$-value (if the parabola opens down) is called the vertex of the parabola. (Sections 5.4, 9.5)

**vertical angles** When two intersecting lines are drawn, the angles that lie opposite each other have the same measure and are called vertical angles. (Section 2.5)

**vertical line test** The vertical line test states that any vertical line will intersect the graph of a function in at most one point. (Section 3.6)

**volume** The volume of a three-dimensional figure is a measure of the space occupied by the figure. (Section 2.5)

## W

**whole numbers** The set of whole numbers is $\{0, 1, 2, 3, 4, \ldots\}$. (Sections 1.1, 1.4)

## X

**$x$-axis** The horizontal number line in a rectangular coordinate system is called the $x$-axis. (Section 3.1)

**$x$-intercept** A point where a graph intersects the $x$-axis is called an $x$-intercept. (Section 3.2)

## Y

**$y$-axis** The vertical number line in a rectangular coordinate system is called the $y$-axis. (Section 3.1)

**$y$-intercept** A point where a graph intersects the $y$-axis is called a $y$-intercept. (Section 3.2)

## Z

**zero-factor property** The zero-factor property states that if two numbers have a product of 0, then at least one of the numbers is 0. (Sections 6.5, 9.1)

# Triangles and Angles

**Right Triangle**
Triangle has one 90° (right) angle.

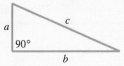

**Pythagorean Theorem (for right triangles)**
$$a^2 + b^2 = c^2$$

**Right Angle**
Measure is 90°.

**Isosceles Triangle**
Two sides are equal.
$$AB = BC$$

**Straight Angle**
Measure is 180°.

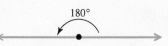

**Equilateral Triangle**
All sides are equal.
$$AB = BC = CA$$

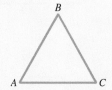

**Complementary Angles**
The sum of the measures of two complementary angles is 90°.

Angles ① and ② are complementary.

**Sum of the Angles of Any Triangle**
$$A + B + C = 180°$$

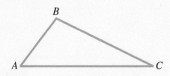

**Supplementary Angles**
The sum of the measures of two supplementary angles is 180°.

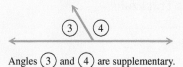

Angles ③ and ④ are supplementary.

**Similar Triangles**
Corresponding angles are equal. Corresponding sides are proportional.
$$A = D, B = E, C = F$$
$$\frac{AB}{DE} = \frac{AC}{DF} = \frac{BC}{EF}$$

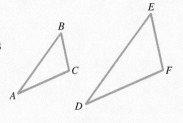

**Vertical Angles**
Vertical angles have equal measures.

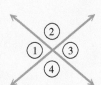

Angle ① = Angle ③
Angle ② = Angle ④

# Formulas

| Figure | Formulas | Illustration |
|---|---|---|
| **Square** | Perimeter: $P = 4s$ <br> Area: $\mathcal{A} = s^2$ | |
| **Rectangle** | Perimeter: $P = 2L + 2W$ <br> Area: $\mathcal{A} = LW$ | |
| **Triangle** | Perimeter: $P = a + b + c$ <br> Area: $\mathcal{A} = \dfrac{1}{2}bh$ | |
| **Parallelogram** | Perimeter: $P = 2a + 2b$ <br> Area: $\mathcal{A} = bh$ | |
| **Trapezoid** | Perimeter: $P = a + b + c + B$ <br> Area: $\mathcal{A} = \dfrac{1}{2}h(b + B)$ | |
| **Circle** | Diameter: $d = 2r$ <br> Circumference: $C = 2\pi r$ <br> $C = \pi d$ <br> Area: $\mathcal{A} = \pi r^2$ | |

# Triangles and Angles

### Right Triangle
Triangle has one 90° (right) angle.

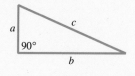

### Pythagorean Formula
(*for right triangles*)

$a^2 + b^2 = c^2$

### Right Angle
Measure is 90°.

### Isosceles Triangle
Two sides are equal.

$AB = BC$

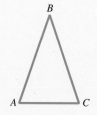

### Straight Angle
Measure is 180°.

### Equilateral Triangle
All sides are equal.

$AB = BC = CA$

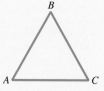

### Complementary Angles
The sum of the measures of two complementary angles is 90°.

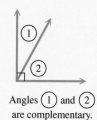

Angles ① and ② are complementary.

### Sum of the Angles of Any Triangle
$A + B + C = 180°$

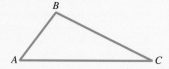

### Supplementary Angles
The sum of the measures of two supplementary angles is 180°.

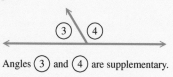

Angles ③ and ④ are supplementary.

### Similar Triangles
Corresponding angles are equal; corresponding sides are proportional.

$A = D, B = E, C = F$

$$\frac{AB}{DE} = \frac{AC}{DF} = \frac{BC}{EF}$$

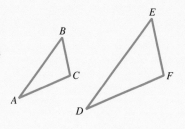

### Vertical Angles
Vertical angles have equal measures.

Angle ① = Angle ③

Angle ② = Angle ④

# Formulas

| Figure | Formulas | Illustration |
|--------|----------|--------------|
| **Square** | Perimeter: $P = 4s$ <br> Area: $A = s^2$ | |
| **Rectangle** | Perimeter: $P = 2L + 2W$ <br> Area: $A = LW$ | |
| **Triangle** | Perimeter: $P = a + b + c$ <br> Area: $A = \dfrac{1}{2}bh$ | |
| **Parallelogram** | Perimeter: $P = 2a + 2b$ <br> Area: $A = bh$ | |
| **Trapezoid** | Perimeter: $P = a + b + c + B$ <br> Area: $A = \dfrac{1}{2}h(b + B)$ | |
| **Circle** | Diameter: $d = 2r$ <br> Circumference: $C = 2\pi r$ <br> $\qquad\qquad\qquad C = \pi d$ <br> Area: $A = \pi r^2$ | |